Control System

Control Systems

Second Edition

A. Anand Kumar

Principal
K.L. University College of Engineering
K.L. University
Green Fields, Vaddeswaram
Guntur District
Andhra Pradesh

PHI Learning Private Limited

Delhi-110092
2014

₹ 495.00

CONTROL SYSTEMS, Second Edition
A. Anand Kumar

ISBN-978-81-203-4939-1

The export rights of this book are vested solely with the publisher.

Ninth Printing (Second Edition)   ...   .   **March, 2014**

Published by Asoke K. Ghosh, PHI Learning Private Limited, Rimjhim House, 111, Patparganj Industrial Estate, Delhi-110092   by Rajkamal Electric Press, B-35/9, G.T. Karnal Road Industrial Area, Delhi-110033.

To the memory of
my parents
Shri A. Nagabhushanam and Smt. A. Ushamani
(Freedom Fighters)

Contents

11. Digital Control Systems 755–821

Preface

After 39 years of my teaching experience, this textbook on control systems is an endeavour towards providing students with a solid grounding in the foundations of this subject. It is suitable for use as a one-semester course material by undergraduate students of Electronics and Communication Engineering, Electrical and Electronics Engineering, Electronics and Instrumentation Engineering, Telecommunication Engineering, Biomedical Engineering, Electronics and Computer Engineering and Mechanical Engineering. Besides, it will also be useful to students undergoing AMIE and grad IETE courses.

The second edition of this text is organized in 11 chapters. The outline of the book is as follows.

Control systems are an integral part of human being's daily life. The need for control system, classification of control systems and typical servomechanisms are discussed in Chapter 1.

Mechanical systems are an essential part of our daily activities. Mechanical systems—translational and rotational—and the analogy between mechanical and electrical systems are discussed in Chapter 2.

Control systems are generally represented by either block diagrams or signal flow graphs. Representation of systems using block diagrams and signal flow graphs and obtaining transfer functions from them are discussed in Chapter 3.

The time response analysis of control systems is very important. The specifications of a control system in time-domain and the transient and steady-state analysis of control systems are discussed in Chapter 4.

Stability is the most important basic requirement of a control system. Routh's method is the easiest method to test the stability of control systems. Routh's method, the difficulties encountered in the application of this method and the ways of overcoming them are discussed in Chapter 5.

Root locus is a very powerful time-domain method of analysis and design of control systems. The determination of absolute as well as relative stabilities and other parameters of control systems and visualization of the complete dynamic response using the root locus method are discussed in Chapter 6.

The analysis and design of control systems in frequency domain is simpler than that in time domain. Correlation between time and frequency responses of a second-order system, polar plots and Bode plots are discussed in Chapter 7.

Nyquist plots are very useful for the determination of absolute as well as relative stabilities and also for the design of control systems. Analysis using Nyquist plots is discussed in Chapter 8.

The design and compensation of control systems can be carried out in time-domain or frequency-domain, but design and compensation in frequency-domain is much simpler. In frequency-domain, compensation using Bode plots is much simpler than using other plots and is discussed in Chapter 9.

State variable approach is the modern direct, time-domain approach for the analysis and design of control systems. Detailed analysis of systems using state variables as well as the controllability and observability of control systems are the topics discussed in Chapter 10.

As the complexity of Control systems increases severe demands of flexibility, adaptability and optimality and even demands to account for economic control function complexity arise. In such situations Digital control systems become a necessity. Analysis of Digital Control Systems, and methods of determining their stability are discussed in Chapter 11.

Matlab programs are included at the end of chapters 2 through 11 to enable the reader to practice and verify the solutions and get correct plots.

A large number of examples have been worked out to help students understand the concepts. Extensive short questions and answers are given at the end of each chapter to enable the students to prepare for the examinations very thoroughly. Review questions, fill in the blank type questions, objective type multiple choice questions and numerical problems are included at the end of each chapter to enable the students to build a clear understanding of the subject matter discussed in the text and also to assess their learning. The answers to all these are also given. Almost all the solved and unsolved problems presented in this book have been classroom tested.

I express my profound gratitude to all those who directly or indirectly helped me in the successful completion of this book and also in bringing out the second edition. First of all I thank Mr. V. Srinivasa Rao of Adam's Engineering College, Palvancha who drew all the figures and typed some part of the manuscript and Mr. P. Venkateswara Rao of SITE who typed the remaining part of the manuscript.

I thank Mr. T.J.V. Subrahmanyeswara Rao, Associate Professor, ECE Department, K.L. University, Vijayawada, Dr. P. Srihari Assistant Professor, ECE Department, NIT Surathkal and Mr. G.N. Sathpathi, research scholar, ECE Department, NIT Surathkal for their help in Matlab Programs.

I am grateful to Mr. Burugupalli Venugopalakrishna, Chairman, Sasi Educational Society, Velivennu, West Godavari (District), AP, for encouraging and providing me with all the facilities for the completion of this book. I also thank Mr. B. Ravi Kumar, Executive Director, Sasi Institute of Technology and Engineering, Tadepalligudem, for his cooperation.

I thank Mr. Koneru Satyanarayana, President, Smt. Siva Kanchana Latha, Secretary and Mr. Lakshman Havish and Raja Harin, Vice Presidents of KLEF (Koneru Lakshmaiah Educaion Foundation), K.L. University, Green Fields, Vaddeswaram, Guntur (District) AP for their constant encouragement.

I express my sincere appreciation to my brother Mr. A. Vijaya Kumar and to my friends Dr. K. Koteswara Rao, Chairman, Gawtham Educational Society, Gudivada Krishna (District) AP and Mr. Ramesh Babu and Smt. Krishna Kumari of Detroit, USA for their constant encouragement.

I thank Dr. K. Raja Rajeswari, Director VITAM College of Engineering, Visakhapatnam, AP and Dr. K.S. Lingamurthy, Professor, EEE Department of GITAM University College of Engineering, Visakhapatnam, AP for their constant words of encouragement.

I thank my publishers M/s PHI Learning for accepting to publish this book. My thanks in particular goes to the former editor, Mr. Sudarshan Das for meticulously editing the manuscript. I also thank Ms. Pushpita Ghosh, Director for her encouragement in the early completion of the manuscript. I also thank Ms. Shivani Garg, Senior Editor who edited the second edition of this book and Ms. Babita Mishra, Editorial Coordinator and Mr. Ajai Kumar Lal Das, Assistant Production Manager for their cooperation.

Finally, I am deeply indebted to my family: my wife A. Jhansi, who is the source of inspiration for this activity and without whose cooperation this work would not have been completed, my sons Dr. A. Anil Kumar and Mr. A. Sunil Kumar, and daughters-in-law Dr. A. Anureet Kaur and A. Apurupa, and granddaughters A. Khushi and A. Shreya for motivating and encouraging me constantly to undertake and complete this work.

The author will gratefully acknowledge constructive criticism from both students and teachers for further improvement of this book.

A. Anand Kumar

Symbols, Notations and Abbreviations

Symbols and Notations

T	Torque
K	Spring constant, Open loop gain
f	Friction coefficient
J	Inertia
θ	Angular displacement
ω	Angular velocity
M	Mass, Modal matrix
ϕ	Flux
i_f	Field current
i_a	Armature current
R	Resistance
L	Inductance, Laplace transform
C	Capacitance
q	Charge
$e(t)$	Error signal
$r(t)$	Input signal
$c(t)$	Output signal
$G(s)H(s)$	Loop transfer function
Δ	Determinant of signal flow graph
θ_d	Damped frequency of oscillation
ω_n	Undamped natural frequency
ξ	Damping ratio
t_d	Delay time
t_r	Rise time
t_p	Peak time
M_p	Peak overshoot
t_s	Settling time
e_{ss}	Steady state error
K_p	Position error constant

K_v	Velocity error constant
K_a	Acceleration error constant
θ_d	Angle of departure
θ_a	Angle of arrival
ω_r	Resonant frequency
u_r	Normalized resonant frequency
ω_b	Bandwidth
M_r	Resonant peak
dB	Decibel
ω_g	Gain crossover frequency
ω_p	Phase crossover frequency
A	System matrix
B	Input matrix
C	Output matrix
D	Transmission matrix
$x(t)$	State vector
$u(t)$	Input vector
$y(t)$	Output vector
$\phi(t)$	State transition matrix (e^{At})
$\phi(s)$	Resolvent matrix
$\delta(n)$	Impulse sequence
$u(n)$	Step sequence
$r(n)$	Ramp sequence
$x(n)$	Discrete signal
$H(z), H(s)$	System function
$G_0(s)$	Transfer function of ZOH
$G(s)$	Forward path transfer function
$H(s)$	Feedback path transfer function
$h(n), h(t)$	Impulse response
ϕ_{pm}	Phase margin

Abbreviations

SISO	Single-Input-Signal-Output
MIMO	Multi-Input-Multi-Output
KCL	Kirchoff's Current Law
KVL	Kirchoff's Voltage Law
GM	Gain Margin
PI	Proportional plus Integral
PID	Proportional plus Integral plus Derivative
BIBO	Bounded-Input-Bounded-Output
CCF	Controllable Canonical Form
OCF	Observable Canonical Form
JCF	Jordan Canonical Form
DCF	Diagonal Canonical Form
PCF	Phase variable Canonical Form
ADC	Analog-to-Digital Converter
DAC	Digital-to-Analog Converter
ZOH	Zero-Order-Hold
SFG	Signal Flow Graph

1

Introduction to Control Systems

1.1 INTRODUCTION

A system is a collection of objects (components) connected together to serve an objective, or a system is a combination of components that act together to perform an objective. A control system is that means by which any quantity of interest in a machine, mechanism, or other equipment is maintained or altered in accordance with a desired manner, or simply a control system is a system in which the output quantity is controlled by varying the input quantity.

A physical system is a collection of physical objects connected together to serve an objective. No physical system can be represented in its full physical intricacies and, therefore, idealizing assumptions are always made for the purpose of analysis and synthesis of systems. An idealized physical system is called a *physical model*. A physical system can be modelled in a number of ways depending upon the specific problem to be dealt with and the desired accuracy. Once a physical model of a physical system is obtained, the next step is to obtain a mathematical model, which is the mathematical representation of the physical model, through use of appropriate physical laws. Depending upon the choice of variables and the coordinate system, a given physical model may lead to different mathematical models. A control system may be modelled as a scalar differential equation describing the system or as a state variable vector-matrix differential equation. The particular mathematical model which gives a greater insight into the dynamic behaviour of the physical system is selected. When the mathematical model of a physical system is solved for various input conditions, the result represents the dynamic response of the system.

Mathematical models of most physical systems are characterized by differential equations. A mathematical model is linear, if the differential equation describing it has coefficients which are either function only of the independent variable or are constants. If the coefficients of the describing differential equation are functions of time (the independent variable), then the mathematical model is linear time-varying. On the other hand, if the coefficients of the describing differential equations are constants, the model is linear time-invariant.

1

The differential equations describing a linear time-invariant system can be reshaped into different forms for the convenience of analysis. For example, for transient response or frequency response analysis of single-input-single-output linear systems, the transfer function representation forms a useful model. On the other hand, when a system has multiple inputs and outputs, the vector-matrix notation may be more convenient. The mathematical model of a system having been obtained, the available mathematical tools can then be utilized for analysis or synthesis of the system.

Powerful mathematical tools like the Fourier and Laplace transforms are available for use in linear systems. Unfortunately, no physical system in nature is perfectly linear. Therefore, certain assumptions must always be made to get a linear model which is a compromise between the simplicity of the mathematical model and the accuracy of results obtained from it. However, it may not always be possible to obtain a valid linear model, for example, in the presence of a strong nonlinearity or in the presence of distributive effects which cannot be represented by lumped parameters.

1.2 CLASSIFICATION OF CONTROL SYSTEMS

Control systems may be classified in a number of ways depending on the purpose of classification.

1. Depending on the hierarchy, control systems may be classified as
   (a) Open-loop control systems
   (b) Closed-loop control systems
   (c) Optimal control systems
   (d) Adaptive control systems
   (e) Learning control systems

2. Depending on the presence of human being as a part of the control system, control systems may be classified as
   (a) Manually controlled systems
   (b) Automatic control systems

3. Depending on the presence of feedback, control systems may be classified as
   (a) Open-loop control systems
   (b) Closed-loop control systems or feedback control systems

4. According to the main purpose of the system, control systems may be classified as
   (a) Position control systems
   (b) Velocity control systems
   (c) Process control systems
   (d) Temperature control systems
   (e) Traffic control systems, etc.

Feedback control systems may be classified in a number of ways depending on the purpose of classification.

1. According to the method of analysis and design, control systems may be classified as linear control systems and nonlinear control systems.

2. Depending on whether the parameters of the system remain constant or vary with time, control systems may be classified as time-varying control systems or time-invariant control systems.

3. According to the types of signals used in the system, control systems may be classified as

    (a) Continuous-data control systems and discrete-data control systems
    (b) ac (modulated) control systems and dc (unmodulated) control systems.

4. Depending on the application, control systems may be classified as position control systems, velocity control systems, process control systems, traffic control systems, etc.

5. Depending on the number of inputs and outputs, control systems may be classified as single-input-single-output (SISO) control systems and multi-input-multi-output (MIMO) control systems. MIMO systems are also called *multivariable systems*.

6. Depending on the number of open-loop poles of the system transfer function present at the origin of the *s*-plane, control systems may by classified as

    (a) Type-0
    (b) Type-1
    (c) Type-2 etc. systems.

7. Depending on the order of the differential equation used to describe the system, control systems may be classified as first-order control systems, second-order control systems, etc.

8. Depending on the type of damping, control systems may be classified as

    (a) Undamped systems
    (b) Underdamped systems
    (c) Critically damped systems
    (d) Overdamped systems.

1.2.1 Open-Loop Control Systems

Those systems in which the output has no effect on the control action, i.e. on the input are called *open-loop control systems*. In other words, in an open-loop control system, the output is neither measured nor fed back for comparison with the input. Open-loop control systems are not feedback systems. Any control system that operates on a time basis is open-loop.

In any open-loop control system, the output is not compared with the reference input. Thus, to each reference input, there corresponds a fixed operating condition; as a result, the accuracy of the system depends on the calibration. In the presence of disturbances, an open-loop control system will not perform the desired task because when the output changes due to disturbances, it is not followed by changes in input to correct the output. In open-loop control systems, the changes in output are corrected by changing the input manually. Open-loop control systems can be used in practice only if the relationship between the input and the output is known and if there are neither internal nor external disturbances. One practical example of an open-loop control system is a washing machine—soaking, washing and rinsing in the washer operate on a time basis. The machine does not measure the output signal, i.e. the cleanliness of the clothes. A traffic control system that operates by means of signals on a time basis is another example of an open-loop control system. A room heater without any temperature sensing device is also an example of an open-loop control system. The general block diagram of an open-loop system is shown in Figure 1.1.

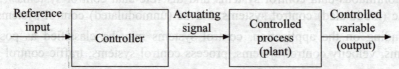

Figure 1.1   General block diagram of an open-loop system.

1.2.2   Closed-Loop Control Systems

Feedback control systems are often referred to as *closed-loop control systems*. In practice, the terms, 'closed-loop control' and 'feedback control' are used interchangeably. In a closed-loop control system, the actuating error signal which is the difference between the input signal and the feedback signal (which may be the output signal itself or a function of the output signal and its derivatives and/or integrals) is fed to the controller so as to reduce the error and bring the output of the system to a desired value. A system that maintains a prescribed relationship between the output and the reference input by comparing them and using the difference as a means of control is called a *feedback control system*. The term 'closed-loop control' always implies the use of feedback control action in order to reduce system error.

The general block diagram of an automatic control system is shown in Figure 1.2. It consists of an error detector, a controller, a plant and feedback path elements.

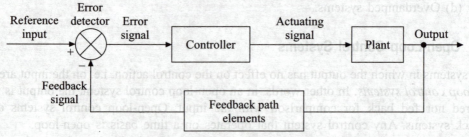

Figure 1.2   General block diagram of a closed-loop control system.

The reference input corresponds to desired output. The feedback path elements convert the output to a signal of the same type as that of the reference signal. The feedback signal is proportional to the output signal and is fed to the error detector. The error signal generated by the error detector is the difference between the reference signal and the feedback signal. The controller modifies and amplifies the error signal to produce better control action. The modified error signal is fed to the plant to correct its output.

An example of a feedback control system is a room temperature control system. By measuring the actual room temperature and comparing it with the reference temperature (desired temperature), the thermostat turns the heating or cooling equipment on or off in such a way as to ensure that the room temperature remains at a comfortable level regardless of outside conditions.

The following are some examples of control systems:

Traffic control system: Traffic control by means of traffic signals operated on a time basis constitutes an open-loop control system. The sequence of control signals is based on a time slot given for each signal. The time slots are decided based on a traffic study. The system will not measure the density of the traffic before giving the signals. It gives the signals in sequence as per the setting irrespective of the actual traffic. Since the time slots do not change according to traffic density, the system is an open-loop control system.

This open-loop traffic control system can be made as a closed-loop system if the time slots of the signals are based on the density of traffic. In a closed-loop traffic control system, the density of the traffic is measured on all the sides and the information is fed to a computer. The timings of the control signals are decided by the computer based on the density of traffic. Since the closed-loop system dynamically changes the timings, the flow of vehicles will be better than in that of an open-loop system.

Room heating system: A room heater without any temperature sensing device is an example of an open-loop control system. In this, an electric furnace is used to heat the room. The output is the desired room temperature. The temperature of the room is risen by the heat generated by the heating element. The output temperature depends on the time during which the supply to the heater remains ON. The ON-OFF time of the heater is set as per some calculation. Whatever may be the room temperature, after the set time, the heater will be OFF. The actual temperature is not compared with the reference temperature and the difference is not used for correction.

The above system becomes a closed-loop system if a thermostat is provided to measure the actual temperature, and the actual temperature is compared with the reference, and the difference is used to control the timing for which the heater is ON.

Washing machine: A washing machine without any cleanliness measuring system is an example of an open-loop control system. In this, the soaking, washing, and rinsing in the washer operate on a time basis. The machine ON time is set based on some calculation. The machine does not measure the output signal, that is the cleanliness of the clothes. Once the set ON time is over, the machine will automatically stop, whatever may be the level of cleanliness.

This can be a closed-loop control system, if the level of cleanliness can be measured and compared with the desired cleanliness (reference input) and the difference is used to control the washing time of the machine.

1.2.3 Closed-Loop System versus Open-Loop System

An open-loop system can be modified as a closed-loop system by providing feedback. The provision of feedback automatically corrects the changes in output due to disturbances. Hence the closed-loop control system is called an automatic control system.

An advantage of the closed-loop control system is the fact that, the use of feedback makes the system response relatively insensitive to external disturbances and internal variations in system parameters. It is thus possible to use relatively inaccurate and inexpensive components to obtain the accurate control of a given plant, whereas doing so is impossible in the case of the open-loop system.

From the point of view of stability, the open-loop control system is easier to build because system stability is not a major problem. On the other hand, stability is a major problem in the closed-loop control system, which may tend to overcorrect errors that can cause oscillations of constant or changing amplitude.

It should be emphasized that for systems in which the inputs are known ahead of time and in which there are no disturbances, it is advisable to use open-loop control. Closed-loop control systems have advantages only when unpredictable disturbances and / or unpredictable variations in system components are present. Note that the output power rating partially determines the cost, weight, and size of a control system. The number of components used in a closed-loop control system is more than that for a corresponding open-loop control system. Thus, the closed-loop control system is generally higher in cost and power. To decrease the required power of a system, open-loop control may be used where applicable. A proper combination of open-loop and closed-loop controls is usually less expensive and will give satisfactory overall system performance.

The advantages and disadvantages of open-loop and closed-loop control systems are summarized in Table 1.1.

Table 1.1 Open-loop vs closed-loop

Open-loop control system	*Closed-loop control system*
1. The open-loop systems are simple and economical.	1. The closed-loop systems are complex and costlier.
2. They consume less power.	2. They consume more power.
3. The open-loop systems are easier to construct because of less number of components required.	3. The closed-loop systems are not easy to construct because of more number of components required.
4. Stability is not a major problem in open-loop control systems. Generally, the open-loop systems are stable.	4. Stability is a major problem in closed-loop control systems and more care is needed to design a stable closed-loop system.
5. The open-loop systems are inaccurate and unreliable.	5. The closed-loop systems are accurate and more reliable.
6. The changes in the output due to external disturbances are not corrected automatically. So they are more sensitive to noise and other disturbances.	6. The changes in the output due to external disturbances are corrected automatically. So they are less sensitive to noise and other disturbances.
	7. The feedback reduces the overall gain of the system.
	8. The feedback in a closed-loop system may lead to oscillatory response, because it may over correct errors, thus causing oscillations of constant or changing amplitude.

1.2.4 Linear versus Nonlinear Control Systems

The classification of control systems into linear and nonlinear is made according to the method of analysis and design. A system is said to be linear, if the principle of superposition applies. The principle of superposition states that the response produced by the simultaneous application of two different forcing functions is equal to the sum of the two individual responses. Hence for the linear system, the response to several inputs can be calculated by treating one input at a time and adding the results. Strictly speaking, linear systems do not exist in practice, since all physical systems are nonlinear to some extent. Linear feedback control systems are idealized models fabricated by the analyst purely for the simplicity of analysis and design. When the magnitudes of signals in a control system are limited to ranges in which system components exhibit linear characteristics, the system is essentially linear, but when the magnitudes of signals are extended beyond the range of the linear operation, depending on the severity of the nonlinearity, the system should no longer be considered linear. Common nonlinear effects focused in control systems are saturation, backlash, dead play between coupled gear members, nonlinear spring characteristics, nonlinear friction force or torque between moving members, and so on. Quite often, nonlinear characteristics are intentionally introduced in a control system to improve its performance, or to provide more effective control. For instance, to achieve minimum time control, an on-off type of controller is used in many missile or spacecraft control systems.

For linear systems, there exist a wealth of analytical and graphical techniques for design and analysis purposes. Nonlinear systems on the other hand are usually difficult to treat mathematically, and there are no general methods available for solving a wide class of nonlinear control systems.

1.2.5 Time-Invariant versus Time-Varying Control Systems

When the parameters of a control system are stationary with respect to time during the operation of the system, the system is called a *time-invariant system*. If the parameters of a control system vary with respect to time during the operation of the system, the system is called a *time-varying system*. In practice, most physical systems contain elements that drift or vary with time. For example, the winding resistance of an electric motor will vary when the motor is first being excited and its temperature is rising. Another example of a time-varying system is a guided missile control system in which the mass of the missile decreases as the fuel on board is being consumed during flight. The analysis and design of linear time-varying systems are usually much more complex than that of the linear time-invariant systems.

1.2.6 Continuous-Data versus Discrete-Data Control Systems

A continuous-data control system is one in which the signals at various parts of the system are all functions of the continuous time variable and among all continuous-data control systems, the signals may be further classified as ac or dc. An ac control system usually means that the signals in the system are modulated by some form of modulation scheme. On the other hand, when a dc control system is referred to, it does not mean that all the signals in the system are unidirectional, then there would be no corrective control movement. A dc control system simply implies that the signals are unmodulated, but they are still ac signals according to the conventional definition.

In practice, not all control systems are strictly of the ac or dc type. A system may incorporate a mixture of ac and dc components using modulators and demodulators to match the signals at various points in the system.

Discrete-data control systems differ from the continuous-data control systems in that the signals at one or more points of the system are in the form of either a pulse train or digital code. Usually discrete-data control systems are subdivided into sampled-data control systems and digital control systems. Sampled-data control systems refer to a more general class of discrete-data control systems, in which the signals are in the form of pulse data. A digital control system refers to the use of a digital computer or controller in the system so that the signals are digitally coded, such as in binary code. In general, a sampled-data control system receives data or information only intermittently at specific instants of time. Strictly, a sampled-data system can also be classified as an ac system, since the signal of the system is pulse modulated.

Sampling may be inherent or intentional. There are many advantages of incorporating sampling into a control system. One important advantage of the sampling operation is that expensive equipment used in the system may be time shared among several control channels. Another advantage is that pulse data are usually less susceptible to noise.

Because digital computers provide many advantages in size and flexibility, computer control has become increasingly popular in recent years.

1.3 WHAT FEEDBACK IS AND WHAT ITS EFFECTS ARE

One use of feedback is for the purpose of reducing the error between the reference input and the system output. The reduction of system error is merely one of the many important effects that feedback may have upon a system. Feedback also has effects on such system performance characteristics as stability, bandwidth, overall gain, disturbance and sensitivity.

When feedback is deliberately introduced for the purpose of control, its existence is easily identified. However, there are numerous situations wherein a physical system that we normally recognize as an inherently nonfeedback system turns out to have feedback when it is observed in a certain manner.

In general, we can state that whenever a closed sequence of cause-and-effect relationships exist among the variables of a system, feedback is said to exist. This view point will inevitably admit feedback in a large number of systems that ordinarily would be identified as nonfeedback systems.

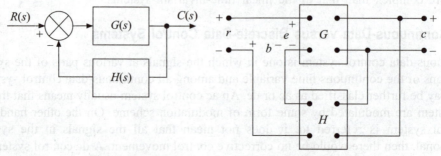

Figure 1.3 Feedback system with one feedback loop.

The input-output relation of a single loop control system shown in Figure 1.3 is given by

$$M = \frac{c}{r} = \frac{G}{1 + GH} \tag{1.1}$$

1.3.1 Effect of Feedback on Overall Gain

As seen from Eq. (1.1), feedback affects the gain G of a nonfeedback system by a factor $1/(1 + GH)$. The system of Figure 1.3 is said to have negative feedback, since a minus sign is assigned to the feedback signal. The quantity GH may itself include a negative sign, so the general effect of feedback is that it may increase or decrease the gain. In a practical control system, G and H are functions of frequency, so the magnitude of $1 + GH$ may be greater than 1 in one frequency range but less than 1 in another. Therefore, feedback could increase the system gain in one frequency range but decrease it in another.

1.3.2 Effect of Feedback on Stability

Stability is a notion that describes whether the system will be able to follow the input command, or be used in general. In a nonrigorous manner, a system is said to be unstable if its output is out of control. To investigate the effect of feedback on stability, refer to Eq. (1.1). If $GH = -1$, the output of the system is infinite for any finite input and the system is said to be unstable. Therefore, we may state that feedback can cause a system that is originally stable to become unstable. Certainly, feedback is a two-edged sword, when used improperly, it can be harmful. In general, $GH = -1$ is not the only condition for instability.

One of the advantages of incorporating feedback is that it can stabilize an unstable system. Let us assume that the feedback system shown in Figure 1.3 is unstable because $GH = -1$. If we introduce another feedback loop through a negative feedback gain of F as shown in Figure 1.4, the input-output relation of the overall system is

$$\frac{c}{r} = \frac{G}{1 + GH + GF} \tag{1.2}$$

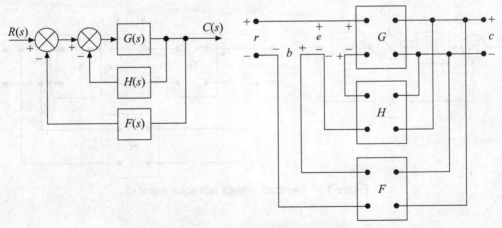

Figure 1.4 Feedback system with two feedback loops.

It is apparent that although the properties of G and H are such that the inner loop feedback system is unstable, because $GH = -1$, the overall system can be stable by proper selection of the outer loop feedback gain F. In practice, GH is a function of frequency, and the stability condition of the closed-loop system depends on the magnitude and phase of GH. So we can conclude that feedback can improve stability or be harmful to stability if it is not applied properly.

1.3.3   Effect of Feedback on External Disturbance or Noise

All physical systems are subject to some types of extraneous signals or noise during operation. Examples of these signals are thermal noise voltage in electronic circuits and brush or commutator noise in electric motors. External disturbances, for example wind gust acting on an antenna, are also quite common in control systems. Therefore, in the design of a control system, considerations should be given so that the system is insensitive to noise and disturbances and sensitive to input commands.

The effect of feedback on noise and disturbance depends greatly on where these extraneous signals occur in the system. No general conclusions can be reached, but in many situations, feedback can reduce the effect of noise and disturbance on system performance. Refer to Figure 1.5 in which r denotes the command signal and n is the noise signal. In the absence of feedback, $H = 0$, the output c due to n acting alone is

$$c = G_2 n \tag{1.3}$$

With the presence of feedback, the system output due to n acting alone is

$$c = \frac{G_2}{1 + G_1 G_2 H} n \tag{1.4}$$

Comparing Eqs. (1.3) and (1.4), we can conclude that the noise component in the output of Eq. (1.4) is reduced by a factor $1 + G_1 G_2 H$, if the latter is greater than unity and the system is kept stable.

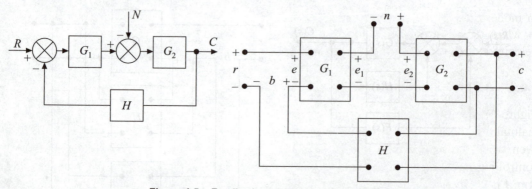

Figure 1.5   Feedback system with noise signal.

1.3.4 Effect of Feedback on Sensitivity

Sensitivity considerations often are important in the design of control systems. Since all physical elements have properties that change with environment and age, we cannot always consider the parameters of a control system to be completely stationary over the entire operating life of the system. For instance, the winding resistance of an electric motor changes as the temperature of the motor rises during operation.

In general, a good control system should be very insensitive to parameter variations but sensitive to input commands. Let us investigate what effect feedback has on the sensitivity to parameter variations. Referring to the general block diagram of a closed-loop control system of Figure 1.3, we consider G to be a gain parameter that may vary. The sensitivity of the gain of the overall system, M, to the variation in G is defined as

$$S_G^M = \frac{\partial M/M}{\partial G/G} = \frac{\text{Percentage change in } M}{\text{Percentage change in } G} \qquad (1.5)$$

where ∂M denotes the incremental change in M due to the incremental change in G, ∂G.

$$S_G^M = \frac{\partial M}{\partial G} \cdot \frac{G}{M} = \frac{1}{1 + GH} \qquad (1.6)$$

This relation shows that if GH is a positive constant, the magnitude of the sensitivity function can be made arbitrarily small by increasing GH, provided that the system remains stable. It is apparent that in an open-loop system, the gain of the system will respond in a one-to-one fashion to the variation in G. (i.e. $S_G^M = 1$). In practice, GH is a function of frequency: The magnitude of $1 + GH$ may be less than unity over some frequency ranges, so that feedback could be harmful to the sensitivity to parameter variations in certain cases. In general, the sensitivity of the system gain of a feedback system to parameter variations depends on where the parameter is located.

1.4 SERVOMECHANISM

In modern usage, the term servomechanism or servo is restricted to feedback control systems in which the controlled variable is mechanical position or time derivatives of position, e.g. velocity and acceleration. Few servo mechanisms are illustrated below.

1.4.1 Automatic Tank Level Control System

Figure 1.6 shows an automatic tank level control system. The purpose of this system is to maintain the liquid level h (output) in the tank as close to the desired liquid level H as possible, even when the output flow rate is varied by opening the valve $\dot{V}_1$. This has to be done by controlling the opening of the valve V_2. The potentiometer acts as an error detector. The slider arm A is positioned corresponding to the desired liquid level H (the reference input). The power amplifier and the motor drive form the control elements. The float forms the feedback path element. The valve V_2 to be controlled is the plant.

The liquid level is sensed by a float and it positions the slider arm *B* on the potentiometer. When the liquid level rises or falls, the potentiometer gives an error voltage proportional to the change in liquid level. The error voltage actuates the motor through a power amplifier which in turn conditions the plant (i.e. decreases or increases the opening of the valve V_2) in order to restore the desired liquid level. Thus, the control system automatically attempts to correct any deviation between the actual and desired liquid levels in the tank.

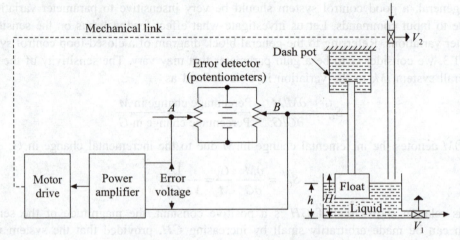

Figure 1.6   Automatic tank level control system.

1.4.2   A Position Control System

Figure 1.7 shows a servosystem used to position a load shaft. In this, the driving motor is geared to the load to be moved. The potentiometer is used as the error detector. The output and desired

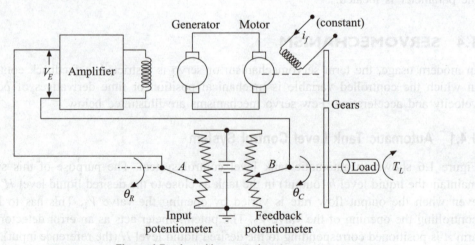

Figure 1.7   A position control system.

positions θ_C and θ_R respectively are measured and compared by the potentiometer pair whose output voltage V_E is proportional to the error in angular position $\theta_E = \theta_R - \theta_C$. The voltage $V_E = K_P\theta_E$ is amplified and is used to control the field current of a dc generator, which supplies armature voltage to the driving motor.

The position control systems have innumerable applications, namely machine tool position control, control of sheet metal thickness in hot rolling mills, radar tracking systems, missile guidance systems, etc.

1.4.3 DC Closed-Loop Control System

Figure 1.8 shows a typical dc (unmodulated) control system. The output signal θ_y represents the actual load position and the reference input θ_r represents the desired position of the load. A potentiometer error detector is used. The electrical error signal proportional to the difference in the positions of the actual and desired load positions is amplified by the dc amplifier and this output drives the dc motor which in turn through the gear box decides the position of the load. The signals are all unmodulated (i.e. dc).

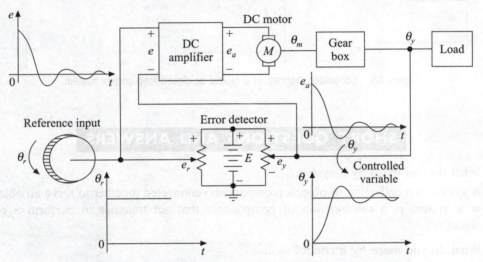

Figure 1.8 Schematic diagram of a typical dc closed-loop system.

1.4.4 AC Closed-Loop Control System

Figure 1.9 shows the schematic diagram of a typical ac control system. The output signal θ_y representing the load position is applied to the synchro control transformer. The reference input θ_r representing the desired output is applied to the synchro transmitter. The synchro pair acts as an error detector. The error signal is amplified by an ac amplifier and drives the ac servomotor which in turn positions the load through the gear box. The signals in this system are modulated (i.e. ac type).

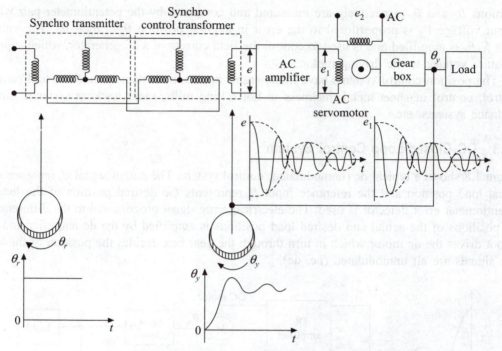

Figure 1.9 Schematic diagram of a typical ac closed-loop control system.

SHORT QUESTIONS AND ANSWERS

1. What do you mean by a system?

A. A system is a collection of objects (components) connected together to serve an objective, or a system is a combination of components that act together to perform a certain objective.

2. What do you mean by a control system?

A. A control system is that means by which any quantity of interest in a machine, mechanism, or some other equipment is maintained or altered in accordance with a desired manner. *or* A control system is a system in which the output quantity is controlled by varying the input quantity.

3. What do you mean by a physical system?

A. A physical system is a collection of physical objects connected together to serve an objective.

4. What do you mean by a physical model?

A. An idealized physical system is called a physical model.

5. What do you mean by a mathematical model?

A. The mathematical representation of the physical model is called the mathematical model.

6. When do you say that the mathematical model is linear?

A. A mathematical model is said to be linear, if the differential equation describing it has coefficients which are either functions only of the independent variable or are constants.

7. When do you say that the model is linear time-varying?

A. If the coefficients of the differential equation describing a system are functions of time (the independent variable), then the mathematical model is said to be linear time varying.

8. When do you say that the model is linear time-invariant?

A. If the coefficients of the differential equation describing a system are constants, then the model is said to be linear time-invariant.

9. How are control systems classified?

A. Control systems may be classified in a number of ways depending on the purpose of classification.

(a) Based on the hierarchy, control systems may be classified as
   (i) open-loop control systems
   (ii) closed-loop control systems
   (iii) optimal control systems
   (iv) adaptive control systems
   (v) learning control systems

(b) Based on the presence of human being as part of the system, control systems may be classified as
   (i) manually controlled systems
   (ii) automatic control systems

(c) Depending on the presence of feedback, control systems may be classified as
   (i) open-loop control systems
   (ii) closed-loop control systems or feedback control systems

(d) Based on the main purpose of the system, control systems may be classified as
   (i) position control systems
   (ii) velocity control systems
   (iii) traffic control systems
   (iv) temperature control systems, etc.

10. How are feedback control systems classified?

A. Feedback control systems may be classified in a number of ways depending on the purpose of classification.

(a) According to the method of analysis and design, control systems may be classified as linear control systems and nonlinear control systems.

(b) Depending on whether the parameters of the system remain constant or vary with time, control systems may be classified as time-invariant control systems and time-varying control systems.

(c) According to the types of signals used in the system, control systems may be classified as continuous-data control systems and discrete-data control systems or ac (modulated) control systems and dc (unmodulated) control systems.

(d) Depending on the application, control systems may be classified as position control systems, velocity control systems, etc.

(e) Depending on the number of inputs and outputs, control systems may be classified as single-input-single-output (SISO) control systems and multi-input-multi-output (MIMO) control systems. MIMO systems are also called multivariable systems.

(f) Depending on the number of open-loop poles of the system transfer function present at the origin of the *s*-plane, control systems may by classified as

(i) Type-0

(ii) Type-1,

(iii) Type-2, etc. control systems.

(g) Depending on the order of the differential equation used to describe the system, control systems may be classified as first-order control systems, second-order control systems, etc.

(h) Depending on the type of damping, control systems may be classified as

(i) undamped systems,

(ii) underdamped systems,

(iii) criticallydamped systems, and

(iv) overdamped systems.

11. What are the two major types of control systems?

A. The two major types of control systems are (a) open-loop control systems and (b) closed-loop control systems.

12. What do you mean by an open-loop control system?

A. An open-loop control system is one in which the output quantity has no effect on the input quantity, that means, the output is not fed back to the input for correction, i.e. a system in which there is no feedback is called an open-loop control system.

13. What do you mean by a closed-loop control system?

A. A closed-loop control system is one in which the output has an effect on the input. The output is fed back, compared with the reference input and the difference between them is used to control and bring the output of the system to a desired level.

14. What do you mean by feedback?

A. Feedback is a control action in which the output is sampled and a proportional signal is given to input for automatic correction of any changes in system output.

15. Which feedback is employed in control systems?

A. Negative feedback is employed in control systems.

16. What are the basic components of a closed-loop control system?

A. The basic components of a feedback control system are: plant, feedback path elements, error detector and controller.

17. Why negative feedback is preferred in control systems?

A. Negative feedback is invariably preferred in closed-loop control systems because negative feedback results in better stability in steady-state and rejects any disturbance signals. It also has low sensitivity to parameter variations.

18. What are the characteristics of negative feedback?

A. The characteristics of negative feedback are as follows:

    (a) Accuracy in tracking steady-state value

    (b) Rejection of disturbance signals

    (c) Low sensitivity to parameter variations

    (d) Reduction in gain at the expense of better stability

19. What is the effect of positive feedback on stability?

A. The effect of positive feedback on stability is—positive feedback increases the error signal and drives the output to instability, but some times positive feedback is used in minor loops in control systems to amplify certain internal signals or parameters.

20. Compare open-loop and closed-loop control systems.

A. Comparison of open-loop and closed-loop control systems is given in the following table:

Open-loop control systems	*Closed-loop control systems*
1. Inaccurate and unreliable.	1. Accurate and reliable.
2. Consume less power.	2. Consume more power.
3. Simple and economical.	3. Complex and costlier.
4. The changes in output due to external disturbances are not corrected automatically.	4. The changes in output due to external disturbances are corrected automatically.
5. They are generally stable.	5. Efforts are needed to design a stable system.

21. Distinguish between linear and nonlinear control systems.

A. A linear control system is one for which the principle of superposition and the principle of homogeneity are valid and a nonlinear control system is one for which the principle of superposition and the principle of homogeneity are not valid.

22. State the principle of superposition.

A. The principle of superposition states that the response produced by the simultaneous application of two different forcing functions is equal to the sum of the two individual responses.

23. Distinguish between time-invariant and time-varying control systems.

A. A time-invariant control system is one in which the parameters of the system are stationary with respect to time during the operation of the system. Its output characteristics do not change with time and it can be represented by constant coefficient differential equations.

A time-varying control system is one in which the parameters of the system are not stationary with respect to time during the operation of the system, i.e. the parameters of the system vary with time. Its output characteristics change with time and the coefficients of its differential equation are functions of time.

24. Distinguish between continuous-data and discrete-data control systems.

A. A continuous-data control system is one in which the signals at various parts of the system are all functions of the continuous time variable.

A discrete-data control system is one in which the signals at one or more points in the system are either in the form of a pulse train or a digital code.

25. Distinguish between ac and dc control systems.

A. The ac control systems are those in which the signals are modulated. The dc control systems are those in which the signals are not pure dc, but they are unmodulated.

26. Distinguish between sampled-data and digital control systems.

A. A sampled-data control system refers to a more general class of discrete-data control systems in which the signals are in the form of pulsed-data.

A digital control system is one which uses a digital computer or controller so that the signals are digitally coded.

27. What is the advantage of sampling?

A. One important advantage of the sampling operation is that expensive equipment used in the system may be time shared among several control channels.

28. What is the effect of feedback on overall gain?

A. The feedback affects the gain G of a nonfeedback system by a factor $1/(1 + GH)$. In a practical control system, G and H are functions of frequency, so the magnitude of $1 + GH$ may be greater than 1 in one frequency range but less than 1 in another. Therefore, feedback could increase the system gain in one frequency range but decrease it in another.

29. What is the effect of feedback on stability?

A. Feedback may cause a system that is originally stable to become unstable. In some cases feedback can stabilise an unstable system. So feedback is a two-edged sword, when used improperly it can be harmful.

30. What is the effect of feedback on external disturbance?

A. The effect of feedback on noise and disturbance depends greatly on where these extraneous signals occur in the system. No general conclusions can be reached, but in many situations feedback can reduce the effect of noise and disturbance on system performance.

31. What is the effect of feedback on sensitivity?

A. In general, a good control system should be very insensitive to parameter variations but sensitive to input commands. Feedback could be harmful to the sensitivity to parameter variations in certain cases. In general, the sensitivity of the system gain of a feedback system to parameter variations depends on where the parameter is located.

REVIEW QUESTIONS

1. With a neat diagram explain the working of an automatic tank level control system.
2. With a neat diagram explain the working of a position control system.
3. With a neat diagram explain the working of a dc position control system.
4. With a neat diagram explain the working of an ac position control system.

FILL IN THE BLANKS

1. A physical system is a collection of _____ connected together.
2. An idealized physical system is called a _____.
3. The mathematical representation of the _____ is called the mathematical model.
4. Based on the hierarchy, control systems may be classified as (i) _____ (ii) _____ (iii) _____ (iv) _____ and (v) _____.
5. Based on the presence of human being as part of the system, control systems may be classified as (i) _____ and (ii) _____.
6. Depending on the presence of feedback, control systems may be classified as (i) _____ and (ii) _____.
7. Based on the main purpose of the system, control systems may be classified as (i) _____ (ii) _____ (iii) _____, etc.
8. According to the method of analysis and design, control systems may be classified as (i) _____ and (ii) _____.
9. Depending on whether the parameters of the system remain constant or vary with time, control systems may be classified as (i) _____ and (ii) _____.
10. According to the type of signals used in the system, control systems may be classified as (i) _____ and (ii) _____ or (i) _____ and (ii) _____.
11. Depending on the application, control systems may be classified as (i) _____ (ii) _____ (iii) _____, etc.
12. Depending on the number of inputs and outputs, control systems may be classified as (i) _____ and (ii) _____.
13. Depending on the number of open-loop poles of the system transfer function present at the origin of the *s*-plane, control systems may be classified as (i) _____ (ii) _____ (iii) _____ systems, etc.
14. Depending on the order of the differential equation used to describe the system, control systems may be classified as (i) _____ (ii) _____ (iii) _____ etc.
15. Depending on the type of damping, control systems may be classified as (i) _____ (ii) _____ (iii) _____ and (iv) _____.
16. The two major types of control systems are (i) _____ and (ii) _____.

17. An open-loop control system is one in which the _____ has no effect on the
_____.

18. A closed-loop control system is one in which the _____ has an effect on the _____.

19. _____ feedback is employed in control systems.

20. The basic components of a feedback control system are (i) _____ (ii) _____
(iii) _____ and (iv) _____.

21. A linear control system is one for which the _____ and the _____ are valid.

22. In ac systems, the signals are _____ whereas in dc systems the signals are _____.

23. Sampling may be _____ or _____.

2
Mathematical Models
of Physical Systems

2.1 MODELLING OF MECHANICAL SYSTEM ELEMENTS

Most control systems contain mechanical as well as electrical components, although some systems even have hydraulic and pneumatic elements. From a mathematical view point, the descriptions of mechanical and electrical elements are analogous. In fact, we can show that given an electrical device, there is usually an analogous mechanical counterpart mathematically and vice versa.

The motion of mechanical elements can be described in various dimensions as translational, rotational, or combinations. The equations governing the motion of mechanical systems are often formulated directly or indirectly from Newton's law of motion. Mechanical translational systems are those in which the motion takes place along a straight line. The variables that are used to describe the translational motion are acceleration, velocity and displacement. Newton's law of motion for translational systems states that the algebraic sum of forces acting on a rigid body in a given direction is equal to the product of the mass of the body and its acceleration in the same direction. This law can be expressed as

$$\sum \text{Forces} = Ma(t) = M\frac{dv(t)}{dt} = M\frac{d^2x(t)}{dt^2}$$

where M denotes the mass of the body and $a(t)$ is the acceleration of the body in the direction considered, $v(t)$ is the linear velocity of the body and $x(t)$ is the displacement of the body.

Mechanical translational systems are modelled by three ideal elements: mass, spring, and damper.

1. Mass: Mass is considered as a property of an element that stores the kinetic energy of translation motion. If W denotes the weight of a body, the mass M is given by

$$M = \frac{W}{g}$$

where g is the acceleration of free fall of the body due to gravity. One end of mass is always connected to the ground.

21

2. Linear Spring: In practice, a linear spring may be a model of a natural spring or a compliance of a cable or belt. In general, a spring is considered to be an element that stores potential energy. All springs in real life are nonlinear to some extent. However, if the deformation of the spring is small, its behaviour can be approximated by a linear relationship.

3. Friction: Whenever there is motion or tendency of motion between two physical elements, frictional forces exist. The frictional forces encountered in physical systems are usually of a nonlinear nature. Three different types of friction are commonly used in practical systems: viscous friction, static friction and coulomb friction.

(a) *Coulomb friction force:* This is the force of sliding friction between dry surfaces. Coulomb friction force is substantially constant.

(b) *Viscous friction force:* This is the force of friction between moving surfaces separated by viscous fluid or the force between a solid body and a fluid medium. Viscous friction force is approximately linearly proportional to velocity over a certain limited velocity range.

(c) *Stiction:* This is the force required to initiate motion between two contacting surfaces.

In most physical situations of interest, the viscous friction predominates. The friction force acts in a direction opposite to that of velocity. The element for viscous friction is often represented by a dash pot.

The translational elements and the corresponding equations of motion are shown in Figure 2.1(a).

1. The mass element

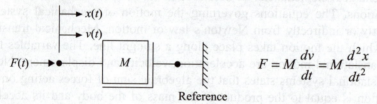

$$F = M\frac{dv}{dt} = M\frac{d^2x}{dt^2}$$

2. The spring element

$$F = K(x_1 - x_2) = Kx$$

$$= K\int_{-\infty}^{t} (v_1 - v_2)\, dt = K\int_{-\infty}^{t} v\, dt$$

3. The damper element

$$F = f(v_1 - v_2) = fv$$

$$= f(\dot{x}_1 - \dot{x}_2) = f\dot{x}$$

The units are x(m), v(m/s), M(kg), F(N), K(N/m), f(N/m/s)

Figure 2.1(a) Ideal elements for mechanical translational systems.

Mechanical rotational systems are those in which the motion is about a fixed axis. Newton's law of motion for rotational systems states that the algebraic sum of moments or torques about a fixed axis is equal to the product of the inertia and the angular acceleration about the axis; or

$$\sum \text{Torques} = J\alpha(t) = J\frac{d\omega(t)}{dt} = J\frac{d^2\theta(t)}{dt^2}$$

where $\theta(t)$ is the angular displacement, $\omega(t)$ is the angular velocity and $\alpha(t)$ is the angular acceleration.

Mechanical rotational systems are modelled by three ideal elements: inertia, torsional spring, and damper.

1. Inertia: Inertia, J, is considered to be the property of an element that stores the kinetic energy of rotational motion. The inertia of a given element depends on the geometric composition about the axis of rotation and its density. One end of the inertia element is always connected to ground.

2. Torsional spring: As with the linear spring for translational motion, a torsional spring constant K can be deviced to represent the compliance of a rod or a shaft when it is subjected to an applied Torque.

3. Friction: The three types of friction for rotational systems are (a) coulomb friction, (b) viscous friction, and (c) stiction—same as for translational systems. Out of these three, viscous friction is the dominant one. This element is often represented by a dash pot.

The rotational elements and the corresponding equations of motion are shown in Figure 2.1(b).

1. The inertia element

$$T = J\frac{d\omega}{dt} = J\frac{d^2\theta}{dt^2}$$

2. The torsional spring element

$$T = K(\theta_1 - \theta_2) = K\theta$$
$$= K\int_{-\infty}^{t}(\omega_1 - \omega_2)\,dt = K\int_{-\infty}^{t}\omega\,dt$$

3. The damper element

$$T = f(\omega_1 - \omega_2) = f\omega$$
$$= f(\dot{\theta}_1 - \dot{\theta}_2) = f\dot{\theta}$$

The units are θ (rad), ω (rad/s), J (kg-m^2), T (N-m), K (N-m/rad), f (N-m/rad/s)

Figure 2.1(b)   Ideal elements for mechanical rotational systems.

2.1.1 Translational Systems

Consider the mechanical system shown in Figure 2.2 (a). It is simply a mass M attached to a spring (stiffness K) and a dash pot (viscous friction coefficient f) on which the force F acts. Displacement x is positive in the direction shown. Let v be the velocity. The zero position is taken to be at the point where the spring and mass are in static equilibrium.

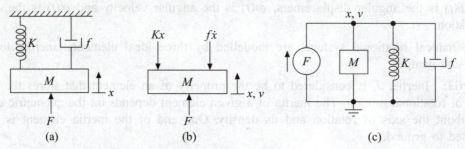

Figure 2.2 (a) Translational system, (b) free-body diagram, and (c) mechanical network.

The systematic way of analyzing such a system is to draw a free-body diagram or mechanical network as shown in Figures 2.2(b) and 2.2(c) respectively. Then, by applying Newton's law of motion (which states that the algebraic sum of the forces acting on a rigid body in a given direction is equal to the product of the mass of the body and its acceleration in the same direction) to the free-body diagram or mechanical network, the force equation can be written in terms of displacement x or velocity v as follows:

$$F - f\frac{dx}{dt} - Kx = M\frac{d^2x}{dt^2} \qquad \text{or} \qquad F = M\frac{d^2x}{dt^2} + f\frac{dx}{dt} + Kx$$

i.e.
$$F - fv - K\int v\,dt = M\frac{dv}{dt} \qquad \text{or} \qquad F = M\frac{dv}{dt} + fv + K\int v\,dt$$

This is a linear, constant coefficient differential equation describing the dynamics of the mechanical system shown in Figure 2.2(a).

The free-body diagram is drawn like this: the free-body diagram for a translational system indicates the elements masses M and all the forces acting on them. For the system shown in Figure 2.2(a), there is only one mass M. An external force F is acting on it to move it by a distance x or with a velocity v. This motion is opposed by the force components of mass M, i.e. $M\ddot{x}$ and the force components due to spring, i.e. Kx and damper, i.e. $f\dot{x}$. So, the free-body diagram is as shown in Figure 2.2(b).

In the free-body diagram, F is the external force applied on the mass M. It is being opposed by the forces $f\dot{x}$ and Kx. The algebraic sum of these three forces, i.e. $F - Kx - f\dot{x}$ is equal to the product of the mass and acceleration of the body, i.e. $M\ddot{x}$. Therefore,

$$F - Kx - f\dot{x} = M\ddot{x}$$

is the governing equation.

The mechanical network for the given translational system of Figure 2.2(a) is drawn like this: one end of F is to be grounded. Also one end of M is to be grounded. So one end of F and M is grounded. The other end of F is connected to the other end of M because F is applied on M. In the mechanical system, one end of K and f is grounded and the other ends of K and f are connected to the free end of M. So in the mechanical network also one end of K and f is grounded and the other ends are connected to the free end of M.

Once a mechanical network is drawn, the differential equations can be written very easily at each node assuming that the displacement or velocity at the node under consideration is higher than the displacement or velocity at all other nodes. In Figure 2.2, only one node is there, the other node is the reference or ground node. Only external force F is towards the node. All other forces, i.e. $M\ddot{x}$, $f\dot{x}$ and Kx are directed away from the node. Now the differential equation is like KCL equation for electrical circuits which says that the sum of currents coming into the node is equal to the sum of currents going out of the node. The force components are similar to currents. Therefore the force $F(t)$ directed towards the node is equal to the sum of the force components $M\ddot{x}$, $f\dot{x}$ and Kx directed away from the node. Therefore, the equation of motion is

$$F = M\frac{d^2x}{dt^2} + f\frac{dx}{dt} + Kx$$

2.1.2 Rotational Systems

Consider the mechanical rotational system shown in Figure 2.3(a) which consists of a rotatable disc of moment of inertia J and a shaft of stiffness K. The disc rotates in a viscous medium with viscous friction coefficient f.

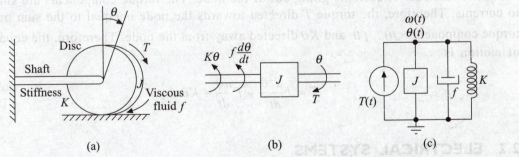

Figure 2.3 (a) Rotational system, (b) free-body diagram, and (c) mechanical network.

Let T be the applied torque which tends to rotate the disc. The free-body diagram and the mechanical network are shown in Figure 2.3(b) and Figure 2.3(c) respectively.

The free-body diagram is drawn like this: the free-body diagram for a rotational system indicates the inertia elements J and all the torques acting on them. For the system shown in

Figure 2.3(a), there is only one inertia element J. An external torque T is acting on it to move it by an angle θ or with an angular velocity ω. This angular motion is opposed by the torque component of J, i.e. $J\ddot{\theta}$ and the torque components due to damper, i.e. $f\dot{\theta}$ and spring, i.e. $K\theta$. So the free-body diagram is drawn as shown in Figure 2.3(b).

In the free-body diagram, T is the external torque applied on the inertia J. It is being opposed by the torques $f\dot{\theta}$ and $K\theta$. The algebraic sum of these three torques is $T - f\dot{\theta} - K\theta$ which is equal to the product of the inertia and angular acceleration of the body, i.e. $J\ddot{\theta}$. Therefore,

$$T - f\frac{d\theta}{dt} - K\theta = J\frac{d^2\theta}{dt^2}$$

is the governing equation.

The mechanical network for the given rotational system of Figure 2.3(a) is drawn like this: one end of T is to be grounded. Also one end of J is to be connected to ground. So one end of T and J is grounded. The other end of T is connected to the other end of J because T is applied on J. In the mechanical system of Figure 2.3(a), one end of f and K is grounded and the other ends are connected to the free end of J. So in the mechanical network also one end of f and K is grounded and the other end is connected to the free end of J.

Once a mechanical network is drawn, the differential equations can be written very easily at each node assuming that the angular displacement or angular velocity at the node under consideration is higher than the angular displacement or angular velocity at all other nodes. In Figure 2.3 only one node is there, the other node is the reference or ground node. Only external torque T is towards the node. All other torques, i.e. $J\ddot{\theta}$, $f\dot{\theta}$ and $K\theta$ are directed away from the node. Now the differential equation is like KCL equation for electrical circuits which says that the sum of currents coming into the node is equal to the sum of currents going out of the node. The torque components are similar to currents. Therefore, the torque T directed towards the node is equal to the sum of the torque components $J\ddot{\theta}$, $f\dot{\theta}$ and $K\theta$ directed away from the node. Therefore, the equation of motion is

$$T = J\frac{d^2\theta}{dt^2} + f\frac{d\theta}{dt} + K\theta$$

2.2 ELECTRICAL SYSTEMS

The resistor, inductor, and capacitor are the three basic elements of electrical circuits. These circuits are analyzed by the application of Kirchoff's voltage and current laws. Out of these three basic elements, inductor and capacitor are the energy storage elements and resistor is the energy dissipative element.

Consider the *R-L-C* series circuit shown in Figure 2.4(a). The equations describing the behaviour of the system in terms of current are as follows:

$$L\frac{di}{dt} + Ri + \frac{1}{C}\int idt = e$$

$$e_o = \frac{1}{C}\int idt$$

$$e_o = e_c$$

In terms of electric charge, $q = \int idt$, the describing equations are as follows:

$$L\frac{d^2q}{dt^2} + R\frac{dq}{dt} + \frac{1}{C}q = e$$

$$e_o = \frac{q}{c}$$

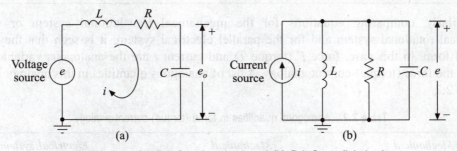

Figure 2.4   (a) *R-L-C* series circuit and (b) *R-L-C* parallel circuit

Similarly, for the *R-L-C* parallel circuit shown in Figure 2.4(b), the describing equation in terms of voltage using Kirchoff's current law is as follows:

$$C\frac{de}{dt} + \frac{e}{R} + \frac{1}{L}\int_{-\infty}^{t} edt = i$$

In terms of magnetic flux linkage, $\phi = \int e\, dt$, the describing equation is as follows:

$$C\frac{d^2\phi}{dt^2} + \frac{1}{R}\frac{d\phi}{dt} + \frac{1}{L}\phi = i$$

2.3 ANALOGOUS SYSTEMS

Comparing equations for the mechanical translational system or for the mechanical rotational system and for the series electrical system, it is seen that they are of identical form. Such systems whose differential equations are of identical form are called *analogous systems*. The force F (torque T) and voltage e are the analogous variables here. This is called the force (torque)-voltage analogy. A list of analogous variables in this analogy is given in Table 2.1.

Table 2.1 Analogous quantities in force (torque)-voltage analogy

Mechanical translational system	*Mechanical rotational system*	*Electrical system*
Force F	Torque T	Voltage e
Mass M	Moment of inertia J	Inductance L
Viscous friction coefficient f	Viscous friction coefficient f	Resistance R
Spring stiffness K	Torsional spring stiffness K	Reciprocal of capacitance $1/C$
Displacement x	Angular displacement θ	Charge q
Velocity v	Angular velocity ω	Current i

Similarly, comparing equations for the mechanical translational system or for the mechanical rotational system and for the parallel electrical system, it is seen that they are of identical form. In this case, force F (torque T) and current i are the analogous variables. This is called the force (torque)-current analogy. A list of analogous quantities in this analogy is given in Table 2.2.

Table 2.2 Analogous quantities in force (torque)-current analogy

Mechanical translational system	*Mechanical rotational system*	*Electrical system*
Force F	Torque T	Current i
Mass M	Moment of inertia J	Capacitance C
Viscous friction coefficient f	Viscous friction coefficient f	Reciprocal of resistance $1/R$
Spring stiffness K	Torsional spring stiffness K	Reciprocal of inductance $1/L$
Displacement x	Angular displacement θ	Magnetic flux linkage ϕ
Velocity v	Angular velocity ω	Voltage e

The concept of analogous system is a useful technique for the study of various systems like electrical, mechanical, thermal, hydraulic, etc. If the solution of one system is obtained, it can be extended to all other systems analogous to it. Generally, it is convenient to study a non-electrical system in terms of its electrical analog as electrical systems are more easily amenable to experimental study.

In this book, we study the systems using linear systems theory. There are two ways of justifying the linear systems approach. One is that the system is basically linear, or the system is operated in the linear region so that most of the conditions of linearity are satisfied. The second is that the system is basically nonlinear or operated in a nonlinear region, but to apply the linear analysis and design tools, we linearize the system about a nominal operating point. The analysis is applicable only for the range of variables in which the linearization is valid.

2.3.1 Impulse Response and Transfer Functions of Linear Systems

The classical way of modelling linear systems is to use transfer functions to represent input-output relations between variables. One way to define the transfer function is to use the impulse response which is defined as follows:

Impulse response: Consider that a linear time-invariant system has the input $r(t)$ and the output $c(t)$. The system can be characterized by its impulse response $g(t)$, which is defined as the output when the input is a unit impulse function $\delta(t)$. Once the impulse response of a linear system is known, the output of the system, $c(t)$, with any input $r(t)$ can be found by using the transfer function.

2.4 TRANSFER FUNCTION: SINGLE-INPUT-SINGLE-OUTPUT SYSTEMS

The transfer function of a linear time-invariant system is defined as the Laplace transform of the impulse response, with all the initial conditions set to zero. Let $G(s)$ denote the transfer function of a single-input-single-output system, with input $r(t)$ and output $c(t)$ and impulse response $g(t)$. Then the transfer function $G(s)$ is defined as

$$G(s) = L\ [g(t)]$$

The transfer function $G(s)$ is related to the Laplace transform of the input and the output through the following relation

$$G(s) = \frac{C(s)}{R(s)}$$

with all the initial conditions set to zero, and $C(s)$ and $R(s)$ are the Laplace transforms of $c(t)$ and $r(t)$ respectively. That is the transfer function is defined as the ratio of the Laplace transform of the output to the Laplace transform of the input with all initial conditions neglected.

Although the transfer function of a linear system is defined in terms of the impulse response, in practice, the input-output relation of a linear time-invariant system with continuous data input is often described by a differential equation, so that it is more convenient to derive the transfer function directly from the differential equation. Let us consider that the input-output relation of a linear time-invariant system is described by the following nth order differential equation with constant real coefficients.

$$a_0 \frac{d^n c(t)}{dt^n} + a_1 \frac{d^{n-1} c(t)}{dt^{n-1}} + a_2 \frac{d^{n-2} c(t)}{dt^{n-2}} + \cdots + a_{n-1} \frac{dc(t)}{dt} + a_n c(t)$$

$$= b_0 \frac{d^m r(t)}{dt^m} + b_1 \frac{d^{m-1} r(t)}{dt^{m-1}} + \cdots + b_{m-1} \frac{dr(t)}{dt} + b_m r(t) \tag{2.1}$$

Once the input $r(t)$ for $t \geq t_0$ and the initial conditions of $c(t)$ and derivatives of $c(t)$ are specified at the initial time $t = t_0$, the output response $c(t)$ for $t \geq t_0$ is determined by solving Eq. (2.1). However, the solution of higher-order differential equations is quite tedious. So the analysis and design of linear systems is done using transfer functions.

To obtain the transfer function of the linear system, simply take the Laplace transform on both sides of Eq. (2.1) and assume zero initial conditions.

The result is

$$(a_0 s^n + a_1 s^{n-1} + \cdots + a_{n-1}s + a_n) \, C(s) = (b_0 s^m + b_1 s^{m-1} + \cdots + b_{m-1}s + b_m) \, R(s)$$

The transfer function between $r(t)$ and $c(t)$ is given by

$$G(s) = \frac{C(s)}{R(s)} = \frac{b_0 s^m + b_1 s^{m-1} + \cdots + b_{m-1}s + b_m}{a_0 s^n + a_1 s^{n-1} + a_2 s^{n-2} + \cdots + a_{n-1}s + a_n}$$

The properties of the transfer function are as follows:

1. The transfer function is defined only for a linear time-invariant system. It is not defined for nonlinear systems.

2. The transfer function between an input variable and an output variable of a system is defined as the Laplace transform of the impulse response.

   Alternatively, the transfer function between a pair of input and output variables of a system is the ratio of the Laplace transform of the output to the Laplace transform of the input.

3. All initial conditions of the system are set to zero.

4. The transfer function is independent of the input of the system.

5. The transfer function of a continuous-data system is expressed only as a function of the complex variable s. It is not a function of the real variable time, or any other variable that is used as the independent variable. For discrete-data systems modelled by difference equations, the transfer function is a function of z when the z-transform is used.

2.4.1 Proper Transfer Function

The transfer function is said to be strictly proper, if the order of the denominator polynomial is greater than that of the numerator polynomial (i.e. $n > m$). The transfer function is said to be proper, if the order of the numerator polynomial is equal to that of the denominator polynomial (i.e. $m = n$). The transfer function is said to be improper, if the order of the numerator polynomial is greater than that of the denominator polynomial (i.e. $m > n$).

2.4.2 Characteristic Equation

The characteristic equation of a linear system is defined as the equation obtained by setting the denominator polynomial of the transfer function to zero. Thus, the characteristic equation of the system described above is

$$a_0 s^n + a_1 s^{n-1} + a_2 s^{n-2} + \cdots + a_{n-1} s + a_n = 0 \qquad (2.2)$$

Equation (2.2) is called the *characteristic equation* because it characterizes the behaviour of the system.

The stability of linear single-input-single-output systems is governed completely by the roots of the characteristic equation.

2.5 TRANSFER FUNCTION (MULTIVARIABLE SYSTEMS)

The definition of a transfer function is easily extended to a system with multiple inputs and outputs. A system of this type is often referred to as a *multivariable system*. In a multivariable system, a differential equation of the form described above may be used to describe the relationship between an input-output pair, when all other inputs are set to zero. Since the principle of superposition is valid for linear systems, the total effect on any output due to all the inputs acting simultaneously is obtained by adding up the outputs due to each input acting alone.

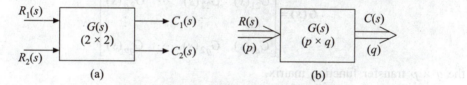

Figure 2.5 Multivariable systems.

If a system has two inputs and two outputs as shown in Figure 2.5(a), then the outputs are given by

$$C_1(s) = G_{11}(s)\,R_1(s) + G_{12}(s)\,R_2(s)$$

$$C_2(s) = G_{21}(s)\,R_1(s) + G_{22}(s)\,R_2(s)$$

The transfer function $G_{11}(s)$ represents the transfer function between output 1 and input 1 when input 2 is zero. Similar definitions can be given to the other transfer functions, $G_{12}(s)$, $G_{21}(s)$ and $G_{22}(s)$.

In general, if a linear system has p inputs and q outputs as shown in Figure 2.5(b), the transfer function between the jth input and the ith output is defined as

$$G_{ij}(s) = \frac{C_i(s)}{R_j(s)}$$

with $R_k(s) = 0$, $k = 1, 2, \ldots, p$, $k \neq j$. Note that $G_{ij}(s)$ is defined with only the jth input in effect, whereas the other inputs are set to zero. When all the p inputs are in action, the ith output transform is written as

$$C_i(s) = G_{i1}(s)R_1(s) + G_{i2}(s)R_2(s) + \cdots + G_{ip}(s)R_p(s)$$

In vector-matrix form, the input-output relation of a multivariable system is

$$\boldsymbol{C(s) = G(s)R(s)}$$

where
$$C(s) = \begin{bmatrix} C_1(s) \\ C_2(s) \\ \vdots \\ C_q(s) \end{bmatrix}$$

is the $q \times 1$ transformed output vector,

$$R(s) = \begin{bmatrix} R_1(s) \\ R_2(s) \\ \vdots \\ R_p(s) \end{bmatrix}$$

is the $p \times 1$ transformed input vector; and

$$G(s) = \begin{bmatrix} G_{11}(s) & G_{12}(s) & \cdots & G_{1p}(s) \\ G_{21}(s) & G_{22}(s) & \cdots & G_{2p}(s) \\ \vdots & \vdots & & \vdots \\ G_{q1}(s) & G_{q2}(s) & \cdots & G_{qp}(s) \end{bmatrix}$$

is the $q \times p$ transfer function matrix.

2.5.1 Sinusoidal Transfer Function

The steady-state response of a control system to a sinusoidal input is obtained by replacing s with $j\omega$ in the transfer function of the system.

The transfer function obtained by replacing s with $j\omega$ in the original transfer function is called the *sinusoidal transfer function*.

2.6 PROCEDURE FOR DERIVING TRANSFER FUNCTIONS

The following assumptions are made in deriving transfer functions of physical systems.

1. It is assumed that there is no loading, i.e. no power is drawn at the output of the system. If the system has more than one non-loading elements in cascade, then the transfer function of each element can be determined independently, and the overall transfer function of the physical system is determined by multiplying the individual transfer functions. In case of systems consisting of elements which load each other, the overall transfer function should be derived by basic analysis without regard to individual transfer functions.

2. The systems should be approximated by linear, lumped, constant parameter models by making suitable assumptions.

To illustrate point 1 above, let us consider two identical *RC* circuits connected in cascade so that the output from the first circuit is fed as input to the second as shown in Figure 2.6.

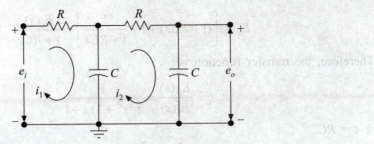

Figure 2.6 RC circuits in cascade.

The describing equations for this system are as follows:

$$\frac{1}{C}\int_{-\infty}^{t}(i_1 - i_2)dt + Ri_1 = e_i \tag{2.3}$$

$$\frac{1}{C}\int_{-\infty}^{t}(i_2 - i_1)dt + Ri_2 = -\frac{1}{C}\int i_2 dt = -e_o \tag{2.4}$$

Taking the Laplace transform of Eqs. (2.3) and (2.4), assuming zero initial conditions, we obtain

$$\frac{1}{Cs}[I_1(s) - I_2(s)] + RI_1(s) = E_i(s) \tag{2.5}$$

$$\frac{1}{Cs}[I_2(s) - I_1(s)] + RI_2(s) = -\frac{1}{Cs}I_2(s) = -E_o(s) \tag{2.6}$$

Reorganizing Eq. (2.5), we get

$$I_1(s)\left[R + \frac{1}{Cs}\right] = E_i(s) + \frac{1}{Cs}I_2(s)$$

or

$$I_1(s) = \frac{E_i(s) + \dfrac{1}{Cs}I_2(s)}{R + \dfrac{1}{Cs}} = \frac{CsE_i(s) + I_2(s)}{1 + RCs} \tag{2.7}$$

Reorganizing Eq. (2.6), we get

$$I_2(s)\left[R + \frac{1}{Cs}\right] - \frac{I_1(s)}{Cs} = -E_o(s)$$

Substituting the value of $I_1(s)$ from Eq. (2.7) in the above equation, we get

$$I_2(s)\left[R + \frac{1}{Cs}\right] - \frac{CsE_i(s) + I_2(s)}{Cs(1 + RCs)} = -E_o(s)$$

i.e.

$$CsE_o(s)\left[\frac{1 + RCs}{Cs}\right] - \frac{E_i(s)}{1 + RCs} - \frac{CsE_o(s)}{Cs(1 + RCs)} = -E_o(s) \qquad [\because I_2(s) = CsE_o(s)]$$

or

$$E_o(s)\left[(1+RCs)+1-\frac{1}{1+RCs}\right]=\frac{E_i(s)}{1+RCs}$$

Therefore, the transfer function is

$$\frac{E_o(s)}{E_i(s)}=\frac{1}{\tau^2 s^2+3\tau s+1}$$

where $\tau = RC$.

The transfer function of each of the individual RC circuits is

$$\frac{\dfrac{1}{Cs}}{R+\dfrac{1}{Cs}}=\frac{1}{1+RCs}=\frac{1}{1+\tau s}$$

If there is no loading, the overall transfer function of the two RC circuits connected in cascade is

$$\frac{1}{1+\tau s}\times\frac{1}{1+\tau s}=\frac{1}{\tau^2 s^2+2\tau s+1}$$

The difference in the transfer functions is due to the fact that while deriving the transfer function of a single RC circuit, it is assumed that the output is unloaded. However, when the input of the second circuit is obtained from the output of the first, a certain amount of energy is drawn from the first circuit and hence its original transfer function is no longer valid. The degree to which the overall transfer function is modified from the product of individual transfer functions depends upon the amount of loading.

Example 2.1   For the mass-spring dashpot system shown in Figure 2.7(a), obtain the transfer function. Also obtain the analogous electrical network based on (a) force-voltage analogy and (b) force-current analogy.

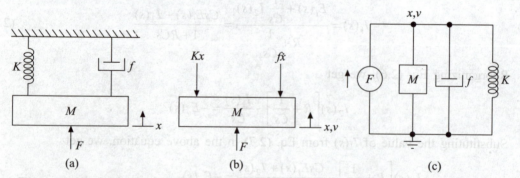

Figure 2.7   Example 2.1: (a) mechanical system, (b) free-body diagram and (c) mechanical network.

Solution: The free-body diagram of the mechanical system of Figure 2.7(a) is shown in Figure 2.7(b). Applying Newton's law of motion that the algebraic sum of the forces acting on a rigid body = mass × acceleration, the equation of motion is

$$F - f\frac{dx}{dt} - Kx = M\frac{d^2x}{dt^2}$$

i.e.

$$F = M\frac{d^2x}{dt^2} + f\frac{dx}{dt} + Kx$$

or

$$F = M\frac{dv}{dt} + fv + K\int v.dt$$

Taking the Laplace transform on both sides and neglecting the initial conditions,

$$F(s) = Ms^2X(s) + fsX(s) + KX(s)$$

∴ Transfer function $= \dfrac{X(s)}{F(s)} = \dfrac{1}{Ms^2 + fs + K}$

Alternative way: For the given mechanical system, first draw the mechanical network shown in Figure 2.7(c).

There is only one node. Let the node variable be displacement x or velocity v. One end of all the three elements is connected to ground so the displacement of that end is zero. The other end of the three elements has a displacement x or velocity v. So the describing equation is

$$F = M\frac{d^2x}{dt^2} + f\frac{dx}{dt} + Kx$$

or

$$F = M\frac{dv}{dt} + fv + K\int vdt$$

The analogous equation of the electrical circuit based on force-current analogy is

$$i = C\frac{d^2\phi}{dt^2} + \frac{1}{R}\frac{d\phi}{dt} + \frac{1}{L}\phi$$

or

$$i = C\frac{de}{dt} + \frac{e}{R} + \frac{1}{L}\int edt$$

and the analogous electrical network is as shown in Figure 2.8(a). It is exactly identical to the mechanical network. Once the mechanical network of a translational system is drawn, the analogous electrical network based on force-current analogy can be easily drawn like this: the structure of the electrical network is exactly the same as the structure of the mechanical network, i.e. series elements in the mechanical network remain as series elements in the electrical network and shunt elements in the mechanical network remain as shunt elements in the electrical network. Just replace the force $F(t)$ by a current source $i(t)$ $(= F(t))$, mass M by capacitance C $(= M)$, friction f by resistance R $(= 1/f)$, spring K by inductance L $(= 1/K)$, displacement x by flux ϕ, and velocity v by voltage e. The node equations of the electrical network will be analogous to the node equations of the mechanical network.

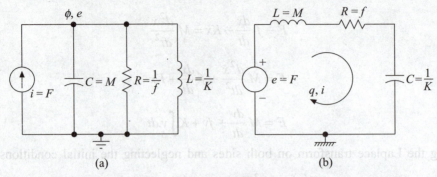

(a) (b)

Figure 2.8 Example 2.1: (a) analogous electrical circuit based on *F-i* analogy and, (b) analogous electrical circuit based on *F-v* analogy.

The analogous equation of the electrical circuit based on force-voltage analogy is

$$e = L\frac{d^2q}{dt^2} + R\frac{dq}{dt} + \frac{1}{C}q$$

or

$$e = L\frac{di}{dt} + Ri + \frac{1}{C}\int idt$$

and the analogous electrical network is as shown in Figure 2.8(b). Once a mechanical network is available, the analogous electrical network based on force-voltage analogy can be drawn easily like this. In this, the series elements of the mechanical network become analogous shunt elements and the shunt elements of the mechanical network become analogous series elements. Replace the force $F(t)$ by a voltage source $e(t)$ $(= F(t))$, mass M by inductance L $(= M)$, friction f by resistance R $(= f)$, spring K by capacitance C $(= 1/K)$, displacement x by charge q and velocity v by current $i(t)$. The loop equations will be analogous to the node equations of mechanical network.

Example 2.2 Write the torque equations of the rotational system shown in Figure 2.9(a). Obtain the transfer function $\dfrac{\theta(s)}{E(s)}$. Also obtain the analogous electrical network based on (a) force-voltage analogy and (b) force-current analogy.

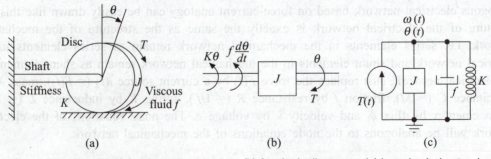

(a) (b) (c)

Figure 2.9 Example 2.2: (a) rotational system, (b) free-body diagram and (c) mechanical network.

Solution: The free-body diagram of the mechanical system of Figure 2.9(a) is shown in Figure 2.9(b). Applying Newton's law of motion that the algebraic sum of torques on a body = moment of inertia × angular acceleration, the equation of motion of the system is

$$T - f\frac{d\theta}{dt} - K\theta = J\frac{d^2\theta}{dt^2}$$

i.e.

$$T = J\frac{d^2\theta}{dt^2} + f\frac{d\theta}{dt} + K\theta$$

Taking the Laplace transform on both sides

$$T(s) = [Js^2 + fs + K]\,\theta(s)$$

The transfer function of the system is therefore

$$\frac{\theta(s)}{T(s)} = \frac{1}{Js^2 + fs + K}$$

Alternative way: For the given mechanical system, first draw the mechanical network as shown in Figure 2.9(c). One end of source (*T*) and moment of inertia (*J*) is always to be connected to ground. In the given system, *T* is applied on the body with moment of inertia *J*. So the other ends of *T* and *J* are to be joined. In Figure 2.9(a), one end of *f* is connected to ground and the other end is connected to *J*. The same is done in drawing the network. In the network, there is only one node. Let the node variable be θ or ω. So the describing equation is

$$T = J\frac{d^2\theta}{dt^2} + f\frac{d\theta}{dt} + K\theta$$

or

$$T = J\frac{d\omega}{dt} + f\omega + K\int_{-\infty}^{t} \omega\, dt$$

The analogous equation of the electrical circuit based on torque-current analogy is

$$i = C\frac{d^2\phi}{dt^2} + \frac{1}{R}\frac{d\phi}{dt} + \frac{1}{L}\phi$$

or

$$i = C\frac{de}{dt} + \frac{1}{R}e + \frac{1}{L}\int_{-\infty}^{t} e\, dt$$

and the analogous electrical circuit is shown in Figure 2.10(a). It is exactly identical to the mechanical network. Once the mechanical network of a rotational system is drawn, the analogous electrical network based on torque-current analogy can be easily drawn like this: the structure of the electrical network is exactly the same as the structure of the mechanical network, i.e. series elements in the mechanical network remain as series elements in the electrical network and shunt elements in the mechanical network remain as shunt elements in the electrical network. So the node equations of the electrical network will be analogous to the node equations of mechanical network. Just replace the torque *T*(*t*) by current source *i*(*t*) (= *T*(*t*)), inertia *J* by capacitance *C* (= *J*), friction *f* by resistance *R* (= 1/*f*), spring *K* by inductance *L* (= 1/*K*), angular displacement θ by ϕ and angular velocity ω by voltage *e*.

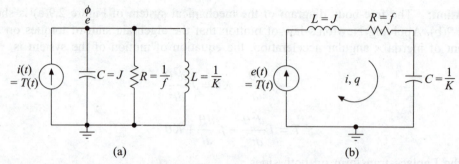

Figure 2.10   Example 2.2: (a) analogous electrical network based on torque-current analogy and (b) analogous electrical network based on torque-voltage analogy.

The analogous equation of the electrical circuit based on torque-voltage analogy is

$$e = L\frac{d^2q}{dt^2} + R\frac{dq}{dt} + \frac{q}{C}$$

or

$$e = L\frac{di}{dt} + Ri + \frac{1}{C}\int_{-\infty}^{t} i\, dt$$

and the analogous electrical circuit is shown in Figure 2.10(b). Once the mechanical network of a rotational system is drawn, the analogous electrical network based on force-voltage analogy can be easily drawn like this. In this, the series elements of the mechanical network become analogous shunt elements and the shunt elements of the mechanical network become analogous series elements. Replace torque $T(t)$ by a voltage source $e(t)$ $(= T(t))$, inertia J by inductance L $(= J)$, friction f by resistance $R(= f)$, spring K by capacitance C $(= 1/K)$, angular displacement θ by charge q, and angular velocity ω by $i(t)$. So the loop equations of the electrical network will be analogous to the node equations of the mechanical network.

Example 2.3   Write the differential equations for the mechanical system shown in Figure 2.11(a).

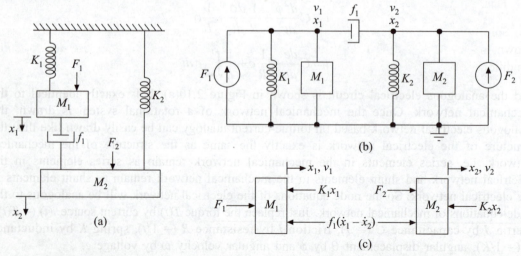

Figure 2.11   Example 2.3: (a) mechanical system, (b) mechanical network and (c) free body diagram.

Solution: The mechanical network for the given mechanical translational system is shown in Figure 2.11(b). The free body diagram is shown in Figure 2.11(c). The differential equations governing the behaviour of that system are given as follows. The node variables may be displacements or velocities.

The differential equations for the system are as follows:

$$M_2 \frac{d^2 x_2}{dt^2} + f_1 \left(\frac{dx_2}{dt} - \frac{dx_1}{dt} \right) + K_2 x_2 = F_2(t)$$

or

$$M_2 \frac{dv_2}{dt} + f_1 (v_2 - v_1) + K_2 \int v_2 \, dt = F_2(t)$$

$$M_1 \frac{d^2 x_1}{dt^2} + f_1 \left(\frac{dx_1}{dt} - \frac{dx_2}{dt} \right) + K_1 x_1 = F_1(t)$$

or

$$M_1 \frac{dv_1}{dt} + f_1 (v_1 - v_2) + K_1 \int v_1 \, dt = F_1(t)$$

Example 2.4 Find the transfer function $\dfrac{X_o(s)}{X_i(s)}$ for the system shown in Figure 2.12(a).

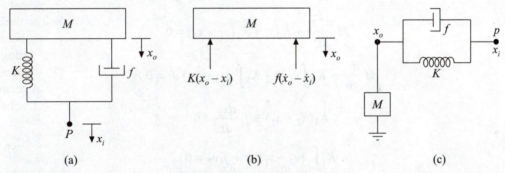

Figure 2.12 Example 2.4: (a) mechanical system, (b) free-body diagram and (c) mechanical network.

Solution: The free-body diagram is shown in Figure 2.12(b). The mechanical network is shown in Figure 2.12(c). No external force is applied. The displacements are due to initial conditions. The differential equation governing the behaviour of the system is

$$M \frac{d^2 x_o}{dt^2} + f \left(\frac{dx_o}{dt} - \frac{dx_i}{dt} \right) + K \left(x_o - x_i \right) = 0$$

Taking the Laplace transform on both sides

$$Ms^2 X_o(s) + fs \left[X_o(s) - X_i(s) \right] + K \left[X_o(s) - X_i(s) \right] = 0$$

i.e.

$$[Ms^2 + fs + K] X_o(s) = (fs + K) X_i(s)$$

The transfer function is therefore

$$\frac{X_o(s)}{X_i(s)} = \frac{fs + K}{Ms^2 + fs + K}$$

Example 2.5 Obtain the differential equations for the mechanical system shown in Figure 2.13(a).

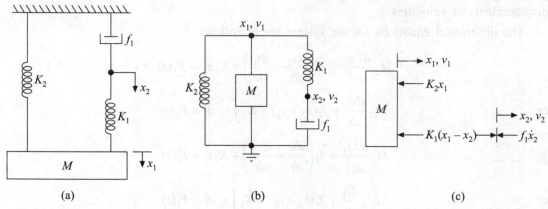

Figure 2.13 Example 2.5: (a) mechanical system, (b) mechanical network and (c) free body diagram.

Solution: The mechanical network is shown in Figure 2.13(b). The free body diagram is shown in Figure 2.13(c). The differential equations for the given mechanical system are

$$M \frac{d^2 x_1}{dt^2} + K_2 x_1 + K_1 (x_1 - x_2) = 0$$

or

$$M \frac{dv_1}{dt} + K_2 \int v_1 \, dt + K_1 \int (v_1 - v_2) \, dt = 0$$

and

$$K_1 (x_2 - x_1) + f_1 \frac{dx_2}{dt} = 0$$

or

$$K_1 \int (v_2 - v_1) \, dt + f_1 v_2 = 0$$

Example 2.6 Consider the mechanical system shown in Figure 2.14(a). Suppose that the system is set into motion by unit impulse force. Find the resulting oscillation. Assume that the system is at rest initially.

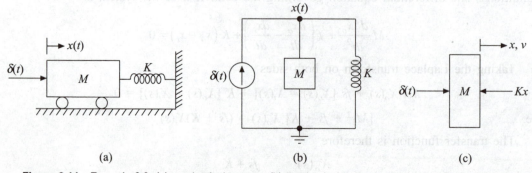

Figure 2.14 Example 2.6: (a) mechanical system, (b) mechanical network and (c) free body diagram.

Solution: The mechanical network is shown in Figure 2.14(b). The free body diagram is shown in Figure 2.14(c).

The differential equation of the system is

$$\delta(t) = Kx + M\frac{d^2x}{dt^2}$$

Taking the Laplace transform on both sides and neglecting the initial conditions.

$$1 = (Ms^2 + K)X(s)$$

i.e.

$$X(s) = \frac{1}{Ms^2 + K} = \frac{1}{M\left(s^2 + \dfrac{K}{M}\right)} = \frac{1}{M}\left[\frac{\sqrt{K/M}}{s^2 + \left(\sqrt{K/M}\right)^2}\right]\frac{1}{\sqrt{K/M}}$$

Taking the inverse Laplace transform

$$x(t) = \frac{1}{\sqrt{MK}}\sin\left(\sqrt{K/M}\right)t$$

The resulting oscillation frequency is $\omega = \sqrt{K/M}$ rad/s.

Example 2.7 Assume that the cart in Figure 2.15(a) is standing still for $t < 0$, $u(t)$ is the displacement of the cart and $y(t)$ is the output. Obtain the transfer function of the system.

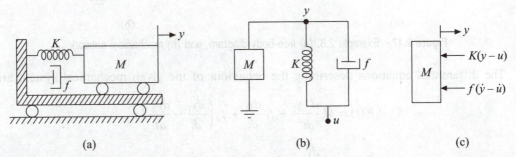

(a) (b) (c)

Figure 2.15 Example 2.7: (a) mechanical system, (b) mechanical network and (c) free body diagram.

Solution: The mechanical network of the system is shown in Figure 2.15(b). The free body diagram is shown in Figure 2.15(c). The differential equation of the system is

$$M\frac{d^2y}{dt^2} + f\left(\frac{dy}{dt} - \frac{du}{dt}\right) + K(y - u) = 0$$

Taking the Laplace transform on both sides and neglecting the initial conditions

$$Ms^2Y(s) + fs[Y(s) - U(s)] + K[Y(s) - U(s)] = 0$$

i.e.

$$[Ms^2 + fs + K]\,Y(s) = [fs + K]\,U(s)$$

Therefore, the transfer function of the mechanical system is

$$\frac{Y(s)}{U(s)} = \frac{fs + K}{Ms^2 + fs + K}$$

Example 2.8 Write the differential equations for the mechanical system shown in Figure 2.16. Obtain the analogous electrical networks based on (a) force-current analogy and (b) force-voltage analogy.

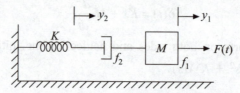

Figure 2.16 Example 2.8: Mechanical system.

Solution: The free-body diagram is shown in Figure 2.17(a). The mechanical network of the system is shown in Figure 2.17(b).

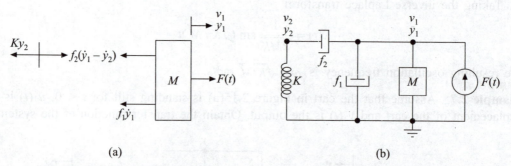

       (a)   (b)

Figure 2.17 Example 2.8: (a) free-body diagram, and (b) mechanical network.

The differential equations describing the behaviour of the given mechanical system are

$$F(t) = M\frac{d^2 y_1}{dt^2} + f_1\frac{dy_1}{dt} + f_2\left(\frac{dy_1}{dt} - \frac{dy_2}{dt}\right)$$

or

$$F(t) = M\frac{dv_1}{dt} + f_1 v_1 + f_2(v_1 - v_2)$$

and

$$0 = f_2\left(\frac{dy_2}{dt} - \frac{dy_1}{dt}\right) + Ky_2$$

or

$$0 = f_2(v_2 - v_1) + K\int_{\infty}^{t} v_2\, dt$$

The electrical networks based on force-current and force-voltage analogies are shown in Figure 2.18(a) and Figure 2.18(b) respectively and the corresponding differential equations are also given as follows:

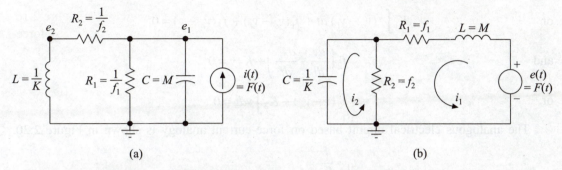

(a)

(b)

Figure 2.18 Example 2.8: (a) electrical network based on force-current analogy and (b) electrical network based on force-voltage analogy.

$$i(t) = C\frac{de_1}{dt} + \frac{e_1}{R_1} + \frac{e_1 - e_2}{R_2} \qquad e(t) = L\frac{di_1}{dt} + R_1 i_1 + R_2(i_1 - i_2)$$

$$\frac{e_2 - e_1}{R_2} + \frac{1}{L}\int e_2\, dt = 0 \qquad 0 = R_2(i_2 - i_1) + \frac{1}{C}\int i_2\, dt$$

Example 2.9 Write the differential equations for the mechanical system shown in Figure 2.19(a). Also draw the analogous electrical circuit based on force-current analogy.

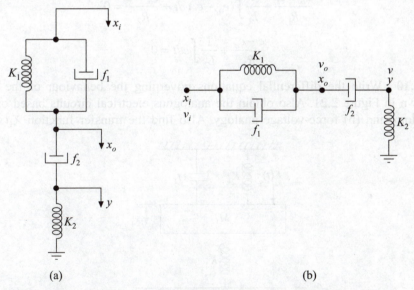

(a)

(b)

Figure 2.19 Example 2.9: (a) mechanical system and (b) mechanical network.

Solution: The mechanical network is shown in Figure 2.19(b). No external force is acting on the system and the displacements are due to initial conditions only.

The differential equations for the system are

$$K_1(x_o - x_i) + f_1\left(\frac{dx_o}{dt} - \frac{dx_i}{dt}\right) + f_2\left(\frac{dx_o}{dt} - \frac{dy}{dt}\right) = 0$$

or

$$K_1 \int (v_o - v_i)\, dt + f_1(v_o - v_i) + f_2(v_o - v) = 0$$

and

$$f_2\left(\frac{dy}{dt} - \frac{dx_o}{dt}\right) + K_2 y = 0$$

or

$$f_2(v - v_o) + K_2 \int v\, dt = 0$$

The analogous electrical circuit based on force-current analogy is shown in Figure 2.20.

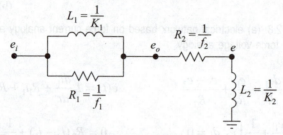

Figure 2.20   Example 2.9: Analogous electrical network based on force-current analogy.

The differential equations for the network of Figure 2.20 are as follows:

$$\frac{e_o - e_i}{R_1} + \frac{1}{L_1} \int (e_o - e_i)\, dt + \frac{e_o - e}{R_2} = 0$$

$$\frac{e - e_o}{R_2} + \frac{1}{L_2} \int e\, dt = 0$$

Example 2.10   Write the differential equations governing the behaviour of the mechanical system shown in Figure 2.21. Also obtain the analogous electrical circuits based on (a) force-current analogy and (b) force-voltage analogy. Also find the transfer function $X_1(s)/F(s)$.

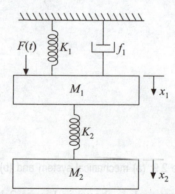

Figure 2.21   Example 2.10: Mechanical system.

Solution: The differential equations governing the behaviour of the mechanical system can be written using the free-body diagram or the mechanical network. Just for illustration both the free-body diagram and mechanical network are drawn as shown in Figure 2.22(a) and Figure 2.22(b) respectively.

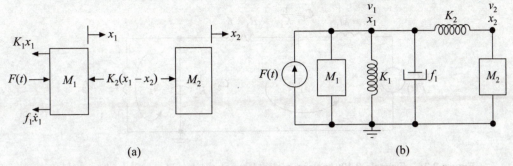

(a)　　　　　　　　　　　　　(b)

Figure 2.22　Example 2.10: (a) free-body diagram and (b) mechanical network.

The differential equations describing the behaviour of the mechanical system are as follows:

$$F(t) = M_1 \frac{d^2 x_1}{dt^2} + f_1 \frac{dx_1}{dt} + K_1 x_1 + K_2(x_1 - x_2)$$

i.e.

$$F(t) = M_1 \frac{dv_1}{dt} + f_1 v_1 + K_1 \int v_1 dt + K_2 \int (v_1 - v_2) dt$$

$$M_2 \frac{d^2 x_2}{dt^2} + K_2(x_2 - x_1) = 0$$

i.e.

$$M_2 \frac{dv_2}{dt} + K_2 \int (v_2 - v_1) \, dt = 0$$

The analogous electrical network based on force-current analogy is shown in Figure 2.23.

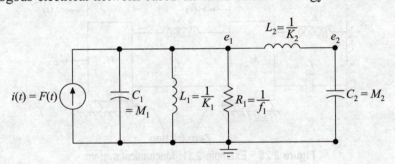

Figure 2.23　Example 2.10: Analogous electrical network based on force-current analogy.

The analogous electrical equations are as follows:

$$i(t) = C_1 \frac{de_1}{dt} + \frac{e_1}{R_1} + \frac{1}{L_1} \int e_1 \, dt + \frac{1}{L_2} \int (e_1 - e_2) \, dt$$

$$C_2 \frac{de_2}{dt} + \frac{1}{L_2} \int (e_2 - e_1) \, dt = 0$$

The analogous electrical network based on force-voltage analogy is shown in Figure 2.24.

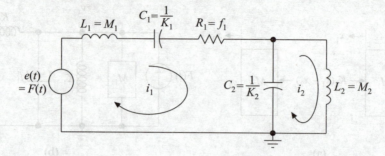

Figure 2.24   Example 2.10: Analogous electrical network based on force-voltage analogy.

The analogous electrical equations are as follows:

$$e(t) = L_1 \frac{di_1}{dt} + R_1 i_1 + \frac{1}{C_1} \int i_1 dt + \frac{1}{C_2} \int (i_1 - i_2)\, dt$$

$$0 = L_2 \frac{di_2}{dt} + \frac{1}{C_2} \int (i_2 - i_1)\, dt$$

Example 2.11   For the mechanical system shown in Figure 2.25, write the differential equations describing its behaviour. Write the analogous electrical equations based on force-voltage analogy, and force-current analogy, and draw the corresponding networks. Also draw the mechanical network and obtain the transfer function $Y_1(s)/F(s)$.

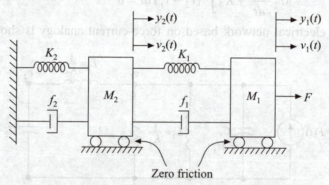

Figure 2.25   Example 2.11: Mechanical system.

Solution: The free-body diagram of the mechanical system is shown in Figure 2.26

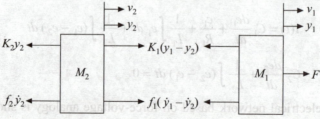

Figure 2.26   Example 2.11: Free-body diagram for mechanical system of Figure 2.25.

The describing equations are as follows:

$$F - f_1\left(\frac{dy_1}{dt} - \frac{dy_2}{dt}\right) - K_1(y_1 - y_2) = M_1\frac{d^2 y_1}{dt^2}$$

i.e.

$$F = M_1\frac{d^2 y_1}{dt^2} + f_1\left(\frac{dy_1}{dt} - \frac{dy_2}{dt}\right) + K_1(y_1 - y_2)$$

$$K_1(y_1 - y_2) + f_1\left(\frac{dy_1}{dt} - \frac{dy_2}{dt}\right) - K_2 y_2 - f_2\frac{dy_2}{dt} = M_2\frac{d^2 y_2}{dt^2}$$

i.e.

$$f_1\left(\frac{dy_2}{dt} - \frac{dy_1}{dt}\right) + K_1(y_2 - y_1) + K_2 y_2 + f_2\frac{dy_2}{dt} + M_2\frac{d^2 y_2}{dt^2} = 0$$

The describing equations in terms of velocities are as follows:

$$F = M_1\frac{dv_1}{dt} + f_1(v_1 - v_2) + K_1\int (v_1 - v_2)\, dt$$

$$f_1(v_2 - v_1) + K_1\int (v_2 - v_1)\, dt + f_2 v_2 + K_2\int v_2\, dt + M_2\frac{dv_2}{dt} = 0$$

The equations of the analogous electrical network based on force-current analogy are as follows:

$$i(t) = C_1\frac{de_1}{dt} + \frac{1}{R_1}(e_1 - e_2) + \frac{1}{L_1}\int (e_1 - e_2)\, dt$$

$$\frac{1}{R_1}(e_2 - e_1) + \frac{1}{L_1}\int (e_2 - e_1)\, dt + \frac{1}{R_2}e_2 + \frac{1}{L_2}\int e_2 dt + C_2\frac{de_2}{dt} = 0$$

The corresponding electrical network is shown in Figure 2.27.

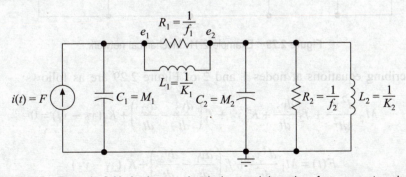

Figure 2.27 Example 2.11: Analogous electrical network based on force-current analogy.

The equations of the analogous electrical network based on force-voltage analogy are as follows:

$$e = L_1 \frac{di_1}{dt} + R_1(i_1 - i_2) + \frac{1}{C_1}\int (i_1 - i_2)\, dt$$

and

$$\frac{1}{C_1}\int (i_2 - i_1)\, dt + R_1(i_2 - i_1) + R_2 i_2 + \frac{1}{C_2}\int i_2 dt + L_2 \frac{di_2}{dt} = 0$$

The corresponding electrical network is shown in Figure 2.28.

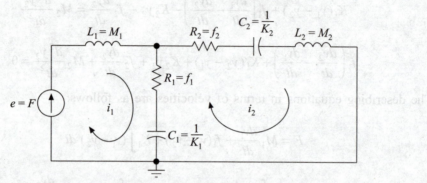

Figure 2.28   Example 2.11: Analogous electrical network based on force-voltage analogy.

The mechanical network for the given mechanical system is shown in Figure 2.29.

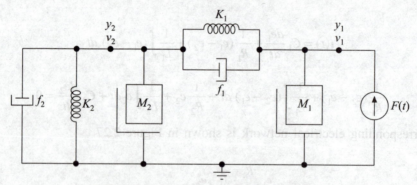

Figure 2.29   Example 2.11: Mechanical network.

The describing equations at nodes 1 and 2 of Figure 2.29 are as follows:

$$M_2 \frac{d^2 y_2}{dt^2} + f_2 \frac{dy_2}{dt} + K_2 y_2 + f_1\left(\frac{dy_2}{dt} - \frac{dy_1}{dt}\right) + K_1(y_2 - y_1) = 0$$

$$F(t) = M_1 \frac{d^2 y_1}{dt^2} + f_1\left(\frac{dy_1}{dt} - \frac{dy_2}{dt}\right) + K_1(y_1 - y_2)$$

To obtain the transfer function, take the Laplace transform of the describing equations of the mechanical system neglecting the initial conditions.

$$F(s) = M_1 s^2 Y_1(s) + f_1 s[Y_1(s) - Y_2(s)] + K_1[Y_1(s) - Y_2(s)]$$

i.e. $\qquad F(s) = [M_1 s^2 + f_1 s + K_1] Y_1(s) - [f_1 s + K_1] Y_2(s) \qquad$ (i)

$$M_2 s^2 Y_2(s) + f_2 s Y_2(s) + K_2 Y_2(s) + f_1 s[Y_2(s) - Y_1(s)] + K_1[Y_2(s) - Y_1(s)] = 0$$

$$[M_2 s^2 + (f_2 + f_1)s + (K_1 + K_2)]Y_2(s) - [f_1 s + K_1]Y_1(s) = 0$$

$\therefore \qquad Y_2(s) = \dfrac{[f_1 s + K_1]Y_1(s)}{M_2 s^2 + (f_2 + f_1)s + (K_1 + K_2)} \qquad$ (ii)

Substituting the value of $Y_2(s)$ from Eq. (ii) in Eq. (i), we get

$$F(s) = [M_1 s^2 + f_1 s + K_1] Y_1(s) - \frac{(f_1 s + K_1)(f_1 s + K_1)Y_1(s)}{M_2 s^2 + (f_2 + f_1)s + (K_2 + K_1)}$$

Therefore, the transfer function is

$$\frac{Y_1(s)}{F(s)} = \frac{M_2 s^2 + (f_2 + f_1)s + (K_2 + K_1)}{(M_1 s^2 + f_1 s + K_1)(M_2 s^2 + (f_2 + f_1)s + (K_2 + K_1)) - (f_1 s + K_1)^2}$$

i.e. $\qquad \dfrac{Y_1(s)}{F(s)} = \dfrac{M_2 s^2 + (f_2 + f_1)s + (K_2 + K_1)}{\begin{aligned} &M_1 M_2 s^4 + (M_1 f_1 + M_1 f_2 + M_2 f_1)s^3 \\ &+ (M_1 K_2 + M_1 K_1 + M_2 K_1 + f_1 f_2)s^2 + (f_1 K_2 + f_2 K_1)s - K_1^2 \end{aligned}}$

Example 2.12 Write the differential equations governing the behaviour of the mechanical system shown in Figure 2.30(a).

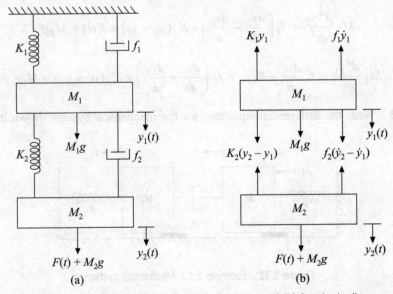

Figure 2.30 Example 2.12: (a) mechanical system and (b) free-body diagram.

Solution: The free-body diagram of the given mechanical system is shown in Figure 2.30(b). The mechanical network corresponding to the mechanical system of Figure 2.30(a) is shown in Figure 2.31.

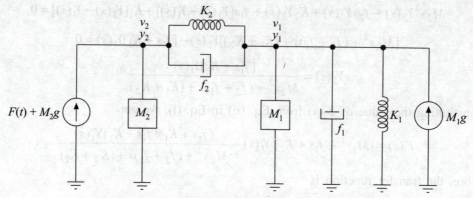

Figure 2.31 Example 2.12: Mechanical network.

The differential equations describing the behaviour of the system in terms of velocities are as follows:

$$M_2 \frac{dv_2}{dt} + f_2(v_2 - v_1) + K_2 \int (v_2 - v_1)\,dt = F(t) + M_2 g$$

$$M_1 \frac{dv_1}{dt} + f_1 v_1 + K_1 \int v_1\,dt + f_2(v_1 - v_2) + K_2 \int (v_1 - v_2) = M_1 g$$

The governing equations in terms of displacements are as follows:

$$M_2 \frac{d^2 y_2}{dt^2} + f_2\left(\frac{dy_2}{dt} - \frac{dy_1}{dt}\right) + K_2(y_2 - y_1) = F(t) + M_2 g$$

$$M_1 \frac{d^2 y_1}{dt^2} + f_1 \frac{dy_1}{dt} + K_1 y_1 + f_2\left(\frac{dy_1}{dt} - \frac{dy_2}{dt}\right) + K_2(y_1 - y_2) = M_1 g$$

Example 2.13 Write the differential equations for the mechanical system shown in Figure 2.32.

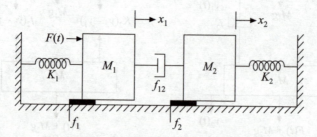

Figure 2.32 Example 2.13: Mechanical system.

Solution: The free-body diagram is shown in Figure 2.33(a). The mechanical network is shown in Figure 2.33 (b). The describing equations can be written based on any one of them.

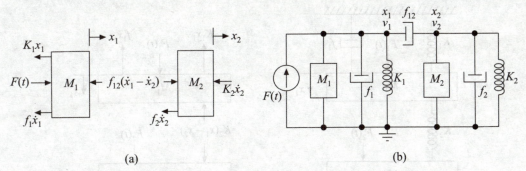

Figure 2.33 Example 2.13: (a) free-body diagram and (b) mechanical network.

The free-body diagram is drawn like this: $F(t)$ is the external force applied on mass M_1 to move it by a distance x_1 from left to right. So direction of $F(t)$ is from left to right. All other forces acting on M_1 will oppose this motion. So the directions of $f_1 \dot{x}_1, K_1 x_1$ and $f_{12}(\dot{x}_1 - \dot{x}_2)$ are opposite to that of $F(t)$. So they act from right to left. f_{12} is connecting M_1 and M_2. Therefore $f_{12}(\dot{x}_1 - \dot{x}_2)$ acts from left to right on M_2. This will cause a displacement of x_2 on M_2. All other forces at M_2, i.e $f_2 \dot{x}_2$ and $K_2 x_2$ act in a direction opposite to that of $f_{12}(\dot{x}_1 - \dot{x}_2)$, i.e. from right to left.

The mechanical network is drawn as follows. There are two masses M_1 and M_2. One end of each mass is to be connected to ground. One end of $F(t)$ is to be connected to ground. The second end of $F(t)$ is to be connected to the second end of M_1. $f_1(t)$ is between M_1 and ground. So one end of f_1 is connected to ground and the other end is connected to the second end of M_1. K_1 is between M_1 and ground. So one end of K_1 is connected to ground and the other end is connected to the second end of M_1. One end of M_2 is grounded. f_{12} is between the second ends of M_1 and M_2. K_2 and f_2 are between M_2 and ground. So one end of K_2 and f_2 is connected to ground and the other ends of K_2 and f_2 are connected to the second end of M_2. The mechanical network is shown in Figure 2.33(b). The displacements x_1 and x_2 or velocities v_1 and v_2 are the node variables at the second ends of M_1 and M_2 respectively.

The differential equations describing the behaviour of the mechanical system are as follows:

$$F(t) = M_1 \frac{d^2 x_1}{dt^2} + f_1 \frac{dx_1}{dt} + K_1 x_1 + f_{12}\left(\frac{dx_1}{dt} - \frac{dx_2}{dt}\right)$$

or

$$F(t) = M_1 \frac{dv_1}{dt} + f_1 v_1 + K_1 \int v_1 dt + f_{12}(v_1 - v_2)$$

$$0 = M_2 \frac{d^2 x_2}{dt^2} + f_2 \frac{dx_2}{dt} + K_2 x_2 + f_{12}\left(\frac{dx_2}{dt} - \frac{dx_1}{dt}\right)$$

or

$$0 = M_2 \frac{dv_2}{dt} + f_2 v_2 + K_2 \int v_2 dt + f_{12}(v_2 - v_1)$$

Example 2.14 Write the differential equations governing the behaviour of the mechanical translational system shown in Figure 2.34(a).

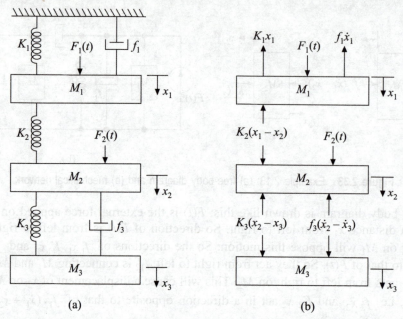

Figure 2.34 Example 2.14: (a) mechanical system and (b) free-body diagram.

Solution: The free-body diagram of the system is shown in Figure 2.34(b). The mechanical network for the given mechanical system is shown in Figure 2.35.

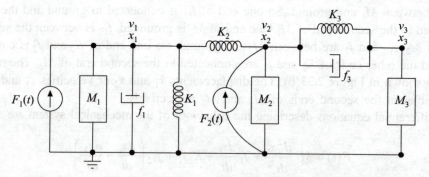

Figure 2.35 Example 2.14: Mechanical network for the mechanical system of Figure 2.34(a).

The differential equations governing the behaviour of the system are as follows:

$$F_1(t) = M_1 \frac{d^2 x_1}{dt^2} + f_1 \frac{dx_1}{dt} + K_1 x_1 + K_2(x_1 - x_2)$$

or
$$F_1(t) = M_1 \frac{dv_1}{dt} + f_1 v_1 + K_1 \int v_1 dt + K_2 \int (v_1 - v_2) dt$$

$$F_2(t) = M_2 \frac{d^2 x_2}{dt^2} + K_2(x_2 - x_1) + f_3 \left(\frac{dx_2}{dt} - \frac{dx_3}{dt} \right) + K_3(x_2 - x_3)$$

or
$$F_2(t) = M_2 \frac{dv_2}{dt} + K_2 \int (v_2 - v_1) dt + f_3(v_2 - v_3) + K_3 \int (v_2 - v_3) dt$$

$$0 = M_3 \frac{d^2 x_3}{dt^2} + f_3 \left(\frac{dx_3}{dt} - \frac{dx_2}{dt} \right) + K_3(x_3 - x_2)$$

or
$$0 = M_3 \frac{dv_3}{dt} + f_3(v_3 - v_2) + K_3 \int (v_3 - v_2) dt$$

Example 2.15 Find the transfer function $X(s)/E(s)$ for the electro-mechanical system shown in Figure 2.36.

[*Hint:* For a simplified analysis, assume that the coil has a back emf $e_b = K_b \, dx/dt$ and the coil current i produces a force $F_C = K_2 \, i$ on the mass M.]

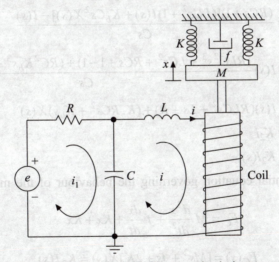

Figure 2.36 Example 2.15: Electromechanical system.

Solution: Let i_1 be the current in loop1 and let i be the current in the loop having the coil. Writing the KVL equations around the loops,

$$e(t) = R i_1(t) + \frac{1}{C} \int [i_1(t) - i(t)] \, dt$$

and

$$L\frac{di}{dt} + e_b(t) + \frac{1}{C}\int[i(t) - i_1(t)]\,dt = 0$$

Taking the Laplace transform on both sides,

$$E(s) = RI_1(s) + \frac{1}{Cs}[I_1(s) - I(s)]$$

i.e.

$$E(s) = \left(R + \frac{1}{Cs}\right)I_1(s) - \frac{1}{Cs}I(s)$$

$$= \frac{(RCs+1)I_1(s) - I(s)}{Cs}$$

and

$$LsI(s) + E_b(s) + \frac{1}{Cs}[I(s) - I_1(s)] = 0$$

i.e.

$$\left(Ls + \frac{1}{Cs}\right)I(s) + K_b sX(s) - \frac{1}{Cs}I_1(s) = 0 \qquad \left[e_b = K_b\frac{dx}{dt}. \quad \therefore \quad E_b(s) = K_b sX(s)\right]$$

$$\therefore \qquad I_1(s) = (LCs^2 + 1)I(s) + K_b Cs^2 X(s)$$

$$\therefore \qquad E(s) = \frac{(RCs+1)[(LCs^2+1)I(s) + K_b Cs^2 X(s)] - I(s)}{Cs}$$

$$= I(s)\frac{(RLC^2 s^3 + LCs^2 + RCs + 1 - 1) + (RC^2 K_b s^3 + K_b Cs^2)X(s)}{Cs}$$

$$= I(s)(RLCs^2 + Ls + R) + (K_b RCs^2 + K_b s)X(s) \tag{i}$$

Given

$$F_C = K_2 i$$

$$\therefore \qquad F_C(s) = K_2 I(s)$$

Writing the differential equation governing the behaviour of the mechanical system,

$$F_C = M\frac{d^2 x}{dt^2} + f\frac{dx}{dt} + Kx + Kx$$

$$\therefore \qquad F_C(s) = [Ms^2 + fs + 2K]X(s) = K_2 I(s)$$

$$\therefore \qquad I(s) = \frac{Ms^2 + fs + 2K}{K_2}X(s) \tag{ii}$$

Substituting the value of $I(s)$ from Eq. (ii) in Eq. (i), we get

$$E(s) = (RLCs^2 + Ls + R)\left(\frac{Ms^2 + fs + 2K}{K_2}\right)X(s) + (K_b RCs^2 + K_b s)X(s)$$

$$= \left(\frac{\begin{aligned} RLCMs^4 + RLCfs^3 + 2KRLCs^2 + LMs^3 + Lfs^2 + 2KLs + RMs^2 \\ + Rfs + 2RK + K_2 K_b RCs^2 + K_2 K_b s \end{aligned}}{K_2} \right) X(s)$$

Therefore, the transfer function is

$$\frac{X(s)}{E(s)} = \frac{K_2}{\begin{aligned} RLCMs^4 + (RLCf + LM)s^3 + (2KRLC + Lf + RM + K_2 K_b RC)s^2 \\ + (2KL + Rf + K_2 K_b)s + 2RK \end{aligned}}$$

Example 2.16 Obtain the transfer function of the mechanical system shown in Figure 2.37.

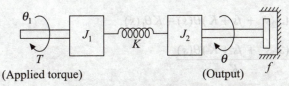

θ_1

J_1

K

J_2

θ

T

(Applied torque)

(Output)

f

Figure 2.37 Example 2.16: Mechanical system.

Solution: The output is the angular displacement θ of shaft on output side. Let θ_1 be the angular displacement of shaft on input side. The free-body diagram is shown in Figure 2.38(a). The mechanical network corresponding to the given mechanical rotational system is drawn as shown in Figure 2.38(b). One end of J_1 is to be connected to ground. One end of torque source is to be grounded. The other end of T is connected to the other end of J_1 at the node 1. Let this node variable be θ_1 or ω_1. One end of J_2 is grounded, and K is connected between the two free ends of J_2 and J_1. One end of f is grounded, the other end of f is joined to the free end of J_2. Let θ, ω be that node variable.

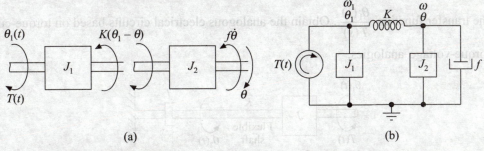

(a)

(b)

Figure 2.38 Example 2.16: (a) free-body diagram and (b) mechanical network.

The differential equations describing the behaviour of the system in Figure 2.37 are as follows:

$$T = J_1 \frac{d^2\theta_1}{dt^2} + K(\theta_1 - \theta) \qquad \text{or} \qquad T = J_1 \frac{d\omega_1}{dt} + K\int(\omega_1 - \omega)\, dt \qquad \text{(i)}$$

and

$$0 = J_2 \frac{d^2\theta}{dt^2} + f\frac{d\theta}{dt} + K(\theta - \theta_1) \qquad \text{or} \qquad 0 = J_2 \frac{d\omega}{dt} + f\omega + K\int(\omega - \omega_1)\, dt \qquad \text{(ii)}$$

(in terms of angular displacement)　　　　　(in terms of angular velocity)

Taking the Laplace transform of Eqs. (i) and (ii), we get

$$T(s) = J_1 s^2 \theta_1(s) + K\theta_1(s) - K\theta(s)$$

i.e.

$$T(s) = (J_1 s^2 + K)\theta_1(s) - K\theta(s)$$

and

$$0 = J_2 s^2 \theta(s) + fs\theta(s) + K\theta(s) - K\theta_1(s)$$

$$= (J_2 s^2 + fs + K)\theta(s) - K\theta_1(s)$$

$$\therefore \qquad \theta_1(s) = \frac{(J_2 s^2 + fs + K)\theta(s)}{K}$$

$$\therefore \qquad T(s) = (J_1 s^2 + K)\left(\frac{J_2 s^2 + fs + K}{K}\right)\theta(s) - K\theta(s)$$

$$= (J_1 J_2 s^4 + J_1 fs^3 + J_1 Ks^2 + J_2 Ks^2 + Kfs + K^2 - K^2)\frac{\theta(s)}{K}$$

Therefore, the transfer function is

$$\frac{\theta(s)}{T(s)} = \frac{K}{J_1 J_2 s^4 + J_1 fs^3 + K(J_1 + J_2)s^2 + Kfs}$$

Example 2.17　Write the torque equations of the rotational system shown in Figure 2.39. Also find the transfer function $\dfrac{\theta_1(s)}{T(s)}$. Obtain the analogous electrical circuits based on torque-current and torque-voltage analogies.

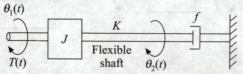

$\theta_1(t)$　　　K　　　f

J　Flexible shaft　$\theta_2(t)$

$T(t)$

Figure 2.39　Example 2.17: Rotational system.

Solution:　The free-body diagram of the given rotational system is shown in Figure 2.40(a). The corresponding mechanical network is shown in Figure 2.40(b).

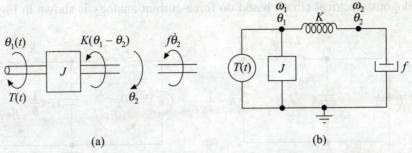

Figure 2.40 Example 2.17: (a) free-body diagram and (b) mechanical network.

The differential equations governing the behavior of the given rotational system are as follows:

$$T(t) = J\frac{d^2\theta_1}{dt^2} + K(\theta_1 - \theta_2) \quad \text{or} \quad T(t) = J\frac{d\omega_1}{dt} + K\int (\omega_1 - \omega_2)dt \quad \text{(i)}$$

and

$$K(\theta_2 - \theta_1) + f\frac{d\theta_2}{dt} = 0 \quad \text{or} \quad K\int (\omega_2 - \omega_1)\,dt + f\omega_2 = 0 \quad \text{(ii)}$$

Taking the Laplace transform of Eqs. (i) and (ii) and neglecting the initial conditions, we get

$$T(s) = Js^2\theta_1(s) + K[\theta_1(s) - \theta_2(s)]$$

$$= [Js^2 + K]\theta_1(s) - K\theta_2(s) \quad \text{(iii)}$$

and

$$K[\theta_2(s) - \theta_1(s)] + fs\theta_2(s) = 0$$

i.e.

$$(fs + K)\theta_2(s) = K\theta_1(s)$$

or

$$\theta_2(s) = \frac{K\theta_1(s)}{fs + K} \quad \text{(iv)}$$

Substituting the value of $\theta_2(s)$ from Eq. (iv) in Eq. (iii), we get

$$T(s) = (Js^2 + K)\theta_1(s) - K\left(\frac{K}{fs + K}\right)\theta_1(s)$$

$$= \theta_1(s)\left(\frac{Jfs^3 + JKs^2 + Kfs + K^2 - K^2}{fs + K}\right)$$

$$\therefore \qquad \frac{\theta_1(s)}{T(s)} = \frac{fs + K}{s(Jfs^2 + JKs + Kf)}$$

The analogous electrical equations based on force-current analogy are as follows:

$$i(t) = C\frac{d^2\phi_1}{dt^2} + \frac{1}{L}(\phi_1 - \phi_2) \quad \text{or} \quad i(t) = C\frac{de_1}{dt} + \frac{1}{L}\int (e_1 - e_2)\,dt$$

and

$$\frac{1}{L}(\phi_2 - \phi_1) + \frac{1}{R}\frac{d\phi_2}{dt} = 0 \quad \text{or} \quad \frac{1}{L}\int (e_2 - e_1)\,dt + \frac{1}{R}e_2 = 0$$

The analogous electrical circuit based on force-current analogy is shown in Figure 2.41(a).

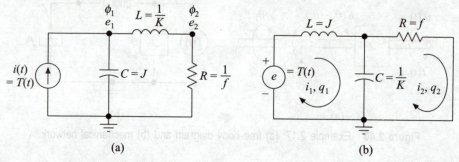

(a)   (b)

Figure 2.41 Example 2.17: Analogous electrical circuits based on (a) torque-current analogy and (b) torque-voltage analogy.

The electrical equations based on force-voltage analogy are as follows:

$$e(t) = L\frac{d^2q_1}{dt^2} + \frac{1}{C}(q_1 - q_2) \quad \text{i.e.} \quad e(t) = \frac{Ldi_1}{dt} + \frac{1}{C}\int (i_1 - i_2)\, dt$$

and

$$\frac{1}{C}(q_2 - q_1) + R\frac{dq_1}{dt} = 0 \quad \text{i.e.} \quad \frac{1}{C}\int (i_2 - i_1)\, dt + Ri_2 = 0$$

The analogous electrical circuit based on force-voltage analogy is shown in Figure 2.41(b).

Example 2.18   Write the torque equations of the rotational system shown in Figure 2.42. Find the transfer function $\dfrac{\theta_1(s)}{T(s)}$.

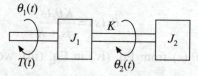

Figure 2.42   Example 2.18: Rotational system.

Solution: The free-body diagram of the rotational system is shown in Figure 2.43(a). The corresponding mechanical network is shown in Figure 2.43(b).

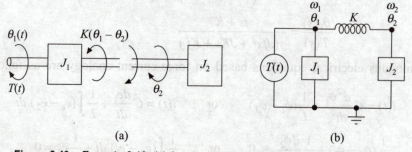

(a)   (b)

Figure 2.43   Example 2.18: (a) free-body diagram and (b) mechanical network.

The differential equations governing the behaviour of the rotational system are as follows:

$$T(t) = J_1 \frac{d^2\theta_1}{dt^2} + K(\theta_1 - \theta_2) \tag{i}$$

and

$$0 = J_2 \frac{d^2\theta_2}{dt^2} + K(\theta_2 - \theta_1) \tag{ii}$$

Taking the Laplace transform on both sides of Eqs. (i) and (ii), we get

$$T(s) = J_1 s^2 \theta_1(s) + K[\theta_1(s) - \theta_2(s)] = (J_1 s^2 + K)\,\theta_1(s) - K\theta_2(s) \tag{iii}$$

and

$$0 = J_2 s^2 \theta_2(s) + K[\theta_2(s) - \theta_1(s)]$$

i.e.

$$(J_2 s^2 + K)\,\theta_2(s) = K\theta_1(s)$$

$\therefore$

$$\theta_2(s) = \frac{K}{J_2 s^2 + K}\,\theta_1(s) \tag{iv}$$

Substituting the value of $\theta_2(s)$ from Eq. (iv) in Eq. (iii), we get

$$T(s) = (J_1 s^2 + K)\,\theta_1(s) - \frac{K \cdot K\theta_1(s)}{J_2 s^2 + K}$$

Therefore, the transfer function of the system is

$$\frac{\theta_1(s)}{T(s)} = \frac{J_2 s^2 + K}{J_1 J_2 s^4 + (J_2 + J_1)Ks^2} = \frac{J_2 s^2 + K}{s^2[J_1 J_2 s^2 + (J_2 + J_1)K]}$$

Example 2.19 Write the torque equations of the rotational system shown in Figure 2.44. Find the transfer function $\dfrac{\theta_1(s)}{T(s)}$.

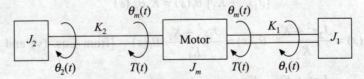

Figure 2.44 Example 2.19: Rotational system.

Solution: The free-body diagram of the given rotational system is shown in Figure 2.45(a). The corresponding mechanical network is shown in Figure 2.45(b).

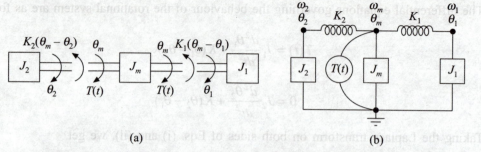

(a)
(b)

Figure 2.45   Example 2.19: (a) free-body diagram and (b) mechanical network.

The differential equations governing the behaviour of the rotational system are as follows:

$$T(t) = J_m \frac{d^2\theta_m}{dt^2} + K_2(\theta_m - \theta_2) + K_1(\theta_m - \theta_1) \tag{i}$$

$$J_2 \frac{d^2\theta_2}{dt^2} + K_2(\theta_2 - \theta_m) = 0 \tag{ii}$$

$$J_1 \frac{d^2\theta_1}{dt^2} + K_1(\theta_1 - \theta_m) = 0 \tag{iii}$$

Taking the Laplace transform of Eqs. (i), (ii) and (iii) and neglecting the initial conditions,

$$T(s) = J_m s^2 \theta_m(s) + K_2[\theta_m(s) - \theta_2(s)] + K_1[\theta_m(s) - \theta_1(s)]$$

i.e.
$$T(s) = [J_m s^2 + (K_2 + K_1)]\, \theta_m(s) - K_2\theta_2(s) - K_1\theta_1(s) \tag{iv}$$

$$J_2 s^2 \theta_2(s) + K_2[\theta_2(s) - \theta_m(s)] = 0$$

i.e.
$$[J_2 s^2 + K_2]\, \theta_2(s) = K_2\theta_m(s) \tag{v}$$

$$J_1 s^2 \theta_1(s) + K_1[\theta_1(s) - \theta_m(s)] = 0$$

i.e.
$$[J_1 s^2 + K_1]\, \theta_1(s) = K_1\theta_m(s) \tag{vi}$$

$$\therefore \qquad \theta_m(s) = \frac{J_2 s^2 + K_2}{K_2}\, \theta_2(s) = \frac{J_1 s^2 + K_1}{K_1}\, \theta_1(s) \quad \text{[from Eqs. (v) and (vi)]}$$

$$\therefore \qquad \theta_2(s) = \frac{J_1 s^2 + K_1}{J_2 s^2 + K_2} \times \frac{K_2}{K_1}\, \theta_1(s)$$

Putting the values of $\theta_m(s)$ and $\theta_2(s)$ in Eq. (iv), we get

$$T(s) = [J_m s^2 + (K_2 + K_1)]\left(\frac{J_1 s^2 + K_1}{K_1}\right)\theta_1(s) - K_2\left(\frac{J_1 s^2 + K_1}{J_2 s^2 + K_2}\right)\frac{K_2}{K_1}\theta_1(s) - K_1\theta_1(s)$$

$$[J_m J_1 s^4 + J_1(K_2 + K_1)s^2 + J_m K_1 s^2 + K_1(K_2 + K_1)](J_2 s^2 + K_2)\,\theta_1(s)$$

$$= \frac{-[K_2^2 J_1 s^2 + K_2^2 K_1 + K_1^2 J_2 s^2 + K_1^2 K_2]\theta_1(s)}{(J_2 s^2 + K_2)K_1}$$

Therefore, the transfer function is

$$\frac{\theta_1(s)}{T(s)} = \frac{(J_2 s^2 + K_2)K_1}{J_1 J_2 J_m s^6 + (K_2 J_m J_1 + J_2 J_1 K_2 + J_2 J_1 K_1 + J_2 J_m K_1)s^4}$$
$$+ (J_2 K_2 K_1 + J_2 K_1^2 + J_1 K_2^2 + J_1 K_1 K_2 + J_m K_1 K_2 - J_1 K_2^2 - J_2 K_1^2)s^2$$
$$+ K_1^2 K_2 + K_2^2 K_1 - K_1^2 K_2 - K_2^2 K_1$$

i.e.

$$\frac{\theta_1(s)}{T(s)} = \frac{(J_2 s^2 + K_2)K_1}{J_1 J_2 J_m s^6 + (K_2 J_m J_1 + J_2 J_1 K_2 + J_2 J_1 K_1 + J_2 J_m K_1)s^4}$$
$$+ (J_2 K_2 K_1 + J_1 K_1 K_2 + J_m K_1 K_2)s^2$$

Example 2.20 Write the torque equations of the rotational system shown in Figure 2.46. Draw the analogous electrical networks based on (a) torque-current and (b) torque-voltage analogies.

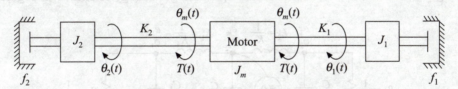

Figure 2.46 Example 2.20: Rotational system.

Solution: The free-body diagram and the mechanical network corresponding to the given rotational system are shown in Figures 2.47(a) and 2.47(b).

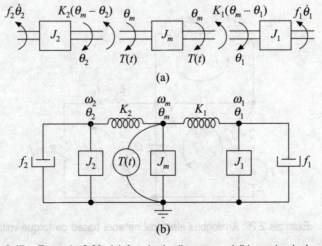

Figure 2.47 Example 2.20: (a) free-body diagram and (b) mechanical network.

The differential equations for the rotational system are as follows:

$$T(t) = J_m \frac{d^2\theta_m}{dt^2} + K_2(\theta_m - \theta_2) + K_1(\theta_m - \theta_1)$$

or

$$T(t) = J_m \frac{d\omega_m}{dt} + K_2 \int (\omega_m - \omega_2)\, dt + K_1 \int (\omega_m - \omega_1)\, dt$$

$$J_1 \frac{d^2\theta_1}{dt^2} + f_1 \frac{d\theta_1}{dt} + K_1(\theta_1 - \theta_m) = 0$$

or

$$J_1 \frac{d\omega_1}{dt} + f_1\omega_1 + K_1 \int (\omega_1 - \omega_m)\, dt = 0$$

$$J_2 \frac{d^2\theta_2}{dt^2} + f_2 \frac{d\theta_2}{dt} + K_2(\theta_2 - \theta_m) = 0$$

or

$$J_2 \frac{d\omega_2}{dt} + f_2\omega_2 + K_2 \int (\omega_2 - \omega_m)\, dt = 0$$

The analogous electrical network based on torque-current analogy is shown in Figure 2.48. The analogous electrical network based on torque-voltage analogy is shown in Figure 2.49.

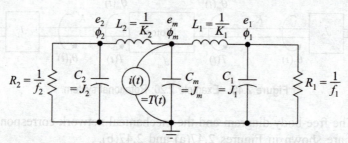

Figure 2.48   Example 2.20: Analogous electrical network based on torque-current analogy.

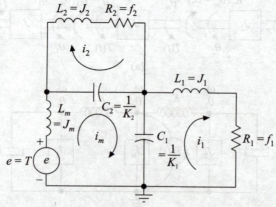

Figure 2.49   Example 2.20: Analogous electrical network based on torque-voltage analogy.

Example 2.21 Write the differential equations governing the mechanical rotational system shown in Figure 2.50 and determine the transfer function $\theta(s)/T(s)$.

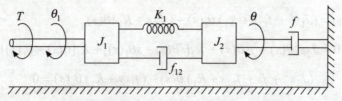

Figure 2.50 Example 2.21: Rotational system.

Solution: The free-body diagram and the mechanical network corresponding to the given rotational system are shown in Figures 2.51 and 2.52 respectively.

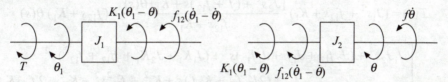

Figure 2.51 Example 2.21: Free-body diagram.

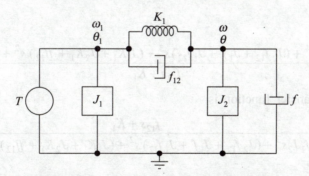

Figure 2.52 Example 2.21: Mechanical network.

The differential equations for the rotational system based on Newton's law of motion (which states that the algebraic sum of torques acting on a rigid body is equal to the product of the moment of inertia and angular acceleration of the body) are as follows:

$$T - K_1(\theta_1 - \theta) - f_{12}\left(\frac{d\theta_1}{dt} - \frac{d\theta}{dt}\right) = J_1 \frac{d^2\theta_1}{dt^2} \tag{i}$$

or

$$T = J_1 \frac{d\omega_1}{dt} + f_{12}(\omega_1 - \omega) + K_1 \int (\omega_1 - \omega)\,dt = 0$$

$$K_1(\theta_1 - \theta) + f_{12}\left(\frac{d\theta_1}{dt} - \frac{d\theta}{dt}\right) - f\frac{d\theta}{dt} = J_2 \frac{d^2\theta}{dt} \tag{ii}$$

or

$$0 = J_2 \frac{d\omega}{dt} + f\omega + f_{12}(\omega - \omega_1) + K_1 \int (\omega - \omega_1)\,dt$$

Taking the Laplace transform of Eqs. (i) and (ii) with zero initial conditions,

$$T(s) = J_1 s^2 \theta_1(s) + f_{12}[s\theta_1(s) - s\theta(s)] + K_1[\theta_1(s) - \theta(s)]$$

i.e.

$$T(s) = (J_1 s^2 + f_{12} s + K_1)\, \theta_1(s) - (f_{12} s + K_1)\theta(s) \tag{iii}$$

$$0 = J_2 s^2 \theta(s) + fs\theta(s) + f_{12}[s\theta(s) - s\theta_1(s)] + K_1[\theta(s) - \theta_1(s)]$$

i.e.

$$(J_2 s^2 + fs + f_{12} s + K_1)\, \theta(s) - (f_{12} s + K_1)\, \theta_1(s) = 0$$

$$\therefore \qquad \theta_1(s) = \frac{(J_2 s^2 + fs + f_{12} s + K_1)\, \theta(s)}{f_{12} s + K_1} \tag{iv}$$

Substituting the value of $\theta_1(s)$ from Eq. (iv) in Eq. (iii), we get

$$T(s) = (J_1 s^2 + f_{12} s + K_1) \frac{[J_2 s^2 + (f + f_{12})s + K_1]\, \theta(s)}{f_{12} s + K_1} - (f_{12} s + K_1)\, \theta(s)$$

i.e.

$$T(s) = \left[\frac{\begin{aligned}J_1 J_2 s^4 + (J_2 f_{12} + J_1 f + J_1 f_{12})s^3 + (J_1 K_1 + J_2 K_1 + f f_{12} + f_{12}{}^2)s^2 \\ + (2K_1 f_{12} + K_1 f)s + K_1{}^2 - f_{12}{}^2 s^2 - K_1{}^2 - 2f_{12} s K_1\end{aligned}}{f_{12} s + K_1} \right] \theta(s)$$

i.e.

$$T(s) = \left[\frac{J_1 J_2 s^4 + (J_2 f_{12} + J_1 f + J_1 f_{12})s^3 + (J_1 K_1 + J_2 K_1 + f f_{12})s^2 + K_1 fs}{f_{12} s + K_1} \right] \theta(s)$$

Therefore, the transfer function is

$$\frac{\theta(s)}{T(s)} = \frac{f_{12} s + K_1}{s[J_1 J_2 s^3 + (J_2 f_{12} + J_1 f + J_1 f_{12})s^2 + (J_1 K_1 + J_2 K_1 + f f_{12})s + K_1 f]}$$

2.7 SERVOMOTORS

The control systems which are used to control the position or time derivatives of position, i.e. velocity and acceleration are called *servomechanisms*. The motors which are used in automatic control systems are called *servomotors*. The servomotors are used to convert an electrical signal (control voltage) applied to them into an angular displacement of the shaft. Depending on the construction, they can operate either in a continuous duty or step duty.

A variety of servomotors are available for control system applications. The suitability of a motor for a particular application depends on the characteristics of the system, the purpose of the system and its operating conditions.

In general, a servomotor should have the following features:

- Linear relationship between speed and electric control signal
- Steady-state stability

- Wide range of speed control
- Linearity of mechanical characteristics throughout the entire speed range
- Low mechanical and electrical inertia
- Fast response

Servomotors are broadly classified as dc servomotors and ac servomotors depending on the power supply required to run the motor. Eventhough dc motors are costlier than ac motors, they have linear characteristics and so it is easier to control. They are generally used for large power applications such as in machine tools and robotics.

The advantages of dc servomotors are as follows:

1. Higher output than from an ac motor of the same size.
2. Easy achievement of linear characteristics.
3. Easier speed control from zero speed to full speed in both the directions.
4. High torque to inertia ratio that gives them quick response to control signals.
5. The dc servomotors have light weight, low inertia and low inductance armature that can respond quickly to commands for a change in position or speed.
6. Low electrical and mechanical time constants.
7. The dc motors are capable of delivering over 3 times their rated torque for a short time compared to the 2 to 2.5 times the rated torque developed by the ac motors.

The advantages of ac servomotors are lower cost, higher efficiency and less maintenance since the brushes and commutator are not there. The disadvantages of ac motors are their characteristics are quite nonlinear and these motors are more difficult to control especially for positioning applications.

The ac motors are best suited for low power applications, such as instrument servo (e.g., control of pen in *x-y* recorders) and computer-related equipment (e.g., disc drives, tape drives, printers, etc.). The three-phase induction motors with pulse width modulation power amplifier are currently gaining popularity in high power control applications.

2.7.1 DC Servomotors

The dc servomotors are broadly classified into (a) sliding contact motors with commutator and brushes and (b) brushless or contact less motors with SCR/transistor commutator.

The sliding contact motors may be classified into (a) permanent magnet motors and (b) electromagnetic field motors.

The permanent magnet motors may be (a) cylindrical armature motors, or (b) disc armature motors, or (c) moving coil motors.

The electromagnetic field motors may be (a) armature-controlled motors, or (b) field-controlled motors, or (c) series motors, or (d) split field motors.

Permanent magnet dc motors: In this type of motors, the armature is placed in rotor and the field winding is replaced by permanent magnet poles fixed to the stator to produce the required magnetic field. Permanent magnet motors are economical for power ratings up to a few kilowatts.

The following are some of the advantages of permanent magnet motors:

1. A simpler and more reliable motor because the field power supply is not required.
2. Higher operating efficiency as the motor has no field losses.
3. Field flux is less affected by temperature rise.
4. Higher torque/inertia ratio.
5. Speed is nearly directly proportional to armature voltage at a given load torque.
6. A more linear torque/speed curve.
7. Higher output power at the same dimensions and temperature limitations.

The disadvantages of permanent magnet motors are: the magnets deteriorate with time and demagnetized with large current transients. These drawbacks are eliminated by high-grade magnetic materials such as ceramic magnets and rear earth magnets. But the cost of these materials is very high.

Electromagnetic field dc motors: Electromagnetic motors are economical for higher power ratings generally above 1 kW. This type of servomotor is similar to a conventional dc motor constructionally but has the following special features:

1. The number of slots and commutator segments is large to improve commutation.
2. Compoles and compensating windings are provided to eliminate sparking.
3. The diameter to length ratio is kept low to reduce inertia.
4. Oversize shafts are employed to withstand the high torque stress.
5. Eddy currents are reduced by complete elimination of the magnetic circuit and by using low loss steel.

In this type of motor, the torque and speed may be controlled by varying the armature current and/or the field current. Generally, one of these is varied to control the torque and the other is held constant. In armature-controlled mode of operation, the field current is held constant and the armature current is varied to control the torque. In the field-controlled mode, the armature current is maintained constant and field current is varied to control the torque.

In servo applications, dc motors are required to produce rapid accelerations from standstill. Therefore, the physical requirements of such a motor are low inertia and high starting torque. Low inertia is attained with reduced armature diameter with a consequent increase in armature length such that the desired power output is achieved. Thus, except for minor differences in constructional features, a dc servomotor is essentially an ordinary dc motor.

In control systems, the dc motors are used mainly in two different control modes: armature control mode with fixed field current and field control mode with fixed armature current.

Armature-controlled dc servomotor: An armature-controlled dc servomotor is a dc shunt motor designed to satisfy the requirement of a servomotor. If the field current is constant, then speed is directly proportional to armature voltage, and torque is directly proportional to armature current. Hence the torque and speed can be controlled by armature voltage. Reversible operation is possible by reversing the armature voltage.

In small motors, the armature voltage is controlled by a variable resistance. But in large motors in order to reduce power loss, armature voltage is controlled by thyristors.

Figure 2.53 shows an armature-controlled dc motor.

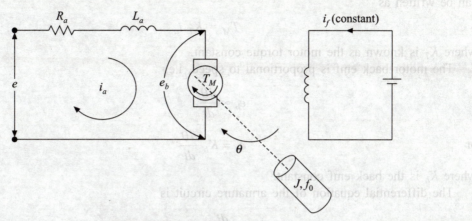

Figure 2.53 Armature-controlled dc motor.

In this system,

R_a = resistance of armature winding (in ohms)

L_a = inductance of armature winding (in henrys)

i_a = armature current (in amperes)

i_f = field current (in amperes)

e = applied armature voltage (in volts)

e_b = back emf (in volts)

T_M = torque developed by motor (in N-m)

θ = angular displacement of motor shaft (in radians)

J = equivalent moment of inertia of motor and load referred to motor shaft (in kg-m²)

f_0 = equivalent viscous friction coefficient of motor and load referred to motor shaft (in N-m/rad/s)

In servo applications, the dc motors are generally used in the linear range of the magnetization curve. Therefore, the air gap flux ϕ is proportional to the field current, i.e.

$$\phi \propto i_f$$

or
$$\phi = K_f\, i_f \qquad (2.8)$$

where K_f is a constant.

The torque T_M developed by the motor is proportional to the product of the air gap flux ϕ and the armature current i_a, i.e.

$$T_M \propto \phi i_a$$

i.e.
$$T_M \propto K_f\, i_f\, i_a$$

or
$$T_M = K_1\, K_f\, i_f\, i_a \qquad (2.9)$$

where K_1 is a constant.

In the armature-controlled dc motor, field current is kept constant, so the equation for T_M can be written as

$$T_M = K_T i_a \tag{2.10}$$

where K_T is known as the motor torque constant.

The motor back emf is proportional to speed, i.e.

$$e_b \propto \frac{d\theta}{dt}$$

or

$$e_b = K_b \frac{d\theta}{dt} \tag{2.11}$$

where K_b is the back emf constant.

The differential equation of the armature circuit is

$$e = L_a \frac{di_a}{dt} + R_a i_a + e_b \tag{2.12}$$

The torque equation is

$$T_M = K_T i_a = J \frac{d^2\theta}{dt^2} + f_0 \frac{d\theta}{dt} \tag{2.13}$$

Taking the Laplace transform of Eqs. (2.11)–(2.13),

$$E_b(s) = K_b s\theta(s) \tag{2.14}$$

$$E(s) = L_a s I_a(s) + R_a I_a(s) + E_b(s) \tag{2.15}$$

$$I_a(s)(L_a s + R_a) = E(s) - E_b(s)$$

i.e.

$$I_a(s) = \frac{E(s) - E_b(s)}{(L_a s + R_a)} \tag{2.16}$$

$$Js^2\theta(s) + f_0 s\theta(s) = T_M(s) = K_T I_a(s)$$

i.e.

$$\theta(s)(Js^2 + f_0 s) = K_T I_a(s)$$

i.e.

$$s\theta(s)[Js + f_0] = K_T \frac{[E(s) - E_b(s)]}{(L_a s + R_a)} = K_T \frac{[E(s) - K_b s\theta(s)]}{(L_a s + R_a)}$$

[Substituting the values of $I_a(s)$ and $E_b(s)$ from Eqs. (2.16) and (2.14)]

i.e.

$$(L_a s + R_a)s(Js + f_0)\theta(s) = K_T E(s) - K_T K_b s\theta(s)$$

i.e.

$$s[(L_a s + R_a)(Js + f_0) + K_T K_b]\theta(s) = K_T E(s)$$

Therefore, the transfer function is

$$\frac{\theta(s)}{E(s)} = \frac{K_T}{s[(L_a s + R_a)(Js + f_0) + K_T K_b]}$$

The block diagram of the dc motor can be obtained as follows. The block diagram representation of the equation

$$I_a(s) = \frac{E(s) - E_b(s)}{(L_a s + R_a)}$$

is shown in Figure 2.54(a), where the circular block representing the differencing action is known as the *summing point*.

The block diagram representation of the equation.

$$\theta(s) = I_a(s) \frac{K_T}{s(Js + f_0)}$$

is shown in Figure 2.54(b). Here the signal is taken off from a take-off point and fed to the feedback block. The block diagram representation of the equation

$$E_b(s) = K_b s \theta(s)$$

is shown in Figure 2.54 (c).

Figure 2.54(d) shows the complete block diagram of the system under consideration obtained by connecting the block diagrams shown in Figure 2.54(a), Figure 2.54(b) and Figure 2.54(c).

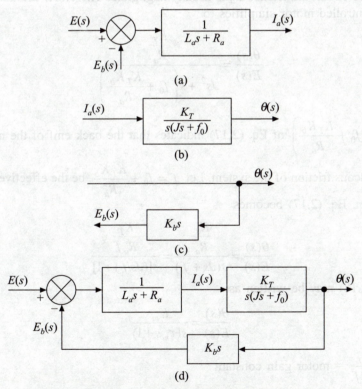

Figure 2.54 Block diagram of armature-controlled dc motor.

The block diagram of the system under consideration can be directly obtained from the physical system of Figure 2.53 by using the mechanical networks derived already.

The voltage applied to the armature circuit is $E(s)$ which is opposed by the back emf $E_b(s)$. The net voltage $E(s) - E_b(s)$ acts on a linear circuit comprised of resistance and inductance in series, having the transfer function $1/(L_a s + R_a)$. The result is an armature current $I_a(s)$. Since the field is fixed, the torque rotates the load at a speed $\theta(s)$ against the moment of inertia J and the viscous friction with a coefficient f_0. The transfer function is $1/(Js + f_0)$. The back emf signal $E_b(s) = K_b\, s\theta(s)$ is taken off from the shaft speed and fed back negatively to the summing point. The angle signal $\theta(s)$ is obtained by integrating (i.e., by multiplying by $1/s$) the speed $s\theta(s)$. This results in the block diagram of Figure 2.55, which is equivalent to that of Figure 2.54.

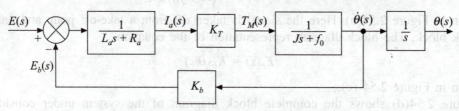

Figure 2.55 Block diagram of armature-controlled dc motor.

The armature circuit inductance L_a is usually negligible. Therefore, the transfer function of the armature-controlled motor simplifies to

$$\frac{\theta(s)}{E(s)} = \frac{\dfrac{K_T}{R_a}}{Js^2 + s\left(f_0 + \dfrac{K_T K_b}{R_a}\right)} \qquad (2.17)$$

The term $\left(f_0 + \dfrac{K_T K_b}{R_a}\right)$ of Eq. (2.17) indicates that the back emf of the motor effectively

increases the viscous friction of the system. Let $f = f_0 + \dfrac{K_T K_b}{R_a}$ be the effective viscous friction coefficient. Then, Eq. (2.17) becomes

$$\frac{\theta(s)}{E(s)} = \frac{\dfrac{K_T}{R_a}}{s(Js + f)} = \frac{\dfrac{K_T}{R_a f}}{s[(Js/f) + 1]} \qquad (2.18)$$

Equation (2.18) may be written as

$$\frac{\theta(s)}{E(s)} = \frac{K_m}{s(\tau_m s + 1)}$$

where $K_m = \dfrac{K_T}{R_a f}$ = motor gain constant

$T_m = \dfrac{J}{f}$ = motor time constant

Field-controlled dc servomotor: A field-controlled dc servomotor, is a dc shunt motor designed to satisfy the requirement of a servomotor. In this motor, the armature is supplied with a constant current or voltage. When armature voltage is constant, the torque is directly proportional to the field flux. Since the field current is proportional to flux, the torque of the motor is controlled by controlling the field current. The response of a field-controlled motor is however slowed by field inductance.

A field controlled dc motor is shown in Figure 2.56(a).

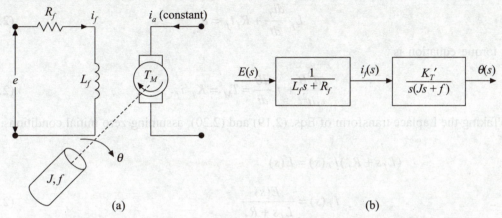

Figure 2.56 (a) Field controlled dc motor and (b) block diagram of field controlled dc motor.

In this system,

R_f = field winding resistance (in ohms)

L_f = field winding inductance (in henrys)

e = field control voltage (in volts)

i_f = field current (in amperes)

T_M = torque developed by motor (in N-m)

J = equivalent moment of inertia of motor and load referred to motor shaft (in kg-m²)

f = equivalent viscous friction coefficient of motor and load referred to motor shaft (in N-m/rad/s)

θ = angular displacement of motor shaft (in radians)

In the field-controlled motor, the armature current is fed from a constant current source. Since the motor is operating in the linear region of the magnetization curve, the flux is proportional to the field current, i.e.

$$\phi \propto i_f$$

or

$$\phi = K_f\, i_f$$

where K_f is a constant.

The torque developed by the motor

$$T_M \propto \phi i_a$$

$\therefore$ $$T_M \propto K_f i_f i_a$$

or $$T_M = K_T K_f i_a i_f = K_T' i_f$$

where K_T' is a constant.

The equation for the field circuit is

$$L_f \frac{di_f}{dt} + R_f i_f = e \tag{2.19}$$

The torque equation is

$$J \frac{d^2\theta}{dt^2} + f \frac{d\theta}{dt} = T_M = K_T' i_f \tag{2.20}$$

Taking the Laplace transform of Eqs. (2.19) and (2.20), assuming zero initial conditions, we get

$$(L_f s + R_f) I_f(s) = E(s)$$

i.e. $$I_f(s) = \frac{E(s)}{L_f s + R_f} \tag{2.21}$$

$$(Js^2 + fs)\theta(s) = T_M(s) = K_T' I_f(s) = \frac{K_T' E(s)}{(L_f s + R_f)}$$

[Substituting the value of $I_f(s)$ from Eq. (2.21)]
Therefore, the transfer function is

$$\frac{\theta(s)}{E(s)} = \frac{K_T'}{s(L_f s + R_f)(Js + f)} = \frac{\dfrac{K_T'}{R_f f}}{s\left(\dfrac{L_f s}{R_f} + 1\right)\left(\dfrac{Js}{f} + 1\right)} = \frac{K_m}{s(\tau_f s + 1)(\tau_m s + 1)}$$

where $K_m = \dfrac{K_T'}{R_f f}$ = motor gain constant

$\tau_f = \dfrac{L_f}{R_f}$ = time constant of field circuit

$\tau_m = \dfrac{J}{f}$ = mechanical time constant

The block diagram of the field controlled dc motor is shown in Figure 2.56(b).

Comparison of armature-controlled and field-controlled modes: For small size motors, field control is advantageous because only a low power servoamplifier is required, while the armature current which is not large can be supplied from an inexpensive current amplifier. For large size motors, it is on the whole cheaper to use armature control scheme. Further, in an armature-controlled motor, back emf contributes additional damping over and above that provided by load friction.

2.7.2   AC Servomotors

An ac servomotor is basically a two-phase induction motor except for certain special design features. A two-phase induction motor consists of two stator windings oriented 90°.

A two-phase servomotor differs in the following two ways from a normal induction motor.

1. The rotor of the servomotor is built with high resistance so that its X/R (inductive reactance/resistance) ratio is small which results in linear speed-torque characteristic, as shown by curve *b* in Figure 2.57. But the conventional induction motors have large X/R ratio which results in high efficiency but in highly nonlinear torque speed characteristics as shown by curve *a* in Figure 2.57. Also because of the positive slope for part of the characteristic, the system using such a motor becomes unstable.

2. The excitation voltage applied to two stator windings should have a phase difference of 90°.

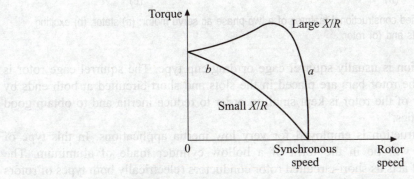

Figure 2.57   Torque-speed characteristics of induction motor.

Construction of ac servomotor: An ac servomotor is basically a two-phase induction motor with some special design features. The stator consists of two pole pairs (*A-B* and *C-D*) mounted on the inner periphery of the stator such that their axes are at an angle of 90° in space. Each pole pair carries a winding. One winding is called reference winding and the other is called control winding. The exciting current in the winding should have a phase displacement of 90°. The supply used to drive the motor is single-phase and so a phase advancing capacitor is connected to one of the phases to produce a phase difference of 90°. The constructional features of an ac servomotor are shown in Figure 2.58.

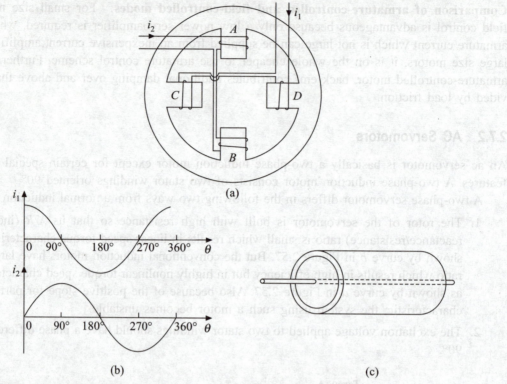

Figure 2.58 Simplified constructional features of a two-phase ac servo motor: (a) stator, (b) exciting currents and (c) rotor.

The rotor construction is usually squirrel cage or drag-cup type. The squirrel cage rotor is made of laminations. The rotor bars are placed in the slots and short-circuited at both ends by end rings. The diameter of the rotor is kept small in order to reduce inertia and to obtain good accelerating characteristics.

The drag-cup construction is employed for very low inertia applications. In this type of construction, the rotor will be in the form of a hollow cylinder made of aluminum. The aluminum cylinder itself acts as short-circuited rotor conductors (electrically both types of rotors are identical).

Working of a two-phase induction motor: Figure 2.59 shows a schematic diagram for balanced operation of the two-phase induction motor. The stator windings are excited by voltages of equal rms magnitude and 90° phase difference. This results in exciting currents i_1 and i_2 that are phase displaced by 90° and have equal rms value. So their respective fields will be 90° apart in both time and space resulting in a magnetic field of constant magnitude rotating at synchronous speed. The direction of rotation depends upon phase relationship of the two currents (voltages). As the field sweeps over the rotor, voltages are induced in it producing current in the short-circuited rotor. The rotating magnetic field interacts with these currents producing a torque on the rotor in the direction of field of rotation and so the rotor starts moving in the same direction as that of rotating magnetic field.

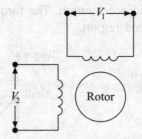

Figure 2.59 Schematic diagram of a two-phase induction motor.

Working of an ac servomotor: In servo applications, the voltages applied to the two stator windings are rarely balanced. Figure 2.60. shows a schematic diagram of an ac servomotor as a control system component. As shown in Figure 2.60, one of the phases known as the reference phase is excited by a constant voltage, and the other phase known as the control phase is energized by a voltage which is 90° out of phase with respect to the voltage of the reference phase. The control phase voltage is supplied from a servo amplifier and it has a variable magnitude and polarity (±90° phase angle with respect to the reference phase). The direction of rotation of the motor reverses as the polarity of the control phase signal changes in sign.

The control signals in control systems are usually of low frequency, in the range of 0 to 20 Hz. For production of rotating magnetic field, the control phase voltage must be of the same frequency as the reference phase voltage and in addition the two voltages must be in time quadrature. Hence, the control signal is modified by a carrier whose frequency is the same as that of the reference voltage and then applied to control winding. The ac supply itself is used as carrier signal for modulation process. The 90°-phase difference between the control-phase and the reference-phase voltages is obtained by the insertion of a capacitor in reference winding.

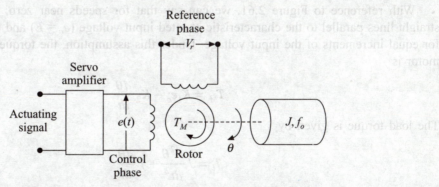

Figure 2.60 Schematic diagram of a two-phase servomotor.

The torque-speed curves of a typical ac servomotor plotted for fixed reference phase voltage and with variable rms control voltage are shown in Figure 2.61. All these curves have a negative slope. Note that the curve for zero control voltage goes through the origin. This means that when the control phase voltage becomes zero, the motor develops a decelerating torque and so the motor stops. The curves show a large torque at zero speed. This is a requirement for a servomotor in order to provide rapid acceleration. The torque-speed curves of ac servomotors are nonlinear except in the low speed region.

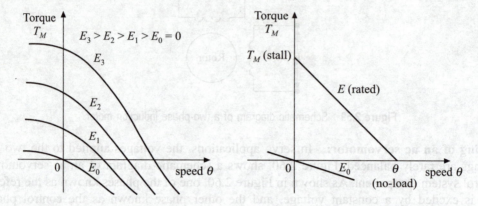

Figure 2.61   Servomotor characteristics.

Transfer function of an ac servomotor: Let

T_M = torque developed by servomotor

θ = angular displacement of rotor

$\omega = d\theta/dt$ = angular speed

T_1 = torque required by the load

J = moment of inertia of load and the rotor

K_1 = slope of control-phase voltage versus torque characteristics

K_2 = slope of torque-speed characteristic

With reference to Figure 2.61, we can say that for speeds near zero, all the curves are straight lines parallel to the characteristic at rated input voltage ($e_c = E$) and are equally spaced for equal increments of the input voltage. Under this assumption, the torque developed by the motor is

$$T_M = K_1 e_c - K_2 \frac{d\theta}{dt} \tag{2.22}$$

The load torque is given by

$$T_l = J \frac{d^2\theta}{dt^2} + f \frac{d\theta}{dt} \tag{2.23}$$

At equilibrium, the motor torque is equal to the load torque. Therefore,

$$\therefore \qquad J \frac{d^2\theta}{dt^2} + f \frac{d\theta}{dt} = K_1 e_c - K_2 \frac{d\theta}{dt} \tag{2.24}$$

Taking the Laplace transform on both sides of Eq. (2.24) and neglecting initial conditions, we get

$$Js^2\theta(s) + fs\theta(s) = K_1 E_c(s) - K_2 s\theta(s)$$

i.e.
$$(Js^2 + fs + K_2 s)\ \theta(s) = K_1 E_c(s)$$

The transfer function of the system is therefore

$$\frac{\theta(s)}{E_c(s)} = \frac{K_1}{Js^2 + fs + K_2 s} = \frac{K_1}{s(f + K_2)\left[\dfrac{Js^2}{s(f + K_2)} + 1\right]}$$

$$= \frac{K_1/(f + K_2)}{s\left(\dfrac{J}{f + K_2}s + 1\right)} = \frac{K_m}{s(\tau_m s + 1)}$$

where $\quad K_m = \dfrac{K_1}{f + K_2}$ = motor gain constant

$\qquad \tau_m = \dfrac{J}{f + K_2}$ = motor time constant

2.8 SYNCHROS

A *synchro* is an electromagnetic *transducer* commonly used to convert an angular position of a shaft into an electric signal. It is commercially known as *selsyn* or *autosyn*. It produces an output voltage depending upon the angular position of the rotor. It works on the principle of an induction motor.

2.8.1 Synchro Transmitter

The basic synchro unit is usually called a *synchro transmitter*. Its construction is similar to that of a three-phase alternator. The two major parts of a synchro transmitter are stator and rotor. The stator (stationary member) is of laminated silicon steel and is slotted on the inner periphery to accommodate a balanced three-phase winding which is usually of concentric coil type (three identical coils are placed in the stator with their axes 120° apart) and is Y connected. The rotor is of dumb-bell construction with a single winding and is wound with a concentric coil. A single-phase ac voltage is applied to the rotor winding through slip rings. The constructional features and a schematic diagram of a synchro transmitter are shown in Figures 2.62. and 2.63 respectively.

Let an ac voltage

$$v_r(t) = V_r \sin \omega_c(t) \tag{2.25}$$

be applied to the rotor of the synchro transmitter as shown in Figure 2.63. This voltage causes a flow of magnetizing current in the rotor coil which produces a sinusoidally time varying flux directed along its axis and distributed nearly sinusoidally in the air gap along the stator periphery. Because of transformer action, voltages are induced in each of the stator coils. As the air gap flux is sinusoidally distributed, the flux linking stator coil is proportional to the cosine of the angle between the rotor and stator coil axes and so is the voltage induced in each stator coil. The stator coil voltages are of course in time phase with each other. Thus we see that the synchro transmitter acts like a single-phase transformer in which the rotor coil is the primary and the stator coils form the three secondaries.

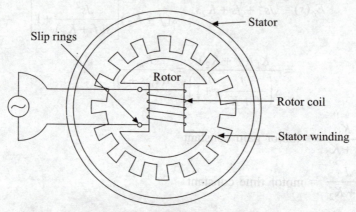

Figure 2.62 Constructional features of a synchro transmitter.

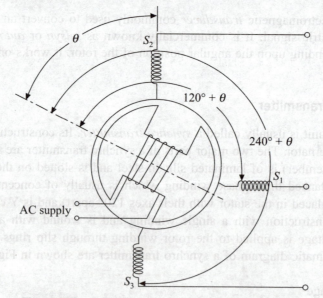

Figure 2.63 Schematic diagram of a synchro transmitter.

Let v_{s1n}, v_{s2n} and v_{s3n} respectively be the voltages in the stator coils S_1, S_2 and S_3 with respect to the neutral. Then, for the rotor position of the synchro transmitter shown in Figure 2.63, where the rotor axis makes an angle θ with the axis of the stator coil S_2,

$$v_{s1n} = KV_r \sin \omega_c t \cos (\theta + 120°)$$
$$v_{s2n} = KV_r \sin \omega_c t \cos \theta \qquad\qquad (2.26)$$
$$v_{s3n} = KV_r \sin \omega_c t \cos (\theta + 240°)$$

The three terminal voltages of the stator are as follows:

$$v_{s1s2} = v_{s1n} - v_{s2n} = \sqrt{3}\, KV_r \sin (\theta + 240°) \sin \omega_c t$$
$$v_{s2s3} = v_{s2n} - v_{s3n} = \sqrt{3}\, KV_r \sin (\theta + 120°) \sin \omega_c t \qquad\qquad (2.27)$$
$$v_{s3s1} = v_{s3n} - v_{s1n} = \sqrt{3}\, KV_r \sin \theta \sin \omega_c t$$

when $\theta = 0$, from the above equations [Eqs. (2.26) and (2.27)] it is seen that maximum voltage is induced in the stator coil S_2, while the terminal voltage v_{s3s1} is zero. This position of the rotor is defined as the electrical zero of the transmitter and is used as reference for specifying the angular position of the rotor.

Thus it is seen that the input to the synchro transmitter is the angular position of its rotor shaft and the output is a set of three stator coil to coil single-phase voltages. The magnitudes of these voltages are functions of the shaft position. So by measuring and identifying the set of voltages at the stator terminals, it is possible to identify the angular position of the rotor.

2.8.2 Synchro Control Transformer

The constructional features of a synchro control transformer are similar to that of a synchro transmitter except for the shape of the rotor. The rotor of the control transformer is made cylindrical in shape so that the air gap is practically uniform. This feature of the control transformer minimizes the changes in the rotor impedance with the rotation of the shaft. Another distinguishing feature is that the stator winding of the control transformer has a higher impedance per phase. This feature permits several control transformers to be fed from a single transmitter. The output of the synchro transmitter is applied to the stator windings of a synchro control transformer.

Working: The rotor shaft is connected to the load whose position has to be maintained at the desired value. Depending on the current position of the rotor and the applied emf on the stator, an emf is produced in the rotor winding. This emf can be measured and used to drive a motor so that the position of the load is corrected.

2.8.3 Synchro as an Error Detector

The synchro error detector is formed by interconnection of the synchro transmitter and the synchro control transformer as shown in Figure 2.64. The stator leads of the transmitter are directly connected to the stator leads of the control transformer. The angular position of the transmitter rotor is the reference input and the rotor is excited by a single-phase ac supply. The control transformer rotor is connected to a servomotor and to the shaft of the load, whose position is the desired output. Initially, the transmitter and the control transformer rotor are assumed to be in their electrical zero position. The angular separation of both rotor axes in this position is 90°. The electrical zero position of a control transformer in a servo system is that position of its rotor for which the output voltage on the rotor winding is zero with the transmitter in its electrical zero position.

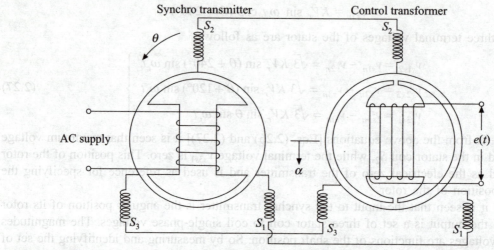

Figure 2.64 Synchro error detector.

When the transmitter rotor is excited, the rotor flux is set up and emfs are induced in stator coils. These induced emfs are impressed on the stator coils of the control transformer. The currents in the stator coils set up flux in the control transformer. Due to the similarity in the magnetic construction, the flux pattern produced in the two synchros will be the same if all losses are neglected.

Let the rotor of the transmitter rotate through an angle θ from its electrical zero position in the direction indicated and let the control transformer rotate in the same direction through an angle α resulting in a net angular separation of $\phi = (90 - \theta + \alpha)$ between the two rotors. So the voltage of the rotor terminals of the control transformer is then

$$e(t) = K'V_r \cos (90 - \theta + \alpha) \sin \omega_c t = K'V_r \cos (\theta - \alpha) \sin \omega_c t \qquad (2.28)$$

Equation (2.28) shows that the output voltage of the synchro error detector is a modulated signal with carrier frequency ω_c.

The synchro transmitter-control transformer pair thus acts as an error detector giving a voltage signal at the rotor terminals of the control transformer proportional to the angular difference between the transmitter and control transformer shaft positions.

2.9 GEAR TRAINS

Gear trains are used in control systems to attain the mechanical matching of the motor to the load. Usually, a servomotor operates at a high speed but at a low torque. To drive a load with a high torque and low speed by such a motor, the torque magnification and speed reduction are achieved by gear trains. Thus in mechanical systems, gear trains act as matching devices like transformers in electrical systems.

Figure 2.65 shows a motor driving a load through a gear train which consists of two gears coupled together. The gear with N_1 teeth is called the *primary gear* (analogous to the primary winding of the transformer) and the gear with N_2 teeth is called the *secondary gear*.

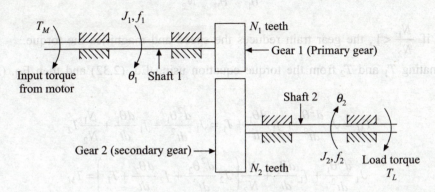

Figure 2.65   Gear train system.

The angular displacements of shafts 1 and 2 are denoted by θ_1 and θ_2 respectively. The moment of inertia and viscous friction of motor and gear 1 are denoted by J_1 and f_1 and those of gear 2 and load by J_2 and f_2 respectively.

For the first shaft, the differential equation is

$$T_M = J_1 \frac{d^2\theta_1}{dt^2} + f_1 \frac{d\theta_1}{dt} + T_1 \tag{2.29}$$

where T_M is the torque developed by the motor and T_1 is the load torque on gear 1 due to the rest of the gear train.

For the second shaft

$$J_2 \frac{d^2\theta_2}{dt^2} + f_2 \frac{d\theta_2}{dt} + T_L = T_2 \tag{2.30}$$

where T_L is the load torque and T_2 is the load torque on gear 2 due to the rest of the gear train.

Let r_1 be the radius of gear 1 and r_2 be the radius of gear 2. Since the linear distance travelled along the surface of each gear is the same, $r_1\theta_1 = r_2\theta_2$. The number of teeth on gear surface being proportional to gear radius, we obtain

$$\frac{\theta_2}{\theta_1} = \frac{r_1}{r_2} = \frac{N_1}{N_2} \tag{2.31}$$

Here the stiffness of the shafts of the gear train is assumed to be infinite. In an ideal case of no loss in power transfer, the work done by gear 1 is equal to that of gear 2. Therefore,

$$T_1\theta_1 = T_2\theta_2$$

$$\therefore \qquad \frac{T_1}{T_2} = \frac{\theta_2}{\theta_1} = \frac{N_1}{N_2} \tag{2.32}$$

Differentiating twice, we have the following relation for speed and acceleration.

$$\frac{\ddot{\theta}_2}{\ddot{\theta}_1} = \frac{\dot{\theta}_2}{\dot{\theta}_1} = \frac{N_1}{N_2} \tag{2.33}$$

Thus, if $\frac{N_1}{N_2} < 1$, the gear train reduces the speed and magnifies the torque.

Eliminating T_1 and T_2 from the torque equation using Eq. (2.32) and then Eq. (2.30), we get

$$T_M = J_1 \frac{d^2\theta_1}{dt^2} + f_1 \frac{d\theta_1}{dt} + T_1 = J_1 \frac{d^2\theta_1}{dt^2} + f_1 \frac{d\theta_1}{dt} + \frac{N_1}{N_2} T_2$$

$$J_1 \frac{d^2\theta_1}{dt^2} + f_1 \frac{d\theta_1}{dt} + \frac{N_1}{N_2} \left(J_2 \frac{d^2\theta_2}{dt^2} + f_2 \frac{d\theta_2}{dt} + T_L \right) = T_M \tag{2.34}$$

Eliminating θ_2 using Eq. (2.32), Eq. (2.34) reduces to

$$\left[J_1 + \left(\frac{N_1}{N_2} \right)^2 J_2 \right] \frac{d^2\theta_1}{dt^2} + \left[f_1 + \left(\frac{N_1}{N_2} \right)^2 f_2 \right] \frac{d\theta_1}{dt} + \left(\frac{N_1}{N_2} \right) T_L = T_M$$

Thus, the equivalent moment of inertia and viscous friction of gear train referred to shaft 1 are

$$J_{1eq} = J_1 + \left(\frac{N_1}{N_2} \right)^2 J_2; \quad f_{1eq} = f_1 + \left(\frac{N_1}{N_2} \right)^2 f_2$$

In terms of equivalent moment of inertia and friction, the equation for T_M, i.e. Eq. (2.29) may be written as

$$J_{1eq} \frac{d^2\theta_1}{dt^2} + f_{1eq} \frac{d\theta_1}{dt} + \left(\frac{N_1}{N_2} \right) T_L = T_M$$

where $\left(\frac{N_1}{N_2} \right) T_L$ is the load torque referred to shaft 1. Similarly, expressing θ_1 in terms of θ_2, the equivalent moment of inertia and viscous friction of gear train referred to load shaft are

$$J_{2eq} = J_2 + \left(\frac{N_2}{N_1} \right)^2 J_1; \quad f_{2eq} = f_2 + \left(\frac{N_2}{N_1} \right)^2 f_1$$

The torque equation referred to the load shaft may then be expressed as

$$J_{2eq} \frac{d^2\theta_2}{dt^2} + f_{2eq} \frac{d\theta_2}{dt} + T_L = \left(\frac{N_2}{N_1} \right) T_M$$

SHORT QUESTIONS AND ANSWERS

1. Most control systems contain which elements?
A. Most control systems contain mechanical as well as electrical components.

2. From a mathematical view point, the descriptions of which systems are analogous?
A. From a mathematical view point, the descriptions of mechanical and electrical systems are analogous. Given an electrical device, there is always an analogous mechanical counterpart mathematically and vice versa.

3. What are the two types of mechanical systems?
A. The two types of mechanical systems are (a) mechanical translational systems and (b) mechanical rotational systems.

4. What do you mean by a mechanical translational system?
A. A mechanical translational system is one in which the motion takes place along a straight line.

5. What do you mean by a mechanical rotational system?
A. A mechanical rotational system is one in which the motion takes place about a fixed axis.

6. Using which law, the equations of motion of mechanical systems are formulated?
A. Using Newton's law of motion, the equations governing the motion of mechanical systems are often formulated directly or indirectly.

7. State Newton's law of motion for mechanical translational systems.
A. Newton's law of motion for mechanical translational systems states that the algebraic sum of the forces acting on a rigid body in a given direction is equal to the product of the mass of the body and its acceleration in the same direction.

8. State Newton's law of motion for mechanical rotational systems.
A. Newton's law of motion for mechanical rotational systems states that the algebraic sum of moments or torques about a fixed axis is equal to the product of the inertia and the angular acceleration about the axis.

9. Using which ideal elements the mechanical translational systems are modelled?
A. The mechanical translational systems are modelled by using three ideal elements: mass, spring and damper.

10. Using which ideal elements the mechanical rotational systems are modelled?
A. The mechanical rotational systems are modelled by using three ideal elements: inertia, torsional spring and friction.

11. Define mass.
A. Mass is considered as a property of an element that stores the kinetic energy of translational motion.

12. Which type of energy does a spring store?

A. A spring is considered to be an element that stores potential energy.

13. When does friction exist?

A. Whenever there is motion or tendency of motion between two physical elements, frictional forces exist.

14. What are the three types of friction? Which one is more predominant?

A. The three types of friction commonly used in practical systems are—viscous friction, static friction, and coulomb friction. In most physical systems, the viscous friction predominates.

15. What do you mean by coulomb friction?

A. The force of sliding friction between dry surfaces is called coulomb friction. This force is substantially constant.

16. What do you mean by viscous friction?

A. The force of friction between moving surfaces separated by viscous fluid or the force between a solid body and a fluid medium is called viscous friction. This force is approximately linearly proportional to velocity over a certain limited velocity range.

17. What do you mean by stiction friction?

A. The force required to initiate motion between two contacting surfaces is called stiction.

18. Which friction is represented by a dash pot?

A. Viscous friction is always represented by a dash pot.

19. Define inertia.

A. Inertia J is considered to be the property of an element that stores the kinetic energy of rotational motion.

20. What does torsional spring constant K represent?

A. The torsional spring constant K represents the compliance of a rod or a shaft when it is subjected to an applied torque.

21. What do you mean by a free-body diagram?

A. A free-body diagram is a diagram showing each mass separately, with all forces acting on the mass marked on it.

22. What do you mean by a mechanical network?

A. A mechanical network is a diagram indicating the interconnection of sources and components of the mechanical system in which one end of the force or torque sources and the mass or inertia elements is connected to ground.

23. Write the force balance equations for an (a) ideal mass, (b) ideal spring and (c) ideal dash pot.

A. The force balance equations for the elements of mechanical translational system are as follows:

$$\text{Mass } (M) \rightarrow F = M\frac{d^2x}{dt^2} \qquad \text{or} \qquad F = M\frac{dv}{dt}$$

Spring $(K) \rightarrow F = Kx$ or $F = K \int v \, dt$

Damper $(f) \rightarrow F = f \dfrac{dx}{dt}$ or $F = fv$

24. Write the torque balance equations for an (a) ideal inertia, (b) ideal spring and (c) ideal dash pot.

A. The torque balance equations for the elements of the mechanical rotational systems are as follows:

Inertia $(J) \rightarrow T = J \dfrac{d^2\theta}{dt^2}$ or $T = J \dfrac{d\omega}{dt}$

Torsional spring $(K) \rightarrow T = K\theta$ or $T = K \int \omega \, dt$

Damper $(f) \rightarrow T = f \dfrac{d\theta}{dt}$ or $T = f\omega$

25. Name the energy storage elements in electrical systems.

A. The capacitor and the inductor are the energy storage elements in electrical systems.

26. Name the energy dissipative elements in electrical systems.

A. The resistor is the energy dissipative element in electrical systems.

27. What is the systematic way of analyzing mechanical systems?

A. The systematic way of analyzing a mechanical system is to draw a free-body diagram or a mechanical network and then write the differential equations describing them.

28. What do you mean by analogous systems?

A. Systems whose differential equations are of identical form are called analogous systems.

29. What are the two types of analogy between mechanical translational and electrical systems?

A. The two types of analogy between mechanical translational and electrical systems are (a) force-voltage analogy and (b) force-current analogy.

30. What are the two types of analogy between mechanical rotational and electrical systems?

A. The two types of analogy between mechanical rotational and electrical systems are (a) torque-voltage analogy and (b) torque-current analogy.

31. Name the analogous electrical elements in force-voltage analogy for the elements of mechanical translational system?

A. In force-voltage analogy, the analogous quantities in mechanical translational and electrical systems are Force (F)-Voltage (e), Mass (M)-Inductance (L), Friction (f)-Resistance (R), Spring constant (K)-Reciprocal of capacitance $(1/C)$, Displacement (x)-Charge (q), Velocity (v)-Current (i).

32. Name the analogous electrical elements in force-current analogy for the elements of mechanical translational system?

A. In force-current analogy, the analogous quantities in mechanical translational and electrical systems are Force (*F*)-Current (*i*), Mass (*M*)-Capacitance (*C*), Friction (*f*)-Reciprocal of resistance (1/*R*), Spring constant (*K*)-Reciprocal of inductance (1/*L*), Displacement (*x*)-Flux linkage (ϕ), Velocity (*v*)-Voltage (*e*).

33. Name the analogous electrical elements in torque-voltage analogy for the elements of mechanical rotational system?

A. In torque-voltage analogy, the analogous quantities in mechanical rotational and electrical systems are Torque (*T*)-Voltage (*e*), Inertia (*J*)-Inductance (*L*), Friction (*f*)-Resistance (*R*), Spring constant (*K*)-Reciprocal of capacitance (1/*C*), Angular displacement (θ)-Charge (*q*), Angular velocity (ω)-Current (*i*).

34. Name the analogous electrical elements in torque-current analogy for the elements of mechanical rotational systems?

A. In torque-current analogy, the analogous quantities in mechanical rotational and electrical systems are Torque (*T*)-Current (*i*), Inertia (*J*)-Capacitance (*C*), Friction (*f*)-Reciprocal of resistance (1/*R*), Spring constant (*K*)-Reciprocal of inductance (1/*L*), Angular displacement (θ)-Flux linkage (ϕ), Angular velocity (ω)-Voltage (*e*).

35. What do you mean by analogy? What is the advantage of finding analogy between systems?

A. Analogy means similarity. Using analogy, it is convenient to study a non-electrical system in terms of its electrical analog as electrical systems are more easily amenable to experimental study. The advantage of finding analogy between two systems is an unfamiliar system can be analyzed easily in terms of the familiar system.

36. Define the term 'Impulse response of a system'.

A. The impulse response of a system is defined as the output when the input is a unit impulse function $\delta(t)$. Once the impulse response of a linear system is known, the output of the system $c(t)$, with any input $r(t)$ can be found by using the transfer function.

37. Give the two definitions of the transfer function.

A. The transfer function of a linear time-invariant system is defined as the Laplace transform of the impulse response of the system, with all the initial conditions set to zero. The transfer function of a linear time-invariant system is also defined as the ratio of the Laplace transform of the output to the Laplace transform of the input with all initial conditions neglected.

38. Can a transfer function be defined for nonlinear systems?

A. No. A transfer function can not be defined for nonlinear systems.

39. For which systems can a transfer function be defined?

A. The transfer function can be defined only for linear time-invariant systems.

40. What do you mean by a strictly proper transfer function?

A. A strictly proper transfer function is one in which the order of the denominator polynomial is greater than that of the numerator polynomial.

41. What do you mean by a proper transfer function?

A. A proper transfer function is one in which the order of the numerator polynomial is equal to that of the denominator polynomial.

42. What do you mean by an improper transfer function?

A. An improper transfer function is one in which the order of the denominator polynomial is lees than that of the numerator polynomial.

43. What do you mean by characteristic equation? Why that name?

A. The characteristic equation of a linear system is defined as the equation obtained by setting the denominator polynomial of the transfer function to zero. This equation characterizes the behaviour of the system. Hence the name characteristic equation.

44. The stability of a linear time-invariant system is governed by what?

A. The stability of a linear time-invariant system is governed completely by the roots of its characteristic equation.

45. What do you mean by a sinusoidal transfer function?

A. The transfer function obtained by replacing s with $j\omega$ in the original transfer function is called the sinusoidal transfer function.

46. What do you mean by multivariable system?

A. A multi-input-multi-output system is called a multivariable system.

47. Does the transfer function of a system depend on the input?

A. No. The transfer function of a system does not depend on the input.

48. How is the transfer function to be derived when a number of systems are cascaded?

A. When loading is considered, the overall transfer function should be derived by basic analysis without regard to individual transfer functions.

When there is no loading, the overall transfer function is equal to the product of the individual transfer functions of the systems connected in cascade.

49. Why are differential equations converted into algebraic equations?

A. The solution of higher-order differential equations is quite a tedious process, so differential equations are converted into algebraic equations by using Laplace transforms.

50. What do you mean by loading in electrical systems?

A. Loading in electrical systems means drawing the current from them.

51. What are servomotors?

A. The motors used in control systems or in servomechanisms are called servomotors. They are used to convert electrical signal into angular motion.

52. What are the characteristics of servomotors?

A. The characteristics of servomotors are as follows:

1. Linear relationship between the speed and the electric control signal
2. Steady-state stability

3. Wide range of speed control
4. Low mechanical and electrical inertia
5. Fast response

53. Compare ac and dc servomotors.

A. The ac and dc servomotors are compared as follows:

ac servomotor	dc servomotor
1. Low power output.	1. Relatively high power output than an ac servomotor of the same size.
2. Characteristics are nonlinear.	2. Characteristics are linear.
3. Slow response due to higher values of time constants.	3. Fast response due to low electrical and mechanical time constants.
4. Suitable for low power applications.	4. Suitable for high power applications.

54. What are the advantages of permanent magnet dc servomotors?

A. The advantages of permanent magnet dc servomotors are as follows:

1. A simpler and more reliable motor because the field power supply is not required.
2. Higher efficiency due to the absence of field losses.
3. Field flux is less affected by temperature rise.
4. Less heating, making it possible to totally enclose the motor.
5. No possibility of over speeding due to loss of field.
6. A more linear torque versus speed curve.
7. Higher power output at the same dimensions and temperature limitations.

55. What are the special features of electromagnetic field dc servomotors?

A. The special features of electromagnetic field dc servomotors are as follows:

1. The number of slots and commutator segments is large to improve commutation.
2. Compoles and compensating windings are provided to eliminate sparking.
3. The diameter to length ratio is kept low to reduce inertia.
4. Oversize shafts are employed to withstand the high torque stress.
5. Eddy currents are reduced by complete lamination of the magnetic circuit and by using low-loss steel.

56. What for dc motors are used in control systems?

A. In servo applications, dc motors are used to produce rapid acceleration from stand still. So the physical requirements of such motors are low inertia and high starting torque.

57. What are the two control modes in which the dc motors are used in control systems?

A. The two control modes in which the dc motors are used in control systems are (a) armature control mode with fixed field current and (b) field control mode with fixed armature current.

58. For which motors field control is preferred and for which motors armature control is preferred?

A. For small size motors, field control is advantageous and for large size motors armature control is preferred.

59. How does an ac servomotor differ from a normal two-phase induction motor?

A. An ac servomotor is basically a two-phase induction motor but it differs from that in two ways.

    1. The ac servomotor has low value of X/R to achieve linear torque-speed characteristics. But normal induction motors have large values of X/R for higher efficiency.

    2. The ac servomotor has low inertia rotor. The inertia of the rotor is reduced by reducing the diameter or by drag-cup construction.

60. What is a synchro?

A. A synchro is an electromagnetic transducer commonly used to convert an angular position of a shaft into an electric signal. It works on the principle of a rotating transformer (induction motor).

61. What are the commercial names of a synchro?

A. The commercial names of a synchro are: selsyn, autosyn and telesyn.

62. What is synchro pair? What for is it used?

A. A synchro pair is a system formed by interconnection of the devices—synchro transmitter and synchro control transformer. A synchro pair may be used either to transmit an angular motion from one place to another or to produce an error voltage proportional to the difference between two angular motions.

63. What are the differences between a synchro transmitter and a synchro control transformer?

A. The differences between a synchro transmitter and a synchro control transformer are as follows:

    1. The rotor of a synchro transmitter is of dumb-bell shape, but the rotor of a synchro control transformer is cylindrical.

    2. The rotor winding of a synchro transmitter is excited by an ac voltage. In a synchro control transformer, the induced emf in the rotor is used as an output signal (error signal).

64. What is electrical zero position of a synchro transmitter?

A. The electrical zero position of a synchro transmitter is a position of its rotor at which one of the coil-to-coil voltage is zero. Any angular motion of the rotor is measured with respect to the electrical zero position of the rotor.

65. What is electrical zero position of a synchro control transformer?

A. The electrical zero position of a synchro control transformer in a servo system is that position of its rotor for which the output voltage on the rotor winding is zero, with the transmitter in its electrical zero position.

66. What is aligned position of a synchro pair?

A. The aligned position of a synchro pair is one in which both the synchro transmitter and the synchro control transformer are in their electrical zero positions. The angular separation of both rotor axes in aligned position is 90°. The error signal is zero in the aligned position.

67. What are the applications of synchros?

A. Synchros are used in servomechanisms (position control systems) as error detectors and to convert angular displacements to proportional electrical signals. They are also used in control systems to transmit angular motions from one place to another.

68. What for gear trains are used in control systems?

A. Gear trains are used in control systems to obtain mechanical matching of motor to load. They are used to alter the speed to torque ratio of the rotational power transmitted from motor to load. This is necessary to meet the torque requirement of the load.

69. What is gear ratio?

A. The gear ratio of a gear train is the ratio of torque, speed, angular displacement, velocity and acceleration between any two gear wheels in that gear train. The gear ratio between gear wheels a and b in a gear train is given by

$$\frac{N_a}{N_b} = \frac{r_a}{r_b} = \frac{T_a}{T_b} = \frac{\theta_b}{\theta_a} = \frac{\omega_b}{\omega_a} = \frac{\alpha_b}{\alpha_a}$$

70. A servomotor is connected through a gear ratio of 12 to a load having moment of inertia J and viscous friction coefficient f. What are the equivalent parameters referred to motor shaft side.

A. Let N_1 = number of teeth in gear wheel connected to motor shaft

N_2 = number of teeth in gear wheel connected to load shaft

Given $N_1/N_2 = 12$

Moment of inertia of load referred to motor shaft = $J(N_1/N_2)^2 = 144\ J$

Coefficient of friction of load referred to motor shaft = $f(N_1/N_2)^2 = 144\ f$

71. How do you compare gear trains and transformers?

A. In mechanical systems, gear trains act as matching devices like transformers in electrical systems.

REVIEW QUESTIONS

1. Derive an expression for the transfer function of a single-loop control system.
2. Derive an expression for the transfer function of an armature controlled dc servomotor.
3. Derive an expression for the transfer function of a field controlled dc servomotor.
4. Explain the construction and working of an ac servomotor.
5. Derive an expression for the transfer function of an ac servomotor.
6. Explain the construction and working of a synchro.
7. Write short notes on gear trains. Derive an expression for the motor torque.

FILL IN THE BLANKS

1. Most control systems contain _____ as well as _____ components.

2. From a mathematical view point, the descriptions of mechanical and electrical elements are _____.

3. The motion of mechanical elements can be described as _____ or _____ or _____.

4. In mechanical _____ systems, motion takes place along a straight line.

5. In mechanical _____ systems, motion takes place about a fixed axis.

6. The variables that are used to describe the translational motion are _____ _____ _____.

7. _____ is considered as a property of an element that stores kinetic energy of translational motion.

8. In general _____ is an element that stores potential energy.

9. The force of sliding friction between dry surfaces is called _____ friction force.

10. The force required to initiate motion between two contacting surfaces is called _____.

11. The element for viscous friction is often represented by a _____.

12. The force of friction between moving surfaces separated by a fluid or the force between a solid body and a fluid medium is called _____ force.

13. _____ is considered as a property of an element that stores the kinetic energy of rotational motion.

14. Systems whose differential equations are identical are called _____ systems.

15. The classical way of modelling linear systems is to use _____ to represent input-output relations between variables.

16. The transfer function is defined only for _____ systems. It is not defined for _____ systems.

17. The transfer function is defined only when the _____ are neglected.

18. The transfer function is independent of the _____ to the system.

19. The transfer function between an input variable and an output variable of a system is defined as the Laplace transform of the _____ of the system.

20. The transfer function is defined as the ratio of the _____ to the _____ with the assumption that all _____ are zero.

21. The transfer function is said to be _____ if the order of the denominator polynomial is greater than that of the numerator polynomial.

22. The transfer function is said to be _____ if the order of the numerator polynomial is equal to that of the denominator polynomial.

23. The transfer function is said to be _____ if the order of the numerator polynomial is greater than that of the denominator polynomial.

24. The characteristic equation of a linear system is defined as the equation obtained by setting the _____ of the _____ to zero.

25. The transfer function obtained by replacing s with $j\omega$ in the original transfer function is called the _____.

26. In servo applications _____ are required to produce rapid acceleration from stand still.

27. In control systems, the dc motors are used in two different control modes (a) _____ and (b) _____.

28. In servo applications, the dc motors are generally used in the _____ range of the magnetization curve.

29. For small size motors _____ is advantageous and for large size motors _____ is preferred.

30. Gear trains are used in control systems to attain mechanical matching of _____ to _____.

31. In mechanical systems, gear trains act as matching devices like _____ in electrical systems.

32. The motors used in automatic control systems or in servomechanisms are called _____.

33. Servomotors are used to convert _____ into _____.

34. The characteristics of _____ servomotors are nonlinear, whereas the characteristics of _____ servomotors are linear.

35. _____ servomotor is suitable for low power applications and _____ servomotor is suitable for high power applications.

36. _____ servomotor has fast response and _____ servomotor has slow response.

37. The ac servomotor has _____ value of X/R, whereas a normal induction motor has a _____ value of X/R.

38. A _____ is an electro magnetic transducer commonly used to convert an angular position of a shaft into an electric signal.

39. A synchro is commonly known as _____ or _____.

40. A synchro pair consists of a _____ and a _____.

41. The rotor of synchro transmitter is of _____ shape, but the shape of synchro control transformer is _____.

42. Any angular motion of the rotor of a transmitter is measured with respect to the _____ of the rotor.

OBJECTIVE TYPE QUESTIONS

1. The motion of mechanical elements can be described as
   (a) purely rotational
   (b) purely translational
   (c) rotational or translational or combination of both
   (d) none of these

2. Translational motion is the motion
   (a) along a straight line
   (b) about a fixed axis
   (c) along a random path
   (d) none of these

3. Rotational motion is the motion
   (a) along a straight line
   (b) about a fixed axis
   (c) along a random path
   (d) none of these

4. An element that stores the kinetic energy of translational motion is called
   (a) mass
   (b) spring
   (c) damper
   (d) none of these

5. An element which stores potential energy is
   (a) mass
   (b) spring
   (c) damper
   (d) none of these

6. The force of sliding friction between dry surfaces is called
   (a) coulomb friction force
   (b) viscous friction force
   (c) stiction
   (d) none of these

7. The force required to initiate motion between two contacting surfaces is called
   (a) coulomb friction force
   (b) viscous friction force
   (c) stiction
   (d) none of these

8. The friction force acts in a direction
   (a) opposite to that of motion
   (b) perpendicular to that of motion
   (c) along that of motion
   (d) none of these

9. The viscous friction force is approximately linearly proportional to
   (a) displacement
   (b) velocity
   (c) acceleration
   (d) none of these

10. An element that stores kinetic energy of rotational motion is called
    (a) inertia
    (b) torsional spring
    (c) damper
    (d) mass

11. The transfer function is defined only for
    (a) linear time-varying systems
    (b) linear time-invariant systems
    (c) linear and nonlinear systems
    (d) all of these

12. The transfer function is defined as the Laplace transform of the response for a
    (a) step input
    (b) impulse input
    (c) ramp input
    (d) parabolic input

13. The transfer function is dependent of the
    (a) parameters of the system
    (b) initial conditions of the system
    (c) input to the system
    (d) output of the system

14. For strictly proper transfer function, the order of the numerator is
    (a) equal to that of the denominator
    (b) greater than that of the denominator
    (c) smaller than that of the denominator
    (d) not related to that of the denominator

15. For proper transfer function, the order of the numerator is
    (a) equal to that of the denominator
    (b) greater than that of the denominator
    (c) smaller than that of the denominator
    (d) not related to that of the denominator

16. For an improper transfer function, the order of the numerator is
    (a) equal to that of the denominator
    (b) greater than that of the denominator
    (c) smaller than that of the denominator
    (d) not related to that of the denominator

PROBLEMS

2.1 *to* 2.12: (a) Write the differential equations governing the behaviour of the mechanical systems shown below.
(b) Draw the analogous electrical circuits based on force-current and force-voltage analogies.
(c) Write the corresponding differential equations.

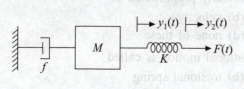

Figure P2.1

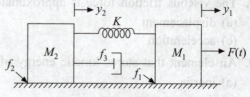

Figure P2.2

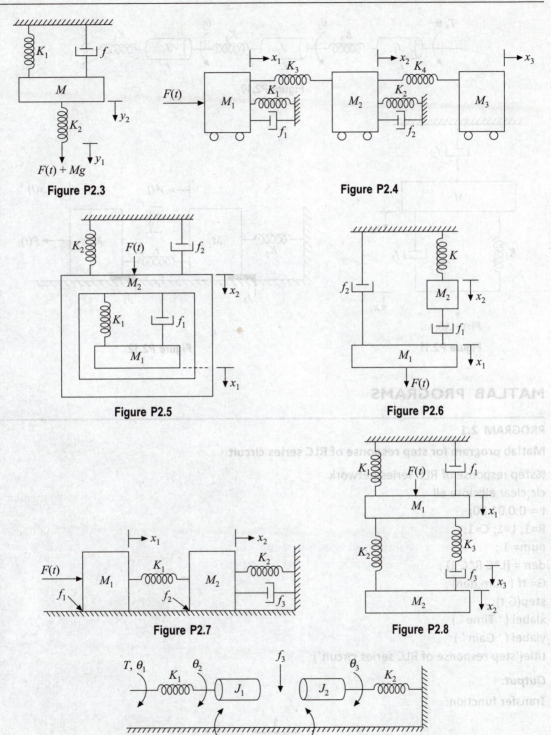

Figure P2.3

Figure P2.4

Figure P2.5

Figure P2.6

Figure P2.7

Figure P2.8

Figure P2.9

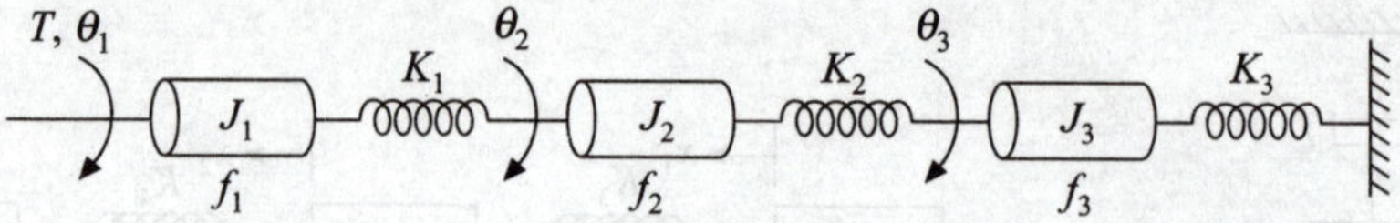

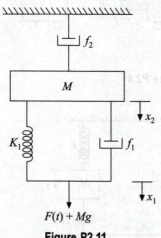

Figure P2.10

Figure P2.11

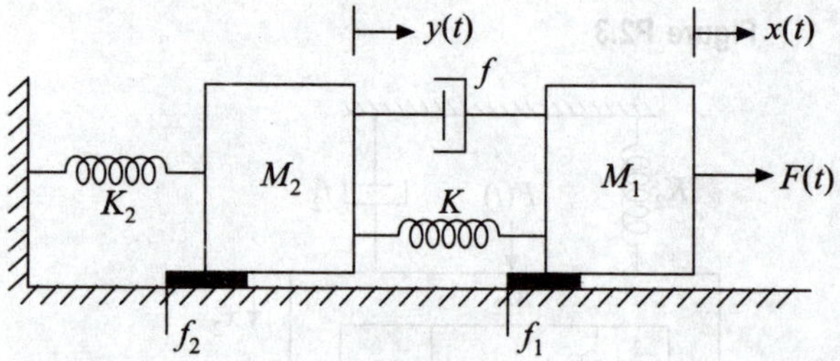

Figure P2.12

MATLAB PROGRAMS

PROGRAM 2.1

Matlab program for step response of RLC series circuit

```
%step response of RLC series network
clc;clear all;close all
t = 0:0.01:20;
R=1; L=1; C=1;
num= 1 ;
den = [L*C R*C 1] ;
G= tf ( num,den) ;
step(G,t);
xlabel ( 'Time' )
ylabel ( 'Gain' )
title('step response of RLC series circuit')
```

Output:

Transfer function:

$$\frac{1}{s^2 + s + 1}$$

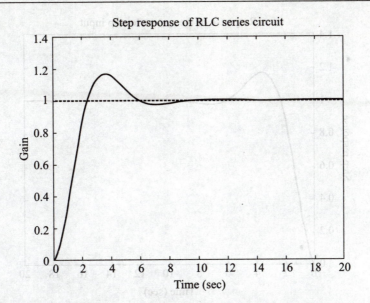

Step response of RLC series circuit

PROGRAM 2.2

Matlab program to obtain the step response for the mechanical system

```
%step response of the given mechanical system
clc;clear all;close all;
t=0:0.01:20;
K=1; M=1; B=1;
num= 1;
den = [M B K] ;
G = tf(num,den)
yl = step (G,t) ;
plot(t, yl);
xlabel( 'Time (Second)' )
ylabel( 'Step Response' )
title( 'Response of the system to step input')
```

Output:

Transfer function:

$$\frac{1}{s^2+s+1}$$

Response of the system to step input

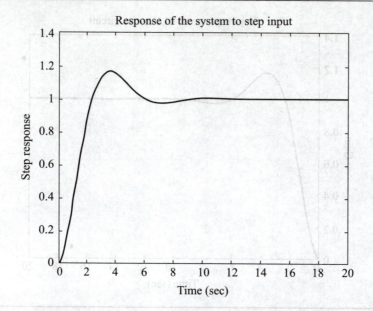

PROGRAM 2.3

Matlab program for the time response of RLC series circuit

```
% Time response for RLC Series Circuit
clc
clear all
close all
x0 = [0.5, 0]; % initial conditions
tspan=[0, 15]; % time interval
[t,x] = ode23('electsys',tspan, x0);
subplot(2, 1, 1),plot(t,x)
title('Time response of an RLC series circuit')
xlabel('Time - sec.')
text(8,1.15, 'Capacitor voltage')
text(8, .1, 'Current')
vc= x(:,1); i = x(:,2);
subplot(2, 1, 2),plot(vc, i)
title('Current versus capacitor voltage ')
xlabel('Capacitor voltage')
ylabel('Current')
```

Output:

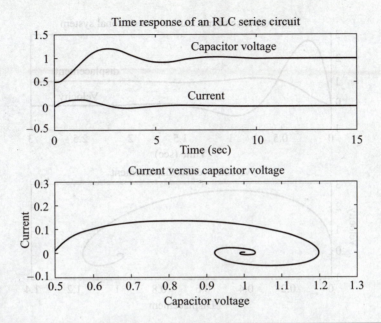

Output:

PROGRAM 2.4

Matlab program to obtain the response of a mechanical system.

```
% Program for force-voltage & force-Current Analogy
clc;clear all;close all;
tspan = [0, 3] ; % time interval
x0 = [0, 0]; % initial conditions
[t,x] = ode23('mechsys', tspan, x0);
subplot(2,1,1),plot(t,x)
title('Time response of mechanical translational system')
xlabel('Time - sec.')
text(2,1.2,'displacement')
text(2,.2,'velocity')
d= x(:,1); v = x(:,2);
subplot(2,1,2), plot(d, v)
title('velocity versus displacement')
xlabel('displacement')
ylabel('velocity')
```

Output:

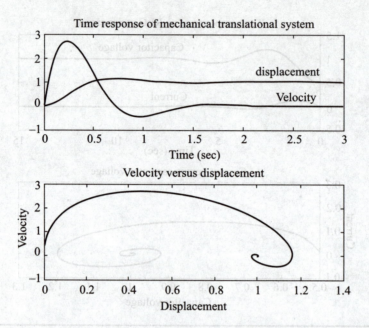

Time response of mechanical translational system

Velocity versus displacement

3

Block Diagram and Signal Flow Graphs

3.1 BLOCK DIAGRAMS

A control system may consist of a number of components. To show the functions performed by each component in control engineering, we commonly use a diagram called the block diagram. *A block diagram of a system is a pictorial representation of the functions performed by each component and of the flow of signals.* Such a diagram depicts the inter relationships that exist among the various components. It can be used together with the transfer functions to describe the cause-and-effect relationships throughout the system. Differing from a purely abstract mathematical representation, a block diagram has the advantage of indicating more realistically the signal flows of the actual system. In general, block diagrams can be used to model linear as well as nonlinear systems.

In a block diagram, all system variables are linked to each other through functional blocks. The functional block or simply block is a symbol for the mathematical operation on the input signal to the block that produces the output. The transfer functions of the components are usually entered in the corresponding blocks, which are connected by arrows to indicate the direction of the flow of signals. The signal can pass only in the direction of the arrows. Thus, the block diagram of a system explicitly shows a unilateral property.

Figure 3.1 shows an element of the block diagram. The arrow head pointing towards the block indicates the input, and the arrow head leading away from the block represents the output. Such arrows are referred to as signals.

Figure 3.1   Element of a block diagram.

The dimensions of the output signals from the block are the dimensions of the input signal to the block multiplied by the dimensions of the transfer function in the block.

101

The advantages of the block diagram representation of a system lie in the fact that it is easy to form the overall block diagram of the entire system by merely connecting the blocks of the components according to the signal flow and that it is possible to evaluate the contribution of each component to the overall performance of the system.

In general, the functional operation of the system can be visualized more readily by examining the block diagram than by examining the physical system itself. A block diagram contains information regarding dynamic behaviour, but it does not include any information on the physical construction of the system. Consequently many dissimilar and unrelated systems can be represented by the same block diagram.

In a block diagram, the main source of energy is not explicitly shown and the block diagram of a system is not unique. A number of different block diagrams can be drawn for a system, depending on the point of view of analysis.

The plus or minus sign at each arrow head indicates whether the signal is to be added or subtracted. It is important that the quantities being added or subtracted have the same dimensions and the same units.

The block diagram elements used frequently in control systems and the related algebra are shown in Figure 3.2. One of the important components of a control system is the sensing device that acts as a junction point for signal comparisons. The physical components involved are: the potentiometer, synchro, resolver, differential amplifier, multiplier and other signal processing transducers. In general, sensing devices perform simple mathematical operations such as addition, subtraction, multiplication (nonlinear) and some times combination of these.

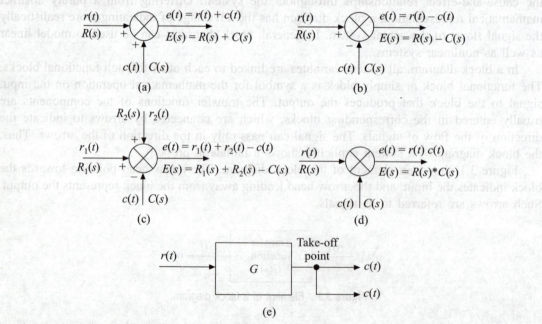

Figure 3.2 (a), (b) and (c) Addition and subtraction operations and (d) multiplication operation and (e) take-off point.

The block diagram representations of these operations are illustrated in Figure 3.2. In Figure 3.2, a circle with a cross is the symbol that indicates a summing operation. The addition and subtraction operations in Figure 3.2(a), Figure (b) and Figure (c) are linear, so that the input and output variables of these block diagram elements can be time-domain variables or Laplace transform variables.

$$e(t) = r(t) - y(t)$$
$$E(s) = R(s) - Y(s)$$

The multiplication operation is nonlinear, so that the input-output relation has meaning only in the real (time) domain.

Branch point: A branch point or a take-off point is a point from which the signal from a block goes concurrently to other blocks or summing points.

3.1.1 Block Diagram of a Closed-Loop System

Figure 3.3 shows an example of a block diagram of a closed-loop system. The output $C(s)$ is fed back to the summing point where it is compared with the reference input. When the output is fed back to the summing point for comparison with the input, it is necessary to convert the form of the output signal to that of the input signal. The role of the feedback element is to modify the output before it is compared with the input. This conversion is accomplished by the feedback element whose transfer function is $H(s)$. The output of the block $C(s)$ in this case is obtained by multiplying the transfer function $G(s)$ by the input to the block $E(s)$. The feedback signal that is fed back to the summing point for comparison with the input is $B(s) = C(s)H(s)$.

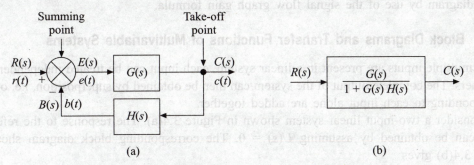

(a)   (b)

Figure 3.3 Block diagram of a closed-loop control system.

The following terminology is defined with reference to the diagram of Figure 3.3:

$r(t)$, $R(s)$ = reference input (command)

$c(t)$, $C(s)$ = output (controlled variable)

$b(t)$, $B(s)$ = feedback signal

$e(t)$, $E(s)$ = error signal

$G(s)$ = forward path transfer function

$H(s)$ = feedback path transfer function

$G(s) H(s) = L(s)$ = loop transfer function or open-loop transfer function

$T(s) = \dfrac{C(s)}{R(s)}$ = closed-loop transfer function or system transfer function

The closed-loop transfer function $T(s)$ can be expressed as a function of $G(s)$ and $H(s)$. From Figure 3.3,

$$C(s) = G(s) E(s) \tag{3.1}$$

and
$$B(s) = C(s) H(s) \tag{3.2}$$

The error signal is

$$E(s) = R(s) - B(s) \tag{3.3}$$

Substituting Eqs. (3.3) and (3.2) in Eq. (3.1), we get

$$
\begin{aligned}
C(s) &= G(s)[R(s) - B(s)] \\
&= G(s)R(s) - G(s)B(s) \\
&= G(s)R(s) - G(s)H(s)C(s)
\end{aligned}
$$

or
$$C(s)[1 + G(s)H(s)] = G(s)R(s) \tag{3.4}$$

$\therefore$
$$\frac{C(s)}{R(s)} = \frac{G(s)}{1 + G(s)H(s)}$$

In general, a control system may contain more than one feedback loop, and evaluation of transfer function from the block diagram by means of the algebraic method described above may be tedious. The transfer function of any linear system can be obtained directly from its block diagram by use of the signal flow graph gain formula.

3.1.2 Block Diagrams and Transfer Functions of Multivariable Systems

When multiple inputs are present in a linear system, each input can be treated independently of the others. The complete output of the system can then be obtained by superposition, i.e. outputs corresponding to each input alone are added together.

Consider a two-input linear system shown in Figure 3.4(a). The response to the reference input can be obtained by assuming $U(s) = 0$. The corresponding block diagram shown in Figure 3.4(b) gives

$$C_R(s) = \text{output due to } R(s) \text{ acting alone}$$

$$= \frac{G_1(s)G_2(s)}{1 + G_1(s)G_2(s)H(s)} R(s) \tag{3.5}$$

Similarly, the response to the input $U(s)$ is obtained by assuming $R(s) = 0$. The block diagram corresponding to this case is shown in Figure 3.4 (c) which gives

$$C_U(s) = \text{output due to } U(s) \text{ acting alone}$$

$$= \frac{G_2(s)}{1 + G_1(s)G_2(s)H(s)} U(s) \tag{3.6}$$

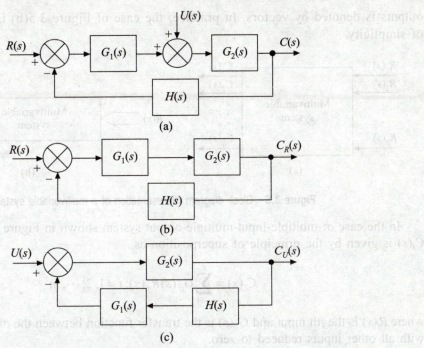

Figure 3.4 (a) Block diagram of a 2-input system, (b) block diagram when $U(s)$ is zero, and (c) block diagram when $R(s)$ is zero.

The response due to the simultaneous application of $R(s)$ and $U(s)$ can be obtained by adding the two individual responses, i.e. Eqs. (3.5) and (3.6).

$$C(s) = C_R(s) + C_U(s)$$

$$= \frac{G_2(s)}{1 + G_1(s)G_2(s)H(s)}[G_1(s)R(s) + U(s)] \qquad (3.7)$$

Consider now the case, where $|G_1(s)H(s)| \gg 1$ and $|G_1(s)G_2(s)H(s)| \gg 1$. In this case, the closed-loop transfer function $C_U(s)/U(s)$ becomes almost zero, and the effect of the disturbance is suppressed. This is an advantage of the closed-loop system.

On the other hand, the closed-loop transfer function $C_R(s)/R(s)$ approaches $1/H(s)$ as the gain $G_1(s)G_2(s)H(s)$ increases. This means that if $|G_1(s)G_2(s)H(s)| \gg 1$, then the closed-loop transfer function $C_R(s)/R(s)$ becomes independent of $G_1(s)$ and $G_2(s)$ and becomes inversely proportional to $H(s)$ so that variations of $G_1(s)$ and $G_2(s)$ do not affect the closed-loop transfer function $C_R(s)/R(s)$. This is another advantage of the closed-loop system. It can easily be seen that any closed-loop system with unity feedback $H(s) = 1$, tends to equalize the input and output.

Two block diagram representations of a multivariable system with p inputs and q outputs are shown in Figure 3.5. In Figure 3.5(a), the individual input and output signals are designated whereas in the block diagram of Figure 3.5(b), the multiplicity of inputs and outputs is denoted by vectors. In practice, the case of Figure 3.5(b) is preferable because of simplicity.

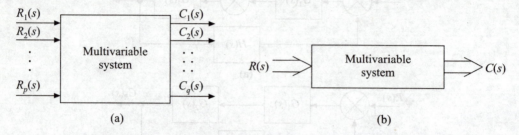

Figure 3.5 Block diagram representation of a multivariable system.

In the case of multiple-input-multiple-output system shown in Figure 3.5(a), the ith output $C_i(s)$ is given by the principle of superposition as

$$C_i(s) = \sum_{j=1}^{r} G_{ij}(s)R_j(s); \ i = 1, 2, \cdots, m \tag{3.8}$$

where $R_j(s)$ is the jth input and $G_{ij}(s)$ is the transfer function between the ith output and jth input with all other inputs reduced to zero.

In matrix form, Eq. (3.8) can be expressed as

$$\begin{bmatrix} C_1(s) \\ C_2(s) \\ \vdots \\ C_q(s) \end{bmatrix} = \begin{bmatrix} G_{11}(s) & G_{12}(s) & \cdots & G_{1p}(s) \\ G_{21}(s) & G_{22}(s) & \cdots & C_{2p}(s) \\ \vdots & & & \\ G_{q1}(s) & G_{q2}(s) & \cdots & G_{qp}(s) \end{bmatrix} \begin{bmatrix} R_1(s) \\ R_2(s) \\ \vdots \\ R_p(s) \end{bmatrix}$$

This can be expressed in compressed matrix notation as

$$C(s) = G(s)R(s) \tag{3.9}$$

where, $R(s)$ = vector of inputs (In Laplace transform) (p)

$G(s)$ = Matrix transfer function ($q \times p$)

$C(s)$ = vector of outputs (In Laplace transform) (q)

The corresponding block diagram can be drawn as in Figure 3.5(b), where thick arrows represent multi-inputs and outputs.

Figure 3.6 shows the block diagram of a multivariable feedback control system. When a feedback loop is present as in Figure 3.6, each feedback signal is obtained by processing in general all the outputs. Thus for ith feedback signal, we can write

$$B_i(s) = \sum_{j=1}^{m} H_{ij}(s)C_j(s) \tag{3.10}$$

The ith error signal is then

$$E_i(s) = R_i(s) - B_i(s) \tag{3.11}$$

Generalizing, in matrix form, we can write

$$E_i(s) = R_i(s) - B_i(s) \tag{3.12}$$

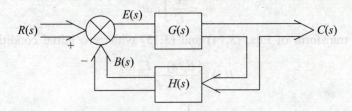

Figure 3.6 Block diagram of a multivariable feedback control system.

The transfer function relationships of the system are expressed in vector-matrix form as

$$C(s) = G(s)E(s)$$

$$E(s) = R(s) - B(s)$$

$$B(s) = C(s) H(s)$$

where $C(s)$ is the $q \times 1$ output vector; $E(s)$, $R(s)$, and $B(s)$ are all $p \times 1$ vectors; and $G(s)$ and $H(s)$ are $q \times p$ and $p \times q$ transfer function matrices respectively. Simplifying

$$C(s) = G(s)E(s) = G(s)[R(s) - B(s)]$$

$$= G(s)R(s) - G(s)B(s)$$

$$= G(s)R(s) - G(s)H(s)C(s)$$

$$\therefore \qquad C(s) = [1 + G(s)H(s)]^{-1} G(s)R(s)$$

Provided that $1 + G(s)H(s)$ is nonsingular. The closed-loop transfer-matrix is defined as

$$T(s) = [1 + G(s)H(s)]^{-1}G(s)$$

$$\therefore \qquad C(s) = T(s)R(s) \tag{3.13}$$

3.1.3 Procedure for Drawing a Block Diagram

A control system can be represented diagrammatically by a block diagram. To draw a block diagram for a system, first write the differential equations that describe the dynamic behaviour of each component. Then take the Laplace transforms of these differential equations, assuming zero initial conditions to obtain the algebraic equations. These equations will have variables and constants. From the working knowledge of the system, the input and output variables are identified and the block diagram for each equation can be drawn. Each equation gives one section of block diagram, the output of one section will be the input for another section. The various sections are interconnected to obtain the overall block diagram of the system.

As an example, consider the *RC* circuit shown in Figure 3.7(a). The equations for the circuit are as follows:

$$i = \frac{e_i - e_o}{R} \tag{3.14}$$

$$e_o = \frac{1}{C} \int i \, dt \tag{3.15}$$

The Laplace transform of Eqs. (3.14) and (3.15) with zero initial conditions yields

$$I(s) = \frac{E_i(s) - E_o(s)}{R} \tag{3.16}$$

$$E_o(s) = \frac{1}{Cs} I(s) \tag{3.17}$$

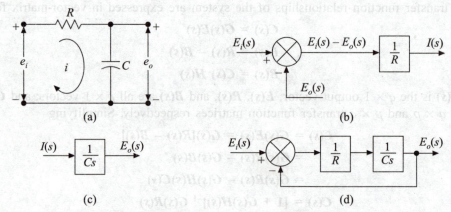

Figure 3.7 Block diagram of an electrical network.

Equation (3.16) represents a summing operation and the corresponding diagram is shown in Figure 3.7(b). Equation (3.17) represents the block as shown in Figure 3.7(c). Assembling these two elements, i.e. $I(s)$ and $E_o(s)$ we obtain the overall block diagram for the system as shown in Figure 3.7(d).

3.1.4 Block Diagram Reduction

It is important to note that blocks can be connected in series, if the output of one block is not affected by the next following block. If there are any loading effects between the components, it is necessary to combine these components into a single block. Any number of cascaded blocks representing non-loading components can be replaced by a single block, the transfer function of which is simply the product of the individual transfer functions.

A complicated block diagram involving many feedback loops can be simplified by a step-by-step rearrangement, using the rules of block diagram algebra. Some of these important rules are given in Table 3.1. They are obtained by writing the same equations in a different way.

Simplification of the block diagram by rearrangements and substitutions considerably reduces the labour needed for subsequent mathematical analysis. It should be noted, however, that as the block diagram is simplified, the transfer functions in new blocks become more complex because new poles and zeros are generated.

In simplifying a block diagram, the following points should be remembered.

1. The product of the transfer functions in the feed forward direction must remain the same.
2. The product of the transfer functions around the loop must remain the same.

Table 3.1 Important rules for block diagram reduction

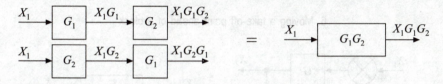

1. Combining blocks in cascade

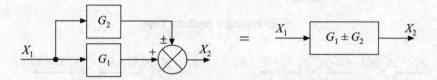

2. Combining blocks in parallel

3. Moving a summing point after a block

4. Moving a summing point ahead of a block

(Contd.)

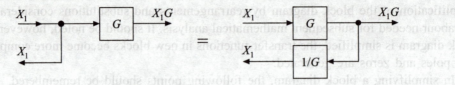

$$=$$

5. Moving a take-off point after a block

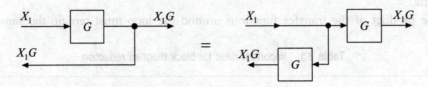

$$=$$

6. Moving a take-off point ahead of a block

$X_1 \longrightarrow \bigotimes \xrightarrow{\pm} \boxed{G} \longrightarrow X_2$ with H feedback $= X_1 \longrightarrow \boxed{\dfrac{G}{1 \mp GH}} \longrightarrow X_2$

7. Eliminating a feedback loop

$X_1 \xrightarrow{} \bigotimes \xrightarrow{X_1 \pm X_2} \bigotimes \xrightarrow{X_1 \pm X_2 \pm X_3}$ with X_2, X_3 $=$ $X_1 \xrightarrow{} \bigotimes \xrightarrow{X_1 \pm X_3} \bigotimes \xrightarrow{X_1 \pm X_2 \pm X_3}$ with X_3, X_2

8. Interchanging summing points

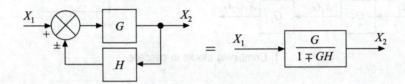

9. Splitting a summing point

$X_1 \xrightarrow{} \bigotimes \xrightarrow{X_1 \pm X_2}$ with X_2 and branch $X_1 \pm X_2$ $=$ two summing points with X_1, X_2 giving $X_1 \pm X_2$

10. Moving a take-off point ahead of a summing point

(Contd.)

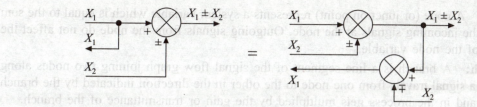

11. Moving a take-off point after a summing point

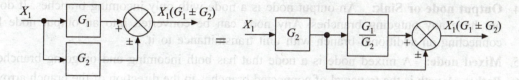

12. Removing a block from a forward path

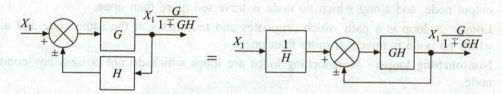

13. Removing a block from a feedback path

3.2 SIGNAL FLOW GRAPHS

A signal flow graph may be regarded as a simplified version of a block diagram. The usual application of signal flow graph is in system diagramming. Signal flow graphs were developed by S.J. Mason. Unlike the block diagram reduction process, they do not require any reduction process to obtain the transfer function of a complicated system, because of the availability of a flow graph gain formula which relates the input and output system variables. Mason's gain formula is especially useful in reducing large and complex system diagrams in one step, without requiring step-by-step reductions. A signal flow graph and a block diagram contain essentially the same information and one is in no sense superior to the other. Besides the difference in physical appearances of the signal flow graph and the block diagram, the signal flow graph may be regarded as constrained by more rigid mathematical rules than the block diagrams.

A signal flow graph is a graphical representation of the relationship between the variables of a set of linear algebraic equations written in the form of cause-and-effect relations. It consists of a network in which nodes representing each of the system variables are connected by directed branches. The directed branches have associated branch gains. A signal can be transmitted through a branch only in the direction of the arrow. Various terms used in the formulation of a signal flow graph are given below.

1. **Node:**   A node (or junction point) represents a system variable which is equal to the sum of all the incoming signals at the node. Outgoing signals from the node do not affect the value of the node variable.

2. **Branch:**   A branch is a line segment of the signal flow graph joining two nodes along which a signal travels from one node to the other in the direction indicated by the branch arrow and in the process gets multiplied by the gain or transmittance of the branch.

3. **Input node or Source:**   An input node is a node with only outgoing branches. It does not have any incoming branches.

4. **Output node or Sink:**   An output node is a node with only incoming branches. It does not have any outgoing branches. Any node can be converted into an output node by connecting an additional branch with unit transmittance to it.

5. **Mixed node:**   A mixed node is a node that has both incoming and outgoing branches.

6. **Path:**   A path is the traversal of connected branches in the direction of the branch arrows such that no node is traversed more than once.

7. **Forward path:**   A forward path is a path that starts at an input node and ends at an output node, and along which no node is traversed more than once.

8. **Loop:**   A loop is a path which originates and terminates at the same node and along which no node is traversed more than once.

9. **Nontouching loops:**   Nontouching loops are loops which do not possess any common node.

10. **Path gain:**   The product of the branch gains encountered in traversing a path is called the path gain.

11. **Forward path gain:**   The product of the branch gains encountered in traversing a forward path is called the forward path gain.

12. **Loop gain:**   The product of the branch gains encountered in traversing the loop is called the loop gain.

13. **Self loop:**   A self loop is a loop consisting of a single branch.

3.2.1   Construction of Signal Flow Graphs

The signal flow graph of a system is constructed from its describing equations. In general, given a set of algebraic equations, the construction of the signal flow graph is basically a matter of following through the cause-and-effect relations relating each variable in terms of itself and others. To outline the procedure, let us consider a system described by the following set of equations.

$$x_2 = a_{12}x_1 + a_{22}x_2 + a_{32}x_3 + a_{42}x_4 + a_{52}x_5$$
$$x_3 = a_{23}x_2$$
$$x_4 = a_{34}x_3 + a_{44}x_4$$
$$x_5 = a_{35}x_3 + a_{45}x_4$$

where x_1 is the input variable and x_5 is the output variable.

The signal flow graph for this system is constructed as shown in Figure 3.8. First, the nodes are located as shown in Figure 3.8(a). The first equation states that x_2 is equal to the sum of five signals and its signal flow graph is shown in Figure 3.8(b). Similarly, the signal flow graphs for the remaining three equations are constructed as shown in Figure 3.8(c), Figures 3.8(d) and 3.8(e) respectively giving the complete signal flow graph of Figure 3.8(f).

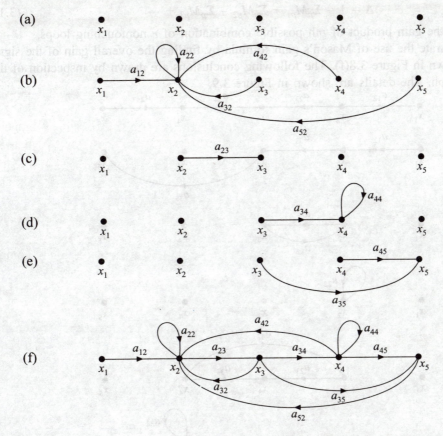

Figure 3.8 Signal flow graph.

The overall gain from input to output may be obtained by applying Mason's gain formula.

The relationship between an input variable and an output variable of a signal flow graph is given by the net gain between the input and output nodes and is known as the overall gain of the system. Mason's gain formula for the determination of the overall system gain is given by

$$T = \frac{\Sigma_k M_k \Delta_k}{\Delta} \tag{3.18}$$

where M_k = path gain of the kth forward path

   Δ_k = value of Δ for that part of the graph not touching the kth forward path

   T = Overall gain of the system

Δ = determinant of the signal flow graph
= 1 – (sum of the loop gains of all individual loops)
+ (sum of the gain products of all possible combinations of two nontouching loops)
– (sum of the gain products of all possible combinations of three nontouching loops)
+ $\cdots$, i.e.

$$\Delta = 1 - \Sigma_p M_{p1} + \Sigma_p M_{p2} - \Sigma_p M_{p3} + \cdots \tag{3.19}$$

where M_{pr} is the gain product of pth possible combination of r nontouching loops.

Let us illustrate the use of Mason's gain formula by finding the overall gain of the signal flow graph shown in Figure 3.8(f). The following conclusions are drawn by inspection of this signal flow graph. The details are shown in Figure 3.9.

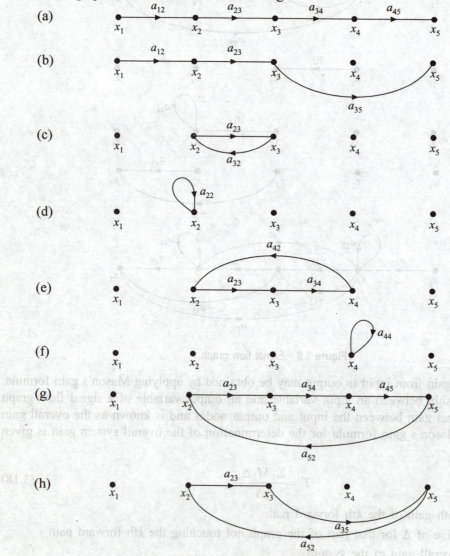

Figure 3.9 (Contd.)

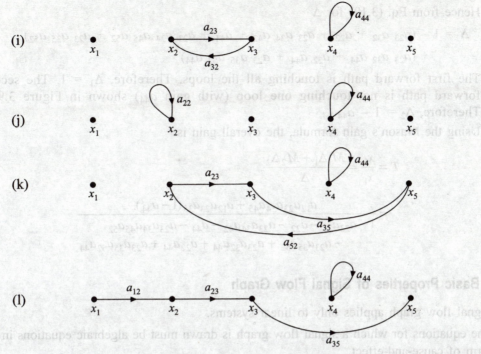

Figure 3.9 Use of Mason's gain formula.

1. There are two forward paths shown in Figure 3.9(a) and (b) with path gains:

   Forward path x_1-x_2-x_3-x_4-x_5 $M_1 = a_{12}\, a_{23}\, a_{34}\, a_{45}$

   Forward path x_1-x_2-x_3-x_5 $M_2 = a_{12}\, a_{23}\, a_{35}$

2. There are six individual loops shown in Figure 3.9(c), (d), (e), (f), (g) and (h) with loop gains:

   Loop x_2-x_3-x_2 $L_1 = a_{23}\, a_{32}$

   Loop x_2-x_2 $L_2 = a_{22}$

   Loop x_2-x_3-x_4-x_2 $L_3 = a_{23}\, a_{34}\, a_{42}$

   Loop x_4-x_4 $L_4 = a_{44}$

   Loop x_2-x_3-x_4-x_5-x_2 $L_5 = a_{23}\, a_{34}\, a_{45}\, a_{52}$

   Loop x_2-x_3-x_5-x_2 $L_6 = a_{23}\, a_{35}\, a_{52}$

3. There are three possible combinations of two nontouching loops shown in Figure 3.9(i), (j) and (k) with loop gain products:

   Loops x_2-x_3-x_2 and x_4-x_4 $L_{14} = a_{23}\, a_{32}\, a_{44}$

   Loops x_2-x_2 and x_4-x_4 $L_{24} = a_{22}\, a_{44}$

   Loops x_2-x_3-x_5-x_2 and x_4-x_4 $L_{64} = a_{23}\, a_{35}\, a_{52}\, a_{44}$

4. There are no combinations of three nontouching loops, four nontouching loops, etc. Therefore,

$$M_{p3} = M_{p4} = \cdots = 0$$

Hence from Eq. (3.19) for Δ

$$\Delta = 1 - (a_{23}\, a_{32} + a_{22} + a_{23}\, a_{34}\, a_{42} + a_{44} + a_{23}\, a_{34}\, a_{45}\, a_{52} + a_{23}\, a_{35}\, a_{52})$$
$$+ (a_{23}\, a_{32}\, a_{44} + a_{22}\, a_{44} + a_{23}\, a_{35}\, a_{52}\, a_{44})$$

5. The first forward path is touching all the loops. Therefore, $\Delta_1 = 1$. The second forward path is not touching one loop (with gain a_{44}) shown in Figure 3.9(l). Therefore, $\Delta_2 = 1 - a_{44}$.

Using the Mason's gain formula, the overall gain is

$$T = \frac{x_5}{x_1} = \frac{M_1\Delta_1 + M_2\Delta_2}{\Delta}$$

$$= \frac{a_{12}a_{23}a_{34}a_{45} + a_{12}a_{23}a_{35}(1 - a_{44})}{1 - a_{23}a_{32} - a_{22} - a_{23}a_{34}a_{42} - a_{44} - a_{23}a_{34}a_{45}a_{52}}$$
$$\frac{}{\qquad\qquad - a_{23}a_{35}a_{52} + a_{23}a_{32}a_{44} + a_{22}a_{44} + a_{23}a_{35}a_{52}a_{44}}$$

3.2.2 Basic Properties of Signal Flow Graph

1. Signal flow graph applies only to linear systems.

2. The equations for which a signal flow graph is drawn must be algebraic equations in the form of cause-and-effect.

3. Nodes are used to represent variables. Normally the nodes are arranged from left to right, from the input to the output following a succession of cause-and-effect relations through the system.

4. Signals travel along branches only in the direction described by the arrows of the branches.

5. The branch directing from node x_k to x_j represents the dependence of x_j upon x_k but not the reverse.

6. A signal x_k traveling along a branch between x_k and x_j is multiplied by the gain of the branch a_{kj} so that a signal $a_{kj}\, x_k$ is delivered at x_j.

7. For a given system, a signal flow graph is not unique. Many different signal flow graphs can be drawn for a given system by writing the system equations differently.

3.2.3 Signal Flow Graph Algebra

Based on the properties of the signal flow graph, we can outline the following manipulation rules and algebra.

1. The value of the variable represented by a node is equal to the sum of all the signals entering the node. For the signal flow graph of Figure 3.10, the value of y_1 is equal to the sum of the signals transmitted through all the incoming branches; i.e.

$$y_1 = a_{21}y_2 + a_{31}y_3 + a_{41}y_4 + a_{51}y_5$$

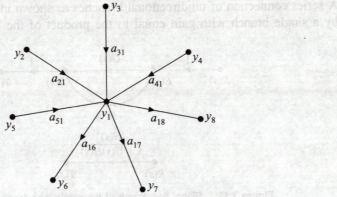

Figure 3.10 Node as a summing point and transmitting point.

2. The value of the variable represented by a node is transmitted through all branches leaving the node. In the signal flow graph of Figure 3.10, we have

$$y_6 = a_{16}y_1$$

$$y_7 = a_{17}y_1$$

$$y_8 = a_{18}y_1$$

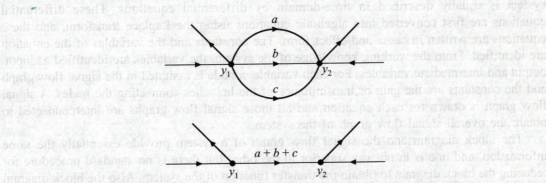

Figure 3.11 Signal flow graph with parallel paths replaced by one with a single branch.

3. Parallel branches in the same direction connecting two nodes can be replaced by a single branch with gain equal to the sum of the gains of the parallel branches. An example of this case illustrated in Figure 3.11

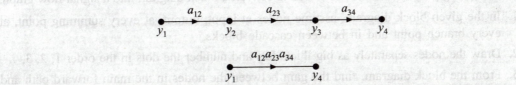

Figure 3.12 Signal flow graph with cascade unidirectional branches replaced by a single branch.

4. A series connection of unidirectional branches as shown in Figure 3.12 can be replaced by a single branch with gain equal to the product of the branch gains.

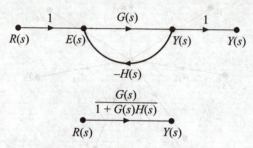

Figure 3.13   Signal flow graph of the single loop feedback control system replaced by a single branch.

5. A single feedback loop can be replaced by a single branch with gain as shown in Figure 3.13.

3.2.4 Construction of Signal Flow Graph for Control Systems

A control system can be represented diagrammatically by a signal flow graph. The control system is usually described in time-domain by differential equations. These differential equations are first converted into algebraic equations using the Laplace transform, and these equations are written in cause-and-effect form. The constants and the variables of the equation are identified. From the working knowledge of the system, the variables are identified as input, output and intermediate variables. For each variable, a node is assigned in the signal flow graph and the constants are the gain or transmittance of the branches connecting the nodes. A signal flow graph is drawn for each equation and all those signal flow graphs are interconnected to obtain the overall signal flow graph of the system.

The block diagram and the signal flow graph of a system provide essentially the same information, and one is in no way superior to the other but there is no standard procedure for reducing the block diagram to obtain the transfer function of the system. Also the block diagram reduction process is tedious and time consuming as it is not systematic, and it is difficult to choose the rule to be applied for simplification. It mainly depends on one's knowledge and experience. On the other hand, there is a standard formula called Mason's gain formula using which the transfer function of a system can be obtained in one step from the signal flow of a system. So, block diagram is to be converted into signal flow graph.

The following procedure can be followed to convert a block diagram into a signal flow graph.

1. In the given block diagram, assume nodes at input, output, at every summing point, at every branch point and in between cascade blocks.

2. Draw the nodes separately as big thick dots and number the dots in the order 1, 2, 3, ...

3. From the block diagram, find the gain between the nodes in the main forward path and connect all the corresponding nodes by directed straight line segments and mark the gain between the nodes on the segment.

4. Draw the feed forward paths between various nodes and mark the gain between nodes on the directed branches.

5. Draw the feedback paths between various nodes and mark the gain of feedback paths along with the sign.

A comparison of a block diagram method and a signal flow method is given in Table 3.2.

Table 3.2 Comparison of block diagram and signal flow graph methods

Block diagram method	*Signal flow graph method*
1. It is a pictorial representation of the functions performed by each component and of the flow of signals.	1. It is a graphical representation of a relationship between variables of a set of linear algebraic equations written in the form of cause-and-effect relations.
2. It can be used to represent linear as well as nonlinear systems.	2. It can be used to represent only linear systems.
3. No direct formula is available to find the over-all transfer function of the system.	3. Mason's gain formula is available to find the overall transfer function of the system.
4. Step-by-step procedure is to be followed to find the transfer function.	4. Transfer function can be obtained in one step.
5. It is not a systematic method.	5. It is a systematic method.
6. It indicates more realistically the signal flows of the system than the original system itself.	6. It is constrained by more rigid mathematical rules than a block diagram.
7. For a given system, the block diagram is not unique. Many dissimilar and unrelated systems can be represented by the same block diagram.	7. For a given system, the signal flow graph is not unique.

Example 3.1 Obtain the transfer function of the control system whose block diagram is shown in Figure 3.14 by (a) block diagram reduction technique and (b) signal flow graph method.

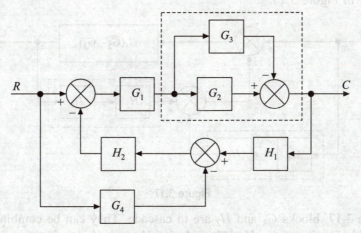

Figure 3.14 Example 3.1.

Solution: (a) *Block diagram reduction technique*

1. In the block diagram shown in Figure 3.14, blocks G_2 and G_3 are in parallel. They can be combined into a single block with a gain of $(G_2 - G_3)$ as shown in Figure 3.15.

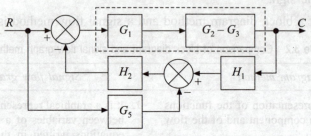

Figure 3.15

2. In Figure 3.15, blocks G_1 and $(G_2 - G_3)$ are in cascade. They can be combined into a single block with a gain of $G_1(G_2 - G_3)$ as shown in Figure 3.16.

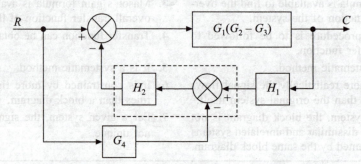

Figure 3.16

3. In Figure 3.16, move the summing point after the block H_2. The resultant block diagram is shown in Figure 3.17.

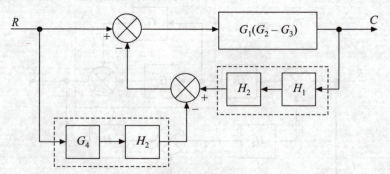

Figure 3.17

4. In Figure 3.17, blocks G_4 and H_2 are in cascade. They can be combined into a single block with a gain of $G_4 H_2$. Also blocks H_1 and H_2 are in cascade. They can be combined into a single block with a gain of $H_1 H_2$ as shown in Figure 3.18.

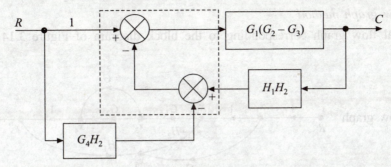

Figure 3.18

5. Interchanging the summing points in Figure 3.18, the block diagram is as shown in Figure 3.19.

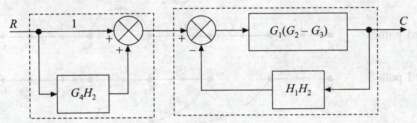

Figure 3.19

6. In Figure 3.19, combining 1 and G_4H_2 into a block with gain of $(1 + G_4H_2)$ and simplifying the feedback arrangement into a single block, the resultant block diagram is as shown in Figure 3.20.

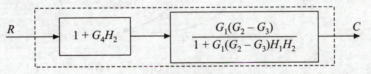

Figure 3.20

7. In Figure 3.20, combining the two blocks in cascade into a single block, the resultant block diagram is as shown in Figure 3.21.

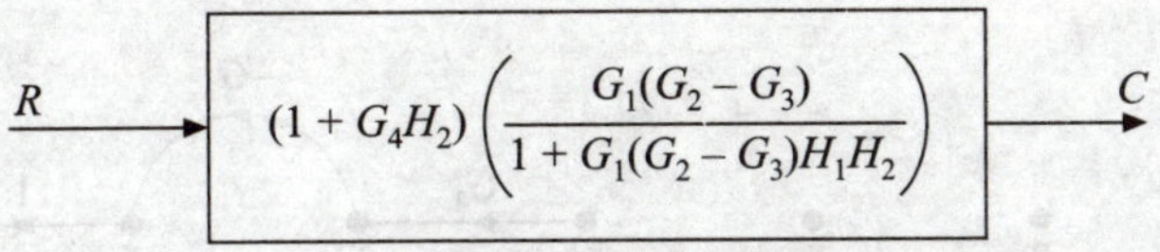

$$R \xrightarrow{\quad} \boxed{(1 + G_4H_2)\left(\dfrac{G_1(G_2 - G_3)}{1 + G_1(G_2 - G_3)H_1H_2}\right)} \xrightarrow{\quad} C$$

Figure 3.21

From Figure 3.21, the overall transfer function is

$$\frac{C}{R} = \frac{G_1G_2 - G_1G_3 + G_1G_2G_4H_2 - G_1G_3G_4H_2}{1 + G_1G_2H_1H_2 - G_1G_3H_1H_2}$$

(a) *Signal flow graph method*

The signal flow graph corresponding to the block diagram of Figure 3.14 is shown in Figure 3.22.

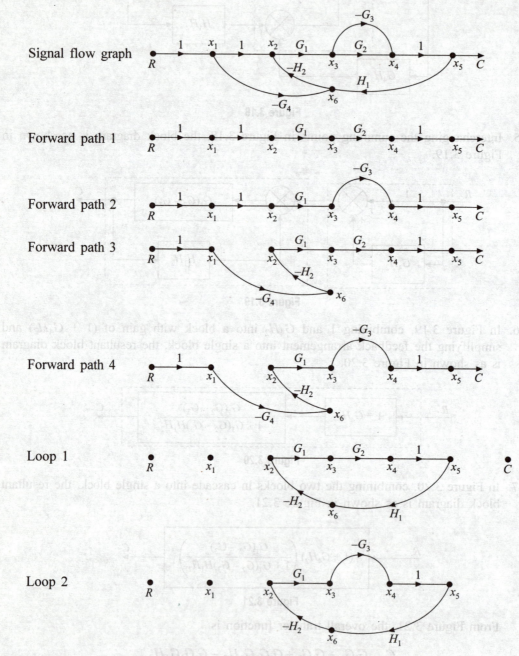

Figure 3.22

The signal flow graph shown in Figure 3.22 has four forward paths and two loops. There are no combinations of two nontouching loops. Both the loops are touching all the four forward paths.

The forward paths, the gains of those forward paths and the values of Δ associated with those paths are given as follows:

Forward path R-x_1-x_2-x_3-x_4-x_5-C

$$M_1 = (1)(1)(G_1)(G_2)(1) = G_1G_2 \qquad\qquad \Delta_1 = 1$$

Forward path R-x_1-x_2-x_3-x_4-x_5-C

$$M_2 = (1)(1)(G_1)(-G_3)(1) = -G_1G_3 \qquad\qquad \Delta_2 = 1$$

Forward path R-x_1-x_6-x_2-x_3-x_4-x_5-C

$$M_3 = (1)(-G_4)(-H_2)(G_1)(G_2)(1) = G_1G_2G_4H_2 \qquad \Delta_3 = 1$$

Forward path R-x_1-x_6-x_2-x_3-x_4-x_5-C

$$M_4 = (1)(-G_4)(-H_2)(G_1)(-G_3)(1) = -G_1G_3G_4H_2 \quad \Delta_4 = 1$$

Loops and the gains associated with them are as follows:

Loop x_2-x_3-x_4-x_5-x_6-x_2 $\qquad L_1 = (G_1)(G_2)(H_1)(-H_2) = -G_1G_2H_1H_2$

Loop x_2-x_3-x_4-x_5-x_6-x_2 $\qquad L_2 = (G_1)(-G_3)(1)(H_1)(-H_2) = G_1G_3H_1H_2$

The determinant of the signal flow graph is $\Delta = 1 - (L_1 + L_2)$

$\therefore \qquad \Delta = 1 - (-G_1G_2H_1H_2 + G_1G_3H_1H_2) = 1 + G_1G_2H_1H_2 - G_1G_3H_1H_2$

Applying Mason's gain formula, the transfer function is

$$\frac{C}{R} = \frac{M_1\Delta_1 + M_2\Delta_2 + M_3\Delta_3 + M_4\Delta_4}{\Delta}$$

$$= \frac{G_1G_2 - G_1G_3 + G_1G_2G_4H_2 - G_1G_3G_4H_2}{1 + G_1G_2H_1H_2 - G_1G_3H_1H_2}$$

Example 3.2 Obtain the transfer function of the feedback control system shown in Figure 3.23 by (a) block diagram reduction technique and (b) signal flow graph method.

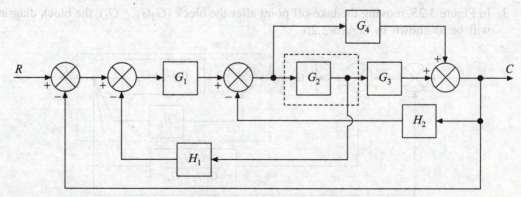

Figure 3.23 Example 3.2.

Solution: (a) *Block diagram reduction method*

1. Moving the take-off point ahead of block G_2, in Figure 3.23, the block diagram will be as shown in Figure 3.24.

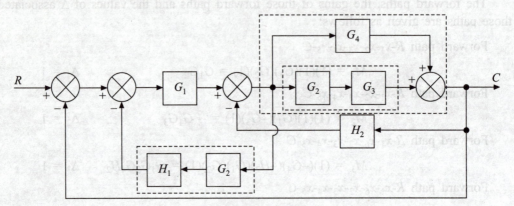

Figure 3.24

2. In Figure 3.24, blocks G_2 and G_3 are in cascade. They can be combined into a single block with a gain of G_2G_3. Now blocks (G_2G_3) and G_4 are in parallel. They can be combined into a single block with a gain of $(G_2G_3 + G_4)$. Also blocks G_2 and H_1 are in cascade. They can be combined into a single block with a gain of G_2H_1. The resultant block diagram is as shown in Figure 3.25.

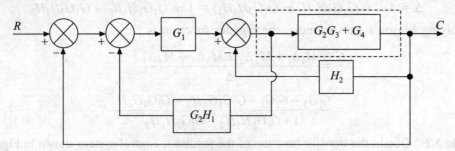

Figure 3.25

3. In Figure 3.25, moving the take-off point after the block $(G_2G_3 + G_4)$, the block diagram will be as shown in Figure 3.26.

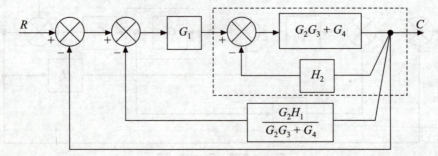

Figure 3.26

4. Simplifying the inner loop of Figure 3.26, the block diagram is as shown in Figure 3.27.

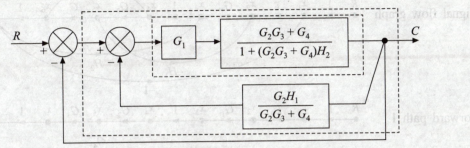

Figure 3.27

5. In Figure 3.27, combining the two blocks in cascade in the forward path and then simplifying the inner loop, the block diagram is as shown in Figure 3.28.

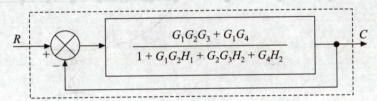

Figure 3.28

6. Simplifying the single loop in Figure 3.28, the block diagram is as shown in Figure 3.29.

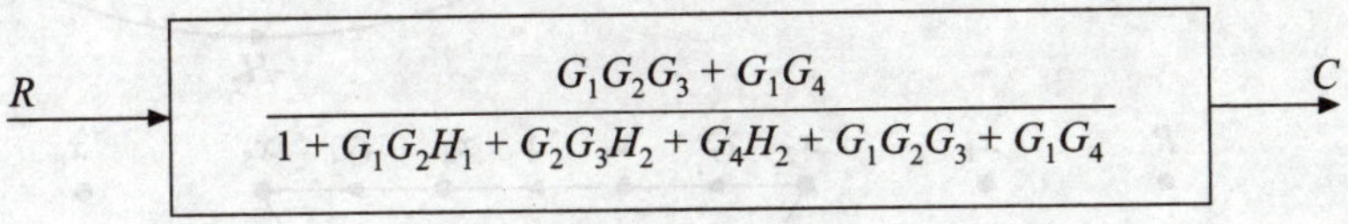

$$\frac{G_1G_2G_3 + G_1G_4}{1 + G_1G_2H_1 + G_2G_3H_2 + G_4H_2 + G_1G_2G_3 + G_1G_4}$$

R ⟶ [ ] ⟶ C

Figure 3.29

From Figure 3.29, the transfer function is therefore

$$\frac{C}{R} = \frac{G_1G_2G_3 + G_1G_4}{1 + G_1G_2H_1 + G_2G_3H_2 + G_4H_2 + G_1G_2G_3 + G_1G_4}$$

(b) *Signal flow graph method*

The signal flow graph for the system with the block diagram of Figure 3.23 is shown in Figure 3.30.

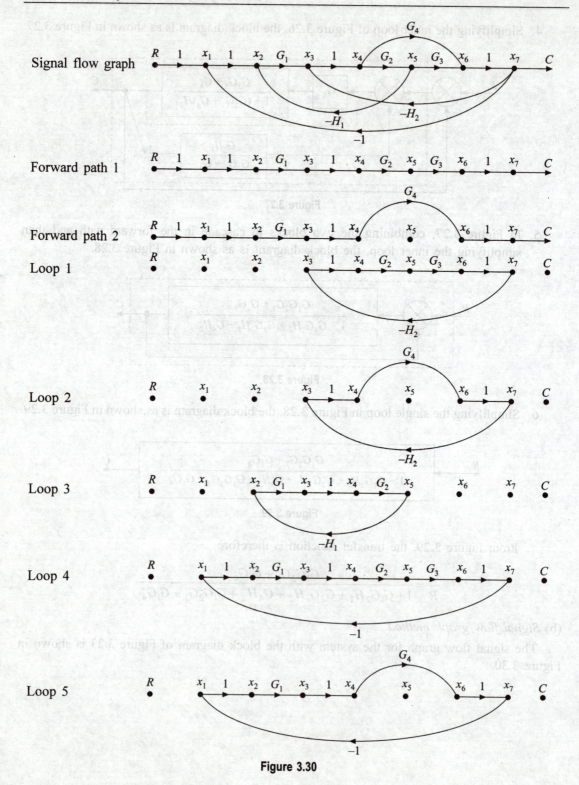

Figure 3.30

In the signal flow graph shown in Figure 3.30, there are two forward paths and five loops as shown and there are no two nontouching loops and all the loops are touching both the forward paths.

The forward paths and the gains associated with them are given as follows:

Forward path R-x_1-x_2-x_3-x_4-x_5-x_6-x_7-C

$$M_1 = (1)(1)(G_1)(1)(G_2)(G_3)(1) = G_1G_2G_3 \qquad \Delta_1 = 1$$

Forward path R-x_1-x_2-x_3-x_4-x_6-x_7-C

$$M_2 = (1)(1)(G_1)(1)(G_4)(1) = G_1G_4 \qquad\qquad \Delta_2 = 1$$

The loops and the gains associated with them are given as follows:

Loop x_3-x_4-x_5-x_6-x_7-x_3 $\qquad L_1 = (1)(G_2)(G_3)(1)(-H_2) = -G_2G_3H_2$

Loop x_3-x_4-x_6-x_7-x_3 $\qquad L_2 = (1)(G_4)(1)(-H_2) = -G_4H_2$

Loop x_2-x_3-x_4-x_5-x_2 $\qquad L_3 = (G_1)(1)(G_2)(-H_1) = -G_1G_2H_1$

Loop x_1-x_2-x_3-x_4-x_5-x_6-x_7-x_1 $\qquad L_4 = (1)(G_1)(1)(G_2)(G_3)(1)(-1) = -G_1G_2G_3$

Loop x_1-x_2-x_3-x_4-x_6-x_7-x_1 $\qquad L_5 = (1)(G_1)(1)(G_4)(1)(-1) = -G_1G_4$

The determinant of the signal flow graph is

$$\Delta = 1 - (L_1 + L_2 + L_3 + L_4 + L_5)$$

$$\Delta = 1 - (-G_2G_3H_2 - G_4H_2 - G_1G_2H_1 - G_1G_2G_3 - G_1G_4)$$
$$= 1 + G_2G_3H_2 + G_4H_2 + G_1G_2H_1 + G_1G_2G_3 + G_1G_4$$

Applying Mason's gain formula, the transfer function is

$$\frac{C}{R} = \frac{M_1\Delta_1 + M_2\Delta_2}{\Delta} = \frac{G_1G_2G_3 + G_1G_4}{1 + G_2G_3H_2 + G_4H_2 + G_1G_2H_1 + G_1G_2G_3 + G_1G_4}$$

Example 3.3 Simplify the block diagram shown in Figure 3.31 and obtain the closed-loop transfer function $C(s)/R(s)$. Verify the result by the signal flow graph method.

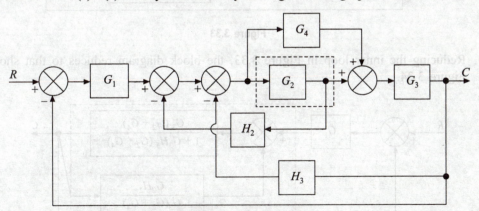

Figure 3.31 Example 3.3.

Solution: (a) *Block diagram reduction technique*

1. In Figure 3.31, moving the take-off point ahead of the block G_2, the block diagram will be as shown in Figure 3.32.

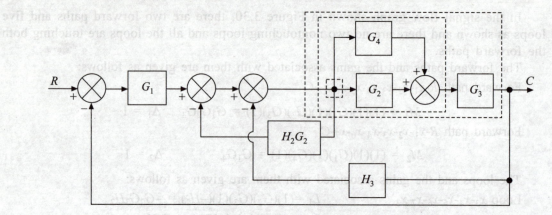

Figure 3.32

2. In Figure 3.32, blocks G_2 and G_4 are in parallel. They can be combined into a single block with a gain of $(G_2 + G_4)$. Now the blocks $(G_2 + G_4)$ and G_3 are in cascade. They can be combined into a single block with a gain of $G_3(G_2 + G_4)$. Moving the take-off point after the block $G_3(G_2 + G_4)$, the block diagram will be as shown in Figure 3.33.

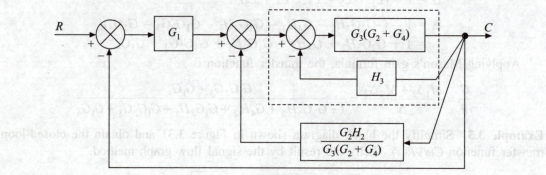

Figure 3.33

3. Reducing the inner loop in Figure 3.33, the block diagram reduces to that shown in Figure 3.34.

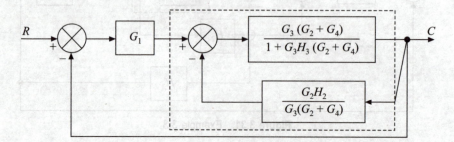

Figure 3.34

4. Reducing the inner loop in Figure 3.34, the block diagram reduces to that shown in Figure 3.35.

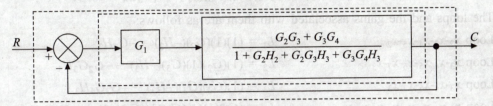

Figure 3.35

5. The two blocks in the forward path of Figure 3.35 are in cascade and can be combined into a single block. Simplifying the loop, the block diagram reduces to that shown in Figure 3.36.

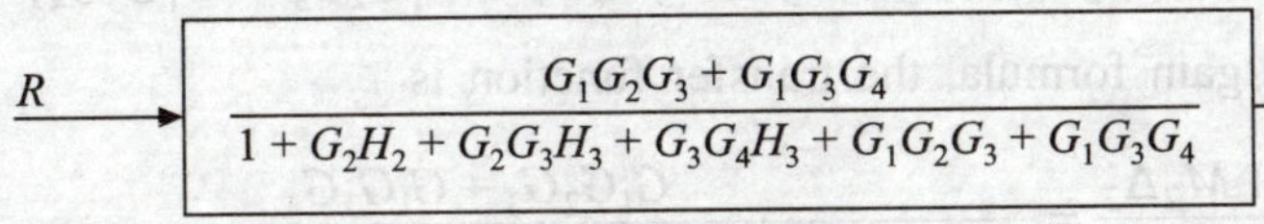

$$R \boxed{\dfrac{G_1G_2G_3 + G_1G_3G_4}{1 + G_2H_2 + G_2G_3H_3 + G_3G_4H_3 + G_1G_2G_3 + G_1G_3G_4}} C$$

Figure 3.36

So, the transfer function of the system is

$$\frac{C}{R} = \frac{G_1G_2G_3 + G_1G_3G_4}{1 + G_2H_2 + G_2G_3H_3 + G_3G_4H_3 + G_1G_2G_3 + G_1G_3G_4}$$

(b) *Signal flow graph method*

The signal flow graph corresponding to the block diagram of Figure 3.31 for the system is shown in Figure 3.37.

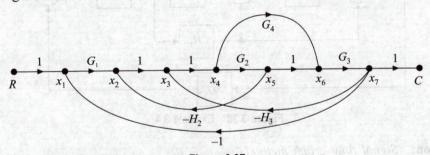

Figure 3.37

The signal flow graph in Figure 3.37 has two forward paths and five loops. There are no pairs of two nontouching loops and all the loops are touching both the forward paths. The forward paths and gains associated with them are as follows:

Forward path $R\text{-}x_1\text{-}x_2\text{-}x_3\text{-}x_4\text{-}x_5\text{-}x_6\text{-}x_7\text{-}C$

$$M_1 = (1)(G_1)(1)(1)(G_2)(1)(G_3)(1) = G_1G_2G_3$$

Forward path R-x_1-x_2-x_3-x_4-x_6-x_7-C

$$M_2 = (1)(G_1)(1)(1)(G_4)(G_3)(1) = G_1G_3G_4$$

The loops and the gains associated with them are as follows:

Loop x_2-x_3-x_4-x_5-x_2 $L_1 = (1)(1)(G_2)(-H_2) = -G_2H_2$

Loop x_3-x_4-x_5-x_6-x_7-x_3 $L_2 = (1)(G_2)(1)(G_3)(-H_3) = -G_2G_3H_3$

Loop x_3-x_4-x_6-x_7-x_3 $L_3 = (1)(G_4)(G_3)(-H_3) = -G_3G_4H_3$

Loop x_1-x_2-x_3-x_4-x_5-x_6-x_7-x_1 $L_4 = (G_1)(1)(1)(G_2)(1)(G_3)(-1) = -G_1G_2G_3$

Loop x_1-x_2-x_3-x_4-x_6-x_7-x_1 $L_5 = (G_1)(1)(1)(G_4)(G_3)(-1) = -G_1G_3G_4$

Since all the loops are touching both the forward paths, $\Delta_1 = 1$ and $\Delta_2 = 1$.
The determinant of the signal flow graph is $\Delta = 1 - (L_1 + L_2 + L_3 + L_4 + L_5)$

$$\therefore \quad \Delta = 1 - (-G_2H_2 - G_2G_3H_3 - G_3G_4H_3 - G_1G_2G_3 - G_1G_3G_4)$$

Applying Mason's gain formula, the transfer function is

$$\frac{C}{R} = \frac{M_1\Delta_1 + M_2\Delta_2}{\Delta} = \frac{G_1G_2G_3 + G_1G_3G_4}{1 + G_2H_2 + G_2G_3H_3 + G_3G_4H_3 + G_1G_2G_3 + G_1G_3G_4}$$

Example 3.4 Obtain the transfer function of the control system represented by the block diagram shown in Figure 3.38, by the signal flow graph method.

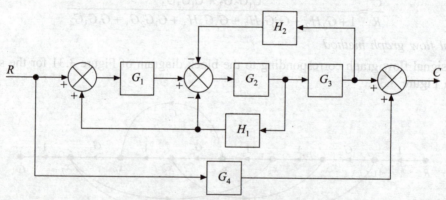

Figure 3.38 Example 3.4.

Solution: *Signal flow graph method*

The signal flow graph of the system obtained from the block diagram of Figure 3.38 is shown in Figure 3.39.

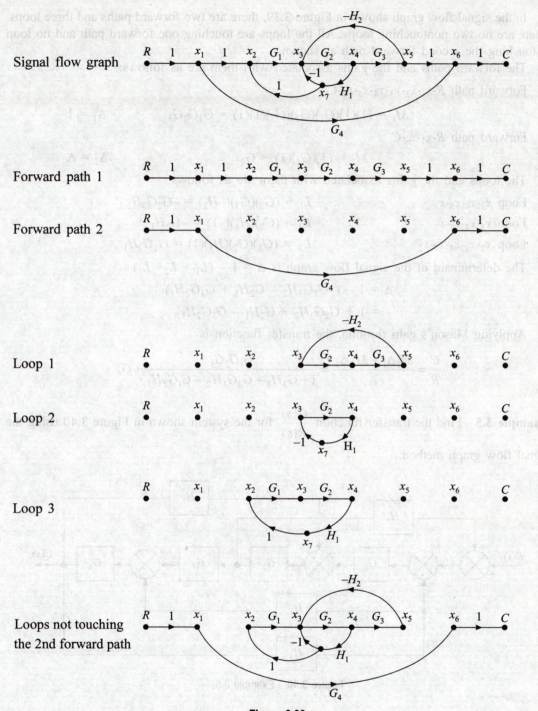

Figure 3.39

In the signal flow graph shown in Figure 3.39, there are two forward paths and three loops. There are no two nontouching loops. All the loops are touching one forward path and no loop is touching the second forward path as shown.

The forward paths and the gains associated with them are as follows:

Forward path R-x_1-x_2-x_3-x_4-x_5-x_6-C

$$M_1 = (1)(1)(G_1)(G_2)(G_3)(1)(1) = G_1G_2G_3 \qquad \Delta_1 = 1$$

Forward path R-x_1-x_6-C

$$M_2 = (1)(G_4)(1) = G_4 \qquad \Delta_2 = \Delta$$

The loops and the gains associated with them are as follows:

Loop x_3-x_4-x_5-x_3 $\qquad\qquad L_1 = (G_2)(G_3)(-H_2) = -G_2G_3H_2$

Loop x_3-x_4-x_7-x_3 $\qquad\qquad L_2 = (G_2)(H_1)(-1) = -G_2H_1$

Loop x_2-x_3-x_4-x_7-x_2 $\qquad\quad L_3 = (G_1)(G_2)(H_1)(1) = G_1G_2H_1$

The determinant of the signal flow graph is $\Delta = 1 - (L_1 + L_2 + L_3)$

$$\Delta = 1 - (-G_2G_3H_2 - G_2H_1 + G_1G_2H_1)$$
$$= 1 + G_2G_3H_2 + G_2H_1 - G_1G_2H_1$$

Applying Mason's gain formula, the transfer function is

$$\frac{C}{R} = \frac{M_1\Delta_1 + M_2\Delta_2}{\Delta} = \frac{G_1G_2G_3}{1 + G_2H_1 + G_2G_3H_2 - G_1G_2H_1} + G_4$$

Example 3.5 Find the transfer function $\dfrac{C(s)}{R(s)}$ for the system shown in Figure 3.40 using the signal flow graph method.

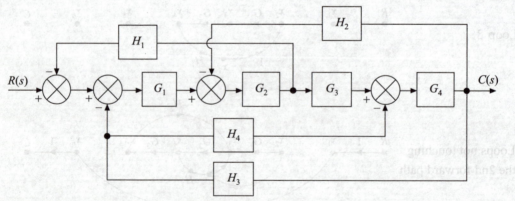

Figure 3.40 Example 3.5.

Solution: The signal flow graph corresponding to the given block diagram of Figure 3.40 is shown in Figure 3.41.

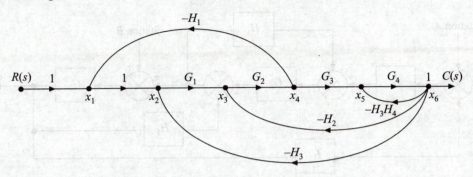

Figure 3.41

The signal flow graph shown in Figure 3.41 has only one forward path and four loops. There is one pair of two nontouching loops and all the four loops are touching the forward path. The forward path and the gain associated with it are as follows:

Forward path $R(s)$-x_1-x_2-x_3-x_4-x_5-x_6-$C(s)$ $\qquad M_1 = (1)(1)(G_1)(G_2)(G_3)(G_4)(1) = G_1G_2G_3G_4$

The loops and the gains associated with them are

Loop x_1-x_2-x_3-x_4-x_1 $\qquad\qquad L_1 = (1)(G_1)(G_2)(-H_1) = -G_1G_2H_1$

Loop x_5-x_6-x_5 $\qquad\qquad\qquad L_2 = (G_4)(-H_3H_4) = -G_4H_3H_4$

Loop x_3-x_4-x_5-x_6-x_3 $\qquad\qquad L_3 = (G_2)(G_3)(G_4)(-H_2) = -G_2G_3G_4H_2$

Loop x_2-x_3-x_4-x_5-x_6-x_2 $\qquad L_4 = (G_1)(G_2)(G_3)(G_4)(-H_3) = -G_1G_2G_3G_4H_3$

The pairs of two nontouching loops x_1-x_2-x_3-x_4-x_1 and x_5-x_6-x_5 and the products of gains associated with them are as follows:

$$L_{12} = (-G_1G_2H_1)(-G_4H_3H_4) = G_1G_2G_4H_1H_3H_4$$

$\Delta_1 = 1$ since all the loops are touching the only forward path.

The determinant of the signal flow graph is

$$\Delta = 1 - (L_1 + L_2 + L_3 + L_4) + (L_{12})$$

The transfer function of the system is given by

$$\frac{C(s)}{R(s)} = \frac{M_1\Delta_1}{\Delta}$$

$$= \frac{G_1G_2G_3G_4}{1-(-G_1G_2H_1 - G_4H_3H_4 - G_2G_3G_4H_2 - G_1G_2G_3G_4H_3)+(G_1G_2G_4H_1H_3H_4)}$$

i.e. $\dfrac{C(s)}{R(s)} = \dfrac{G_1G_2G_3G_4}{1+G_1G_2H_1 + G_4H_3H_4 + G_2G_3G_4H_2 + G_1G_2G_3G_4H_3 + G_1G_2G_4H_1H_3H_4}$

Example 3.6 For the system represented by the block diagram shown in Figure 3.42, evaluate the closed-loop transfer function when the input R is (a) at station A and (b) at station B.

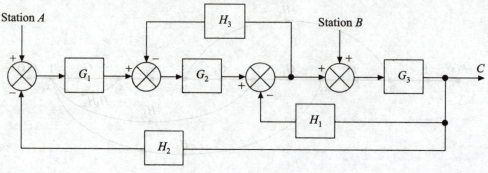

Figure 3.42 Example 3.6.

Solution:

(a) The input R is at station A and so the input at station B is made zero. Let the output be C_1. Since there is no input at station B, that summing point can be removed and the resultant block diagram will be as shown in Figure 3.43.

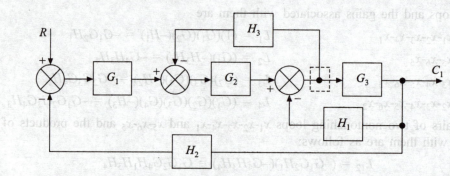

Figure 3.43

Step 1. Moving the take-off point in Figure 3.43 after block G_3, the block diagram will be as shown in Figure 3.44.

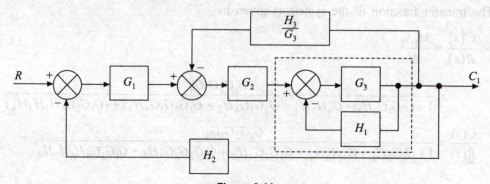

Figure 3.44

Step 2. Eliminating the inner loop in Figure 3.44 and combining the result with G_2 and rearranging, the block diagram will be as shown in Figure 3.45.

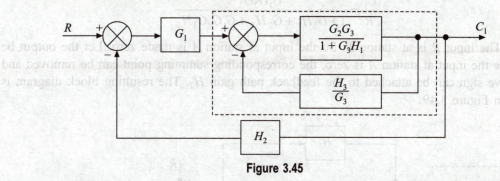

Figure 3.45

Step 3. Eliminating the inner loop in Figure 3.45, the block diagram is as shown in Figure 3.46.

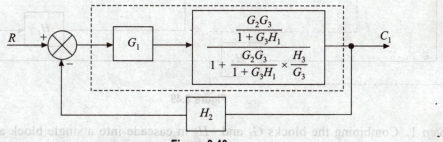

Figure 3.46

Step 4. Combining the blocks in cascade in Figure 3.46, the block diagram will be as shown in Figure 3.47.

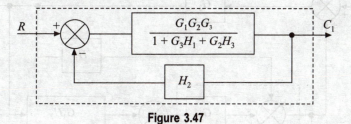

Figure 3.47

Step 5. Eliminating the only loop in Figure 3.47, the block diagram will be as shown in Figure 3.48.

$$R \longrightarrow \boxed{\dfrac{\dfrac{G_1 G_2 G_3}{1 + G_3 H_1 + G_2 H_3}}{1 + \dfrac{G_1 G_2 G_3}{1 + G_3 H_1 + G_2 H_3} \times H_2}} \longrightarrow C_1$$

Figure 3.48

Step 6. After simplification, the closed-loop transfer function is

$$\frac{C_1}{R} = \frac{G_1 G_2 G_3}{1 + G_3 H_1 + G_2 H_3 + G_1 G_2 G_3 H_2}$$

(b) The input R is at station B. So the input at station A is made zero. Let the output be C_2. Since the input at station A is zero, the corresponding summing point can be removed and a negative sign can be attached to the feedback path gain H_2. The resulting block diagram is shown in Figure 3.49.

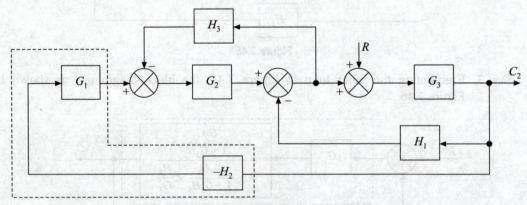

Figure 3.49

Step 1. Combining the blocks G_1 and $-H_2$ in cascade into a single block and rearranging the diagram in Figure 3.49, the resultant block diagram is as shown in Figure 3.50.

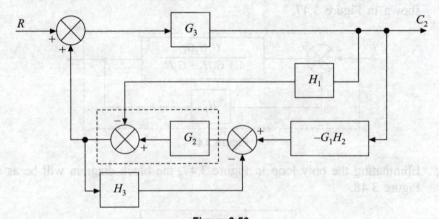

Figure 3.50

Step 2. Moving the summing point before the block G_2 in Figure 3.50, the block diagram will be as shown in Figure 3.51.

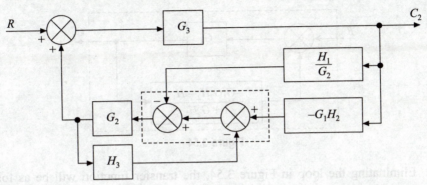

Figure 3.51

Step 3. Interchanging the summing points in Figure 3.51, the block diagram will be as shown in Figure 3.52.

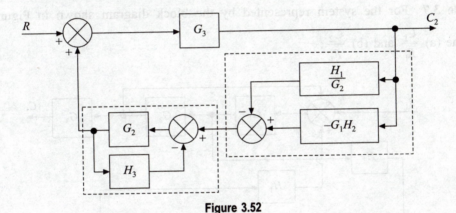

Figure 3.52

Step 4. Eliminating the loop and combining the parallel blocks in the feedback path in Figure 3.52, the block diagram will be as shown in Figure 3.53.

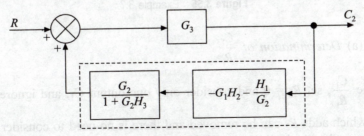

Figure 3.53

Step 5. Combining the two blocks in cascade in Figure 3.53, the block diagram will be as shown in Figure 3.54.

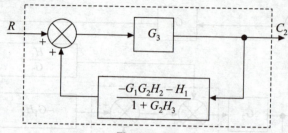

Figure 3.54

Step 6. Eliminating the loop in Figure 3.54, the transfer function will be as follows:

$$\frac{C_2}{R} = \frac{G_3}{1 - \dfrac{G_3(-G_1G_2H_2 - H_1)}{1 + G_2H_3}} = \frac{G_3(1 + G_2H_3)}{1 + G_2H_3 + G_3H_1 + G_1G_2G_3H_2}$$

Example 3.7 For the system represented by the block diagram shown in Figure 3.55, determine (a) $\dfrac{C_1}{R_1}$ and (b) $\dfrac{C_2}{R_1}$.

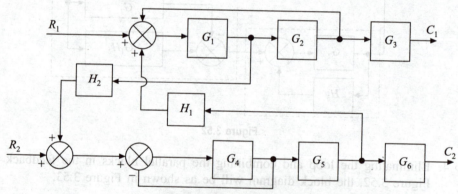

Figure 3.55 Example 3.7.

Solution: (a) *Determination of* $\dfrac{C_1}{R_1}$

To determine $\dfrac{C_1}{R_1}$, set $R_2 = 0$ and consider only one output C_1, and ignore C_2. Hence, the summing point which adds R_2 can be removed and there is no need to consider block G_6. With these modifications, the block diagram will be as shown in Figure 3.56.

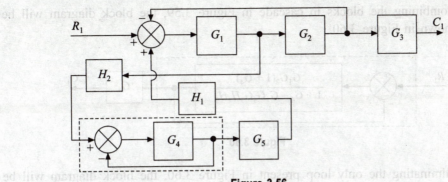

Figure 3.56

Step 1. Eliminating the feedback loop involving block G_4 in Figure 3.56, the block diagram will be as shown in Figure 3.57.

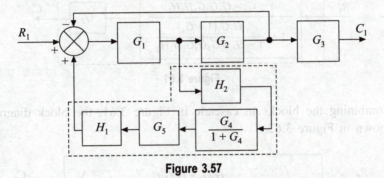

Figure 3.57

Step 2. Combining the blocks in cascade in the feedback path in Figure 3.57, the block diagram will be as shown in Figure 3.58.

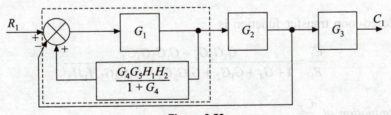

Figure 3.58

Step 3. Eliminating the inner loop in Figure 3.58, the block diagram will be as shown in Figure 3.59.

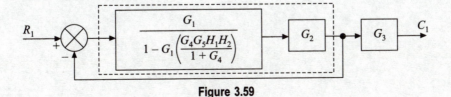

Figure 3.59

Step 4. Combining the blocks in cascade in Figure 3.59, the block diagram will be as shown in Figure 3.60.

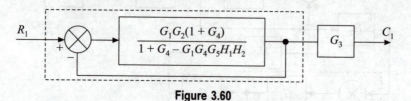

Figure 3.60

Step 5. Eliminating the only loop present in Figure 3.60, the block diagram will be as shown in Figure 3.61.

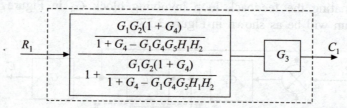

Figure 3.61

Step 6. Combining the blocks in cascade in Figure 3.61, the block diagram will be as shown in Figure 3.62.

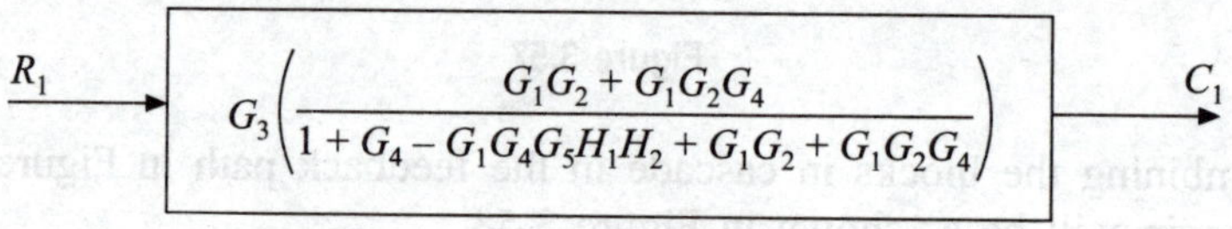

$$R_1 \rightarrow \boxed{G_3\left(\frac{G_1G_2 + G_1G_2G_4}{1 + G_4 - G_1G_4G_5H_1H_2 + G_1G_2 + G_1G_2G_4}\right)} \rightarrow C_1$$

Figure 3.62

So the closed-loop transfer function is

$$\frac{C_1}{R_1} = \frac{G_1G_2G_3 + G_1G_2G_3G_4}{1 + G_4 + G_1G_2 + G_1G_2G_4 - G_1G_4G_5H_1H_2}$$

(b) *Determination of* $\dfrac{C_2}{R_1}$

In this case, $R_2 = 0$ and C_1 need not be considered. Since $R_2 = 0$, we can remove the summing point which adds R_2, and since C_1 is not considered, block G_3 is open and can be ignored. The resultant block diagram is as shown in Figure 3.63.

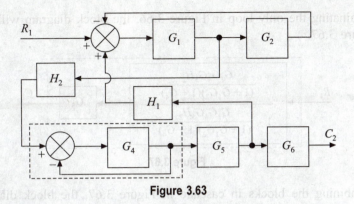

Figure 3.63

Step 1. Eliminating the unity feedback loop comprising G_4 in Figure 3.63, and redrawing Figure 3.63, the block diagram will be as shown in Figure 3.64.

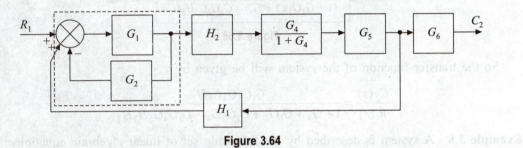

Figure 3.64

Step 2. Eliminating the inner loop comprising blocks G_1 and G_2 in Figure 3.64, the block diagram will be as shown in Figure 3.65.

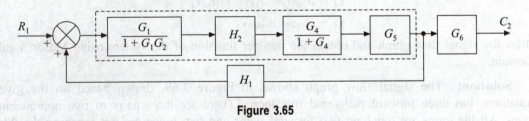

Figure 3.65

Step 3. Combining the blocks in cascade in Figure 3.65, the block diagram will be as shown in Figure 3.66.

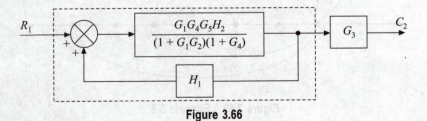

Figure 3.66

Step 4. Eliminating the only loop in Figure 3.66, the block diagram will be as shown in Figure 3.67.

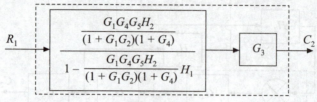

Figure 3.67

Step 5. Combining the blocks in cascade in Figure 3.67, the block diagram will be as shown in Figure 3.68.

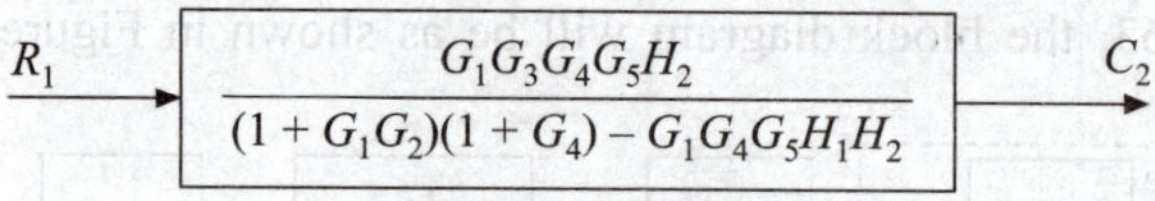

$$R_1 \longrightarrow \boxed{\dfrac{G_1 G_3 G_4 G_5 H_2}{(1 + G_1 G_2)(1 + G_4) - G_1 G_4 G_5 H_1 H_2}} \longrightarrow C_2$$

Figure 3.68

So the transfer function of the system will be given by

$$\frac{C_2(s)}{R_1(s)} = \frac{G_1 G_3 G_4 G_5 H_2}{1 + G_4 + G_1 G_2 + G_1 G_2 G_4 - G_1 G_4 G_5 H_1 H_2}$$

Example 3.8 A system is described by the following set of linear algebraic equations:

$$x_2 = a_{12} x_1 + a_{22} x_2 + a_{32} x_3$$
$$x_3 = a_{23} x_2 + a_{43} x_4$$
$$x_4 = a_{24} x_2 + a_{34} x_3 + a_{44} x_4$$
$$x_5 = a_{25} x_2 + a_{45} x_4$$

Draw the signal flow graph and obtain the transfer function of the system using Mason's gain formula.

Solution: The signal flow graph shown in Figure 3.69, drawn based on the given equations, has three forward paths and five loops. There are three pairs of two nontouching loops. All the loops are touching two forward paths and two loops are not touching the third forward path.

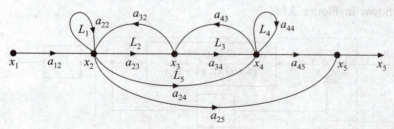

Figure 3.69 Example 3.8.

The forward paths and the gains associated with them are as follows:

Forward path x_1-x_2-x_3-x_4-x_5

$$M_1 = (a_{12})(a_{23})(a_{34})(a_{45}) = a_{12}a_{23}a_{34}a_{45} \qquad \Delta_1 = 1$$

Forward path x_1-x_2-x_4-x_5

$$M_2 = (a_{12})(a_{24})(a_{45}) = a_{12}a_{24}a_{45} \qquad\qquad \Delta_2 = 1$$

Forward path x_1-x_2-x_5

$$M_3 = (a_{12})(a_{25}) = a_{12}a_{25} \qquad\qquad \Delta_3 = 1 - (a_{34}a_{43} + a_{44})$$

The loops and the gains associated with them are as follows:

Loop x_2-x_2 $\qquad\qquad\qquad\qquad$ $L_1 = a_{22}$

Loop x_2-x_3-x_2 $\qquad\qquad\qquad$ $L_2 = (a_{23})(a_{32}) = a_{23}a_{32}$

Loop x_3-x_4-x_3 $\qquad\qquad\qquad$ $L_3 = (a_{34})(a_{43}) = a_{34}a_{43}$

Loop x_4-x_4 $\qquad\qquad\qquad\qquad$ $L_4 = a_{44}$

Loop x_2-x_4-x_3-x_2 $\qquad\qquad$ $L_5 = (a_{24})(a_{43})(a_{32}) = a_{24}a_{43}a_{32}$

The pairs of two nontouching loops and the products of gains associated with them are as follows:

Loops L_1 and L_3 $\qquad\qquad\qquad$ $L_{13} = (a_{22})(a_{34}a_{43}) = a_{22}a_{34}a_{43}$

Loops L_1 and L_4 $\qquad\qquad\qquad$ $L_{14} = (a_{22})(a_{44}) = a_{22}a_{44}$

Loops L_2 and L_4 $\qquad\qquad\qquad$ $L_{24} = (a_{23}a_{32})(a_{44}) = a_{23}a_{32}a_{44}$

The determinant of the signal flow graph is

$$\Delta = 1 - (L_1 + L_2 + L_3 + L_4 + L_5) + (L_{13} + L_{14} + L_{24})$$

$$\therefore \quad \Delta = 1 - (a_{22} + a_{23}a_{32} + a_{34}a_{43} + a_{44} + a_{24}a_{43}a_{32}) + (a_{22}a_{34}a_{43} + a_{22}a_{44} + a_{23}a_{32}a_{44})$$

Applying Mason's gain formula, the transfer function is

$$T = \frac{C}{R} = \frac{M_1\Delta_1 + M_2\Delta_2 + M_3\Delta_3}{\Delta}$$

$$= \frac{a_{12}a_{23}a_{34}a_{45} + a_{12}a_{24}a_{45} + a_{12}a_{25}(1 - a_{34}a_{43} - a_{44})}{1 - a_{22} - a_{23}a_{32} - a_{34}a_{43} - a_{44} - a_{24}a_{43}a_{32} + a_{22}a_{34}a_{43} + a_{22}a_{44} + a_{23}a_{32}a_{44}}$$

Example 3.9 For the system represented by the following equations, find the transfer function $X(s)/U(s)$ by the signal flow graph technique.

$$x = x_1 + \alpha_0 u$$

$$\frac{dx_1}{dt} = -\alpha_1 x_1 + x_2 + \alpha_2 u$$

$$\frac{dx_2}{dt} = -\alpha_2 x_1 + \alpha_1 u$$

Solution: The given equations are a set of first-order differential equations. For the signal flow graph, the describing equations must be linear algebraic equations. The differential equations may be converted into algebraic equations by using the Laplace transform.

$$X(s) = X_1(s) + \alpha_0 U(s)$$

$$sX_1(s) = -\alpha_1 X_1(s) + X_2(s) + \alpha_2 U(s)$$

$$sX_2(s) = -\alpha_2 X_1(s) + \alpha_1 U(s)$$

i.e.
$$X(s) = X_1(s) + \alpha_0 U(s)$$

$$X_1(s) = \frac{-\alpha_1}{s} X_1(s) + \frac{1}{s} X_2(s) + \frac{\alpha_2}{s} U(s)$$

$$X_2(s) = \frac{-\alpha_2}{s} X_1(s) + \frac{\alpha_1}{s} U(s)$$

Based on these equations, the signal flow graph is drawn as shown in Figure 3.70.

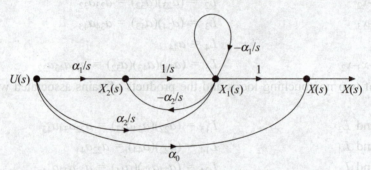

Figure 3.70 Example 3.9.

In the signal flow graph of Figure 3.70, there are three forward paths and two loops. There are no pairs of nontouching loops. Both the loops are touching two forward paths and both the loops are not touching the third forward path.

The forward paths and the gains associated with them are as follows:

Forward path $U(s)$-$X_2(s)$-$X_1(s)$-$X(s)$ $M_1 = \dfrac{\alpha_1}{s} \cdot \dfrac{1}{s} \cdot 1 = \dfrac{\alpha_1}{s^2}$

Forward path $U(s)$-$X_1(s)$-$X(s)$ $M_2 = \dfrac{\alpha_2}{s} \cdot 1 = \dfrac{\alpha_2}{s}$

Forward path $U(s)$-$X(s)$ $M_3 = \alpha_0$

The loops and the gains associated with them are as follows:

Loop $X_2(s)$-$X_1(s)$-$X_2(s)$ $L_1 = \left(\dfrac{-\alpha_2}{s} \right)\left(\dfrac{1}{s} \right) = \dfrac{-\alpha_2}{s^2}$

Loop $X_1(s)$-$X_1(s)$ $L_2 = \dfrac{-\alpha_1}{s}$

Both the loops are touching the first and second forward paths and no loop is touching the third forward path

$$\therefore \qquad \Delta_1 = 1, \Delta_2 = 1, \Delta_3 = 1 - \left(-\frac{\alpha_2}{s^2} - \frac{\alpha_1}{s} \right) = 1 + \frac{\alpha_1}{s} + \frac{\alpha_2}{s^2} = \Delta$$

The determinant of the signal flow graph is $D = 1 - (L_1 + L_2)$

$$\therefore \qquad \Delta = 1 - \left(-\frac{\alpha_2}{s^2} - \frac{\alpha_1}{s} \right) = 1 + \frac{\alpha_1}{s} + \frac{\alpha_2}{s^2}$$

Using Mason's gain formula, the transfer function is

$$\frac{X(s)}{U(s)} = \frac{M_1\Delta_1 + M_2\Delta_2 + M_3\Delta_3}{\Delta} = \frac{\dfrac{\alpha_1}{s^2} + \dfrac{\alpha_2}{s}}{1 + \dfrac{\alpha_1}{s} + \dfrac{\alpha_2}{s^2}} + \alpha_0 = \alpha_0 + \frac{\alpha_1 + \alpha_2 s}{s^2 + \alpha_1 s + \alpha_2}$$

$$\frac{X(s)}{U(s)} = \frac{\alpha_0(s^2 + \alpha_1 s + \alpha_2) + \alpha_1 + \alpha_2 s}{s^2 + \alpha_1 s + \alpha_2}$$

Example 3.10 Apply the gain formula to the signal flow graph shown in Figure 3.71, to find the following transfer functions:

$$\frac{x_5}{x_1}, \frac{x_4}{x_1}, \frac{x_2}{x_1}, \frac{x_5}{x_2}, \frac{x_4}{x_2}$$

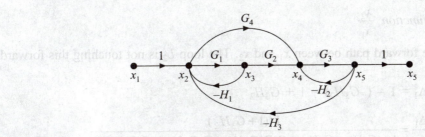

Figure 3.71 Example 3.10.

Solution: The signal flow graph shown in Figure 3.71 has two forward paths, four loops, and one pair of two nontouching loops. All the loops are touching both the forward paths.

The forward paths and the gains associated with them are as follows:

Forward path x_1-x_2-x_3-x_4-x_5 $\qquad M_1 = (1)(G_1)(G_2)(G_3)(1) = G_1 G_2 G_3 \qquad \Delta_1 = 1$

Forward path x_1-x_2-x_4-x_5 $\qquad M_2 = (1)(G_4)(G_3)(1) = G_4 G_3 \qquad\qquad \Delta_2 = 1$

The loops and the gains associated with them are as follows:

Loop x_2-x_3-x_2 $\qquad L_1 = (G_1)(-H_1) = -G_1 H_1$

Loop x_4-x_5-x_4 $\qquad L_2 = (G_3)(-H_2) = -G_3 H_2$

Loop x_2-x_3-x_4-x_5-x_2 $\qquad L_3 = (G_1)(G_2)(G_3)(-H_3) = -G_1 G_2 G_3 H_3$

Loop x_2-x_4-x_5-x_2 $\qquad L_4 = (G_4)(G_3)(-H_3) = -G_4 G_3 H_3$

The pairs of two nontouching loops and the products of gains associated with them are as follows:

Loops x_2-x_3-x_2 and x_4-x_5-x_4 $\qquad L_{12} = (-G_1 H_1)(-G_3 H_2) = G_1 G_3 H_1 H_2$

The determinant of the signal flow graph is $\Delta = 1 - (L_1 + L_2 + L_3 + L_4) + (L_{12})$

$\therefore \qquad \Delta = 1 - (-G_1H_1 - G_3H_2 - G_1G_2G_3H_3 - G_3G_4H_3) + G_1G_3H_1H_2$

$\qquad\qquad = 1 + G_1H_1 + G_3H_2 + G_1G_2G_3H_3 + G_3G_4H_3 + G_1G_3H_1H_2$

The transfer function is

$$\frac{x_5}{x_1} = \frac{M_1\Delta_1 + M_2\Delta_2}{\Delta} = \frac{G_1G_2G_3 + G_3G_4}{1 + G_1H_1 + G_3H_2 + G_1G_2G_3H_3 + G_3G_4H_3 + G_1G_3H_1H_2}$$

To find the transfer function $\dfrac{x_4}{x_1}$

There are two forward paths between x_1 and x_4 and there are no loops which are not touching these forward paths

Forward path x_1-x_2-x_3-x_4 $\qquad M_1 = (1)(G_1)(G_2) = G_1G_2 \qquad \Delta_1 = 1$

Forward path x_1-x_2-x_4 $\qquad\qquad M_2 = (1)(G_4) = G_4 \qquad\qquad \Delta_2 = 1$

$\therefore \qquad \dfrac{x_4}{x_1} = \dfrac{M_1\Delta_1 + M_2\Delta_2}{\Delta} = \dfrac{G_1G_2 + G_4}{1 + G_1H_1 + G_3H_2 + G_1G_2G_3H_3 + G_3G_4H_3 + G_1G_3H_1H_2}$

To find the transfer function $\dfrac{x_2}{x_1}$

There is only one forward path between x_1 and x_2. The loop L_2 is not touching this forward path

$$M_1 = 1, \, \Delta_1 = 1 - (-G_3H_2) = 1 + G_3H_2$$

$\therefore \qquad \dfrac{x_2}{x_1} = \dfrac{M_1\Delta_1}{\Delta} = \dfrac{1 \cdot (1 + G_3H_2)}{1 + G_1H_1 + G_3H_2 + G_1G_2G_3H_3 + G_3G_4H_3 + G_1G_3H_1H_2}$

To find the transfer function $\dfrac{x_5}{x_2}$

Find $\dfrac{x_5}{x_1}$ and $\dfrac{x_2}{x_1}$ and divide one by the other, i.e.

$$\frac{x_5}{x_2} = \frac{\dfrac{x_5}{x_1}}{\dfrac{x_2}{x_1}} = \frac{\dfrac{G_1G_2G_3 + G_3G_4}{\Delta}}{\dfrac{1 + G_3H_2}{\Delta}} = \frac{G_1G_2G_3 + G_3G_4}{1 + G_3H_2}$$

To find the transfer function $\dfrac{x_4}{x_2}$

Find $\dfrac{x_4}{x_1}$ and $\dfrac{x_2}{x_1}$ and divide one by the other, i.e.

$$\frac{x_4}{x_2} = \frac{\dfrac{x_4}{x_1}}{\dfrac{x_2}{x_1}} = \frac{\dfrac{G_1 G_2 + G_4}{\Delta}}{\dfrac{1 + G_3 H_2}{\Delta}} = \frac{G_1 G_2 + G_4}{1 + G_3 H_2}$$

Example 3.11 Apply the gain formula to the signal flow graph shown in Figure 3.72.

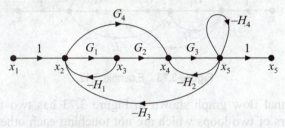

Figure 3.72 Example 3.11.

Solution: In the signal flow graph shown in Figure 3.72, there are two forward paths, five loops and two pairs of two nontouching loops. All the loops are touching both the forward paths.

The forward paths and the gains associated with them are as follows:

Forward path x_1-x_2-x_3-x_4-x_5 $M_1 = (1)(G_1)(G_2)(G_3)(1) = G_1 G_2 G_3$ $\Delta_1 = 1$

Forward path x_1-x_2-x_4-x_5 $M_2 = (1)(G_4)(G_3)(1) = G_4 G_3$ $\Delta_2 = 1$

The loops and the gains associated with them are as follows:

Loop x_2-x_3-x_2 $L_1 = (G_1)(-H_1) = -G_1 H_1$

Loop x_4-x_5-x_4 $L_2 = (G_3)(-H_2) = -G_3 H_2$

Loop x_2-x_3-x_4-x_5-x_2 $L_3 = (G_1)(G_2)(G_3)(-H_3) = -G_1 G_2 G_3 H_3$

Loop x_2-x_4-x_5-x_2 $L_4 = (G_4)(G_3)(-H_3) = -G_4 G_3 H_3$

Loop x_5-x_5 $L_5 = -H_4$

The pairs of two nontouching loops and the products of gains associated with them are as follows:

Loops x_2-x_3-x_2 and x_4-x_5-x_4 $L_{12} = (-G_1 H_1)(-G_3 H_2) = G_1 G_3 H_1 H_2$

Loops x_2-x_3-x_2 and x_5-x_5 $L_{15} = (-G_1 H_1)(-H_4) = G_1 H_1 H_4$

The determinant of the signal flow graph is $\Delta = 1 - (L_1 + L_2 + L_3 + L_4 + L_5) + (L_{12} + L_{15})$

$\Delta = 1 - (-G_1 H_1 - G_3 H_2 - G_1 G_2 G_3 H_3 - G_4 G_3 H_3 - H_4) + (G_1 G_3 H_1 H_2 + G_1 H_1 H_4)$

$= 1 + G_1 H_1 + G_3 H_2 + G_1 G_2 G_3 H_3 + G_4 G_3 H_3 + H_4 + G_1 G_3 H_1 H_2 + G_1 H_1 H_4$

Applying Mason's gain formula, the transfer function is

$$\frac{x_5}{x_1} = \frac{M_1 \Delta_1 + M_2 \Delta_2}{\Delta}$$

$$= \frac{G_1 G_2 G_3 + G_4 G_3}{1 + G_1 H_1 + G_3 H_2 + G_1 G_2 G_3 H_3 + G_4 G_3 H_3 + H_4 + G_1 G_3 H_1 H_2 + G_1 H_1 H_4}$$

Example 3.12   Find the transfer function $\dfrac{x_5}{x_1}$, for the system whose signal flow graph is shown in Figure 3.73, by applying the gain formula.

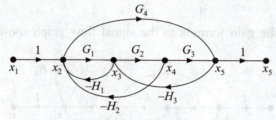

Figure 3.73   Example 3.12.

Solution: The signal flow graph shown in Figure 3.73 has two forward paths and five loops. There are no pairs of two loops which are not touching each other, and all the loops are touching both the forward paths.

The forward paths and the gains associated with them are as follows:

Forward path x_1-x_2-x_3-x_4-x_5 $M_1 = (1)(G_1)(G_2)(G_3)(1) = G_1G_2G_3$ $\Delta_1 = 1$

Forward path x_1-x_2-x_5 $M_2 = (1)(G_4)(1) = G_4$ $\Delta_2 = 1$

The loops and the gains associated with them are as follows:

Loop x_2-x_3-x_2 $L_1 = (G_1)(-H_1) = -G_1H_1$

Loop x_2-x_3-x_4-x_2 $L_2 = (G_1)(G_2)(-H_2) = -G_1G_2H_2$

Loop x_3-x_4-x_5-x_3 $L_3 = (G_2)(G_3)(-H_3) = -G_2G_3H_3$

Loop x_2-x_5-x_3-x_2 $L_4 = (G_4)(-H_3)(-H_1) = G_4H_3H_1$

Loop x_2-x_5-x_3-x_4-x_2 $L_5 = (G_4)(-H_3)(G_2)(-H_2) = G_4G_2H_3H_2$

The determinant of the signal flow graph is $\Delta = 1 - (L_1 + L_2 + L_3 + L_4 + L_5)$

$$\Delta = 1 - (-G_1H_1 - G_1G_2H_2 - G_2G_3H_3 + G_4G_3H_1 + G_4G_2H_3H_2)$$

$$= 1 + G_1H_1 + G_1G_2H_2 + G_2G_3H_3 - G_4G_3H_1 - G_4G_2H_3H_2$$

Applying Mason's gain formula, the transfer function is

$$\frac{x_5}{x_1} = \frac{M_1\Delta_1 + M_2\Delta_2}{\Delta} = \frac{G_1G_2G_3 + G_4}{1 + G_1H_1 + G_1G_2H_2 + G_2G_3H_3 - G_4H_3H_1 - G_4G_2H_3H_2}$$

Example 3.13   Apply the gain formula to the signal flow graph shown in Figure 3.74, to find the transfer function $\dfrac{x_5}{x_1}$.

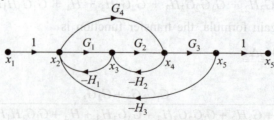

Figure 3.74   Example 3.13.

Solution: The signal flow graph shown in Figure 3.74 has two forward paths, and five loops. There are no pairs of two nontouching loops and all the loops are touching both the forward paths.

The forward paths and the gains associated with them are as follows:

Forward path x_1-x_2-x_3-x_4-x_5 $M_1 = (1)(G_1)(G_2)(G_3)(1) = G_1G_2G_3$ $\Delta_1 = 1$

Forward path x_1-x_2-x_4-x_5 $M_2 = (1)(G_4)(G_3)(1) = G_4G_3$ $\Delta_2 = 1$

The loops and the gains associated with them are as follows:

Loop x_2-x_3-x_2 $L_1 = (G_1)(-H_1) = -G_1H_1$

Loop x_3-x_4-x_3 $L_2 = (G_2)(-H_2) = -G_2H_2$

Loop x_2-x_4-x_3-x_2 $L_3 = (G_4)(-H_2)(-H_1) = G_4H_2H_1$

Loop x_2-x_4-x_5-x_2 $L_4 = (G_4)(G_3)(-H_3) = -G_4G_3H_3$

Loop x_2-x_3-x_4-x_5-x_2 $L_5 = (G_1)(G_2)(G_3)(-H_3) = -G_1G_2G_3H_3$

The determinant of the signal flow graph is $\Delta = 1 - (L_1 + L_2 + L_3 + L_4 + L_5)$

$$\Delta = 1 - (-G_1H_1 - G_2H_2 + G_4H_2H_1 - G_4G_3H_2 - G_1G_2G_3H_3)$$

Applying Mason's gain formula, the transfer function is

$$\frac{x_5}{x_1} = \frac{M_1\Delta_1 + M_2\Delta_2}{\Delta} = \frac{G_1G_2G_3 + G_4G_3}{1 + G_1H_1 + G_2H_2 + G_4G_3H_3 + G_1G_2G_3H_3 - G_4H_2H_1}$$

Example 3.14 Apply the gain formula to the signal flow graph shown in Figure 3.75, to find the transfer function $\dfrac{x_5}{x_1}$.

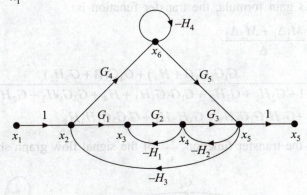

Figure 3.75 Example 3.14.

Solution: The signal flow graph shown in Figure 3.75 has two forward paths and five loops. There are four pairs of two nontouching loops and each forward path has got one nontouching loop.

The forward paths and gains associated with them are as follows:

Forward path x_1-x_2-x_3-x_4-x_5 $M_1 = (1)(G_1)(G_2)(G_3)(1) = G_1G_2G_3$

Forward path x_1-x_2-x_6-x_5 $M_2 = (1)(G_4)(G_5)(1) = G_4G_5$

The loops and the gains associated with them are

Loop x_3-x_4-x_3 $L_1 = (G_2)(-H_1) = -G_2H_1$

Loop x_4-x_5-x_4 $L_2 = (G_3)(-H_2) = -G_3H_2$

Loop x_2-x_3-x_4-x_5-x_2 $L_3 = (G_1)(G_2)(G_3)(-H_3) = -G_1G_2G_3H_3$

Loop x_6-x_6 $L_4 = -H_4$

Loop x_2-x_6-x_5-x_2 $L_5 = (G_4)(G_5)(-H_3) = -G_4G_5H_3$

The pairs of two nontouching loops and the products of gains associated with them are as follows:

Loops x_3-x_4-x_3 and x_6-x_6 $L_{14} = (-G_2H_1)(-H_4) = G_2H_1H_4$

Loops x_3-x_4-x_3 and x_2-x_6-x_5-x_2 $L_{15} = (-G_2H_1)(-G_4G_5H_3) = G_2H_1G_4G_5H_3$

Loops x_4-x_5-x_4 and x_6-x_6 $L_{24} = (-G_3H_2)(-H_4) = G_3H_2H_4$

Loops x_2-x_3-x_4-x_5-x_2 and x_6-x_6 $L_{34} = (-G_1G_2G_3H_3)(-H_4) = G_1G_2G_3H_3H_4$

The determinant of the signal flow graph is

$$\Delta = 1 - (L_1 + L_2 + L_3 + L_4 + L_5) + (L_{14} + L_{15} + L_{24} + L_{34})$$

$$\Delta = 1 - (-G_2H_1 - G_3H_2 - G_1G_2G_3H_3 - H_4 - G_4G_5H_3)$$
$$+ (G_2H_1H_4 + G_2H_1G_4G_5H_3 + G_3H_2H_4 + G_1G_2G_3H_3H_4)$$

$$= 1 + G_2H_1 + G_3H_2 + G_1G_2G_3H_3 + H_4 + G_4G_5H_3 + G_2H_1H_4$$
$$+ G_2H_1G_4G_5H_3 + G_3H_2H_4 + G_1G_2G_3H_3H_4$$

L_4 is not touching the first forward path and L_1 is not touching the second forward path

$\therefore$ $\Delta_1 = 1 - (-H_4) = 1 + H_4$

and $\Delta_2 = 1 - (-G_2H_1) = 1 + G_2H_1$

Applying Mason's gain formula, the transfer function is

$$\frac{x_5}{x_1} = \frac{M_1\Delta_1 + M_2\Delta_2}{\Delta}$$

$$= \frac{G_1G_2G_3(1 + H_4) + G_4G_5(1 + G_2H_1)}{1 + G_2H_1 + G_3H_2 + G_1G_2G_3H_3 + H_4 + G_4G_5H_3 + G_2H_1H_4}$$
$$+ G_2H_1G_4G_5H_3 + G_3H_2H_4 + G_1G_2G_3H_3H_4$$

Example 3.15 Find the transfer function $\dfrac{x_7}{x_1}$ of the signal flow graph shown in Figure 3.76.

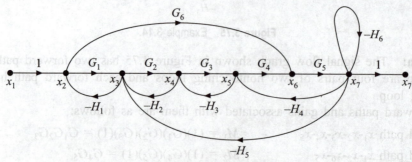

Figure 3.76 Example 3.15.

Solution: The signal flow graph shown in Figure 3.76 has two forward paths and eight loops. There are seven pairs of two nontouching loops. There is one combination of three nontouching loops. All loops are touching one forward path and two loops are not touching the second forward path.

The forward paths and the gains associated with them are as follows:

Forward path x_1-x_2-x_3-x_4-x_5-x_6-x_7 $\qquad M_1 = (1)(G_1)(G_2)(G_3)(G_4)(G_5)(1) = G_1G_2G_3G_4G_5$

Forward path x_1-x_2-x_6-x_7 $\qquad\qquad M_2 = (1)(G_6)(G_5)(1) = G_6G_5$

The loops and the gains associated with them are as follows:

Loop x_2-x_3-x_2 $\qquad\qquad\qquad L_1 = (G_1)(-H_1) = -G_1H_1$

Loop x_3-x_4-x_3 $\qquad\qquad\qquad L_2 = (G_2)(-H_2) = -G_2H_2$

Loop x_4-x_5-x_4 $\qquad\qquad\qquad L_3 = (G_3)(-H_3) = -G_3H_3$

Loop x_5-x_6-x_7-x_5 $\qquad\qquad L_4 = (G_4)(G_5)(-H_4) = -G_4G_5H_4$

Loop x_7-x_7 $\qquad\qquad\qquad\quad L_5 = -H_6$

Loop x_3-x_4-x_5-x_6-x_7-x_3 $\qquad L_6 = (G_2)(G_3)(G_4)(G_5)(-H_5) = -G_2G_3G_4G_5H_5$

Loop x_2-x_6-x_7-x_5-x_4-x_3-x_2 $\quad L_7 = (G_6)(G_5)(-H_4)(-H_3)(-H_2)(-H_1) = G_6G_5H_4H_3H_2H_1$

Loop x_2-x_6-x_7-x_3-x_2 $\qquad\quad L_8 = (G_6)(G_5)(-H_5)(-H_1) = G_6G_5H_5H_1$

The pairs of two nontouching loops and the products of gains associated with them are as follows:

Loops x_2-x_3-x_2 and x_4-x_5-x_4 $\qquad L_{13} = (-G_1H_1)(-G_3H_3) = G_1H_1G_3H_3$

Loops x_2-x_3-x_2 and x_5-x_6-x_7-x_5 $\quad L_{14} = (-G_1H_1)(-G_4G_5H_4) = G_1H_1G_4G_5H_4$

Loops x_2-x_3-x_2 and x_7-x_7 $\qquad\quad L_{15} = (-G_1H_1)(-H_6) = G_1H_1H_6$

Loops x_3-x_4-x_3 and x_5-x_6-x_7-x_5 $\quad L_{24} = (-G_2H_2)(-G_4G_5H_4) = G_2H_2G_4G_5H_4$

Loops x_3-x_4-x_3 and x_7-x_7 $\qquad\quad L_{25} = (-G_2H_2)(-H_6) = G_2H_2H_6$

Loops x_4-x_5-x_4 and x_7-x_7 $\qquad\quad L_{35} = (-G_3H_3)(-H_6) = G_3H_3H_6$

Loops x_4-x_5-x_4 and x_2-x_6-x_7-x_3-x_2 $\quad L_{38} = (-G_3H_3)(G_6G_5H_5H_1) = -G_3H_3G_6G_5H_5H_1$

The combinations of three nontouching loops and the products of gains associated with them are as follows:

Loops x_2-x_3-x_2, x_4-x_5-x_4, and x_7-x_7 $\quad L_{135} = (-G_1H_1)(-G_3H_3)(-H_6) = -G_1H_1G_3H_3H_6$

The determinant of the signal flow graph is

$$\Delta = 1 - (L_1 + L_2 + L_3 + L_4 + L_5 + L_6 + L_7 + L_8)$$
$$+ (L_{13} + L_{14} + L_{15} + L_{24} + L_{25} + L_{35} + L_{38}) - (L_{135})$$

$$\therefore \quad \Delta = 1 - (-G_1H_1 - G_2H_2 - G_3H_3 - G_4G_5H_4 - H_6 - G_2G_3G_4G_5H_5$$
$$+ G_6G_5H_4H_3H_2H_1 + G_6G_5H_5H_1)$$
$$+ (G_1H_1G_3H_3 + G_1H_1G_4G_5H_4 + G_1H_1H_6 + G_2H_2H_6 + G_3H_3H_6$$
$$- G_3H_3G_6G_5H_5H_1 + G_2H_2G_4G_5H_4) - (-G_1H_1G_3H_3H_6)$$

All loops are touching the first forward path and L_2 and L_6 are not touching the second forward path

$$\therefore \qquad\qquad\qquad \Delta_1 = 1 \text{ and } \Delta_2 = 1 - (-G_2H_2 - G_3H_3)$$

Applying the Mason's gain formula, the transfer function is

$$\frac{x_7}{x_1} = \frac{M_1\Delta_1 + M_2\Delta_2}{\Delta} = \frac{G_1G_2G_3G_4G_5 + G_6G_5(1 + G_2H_2 + G_3H_3)}{\Delta}$$

Example 3.16 Find the transfer function $\dfrac{x_7}{x_1}$ of the signal flow graph shown in Figure 3.77.

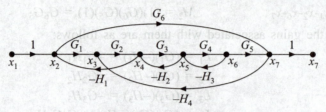

Figure 3.77 Example 3.16.

Solution: The signal flow graph shown in Figure 3.77 has two forward paths and five loops. There are two pairs of loops which are not touching each other. All the loops are touching one forward path and two loops are not touching the second forward path.

The forward paths and the gains associated with them are as follows:

Forward path x_1-x_2-x_3-x_4-x_5-x_6-x_7 $M_1 = (1)(G_1)(G_2)(G_3)(G_4)(G_5)(1) = G_1G_2G_3G_4G_5$

Forward path x_1-x_2-x_7 $M_2 = (1)(G_6)(1) = G_6$

The loops and the gains associated with them are as follows:

Loop x_2-x_3-x_4-x_2 $L_1 = (G_1)(G_2)(-H_1) = -G_1G_2H_1$

Loop x_4-x_5-x_4 $L_2 = (G_3)(-H_2) = -G_3H_2$

Loop x_5-x_6-x_5 $L_3 = (G_4)(-H_3) = -G_4H_3$

Loop x_3-x_4-x_5-x_6-x_7-x_3 $L_4 = (G_2)(G_3)(G_4)(G_5)(-H_4) = -G_2G_3G_4G_5H_4$

Loop x_2-x_7-x_3-x_4-x_2 $L_5 = (G_6)(-H_4)(G_2)(-H_1) = G_2G_6H_1H_4$

The pairs of two nontouching loops and the products of gains associated with them are as follows:

Loops x_2-x_3-x_4-x_2 and x_5-x_6-x_5 $L_{13} = (-G_1G_2H_1)(-G_4H_3) = G_1G_2H_1G_4H_3$

Loops x_5-x_6-x_5 and x_2-x_7-x_3-x_4-x_2 $L_{35} = (-G_4H_3)(G_6G_2H_4H_1) = -G_4H_3G_6G_2H_4H_1$

The determinant of the signal flow graph is $\Delta = 1 - (L_1 + L_2 + L_3 + L_4 + L_5) + (L_{13} + L_{35})$

$$\Delta = 1 - (-G_1G_2H_1 - G_3H_2 - G_4H_3 - G_2G_3G_4G_5H_4 + G_2G_6H_1H_4)$$
$$+ (G_1G_2H_1G_4H_3 - G_4G_3G_6G_2H_4H_1)$$

All loops are touching the first forward path and L_2 and L_3 are not touching the second forward path

$\therefore$ $\Delta_1 = 1$ and $\Delta_2 = 1 - (-G_3H_2 - G_4H_3) = 1 + G_3H_2 + G_4H_3$

Applying Mason's gain formula, the transfer function is

$$\frac{x_7}{x_1} = \frac{M_1\Delta_1 + M_2\Delta_2}{\Delta} = \frac{G_1G_2G_3G_4G_5 + G_6(1 + G_3H_2 + G_4H_3)}{\Delta}$$

Example 3.17 Find the transfer function $\dfrac{C}{R}$ of the signal flow graph shown in Figure 3.78.

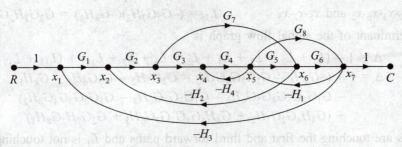

Figure 3.78 Example 3.17.

Solution: The signal flow graph shown in Figure 3.78 has three forward paths and eight loops. There are three pairs of two nontouching loops. All the loops are touching two forward paths and one loop is not touching the third forward path.

The forward paths and gains associated with them are as follows:

Forward path R-x_1-x_2-x_3-x_4-x_5-x_6-x_7-C $M_1 = (1)(G_1)(G_2)(G_3)(G_4)(G_5)(G_6)(1)$

$$= G_1G_2G_3G_4G_5G_6$$

Forward path R-x_1-x_2-x_3-x_6-x_7-C $M_2 = (1)(G_1)(G_2)(G_7)(G_6)(1) = G_1G_2G_7G_6$

Forward path R-x_1-x_2-x_3-x_4-x_5-x_7-C $M_3 = (1)(G_1)(G_2)(G_3)(G_4)(G_8)(1)$

$$= G_1G_2G_3G_4G_8$$

The loops and the gains associated with them are as follows:

Loop x_4-x_5-x_4 $L_1 = (G_4)(-H_4) = -G_4H_4$

Loop x_2-x_3-x_4-x_5-x_6-x_2 $L_2 = (G_2)(G_3)(G_4)(G_5)(-H_2)$

$$= -G_2G_3G_4G_5H_2$$

Loop x_2-x_3-x_6-x_2 $L_3 = (G_2)(G_7)(-H_2) = -G_2G_7H_2$

Loop x_5-x_6-x_7-x_5 $L_4 = (G_5)(G_6)(-H_1) = -G_5G_6H_1$

Loop x_5-x_7-x_5 $L_5 = (G_8)(-H_1) = -G_8H_1$

Loop x_1-x_2-x_3-x_4-x_5-x_6-x_7-x_1 $L_6 = (G_1)(G_2)(G_3)(G_4)(G_5)(G_6)(-H_3)$

$$= -G_1G_2G_3G_4G_5G_6H_3$$

Loop x_1-x_2-x_3-x_6-x_7-x_1 $L_7 = (G_1)(G_2)(G_7)(G_6)(-H_3)$

$$= -G_1G_2G_7G_6H_3$$

Loop x_1-x_2-x_3-x_4-x_5-x_7-x_1 $L_8 = (G_1)(G_2)(G_3)(G_4)(G_8)(-H_3)$

$$= -G_1G_2G_3G_4G_8H_3$$

The pairs of two nontouching loops and the products of gains associated with them are as follows:

Loops x_4-x_5-x_4 and x_2-x_3-x_6-x_2 $L_{13} = (-G_4H_4)(-G_2G_7H_2) = G_4H_4G_2G_7H_2$

Loops x_4-x_5-x_4 and x_1-x_2-x_3-x_6-x_7-x_1 $L_{17} = (-G_4H_4)(-G_1G_2G_7G_6H_3)$
$$= G_4H_4G_1G_2G_7G_6H_3$$

Loops x_2-x_3-x_6-x_2 and x_5-x_7-x_5 $L_{35} = (-G_2G_7H_2)(-G_8H_1) = G_2G_7H_2G_8H_1$

The determinant of the signal flow graph is

$$\Delta = 1 - (L_1 + L_2 + L_3 + L_4 + L_5 + L_6 + L_7 + L_{18}) + (L_{13} + L_{17} + L_{35})$$
$$\Delta = 1 - (-G_4H_4 - G_2G_3G_4G_5H_2 - G_2G_7H_2 - G_5G_6H_1 - G_8H_1$$
$$- G_1G_2G_3G_4G_5G_6H_3 - G_1G_2G_7G_6H_3 - G_1G_2G_3G_4G_8H_3)$$
$$+ (G_4H_4G_2G_7H_2 + G_4H_4G_1G_2G_7G_6H_3 + G_2G_7H_2G_8H_1)$$

All loops are touching the first and third forward paths and L_1 is not touching the second forward path

$$\therefore \qquad \Delta_1 = 1, \; \Delta_2 = 1 - L_1 = 1 - (-G_4H_4) = 1 + G_4H_4, \; \Delta_3 = 1$$

Applying Mason's gain formula, the transfer function is

$$\frac{C}{R} = \frac{M_1\Delta_1 + M_2\Delta_2 + M_3\Delta_3}{\Delta}$$

i.e.
$$\frac{C}{R} = \frac{G_1G_2G_3G_4G_5G_6 + G_1G_2G_7G_6(1 + G_4H_4) + G_1G_2G_3G_4G_8}{\Delta}$$

Example 3.18   Find the transfer function of the system whose signal flow graph is shown in Figure 3.79.

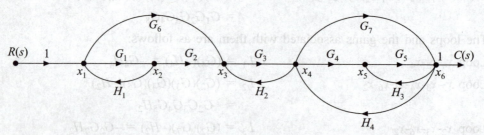

Figure 3.79   Example 3.18.

Solution: The given signal flow graph shown in Figure 3.79 has four forward paths and five loops. All the loops are touching all the forward paths. There are five pairs of two nontouching loops and one combination of three nontouching loops.

The forward paths and the gains associated with them are as follows:

Forward path R-x_1-x_2-x_3-x_4-x_5-x_6-C $M_1 = (1)(G_1)(G_2)(G_3)(G_4)(G_5)(1)$
$$= G_1G_2G_3G_4G_5$$

Forward path R-x_1-x_3-x_4-x_5-x_6-C $M_2 = (1)(G_6)(G_3)(G_4)(G_5)(1) = G_6G_3G_4G_5$

Forward path R-x_1-x_2-x_3-x_4-x_6-C $M_3 = (1)(G_1)(G_2)(G_3)(G_7)(1) = G_1G_2G_3G_7$

Forward path R-x_1-x_3-x_4-x_6-C $M_4 = (1)(G_6)(G_3)(G_7)(1) = G_6G_3G_7$

The loops and the gains associated with them are as follows:

Loop x_1-x_2-x_1 $L_1 = (G_1)(H_1) = G_1H_1$

Loop x_3-x_4-x_3 $L_2 = (G_3)(H_2) = G_3H_2$

Loop x_5-x_6-x_5 $\qquad\qquad\qquad$ $L_3 = (G_5)(H_3) = G_5H_3$

Loop x_4-x_5-x_6-x_4 $\qquad\qquad$ $L_4 = (G_4)(G_5)(H_4) = G_4G_5H_4$

Loop x_4-x_6-x_4 $\qquad\qquad\quad$ $L_5 = (G_7)(H_4) = G_7H_4$

The pairs of two nontouching loops and the products of gains associated with them are as follows:

Loops x_1-x_2-x_1 and x_3-x_4-x_3 $\qquad$ $L_{12} = (G_1H_1)(G_3H_2) = G_1H_1G_3H_2$

Loops x_1-x_2-x_1 and x_5-x_6-x_5 $\qquad$ $L_{13} = (G_1H_1)(G_5H_3) = G_1H_1G_5H_3$

Loops x_3-x_4-x_3 and x_5-x_6-x_5 $\qquad$ $L_{23} = (G_3H_2)(G_5H_3) = G_3G_5H_2H_3$

Loops x_1-x_2-x_1 and x_4-x_5-x_6-x_4 $\quad$ $L_{14} = (G_1H_1)(G_4G_5H_4) = G_1H_1G_4G_5H_4$

Loops x_1-x_2-x_1 and x_4-x_6-x_4 $\qquad$ $L_{15} = (G_1H_1)(G_7H_4) = G_1G_7H_1H_4$

Combinations of three nontouching loops and the gains associated with them are as follows:

Loops L_1, L_2 and L_3 $\qquad\qquad$ $L_{123} = (G_1H_1)(G_3H_2)(G_5H_3)$

$\qquad\qquad\qquad\qquad\qquad\qquad\quad$ $= G_1H_1G_3H_2G_5H_3$

Since all the loops are touching all the forward paths, $\Delta_1 = 1$, $\Delta_2 = 1$, $\Delta_3 = 1$, and $\Delta_4 = 1$. The determinant of the signal flow graph is given by

$$\Delta = 1 - (L_1 + L_2 + L_3 + L_4 + L_5) + (L_{12} + L_{13} + L_{14} + L_{15} + L_{23}) - (L_{123})$$

Therefore, the closed-loop transfer function $\dfrac{C}{R}$ is

$$\frac{C}{R} = \frac{M_1\Delta_1 + M_2\Delta_2 + M_3\Delta_3 + M_4\Delta_4}{\Delta} = \frac{G_1G_2G_3G_4G_5 + G_6G_3G_4G_5 + G_1G_2G_3G_7 + G_6G_3G_7}{\Delta}$$

$$= \frac{G_1G_2G_3G_4G_5 + G_6G_3G_4G_5 + G_1G_2G_3G_7 + G_6G_3G_7}{\begin{aligned} 1 - (G_1H_1 + G_3H_2 + G_5H_3 + G_4G_5H_4 + G_7H_4) + (G_1H_1G_3H_2 + G_1H_1G_5H_3 + G_3G_5H_2H_3 \\ + G_1H_1G_4G_5H_4 + G_1G_7H_1H_4) - G_1H_1G_3H_2G_5H_3 \end{aligned}}$$

Example 3.19 Obtain the transfer function of the system whose signal flow graph is shown in Figure 3.80. Also determine $\dfrac{x_2}{x_1}, \dfrac{x_4}{x_1}, \dfrac{x_7}{x_2}, \dfrac{x_4}{x_2}$ and $\dfrac{x_7}{x_4}$.

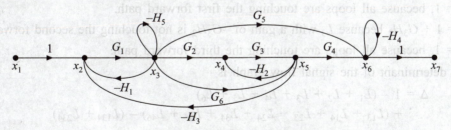

Figure 3.80 Example 3.19.

Solution: The signal flow graph shown in Figure 3.80 has three forward paths and six loops. There are seven pairs of two nontouching loops and two pairs of three nontouching loops. All loops are touching two forward paths and one loop is not touching the third forward path.

The forward paths and the gains associated with them are as follows:

Forward path x_1-x_2-x_3-x_4-x_5-x_6-x_7 $M_1 = (1)(G_1)(G_2)(G_3)(G_4)(1) = G_1G_2G_3G_4$

Forward path x_1-x_2-x_3-x_6-x_7 $M_2 = (1)(G_1)(G_5)(1) = G_1G_5$

Forward path x_1-x_2-x_3-x_5-x_6-x_7 $M_3 = (1)(G_1)(G_6)(G_4)(1) = G_1G_6G_4$

The loops and the gains associated with them are as follows:

Loop x_2-x_3-x_2 $L_1 = (G_1)(-H_1) = -G_1H_1$

Loop x_3-x_3 $L_2 = -H_5$

Loop x_4-x_5-x_4 $L_3 = (G_3)(-H_2) = -G_3H_2$

Loop x_6-x_6 $L_4 = -H_4$

Loop x_2-x_3-x_4-x_5-x_2 $L_5 = (G_1)(G_2)(G_3)(-H_3) = -G_1G_2G_3H_3$

Loop x_2-x_3-x_5-x_2 $L_6 = (G_1)(G_6)(-H_3) = -G_1G_6H_3$

The pairs of two nontouching loops and the products of gains associated with them are as follows:

Loops x_2-x_3-x_2 and x_4-x_5-x_4 $L_{13} = (-G_1H_1)(-G_3H_2) = G_1H_1G_3H_2$

Loops x_2-x_3-x_2 and x_6-x_6 $L_{14} = (-G_1H_1)(-H_4) = G_1H_1H_4$

Loops x_3-x_3 and x_4-x_5-x_4 $L_{23} = (-H_5)(-G_3H_2) = G_3H_2H_5$

Loops x_3-x_3 and x_6-x_6 $L_{24} = (-H_5)(-H_4) = H_5H_4$

Loops x_4-x_5-x_4 and x_6-x_6 $L_{34} = (-G_3H_2)(-H_4) = G_3H_2H_4$

Loops x_2-x_3-x_4-x_5-x_2 and x_6-x_6 $L_{45} = (-G_1G_2G_3H_3)(-H_4) = G_1G_2G_3H_3H_4$

Loops x_2-x_3-x_5-x_2 and x_6-x_6 $L_{46} = (-G_1G_6H_3)(-H_4) = G_1G_6H_3H_4$

There are two pairs of three nontouching loops. Those combinations and the products of gains associated with them are as follows:

Loops x_3-x_3, x_4-x_5-x_4, and x_6-x_6 $L_{234} = (-H_5)(-G_3H_2)(-H_4) = -G_3H_2H_4H_5$

Loops x_2-x_3-x_2, x_4-x_5-x_4, and x_6-x_6 $L_{134} = (-G_1H_1)(-G_3H_2)(-H_4) = -G_1H_1G_3H_2H_4$

The values of Δ_1, Δ_2 and Δ_3 are as follows:

$\Delta_1 = 1$, because all loops are touching the first forward path.

$\Delta_2 = 1 + G_3H_2$ because L_3 with a gain of $-G_3H_2$ is not touching the second forward path.

$\Delta_3 = 1$, because all loops are touching the third forward path.

The determinant of the signal flow graph is

$$\Delta = 1 - (L_1 + L_2 + L_3 + L_4 + L_5 + L_6)$$
$$+ (L_{13} + L_{14} + L_{23} + L_{24} + L_{34} + L_{45} + L_{46}) - (L_{134} + L_{234})$$

$\therefore$ $\Delta = 1 - (-G_1H_1 - H_5 - G_3H_2 - H_4 - G_1G_2G_3H_3 - G_1G_6H_3)$
$$+ (G_1G_3H_1H_2 + G_1H_1H_4 + H_4H_5 + G_3H_2H_5 + G_3H_2H_4$$
$$+ G_1G_2G_3H_3H_4 + G_1G_6H_3H_4) - (-G_1G_3H_1H_2H_4 - G_3H_2H_4H_5)$$

The transfer function

$$T = \frac{x_7}{x_1} = \frac{M_1\Delta_1 + M_2\Delta_2 + M_3\Delta_3}{\Delta}$$

$$\therefore \quad \frac{x_7}{x_1} = \frac{G_1G_2G_3G_4 + G_1G_5(1+G_3H_2) + G_1G_4G_6}{\begin{array}{l} 1 + G_1H_1 + H_5 + G_3H_2 + H_4 + G_1G_2G_3H_3 + G_1G_6H_3 + G_1G_3H_1H_2 \\ + G_1H_1H_4 + H_4H_5 + G_3H_2H_5 + G_3H_2H_4 + G_1G_2G_3H_3H_4 + G_1G_6H_3H_4 \\ + G_1G_3H_1H_2H_4 + G_3H_2H_4H_5 \end{array}}$$

Determination of $\dfrac{x_2}{x_1}$

To determine $\dfrac{x_2}{x_1}$, there is only one forward path between x_1 and x_2 and the gain of that forward path is unity. Loops 2, 3 and 4 are not touching this forward path. Combinations of two nontouching loops which are not touching this forward path are L_{23}, L_{34} and L_{24}. One combination of three nontouching loops which are not touching this forward path is L_{234}. Therefore

$$\frac{x_2}{x_1} = \frac{M_1\Delta_1}{\Delta}$$

where $M_1 = 1$

and $\Delta_1 = 1 - (-H_5 - G_3H_2 - H_4) + (G_3H_2H_5 + G_3H_2H_4 + H_4H_5) - (-G_3H_2H_4H_5)$

$\qquad = 1 + H_5 + H_4 + G_3H_2 + G_3H_2H_5 + G_3H_2H_4 + H_4H_5 + G_3H_2H_4H_5$

$$\therefore \quad \frac{x_2}{x_1} = \frac{1 + H_5 + H_4 + G_3H_2 + G_3H_2H_5 + G_3H_2H_4 + H_4H_5 + G_3H_2H_4H_5}{\Delta}$$

Determination of $\dfrac{x_4}{x_1}$

To determine $\dfrac{x_4}{x_1}$, there are two forward paths between x_1 and x_4. Only one loop L_4 is not touching both these two forward paths.

Forward path x_1-x_2-x_3-x_4 $\qquad M_1 = G_1G_2 \qquad \Delta_1 = 1 - (-H_4) = 1 + H_4$

Forward path x_1-x_2-x_3-x_5-x_4 $\qquad M_2 = -G_1G_6H_2 \qquad \Delta_2 = 1 - (-H_4) = 1 + H_4$

$$\therefore \quad \frac{x_4}{x_1} = \frac{M_1\Delta_1 + M_2\Delta_2}{\Delta} = \frac{(G_1G_2 - G_1G_6H_2)(1+H_4)}{\Delta}$$

Determination of $\dfrac{x_7}{x_2}$

$$\frac{x_7}{x_2} = \frac{\dfrac{x_7}{x_1}}{\dfrac{x_2}{x_1}} = \frac{\dfrac{G_1G_2G_3G_4 + G_1G_5(1+G_3H_2) + G_1G_4G_6}{\Delta}}{\dfrac{1 + H_5 + H_4 + G_3H_2 + G_3H_2H_5 + G_3H_2H_4 + H_4H_5 + G_3H_2H_4H_5}{\Delta}}$$

i.e.
$$\frac{x_7}{x_2} = \frac{G_1G_2G_3G_4 + G_1G_5(1+G_3H_2) + G_1G_4G_6}{1 + H_5 + H_4 + G_3H_2 + G_3H_2H_5 + G_3H_2H_4 + H_4H_5 + G_3H_2H_4H_5}$$

Determination of $\dfrac{x_7}{x_4}$

$$\frac{x_7}{x_4} = \frac{\dfrac{x_7}{x_1}}{\dfrac{x_4}{x_1}} = \frac{\dfrac{G_1G_2G_3G_4 + G_1G_5(1+G_3H_2) + G_1G_4G_6}{\Delta}}{\dfrac{(G_1G_2 - G_1G_6H_2)(1+H_4)}{\Delta}}$$

i.e.
$$\frac{x_7}{x_4} = \frac{G_1G_2G_3G_4 + G_1G_5(1+G_3H_2) + G_1G_4G_6}{(G_1G_2 - G_1G_6H_2)(1+H_4)}$$

Determination of $\dfrac{x_4}{x_2}$

$$\frac{x_4}{x_2} = \frac{\dfrac{x_4}{x_1}}{\dfrac{x_2}{x_1}} = \frac{(G_1G_2 - G_1G_6H_2)(1+H_4)}{1 + H_5 + H_4 + G_3H_2 + G_3H_2H_5 + G_3H_2H_4 + H_4H_5 + G_3H_2H_4H_5}$$

Example 3.20 Obtain the overall transfer function C/R from the signal flow graph shown in Figure 3.81.

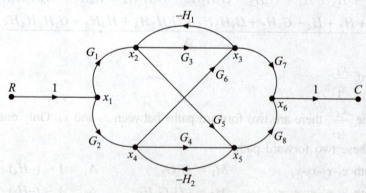

Figure 3.81 Example 3.20.

Solution: For the signal flow graph shown in Figure 3.81, there are six forward paths, three loops and one pair of two nontouching loops. One loop is not touching one forward path and another loop is not touching another forward path.

The forward paths and the gains associated with them are as follows:

Forward path R-x_1-x_2-x_3-x_6-C $M_1 = (1)(G_1)(G_3)(G_7)(1) = G_1G_3G_7$

Forward path R-x_1-x_2-x_5-x_6-C $M_2 = (1)(G_1)(G_5)(G_8)(1) = G_1G_5G_8$

Forward path R-x_1-x_2-x_5-x_4-x_3-x_6-C $M_3 = (1)(G_1)(G_5)(-H_2)(G_6)(G_7)(1)$

$$= -G_1G_5H_2G_6G_7$$

Forward path R-x_1-x_4-x_5-x_6-C $M_4 = (1)(G_2)(G_4)(G_8)(1) = G_2G_4G_8$

Forward path R-x_1-x_4-x_3-x_6-C $M_5 = (1)(G_2)(G_6)(G_7)(1) = G_2G_6G_7$

Forward path R-x_1-x_4-x_3-x_2-x_5-x_6-C $M_6 = (1)(G_2)(G_6)(-H_1)(G_5)(G_8)(1)$

$$= -G_2G_5G_6G_8H_1$$

The loops and the gains associated with them are as follows:

Loop x_2-x_3-x_2 $L_1 = (G_3)(-H_1) = -G_3H_1$

Loop x_4-x_5-x_4 $L_2 = (G_4)(-H_2) = -G_4H_2$

Loop x_2-x_5-x_4-x_3-x_2 $L_3 = (G_5)(-H_2)(G_6)(-H_1) = G_5G_6H_1H_2$

The pairs of two nontouching loops and the products of gains associated with them are as follows:

Loops x_2-x_3-x_2 and x_4-x_5-x_4 $L_{12} = (-G_3H_1)(-G_4H_2) = G_3G_4H_1H_2$

Loop 2 is not touching the first forward path. Therefore,

$$\Delta_1 = 1 - (-G_4H_2) = 1 + G_4H_2$$

Loop 1 is not touching the fourth forward path. Therefore,

$$\Delta_4 = 1 - (-G_3H_1) = 1 + G_3H_1$$

All the loops are touching all other forward paths. Therefore

$$\Delta_2 = 1 = \Delta_3 = \Delta_5 = \Delta_6$$

The determinant of the signal flow graph is

$$\Delta = 1 - (L_1 + L_2 + L_3) + (L_{12})$$

$$= 1 - (-G_3H_1 - G_4H_2 + G_5G_6H_1H_2) + G_3G_4H_1H_2$$

Applying Mason's gain formula, the transfer function is

$$\frac{C}{R} = \frac{M_1\Delta_1 + M_2\Delta_2 + M_3\Delta_3 + M_4\Delta_4 + M_5\Delta_5 + M_6\Delta_6}{\Delta}$$

$$= \frac{\begin{matrix} G_1G_3G_7\left(1 + G_4H_2\right) + G_1G_5G_8 - G_1G_5G_6G_7H_2 \\ + G_2G_4G_8(1 + G_3H_1) + G_2G_6G_7 - G_2G_5G_6G_8H_1 \end{matrix}}{1 + G_3H_1 + G_4H_2 - G_5G_6H_1H_2 + G_3G_4H_1H_2}$$

Example 3.21 Figure 3.82 shows the signal flow graph of a system with two inputs and two outputs. Find expressions for outputs C_1 and C_2. Also determine the condition that makes C_1 independent of R_2, and C_2 independent of R_1.

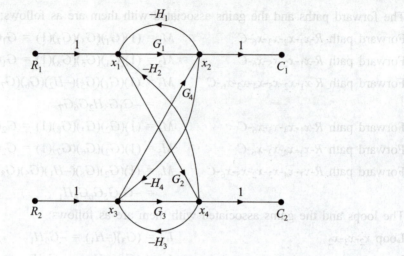

Figure 3.82 Example 3.21.

Solution: For the signal flow graph shown in Figure 3.82, there are two forward paths from R_1 to C_1 and two forward paths from R_2 to C_1, six loops and two pairs of two nontouching loops. One loop is not touching one forward path and another loop is not touching another forward path.

The forward paths from R_1 to C_1 and the gains associated with them are as follows:

Forward path R_1-x_1-x_2-C_1 $\qquad M_1 = (1)(G_1)(1) = G_1$

Forward path R_1-x_1-x_4-x_3-x_2-C_1 $\qquad M_2 = (1)(G_2)(-H_3)(G_4)(1) = -G_2G_4H_3$

The forward paths from R_2 to C_1 and the gains associated with them are as follows:

Forward path R_2-x_3-x_2-C_1 $\qquad M_3 = (1)(G_4)(1) = G_4$

Forward path R_2-x_3-x_4-x_1-x_2-C_1 $\qquad M_4 = (1)(G_3)(-H_2)(G_1)(1) = -G_1G_3H_2$

The forward paths from R_2 to C_2 and the gains associated with them are as follows:

Forward path R_2-x_3-x_4-C_2 $\qquad M_5 = (1)(G_3)(1) = G_3$

Forward path R_2-x_3-x_2-x_1-x_4-C_2 $\qquad M_6 = (1)(G_4)(-H_1)(G_2)(1) = -G_2G_4H_1$

The forward paths from R_1 to C_2 and the gains associated with them are as follows:

Forward path R_1-x_1-x_4-C_2 $\qquad M_7 = (1)(G_2)(1) = G_2$

Forward path R_1-x_1-x_2-x_3-x_4-C_2 $\qquad M_8 = (1)(G_1)(-H_4)(G_3)(1) = -G_1G_3H_4$

The loops and the gains associated with them are as follows:

Loop x_1-x_2-x_1 $\qquad L_1 = (G_1)(-H_1) = -G_1H_1$

Loop x_1-x_4-x_1 $\qquad L_2 = (G_2)(-H_2) = -G_2H_2$

Loop x_1-x_4-x_3-x_2-x_1 $\qquad L_3 = (G_2)(-H_3)(G_4)(-H_1) = G_2G_4H_1H_3$

Loop x_3-x_4-x_3 $\qquad L_4 = (G_3)(-H_3) = -G_3H_3$

Loop x_3-x_2-x_3 $\qquad L_5 = (G_4)(-H_4) = -G_4H_4$

Loop x_1-x_2-x_3-x_4-x_1 $\qquad L_6 = (G_1)(-H_4)(G_3)(-H_2) = G_1G_3H_2H_4$

The pairs of two nontouching loops and the products of gains associated with them are as follows:

Loops x_1-x_2-x_1 and x_3-x_4-x_3 $\qquad L_{14} = (-G_1H_1)(-G_3H_3) = G_1H_1G_3H_3$

Loops x_1-x_4-x_1 and x_3-x_2-x_3 $\qquad L_{25} = (-G_2H_2)(-G_4H_4) = G_2H_2G_4H_4$

The determinant of the signal flow graph is

$$\Delta = 1 - (L_1 + L_2 + L_3 + L_4 + L_5 + L_6) + (L_{14} + L_{25})$$

$$= 1 - (-G_1H_1 - G_2H_2 + G_2G_4H_1H_3 - G_3H_3 - G_4H_4 + G_1G_3H_2H_4)$$
$$+ (G_1H_1G_3H_3 + G_2G_4H_2H_4)$$

i.e. $\qquad \Delta = 1 + G_1H_1 + G_2H_2 - G_2G_4H_1H_3 + G_3H_3 + G_4H_4 - G_1G_3H_2H_4$
$$+ G_1G_3H_1H_3 + G_2G_4H_2H_4$$

L_4 is not touching the first forward path. Hence

$$\Delta_1 = 1 - (-G_3H_3) = 1 + G_3H_3$$

L_2 is not touching the third forward path. Hence

$$\Delta_3 = 1 - (-G_2H_2) = 1 + G_2H_2$$

L_1 is not touching the fifth forward path. Hence

$$\Delta_5 = 1 - (-G_1H_1) = 1 + G_1H_1$$

L_5 is not touching the seventh forward path. Hence

$$\Delta_7 = 1 - (-G_4H_4) = 1 + G_4H_4$$

There are two forward paths between C_1 and R_1 and two forward paths between C_1 and R_2. Applying the superposition principle,

$$C_1 = (M_1\Delta_1 + M_2\Delta_2)R_1 + (M_3\Delta_3 + M_4\Delta_4)R_2$$

$\therefore \qquad C_1 = \dfrac{[G_1(1+G_3H_3) - G_2G_4H_3]R_1 + [G_4(1+G_2H_2) - G_1G_3H_2]R_2}{\Delta}$

There are two forward paths between C_2 and R_1 and two forward paths between C_2 and R_2. Applying the superposition principle,

$$C_2 = (M_5\Delta_5 + M_6\Delta_6)R_2 + (M_7\Delta_7 + M_8\Delta_8)R_1$$

$$C_2 = \dfrac{[G_3(1+G_1H_1) - G_2G_4H_1]R_2 + [G_2(1+G_4H_4) - G_1G_3H_4]R_1}{\Delta}$$

For C_1 to be independent of R_2, the coefficient of R_2 in the expression for C_1 must be zero.

$$G_4(1 + G_2H_2) - G_1G_3H_2 = 0$$

i.e. $\qquad G_4 + (G_4G_2 - G_1G_3)H_2 = 0$

i.e. $\qquad H_2 = \dfrac{-G_4}{G_4G_2 - G_1G_3}$

For C_2 to be independent of R_1, the coefficient of R_1 in the expression for C_2 must be zero.

i.e. $\qquad G_2 + G_2G_4H_4 - G_1G_3H_4 = 0$

i.e.

$$G_2 + (G_2G_4 - G_1G_3)(H_4) = 0$$

i.e.

$$H_4 = \frac{-G_2}{G_2G_4 - G_1G_3} = \frac{G_2}{G_1G_3 - G_2G_4}$$

SHORT QUESTIONS AND ANSWERS

1. What is $G(s)H(s)$?

A. $G(s)H(s)$ is called the loop transfer function or the open-loop transfer function of a control system.

2. The principle of superposition is applied to which systems?

A. The principle of superposition is applied to linear systems.

3. What do you mean by a block?

A. A block is a symbol for the mathematical operation on the input signal to the block that produces the output.

4. What do you mean by a block diagram?

A. A block diagram of a system is a pictorial representation of the functions performed by each component of the system and of the flow of signals. A block diagram depicts the interrelationships that exist among the various components.

5. Can the block diagrams be used to model nonlinear systems?

A. Yes. The block diagrams can be used to model linear as well as nonlinear systems.

6. What is the advantage of a block diagram?

A. A block diagram can be used together with the transfer function to describe the cause-and-effect relationships throughout the system. It has the advantage of indicating more realistically the signal flows of the actual system. In general, the functional operation of the system can be visualized more readily by examining the block diagram than by examining the physical system itself.

7. In a block diagram, what does the arrow heads pointing towards the block and leading away from the block indicate?

A. In a block diagram, the arrow head pointing towards the block indicates the input and the arrow head leading away from the block represents the output.

8. Can many dissimilar and unrelated systems be represented by the same block diagram?

A. Yes. Many dissimilar and unrelated systems can be represented by the same block diagram.

9. Does the block diagram include any information on the physical construction of the system?

A. No. A block diagram contains information regarding only the dynamic behaviour, but it does not include any information on the physical construction of the system.

10. Can many block diagrams be drawn for a single system?

A. Yes. A number of different block diagrams can be drawn for a single system depending on the point of view of analysis.

11. What are the functions that can be performed by sensing devices?

A. In general, sensing devices perform simple mathematical operations such as addition, subtraction, multiplication and sometimes combinations of these.

12. In block diagrams, which device acts as a junction point for signal comparisons?

A. In block diagrams, a sensing device acts as a junction point for signal comparisons.

13. Name the components of the block diagram.

A. The basic elements of a block diagram are: block, branch point, and summing point.

14. What is a summing point?

A. A summing point is a point at which all the incoming signals are added.

15. What is a take-off point?

A. A take-off point or a branch point is a point from which the signal from a block goes concurrently to other blocks or summing points.

16. What is the total gain of a number of blocks connected in cascade?

A. The total gain of a number of blocks connected in cascade is equal to the product of the gains of all those blocks.

17. What is the total gain of a number of blocks connected in parallel?

A. The total gain of a number of blocks connected in parallel is equal to the sum of the gains of all those blocks.

18. What do you mean by a signal flow graph?

A. A signal flow graph is a graphical representation of the relationships between the variables of a set of linear algebraic equations written in the form of cause-and-effect relations.

19. What type of equations are required to draw a signal flow graph?

A. Algebraic equations written in the form of cause-and-effect relations are required to draw a signal flow graph.

20. Who developed signal flow graphs?

A. S.J. Mason developed the signal flow graphs.

21. What is the use of Mason's gain formula?

A. Mason's gain formula is useful in reducing large and complex system diagrams in one step, without requiring step-by-step reductions.

22. Can a signal flow graph be drawn for nonlinear systems?

A. No. A signal flow graph cannot be drawn for nonlinear systems. It can be drawn only for linear systems.

23. Which one is superior—signal flow graph or block diagram?

A. The signal flow graph and the block diagram contain essentially the same information and one is in no sense superior to the other.

24. For a given system, is the signal flow graph unique?

A. For a given system, a signal flow graph is not unique. Many different signal flow graphs can be drawn for a given system by writing the system equations differently.

25. What do you mean by a node?

A. A node is a junction point. It represents a system variable which is equal to the sum of all the incoming signals at the node. Outgoing signals from the node do not effect the value of the node variable.

26. What do you mean by a branch ?

A. A branch is a line segment of the signal flow graph joining two nodes along which a signal travels from one node to the other in the direction indicated by the branch arrow and in the process gets multiplied by the gain or transmittance of the branch.

27. What do you mean by an input node?

A. An input node or source is a node with only outgoing branches. It does not have any incoming branches.

28. What do you mean by an output node?

A. An output node or sink is a node with only incoming branches. It does not have any outgoing branches. Any node can be converted in to an output node by connecting an additional branch with unit transmittance to it.

29. What do you mean by a mixed node?

A. A mixed node is a node that has both incoming and outgoing branches.

30. What do you mean by a path?

A. A path is the traversal of connected branches in the direction of the branch arrows such that no node is traversed more than once.

31. What do you mean by a forward path?

A. A forward path is a path that starts from the input node and ends at the output node.

32. What do you mean by a loop?

A. A loop is a path which originates and terminates at the same node and along which no node is traversed more than once.

33. What do you mean by nontouching loops?

A. Nontouching loops are loops which do not possess any common node.

34. What do you mean by path gain?

A. The product of the branch gains encountered in traversing a path is called the path gain.

35. What do you mean by forward path gain?

A. The product of the branch gains encountered in traversing a forward path is called the forward path gain.

36. What do you mean by loop gain?

A. The product of the branch gains encountered in traversing a loop is called the loop gain.

37. What do you mean by a self loop?

A. A self loop is a loop consisting of a single branch.

38. State Mason's gain formula.

A. Mason's gain formula for the determination of the overall system gain is given by

$$T = \sum_k \frac{M_k \Delta_k}{\Delta}$$

where M_k is the path gain of the kth forward path.

  Δ = determinant of the signal flow graph

  = 1 – (sum of the loop gains of all individual loops)

  + (sum of the gain products of all possible combinations of two nontouching loops)

  – (sum of the gain products of all possible combinations of three nontouching loops)

  + $\cdots$

  Δ_k = The value of Δ for that part of the graph not touching the kth forward path.

  T = overall gain of the system

39. What is the common application of signal flow graphs?

A. The common application of signal flow graphs is in system diagramming.

40. What is the basis for framing the rules for block diagram reduction?

A. The basis for framing the rules for block diagram reduction is that any modification made on the diagram does not alter the input-output relation.

41. Compare block diagram and signal flow graph methods?

A.

Comparison of block diagram and signal flow graph methods

Block diagram method	*Signal flow graph method*
1. It is a pictorial representation of the functions performed by each component and of the flow of signals.	1. It is a graphical representation of the relationships between variables of a set of linear algebraic equations written in the form of cause-and-effect relations.
2. It can be used to represent linear as well as nonlinear systems.	2. It can be used to represent only linear systems.
3. No direct formula is available to find the overall transfer function of the system.	3. Mason's gain formula is available to find the overall transfer function of the system.
4. Step-by-step procedure is to be followed to find the transfer function.	4. Transfer function can be obtained in one step itself.
5. It is not a systematic method.	5. It is a systematic method.
6. It indicates more realistically the signal flows of the system than the original system itself.	6. It is constrained by more rigid mathematical rules than a block diagram.
7. For a given system, the block diagram is not unique. Many dissimilar and unrelated systems can be represented by the same block diagram.	7. For a given system, the signal flow graph is not unique.

Note: A signal flow graph and block diagram contain essentially the same information and one is in no sense superior to the other.

42. Write the properties of signal flow graphs.

A. The properties of signal flow graphs are as follows:

   (a) Signal flow graph applies only to linear systems.

   (b) The equations for which a signal flow graph is drawn must be algebraic equations written in the form of cause-and-effect.

   (c) Nodes are used to represent variables. Normally the nodes are arranged from left to right, from the input to the output following a succession of cause-and-effect relations through the system.

   (d) Signals travel along branches only in the direction described by the arrows of the branches.

   (e) The branch directing from node x_k to x_j represents the dependence of x_j upon x_k but not the reverse.

   (f) A signal x_k traveling along a branch between x_k and x_j is multiplied by the gain of the branch a_{kj} so that a signal $a_{kj} x_k$ is delivered at x_j.

   (g) For a given system, a signal flow graph is not unique. Many different signal flow graphs can be drawn for a given system by writing the system equations differently.

FILL IN THE BLANKS

1. A block diagram of a system is a _____ representation of the functions performed by each component of the system and of the flow of signals.

2. Block diagrams can be used to model _____ as well as _____ systems.

3. In a block diagram, the arrow head pointing towards the block indicates the _____ and the arrow head leading away from the block represents the _____.

4. In general, the functional operation of the system can be visualized more readily by examining the _____ than by examining the physical system itself.

5. A _____ adds the incoming signals.

6. A _____ point or a _____ point is a point from which the signal from a block goes concurrently to other blocks or summing points.

7. _____ is called the loop transfer function or open-loop transfer function.

8. Signal flow graph is applied only to _____.

9. The equations for which a signal flow graph is drawn must be _____ equations in the form of _____ and _____ relations.

10. _____ are used to represent variables.

11. Signals travel along branches only in the direction described by the _____ of the branches.

12. A signal flow graph may be regarded as a _____ of the block diagram.

13. Signal flow graphs were developed by _____.

14. _____ is especially useful in reducing large and complex system diagrams in one step, without requiring step-by-step reductions.

15. A signal flow graph and block diagram contain essentially the _____ and one is in no sense _____ to the other.

16. Besides the difference in physical appearance of the signal flow graph and the block diagram, the _____ may be regarded as constrained by more rigid mathematical rules than the _____.

17. A signal flow graph is a graphical representation of the relationship between the variables of a set of linear _____ written in the form of _____ relations.

18. For a given system, a signal flow graph is not _____.

19. A _____ represents a system variable which is equal to the sum of all the incoming signals at that _____.

20. An _____ node or _____ is a node with only outgoing branches. It does not have any incoming branch.

21. An _____ node or _____ is a node with only incoming branches.

22. A _____ is a node that has both incoming and outgoing branches.

23. _____ loops are loops which do not possess any common node.

24. A _____ loop is loop consisting of a single branch.

25. A _____ loop is a path which originates and terminates at the same node and along which no node is traversed more than once.

OBJECTIVE TYPE QUESTIONS

1. Block diagrams can be used to represent
   (a) only linear systems
   (b) only nonlinear systems
   (c) both linear and nonlinear systems
   (d) time-invariant as well as time-varying systems.

2. Signal flow graphs can be used to represent
   (a) only linear systems
   (b) only nonlinear systems
   (c) both linear and nonlinear systems
   (d) time-invariant as well as time-varying systems.

3. The equations based on which a signal flow graph is drawn must be
   (a) differential equations
   (b) algebraic equations
   (c) algebraic equations in the form of cause-and-effect relations
   (d) differential equations in form of cause-and-effect relations.

4. A node which has only outgoing branches is called a
   (a) input node   (b) output node
   (c) mixed node   (d) general node

5. A node which has only incoming branches is called a/an
   (a) input node   (b) output node
   (c) mixed node   (d) general node

6. A node which has both incoming and outgoing branches is called a/an
   (a) input node   (b) output node
   (c) mixed node   (d) general node

7. Three blocks with gains of 5, 8 and 4 are connected in cascade. The total gain of the arrangement is
   (a) 17   (b) 160
   (c) 44   (d) 37.

8. Three blocks with gains of 4, 6 and 8 are connected in parallel. The total gain of the arrangement is
   (a) 18   (b) 196
   (c) 32   (d) 52

9. A given system can be represented by
   (a) only one SFG   (b) only two SFGs
   (c) many different SFGs   (d) none of these

10. A given block diagram can represent
   (a) only one system   (b) 2 or 3 systems
   (c) many systems   (d) none of these

PROBLEMS

3.1 *to* 3.10: For the systems represented by the block diagrams shown in figures below, obtain the transfer function by using block diagram reduction technique. Verify the result using signal flow graphs.

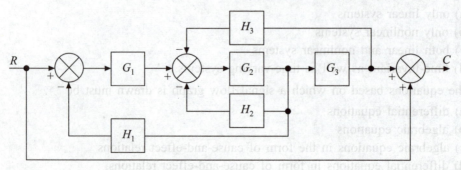

Figure P3.1

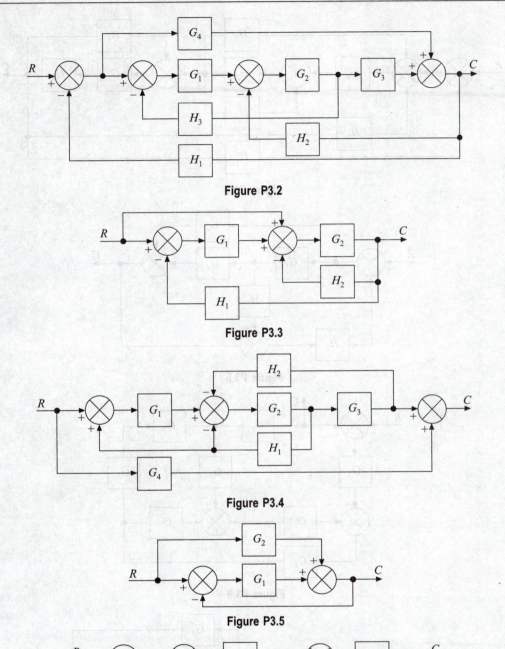

Figure P3.2

Figure P3.3

Figure P3.4

Figure P3.5

Figure P3.6

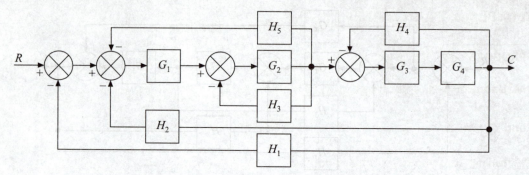

Figure P3.7

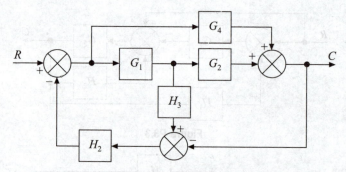

Figure P3.8

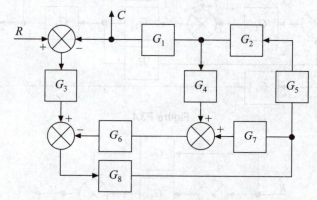

Figure P3.9

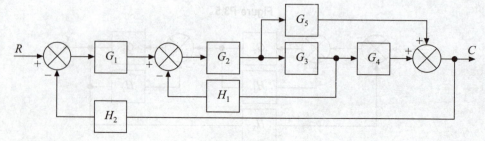

Figure P3.10

MATLAB PROGRAMS

PROGRAM 3.1

Matlab program to find the transfer function of the system when blocks $G_1(s) = \dfrac{4}{(s^2 + 2s + 1)}$

and $G_2(s) = \dfrac{7}{(s + 5)}$ **are connected in (a) Series (b) Parallel (c) Feedback.**

```
% Transfer function for various conditions
clc;close all;clear all;
num1=[4];
den1=[1 2 1];
num2=[7];
den2=[1 5];
% series connection
[num,den]=series(num1,den1,num2,den2);
disp('series connection');
tf(num,den)
% parallel connection
[num,den]=parallel(num1,den1,num2,den2);
disp('parallel connection');
tf(num,den)
% feedback connection
[num,den]=feedback(num1,den1,num2,den2);
disp('feedback connection');
tf(num,den)
```

Output:

series connection
Transfer function:

$$\frac{28}{s^3 + 7s^2 + 11s + 5}$$

parallel connection
Transfer function:

$$\frac{7s^2 + 18s + 27}{s^3 + 7s^2 + 11s + 5}$$

feedback connection
Transfer function:

$$\frac{4s + 20}{s^3 + 7s^2 + 11s + 33}$$

PROGRAM 3.2

Matlab program for combining blocks in cascade

```
% Combining blocks in Cacade
%method 1
clc;clear all;close all;
s=tf('s');
g1=1/(s+2);
g2=(s+3)/(s+4);
G=g1*g2;
disp('Transfer function of First block')
g1
disp('Transfer function of Second block')
g2
disp('The transfer function of combining blocks in cascade is')
G
```

Output:

Transfer function of First block
Transfer function:

$$\frac{1}{s+2}$$

Transfer function of Second block
Transfer function:

$$\frac{s+3}{s+4}$$

The transfer function of combining blocks in cascade is
Transfer function:

$$\frac{s+3}{s^2+6s+8}$$

PROGRAM 3.3

Matlab program for combining blocks in cascade

```
% Combining blocks in Cacade
clc;clear all;close all;
s=tf('s');
g1=1/(s+2);
g2=(s+3)/(s+4);
G=series(g1,g2);
disp('Transfer function of First block')
```

g1
disp('Transfer function of Second block')
g2
disp('The transfer function of combining blocks in cascade is')
G

Output:

Transfer function of First block
Transfer function:

$$\frac{1}{s+2}$$

Transfer function of Second block
Transfer function:

$$\frac{s+3}{s+4}$$

The transfer function of combining blocks in cascade is
Transfer function:

$$\frac{s+3}{s^2+6s+8}$$

PROGRAM 3.4

Matlab program for combining blocks in parallel

```
% Combining blocks in parallel
clc;clear all;close all;
s=tf('s');
g1=1/(s+2);
g2=(s+3)/(s+4);
G=g1+g2;
disp('Transfer function of First block')
g1
disp('Transfer function of Second block')
g2
disp('The transfer function of combining blocks in parallel is')
G
```

Output:

Transfer function of First block
Transfer function:

$$\frac{1}{s+2}$$

Transfer function of Second block

Transfer function:

$$\frac{s+3}{s+4}$$

The transfer function of combining blocks in parallel is

Transfer function:

$$\frac{s^2+6s+10}{s^2+6s+8}$$

PROGRAM 3.5

Matlab program for combining blocks in parallel

```
% Combining blocks in parall
clc;clear all;close all;
s=tf('s');
g1=1/(s+2);
g2=(s+3)/(s+4);
G=parallel(g1,g2);
disp('Transfer function of First block')
g1
disp('Transfer function of Second block')
g2
disp('The transfer function of combining blocks in parallel is')
G
```

Output:

Transfer function of First block

Transfer function:

$$\frac{1}{s+2}$$

Transfer function of Second block

Transfer function:

$$\frac{s+3}{s+4}$$

The transfer function of combining blocks in parallel is

Transfer function:

$$\frac{s^2+6s+10}{s^2+6s+8}$$

PROGRAM 3.6

Matlab program to remove feedback loop in a given block diagram

```
%removing feed back loop
clc;clear all;close all;
s=tf('s');
g1=1/(s+2);
g2=(s+3)/(s+4);
G=g1/(1+g1*g2);
disp('Transfer function of First block')
g1
disp('Transfer function of Second block')
g2
disp('The transfer function of removing feedback loop is')
G
```

Output:

Transfer function of First block
Transfer function:

$$\frac{1}{s+2}$$

Transfer function of Second block
Transfer function:

$$\frac{s+3}{s+4}$$

The transfer function of removing feedback loop is
Transfer function:

$$\frac{s^2+6s+8}{s^3+9s^2+25s+22}$$

PROGRAM 3.7

Matlab program to remove feedback loop in a given block diagram

```
%removing feed back loop
clc;clear all;close all;
s=tf('s');
g1=1/(s+2);
g2=(s+3)/(s+4);
G=feedback(g1,g2);
disp('Transfer function of First block')
g1
```

disp('Transfer function of Second block')
g2
disp('The transfer function of removing feedback loop is')
G

Output:

Transfer function of First block
Transfer function:

$$\frac{1}{s+2}$$

Transfer function of Second block
Transfer function:

$$\frac{s+3}{s+4}$$

The transfer function of removing feedback loop is
Transfer function:

$$\frac{s+4}{s^2+7s+11}$$

4

Time Response Analysis

4.1 TIME RESPONSE OF CONTROL SYSTEMS

The time response of a system is the output of the closed-loop system as a function of time. The time response of a control system is usually divided into two parts: the transient response and the steady-state response. Let $c(t)$ denote the time response of a continuous-data system; then, in general, it can be written as

$$c(t) = c_t(t) + c_{ss}(t)$$

where $c_t(t)$ denotes the transient response, and $c_{ss}(t)$ denotes the steady-state response.

In control systems, transient response is defined as that part of the time response that goes to zero as time becomes very large. Thus $c_t(t)$ has the property that

$$\underset{t \to \infty}{\text{Lt}}\, c_t(t) = 0$$

The transient response is also called the dynamic response of the system.

The steady-state response is simply that part of the total response that remains after the transient has died out. Thus, the steady-state response can still vary in a fixed pattern such as a sine wave or a ramp function that increases with time.

A feedback control system has the inherent capability that its parameters can be adjusted to alter both its transient and steady-state behaviour. In order to analyze the transient and steady-state behaviour of control systems, the first step always is to obtain a mathematical model of the system. For any specific input signal, a complete time response can then be obtained through the Laplace transform inversion. This expression yields the steady-state behaviour of the system with time tending to infinity. In the case of simple deterministic signals, the steady-state response can also be obtained directly without obtaining the time response expression by use of the final value theorem.

Before proceeding with the time response analysis of control systems, it is necessary to test the stability of the system. System stability can be tested through indirect tests without actually obtaining the transient response. In case the system happens to be unstable, we need not proceed with the transient response analysis.

Unlike electrical networks and communication systems, the inputs to many practical systems are not exactly known ahead of time. In many cases, the actual inputs of a control system may vary in a random fashion with respect to time. For instance, in a radar tracking system for anti-aircraft missiles, the position and speed of the target to be tracked may vary in an unpredictable manner so that they cannot be predetermined. This poses a problem for the designer since it is difficult to design a control system so that it will perform satisfactorily for all possible forms of input signals. For the purpose of analysis and design, it is necessary to assume some basic types of test signals so that the performance of a system can be evaluated. The characteristics of actual signals which severely strain a control system are a sudden shock, a sudden change, a constant velocity, and a constant acceleration. System dynamic behaviour for analysis and design is therefore judged and compared under application of standard test signals—*an impulse, a step, a constant velocity* (*a ramp input*), *and constant acceleration* (*a parabolic input*).

The nature of the transient response is revealed by any one of these test signals as this nature is dependent upon system poles and not upon the type of input. It is therefore sufficient to analyze the transient response to one of the standard test signals—a step is generally used for this purpose as this signal can be easily generated. Steady-state response is then examined to this particular test signal as well as other test signals; the ramp, and parabolic signal. So except for the step test signal, the time consuming transient analysis need not be carried out for the ramp and parabolic signals, while their steady-state error can be quickly determined by the final value theorem. This approach is particularly useful for linear systems since the response to complex signals can be determined by superposing those due to simple test signals. Control systems are inherently time-domain systems subjected to time-varying inputs and are to be tested, analyzed and designed by the time-domain test signals such as step, ramp and parabolic.

When the response of a linear time-invariant system is analyzed in the frequency-domain, a sinusoidal signal with variable frequency is used. It is possible to predict the time-domain behaviour of the system from its frequency-domain characteristics.

Since a physical control system involves energy storage, the output of the system, when subjected to an input, cannot follow the input immediately, but exhibits a transient response before a steady-state can be reached. The transient response of a practical control system often exhibits damped oscillations before reaching a steady-state. If the output of a system at steady-state does not exactly agree with the input, the system is said to have steady-state error. This error is indicative of the accuracy of the system. In analyzing a control system, we must examine transient response behaviour and steady-state behaviour.

4.2 STANDARD TEST SIGNALS

To facilitate the time-domain analysis, the following deterministic test signals are used.

4.2.1 Step Signal

The *step* is a signal whose value changes from one level (usually zero) to another level *A* in zero time. The mathematical representation of the step function is

$$r(t) = Au(t)$$

where $\quad u(t) = 1; \; t > 0$

$\qquad\qquad = 0; \; t < 0$

is called the unit-step function.

In the Laplace transform form

$$R(s) = A/s$$

The graphical representation of a step signal is shown in Figure 4.1(a). The step function is very useful as a test signal since its initial instantaneous jump in amplitude reveals a great deal about a system's quickness in responding to inputs with abrupt changes. Also, since the step function contains, in principle, a wide band of frequencies in its spectrum as a result of the jump discontinuity, it is equivalent to the application of numerous sinusoidal signals with a wide range of frequencies.

4.2.2 Ramp Signal

The *ramp* is a signal which starts at a value of zero and increases linearly with time. Mathematically,

$$r(t) = At; \; t > 0$$

$$= 0; \; t < 0$$

In the Laplace transform form

$$R(s) = A/s^2$$

The graphical representation of a ramp signal is shown in Figure 4.1(b). The ramp signal is integral of a step signal. The ramp signal has the ability to test how the system would respond to a signal that changes linearly with time.

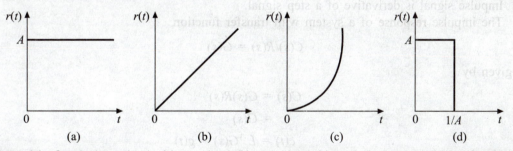

Figure 4.1 Standard test signals: (a) step signal, (b) ramp signal, (c) parabolic signal and (d) impulse signal.

4.2.3 Parabolic Signal

The parabolic function represents a signal that is one order faster than the ramp function. The mathematical representation of this signal is

$$r(t) = At^2/2; \; t > 0$$
$$= 0; \; t < 0$$

In the Laplace transform form

$$R(s) = A/s^3$$

The graphical representation of a parabolic signal is shown in Figure 4.1(c). The parabolic signal is integral of a ramp signal.

These signals all have the common feature that they are simple to describe mathematically. From the impulse function to the parabolic function, the signals become progressively faster with respect to time. In theory, we can define signals with still higher rates such as t^3, which is called the *jerk function*, and so on. However, in reality, we seldom find it necessary or feasible to use a test signal faster than a parabolic function. This is because, in order to track a higher-order input accurately, the system must have higher-order integrations in the loop, which usually lead to serious stability problems.

4.2.4 Impulse Signal

A unit-impulse is defined as a signal which has zero value everywhere except at $t = 0$ where its magnitude is infinite. It is generally called the δ-function and has the following property.

$$\delta(t) = 0; \; t \neq 0$$

$$\int_{-\epsilon}^{\epsilon} \delta(t) \, dt = 1$$

where ϵ tends to zero.

In the Laplace transform form, $\delta(s) = 1$.

Since a perfect impulse cannot be achieved in practice, it is usually approximated by a pulse of small width but unit area as shown in Figure 4.1(d).

Impulse signal is derivative of a step signal.

The impulse response of a system with transfer function

$$C(s)/R(s) = G(s)$$

is given by

$$C(s) = G(s)R(s)$$
$$= G(s)$$

or

$$c(t) = L^{-1}G(s) = g(t)$$

Thus, the impulse response of a system, indicated by $g(t)$, is the inverse Laplace transform of its transfer function. This is sometimes referred to as *weighting function* of the system. The weighting function of a system can be used to find the system's responses to any input $r(t)$ by means of the convolution integral. Thus,

$$c(t) = \int_0^t g(t - \tau) \, r(\tau) \, d\tau$$

4.3 TIME RESPONSE OF FIRST-ORDER SYSTEMS

Consider the first-order unity feedback system shown in Figure 4.2(a). Physically the system may represent an *RC* circuit, thermal system or the like. A simplified block diagram is shown in Figure 4.2(b). The input-output relationship (transfer function) is given by

$$\frac{C(s)}{R(s)} = \frac{1}{Ts+1}$$

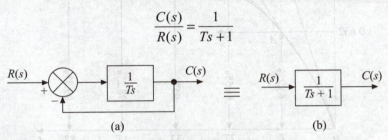

Figure 4.2 Block diagram of a first-order system.

In the following, we shall analyze the system responses to such inputs as the unit-step, unit-ramp, and unit-impulse functions. The initial conditions are assumed to be zero.

All systems having the same transfer function will exhibit the same output in response to the same input.

4.3.1 Unit-Step Response of First-Order Systems

For the unit-step input, $R(s) = 1/s$. So the output response is given by

$$C(s) = \frac{1}{s} \cdot \frac{1}{Ts+1} \tag{4.1}$$

Expanding Eq. (4.1) into partial fractions,

$$C(s) = \frac{1}{s} - \frac{T}{Ts+1} = \frac{1}{s} - \frac{1}{s+1/T} \tag{4.2}$$

Taking the inverse Laplace transform of Eq. (4.2), we obtain

$$c(t) = 1 - e^{-t/T}, \text{ for } t \geq 0 \tag{4.3}$$

This states that the output rises exponentially from zero value to the final value of unity. One important characteristic of such an exponential response curve $c(t)$ shown in Figure 4.3 is that at $t = T$, the value of $c(t)$ is 0.632, or the response $c(t)$ has reached 63.2% of its total change. This may be easily seen by substituting $t = T$ in Eq. (4.3). That is

$$c(T) = 1 - e^{-1} = 0.632$$

The initial slope of the curve at $t = 0$ is given by

$$\left.\frac{dc}{dt}\right|_{t=0} = \left.\frac{1}{T}e^{-t/T}\right|_{t=0} = \frac{1}{T}$$

where T is known as the time constant of the system. The output would reach the final value at $t = T$, if it maintained its initial speed of response. The slope of the response curve decreases monotonically from $1/T$ at $t = 0$ to zero at $t = \infty$.

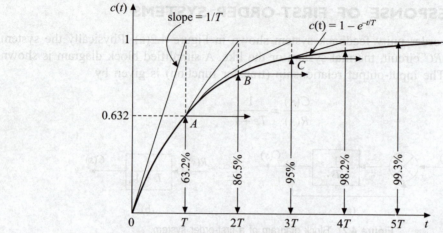

Figure 4.3 Unit-step response of a first-order system.

The time constant is indicative of how fast the system tends to reach the final value. A large time constant corresponds to a sluggish system and a small time constant corresponds to a fast response as shown in Figure 4.4. The speed of response can be quantitatively defined as the time for the output to become a particular percentage of its final value.

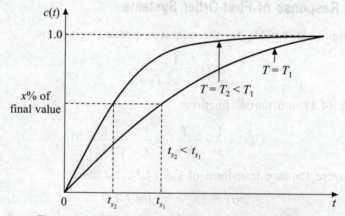

Figure 4.4 Effect of time constant on system response.

The error response of the system is given by

$$e(t) = r(t) - c(t) = e^{-t/T}$$

The steady-state error is given by

$$e_{ss} = \underset{t \to \infty}{\text{Lt}} \; e(t) = 0$$

That means, the first-order system tracks the unit-step input with zero steady-state error. For $t \geq 4T$, the response remains within 2% of the final value.

The steady-state is reached mathematically only after an infinite time. In particular, however, a reasonable estimate of the response time is the length of time the response curve needs to reach and stay within the 2% line of the final value, or four time constants.

4.3.2 Unit-Ramp Response of First-Order Systems

The output response of a first-order system for the unit-ramp input ($R(s) = 1/s^2$) is given by

$$C(s) = \frac{1}{s^2} \cdot \frac{1}{Ts+1} \tag{4.4}$$

Expanding Eq. (4.4) into partial fractions, we have

$$C(s) = \frac{1}{s^2} - \frac{T}{s} + \frac{T^2}{Ts+1} = \frac{1}{s^2} - \frac{T}{s} + \frac{T}{s+1/T} \tag{4.5}$$

Taking the inverse Laplace transform of Eq. (4.5), we get

$$c(t) = t - T + Te^{-t/T} = t - T(1 - e^{-t/T}) \text{ for } t \geq 0 \tag{4.6}$$

The error signal is then

$$e(t) = r(t) - c(t)$$
$$= T(1 - e^{-t/T})$$

and the steady-state error is given by

$$e_{ss} = \underset{t \to \infty}{\text{Lt}} \ e(t) = T$$

Thus, the first-order system under consideration will track the unit-ramp input with a steady-state error T, which is equal to the time constant of the system as shown in Figure 4.5. The smaller the time constant T, the smaller the steady-state error in following the ramp input. Reducing the time constant therefore not only improves its speed of response but also reduces its steady-state error to a ramp input.

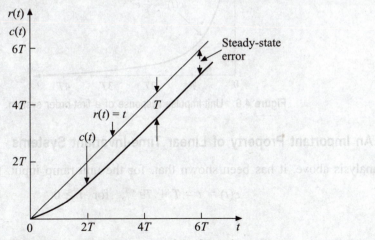

Figure 4.5 Unit-ramp response of the first-order system.

The steady-state error to a ramp input can also be obtained by applying the final value theorem.

$$e_{ss} = \underset{t \to \infty}{\text{Lt}}\ e(t) = \underset{s \to 0}{\text{Lt}}\ sE(s)$$

$$= \underset{s \to 0}{\text{Lt}}\ s[R(s) - C(s)]$$

$$= \underset{s \to 0}{\text{Lt}}\ s\left[\frac{1}{s^2} - \frac{1}{s^2(Ts+1)}\right]$$

$$= T$$

4.3.3 Unit-Impulse Response of First-Order Systems

For the unit-impulse input, $R(s) = 1$ and the output of the system can be obtained as

$$C(s) = 1 \cdot \frac{1}{Ts+1} = \frac{1}{Ts+1} = \frac{1}{T\left(s + \dfrac{1}{T}\right)} \tag{4.7}$$

Taking the inverse Laplace transform of Eq. (4.7), we get

$$c(t) = \frac{1}{T}e^{-t/T}, \quad \text{for} \quad t \geq 0 \tag{4.8}$$

The response curve is as shown in Figure 4.6.

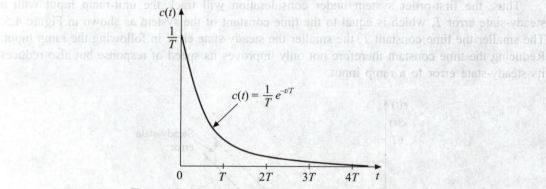

Figure 4.6 Unit-impulse response of a first-order system.

4.3.4 An Important Property of Linear Time-Invariant Systems

In the analysis above, it has been shown that, for the unit-ramp input, the output $c(t)$ is

$$c(t) = t - T + Te^{-t/T}, \quad \text{for} \quad t \geq 0$$

For the unit-step input, which is the derivative of the unit-ramp input, the output $c(t)$ is

$$c(t) = 1 - e^{-t/T}, \quad \text{for} \quad t \geq 0$$

Finally, for the unit-impulse input, which is the derivative of the unit-step input, the output $c(t)$ is

$$c(t) = \frac{1}{T} e^{-t/T}, \quad \text{for} \quad t \geq 0$$

Comparison of the system responses to these three inputs clearly indicates that the response of the derivative of an input signal can be obtained by differentiating the response of the system to the original signal. It can also be seen that the response to the integral of the original signal can be obtained by integrating the response of the system to the original signal and by determining the integration constant from the zero output initial conditions. This is a property of linear time-invariant systems. Linear time-varying systems and nonlinear systems do not possess this property.

4.4 SECOND-ORDER SYSTEMS

4.4.1 Response of Second-Order System to the Unit-Step Input

Consider the second-order system shown in Figure 4.7. The closed-loop transfer function $C(s)/R(s)$ of the system is given by

$$\frac{C(s)}{R(s)} = \frac{\omega_n^2}{s^2 + 2\xi\omega_n s + \omega_n^2} \tag{4.9}$$

where ξ = damping ratio (or damping factor)
and ω_n = undamped natural frequency.

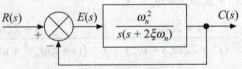

Figure 4.7   Second-order system.

This form is called the standard form of the second-order system. The dynamic behaviour of the second-order system can then be described in terms of two parameters ξ and ω_n.

If $\xi = 0$, the poles are purely imaginary and lie on the $j\omega$-axis. The system is then called undamped. The transient response does not die out. It is purely oscillatory. If $0 < \xi < 1$, the closed-loop poles are complex conjugates and lie in the left half of the s-plane. The system is then called underdamped, and the transient response is oscillatory. If $\xi = 1$, the poles are real, negative and equal. The system is called critically damped. The response rises slowly and reaches the final value. If $\xi > 1$, the poles are real, negative and unequal. The system is called overdamped. The output rises towards its final value slowly. Critically-damped and overdamped systems do not exhibit any overshoot.

The time response of any system is characterized by the roots of the denominator polynomial $q(s)$, which in fact are the poles of the transfer function.

The denominator polynomial $q(s)$ is therefore called the characteristic polynomial and

$$q(s) = 0$$

is called the *characteristic equation*. The characteristic equation of the system under consideration is

$$s^2 + 2\xi\omega_n s + \omega_n^2 = 0$$

The roots of this characteristic equation are given by

$$s^2 + 2\xi\omega_n s + \omega_n^2 = (s - s_1)(s - s_2)$$

For $\xi < 1$,

$$s_1, s_2 = -\xi\omega_n \pm j\omega_n \sqrt{1 - \xi^2} = -\xi\omega_n \pm j\omega_d$$

where $\omega_d = \omega_n \sqrt{1 - \xi^2}$, is called the *damped natural frequency*.

Most control systems with the exception of robotic control systems are designed with damping factor $\xi < 1$, to have high response speed.

Response of an underdamped system $(0 < \xi < 1)$: In this case, $C(s)/R(s)$ can be written as

$$\frac{C(s)}{R(s)} = \frac{\omega_n^2}{s^2 + 2\xi\omega_n s + \omega_n^2} = \frac{\omega_n^2}{(s + \xi\omega_n + j\omega_d)(s + \xi\omega_n - j\omega_d)} \tag{4.10}$$

For a unit-step input, $R(s) = 1/s$. Therefore, Eq. (4.10) becomes

$$C(s) = \frac{\omega_n^2}{s(s^2 + 2\xi\omega_n s + \omega_n^2)}$$

$$= \frac{1}{s} - \frac{s + 2\xi\omega_n}{(s^2 + 2\xi\omega_n s + \omega_n^2)} = \frac{1}{s} - \frac{s + 2\xi\omega_n}{[(s + \xi\omega_n)^2 + \omega_n^2 - \omega_n^2\xi^2]}$$

$$= \frac{1}{s} - \frac{s + \xi\omega_n}{(s + \xi\omega_n)^2 + \omega_d^2} - \frac{\xi\omega_n}{\omega_d} \cdot \frac{\omega_d}{(s + \xi\omega_n)^2 + \omega_d^2}$$

$$= \frac{1}{s} - \frac{s + \xi\omega_n}{(s + \xi\omega_n)^2 + \omega_d^2} - \frac{\xi}{\sqrt{1 - \xi^2}} \cdot \frac{\omega_d}{(s + \xi\omega_n)^2 + \omega_d^2} \tag{4.11}$$

Taking the inverse Laplace transform of Eq. (4.11),

$$c(t) = 1 - e^{-\xi\omega_n t} \cos \omega_d t - \frac{\xi e^{-\xi\omega_n t}}{\sqrt{1 - \xi^2}} \sin \omega_d t$$

$$= 1 - \frac{e^{-\xi\omega_n t}}{\sqrt{1 - \xi^2}} \left(\sqrt{1 - \xi^2} \cos \omega_d t + \xi \sin \omega_d t \right)$$

$$= 1 - \frac{e^{-\xi\omega_n t}}{\sqrt{1-\xi^2}} (\sin\theta\cos\omega_d t + \cos\theta\sin\omega_d t)$$

$$= 1 - \frac{e^{-\xi\omega_n t}}{\sqrt{1-\xi^2}} \sin(\omega_d t + \theta)$$

$$= 1 - \frac{e^{-\xi\omega_n t}}{\sqrt{1-\xi^2}} \sin\left(\omega_n\sqrt{1-\xi^2}\,t + \tan^{-1}\frac{\sqrt{1-\xi^2}}{\xi}\right) \quad \text{for } t \geq 0$$

The error signal for this system is the difference between the input and the output and is

$$e(t) = r(t) - c(t)$$

$$= e^{-\xi\omega_n t}\left(\cos\omega_d t + \frac{\xi}{\sqrt{1-\xi^2}}\sin\omega_d t\right), \quad \text{for } t \geq 0$$

The error signal exhibits a damped sinusoidal oscillation. At steady-state, or at $t = \infty$, no error exists between the output and the input.

If $\xi = 0$, the response becomes undamped and oscillations continue indefinitely. The response $c(t)$ for the zero damping case is

$$c(t) = 1 - \cos\omega_n t \quad \text{for } t \geq 0$$

Thus, ω_n represents the undamped natural frequency.

$$\omega_d = \omega_n \quad \text{for } \xi = 0$$
$$\omega_d < \omega_n \quad \text{for } \xi > 0$$

The time response of an underdamped ($\xi > 1$) second-order system is plotted in Figure 4.8.

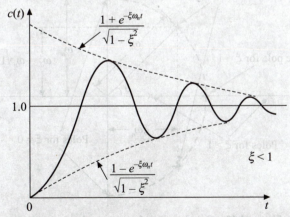

Figure 4.8 Unit-step response of a second-order underdamped system.

It is damped sinusoid. The response reaches a steady-state value of $c_{ss} = 1$, i.e. the steady-state error of this system approaches zero. The time response for various values of ξ plotted against normalized time $\omega_n t$ is shown in Figure 4.9. The system breaks into continuous oscillations for $\xi = 0$.

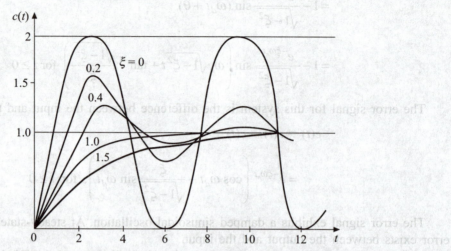

Figure 4.9   Unit-step response curves of second-order systems.

As ξ is increased, the response becomes progressively less oscillatory till it becomes critically damped (just non-oscillatory) for $\xi = 1$, and becomes overdamped for $\xi > 1$.

Figure 4.10 shows the locus of the poles of the second-order system discussed above with ω_n held constant and ξ varying from 0 to ∞. As ξ increases, the poles move away from the imaginary axis along a circular path of radius ω_n meeting at the point $\sigma = -\omega_n$ and then

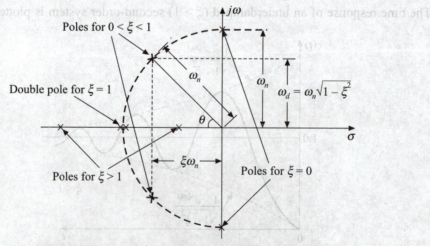

Figure 4.10   Pole locations for a second-order system.

separating and travelling along the real axis, one towards zero and the other towards infinity. For $0 < \xi < 1$, the poles are complex conjugate pair making an angle of $\theta = \cos^{-1} \xi$ with the negative real axis.

4.4.2 Time Response Specifications

Control systems are generally designed with damping less than one, i.e. oscillatory step response. High-order control systems usually have a pair of complex conjugate poles with damping less than one which dominate over other poles. Therefore, the time response of second- and higher-order control systems to a step input is generally of damped oscillatory nature as shown in Figure 4.11. From Figure 4.11, it can be observed that the step response has a number of overshoots and undershoots with respect to the final steady value. Since the overshoots and undershoots decay exponentially, the peak overshoot is the first overshoot and is the same as the peak of the complete time response.

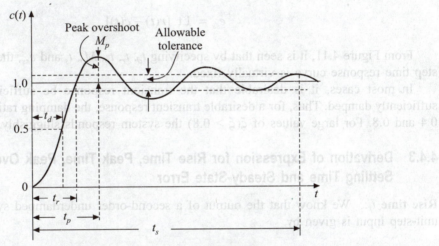

Figure 4.11 Time response specifications.

The transient response of a system to a unit-step input depends on the initial conditions. For convenience, it is a common practice to assume that the system is at rest initially with the output and all time derivatives thereof zero.

The transient response specifications are as follows:

1. *Delay time t_d:* The delay time is the time required for the response to reach 50% of the final value the very first time.

2. *Rise time t_r:* The rise time is the time required for the response to rise from 0 to 100% of the final value for underdamped systems and from 10% to 90% of the final value for overdamped systems.

3. *Peak time t_p:* The peak time is the time required for the response to reach the first peak of the overshoot.

4. *Peak overshoot M_p:* The peak or maximum overshoot is the maximum peak value of the response curve measured from unity. If the final steady-state value of the response differs from unity, then it is common to use the maximum percent overshoot. It is defined by

$$\text{Maximum percent overshoot} = \frac{c(t_p) - c(\infty)}{c(\infty)} \times 100\%$$

The amount of maximum (percent) overshoot directly indicates the relative stability of the system.

5. *Settling time t_s:* The settling time is the time required for the response curve to reach and stay within a particular tolerance band (usually 2% or 5% of its final value).

6. *Steady-state error e_{ss}:* It indicates the error between the actual output and the desired output as t tends to infinity, i.e.

$$e_{ss} = \underset{t \to \infty}{\text{Lt}} \ [r(t) - c(t)]$$

From Figure 4.11, it is seen that by specifying t_d, t_r, t_p, M_p, t_s and e_{ss}, the shape of the unit-step time response curve is virtually fixed.

In most cases, it is desirable that the transient response be sufficiently fast and be sufficiently damped. Thus, for a desirable transient response, the damping ratio must be between 0.4 and 0.8. For large values of $\xi(\xi > 0.8)$ the system responds sluggishly.

4.4.3 Derivation of Expression for Rise Time, Peak Time, Peak Overshoot, Settling Time and Steady-State Error

Rise time t_r: We know that the output of a second-order underdamped system excited by a unit-step input is given by

$$c(t) = 1 - \frac{e^{-\xi\omega_n t}}{\sqrt{1 - \xi^2}} \sin(\omega_d t + \theta) \tag{4.12}$$

Rise time is defined as the time taken by the output to rise from 0 to 100% of the final value. At $t = t_r$,

$$c(t_r) = 1$$

Therefore, Eq. (4.12) becomes

$$1 = 1 - \frac{e^{-\xi\omega_n t_r}}{\sqrt{1 - \xi^2}} \sin(\omega_d t_r + \theta)$$

or

$$\frac{e^{-\xi\omega_n t_r}}{\sqrt{1 - \xi^2}} \sin(\omega_d t_r + \theta) = 0 \tag{4.13}$$

Since in Eq. (4.13)

$$\frac{e^{-\xi\omega_n t_r}}{\sqrt{1-\xi^2}} \neq 0$$

$\sin(\omega_d t_r + \theta)$ must be equal to zero. Therefore,

$$\sin(\omega_d t_r + \theta) = 0 = \sin \pi$$

$$\therefore \qquad \omega_d t_r + \theta = \pi$$

or

$$\omega_d t_r = \pi - \theta$$

Therefore, the rise time

$$t_r = \frac{\pi - \theta}{\omega_d} = \frac{\pi - \tan^{-1}\dfrac{\sqrt{1-\xi^2}}{\xi}}{\omega_n\sqrt{1-\xi^2}} \qquad (4.14)$$

For a small value of t_r, ω_d must be large.

Peak time t_p: We know that the output of a second-order underdamped system excited by a unit-step input is given by

$$c(t) = 1 - \frac{e^{-\xi\omega_n t}}{\sqrt{1-\xi^2}} \sin(\omega_d t + \theta)$$

Peak time is defined as the time at which the maximum value of magnitude occurs. Therefore, at $t = t_p$, the slope of $c(t)$ must be zero. Therefore,

$$\frac{dc(t)}{dt}\bigg|_{t=t_p} = -\frac{e^{-\xi\omega_n t}}{\sqrt{1-\xi^2}} \cos(\omega_d t + \theta).\omega_d - \sin(\omega_d t + \theta)\frac{e^{-\xi\omega_n t}}{\sqrt{1-\xi^2}}(-\xi\omega_n)\bigg|_{t=t_p} = 0$$

i.e. $\qquad \xi\omega_n \sin(\omega_d t_p + \theta) - \omega_n\sqrt{1-\xi^2} \cos(\omega_d t_p + \theta) = 0$

i.e. $\qquad \xi \sin(\omega_d t_p + \theta) - \sqrt{1-\xi^2} \cos(\omega_d t_p + \theta) = 0$

i.e. $\qquad \cos\theta \sin(\omega_d t_p + \theta) - \sin\theta \cos(\omega_d t_p + \theta) = 0$

i.e. $\qquad \sin(\omega_d t_p + \theta - \theta) = 0 = \sin \pi$

$$\therefore \qquad \omega_d t_p = \pi$$

Therefore, the peak time

$$t_p = \frac{\pi}{\omega_d} = \frac{\pi}{\omega_n\sqrt{1-\xi^2}} \qquad (4.15)$$

The relation between θ and ξ is shown in Figure 4.12.

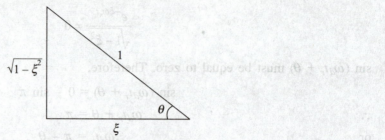

Figure 4.12 Relation between θ and ξ.

The first undershoot occurs at $t = \dfrac{2\pi}{\omega_d}$

The second overshoot occurs at $t = \dfrac{3\pi}{\omega_d}$, and so on.

Peak overshoot M_p: We know that the output of a second-order underdamped system excited by a unit-step input is given by

$$c(t) = 1 - \frac{e^{-\xi \omega_n t}}{\sqrt{1 - \xi^2}} \sin (\omega_d t + \theta)$$

The peak overshoot is the difference between the peak value and the reference input. Therefore,

$$M_p = c(t_p) - 1 = \left[1 - \frac{e^{-\xi \omega_n t_p}}{\sqrt{1 - \xi^2}} \sin (\omega_d t_p + \theta) \right] - 1$$

$$= -\frac{e^{-\xi \omega_n t_p}}{\sqrt{1 - \xi^2}} \sin (\omega_d t_p + \theta)$$

Substituting Eq. (4.15), we get

$$M_p = -\frac{e^{-\xi \omega_n \frac{\pi}{\omega_n \sqrt{1 - \xi^2}}}}{\sqrt{1 - \xi^2}} \sin \left(\omega_d \frac{\pi}{\omega_d} + \theta \right)$$

$$= -\frac{e^{-\pi \xi / \sqrt{1 - \xi^2}}}{\sqrt{1 - \xi^2}} (-\sin \theta)$$

$$= \frac{e^{-\pi \xi / \sqrt{1 - \xi^2}}}{\sqrt{1 - \xi^2}} \sqrt{1 - \xi^2} = e^{-\pi \xi / \sqrt{1 - \xi^2}} \qquad (4.16)$$

Therefore, the peak percent overshoot is

$$100 \times e^{-\pi \xi / \sqrt{1 - \xi^2}} \%$$

Peak overshoot M_p and normalized peak time $\omega_n t_p$ versus damping ratio ξ for a second-order system are shown in Figure 4.13.

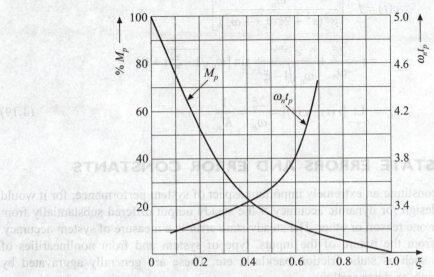

Figure 4.13 M_p and $\omega_n t_p$ versus ξ for a second-order system.

Settling time t_s: The settling time is given by

$$t_s = 4T = \frac{4}{\sigma} = \frac{4}{\xi \omega_n} \quad (2\% \text{ criterion}) \tag{4.17}$$

or

$$t_s = 3T = \frac{3}{\sigma} = \frac{3}{\xi \omega_n} \quad (5\% \text{ criterion}) \tag{4.18}$$

The settling time reaches a minimum value around $\xi = 0.76$ (for the 2% criterion) or $\xi = 0.68$ (for the 5% criterion) and then increases almost linearly for large values of ξ.

t_s is inversely proportional to ω_n for given ξ.

The equations for obtaining the rise time, peak time, maximum overshoot, and settling time are valid only for the standard second-order system.

Steady-state error e_{ss}: We know that the output of a second-order underdamped system excited by a unit-step input is given by

$$c(t) = 1 - \frac{e^{-\xi \omega_n t}}{\sqrt{1 - \xi^2}} \sin (\omega_d t + \theta)$$

$$e_{ss} = \underset{t \to \infty}{\text{Lt}}\, e(t) = \underset{t \to \infty}{\text{Lt}}\, [1 - c(t)] = \underset{t \to \infty}{\text{Lt}} \left[\frac{e^{-\xi \omega_n t}}{\sqrt{1 - \xi^2}} \sin (\omega_d t + \theta) \right] = 0$$

Thus the second-order system has zero steady-state error to a unit-step input.

The response to a ramp input $[r(t) = t,\ R(s) = 1/s^2]$ is

$$c(t) = L^{-1}\left[\frac{\omega_n^2}{s^2(s^2 + 2\xi\omega_n s + \omega_n^2)}\right]$$

$$= t - \frac{2\xi}{\omega_n} + \frac{e^{-\xi\omega_n t}}{\omega_n\sqrt{1-\xi^2}}\sin[\omega_n\sqrt{1-\xi^2}\,t + \theta]$$

$$e_{ss} = \underset{t\to\infty}{\mathrm{Lt}}\,[r(t) - c(t)] = \frac{2\xi}{\omega_n} = \frac{1}{K_v} \tag{4.19}$$

4.5 STEADY-STATE ERRORS AND ERROR CONSTANTS

Steady-state errors constitute an extremely important aspect of system performance; for it would be meaningless to design for dynamic accuracy if the steady output differed substantially from the desired value for one reason or other. The steady-state error is a measure of system accuracy. These errors arise from the nature of the inputs, type of system and from nonlinearities of system components such as static friction backlash, etc. These are generally aggravated by amplifier drifts, ageing or deterioration.

Control systems may be classified according to their ability to follow step inputs, ramp inputs, parabolic inputs and so on as type-0, type-1, type-2 and so on systems. The magnitudes of the steady-state errors due to these individual inputs are indicative of the goodness of the system. Consider a unity feedback system shown in Figure 4.14.

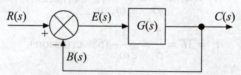

Figure 4.14 Unity feedback system.

The closed-loop transfer function is

$$\frac{C(s)}{R(s)} = \frac{G(s)}{1 + G(s)}$$

The error signal is

$$E(s) = C(s)/G(s)$$

∴

$$E(s) = \frac{R(s)}{1 + G(s)}$$

or

$$\frac{E(s)}{R(s)} = \frac{1}{1 + G(s)}$$

The steady-state error e_{ss} may be found by using the final-value theorem.

$$e_{ss} = \underset{t \to \infty}{\text{Lt}} \; e(t) = \underset{s \to 0}{\text{Lt}} \; sE(s) = \underset{s \to 0}{\text{Lt}} \; \frac{sR(s)}{1 + G(s)} \qquad (4.20)$$

Equation (4.20) for e_{ss} shows that the steady-state error depends upon the input $R(s)$ and the forward path transfer function.

4.5.1 Static Position Error Constant K_p

The steady-state error of the system for a unit-step input $[r(t) = 1, \; R(s) = 1/s]$ is

$$e_{ss} = \underset{s \to 0}{\text{Lt}} \; sE(s) = \underset{s \to 0}{\text{Lt}} \; s \cdot \frac{R(s)}{1 + G(s)} = \underset{s \to 0}{\text{Lt}} \; \frac{s \cdot 1/s}{1 + G(s)}$$

$$= \frac{1}{1 + \underset{s \to 0}{\text{Lt}} \; G(s)} = \frac{1}{1 + G(0)} = \frac{1}{1 + K_p} \qquad (4.21)$$

where $K_p = \underset{s \to 0}{\text{Lt}} \; G(s) = G(0)$ is defined as the *position error constant*.

4.5.2 Static Velocity Error Constant K_v

The steady-state error of the system for a unit-ramp input $[r(t) = t, \; R(s) = 1/s^2]$ is

$$e_{ss} = \underset{s \to 0}{\text{Lt}} \; sE(s) = \underset{s \to 0}{\text{Lt}} \; s \cdot \frac{R(s)}{1 + G(s)} = \underset{s \to 0}{\text{Lt}} \; \frac{s \cdot \dfrac{1}{s^2}}{1 + G(s)}$$

$$= \frac{1}{\underset{s \to 0}{\text{Lt}} \; sG(s)} = \frac{1}{K_v} \qquad (4.22)$$

where $K_v = \underset{s \to 0}{\text{Lt}} \; sG(s)$ is defined as the *velocity error constant*.

4.5.3 Static Acceleration Error Constant K_a

The steady-state error of the system for a unit-parabolic input $\left[r(t) = \dfrac{t^2}{2}, \; R(s) = \dfrac{1}{s^3} \right]$ is

$$e_{ss} = \underset{s \to 0}{\text{Lt}} \; sE(s) = \underset{s \to 0}{\text{Lt}} \; s \cdot \frac{R(s)}{1 + G(s)} = \underset{s \to 0}{\text{Lt}} \; \frac{s \cdot \dfrac{1}{s^3}}{1 + G(s)}$$

$$= \frac{1}{\underset{s \to 0}{\text{Lt}} \; s^2 G(s)} = \frac{1}{K_a} \qquad (4.23)$$

where $K_a = \underset{s \to 0}{\text{Lt}} \; s^2 G(s)$ is defined as the *acceleration error constant*.

4.6   TYPES OF CONTROL SYSTEMS

The open-loop transfer function of a unity feedback system can be written in two standard forms: the time-constant form and the pole-zero form. In these two forms, $G(s)$ is given as follows:

$$G(s) = \frac{K(1+T_{z1}s)(1+T_{z2}s)\cdots}{s^n(1+T_{p1}s)(1+T_{p2}s)\cdots} \qquad \text{(time-constant form)} \qquad (4.24)$$

$$G(s) = \frac{K'(s+z_1)(s+z_2)\cdots}{s^n(s+p_1)(s+p_2)\cdots} \qquad \text{(pole-zero form)} \qquad (4.25)$$

The gains in the two forms are related by

$$K = K'\frac{\Pi_i z_i}{\Pi_j p_j}, \quad i=1,2,\ldots \quad j=1,2,\ldots \qquad (4.26)$$

The term s^n in the denominator of Eqs. (4.24) and (4.25) corresponds to the number of integrations in the system. As s tends to zero, this term dominates in determining the steady-state error. Control systems are therefore classified in accordance with the number of integrations in the open-loop transfer function $G(s)$, as

Type-0 system ($n = 0$, no integration, i.e. no pole of $G(s)$ at the origin of s-plane)

Type-1 system ($n = 1$, one integration, i.e. one pole of $G(s)$ at the origin of s-plane)

Type-2 system ($n = 2$, two integrations, i.e. two poles of $G(s)$ at the origin of s-plane) and so on

4.6.1   Steady-State Error: Type-0 System

For a type-0 system,

$$G(s) = \frac{K(1+T_{z1}s)(1+T_{z2}s)\cdots}{(1+T_{p1}s)(1+T_{p2}s)\cdots}$$

$$K_p = \underset{s\to 0}{\text{Lt}}\ \frac{K(1+T_{z1}s)(1+T_{z2}s)\cdots}{(1+T_{p1}s)(1+T_{p2}s)\cdots} = K$$

$$\therefore \qquad e_{ss}(\text{position}) = \frac{1}{1+K_p} = \frac{1}{1+K} = \text{finite value}$$

$$K_v = \underset{s\to 0}{\text{Lt}}\ sG(s) = \underset{s\to 0}{\text{Lt}}\ s\cdot\frac{K(1+T_{z1})(1+T_{z2}s)\cdots}{(1+T_{p1}s)(1+T_{p2}s)\cdots} = 0$$

$$\therefore \qquad e_{ss}(\text{velocity}) = \frac{1}{K_v} = \frac{1}{0} = \infty$$

$$K_a = \underset{s\to 0}{\text{Lt }} s^2 G(s) = \underset{s\to 0}{\text{Lt }} s^2 \frac{K(1+T_{z1}s)(1+T_{z2}s)\cdots}{(1+T_{p1}s)(1+T_{p2}s)\cdots} = 0$$

$$\therefore \quad e_{ss}\,(\text{acceleration}) = \frac{1}{K_a} = \frac{1}{0} = \infty$$

Thus, a system with $n = 0$, or no integration in $G(s)$ (type-0 system) has a constant position error, infinite velocity and acceleration errors. The position error constant is given by the open-loop gain of the transfer function in the time-constant form.

4.6.2 Steady-State Error: Type-1 System

For a type-1 system,

$$G(s) = \frac{K(1+T_{z1}s)(1+T_{z2}s)\cdots}{s(1+T_{p1}s)(1+T_{p2}s)\cdots}$$

$$K_p = \underset{s\to 0}{\text{Lt }} G(s) = \underset{s\to 0}{\text{Lt }} \frac{K(1+T_{z1}s)(1+T_{z2}s)\cdots}{s(1+T_{p1}s)(1+T_{p2}s)\cdots} = \infty$$

$$\therefore \quad e_{ss}\,(\text{position}) = \frac{1}{1+K_p} = \frac{1}{1+\infty} = 0$$

$$K_v = \underset{s\to 0}{\text{Lt }} sG(s) = \underset{s\to 0}{\text{Lt }} \frac{sK(1+T_{z1}s)(1+T_{z2}s)\cdots}{s(1+T_{p1}s)(1+T_{p2}s)\cdots} = K$$

$$\therefore \quad e_{ss}\,(\text{velocity}) = \frac{1}{K_v} = \frac{1}{K} = \text{finite value}$$

$$K_a = \underset{s\to 0}{\text{Lt }} s^2 G(s) = \underset{s\to 0}{\text{Lt }} s^2 \frac{K(1+T_{z1}s)(1+T_{z2}s)\cdots}{s(1+T_{p1}s)(1+T_{p2}s)\cdots} = 0$$

$$\therefore \quad e_{ss}\,(\text{acceleration}) = \frac{1}{K_a} = \frac{1}{0} = \infty$$

Thus, a system with $n = 1$ or one integration in $G(s)$ (type-1 system) has zero position error, a constant velocity error and an infinite acceleration error at steady-state. The velocity error constant is given by the open-loop gain of the transfer function in the time constant form.

4.6.3 Steady-State Error: Type-2 System

For a type-2 system,

$$G(s) = \frac{K(1+T_{z1}s)(1+T_{z2}s)\cdots}{s^2(1+T_{p1}s)(1+T_{p2}s)\cdots}$$

$$K_p = \operatorname*{Lt}_{s \to 0} G(s) = \operatorname*{Lt}_{s \to 0} \frac{K(1 + T_{z1}s)(1 + T_{z2}s)\cdots}{s^2(1 + T_{p1}s)(1 + T_{p2}s)\cdots} = \infty$$

$$\therefore \qquad e_{ss}(\text{position}) = \frac{1}{1 + K_p} = \frac{1}{1 + \infty} = 0$$

$$K_v = \operatorname*{Lt}_{s \to 0} sG(s) = \operatorname*{Lt}_{s \to 0} \frac{sK(1 + T_{z1}s)(1 + T_{z2}s)\cdots}{s^2(1 + T_{p1}s)(1 + T_{p2}s)\cdots} = \infty$$

$$\therefore \qquad e_{ss}(\text{velocity}) = \frac{1}{K_v} = \frac{1}{\infty} = 0$$

$$K_a = \operatorname*{Lt}_{s \to 0} s^2 G(s) = \operatorname*{Lt}_{s \to 0} s^2 \frac{K(1 + T_{z1}s)(1 + T_{z2}s)\cdots}{s^2(1 + T_{p1}s)(1 + T_{p2}s)\cdots} = K$$

$$\therefore \qquad e_{ss}(\text{acceleration}) = \frac{1}{K_a} = \frac{1}{K} = \text{finite value}$$

Thus, a system with $n = 2$ or two integrations in $G(s)$ (type-2 system) has zero position error, zero velocity error, and a constant acceleration error at steady-state. The acceleration error constant is given by the open-loop gain of the transfer function in the time-constant form.

Steady-state errors for various inputs and systems are summarized in Table 4.1.

Table 4.1 Steady-state errors for various inputs and systems.

Type of input	Steady-state error		
	Type-0 system	*Type-1 system*	*Type-2 system*
Unit-step	$1/1 + K_p$	0	0
Unit-ramp	∞	$1/K_v$	0
Unit-parabolic	∞	∞	$1/K_a$
	$K_p = \operatorname*{Lt}_{s \to 0} G(s)$	$K_v = \operatorname*{Lt}_{s \to 0} sG(s)$	$K_a = \operatorname*{Lt}_{s \to 0} s^2 G(s)$

The error constants for non-unity feedback systems may be obtained by replacing $G(s)$ by $G(s)H(s)$ in Table 4.1. The terms 'position error', 'velocity error', and 'acceleration error' mean steady-state deviations in output position.

The error constants K_p, K_v and K_a describe the ability of a system to reduce or eliminate steady-state errors. Therefore, they are indicative of the steady-state performance. As the type of system becomes higher, progressively more steady-state errors are eliminated. Systems of type higher than 2, i.e. with more than two integrations are not employed in practice because of two reasons:

1. These are more difficult to stabilize.
2. The dynamic errors for such systems tend to be larger than those for type-0, type-1 and type-2 systems, although their steady-state performance is desirable.

The disadvantages of static error constants are as follows:

1. They do not give any information on the steady-state error, when inputs are other than the three basic types—step, ramp and parabolic.

2. They fail to indicate the exact manner in which the error function changes with time.

The dynamic error may be evaluated using the dynamic error coefficients—the concept generalized to include inputs of any arbitrary function of time.

For a unity feedback system, express the numerator and denominator of

$$\frac{E(s)}{R(s)} = \frac{1}{1 + G(s)} = F(s)$$

in ascending powers of s and perform long division. Therefore,

$$\frac{E(s)}{R(s)} = \frac{1}{1 + G(s)} = C_0 + C_1 s + \frac{C_2}{2!} s^2 + \frac{C_3}{3!} s^3 + \cdots$$

Coefficients $C_0, C_1, C_2, C_3 \cdots$ are defined to be *dynamic error coefficients* or *generalized error coefficients*. Therefore,

$$E(s) = C_0 R(s) + C_1 s R(s) + \frac{C_2}{2!} s^2 R(s) + \frac{C_3}{3!} s^3 R(s) + \cdots$$

Taking the inverse Laplace transform, the dynamic error is given by

$$e(t) = C_0 r(t) + C_1 \dot{r}(t) + \frac{C_2}{2!} \ddot{r}(t) + \frac{C_3}{3!} \dddot{r}(t) + \cdots$$

The generalized error coefficients are evaluated as follows:

$$C_0 = \underset{s \to 0}{\text{Lt}}\, F(s) \qquad\qquad C_1 = \underset{s \to 0}{\text{Lt}}\, \frac{d}{ds} F(s)$$

$$C_2 = \underset{s \to 0}{\text{Lt}}\, \frac{d^2}{ds^2} F(s) \cdots \qquad\qquad C_n = \underset{s \to 0}{\text{Lt}}\, \frac{d^n}{ds^n} F(s)$$

Correlation between static and dynamic error coefficients: The values of dynamic error coefficients can be used to calculate static error coefficients. The following expressions show the relation between them.

$$C_0 = \frac{1}{1 + K_p} \qquad C_1 = \frac{1}{K_v} \qquad C_2 = \frac{1}{K_a}$$

4.7 EFFECT OF ADDING POLES AND ZEROS TO TRANSFER FUNCTIONS

Although the roots of the characteristic equation, which are the poles of the closed-loop transfer function, affect the transient response of linear time-invariant systems, particularly the stability, the zeros of the transfer function, if there are any, are also important. Thus the addition of poles and zeros and/or cancellation of undesirable poles and zeros of the transfer function often are necessary in achieving satisfactory time-domain performance of control systems.

4.7.1 Addition of a Pole to the Forward Path Transfer Function

The addition of a pole increases the order of the system, increases the overshoot and reduces the stability. It increases the rise time of the step response, reduces the bandwidth and pushes and bends the complex conjugate portion of the root loci of the second-order system to the right half of the *s*-plane.

4.7.2 Addition of a Pole to the Closed-Loop Transfer Function

The addition of a pole to the closed-loop transfer function increases the rise time and decreases the overshoot. Thus as far as overshoot is concerned, adding a pole to the closed-loop transfer function has just the opposite effect to that of adding a pole to the forward path transfer function.

4.7.3 Addition of a Zero to the Closed-Loop Transfer Function

Adding a zero to the closed-loop transfer function decreases the rise time, and increases the maximum overshoot of the step response.

4.7.4 Addition of a Zero to the Forward Path Transfer Function

When the added zero is very far away from the imaginary axis, the overshoot is large and the damping is very poor. The overshoot is reduced and damping improves when the zero moves to the right. Again when the zero moves closer to the origin, the overshoot increases but damping improves.

The conclusion is that although the characteristic equation roots are generally used to study the relative damping and relative stability of linear control systems, the zeros of the transfer function should not be overlooked in their effects on the transient performance of the system.

4.8 DOMINANT POLES OF TRANSFER FUNCTIONS

The location of the poles of a transfer function in the *s*-plane greatly affects the transient response of the system. For analysis and design purposes, it is important to sort out the poles that have a dominant effect on the transient response and call these poles *dominant poles*.

Since most control systems in practice are of orders higher than two, they can be approximated by second-order systems maintaining the same transient response. In design, the dominant poles of the system are used to control the dynamic performance of the system, whereas the insignificant poles are used for the purpose of ensuring that the controller transfer function can be realized by physical components.

For all practical purposes, we can divide the *s*-plane into regions in which the dominant and insignificant poles can lie.

The poles that are close to the imaginary axis in the left half *s*-plane give rise to transient responses that will decay relatively slowly and are called *dominant poles*, whereas the poles that are far away from the imaginary axis (relative to the dominant poles) correspond to fast-decaying time responses and are called *insignificant poles*. In practice, if the magnitude of the real part of a pole is at least 5 to 10 times that of a dominant pole or a pair of complex dominant poles, then the pole may be regarded as insignificant in so far as the transient response is concerned. The roots that are closer to the imaginary axis will dominate the transient response, and these are defined as the dominant roots of the characteristic equation of the system.

4.8.1 The Relative Damping Ratio

When a system is higher than the second order, we can no longer strictly use the damping ratio ξ and the undamped natural frequency ω_n, which are defined for the prototype second-order systems. However, if the system dynamics can be accurately represented by a pair of complex conjugate dominant poles, then we can still use ξ and ω_n to indicate the dynamics of the transient response and the damping ratio in this case is referred to as the relative damping ratio of the system.

For example, consider the following closed-loop transfer function:

$$M(s) = \frac{C(s)}{R(s)} = \frac{20}{(s+10)(s^2 + 2s + 2)}$$

The pole at $s = -10$ is ten times the real part of the complex conjugate poles, which are at $-1 \pm j1$. We can refer to the relative damping ratio of the system as 0.707.

4.8.2 The Proper Way of Neglecting Insignificant Poles with Consideration of Steady-State Response

If the insignificant poles are neglected as they are, the transient response is unchanged, but the steady-state response gets affected.

For example, consider the following closed-loop transfer function:

$$M(s) = \frac{C(s)}{R(s)} = \frac{20}{(s+10)(s^2 + 2s + 2)}$$

Neglecting the pole far away from the origin, the third-order system can be approximated by a second-order system with the transfer function

$$\frac{C(s)}{R(s)} = \frac{20}{(s^2 + 2s + 2)}$$

The transient response of the above two transfer functions will be the same but their steady-state responses will be different. To maintain the same steady-state response, the transfer function can be written as

$$\frac{C(s)}{R(s)} = \frac{20}{10(s/10 + 1)(s^2 + 2s + 2)}$$

The term $s/10$ can be neglected compared to 1. So the third-order system can be written in terms of a second-order system as

$$\frac{C(s)}{R(s)} = \frac{20}{10(s^2 + 2s + 2)}$$

Both the above systems will have the same steady-state error.

Example 4.1   For the system with the following transfer function, determine the type and order of the system:

(a) $G(s)H(s) = \dfrac{K(s+3)}{s^2(s+2)(s+5)}$

(b) $G(s)H(s) = \dfrac{K}{s(s+1)(s^2+2s+3)}$

(c) $G(s)H(s) = \dfrac{s+2}{(s-3)(s+0.1)}$

(d) $G(s)H(s) = \dfrac{20}{s^3(s^4+8s^2+16)}$

Solution:

(a) The open-loop transfer function has two poles at the origin of the s-plane, so it is a type-2 system. The highest power of s present in the denominator is 4, so it is a fourth-order system.

(b) The open-loop transfer function has one pole at the origin of the s-plane, so it is a type-1 system. The highest power of s present in the denominator is 4, so it is a fourth-order system.

(c) The open-loop transfer function has no pole at the origin of the s-plane, so it is type-0 system. The highest power of s present in the denominator is 2, so it is a second-order system.

(d) The open-loop transfer function has three poles at the origin of the s-plane, so it is a type-3 system. The highest power of s present in the denominator is 7, so it is a seventh-order system.

Example 4.2   The closed-loop transfer functions of certain second-order unity feedback control systems are given below. Determine the type of damping in the systems.

(a) $\dfrac{C(s)}{R(s)} = \dfrac{8}{s^2 + 3s + 8}$

(b) $\dfrac{C(s)}{R(s)} = \dfrac{2}{s^2 + 4s + 2}$

(c) $\dfrac{C(s)}{R(s)} = \dfrac{2}{s^2 + 2s + 1}$

(d) $\dfrac{C(s)}{R(s)} = \dfrac{2}{s^2 + 4}$

Solution: Comparing the given transfer functions with the standard form of the transfer function of a second-order system, i.e. with

$$\frac{C(s)}{R(s)} = \frac{\omega_n^2}{s^2 + 2\xi\omega_n s + \omega_n^2}$$

(a)
$$\frac{C(s)}{R(s)} = \frac{8}{s^2 + 3s + 8} = \frac{\omega_n^2}{s^2 + 2\xi\omega_n s + \omega_n^2}$$

$\therefore$ $\qquad \omega_n^2 = 8$

i.e. $\qquad \omega_n = \sqrt{8} = 2.82$

$\qquad 2\xi\omega_n = 3$

i.e. $\qquad \xi = \dfrac{3}{2\omega_n} = \dfrac{3}{2 \times 2.82} = 0.53$

Since $\xi < 1$, it is an underdamped system.

(b)
$$\frac{C(s)}{R(s)} = \frac{2}{s^2 + 4s + 2} = \frac{\omega_n^2}{s^2 + 2\xi\omega_n s + \omega_n^2}$$

$\therefore$ $\qquad \omega_n^2 = 2$

i.e. $\qquad \omega_n = \sqrt{2} = 1.414$

$\qquad 2\xi\omega_n = 4$

i.e. $\qquad \xi = \dfrac{4}{2\omega_n} = \dfrac{4}{2 \times 1.414} = 1.41$

Since $\xi > 1$, it is an overdamped system.

(c)
$$\frac{C(s)}{R(s)} = \frac{2}{s^2 + 2s + 1} = \frac{\omega_n^2}{s^2 + 2\xi\omega_n s + \omega_n^2}$$

$\therefore$ $\qquad \omega_n^2 = 1$

i.e. $\qquad \omega_n = 1$

$\qquad 2\xi\omega_n = 2$

i.e. $\qquad \xi = \dfrac{2}{2\omega_n} = \dfrac{2}{2 \times 1} = 1$

Since $\xi = 1$, it is a critically-damped system.

(d)
$$\frac{C(s)}{R(s)} = \frac{2}{s^2 + 4} = \frac{\omega_n^2}{s^2 + 2\xi\omega_n s + \omega_n^2}$$

$\therefore$ $\qquad \omega_n^2 = 4$

i.e. $\qquad \omega_n = 2$

$\qquad 2\xi\omega_n = 0$

i.e. $\qquad \xi = 0$

Since $\xi = 0$, it is an undamped system.

Example 4.3 A first-order system and its response to a unit-step input are shown in Figure 4.15. Determine the system parameters a and K.

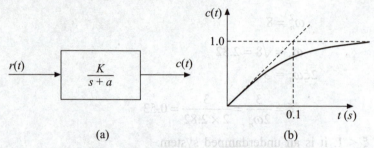

(a)   (b)

Figure 4.15 Example 4.3: (a) system and (b) response.

Solution: The system transfer function is

$$M(s) = \frac{C(s)}{R(s)} = \frac{K}{s+a}$$

For a unit-step input,

$$R(s) = \frac{1}{s}$$

Therefore, the output

$$C(s) = R(s)M(s) = \frac{1}{s} \cdot \frac{K}{s+a}$$

The steady-state value of the output is

$$\underset{t\to\infty}{\text{Lt}}\ c(t) = \underset{t\to\infty}{\text{Lt}}\ L^{-1}\left[\frac{K}{s(s+a)}\right] = \frac{K}{a}\underset{t\to\infty}{\text{Lt}}\ L^{-1}\left(\frac{1}{s} - \frac{1}{s+a}\right)$$

$$= \frac{K}{a}\underset{t\to\infty}{\text{Lt}}\ (1 - e^{-at}) = \frac{K}{a}$$

From Figure 4.15(b), $c(\infty) = 1$. Therefore,

$$\frac{K}{a} = 1$$

or

$$K = a$$

The initial slope of the output $= \underset{t\to 0}{\text{Lt}}\left[\frac{d}{dt}c(t)\right] = \frac{1}{0.1} = 10$

$$L\left[\frac{d}{dt}c(t)\right] = sC(s) = s\left[\frac{K}{s(s+a)}\right] = \frac{K}{s+a}$$

$$\therefore \qquad \text{Slope of the output} = \frac{d}{dt}c(t) = L^{-1}\left[\frac{K}{s+a}\right] = Ke^{-at}$$

$$\text{The initial slope} = \mathop{\text{Lt}}_{t\to 0}\left[\frac{d}{dt}c(t)\right] = K$$

$$\therefore \qquad\qquad\qquad K = 10$$

$$\therefore \qquad\qquad\qquad a = K = 10$$

Example 4.4 Obtain the response of a unity feedback system whose open-loop transfer function is

$$G(s) = \frac{3}{s(s+4)}$$

for a unit-step input.

Solution: The closed-loop unity feedback system is shown in Figure 4.16.

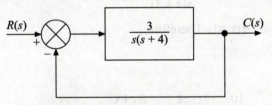

Figure 4.16   Example 4.4: Block diagram.

$$\frac{C(s)}{R(s)} = \frac{G(s)}{1+G(s)} = \frac{\dfrac{3}{s(s+4)}}{1+\dfrac{3}{s(s+4)}} = \frac{3}{s^2+4s+3} = \frac{3}{(s+1)(s+3)}$$

For a unit-step input, $r(t) = 1$. Therefore,

$$R(s) = \frac{1}{s}$$

$$\therefore \qquad C(s) = \frac{3}{s(s+1)(s+3)} = \frac{1}{s} - \frac{\dfrac{3}{2}}{s+1} + \frac{\dfrac{1}{2}}{s+3}$$

Taking the inverse Laplace transform, the response is

$$c(t) = 1 - \frac{3}{2}e^{-t} + \frac{1}{2}e^{-3t}$$

Example 4.5 A positional control system with velocity feedback is shown in Figure 4.17. What is the response of the system for a unit-step input?

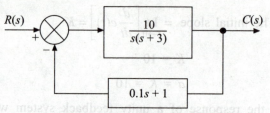

Figure 4.17 Example 4.5: Block diagram.

Solution: The closed-loop transfer function of the system is

$$\frac{C(s)}{R(s)} = \frac{\dfrac{10}{s(s+3)}}{1 + \dfrac{10}{s(s+3)} \times (0.1s+1)} = \frac{10}{s^2 + 4s + 10}$$

For a unit-step input, $r(t) = 1$. Therefore,

$$R(s) = \frac{1}{s}$$

so

$$C(s) = \frac{1}{s} \times \frac{10}{s^2 + 4s + 10} = \frac{A}{s} + \frac{Bs+C}{s^2 + 4s + 10}$$

$$= \frac{1}{s} - \frac{s+4}{s^2 + 4s + 10} = \frac{1}{s} - \frac{s+2}{(s+2)^2 + (\sqrt{6})^2} - \frac{2}{\sqrt{6}} \cdot \frac{\sqrt{6}}{(s+2)^2 + (\sqrt{6})^2}$$

Taking the inverse Laplace transform, the response is

$$c(t) = 1 - e^{-2t} \cos \sqrt{6}t - \frac{2}{\sqrt{6}} e^{-2t} \sin \sqrt{6}t$$

Example 4.6 The open-loop transfer function of a unity feedback system is

$$G(s) = \frac{4}{s(s+1)}$$

Determine the nature of response of the closed-loop system for a unit-step input. Also determine the rise time, peak time, peak overshoot and settling time.

Solution: Given $G(s) = \dfrac{4}{s(s+1)}$, the closed-loop transfer function is

$$\frac{C(s)}{R(s)} = \frac{\dfrac{4}{s(s+1)}}{1 + \dfrac{4}{s(s+1)}} = \frac{4}{s^2 + s + 4}$$

Comparing it with the standard form of the closed-loop transfer function of a second-order system,

$$\frac{C(s)}{R(s)} = \frac{4}{s^2 + s + 4} = \frac{\omega_n^2}{s^2 + 2\xi\omega_n s + \omega_n^2}$$

$$\therefore \qquad \omega_n^2 = 4$$

i.e. $$\omega_n = \sqrt{4} = 2$$

$$2\xi\omega_n = 1$$

i.e. $$\xi = \frac{1}{2\omega_n} = \frac{1}{2 \times 2} = 0.25$$

Since $\xi < 1$, the system is an underdamped one.

$$\omega_n = 2 \quad \text{and} \quad \xi = 0.25.$$

Therefore,

$$\omega_d = \omega_n \sqrt{1 - \xi^2} = 2 \times \sqrt{1 - 0.25^2} = 1.936 \text{ rad/s}$$

$$\theta = \tan^{-1} \frac{\sqrt{1 - \xi^2}}{\xi} = \tan^{-1} \frac{\sqrt{1 - 0.25^2}}{0.25} = 1.310 \text{ rad}$$

The rise time

$$t_r = \frac{\pi - \theta}{\omega_d} = \frac{3.141 - 1.310}{1.936} = 0.945 \text{ s}$$

The peak time

$$t_p = \frac{\pi}{\omega_d} = \frac{3.141}{1.936} = 1.622 \text{ s}$$

The peak overshoot

$$M_p = e^{-\pi\xi/\sqrt{1-\xi^2}} = 0.4326$$

Therefore, percentage of peak overshoot is

$$M_p \times 100\% = 43.26\%$$

The settling time for 5% error

$$t_s = \frac{3}{\xi\omega_n} = \frac{3}{0.25 \times 2} = 6\,\text{s}$$

The settling time for 2% error

$$t_s = \frac{4}{\xi\omega_n} = \frac{4}{0.25 \times 2} = 8\,\text{s}$$

Example 4.7   Measurements conducted on a servo mechanism show the system response to be

$$c(t) = 1 + 0.2e^{-60t} - 1.2e^{-10t}$$

when subjected to a unit-step input
  (a) Obtain the expression for the closed-loop transfer function.
  (b) Determine the undamped natural frequency and the damping ratio of the system.

Solution:
  (a) *Calculation of the closed-loop transfer function*
      The system response is

$$c(t) = 1 + 0.2e^{-60t} - 1.2e^{-10t}$$

Taking the Laplace transform on both sides,

$$C(s) = \frac{1}{s} + \frac{0.2}{s+60} - \frac{1.2}{s+10}$$

$$= \frac{(s+10)(s+60) + 0.2(s+10)s - 1.2(s+60)s}{s(s+10)(s+60)}$$

$$= \frac{600}{s(s^2 + 70s + 600)}$$

For a unit-step input, $r(t) = 1$, therefore, $R(s) = \dfrac{1}{s}$.

Hence, the transfer function is

$$\frac{C(s)}{R(s)} = \frac{\dfrac{600}{s(s^2 + 70s + 600)}}{\dfrac{1}{s}} = \frac{600}{s^2 + 70s + 600}$$

  (b) *Calculation of ω_n and ξ*
      Comparing the obtained transfer function with the standard form of the transfer function of a second-order system, we get

$$\frac{C(s)}{R(s)} = \frac{600}{s^2 + 70s + 600} = \frac{\omega_n^2}{s^2 + 2\xi\omega_n s + \omega_n^2}$$

$$\omega_n^2 = 600$$

or
$$\omega_n = \sqrt{600} = 24.49 \text{ rad/s}$$

$$2\xi\omega_n = 70$$

or
$$\xi = \frac{70}{2\omega_n} = \frac{70}{2 \times 24.49} = 1.43$$

Hence the undamped natural frequency of the system is $\omega_n = 24.49$ rad/s, and the damping ratio of the system is $\xi = 1.43$.

Example 4.8 A unity feedback system is characterized by an open-loop transfer function

$$G(s) = \frac{K}{s(s+10)}$$

Determine the gain K so that the system will have a damping ratio of 0.5. For this value of K determine the settling time, peak overshoot and time to peak overshoot for a unit-step input.

Solution: The closed-loop transfer function of the given unity feedback system is

$$\frac{C(s)}{R(s)} = \frac{G(s)}{1+G(s)} = \frac{\dfrac{K}{s(s+10)}}{1+\dfrac{K}{s(s+10)}} = \frac{K}{s^2 + 10s + K}$$

Comparing it with the standard form of the transfer function of a second-order system, we have

$$\frac{C(s)}{R(s)} = \frac{K}{s^2 + 10s + K} = \frac{\omega_n^2}{s^2 + 2\xi\omega_n s + \omega_n^2}$$

$$\omega_n^2 = K$$

or
$$\omega_n = \sqrt{K}$$

$$2\xi\omega_n = 10$$

i.e.
$$2 \times 0.5 \times \omega_n = 10$$

or
$$\omega_n = 10$$

∴
$$K = \omega_n^2 = 10^2 = 100$$

So the gain $K = 100$ so that the system will have a damping ratio of 0.5.

The settling time for 2% criterion is

$$t_s = \frac{4}{\xi \omega_n} = \frac{4}{0.5 \times 10} = 0.8\,\text{s}$$

The settling time for 5% criterion is

$$t_s = \frac{3}{\xi \omega_n} = \frac{3}{0.5 \times 10} = 0.6\,\text{s}$$

The peak overshoot is

$$M_p = e^{-\pi \xi / \sqrt{1-\xi^2}} = e^{-3.14 \times 0.5 / \sqrt{1-0.5^2}} = 0.163$$

The percentage peak overshoot is

$$\%M_p = M_p \times 100 = 0.163 \times 100 = 16.3\%$$

The peak time $t_p = \dfrac{\pi}{\omega_d} = \dfrac{\pi}{\omega_n \sqrt{1-\xi^2}} = \dfrac{3.14}{10 \times \sqrt{1-0.5^2}} = 0.363\,\text{s}$

That is the time to peak overshoot is $t_p = 0.363\text{s}$.

Example 4.9   A second-order control system is represented by a transfer function given below

$$\frac{Q_0(s)}{T(s)} = \frac{1}{Js^2 + fs + K}$$

where $Q_0(s)$ is the proportional output and T is the input torque. A step input 10 N-m is applied to the system and the test results are given below.

(a) Peak overshoot $M_p = 6\%$
(b) Peak time $t_p = 1\text{s}$
(c) The steady-state output of the system is 0.5 radian.

Determine the values of J, K and f.

Solution: Given, the input torque T is a step of 10 N-m. Therefore,

$$T(s) = \frac{10}{s}$$

so

$$Q_0(s) = \frac{T(s)}{Js^2 + fs + K} = \frac{10}{s(Js^2 + fs + K)}$$

The steady-state value of output $= \underset{s \to 0}{\text{Lt}}\ sQ_0(s)$. Therefore,

$$0.5 = \underset{s \to 0}{\text{Lt}}\ s \cdot \frac{10}{s(Js^2 + fs + K)}$$

i.e.
$$0.5 = \frac{10}{K}$$

or
$$K = 20$$

Given the peak overshoot $M_p = 6\% = 0.06$. Therefore,

$$0.06 = e^{-\pi\xi/\sqrt{1-\xi^2}}$$

or
$$\xi = 0.667$$

Given the peak time, $t_p = 1s$. Therefore,

$$1 = \frac{\pi}{\omega_d} = \frac{\pi}{\omega_n\sqrt{1-\xi^2}}$$

$$\therefore \qquad \omega_n = 4.21 \text{ rad/s}$$

Comparing the given characteristic equation with the standard form of the characteristic equation of a second-order system

$$s^2 + \frac{f}{J}s + \frac{K}{J} = s^2 + 2\xi\omega_n s + \omega_n^2 = 0$$

$$\omega_n^2 = \frac{K}{J}$$

$$\therefore \qquad J = \frac{K}{\omega_n^2} = \frac{20}{4.21^2} = 1.128 \text{ kg-m}^2$$

$$2\xi\omega_n = \frac{f}{J}$$

$$\therefore \qquad f = 2\xi\omega_n J = 2 \times 0.667 \times 4.21 \times 1.128 = 6.34 \text{ N-m/rad/s}$$

Example 4.10   The system shown in Figure 4.18(a) when subjected to a unit-step input gives the output response shown in Figure 4.18(b). Determine the values of K and T from the response curve.

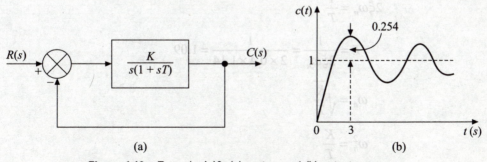

(a)   (b)

Figure 4.18   Example 4.10: (a) system and (b) output response.

Solution: Given $G(s) = \dfrac{K}{s(1+sT)}$ and $H(s) = 1$.

The closed-loop transfer function is

$$\frac{C(s)}{R(s)} = \frac{G(s)}{1+G(s)} = \frac{\dfrac{K}{s(1+sT)}}{1+\dfrac{K}{s(1+sT)}} = \frac{K}{s^2 T + s + K} = \frac{\dfrac{K}{T}}{s^2 + \dfrac{1}{T}s + \dfrac{K}{T}}$$

Comparing it with the standard form of the transfer function of a second-order system, i.e. with

$$\frac{C(s)}{R(s)} = \frac{\omega_n^2}{s^2 + 2\xi\omega_n s + \omega_n^2}$$

We get

$$\omega_n = \sqrt{\frac{K}{T}}$$

and

$$2\xi\omega_n = \frac{1}{T}$$

The peak overshoot $M_p = 0.254$ (as seen from Figure 4.18(b)). Therefore,

$$e^{-\pi\xi/\sqrt{1-\xi^2}} = 0.254$$

or

$$\xi = 0.4$$

The peak time $t_p = \dfrac{\pi}{\omega_d} = \dfrac{\pi}{\omega_n\sqrt{1-\xi^2}} = 3\,\text{s}$ (as seen from Figure 4.18(b))

$$\therefore \qquad \omega_n = \frac{\pi}{3\sqrt{1-\xi^2}} = \frac{\pi}{3\sqrt{1-0.4^2}} = 1.14 \ \text{rad/s}$$

$$2\xi\omega_n = \frac{1}{T}$$

or

$$T = \frac{1}{2\xi\omega_n} = \frac{1}{2\times 0.4\times 1.14} = 1.09$$

$$\omega_n = \sqrt{\frac{K}{T}}$$

or

$$\omega_n^2 = \frac{K}{T}$$

or

$$K = \omega_n^2 T = 1.14^2 \times 1.09 = 1.42$$

Example 4.11 For the *RLC* series circuit shown in Figure 4.19, determine the undamped natural frequency, and damping ratio of the circuit. Assume zero initial conditions.

$$R = 1 \text{ k}\Omega, \ L = 10 \text{ mH}, \ C = 0.01 \text{ μF}$$

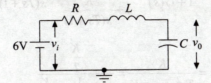

Figure 4.19 Example 4.11: Circuit.

Solution: The transfer function of the system is

$$\frac{V_o(s)}{V_i(s)} = \frac{\dfrac{1}{Cs}}{R + Ls + \dfrac{1}{Cs}} = \frac{1}{CLs^2 + RCs + 1} = \frac{\dfrac{1}{LC}}{s^2 + \dfrac{R}{L}s + \dfrac{1}{LC}}$$

Comparing the above characteristic polynomial with $s^2 + 2\xi\omega_n s + \omega_n^2$

$$\omega_n^2 = \frac{1}{LC}$$

or

$$\omega_n = \frac{1}{\sqrt{LC}} = \frac{1}{\sqrt{10 \times 10^{-3} \times 0.01 \times 10^{-6}}} = 10^5 \text{ rad/s}$$

$$2\xi\omega_n = \frac{R}{L}$$

i.e.

$$2\xi\frac{1}{\sqrt{LC}} = \frac{R}{L}$$

∴

$$\xi = \frac{R}{2}\sqrt{\frac{C}{L}} = \frac{1 \times 10^3}{2}\sqrt{\frac{0.01 \times 10^{-6}}{10 \times 10^{-3}}} = 0.5$$

Therefore, the undamped natural frequency $\omega_n = 10^5$ rad/s and the damping ratio $\xi = 0.5$.

Example 4.12 The open-loop transfer function of a unity feedback system is given by

$$G(s) = \frac{K}{s(Ts + 1)}$$

where K and T are positive constants. By what factor should the amplifier gain K be reduced so that the peak overshoot of unit-step response of the system is reduced from 75% to 25%.

Solution: The closed-loop transfer function of the system is

$$\frac{C(s)}{R(s)} = \frac{G(s)}{1+G(s)} = \frac{\dfrac{K}{s(Ts+1)}}{1+\dfrac{K}{s(Ts+1)}} = \frac{K}{s(Ts+1)+K}$$

$$= \frac{K}{Ts^2+s+K} = \frac{\dfrac{K}{T}}{s^2+\dfrac{1}{T}s+\dfrac{K}{T}}$$

Comparing this transfer function with the standard form of the transfer function of a second-order system to obtain the expressions for ξ and ω_n

$$\frac{C(s)}{R(s)} = \frac{\omega_n^2}{s^2+2\xi\omega_n s+\omega_n^2} = \frac{\dfrac{K}{T}}{s^2+\dfrac{1}{T}s+\dfrac{K}{T}}$$

$$\omega_n^2 = \frac{K}{T}$$

or

$$\omega_n = \sqrt{\frac{K}{T}}$$

$$2\xi\omega_n = \frac{1}{T}$$

∴

$$\xi = \frac{1}{2\omega_n T} = \frac{1}{2\sqrt{\dfrac{K}{T}} \times T} = \frac{1}{2\sqrt{KT}}$$

so,

$$\xi^2 = \frac{1}{4KT}$$

The peak overshoot M_p is reduced by increasing the damping ratio ξ. The damping ratio ξ is increased by reducing the gain K.

When $\qquad M_p = 0.75$, let $\xi = \xi_1$ and $K = K_1$.

When $\qquad M_p = 0.25$, let $\xi = \xi_2$ and $K = K_2$.

The peak overshoot is given by

$$M_p = e^{-\pi\xi/\sqrt{1-\xi^2}}$$

Taking the natural logarithm on both sides,

$$\ln M_p = \frac{-\pi \xi}{\sqrt{1-\xi^2}}$$

Squaring both sides

$$(\ln M_p)^2 = \frac{\pi^2 \xi^2}{1-\xi^2}$$

i.e.

$$(1-\xi^2)(\ln M_p)^2 = \pi^2 \xi^2$$

i.e.

$$(\ln M_p)^2 = \xi^2[\pi^2 + (\ln M_p)^2]$$

or

$$\xi^2 = \frac{(\ln M_p)^2}{\pi^2 + (\ln M_p)^2}$$

Equating both the expressions for ξ^2,

$$\xi^2 = \frac{(\ln M_p)^2}{\pi^2 + (\ln M_p)^2} = \frac{1}{4KT}$$

i.e.

$$K = \frac{\pi^2 + (\ln M_p)^2}{4T(\ln M_p)^2}$$

When $K = K_1$, $M_p = 0.75$. Therefore,

$$K_1 = \frac{\pi^2 + (\ln 0.75)^2}{4T(\ln 0.75)^2} = \frac{9.952}{0.331T} = \frac{30.06}{T}$$

When $K = K_2$, $M_p = 0.25$. Therefore,

$$K_2 = \frac{\pi^2 + (\ln 0.25)^2}{4T(\ln 0.25)^2} = \frac{11.79}{7.68T} = \frac{1.53}{T}$$

$$\therefore \qquad \frac{K_1}{K_2} = \frac{(1/T) \times 30.06}{(1/T) \times 1.53} = 19.6$$

i.e.

$$K_1 = 19.6 \, K_2$$

or

$$K_2 = \frac{1}{19.6} K_1$$

This indicates that, to reduce the peak overshoot from 0.75 to 0.25, K should be reduced by 19.6 times.

Example 4.13   A closed-loop control system is represented by the differential equation

$$\frac{d^2c}{dt^2} + 4\frac{dc}{dt} = 16e$$

where $e = r - c$ is the error signal. Determine the undamped natural frequency, damping ratio, and percentage maximum overshoot for a unit-step input.

Solution: The mathematical equations governing the behaviour of the system are as follows:

$$\frac{d^2c}{dt^2} + 4\frac{dc}{dt} = 16e$$

and

$$e = r - c$$

∴

$$\frac{d^2c}{dt^2} + 4\frac{dc}{dt} = 16(r - c)$$

i.e.

$$\frac{d^2c}{dt^2} + 4\frac{dc}{dt} + 16c = 16r$$

Taking the Laplace transform on both sides and neglecting the initial conditions,

$$s^2C(s) + 4sC(s) + 16C(s) = 16\ R(s)$$

Therefore, the transfer function is

$$\frac{C(s)}{R(s)} = \frac{16}{s^2 + 4s + 16}$$

Comparing it with the standard form of the transfer function of a second-order system,

$$\frac{C(s)}{R(s)} = \frac{\omega_n^2}{s^2 + 2\xi\omega_n s + \omega_n^2} = \frac{16}{s^2 + 4s + 16}$$

∴

$$\omega_n^2 = 16$$

i.e.

$$\omega_n = 4$$

and

$$2\xi\omega_n = 4$$

i.e.

$$\xi = \frac{4}{2\omega_n} = \frac{4}{2 \times 4} = 0.5$$

The peak overshoot

$$M_p = e^{-\pi\xi/\sqrt{1-\xi^2}} = e^{-3.141 \times 0.5/\sqrt{1-0.5^2}} = 0.163$$

The % peak overshoot is

$$M_p \times 100\% = 0.163 \times 100\% = 16.3\%$$

Example 4.14 A unity feedback control system has an open-loop transfer function

$$G(s) = \frac{5}{s(s+1)}$$

Find the rise time, percentage overshoot, peak time and settling time for a step input of 10 units. Also determine the peak overshoot.

Solution: Note that the formulae for the rise time, percentage overshoot, peak time and settling time remain the same for unit-step input and step input of any amplitude. Only the peak overshoot varies. The peak overshoot for a step input of 10 units is 10 times the peak overshoot for a unit-step input.

The closed-loop transfer function of the system is

$$\frac{C(s)}{R(s)} = \frac{G(s)}{1+G(s)} = \frac{\dfrac{5}{s(s+1)}}{1+\dfrac{5}{s(s+1)}} = \frac{5}{s^2+s+5}$$

Comparing this transfer function with the standard form of the transfer function of a second-order system,

$$\frac{C(s)}{R(s)} = \frac{\omega_n^2}{s^2+2\xi\omega_n s+\omega_n^2} = \frac{5}{s^2+s+5}$$

$$\therefore \qquad \omega_n^2 = 5$$

or

$$\omega_n = \sqrt{5} = 2.236 \text{ rad/s}$$

$$2\xi\omega_n = 1$$

$$\therefore \qquad \xi = \frac{1}{2\omega_n} = \frac{1}{2 \times 2.236} = 0.223$$

$$\omega_d = \omega_n\sqrt{1-\xi^2} = 2.236\sqrt{1-0.223^2} = 2.124 \text{ rad/s}$$

$$\theta = \tan^{-1}\frac{\sqrt{1-\xi^2}}{\xi} = \tan^{-1}\frac{\sqrt{1-0.223^2}}{0.223} = 1.346 \text{ rad/s}$$

The rise time

$$t_r = \frac{\pi-\theta}{\omega_d} = \frac{3.141-1.346}{2.124} = 0.845 \text{ s}$$

The percentage overshoot

$$\%M_p = e^{(-\pi\xi/\sqrt{1-\xi^2})} \times 100\%$$

$$= e^{(-\pi \times 0.223/\sqrt{1-0.223^2})} \times 100\%$$

$$= 0.478 \times 100 = 47.8\%$$

The peak overshoot for a unit-step input is

$$\frac{47.8}{100} = 0.478$$

For an input of 10 units, the peak overshoot is

$$0.478 \times 10 = 4.78$$

The peak time

$$t_p = \frac{\pi}{\omega_d} = \frac{\pi}{2.124} = 1.479\,\text{s}$$

The time constant

$$T = \frac{1}{\xi\omega_n} = \frac{1}{0.223 \times 2.236} = 2\,\text{s}$$

For 5% error, the settling time

$$t_s = 3T = 3 \times 2 = 6\text{s}$$

For 2% error, the settling time

$$t_s = 4T = 4 \times 2 = 8\text{s}$$

Example 4.15 A unity feedback control system is characterized by the following open-loop transfer function

$$G(s) = \frac{0.4s+1}{s(s+0.6)}$$

Determine its transient response for a unit-step input. Evaluate the maximum overshoot and the corresponding peak time.

Solution: The closed-loop transfer function of the system is

$$\frac{C(s)}{R(s)} = \frac{G(s)}{1+G(s)} = \frac{\dfrac{0.4s+1}{s(s+0.6)}}{1+\dfrac{0.4s+1}{s(s+0.6)}}$$

$$= \frac{0.4s+1}{s^2+s+1}$$

For a unit-step input, $r(t) = 1$. Therefore,

$$R(s) = \frac{1}{s}$$

The output of the system is therefore given by

$$C(s) = R(s) \times \frac{G(s)}{1+G(s)} = \frac{1}{s} \times \frac{0.4s+1}{s^2+s+1}$$

$$\therefore \qquad C(s) = \frac{A}{s} + \frac{Bs+C}{s^2+s+1} = \frac{1}{s} - \frac{s+0.6}{s^2+s+1}$$

$$= \frac{1}{s} - \frac{s+0.5}{s^2+s+0.25+0.75} - \frac{0.1}{s^2+s+0.25+0.75}$$

$$= \frac{1}{s} - \frac{s+0.5}{(s+0.5)^2+(\sqrt{0.75})^2} - \frac{0.1}{(\sqrt{0.75})} \frac{(\sqrt{0.75})}{(s+0.5)^2+(\sqrt{0.75})^2}$$

Taking the inverse Laplace transform on both sides

$$c(t) = 1 - e^{-0.5t}\left[\cos\sqrt{0.75}t - \frac{0.1}{\sqrt{0.75}}\sin\sqrt{0.75}t\right]$$

This value of $c(t)$ gives the total time response of the system.

The transient response is that part of the time response which tends to zero as t tends to infinity. Here in the expression for $c(t)$, as $t \to \infty$, the exponential component $e^{-0.5t}$ tends to zero. Hence the transient response is given by the damped sinusoidal component.

Hence the transient response is

$$c(t) = e^{-0.5t}\left[\cos\sqrt{0.75}t - \frac{0.1}{\sqrt{0.75}}\sin\sqrt{0.75}t\right]$$

The values of ξ and ω_n can be estimated by comparing the characteristic equation of the system transfer function with the standard form of the second-order characteristic equation. Therefore,

$$s^2 + 2\xi\omega_n s + \omega_n^2 = s^2 + s + 1$$

$$\omega_n^2 = 1$$

or

$$\omega_n = 1$$

$$2\xi\omega_n = 1$$

$$\therefore \qquad \xi = \frac{1}{2\omega_n} = \frac{1}{2\times 1} = 0.5$$

The maximum overshoot

$$M_p = e^{-\pi\xi/\sqrt{1-\xi^2}} = e^{-3.147\times0.5/\sqrt{1-0.5^2}} = 0.163$$

The % maximum overshoot is

$$M_p \times 100 = 0.163 \times 100 = 16.3\%$$

The peak time

$$t_p = \frac{\pi}{\omega_d} = \frac{\pi}{\omega_n\sqrt{1-\xi^2}} = \frac{\pi}{1\times\sqrt{1-0.5^2}} = 3.628 \text{ s}$$

Example 4.16   The open-loop transfer function of a unity feedback control system is given by

$$G(s) = \frac{K}{s(1+sT)}$$

(a) By what factor the amplifier gain K should be multiplied so that the damping ratio is increased from 0.2 to 0.8?

(b) By what factor the time constant T should be multiplied so that the damping ratio is reduced from 0.9 to 0.3?

Solution: The closed-loop transfer function of the system is

$$\frac{C(s)}{R(s)} = \frac{\dfrac{K}{s(1+sT)}}{1+\dfrac{K}{s(1+sT)}} = \frac{\dfrac{K}{T}}{s^2 + \dfrac{s}{T} + \dfrac{K}{T}}$$

Comparing the characteristic equation $s^2 + \dfrac{s}{T} + \dfrac{K}{T} = 0$, with the standard form of the characteristic equation $s^2 + 2\xi\omega_n s + \omega_n^2 = 0$ of a second-order system.

$$2\xi\omega_n = \frac{1}{T}$$

and

$$\omega_n^2 = \frac{K}{T}$$

i.e.

$$\omega_n = \sqrt{\frac{K}{T}}$$

$\therefore$

$$2\xi\sqrt{\frac{K}{T}} = \frac{1}{T}$$

or

$$\xi = \frac{1}{2\sqrt{KT}}$$

(a) When $\xi = \xi_1 = 0.2$, let $K = K_1$.

When $\xi = \xi_2 = 0.8$, let $K = K_2$.

$\therefore$

$$\frac{\xi_1}{\xi_2} = \frac{0.2}{0.8} = \frac{1}{4} = \frac{1}{2\sqrt{K_1 T}} \times 2\sqrt{K_2 T} = \sqrt{\frac{K_2}{K_1}}$$

i.e.

$$\frac{K_2}{K_1} = \left(\frac{\xi_1}{\xi_2}\right)^2 = \frac{1}{16}$$

or

$$K_2 = \frac{1}{16}K_1$$

Hence the gain K_1, at which $\xi = 0.2$ should be multiplied by 1/16 to increase the damping ratio from 0.2 to 0.8.

  (b) When $\xi = \xi_1 = 0.9$, let $T = T_1$.

  When $\xi = \xi_2 = 0.3$, let $T = T_2$.

$$\frac{\xi_1}{\xi_2} = \frac{0.9}{0.3} = 3 = \frac{1}{2\sqrt{KT_1}} \times 2\sqrt{KT_2} = \sqrt{\frac{T_2}{T_1}}$$

$$\therefore \qquad \frac{T_2}{T_1} = \left(\frac{\xi_1}{\xi_2}\right)^2 = 9$$

or

$$T_2 = 9T_1$$

Hence the original time constant T_1 should be multiplied by 9 to reduce the damping ratio from 0.9 to 0.3.

Example 4.17   A unity feedback control system has an amplifier with gain $K_A = 16$ and gain ratio,

$$G(s) = \frac{1}{s(s+4)}$$

in the forward path. A derivative feedback $H(s) = sK_0$ is introduced as a minor loop around $G(s)$. Determine the derivative feedback constant K_0 so that the system damping factor is 0.5.

  Solution: The given system can be represented by the block diagram shown in Figure 4.20.

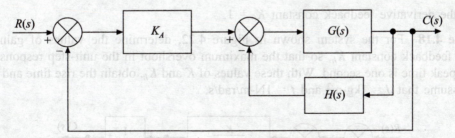

Figure 4.20   Example 4.17: Block diagram.

Here $K_A = 16$, $G(s) = \dfrac{1}{s(s+3)}$ and $H(s) = sK_0$.

The closed-loop transfer function can be obtained by using the signal flow graph method as shown in Figure 4.21.

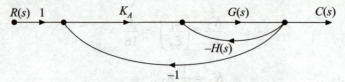

Figure 4.21 Example 4.17: Signal flow graph.

$$\frac{C(s)}{R(s)} = \frac{K_A G(s)}{1 - [-G(s)H(s) - K_A G(s)]}$$

$$= \frac{16 \times \dfrac{1}{s(s+3)}}{1 + \dfrac{sK_0}{s(s+3)} + \dfrac{16}{s(s+3)}}$$

$$= \frac{16}{s^2 + (3 + K_0)s + 16}$$

Looking at the transfer function, we observe that the given system is a second-order system. Comparing it with the standard form of the transfer function of a second-order system,

$$\frac{C(s)}{R(s)} = \frac{\omega_n^2}{s^2 + 2\xi\omega_n s + \omega_n^2} = \frac{16}{s^2 + (3 + K_0)s + 16}$$

$$\omega_n^2 = 16$$

i.e. $$\omega_n = \sqrt{16} = 4$$

$$2\xi\omega_n = 3 + K_0$$

∴ $$2 \times 0.5 \times 4 = 3 + K_0$$

or $$K_0 = 1$$

So the derivative feedback constant $K_0 = 1$.

Example 4.18 For the system shown in Figure 4.22, determine the values of gain K and velocity feedback constant K_h, so that the maximum overshoot in the unit-step response is 0.2 and the peak time is one second. With these values of K and K_h, obtain the rise time and settling time. Assume that $J = 1$kg-m^2 and $f = 1$N-m/rad/s.

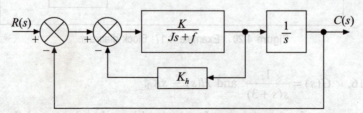

Figure 4.22 Example 4.18: Block diagram.

Solution: The block diagram shown in Figure 4.22 can be simplified as shown in Figure 4.23.

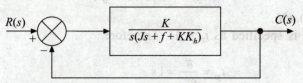

Figure 4.23 Example 4.18: Simplified block diagram.

The transfer function of the system is given by

$$\frac{C(s)}{R(s)} = \frac{K}{Js^2 + (f + KK_h)s + K}$$

$$= \frac{\dfrac{K}{J}}{s^2 + \dfrac{f + KK_h}{J} + \dfrac{K}{J}}$$

Comparing it with the transfer function of a standard second-order system,

$$\frac{C(s)}{R(s)} = \frac{\omega_n^2}{s^2 + 2\xi\omega_n s + \omega_n^2}$$

$$\omega_n = \sqrt{\frac{K}{J}}$$

and

$$2\xi\omega_n = \frac{f + KK_h}{J}$$

∴

$$\xi = \frac{f + KK_h}{2\sqrt{\dfrac{K}{J}} \cdot J} = \frac{f + KK_h}{2\sqrt{KJ}}$$

Determination of the values of K and K_h

The maximum overshoot M_p is given

$$M_p = e^{-\pi\xi/\sqrt{1-\xi^2}}$$

This value must be 0.2. Thus

$$e^{-\pi\xi/\sqrt{1-\xi^2}} = 0.2 = e^{-1.61}$$

∴

$$\frac{\pi\xi}{\sqrt{1-\xi^2}} = 1.61$$

or
$$\pi\xi = 1.61\sqrt{1-\xi^2}$$

i.e.
$$(\pi\xi)^2 = 1.61^2(1-\xi^2)$$

This yields $\xi = 0.456$.

The peak time t_p is specified as $t_p = 1$s. Therefore,

$$t_p = \frac{\pi}{\omega_d} = 1\,\text{s}$$

or
$$\omega_d = \frac{\pi}{t_p} = \frac{3.14}{1} = 3.14\,\text{rad/s}$$

We know that
$$\omega_d = \omega_n\sqrt{1-\xi^2}$$

Since $\xi = 0.456$, ω_n is therefore given by

$$\omega_n = \frac{\omega_d}{\sqrt{1-\xi^2}} = \frac{3.14}{\sqrt{1-0.456^2}} = 3.53\,\text{rad/s}$$

The natural frequency ω_n is equal to $\sqrt{\dfrac{K}{J}}$. Therefore,

$$K = J\omega_n^2 = 1 \times 3.53^2 = 12.5\,\text{N-m}$$

Since
$$\xi = \frac{f + KK_h}{2\sqrt{KJ}}$$

K_h is given by

$$K_h = \frac{2\xi\sqrt{KJ} - f}{K} = \frac{2 \times 0.456\sqrt{125 \times 1} - 1}{12.5} = 0.178\,\text{s}$$

The rise time t_r is given by

$$t_r = \frac{\pi - \theta}{\omega_d} = \frac{\pi - \tan^{-1}\dfrac{\sqrt{1-\xi^2}}{\xi}}{\omega_n\sqrt{1-\xi^2}}$$

$$= \frac{\pi - \tan^{-1}\dfrac{\sqrt{1-0.456^2}}{0.456}}{3.53 \times \sqrt{1-0.456^2}} = 0.651\,\text{s}$$

Settling time t_s

For the 2% criterion

$$t_s = 4T = \frac{4}{\xi\omega_n} = \frac{4}{0.456 \times 3.53} = 2.48 \text{ s}$$

For the 5% criterion

$$t_s = 3T = \frac{3}{\xi\omega_n} = \frac{3}{0.456 \times 3.53} = 1.86 \text{ s}$$

Example 4.19 The closed-loop poles of a system are shown in Figure 4.24. Find the unit-step response of the system and the settling time for 2% tolerance.

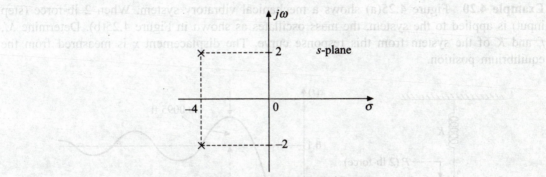

Figure 4.24   Example 4.19: Pole location.

Solution: From the pole location shown in Figure 4.24, the real part of the complex poles is

$$-\xi\omega_n = -4$$

i.e.

$$\xi\omega_n = 4$$

or

$$\omega_n = \frac{4}{\xi}$$

and

$$\omega_d = 2$$

We know

$$\omega_d = \omega_n\sqrt{1-\xi^2}$$

i.e.

$$2 = \frac{4}{\xi}\sqrt{1-\xi^2}$$

∴

$$\xi = 2\sqrt{1-\xi^2}$$

i.e.

$$\xi^2 = 4(1-\xi^2)$$

i.e.

$$\xi^2 = \frac{4}{5} = 0.8$$

or

$$\xi = 0.894$$

∴

$$\omega_n = \frac{4}{\xi} = \frac{4}{0.894} = 4.474 \text{ rad/s}$$

The unit-step response of the system is

$$c(t) = 1 - \frac{e^{-\xi\omega_n t}}{\sqrt{1-\xi^2}} \sin\left(\omega_d t + \tan^{-1}\frac{\sqrt{1-\xi^2}}{\xi}\right)$$

$$= 1 - \frac{e^{-4t}}{0.447} \sin\left(2t + \tan^{-1}\frac{0.447}{0.894}\right)$$

The settling time

$$t_s = \frac{4}{\xi\omega_n} = \frac{4}{4} = 1\,\text{s}$$

Example 4.20 Figure 4.25(a) shows a mechanical vibratory system. When 2 lb-force (step input) is applied to the system, the mass oscillates as shown in Figure 4.25(b). Determine M, f, and K of the system from this response curve. The displacement x is measured from the equilibrium position.

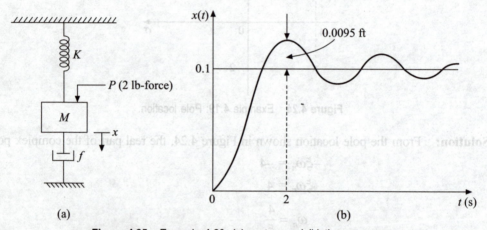

Figure 4.25 Example 4.20: (a) system and (b) time response.

Solution: The differential equation describing the behaviour of the mechanical vibratory system of Figure 4.25(a) is

$$P = M\ddot{x} + f\dot{x} + Kx$$

$$\therefore \qquad P(s) = (Ms^2 + fs + K)\,X(s)$$

So the transfer function of the given system is

$$\frac{X(s)}{P(s)} = \frac{1}{Ms^2 + fs + K}$$

Given $P = 2$ lb-force. Therefore,

$$P(s) = \frac{2}{s}$$

∴
$$X(s) = \frac{2}{s(Ms^2 + fs + K)}$$

From Figure 4.25(b), it can be observed that $x(\infty) = 0.1$. Therefore,

$$x(\infty) = \underset{s \to 0}{\text{Lt}}\ sX(s) = \underset{s \to 0}{\text{Lt}}\ s.\frac{2}{s(Ms^2 + fs + K)} = \frac{2}{K} = 0.1\,\text{ft}$$

Hence

$$K = 2/0.1 = 20\ \text{lb/ft}$$

$$M_p = 0.095 = e^{-\pi\xi/\sqrt{1-\xi^2}}$$

This yields $\xi = 0.6$.

From Figure 4.25(b), $t_p = 2$s. Therefore,

$$t_p = \frac{\pi}{\omega_d} = \frac{\pi}{\omega_n\sqrt{1-\xi^2}} = \frac{\pi}{0.8\omega_n} = 2$$

∴
$$\omega_n = \frac{\pi}{2 \times 0.8} = 1.96\ \text{rad/s}$$

Comparing the transfer function of this system with the standard form of the transfer function of a second-order system,

$$\frac{X(s)}{P(s)} = \frac{1/M}{Ms^2 + (f/M)s + (K/M)} = \frac{1}{K} \times \frac{K/M}{[Ms^2 + (f/M)s + K/M]} = \frac{\omega_n^2}{s^2 + 2\xi\omega_n s + \omega_n^2}$$

$$\omega_n^2 = \frac{K}{M} = \frac{20}{M}$$

∴
$$M = \frac{20}{\omega_n^2} = \frac{20}{1.96^2} = 5.2\ \text{slugs} = 166\ \text{lb}$$

$$2\xi\omega_n = \frac{f}{M}$$

or
$$f = 2\xi\omega_n M = 2 \times 0.6 \times 1.92 \times 5.2 = 12.2\ \text{lb/ft/s}$$

Example 4.21 Determine the values of K and P of the closed-loop system shown in Figure 4.26, so that the maximum overshoot in the unit-step response is 25% and the peak time is 2 seconds. Assume that $J = 1$kg-m^2.

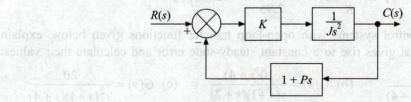

Figure 4.26 Example 4.21: Block diagram.

Solution: The closed-loop transfer function is

$$\frac{C(s)}{R(s)} = \frac{K/Js^2}{1 + (K/Js^2)(1 + Ps)} = \frac{K}{Js^2 + KPs + K}$$

Since $J = 1$ kg-m^2,

$$\frac{C(s)}{R(s)} = \frac{K}{s^2 + KPs + K}$$

Comparing this with the standard form of the transfer function of a second-order system,

$$\omega_n^2 = K,$$

i.e.

$$\omega_n = \sqrt{K}$$

$$2\xi\omega_n = KP$$

The peak overshoot

$$M_p = e^{-\pi\xi/\sqrt{1-\xi^2}} = 0.25 = e^{-1.386}$$

∴

$$\frac{\pi\xi}{\sqrt{1-\xi^2}} = 1.386$$

or

$$\xi = 0.404$$

The peak time t_p is specified as 2 seconds. So

$$t_p = \frac{\pi}{\omega_d} = 2$$

∴

$$\omega_d = \frac{\pi}{2} = 1.57 \text{ rad/s}$$

The undamped natural frequency

$$\omega_n = \frac{\omega_d}{\sqrt{1-\xi^2}} = \frac{1.57}{\sqrt{1-(0.404)^2}} = 1.72 \text{ rad/s}$$

∴

$$K = \omega_n^2 = 1.72^2 = 2.95 \text{ N-m}$$

$$P = \frac{2\xi\omega_n}{K} = \frac{2 \times 0.404 \times 1.72}{2.95} = 0.471 \text{ s}$$

Example 4.22 For control systems with open-loop transfer functions given below, explain what type of input signal gives rise to a constant steady-state error and calculate their values.

(a) $G(s) = \dfrac{20}{(s+1)(s+4)}$ (b) $G(s) = \dfrac{10(s+4)}{s(s+1)(s+2)}$ (c) $G(s) = \dfrac{20}{s^2(s+1)(s+4)}$

Solution:

(a) $G(s) = \dfrac{20}{(s+1)(s+4)}$

The open-loop transfer function does not have any pole at the origin. So it is a type-0 system. Therefore, only a step signal gives rise to a constant steady-state error. Hence

$$K_p = \underset{s \to 0}{\text{Lt}} \ G(s) = \underset{s \to 0}{\text{Lt}} \ \frac{20}{(s+1)(s+4)} = \frac{20}{4} = 5, \ K_v = 0 \text{ and } K_a = 0$$

Therefore, the steady-state error for unit-step input is

$$e_{ss}(t) = \frac{1}{1+K_p} = \frac{1}{1+5} = \frac{1}{6}$$

(b) $G(s) = \dfrac{10(s+4)}{s(s+1)(s+2)}$

The open-loop transfer function has got one pole at the origin of the s-plane. So, it is a type-1 system. Therefore, only a ramp signal gives rise to a constant steady-state error. Hence

$$K_p = \infty, \ K_a = 0$$

and $$K_v = \underset{s \to 0}{\text{Lt}} \ sG(s) = \underset{s \to 0}{\text{Lt}} \ s \times \frac{10(s+4)}{s(s+1)(s+2)} = 20$$

Therefore, the steady-state error for a unit-ramp input is

$$e_{ss}(t) = \frac{1}{K_v} = \frac{1}{20} = 0.05$$

(c) $G(s) = \dfrac{20}{s^2(s+1)(s+4)}$

The open-loop transfer function has got two poles at the origin of the s-plane. So it is a type-2 system. Therefore, only a parabolic signal gives rise to a constant steady-state error. Hence

$$K_p = \infty, \ K_v = \infty$$

and $$K_a = \underset{s \to 0}{\text{Lt}} \ s^2 G(s) = \underset{s \to 0}{\text{Lt}} \ s^2 \times \frac{20}{s^2(s+1)(s+4)} = 5$$

Therefore, the steady-state error for a unit-parabolic input is

$$e_{ss}(t) = \frac{1}{K_a} = \frac{1}{5} = 0.2$$

Example 4.23 A unity feedback system is characterized by the open-loop transfer function

$$G(s) = \frac{1}{s(0.5s+1)(0.2s+1)}$$

Determine the steady-state errors for unit-step, unit-ramp and unit-acceleration input.

Solution: For a unity feedback system, $H(s) = 1$.

The position error constant

$$K_p = \underset{s\to 0}{Lt}\ G(s)$$

$$= \underset{s\to 0}{Lt}\ \frac{1}{s(0.5s+1)(0.2s+1)} = \infty$$

Therefore, the steady-state error for a unit-step input is

$$e_{ss}(t) = \frac{1}{1+K_p} = \frac{1}{1+\infty} = 0$$

The velocity error constant

$$K_v = \underset{s\to 0}{Lt}\ sG(s)$$

$$= \underset{s\to 0}{Lt}\ s \times \frac{1}{s(0.5s+1)(0.2s+1)} = 1$$

Therefore, the steady-state error for a unit-ramp input is

$$e_{ss}(t) = \frac{1}{K_v} = \frac{1}{1} = 1$$

The acceleration error constant

$$K_a = \underset{s\to 0}{Lt}\ s^2 G(s)$$

$$= \underset{s\to 0}{Lt}\ s^2 \times \frac{1}{s(0.5s+1)(0.2s+1)} = 0$$

Therefore, the steady-state error for a unit-acceleration input is

$$e_{ss}(t) = \frac{1}{K_a} = \frac{1}{0} = \infty$$

Example 4.24 Consider a unity feedback system with a closed transfer function

$$\frac{C(s)}{R(s)} = \frac{Ks+b}{s^2+as+b}$$

Determine the open-loop transfer function $G(s)$. Show that the steady-state error with unit-ramp input is given by $\dfrac{a-K}{b}$.

Solution: For the given unity feedback control system, the closed-loop transfer function is

$$\frac{C(s)}{R(s)} = \frac{G(s)}{1+G(s)} = \frac{Ks+b}{s^2+as+b}$$

Cross multiplying the above equation,

$$(s^2+as+b)G(s) = (Ks+b) + (Ks+b)G(s)$$

i.e.
$$G(s)[(s^2+as+b) - (Ks+b)] = (Ks+b)$$

$\therefore$
$$G(s) = \frac{Ks+b}{s[s+(a-K)]}$$

The velocity error constant

$$K_v = \underset{s\to0}{\text{Lt}}\ sG(s)$$

$$= \underset{s\to0}{\text{Lt}}\ s \times \frac{Ks+b}{s[s+(a-K)]} = \frac{b}{a-K}$$

Therefore, the steady-state error for a unit-ramp input is

$$e_{ss}(t) = \frac{1}{K_v} = \frac{1}{\dfrac{b}{a-K}} = \frac{a-K}{b}$$

Example 4.25 A unity feedback system has the forward path transfer function

$$G(s) = \frac{K_1(2s+1)}{s(5s+1)(s+1)^2}$$

The input $r(t) = 1 + 6t$ is applied to the system. Determine the minimum value of K_1 if the steady-state error is to be less than 0.1.

Solution: The given system is a type-1 system. Therefore,

$$K_p = \infty$$

$$K_v = \underset{s\to0}{\text{Lt}}\ s\,\frac{K_1(2s+1)}{s(5s+1)(1+s)^2} = K_1$$

and
$$K_a = 0$$

Since the input is $r(t) = 1 + 6t$, applying the superposition theorem, the steady-state error for the input

$$r(t) = 1 + 6t = 1 \times \text{(steady-state error for a unit-step input)}$$
$$+\ 6 \times \text{(steady-state error for a unit-ramp input)}$$

$$= 1 \times \left(\frac{1}{1 + K_p} \right) + 6 \times \left(\frac{1}{K_v} \right) = \frac{1}{1 + \infty} + \frac{6}{K_1} = \frac{6}{K_1}$$

Given that $e_{ss} < 0.1$, for minimum value of K_1

$$e_{ss}(t) = 0.1 = \frac{6}{K_1}$$

or

$$K_1 = \frac{6}{0.1} = 60$$

So the minimum value of K_1 is 60.

Example 4.26   The open-loop transfer function of a servo system with unity feedback is

$$G(s) = \frac{10}{s(0.1s + 1)}$$

Evaluate the static error coefficients (K_p K_v, K_a) for the system. Obtain the steady-state error of the system when subjected to an input given by the polynomial

$$r(t) = a_0 + a_1 t + \frac{a_2}{2} t^2$$

Also evaluate the dynamic error using the dynamic error coefficients.

Solution: (a) The position error constant

$$K_p = \underset{s \to 0}{\text{Lt }} G(s)$$

$$= \underset{s \to 0}{\text{Lt }} \frac{10}{s(0.1s + 1)} = \infty$$

Therefore, the steady-state error for a unit-step input is

$$e_{ss}(t) = \frac{1}{1 + K_p} = \frac{1}{1 + \infty} = 0$$

The velocity error constant

$$K_v = \underset{s \to 0}{\text{Lt }} sG(s)$$

$$= \underset{s \to 0}{\text{Lt }} s \times \frac{10}{s(0.1s + 1)} = 10$$

Therefore, the steady-state error for a unit-ramp input is

$$e_{ss}(t) = \frac{1}{K_v} = \frac{1}{10} = 0.1$$

The acceleration error constant

$$K_a = \underset{s \to 0}{\text{Lt}}\ s^2 G(s)$$

$$= \underset{s \to 0}{\text{Lt}}\ s^2 \times \frac{10}{s(0.1s+1)} = 0$$

Therefore, the steady-state error for a unit-acceleration input is

$$e_{ss}(t) = \frac{1}{K_a} = \frac{1}{0} = \infty$$

For a linear system, we can apply the principle of superposition. Therefore, the steady-state error for an input

$$r(t) = a_0 + a_1 t + a_2 \frac{t^2}{2}$$

$$= a_0 \times \text{(steady-state error for a unit-step input)} +$$
$$a_1 \times \text{(steady-state error for a unit-ramp input)} +$$
$$a_2 \times \text{(steady-state error for a unit-parabolic input)}$$

$$= a_0 \times (0) + a_1 \times (0.1) + a_2 \times (\infty) = 0 + 0.1a_1 + \infty = \infty$$

(b) For the given unity feedback system,

$$\frac{E(s)}{R(s)} = \frac{1}{1+G(s)} = \frac{1}{1 + \dfrac{10}{s(0.1s+1)}} = \frac{0.1s^2 + s}{0.1s^2 + s + 10}$$

For expanding it into an infinite series in ascending powers of s, write the numerator and denominator polynomials in ascending powers of s, i.e.

$$\frac{E(s)}{R(s)} = \frac{s + 0.1s^2}{10 + s + 0.1s^2} = \frac{s}{10} - \frac{s^3}{1000} + \frac{s^4}{10000}$$

$$
\begin{array}{r}
\dfrac{s}{10} - \dfrac{s^3}{1000} + \dfrac{s^4}{10000} \cdots \\[2mm]
10 + s + 0.1s^2\ \overline{\big)\ s + 0.1s^2} \\[1mm]
\underline{s + 0.1s^2 + 0.01s^3} \\[1mm]
-0.01s^3 \\[1mm]
\underline{-0.01s^3 - 0.001s^4 - 0.0001s^5} \\[1mm]
0.001s^4 + 0.0001s^5
\end{array}
$$

Equating it with

$$\frac{E(s)}{R(s)} = C_0 + C_1 s + \frac{C_2}{2!}s^2 + \frac{C_3}{3!}s^3 + \cdots$$

The dynamic error coefficients are as follows:

$$C_0 = 0, \quad C_1 = \frac{1}{10} = 0.1, \quad C_2 = 0$$

Therefore, the dynamic error is

$$e(t) = C_0 r(t) + C_1 \frac{dr(t)}{dt} + \frac{C_2}{2!} \frac{d^2 r(t)}{dt^2} + \frac{C_3}{3!} \frac{d^3 r(t)}{dt^3} + \cdots$$

$$= \frac{1}{\infty}\left(a_0 + a_1 t + \frac{a_2 t^2}{2}\right) + \frac{1}{10}\left[\frac{d}{dt}\left(a_0 + a_1 t + \frac{a_2 t^2}{2}\right)\right] + \frac{1}{\infty}\left[\frac{d^2}{dt^2}\left(a_0 + a_1 t + \frac{a_2 t^2}{2}\right)\right] \times \frac{1}{2}$$

$$= 0 + 0.1(a_1 + a_2 t) + 0$$

$$= 0.1(a_1 + a_2 t)$$

Therefore, the steady-state error

$$e_{ss}(t) = \underset{t \to \infty}{\text{Lt}}\ e(t) = \underset{t \to \infty}{\text{Lt}}\ 0.1(a_1 + a_2 t) = \infty$$

Example 4.27 A unity feedback system has

$$G(s) = \frac{K}{s(s+1)(0.1s+1)} \quad \text{and} \quad r(t) = 10t$$

(a) If $K = 2\ \text{s}^{-1}$, determine $e_{ss}(t)$.
(b) Find the minimum value of K for $e_{ss}(t) < 0.1$, for a unit-ramp input.

Solution:
(a)

$$\text{Input } r(t) = 10t$$

Therefore,

$$R(s) = \frac{10}{s^2}$$

The steady-state error for a unity feedback system is given by

$$e_{ss}(t) = \underset{s \to 0}{\text{Lt}}\ sE(s) = \underset{s \to 0}{\text{Lt}}\ s\frac{R(s)}{1 + G(s)}$$

$$= \underset{s \to 0}{\text{Lt}}\ \frac{s\left(\dfrac{10}{s^2}\right)}{1 + \dfrac{K}{s(s+1)(0.1s+1)}}$$

$$= \underset{s \to 0}{\text{Lt}}\ \frac{s\left(\dfrac{10}{s^2}\right)s(s+1)(0.1s+1)}{s(s+1)(0.1s+1) + K}$$

If $K = 2$,

$$e_{ss}(t) = \underset{s \to 0}{\text{Lt}} \, \frac{10(s+1)(0.1s+1)}{s(s+1)(0.1s+1)+2}$$

$$= \frac{10}{2} = 5$$

(b)   Input $r(t) = t$

Therefore, $R(s) = \dfrac{1}{s^2}$

It is desired to have $e_{ss}(t) < 0.1$.
Therefore, we have

$$e_{ss}(t) = \underset{s \to 0}{\text{Lt}} \, \frac{s\left(\dfrac{1}{s^2}\right)}{1 + \dfrac{K}{s(s+1)(0.1s+1)}} < 0.1$$

i.e. $\underset{s \to 0}{\text{Lt}} \, \dfrac{(s+1)(0.1s+1)}{s(s+1)(0.1s+1)+K} < 0.1$

i.e. $\dfrac{1}{K} < 0.1$

or $K > 10$

Therefore, the minimum value of K is 10.

Example 4.28   A servo mechanism is designed to keep a radar antenna pointed at a flying aeroplane. If the aeroplane is flying with a velocity of 600 km/h, at a range of 2 km, and the maximum tracking error is to be within 0.1°, determine the required velocity error coefficient.

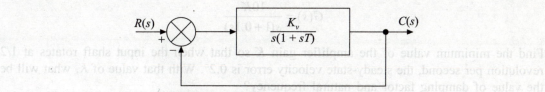

Figure 4.27   Example 4.28: Block diagram.

Solution: The block diagram of the given servomechanism is shown in Figure 4.27.
         Linear velocity = 600 km/h
         Radius r = 2 km
The angular velocity

$$\omega = \frac{600}{2} = 300 \text{ rad/h}$$

$$= \frac{300}{3600} = 0.083 \text{ rad/s}$$

$$\therefore \qquad R(s) = \frac{0.083}{s^2}$$

The steady-state error

$$e_{ss} = \underset{s \to 0}{\text{Lt}}\ sE(s)$$

$$= \underset{s \to 0}{\text{Lt}}\ s \cdot \frac{R(s)}{1 + G(s)H(s)}$$

$$= \underset{s \to 0}{\text{Lt}}\ s \times \frac{0.083}{s^2} \cdot \frac{1}{1 + \dfrac{K_v}{s(1 + sT)}}$$

$$= \underset{s \to 0}{\text{Lt}}\ \frac{0.083}{s} \cdot \frac{s(1 + sT)}{s(1 + sT) + K_v}$$

$$= \frac{0.083}{K_v}$$

Given the maximum tracking error $e_{ss} = 0.1°$. Therefore,

$$e_{ss}(t) = 0.1 = \frac{0.083}{K_v}$$

or

$$K_v = \frac{0.083}{0.1} = 0.83 \text{ per degree}$$

Therefore, the required velocity error coefficient $K_v = 0.83$ per degree.

Example 4.29 The open-loop transfer function of a unity feedback ac position control system is

$$G(s) = \frac{10K}{s(1 + 0.1s)}$$

Find the minimum value of the amplifier gain K so that when the input shaft rotates at 1/2 revolution per second, the steady-state velocity error is 0.2°. With that value of K, what will be the value of damping factor and natural frequency?

Solution: Input velocity $= \dfrac{1}{2}$ revolution per second $= \dfrac{1}{2} \times 2\pi = \pi\ = 3.14$ rad/s

Therefore, the ramp input, $R = 3.14$ rad/s.

The steady-state error

$$e_{ss} = 0.2° = \frac{0.2 \times \pi}{180} \text{ rad}$$

For a ramp input of R units

$$e_{ss} = \frac{R}{K_v}$$

$$\therefore \qquad K_v = \frac{R}{e_{ss}} = \frac{3.14 \times 180}{0.2 \times 3.14} = 900$$

But

$$K_v = \underset{s \to 0}{\text{Lt}} \, sG(s) = \underset{s \to 0}{\text{Lt}} \, s \frac{10K}{s(1+0.1s)} = 10K$$

$$\therefore \qquad 10K = 900$$

or

$$K = 90$$

The closed-loop transfer function is

$$\frac{C(s)}{R(s)} = \frac{G(s)}{1+G(s)} = \frac{\dfrac{900}{s(1+0.1s)}}{1+\dfrac{900}{s(1+0.1s)}} = \frac{9000}{s^2 + 10s + 9000}$$

Comparing this with the standard form of the transfer function of a second-order system,

i.e. with

$$\frac{C(s)}{R(s)} = \frac{\omega_n^2}{s^2 + 2\xi\omega_n s + \omega_n^2}, \quad \text{we get } \omega_n^2 = 9000$$

Therefore, the natural frequency

$$\omega_n = \sqrt{9000} = 94.87 \text{ rad/s}$$

$$2\xi\omega_n = 10$$

Therefore, the damping ratio

$$\xi = \frac{10}{2\omega_n} = \frac{10}{2 \times 94.87} = 0.053$$

Example 4.30 A control system is designed to keep the antenna of a tracking radar pointed at a flying target. The system must be able to follow a target travelling in a straight line with a speed of 200 m/s with maximum permissible error of 0.01 degree. The shortest distance from the antenna to the target is 250 m. Find the value of error constant K_v in order to satisfy the requirements.

Figure 4.28 shows the arrangement.

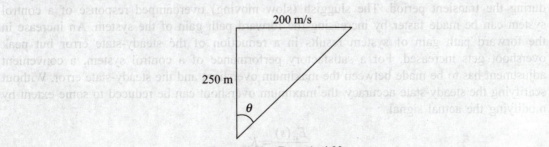

Figure 4.28   Example 4.30.

Solution:
$$\text{Speed} = 200\text{m/s}$$

$$\text{Angular velocity} = \tan^{-1}\frac{200}{250} = 38.66 \text{ deg/s} = 0.675 \text{ rad/s}$$

The steady-state error

$$e_{ss} = \frac{\text{Angular velocity}}{K_v}$$

$\therefore$

$$K_v = \frac{\text{Velocity}}{\text{Error}} = \frac{38.66}{0.01} = 3866$$

or

the steady-state error $= 0.01° = 0.01 \times \dfrac{\pi}{180}$ rad

$\therefore$

$$K_v = \frac{0.675}{0.01 \times \dfrac{\pi}{180}} = \frac{0.675 \times 180}{0.01 \times \pi} = 3867$$

4.9   RESPONSE WITH P, PI, PD AND PID CONTROLLERS

4.9.1   Proportional Control

In proportional control, the actuating signal $E_a(s)$ is proportional to the error signal $E(s)$. Hence the name proportional control system. The block diagram of Figure 4.29 shows the proportional control action.

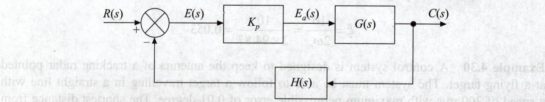

Figure 4.29   Block diagram of proportional control system.

For quick response, it is necessary that the control system should be underdamped. An underdamped control system has exponentially decaying oscillations in the output time response during the transient period. The sluggish (slow moving) overdamped response of a control system can be made faster by increasing the forward path gain of the system. An increase in the forward path gain of system results in a reduction of the steady-state error but peak overshoot gets increased. For a satisfactory performance of a control system, a convenient adjustment has to be made between the maximum overshoot and the steady-state error. Without scarifying the steady-state accuracy, the maximum overshoot can be reduced to some extent by modifying the actual signal.

$$\frac{E_a(s)}{E(s)} = K_p$$

where K_p is known as proportional gain.

4.9.2 Derivative Control

In derivative control, the actuating signal consists of proportional error signal and derivative of the error signal, i.e.

$$e_a(t) = e(t) + T_d \frac{d}{dt} e(t) \tag{4.27}$$

Taking the Laplace transform on both sides of Eq. (4.27),

$$E_a(s) = E(s) + T_d s E(s)$$

i.e.
$$E_a(s) = (1 + sT_d) E(s)$$

Figure 4.30 shows a block diagram of a second-order unity feedback control system using derivative control.

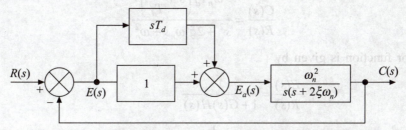

Figure 4.30 Block diagram of a control system with derivative control.

The overall transfer function of the system of Figure 4.30 is given by

$$\frac{C(s)}{R(s)} = \frac{(1 + sT_d) \dfrac{\omega_n^2}{s(s + 2\xi\omega_n)}}{1 + (1 + sT_d) \times \dfrac{\omega_n^2}{s(s + 2\xi\omega_n)}}$$

$$= \frac{\omega_n^2(1 + sT_d)}{s^2 + 2\xi\omega_n s + \omega_n^2 + sT_d\omega_n^2}$$

$$= \frac{\omega_n^2(1 + sT_d)}{s^2 + (2\xi\omega_n + \omega_n^2 T_d)s + \omega_n^2}$$

So, the characteristic equation is

$$s^2 + (2\xi\omega_n + \omega_n^2 T_d)s + \omega_n^2 = 0 \tag{4.28}$$

If ξ' is the effective damping ratio of the second-order system with derivative control, its characteristic equation should be

$$s^2 + 2\xi'\omega_n s + \omega_n^2 = 0 \tag{4.29}$$

Comparing Eqs. (4.28) and (4.29),

$$2\xi'\omega_n = 2\xi\omega_n + \omega_n^2 T_d$$

i.e.

$$\xi' = \frac{2\xi\omega_n + \omega_n^2 T_d}{2\omega_n}$$

i.e.

$$\xi' = \xi + \frac{\omega_n T_d}{2} \qquad (4.30)$$

Equation (4.30) shows that the damping ratio is increased using derivative control, but the maximum overshoot is reduced. Now the overall transfer function of the system of Figure 4.30 can be written as

$$\frac{C(s)}{R(s)} = \frac{\omega_n^2 T_d \left(s + \dfrac{1}{T_d}\right)}{s^2 + 2\xi'\omega_n s + \omega_n^2}$$

The error function is given by

$$\frac{E(s)}{R(s)} = \frac{1}{1 + G(s)H(s)}$$

$$= \frac{1}{1 + \dfrac{\omega_n^2(1 + sT_d)}{s(s + 2\xi\omega_n)}}$$

$$= \frac{s(s + 2\xi\omega_n)}{s(s + 2\xi\omega_n) + \omega_n^2(1 + sT_d)}$$

i.e.

$$\frac{E(s)}{R(s)} = \frac{s(s + 2\xi\omega_n)}{s^2 + (2\xi\omega_n + \omega_n^2 T_d)s + \omega_n^2}$$

For a ramp input,

$$r(t) = t$$

$\therefore$

$$R(s) = \frac{1}{s^2}$$

Therefore, the error signal

$$E(s) = \frac{1}{s^2} \cdot \frac{s(s + 2\xi\omega_n)}{s^2 + (2\xi\omega_n + \omega_n^2 T_d)s + \omega_n^2}$$

The steady-state error for a unit-ramp input is given by

$$e_{ss}(t) = \underset{s \to 0}{\mathrm{Lt}}\; sE(s)$$

$$= \underset{s \to 0}{\text{Lt }} s \cdot \frac{1}{s^2} \cdot \frac{s(s + 2\xi\omega_n)}{s^2 + (2\xi\omega_n + \omega_n^2 T_d)s + \omega_n^2}$$

$$= \frac{2\xi\omega_n}{\omega_n^2}$$

i.e. $$e_{ss}(t) = \frac{2\xi}{\omega_n}$$

Comparing this with the steady-state error of a second-order system without derivative control, we see that both values are the same. Thus, the steady-state error is not effected by derivative control action.

Comparing the transfer functions of the second-order system with and without derivative control, we see that ω_n is unchanged but a zero has been added at $s = -1/T_d$, which has resulted in a different expression for time response wherein the rise time t_r is reduced.

4.9.3 Derivative Feedback Control

The derivative feedback control or rate feedback control is also known as *tachometer feedback control*. In derivative feedback control, the actuating signal is the difference of the proportional error signal and the derivative of the output signal. The actuating signal is therefore given by

$$e_a(t) = e(t) - K_t \frac{dc(t)}{dt} \tag{4.31}$$

Taking the Laplace transform on both sides of Eq. (4.31),

$$E_a(s) = E(s) - K_t s C(s)$$

The block diagram of a second-order unity feedback control system incorporating derivative feedback control is shown in Figure 4.31.

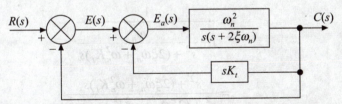

Figure 4.31 Block diagram of a control system with derivative feedback control.

Figure 4.32 shows a simplified block diagram of Figure 4.31.

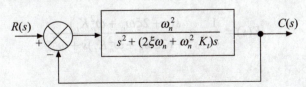

Figure 4.32 Simplified block diagram.

The transfer function of the system of Figure 4.31 is

$$\frac{C(s)}{R(s)} = \frac{\dfrac{\omega_n^2}{s^2 + (2\xi\omega_n + \omega_n^2 K_t)s}}{1 + \dfrac{\omega_n^2}{s^2 + (2\xi\omega_n + \omega_n^2 K_t)s}}$$

$$= \frac{\omega_n^2}{s^2 + (2\xi\omega_n + \omega_n^2 K_t)s + \omega_n^2}$$

The characteristic equation is

$$s^2 + (2\xi\omega_n + \omega_n^2 K_t)s + \omega_n^2 = 0 \qquad (4.32)$$

If ξ' is the damping ratio of the system with derivative feedback control, its characteristic equation should be

$$s^2 + 2\xi'\omega_n s + \omega_n^2 = 0 \qquad (4.33)$$

Comparing the characteristic equations [Eqs. (4.32) and (4.33)],

$$2\xi'\omega_n = 2\xi\omega_n + \omega_n^2 K_t$$

i.e.

$$\xi' = \xi + \frac{\omega_n K_t}{2}$$

This shows that, by using the derivative feedback control, the damping ratio is increased and so the maximum overshoot is reduced. From the reduced block diagram of Figure 4.32, we see that

$$\frac{E(s)}{R(s)} = \frac{1}{1 + G(s)H(s)}$$

$$= \frac{1}{1 + \dfrac{\omega_n^2}{s^2 + (2\xi\omega_n + \omega_n^2 K_t)s}}$$

$$= \frac{s^2 + (2\xi\omega_n + \omega_n^2 K_t)s}{s^2 + (2\xi\omega_n + \omega_n^2 K_t)s + \omega_n^2}$$

For a ramp input, $r(t) = t$ and so $R(s) = \dfrac{1}{s^2}$. Therefore, the error signal

$$E(s) = \frac{1}{s^2} \cdot \frac{s(s + 2\xi\omega_n + \omega_n^2 K_t)}{s^2 + (2\xi\omega_n + \omega_n^2 K_t)s + \omega_n^2}$$

The steady-state error is given by

$$e_{ss}(t) = \underset{s \to 0}{\text{Lt}}\, sE(s)$$

$$= \underset{s \to 0}{\text{Lt}}\, s.\frac{1}{s^2}.\frac{s(s + 2\xi\omega_n + \omega_n^2 K_t)}{s^2 + (2\xi\omega_n + \omega_n^2 K_t)s + \omega_n^2}$$

$$= \frac{2\xi\omega_n + \omega_n^2 K_t}{\omega_n^2}$$

$$= \frac{2\xi}{\omega_n} + K_t$$

Hence, we see that by using derivative feedback control the steady-state error is increased.

Example 4.31   A closed-loop control system with unity feedback is shown in Figure 4.33. By using derivative control, the damping ratio is to be made 0.75. Determine the value of T_d. Also determine the rise time, peak time and peak overshoot without derivative control and with derivative control. The input to the system is a unit-step.

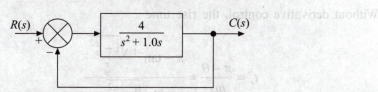

Figure 4.33   Example 4.31: Block diagram.

Solution: The closed-loop transfer function of the system is

$$\frac{C(s)}{R(s)} = \frac{\dfrac{4}{s^2 + 1.0s}}{1 + \dfrac{4}{s^2 + 1.0s}} = \frac{4}{s^2 + 1.0s + 4}$$

Therefore, the characteristic equation is

$$s^2 + 1.0s + 4 = 0,$$

Comparing it with

$$s^2 + 2\xi\omega_n s + \omega_n^2 = 0$$

$$\omega_n^2 = 4$$

$$\therefore \qquad \omega_n = 2 \text{ rad/s}$$

and

$$2\xi\omega_n = 1$$

$$\therefore \qquad \xi = \frac{1}{2\omega_n} = \frac{1}{2 \times 2} = 0.25$$

The damping ratio with derivative control is

$$\xi' = \xi + \frac{\omega_n T_d}{2}$$

Since the damping ratio with derivative control is to be 0.75 and $\omega_n = 2$, we have

$$0.75 = 0.25 + \frac{2 \times T_d}{2}$$

$\therefore$

$$T_d = 0.5$$

Therefore, the block diagram with derivative control is as shown in Figure 4.34.

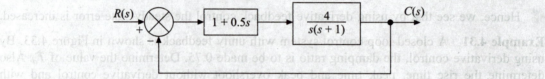

Figure 4.34 Example 4.31: Block diagram with derivative control.

Without derivative control, the rise time

$$t_r = \frac{\pi - \theta}{\omega_d} = \frac{\pi - \tan^{-1}\dfrac{\sqrt{1-\xi^2}}{\xi}}{\omega_n\sqrt{1-\xi^2}}$$

$$= \frac{\pi - \tan^{-1}\dfrac{\sqrt{1-0.25^2}}{0.25}}{2 \times \sqrt{1-0.25^2}} = \frac{1.823}{1.936} = 0.942 \text{ s}$$

The peak time

$$t_p = \frac{\pi}{\omega_d} = \frac{\pi}{\omega_n\sqrt{1-\xi^2}}$$

$$= \frac{\pi}{2\sqrt{1-0.25^2}} = 1.62 \text{ s}$$

The peak overshoot is given by

$$M_p = e^{-\pi\xi/\sqrt{1-\xi^2}}$$

$$= e^{-\pi \times 0.25/\sqrt{1-0.25^2}}$$

$$= 0.4443$$

The overall transfer function with derivative control is

$$\frac{C(s)}{R(s)} = \frac{\dfrac{4(1+0.5s)}{s(s+1)}}{1+\dfrac{4(1+0.5s)}{s(s+1)}} = \frac{4(1+0.5s)}{s^2+3s+4}$$

$$= \frac{4+2s}{s^2+3s+4}$$

For a unit-step input, $r(t) = 1$

$$\therefore \qquad R(s) = \frac{1}{s}$$

$$C(s) = \frac{4+2s}{s(s^2+3s+4)}$$

$$= \frac{A}{s} + \frac{Bs+C}{s^2+3s+4}$$

$$= \frac{1}{s} - \frac{(s+1)}{s^2+3s+4} = \frac{1}{s} - \frac{s+1}{(s+1.5)^2+1.75}$$

$$= \frac{1}{s} - \frac{(s+1)}{(s+1.5)^2+1.32^2} = \frac{1}{s} - \frac{(s+1.5)-0.5}{(s+1.5)^2+1.32^2}$$

$$= \frac{1}{s} - \frac{(s+1.5)}{(s+1.5)^2+1.32^2} + \frac{0.5}{1.32}\frac{1.32}{(s+1.5)^2+1.32^2}$$

$$c(t) = 1 - e^{-1.5t}\cos 1.32t + 0.378 e^{-1.5t}\sin 1.32t$$
$$= 1 - e^{-1.5t}(\cos 1.32t - 0.378\sin 1.32t)$$

At $\qquad t = t_r,$

$$c(t) = 1$$

i.e. $\qquad c(t_r) = 1$

$$\therefore \qquad 1 = 1 - e^{-1.5t_r}(\cos 1.32t_r - 0.378\sin 1.32t_r)$$

$$\therefore \qquad \cos 1.32t_r = 0.378\sin 1.32t_r$$

$$\tan 1.32t_r = 1/0.378 = 2.645$$

$$\therefore \qquad 1.32t_r = \tan^{-1} 2.645 = 69.28° = 1.209 \text{ rad}$$

$$\therefore \qquad t_r = 1.209/1.32 = 0.916\text{s}$$

For peak time, differentiating the output equation with respect to t and equating to zero

$$\left.\frac{d}{dt}c(t)\right|_{t=t_p} = \left.\frac{d}{dt}[1 - e^{-1.5t}(\cos 1.32t - 0.378\sin 1.32t)]\right|_{t=t_p} = 0$$

i.e. $-e^{-1.5t}[-\sin 1.32t\,(1.32) - 0.378 \times 1.32 \cos 1.32t]$

$-e^{-1.5t}(-1.5)[\cos 1.32t - 0.378 \sin 1.32t]\big|_{t=t_p} = 0$

i.e. $-1.32 \sin 1.32t_p - 0.498 \cos 1.32t_p + 0.567 \sin 1.32t_p - 1.5 \cos 1.32t_p = 0$

i.e. $-0.753 \sin 1.32t_p - 1.998 \cos 1.32t_p = 0$

$\tan 1.32t_p = -1.998/0.753 = -2.653$

$\therefore \qquad t_p = \dfrac{\tan^{-1}(-2.63)}{1.32} = \dfrac{\pi - \tan^{-1} 2.63}{1.32} = \dfrac{\pi - 1.207}{1.32} = 1.46\,\text{s}$

Peak output occurs at $t = t_p$

$$c(t_p) = 1 - e^{-1.5t_p}(\cos 1.32t_p - 0.378 \sin 1.32t_p)$$

$$= 1 - e^{-1.5 \times 1.46}(\cos 1.32 \times 1.46 - 0.378 \sin 1.32 \times 1.46)$$

$$= 1 - e^{-2.19}(\cos 1.927 - 0.378 \sin 1.927)$$

$$= 1 - 0.119(\cos 110.4° - 0.378 \sin 110.4°)$$

$$= 1 - 0.119(-0.348 - 0.354)$$

$$= 1.08$$

Therefore, the peak overshoot

$$M_p = c(t_p) - c(\infty)$$

$$= 1.08 - 1 = 0.08$$

$$\%M_p = 8\%$$

Example 4.32   In Example 4.31, it is desired the damping ratio be 0.75. Determine the derivative rate feedback K_t. Also determine the peak time, rise time, steady-state error and maximum overshoot with and without feedback for unit-ramp input.

Solution: The characteristic equation is

$$s^2 + s + 4 = 0$$

$\therefore \qquad\qquad\qquad\qquad \xi = 0.25$

and $\qquad\qquad\qquad\qquad \omega_n = 2$

Let ξ' be the damping ratio with derivative feedback. Therefore,

$$\xi' = \xi + \frac{\omega_n K_t}{2}$$

Putting values in the above equation, we get

$$0.75 = 0.25 + \frac{2K_t}{2}$$

$\therefore \qquad\qquad\qquad\qquad K_t = 0.5$

The steady-state error without feedback is

$$e_{ss} = \frac{2\xi}{\omega_n} = \frac{2 \times 0.25}{2} = 0.25$$

Already we have determined t_r, t_p and M_p to be

$$t_r = 0.942 \text{ s}, \ t_p = 1.62 \text{ s}, \text{ and } M_p = 0.444$$

The overall transfer function using derivative feedback control is

$$\frac{C(s)}{R(s)} = \frac{\omega_n^2}{s^2 + (2\xi\omega_n + \omega_n^2 K_t)s + \omega_n^2}$$

Given that $\xi = 0.25$ and $\omega_n = 2$ rad/s, $K_t = 0.5$

$$\therefore \qquad \frac{C(s)}{R(s)} = \frac{\omega_n^2}{s^2 + 3s + \omega_n^2} = \frac{4}{s^2 + 3s + 4}$$

The characteristic equation is

$$s^2 + 3s + 4 = 0$$

i.e.
$$\xi = 0.75$$

and
$$\omega_n = 2$$

The rise time

$$t_r = \frac{\pi - \theta}{\omega_d} = \frac{\pi - \tan^{-1} \dfrac{\sqrt{1 - \xi^2}}{\xi}}{\omega_n \sqrt{1 - \xi^2}}$$

$$= \frac{\pi - \tan^{-1} \dfrac{\sqrt{1 - 0.75^2}}{0.75}}{2 \times \sqrt{1 - 0.75^2}}$$

$$= \frac{2.419}{1.322} = 1.829 \text{ s}$$

The peak time

$$t_p = \frac{\pi}{\omega_d} = \frac{\pi}{\omega_n \sqrt{1 - \xi^2}} = \frac{\pi}{2\sqrt{1 - 0.75^2}} = 3.59 \text{ s}$$

The maximum overshoot

$$M_p = e^{-\pi\xi / \sqrt{1 - \xi^2}}$$

$$= e^{-\pi \times 0.75 / \sqrt{1 - 0.75^2}}$$

$$= 0.074 = 7.4\%$$

The steady-state error

$$e_{ss} = \frac{2\xi}{\omega_n} + K_t$$

$$= \frac{2 \times 0.75}{2} + 0.5 = 1.25$$

4.9.4 Integral Control

For integral control action, the actuating signal consists of proportional error signal added with integral error signal, i.e.

$$e_a(t) = e(t) + K_i \int e(t)\, dt \qquad (4.34)$$

where K_i is a constant.

Taking the Laplace transform on both sides of Eq. (4.34),

$$E_a(s) = E(s) + K_i \frac{E(s)}{s} = E(s)\left(1 + \frac{K_i}{s}\right) \qquad (4.35)$$

Figure 4.35 shows the block diagram of a system with integral control action.

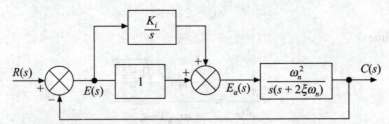

Figure 4.35 Block diagram of a control system with integral control.

From the block diagram, the closed-loop transfer function is

$$\frac{C(s)}{R(s)} = \frac{\left(1 + \dfrac{K_i}{s}\right)\left(\dfrac{\omega_n^2}{s^2 + 2\xi\omega_n s}\right)}{1 + \left(1 + \dfrac{K_i}{s}\right)\left(\dfrac{\omega_n^2}{s^2 + 2\xi\omega_n s}\right)}$$

$$= \frac{(s + K_i)\,\omega_n^2}{s^3 + 2\xi\omega_n s^2 + \omega_n^2 s + K_i \omega_n^2}$$

The characteristic equation $s^3 + 2\xi\omega_n s^2 + \omega_n^2 s + K_i \omega_n^2 = 0$ is of third-order. So we see that the second-order system has become a third-order system due to the inclusion of the integral control.

From Figure 4.35 we see that the forward path transfer function is

$$G(s) = \frac{(s + K_i)\omega_n^2}{s^2(s + 2\xi\omega_n)}$$

and the feedback path transfer function is

$$H(s) = 1$$

The error function is therefore given by

$$\frac{E(s)}{R(s)} = \frac{1}{1 + G(s)H(s)}$$

$$= \frac{1}{1 + \left[\dfrac{(s + K_i)\omega_n^2}{s^2(s + 2\xi\omega_n)}\right]}$$

$$= \frac{s^2(s + 2\xi\omega_n)}{s^3 + 2\xi\omega_n s^2 + \omega_n^2 s + K_i\omega_n^2}$$

$$\therefore \qquad E(s) = R(s).\frac{s^2(s + 2\xi\omega_n)}{s^3 + 2\xi\omega_n s^2 + \omega_n^2 s + K_i\omega_n^2}$$

For a unit-ramp input,

$$r(t) = t$$

$$\therefore \qquad R(s) = \frac{1}{s^2}$$

Since

$$e_{ss} = \underset{s \to 0}{\mathrm{Lt}} \; sE(s)$$

for a ramp input, the steady-state error is

$$e_{ss} = \underset{s \to 0}{\mathrm{Lt}} \; s.\frac{1}{s^2}\frac{s^2(s + 2\xi\omega_n)}{s^3 + 2\xi\omega_n s^2 + \omega_n^2 s + K_i\omega_n^2} = 0$$

For a unit-parabolic input

$$r(t) = \frac{t^2}{2}$$

$$\therefore \qquad R(s) = \frac{1}{s^3}$$

So the steady-state error for a unit-parabolic input is

$$e_{ss} = \underset{s \to 0}{Lt} \; s \cdot \frac{1}{s^3} \cdot \frac{s^2(s + 2\xi\omega_n)}{s^3 + 2\xi\omega_n s^2 + \omega_n^2 s + K_i \omega_n^2}$$

$$= \frac{2\xi\omega_n}{K_i \omega_n^2} = \frac{2\xi}{K_i \omega_n}$$

4.9.5 Proportional-plus-Integral Plus Derivative Control (PID Control)

In PID control, the actuating signal consists of proportional error signal added with integral and derivative of error signal.

The actuating signal for the PID control is given by

$$e_a(t) = e(t) + T_d \frac{de(t)}{dt} + K_i \int e(t)\, dt \tag{4.36}$$

Taking the Laplace transform on both sides of Eq. (4.35),

$$E_a(s) = E(s) + T_d s E(s) + K_i \frac{E(s)}{s}$$

i.e.

$$E_a(s) = \left[1 + T_d s + \frac{K_i}{s} \right] E(s) \tag{4.37}$$

The block diagram of a second-order control system employing PID controller is shown in Figure 4.36.

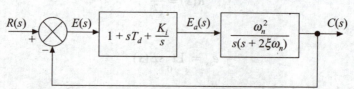

Figure 4.36 Block diagram of a control system with PID control.

Proportional, integral and derivative actions and their various combinations are not the only control laws possible, but they are the most common. It has been estimated that 90% of the controllers are of the PI type. This percentage will probably decrease as digital control with its great flexibility becomes more widely used. But the PI and PID controllers will remain for some time as standard against which any new designs must compete.

Example 4.33 The system illustrated in Figure 4.37 is a unity feedback control system with a minor feedback loop (output derivative feedback).

(a) In the absence of derivative feedback ($K_t = 0$), determine the damping factor and natural frequency for $K_A = 15$. Also determine the steady-state error resulting from a unit-ramp input.

(b) Determine the derivative feedback constant K_t which will increase the damping factor of the system to 0.7. What is the steady-state error to a unit-ramp input with this setting of the derivative feedback constant?

(c) Find suitable values of the parameters K_A and K_t so that the damping ratio of the system is increased to 0.8 without affecting the steady-state error as obtained in part(a).

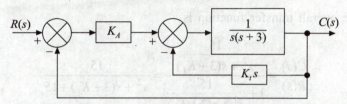

Figure 4.37 Example 4.33: Block diagram.

Solution: (a) In the absence of derivative feedback, that is, with $K_t = 0$,

$$G(s) = \frac{K_A}{s(s+3)} = \frac{15}{s(s+3)}$$

and $\qquad\qquad\qquad\qquad H(s) = 1$

The closed-loop transfer function is therefore

$$\frac{C(s)}{R(s)} = \frac{G(s)}{1+G(s)} = \frac{\dfrac{15}{s(s+3)}}{1+\dfrac{15}{s(s+3)}} = \frac{15}{s^2+3s+15}$$

Comparing the characteristic equation $s^2 + 3s + 15 = 0$ with $s^2 + 2\xi\omega_n s + \omega_n^2 = 0$,

$$\omega_n^2 = 15$$

∴ $$\omega_n = \sqrt{15} = 3.873 \text{ rad/s}$$

$$2\xi\omega_n = 3$$

∴ $$\xi = \frac{3}{2\omega_n} = \frac{3}{2\times3.873} = 0.387$$

The system velocity error constant

$$K_v = \underset{s\to0}{\text{Lt}}\ sG(s)$$

∴ $$K_v = \underset{s\to0}{\text{Lt}}\ s\times\frac{15}{s(s+3)} = 5$$

Therefore, the steady-state error for a ramp input is

$$e_{ss} = \frac{1}{K_v} = \frac{1}{5} = 0.2 \text{ rad}$$

(b) *With derivative feedback*

$$G(s) = 15 \times \frac{\dfrac{1}{s(s+3)}}{1 + \dfrac{1}{s(s+3)} \times K_t s} = \frac{15}{s^2 + (3+K_t)s}$$

Therefore, the overall transfer function is

$$\frac{C(s)}{R(s)} = \frac{\dfrac{15}{s^2 + s(3+K_t)}}{1 + \dfrac{15}{s^2 + s(3+K_t)}} = \frac{15}{s^2 + s(3+K_t) + 15}$$

Comparing the characteristic equation $s^2 + (3 + K_t)s + 15 = 0$ with $s^2 + 2\xi\omega_n s + \omega_n^2 = 0$, we get

$$\omega_n^2 = 15$$

$\therefore$ $$\omega_n = \sqrt{15} = 3.873 \text{ rad/s}$$

$$2\xi\omega_n = 3 + K_t$$

i.e. $$2 \times 0.7 \times 3.873 = 3 + K_t$$

$\therefore$ $$K_t = 2 \times 0.7 \times 3.873 - 3 = 2.422$$

$\therefore$ $$G(s) = \frac{15}{s^2 + (3+2.442)s} = \frac{15}{s^2 + 5.422s}$$

For a unit-ramp input

$$K_v = \underset{s\to 0}{\text{Lt}}\ sG(s)$$

$$= \underset{s\to 0}{\text{Lt}}\ s. \frac{15}{s(s+5.422)} = \frac{15}{5.422} = 2.766$$

$\therefore$ $$e_{ss} = \frac{1}{K_v} = \frac{1}{2.766} = 0.3615 \text{ rad}$$

(c) The overall transfer function of the system is

$$\frac{C(s)}{R(s)} = \frac{K_A}{s^2 + (3+K_t)s + K_A}$$

Comparing the characteristic equation $s^2 + (3 + K_t)s + K_A = 0$ with $s^2 + 2\xi\omega_n s + \omega_n^2 = 0$, we get

$$\omega_n^2 = K_A$$

$\therefore$ $$\omega_n = \sqrt{K_A}$$

$$2\xi\omega_n = 3 + K_t$$

i.e.
$$2 \times 0.8 \times \sqrt{K_A} = 3 + K_t$$

The open-loop transfer function of the system is

$$G(s) = \frac{K_A}{s(s+3+K_t)}$$

For a ramp input

$$K_v = \underset{s \to 0}{\text{Lt}} \ sG(s)$$

$$= \underset{s \to 0}{\text{Lt}} \ s.\frac{K_A}{s(s+3+K_t)}$$

$$= \frac{K_A}{(3+K_t)}$$

The steady-state error

$$e_{ss} = \frac{1}{K_v} = \frac{3+K_t}{K_A}$$

Given that, the steady-state error $e_{ss} = 0.2$. Therefore,

$$0.2 = \frac{3+K_t}{K_A}$$

i.e.
$$0.2 K_A = 3 + K_t = 2\xi\omega_n = 2 \times 0.8 \times \sqrt{K_A}$$

$$\therefore \qquad \sqrt{K_A} = \frac{2 \times 0.8}{0.2} = 8$$

or
$$K_A = 64$$

$$3 + K_t = 0.2 K_A = 0.2 \times 64 = 12.8$$

$$\therefore \qquad K_t = 12.8 - 3 = 9.8$$

The values of K_A and K_t for $\xi = 0.8$, for a steady-state error of $e_{ss} = 0.2$ for a ramp input are $K_A = 64$ and $K_t = 9.8$.

Example 4.34 The control system shown in Figure 4.38 employs proportional plus error rate control. Determine the value of error rate constant K_e so that the damping ratio is 0.6

(a) Determine the value of settling time and maximum overshoot. Find the steady-state error if the input is a unit-ramp.

(b) What will be those values without error rate control?

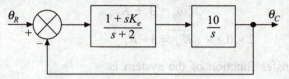

Figure 4.38 Example 4.34: Block diagram.

Solution: (a) *With error rate control*

$$G(s) = \frac{10(1 + sK_e)}{s(s + 2)}$$

Therefore, the closed-loop transfer function is

$$\frac{\theta_C(s)}{\theta_R(s)} = \frac{\dfrac{10(1 + sK_e)}{s(s + 2)}}{1 + \dfrac{10(1 + sK_e)}{s(s + 2)}} = \frac{10 + 10sK_e}{s^2 + s(2 + 10K_e) + 10}$$

Comparing the characteristic equation $s^2 + s(2 + 10K_e) + 10 = 0$ with the standard form of the characteristic equation of a second-order system $s^2 + 2\xi\omega_n s + \omega_n^2 = 0$, we get

$$\omega_n^2 = 10, \quad \therefore \quad \omega_n = \sqrt{10} = 3.16 \text{ rad/s}$$

$$2\xi\omega_n = 2 + 10K_e$$

$$\therefore \qquad K_e = \frac{2\xi\omega_n - 2}{10} = \frac{2 \times 0.6 \times 3.16 - 2}{10} = 0.18$$

The settling time

$$t_s = \frac{4}{\xi\omega_n} = \frac{4}{0.6 \times 3.16} = 2.11 \text{ s}$$

The peak overshoot

$$M_p = e^{-\pi\xi/\sqrt{1-\xi^2}} = e^{-\pi \times 0.6/\sqrt{1-0.6^2}} = 0.0949$$

The peak % overshoot

$$M_p \times 100\% = 0.0949 \times 100\% = 9.49\%$$

Therefore, the steady-state error

$$e_{ss} = \frac{R}{K_v} = \frac{1}{K_v} = \frac{1}{\underset{s \to 0}{\text{Lt}}\, sG(s)} = \frac{1}{\underset{s \to 0}{\text{Lt}}\, s\dfrac{10(1 + sK_e)}{s(s + 2)}} = \frac{1}{5} = 0.2 \text{ rad}$$

(b) *Without error rate control*

When $K_e = 0$,

$$G(s) = \frac{10}{s(s+2)}$$

Therefore, the closed-loop transfer function is

$$\frac{\theta_C(s)}{\theta_R(s)} = \frac{\dfrac{10}{s(s+2)}}{1 + \dfrac{10}{s(s+2)}} = \frac{10}{s^2 + 2s + 10}$$

Comparing this transfer function with the standard form of the transfer function of a second-order system $\dfrac{\omega_n^2}{s^2 + 2\xi\omega_n s + \omega_n^2}$, we get

$$\omega_n^2 = 10$$

$$\therefore \qquad \omega_n = \sqrt{10} = 3.16 \text{ rad/s}$$

$$2\xi\omega_n = 2$$

$$\therefore \qquad \xi = \frac{2}{2\omega_n} = \frac{2}{2 \times 3.16} = 0.32$$

The settling time

$$t_s = \frac{4}{\xi\omega_n} = \frac{4}{0.32 \times 3.16} = 4 \text{ s}$$

The peak overshoot

$$M_p = e^{-\pi\xi/\sqrt{1-\xi^2}} = e^{-\pi \times 0.32/\sqrt{1-0.32^2}} = 0.351$$

The steady-state error

$$e_{ss}(t) = \frac{1}{K_v} = \frac{1}{\underset{s \to 0}{\text{Lt}}\, sG(s)} = \frac{1}{\underset{s \to 0}{\text{Lt}}\, s\dfrac{10}{s(s+2)}} = \frac{1}{5} = 0.2 \text{ rad}$$

SHORT QUESTIONS AND ANSWERS

1. What do you mean by time response of a control system?

A. The time response of a control system is the output of the system as a function of time. It is given by the inverse Laplace transform of the product of input and system transfer functions. The time response of a control system is the sum of the transient response and the steady-state response.

2. What do you mean by transient response? On what does it depend?

A. The transient response of a system is that part of the time response which tends to zero as *t* tends to infinity. It is the response of the system when the input changes from one state to the other. The nature of the transient response is dependent only on the system poles and not on the type of input. The transient response of a system is also called the dynamic response.

3. What do you mean by steady-state response? On what does it depend?

A. The steady-state response of a system is that part of the time response which remains constant as $t \rightarrow \infty$. It is dependent on the system poles as well as on the type of the input.

4. What is the importance of test signals?

A. The importance of test signals is: the test signals can be easily generated in the laboratories and the characteristics of test signals resemble the characteristics of actual signals. The test signals are used to pre-determine the performance of the system. If the response of a system is satisfactory for a test signal, then the system will be suitable for practical applications.

5. Name the standard test signals used in control systems.

A. The standard test signals used in control systems are: impulse, step, ramp, parabolic and sinusoidal.

6. Why are test signals needed?

A. Usually the input signals to a control system are not known fully ahead of time. They may be random in nature. But to test the performance of a system while designing, some inputs are required to be given. They are called test signals.

7. Define the test signals: (a) step (b) ramp (c) parabolic and (d) impulse.

A. A unit-step signal is one which remains at zero level for $t < 0$ and changes suddenly to a level of unity at $t = 0$ and remains at 1 for $t > 0$, i.e. $u(t) = 0$ for $t < 0$ and $u(t) = 1$, for $t > 0$.

A unit-ramp signal is one which remains at zero level for $t < 0$ and increases linearly with time for $t > 0$, i.e. $r(t) = 0$, for $t < 0$ and $r(t) = t$ for $t > 0$.

A unit-parabolic signal is one which remains at zero level for $t < 0$ and increases as per the equation $t^2/2$ for $t > 0$, i.e. $r(t) = 0$, for $t < 0$, and $r(t) = t^2/2$ for $t > 0$.

A unit-impulse signal is defined as a signal which has zero value everywhere except at $t = 0$, where its magnitude is infinity. $\delta(t) = 0$, for $t \neq 0$; $\delta(t) = \infty$, at $t = 0$.

8. What do you mean by weighing function?

A. The system's impulse response is referred to as weighing function of the system.

9. Define the impulse response of a system?

A. The impulse response of a system is the response or the output of a system for a unit-impulse input. The impulse response of a system is also defined as the inverse Laplace transform of its transfer function. It is also referred to as the weighting function of the system.

10. How are higher-order systems approximated to second-order systems?

A. Higher-order systems usually have a pair of complex conjugate poles with damping less than one which dominate over other poles. So they can be represented by second-order systems considering only the dominant poles and neglecting all other poles.

11. Define the terms:

(a) Pole

(b) Zero

A. The pole of a function $F(s)$ is the value of s for which the function $F(s)$ becomes infinite. The zero of a function $F(s)$ is the value of s for which the function $F(s)$ becomes zero.

12. What do you mean by the term 'order' of a control system?

A. The term 'order' of a system indicates the order of the differential equation used to describe the system. It is also given by the highest power of s present in the denominator of the closed-loop transfer function. The highest power of s in the denominator gives the number of poles of the system and so the order of the system is also given by the number of poles of the transfer function.

13. What do you mean by time constant of a system? What does it indicate?

A. The time constant of a system is defined as the time taken by the output to reach 100% of the input step if the initial slope of the output is maintained constant. It is indicative of how fast the system tends to reach the final value. A large time constant corresponds to a sluggish system and a small time constant corresponds to fast response.

14. How is the speed of response defined?

A. The speed of response can be quantitatively defined as the time required for the output to become a particular percentage of its final value.

15. Define the characteristic polynomial.

A. The denominator polynomial of the closed-loop transfer function is called the characteristic polynomial.

16. Define the characteristic equation. Why that name?

A. The denominator of the closed-loop transfer function equated to zero is called the characteristic equation. The roots of the characteristic equation characterize the behaviour of the system. Hence that name.

17. How are the poles of a closed-loop system and roots of the characteristic equation related?

A. The roots of the characteristic equation are the same as the poles of the closed-loop transfer function.

18. What does the time constant of a system indicate?

A. The time constant of a system is indicative of how fast the system tends to reach the final value. A large time constant corresponds to a sluggish system and a small time constant corresponds to fast response.

19. Define the term 'damping ratio' of a system.

A. The damping factor or damping ratio ξ of a system is defined as the ratio of actual damping to critical damping.

20. How are control systems classified depending on the value of damping?

A. Depending on the value of damping, control systems may be classified as follows:

(a) Undamped systems, $\xi = 0$ (b) Underdamped systems, $\xi < 1$

(c) Criticallydamped systems, $\xi = 1$ (d) Overdamped systems, $\xi > 1$

21. What is the location of poles for different types of damped systems?

A. (a) For undamped systems, $\xi = 0$. The poles are on the imaginary axis and are conjugate of each other.

(b) For underdamped systems, $0 < \xi < 1$. The poles are in the left half of the s-plane and are the complex conjugate of each other.

(c) For critically-damped systems, $\xi = 1$. Both the poles are real, negative and equal.

(d) For overdamped systems, $\xi > 1$. The poles are real, negative and unequal.

22. What is the nature of response of a second-order system with different types of damping?

A. The nature of response of a second-order system with different types of damping is as follows:

(a) For undamped systems, the response is purely oscillatory.

(b) For underdamped systems, the response is damped oscillatory.

(c) For critically-damped systems, the response is exponentially rising.

(d) For overdamped systems, the response is exponentially rising but the rise time will be very large.

23. For quick response, what type of damping is preferred?

A. For quick response, the control system should be underdamped. So control systems are normally designed with $\xi < 1$, i.e. mostly they are underdamped systems.

24. What do you mean by undamped natural frequency?

A. The undamped natural frequency ω_n is the frequency at which the system will oscillate in the absence of any damping.

25. What do you mean by damped frequency of oscillation?

A. The damped frequency of oscillation, $\omega_d = \omega_n\sqrt{1-\xi^2}$ is the frequency of damped oscillations of an underdamped system.

26. List the time-domain specifications of a second-order underdamped system excited by a unit-step input.

A. The time-domain specifications of a second-order underdamped system excited by a step input are (a) delay time, (b) rise time, (c) peak time, (d) maximum overshoot, (e) settling time and (f) steady-state error.

27. Define the following terms:

    (a) Delay time   (b) Rise time   (c) Peak time

    (d) Peak overshoot   (e) Settling time   (f) Steady-state error

A. (a) The delay time t_d is defined as the time required for the response to reach 50% of the final value in the first attempt.

    (b) The rise time t_r is defined as the time required for the response to rise from 10% to 90% of the final value for overdamped systems and 0 to 100% of the final value for underdamped systems.

    (c) The peak time t_p is defined as the time required for the response to reach the peak of the time response or the peak overshoot.

    (d) The peak overshoot M_p is defined as the difference between the time response peak and the steady-state output, i.e.

$$M_p = c(t_p) - c(\infty)$$

    Peak per cent overshoot

$$M_p = \frac{c(t_p) - c(\infty)}{c(\infty)} \times 100\%$$

    (e) The settling time t_s is defined as the time required for the response to reach and stay within a particular percentage of its final value.

    (f) The steady-state error $e_{ss}(t)$ is defined as the error between the actual output and the desired output as t tends to infinity.

28. What does the term 'type' of a system indicate? What is its significance?

A. The type number of a system indicates the number of open-loop poles present at the origin of the s-plane. It decides the steady-state error.

29. What are type-0, type-1 and type-2 systems?

A. A type-0 system is a system with no open-loop pole at the origin of the s-plane. It can track a step input with a finite steady-state error. It cannot track the ramp and the acceleration inputs.

A type-1 system is a system with one open-loop pole at the origin of the s-plane. It can track a step input with zero steady-state error, a ramp input with a finite steady-state error and it cannot track a parabolic input.

A type-2 system is a system with two open-loop poles at the origin of the s-plane. It can track step and ramp inputs with zero steady-state error, and an acceleration input with a finite steady-state error.

30. Why are systems of type more than 2 not used normally?

A. As type of system becomes higher, progressively more steady-state errors are eliminated, but systems of type higher than 2, i.e. with more than two integrators are not employed in practice, because they are more difficult to stabilize and the dynamic errors for such systems tend to be larger than those for type-0, type-1, and type-2 systems, although their steady-state performance is desirable.

31. Distinguish between type and order of a control system.

A. The difference between the type and order of a system is as follows. The type number indicates the number of open-loop poles present at the origin of the s-plane. It indicates the number of integrators present in the system whereas the order of a system indicates the number of poles present in the system transfer function. The type number is specified based on the number of open-loop poles at the origin of the s-plane but order can be specified for open-loop systems as well as closed-loop systems.

32. What is steady-state error?

A. The steady-state error is the value of error signal $e(t)$, when t tends to infinity. It is a measure of system accuracy.

33. What are static error constants? What is their significance?

A. The position error constant K_p, the velocity error constant K_v and the acceleration error constant K_a are called the static error constants. These constants are associated with steady-state error in a particular type of system and for a standard input. The error constants K_p, K_v and K_a describe the ability of a system to reduce or eliminate steady-state errors.

34. Name and define the static error coefficients.

A. The static error coefficients are as follows:

(a) The position error constant $K_p = \underset{s \to 0}{\text{Lt}}\ G(s)$, which is indicative of the error in output for a unit-step input.

(b) The velocity error constant $K_v = \underset{s \to 0}{\text{Lt}}\ sG(s)$, which is indicative of the error in output for a unit-ramp input.

(c) The acceleration error constant $K_a = \underset{s \to 0}{\text{Lt}}\ s^2G(s)$, which is indicative of the error in output for a unit-parabolic input.

35. What are the drawbacks of static error coefficients?

A. The drawbacks of static error coefficients K_p, K_v and K_a are as follows. They do not give any information on the steady-state error when inputs are other than the three basic types—step, ramp and parabolic. Also they fail to indicate the exact manner in which the error function changes with time.

36. How is the steady-state performance of a system judged?

A. The steady-state performance of a stable control system is generally judged by its steady-state error to step, ramp, and parabolic inputs. The steady-state errors arise from the nature of inputs, type of system and from nonlinearities of the system components.

37. What are dynamic error coefficients? What are their advantages?

A. Dynamic error coefficients are the coefficients used to express dynamic error. Their advantages are as follows:

(a) Dynamic error coefficients give error signal as a function of time.

(b) Using dynamic error coefficients, the steady-state error can be determined for any type of input.

38. Give the relation between static and dynamic error coefficients.

A. The relation between static and dynamic error coefficients is as follows:

$$C_0 = \frac{1}{1 + K_p} \qquad C_1 = \frac{1}{K_v} \qquad C_2 = \frac{1}{K_a}$$

39. What is the effect of addition of a pole to the forward path transfer function?

A. The addition of a pole to the forward path transfer function increases the order of the system, increases the overshoot, and reduces the stability. It also increases the rise time of the step response, reduces the bandwidth and pushes and bends the complex conjugate portion of the root loci of the second-order system to the right half of the s-plane.

40. What is the effect of addition of a pole to the closed-loop transfer function?

A. The addition of a pole to the closed-loop transfer function increases the rise time and decreases the overshoot. Thus, as far as overshoot is concerned, adding a pole to the closed-loop transfer function has just the opposite effect to that of adding a pole to the forward path transfer function.

41. What is the effect of addition of a zero to the closed-loop transfer function?

A. The addition of a zero to the closed-loop transfer function decreases the rise time, and increases the maximum overshoot of the step response.

42. What is the effect of addition of a zero to the forward path transfer function?

A. When the zero added to the forward path transfer function is very far away from the imaginary axis, the overshoot is large and the damping is very poor. The overshoot is reduced and damping improved when the zero moves to the right. Again, when the zero moves closer to the origin, the overshoot increases but damping improves.

43. What do you mean by proportional control?

A. Proportional control is one in which the actuating signal for the control action is proportional to the error signal.

44. What is the effect of a proportional controller on the performance of a system?

A. The effect of a proportional controller on the performance of a system is that it improves the steady-state tracking accuracy, disturbance signal rejection and relative stability of the system. It also increases the open-loop gain of the system which results in reducing the sensitivity of the system.

45. What is the disadvantage of a proportional controller?

A. The disadvantage of a proportional controller is that it produces a constant steady-state error.

46. What is the effect of increasing the forward path gain of a system?

A. The effect of increasing the forward path gain of a system is as follows:
   (a) The sluggish overdamped response of a control system is made faster and the steady-state error is reduced.
   (b) The damping ratio is also reduced, so peak overshoot is increased.

47. What do you mean by derivative control?

A. Derivative control is one in which the actuating error signal consists of proportional error signal added to derivative of error signal.

48. What is the effect of derivative control on damping ratio, peak overshoot, steady-state error and rise time?

A. The steady-state error is not affected by derivative control.

The value of undamped natural frequency ω_n is not affected by derivative control.

Derivative control results in the addition of a zero and so in reduction of rise time.

Derivative control results in increase of effective damping, so maximum overshoot is reduced.

49. What is the effect of a PD controller on the system performance?

A. The effect of a PD controller on the system performance is to increase the damping ratio of the system and so the peak overshoot is reduced.

50. Why is the derivative controller not used in control systems?

A. The derivative control is not used in control systems because, the derivative controller produces a control action based on the rate of change of error signal and it does not produce corrective measures for any constant error.

51. What do you mean by derivative feedback control?

A. Derivative feedback control is one in which the actuating signal is the difference of proportional error signal and the derivative of the output. The derivative feedback control is also known as the tachometer feedback control.

52. What is the affect of derivative feedback control on damping ratio, maximum overshoot and steady-state error?

A. Derivative feedback control increases the damping ratio and so the maximum overshoot is reduced. Derivative feedback control results in an increase in steady-state error.

53. What do you mean by integral control?

A. Integral control is one in which the actuating signal consists of proportional error signal added to the integral of error signal.

54. What is the effect of a PI controller on the system performance?

A. The effect of a PI controller on the system performance is that it increases the order of the system by one, which results in the reduction of the steady-state error. But the system becomes less stable than the original one.

55. What do you mean by a PID controller?

A. A PID controller is one in which the actuating signal consists of proportional error signal added with derivative and integral of error signal.

56. What do you mean by dominant poles of transfer functions?

A. The poles that are close to the imaginary axis in the left-half s-plane give rise to transient response that will decay relatively slowly and are called dominant poles. They are called dominant poles because they dominate the response of the system.

57. What do you mean by insignificant poles?

A. The poles that are far away from the imaginary axis (relative to the dominant poles) correspond to fast decaying time responses and are called insignificant poles.

58. What do you mean by relative damping ratio?

A. If the system dynamics of a higher-order system can be accurately represented by a pair of complex conjugate dominant poles, then the damping ratio ξ is called the relative damping ratio of the system.

59. What is the effect of neglecting the insignificant poles as they are?

A. If the insignificant poles are neglected as they are, the transient response is unchanged, but the steady-state response gets affected.

60. What is the proper way of neglecting insignificant poles with consideration of steady-state response?

A. The proper way of neglecting insignificant poles with consideration of steady-state response is to write the transfer function in time constant form and then to neglect the insignificant poles so that the steady-state response is not affected.

REVIEW QUESTIONS

1. Sketch the response of a second-order (a) undamped system, (b) underdamped system, (c) critically-damped system, (d) overdamped system.
2. Derive expressions for the time response of a first-order system excited by (a) a step input and (b) a ramp input.
3. Derive an expression for the time response of a second-order system excited by a unit-step input.
4. Derive expressions for rise time, peak time and peak overshoot of a second-order system excited by a step input.
5. Derive expressions for the steady-state errors of type-0, type-1 and type-2 systems excited by unit-step, unit-ramp and unit-parabolic inputs.
6. Show that derivative control (a) increases the damping ratio and (b) does not alter the steady-state error of the system.
7. Show that derivative feedback control (a) increases the damping ratio and (b) increases the steady-state error of the system.
8. Show that with integral control the steady-state error is zero for a ramp input.

FILL IN THE BLANKS

1. A feedback control system has the inherent capability that its _____ can be adjusted to alter both its transient and steady-state behaviour.
2. Usually the input signals to a control system are _____ fully ahead of time.

3. The characteristics of actual signals which severely strain a control system are _____, _____, _____, and _____.

4. The nature of the transient response is dependent only _____ and not on the type of _____.

5. The steady-state response is dependent on the _____ as well as on the type of _____.

6. The standard test signals are _____, _____, _____, _____, and _____.

7. The inverse Laplace transform of the transfer function of a system is its _____.

8. A signal which has zero value everywhere except at $t = 0$, where its magnitude is infinity is called a _____ signal.

9. The system's impulse response is referred to as the _____ of the system.

10. A signal which remains at zero level for $t < 0$, and changes suddenly to a level of A at $t = 0$, and remains constant at that level for $t > 0$ is called a _____ signal.

11. A signal which remains at zero level for $t < 0$, and increases linearly with time for $t > 0$ is called a _____ signal.

12. A signal which remains at zero level for $t < 0$, and increases as per the equation $t^2/2$ for $t > 0$ is called a _____ signal.

13. The time response of a control system is the sum of the _____ and the _____.

14. The transient response of the system is also called the _____.

15. That part of the time response which tends to zero as t tends to infinity is called the _____ response of the system.

16. The time constant of a system is indicative of _____ the system tends to reach the final value.

17. A large time constant corresponds to a _____ system and a small time constant corresponds to a _____ response.

18. The ratio of actual damping to critical damping is called the _____ of the system.

19. The frequency at which the system oscillates in the absence of any damping is called the _____.

20. The denominator polynomial of the closed-loop transfer function is called the _____.

21. The denominator of the closed-loop transfer function equated to zero is called the _____.

22. The roots of the characteristic equation are the same as the _____ of the closed-loop transfer function.

23. The roots of the characteristic equation _____ the behaviour of the system. Hence the name for the equation.

24. The frequency of damped oscillations of an underdamped system is called the _____ natural frequency.

25. Control systems are normally designed with ξ _____ 1.

26. Systems with $\xi = 0$ are called _____ systems.

27. Systems with $0 < \xi < 1$ are called _____ systems.

28. Systems with $\xi = 1$ are called _____ systems.

29. Systems with $\xi > 1$ are called _____ systems.

30. As ξ is increased from 0 to 1, the response becomes progressively _____ oscillatory.

31. The time required for the response to reach 50% of the final value in the first attempt is called the _____.

32. The time required for the response to rise from 0 to 100% of the final value is called the _____.

33. The time required for the response to reach the peak of the time response is called _____.

34. The difference between the time response peak and the steady output is called the _____.

35. The time required for the response to reach and stay within a particular percentage of its final value is called the _____.

36. The normalized settling time is given by _____.

37. The _____ error is a measure of system accuracy.

38. The steady-state errors arise from the _____, _____, and from _____ of system components.

39. The steady-state performance of a stable control system is generally judged by its steady-state error to _____, _____ and _____ inputs.

40. The position error constant K_p is indicative of the error in output for a _____ input.

41. The velocity error constant K_v is indicative of the error in output for a _____ input.

42. The acceleration error constant K_a is indicative of the error in output for a _____ input.

43. Control systems are classified in accordance with the number of integrations in the open-loop transfer function as _____, _____, _____ systems etc.

44. A system with no open-loop poles at the origin of the s-plane is called a _____ system.

45. A system with one open-loop pole at the origin of the s-plane is called a _____ system.

46. A system with two open-loop poles at the origin of the s-plane is called a _____ system.

47. The number of open-loop poles at the origin of the *s*-plane indicates the _____ of the system.

48. A type-0 system has _____ position error, _____ velocity error and _____ acceleration error.

49. A type-1 system has _____ position error, _____ velocity error and _____ acceleration error.

50. A type-2 system has _____ position error, _____ velocity error and _____ acceleration error.

51. The _____ describe the ability of a system to reduce or eliminate steady-state errors.

52. As _____ of system becomes higher, progressively more steady-state errors are eliminated but it is more difficult to _____ the system and the _____ errors for such systems tend to be larger.

53. The highest power of *s* present in the denominator of the closed-loop transfer function indicates the _____ of the control system.

54. The time-domain specifications of a control system are _____, _____, _____, _____, and _____.

55. The relation between the static and dynamic error coefficients is $C_0 = $ _____, $C_1 = $ _____, and $C_2 = $ _____.

56. In proportional control, the actuating signal is _____ to the error signal.

57. It is necessary that the control system must be _____ for quick response.

58. The sluggish overdamped system can be made faster by increasing the _____ of the system.

59. Due to the increase in the forward path gain, the _____ gets reduced but the _____ increases.

60. The actuating signal for derivative control action consists of _____ error signal added with _____ error signal.

61. Derivative control results in an _____ of damping ratio but the _____ is reduced.

62. Derivative control does not affect _____.

63. Derivative control results in the addition of a _____ to the transfer function.

64. Derivative control _____ the value of ω_n.

65. The introduction of zero in derivative control results in _____ of rise time t_r.

66. In integral control, the actuating signal consists of _____ error signal added with _____ of the error signal.

67. The derivative feedback control is also called the _____ feedback control or _____ feedback control.

68. In derivative feedback control, the actuating signal is the difference between the _____ error signal and _____ of the output signal.

69. Derivative feedback control _____ the damping ratio and so the maximum overshoot will be _____.

70. Derivative feedback control _____ the steady-state error of the control system.

71. Integral control _____ the order of a control system.

72. The addition of a pole to the forward path transfer function _____ the order of the system, _____ the overshoot, _____ the stability, _____ the rise time and _____ the bandwidth.

73. The addition of a pole to the closed-loop transfer function _____ the rise time and _____ the overshoot.

74. The addition of a zero to the closed-loop transfer function _____ the rise time and _____ the maximum overshoot.

75. The poles which are very near to the imaginary axis are called _____ poles and the poles which are far away from the imaginary axis are called _____ poles.

76. In design of higher-order systems, the _____ poles of the system are used to control the dynamic performance of the system whereas the _____ poles are used for the purpose of ensuring that the controller transfer function can be realized by physical components.

77. If the system dynamics of a higher-order system can be accurately represented by a pair of complex conjugate dominant poles, then that ξ is called _____ damping ratio.

78. If the significant poles are neglected as they are, the _____ response is unchanged, but the _____ response gets affected.

79. To maintain the same steady-state response, the transfer function has to be written in _____ form.

80. A pole may be regarded as insignificant, if the magnitude of the real part of the pole is at least _____ times that of a dominant pole or a pair of complex dominant poles.

OBJECTIVE TYPE QUESTIONS

1. Knowledge of the transfer function of a system is necessary for the calculation of
   (a) time constant
   (b) output for a given input
   (c) order of the system
   (d) none of these

2. Zero initial conditions means that the system is
   (a) working with zero stored energy
   (b) working with zero reference signal
   (c) at rest and no energy is stored in any of its components
   (d) none of these

3. The transfer function is defined for
   (a) linear time-invariant systems
   (b) linear time-varying systems
   (c) nonlinear systems
   (d) none of these

4. The error signal in a control system is

(a) the difference between the measured value and the set value

(b) the sum of measured value and set value

(c) the ratio of measured value to set value

(d) none of these

5. The transfer function is the ratio of

(a) output to input

(b) the Laplace transform of output to the Laplace transform of input

(c) the Laplace transform of input to the Laplace transform of output

(d) the inverse Laplace transform of output to the inverse Laplace transform of input

6. With feedback, the transient response of the system as compared to that without feedback

(a) decays slowly   (b) rises at faster rate

(c) rises at slower rate   (d) none of these

7. A unit-impulse signal has zero value everywhere except at $t = 0$, where its magnitude is

(a) unity   (b) small finite value

(c) infinity   (d) none of these

8. The area under a unit-impulse function is

(a) infinity   (b) zero

(c) unity   (d) none of these

9. The nature of the transient response of a system is dependent

(a) only on system poles

(b) only on the inputs applied

(c) both on the system poles and the applied inputs

(d) none of these

10. The Laplace transform of impulse function is

(a) zero   (b) one

(c) $1/s$ (d) none of these

11. The system's impulse response is sometimes referred to as the

(a) weighting function of the system   (b) transfer function of the system

(c) transient response of the system   (d) steady-state response of the system

12. The impulse response of a system is

(a) the inverse Laplace transform of its transfer function

(b) the inverse Laplace transform of $G(s)$

(c) the inverse Laplace transform of $G(s)H(s)$

(d) none of these

13. A large time constant corresponds to a

(a) sluggish system   (b) faster system

(c) overdamped system   (d) underdamped system

14. The steady-state error of a first-order system to a ramp input is equal to
    (a) the time constant of the system
    (b) zero
    (c) infinity
    (d) none of these

15. Control systems are normally designed with damping factor
    (a) $\xi = 0$
    (b) $\xi = 1$
    (c) $\xi > 1$
    (d) $\xi < 1$

16. For a stable second-order underdamped system, the poles are
    (a) purely imaginary
    (b) complex conjugate of each other
    (c) real and unequal
    (d) real and equal

17. For a second-order overdamped system, the poles are
    (a) purely imaginary
    (b) complex conjugate of each other
    (c) real and equal
    (d) real and unequal

18. For a second-order critically-damped system, the poles are
    (a) purely imaginary
    (b) complex conjugate of each other
    (c) real and equal
    (d) real and unequal

19. For a second-order undamped system, the poles are
    (a) purely imaginary
    (b) real and equal
    (c) real and unequal
    (d) complex conjugate of each other

20. For undamped systems, the damping ratio is
    (a) $\xi = 0$
    (b) $\xi = 1$
    (c) $\xi < 1$
    (d) $\xi > 1$

21. For overdamped systems, the damping ratio is
    (a) $\xi = \infty$
    (b) $\xi = 0$
    (c) $\xi = 1$
    (d) $\xi > 1$

22. For critically-damped systems, the damping ratio is
    (a) $\xi = 0$
    (b) $\xi = \infty$
    (c) $\xi < 1$
    (d) $\xi = 1$

23. For underdamped systems, the damping ratio is
    (a) $\xi = 0$
    (b) $\xi < 1$
    (c) $\xi < 0$
    (d) $\xi = 1$

24. For a second-order system as ξ is increased from zero, the response becomes
    (a) progressively more oscillatory
    (b) progressively less oscillatory
    (c) zero
    (d) infinity

25. If the characteristic equation of a system is $s^2 + 2s + 1 = 0$, the system is
    (a) undamped
    (b) overdamped
    (c) critically-damped
    (d) underdamped

26. If the characteristic equation of a system is $s^2 + 4s + 10 = 0$, the system is
    (a) undamped
    (b) overdamped
    (c) critically-damped
    (d) underdamped

27. If the characteristic equation of a system is $s^2 + 6s + 8 = 0$, the system is
    (a) undamped
    (b) underdamped
    (c) critically-damped
    (d) overdamped

28. If the characteristic equation of a system is $s^2 + 2 = 0$, the system is
    (a) undamped
    (b) underdamped
    (c) critically-damped
    (d) overdamped

29. The response of a control system having damping factor as unity will be
    (a) oscillatory
    (b) underdamped
    (c) critically-damped
    (d) none of these

30. The steady-state error of a type-1, second-order system to a unit-ramp input is
    (a) $2\xi\omega_n$
    (b) $\dfrac{\omega_n}{2\xi}$
    (c) $\dfrac{2\xi}{\omega_n}$
    (d) $\dfrac{2\omega_n}{\xi}$

31. In a type-1, second-order system, the first peak overshoot occurs at a time
    (a) $t_p = \dfrac{\pi\omega_n}{\sqrt{1-\xi^2}}$
    (b) $t_p = \dfrac{\pi}{\omega_n\sqrt{1-\xi^2}}$
    (c) $t_p = \dfrac{2\pi}{\omega_n\sqrt{1-\xi^2}}$
    (d) $t_p = \dfrac{\omega_n}{\sqrt{1-\xi^2}}$

32. The rise time for a type-1, second-order system is given by
    (a) $t_r = \dfrac{\tan^{-1}\left(\dfrac{\sqrt{1-\xi^2}}{\xi}\right)}{\omega_n\sqrt{1-\xi^2}}$
    (b) $t_r = \dfrac{\pi - \cos^{-1}\xi}{\omega_n\sqrt{1-\xi^2}}$
    (c) $t_r = \dfrac{\pi - \cos^{-1}\left(\dfrac{\sqrt{1-\xi^2}}{\xi}\right)}{\omega_n\sqrt{1-\xi^2}}$
    (d) $t_r = \dfrac{\pi - \sin^{-1}\left(\dfrac{\sqrt{1-\xi^2}}{\xi}\right)}{\omega_n\sqrt{1-\xi^2}}$

33. The rise time of a second-order underdamped system is the time taken by the output to rise
    (a) from 10% to 90% of its final steady-state value
    (b) from 0% to 100% of its final steady-state value

(c) from 5% to 95% of its final steady-state value

(d) from 0% to 50% of its final steady-state value

34. The rise time is the time taken by the output to rise from 10% to 90% of its final steady-state value, in case of

(a) undamped systems

(b) underdamped systems

(c) overdamped systems

(d) critically-damped systems

35. In a type-1, second-order system, the first undershoot occurs at a time

(a) $t_p = \dfrac{\pi}{\omega_d}$

(b) $t_p = \dfrac{2\pi}{\omega_d}$

(c) $t_p = \dfrac{\pi}{2\omega_d}$

(d) $t_p = \dfrac{\omega_d}{2\pi}$.

36. In general, which of the following systems is preferred.

(a) overdamped

(b) critically-damped

(c) undamped

(d) underdamped

37. The settling time of the second-order linear system is

(a) 4 times the time constant of the system

(b) 2 times the time constant of the system

(c) 1/4 times the time constant of the system

(d) none of these

38. A system is critically damped. If the gain of the system is increased, the system will behave as

(a) undamped

(b) underdamped

(c) overdamped

(d) no effect of gain

39. The position error constant of a type-2 canonical feedback system is given by

(a) $\underset{s \to 0}{\mathrm{Lt}}\ G(s)$

(b) $\underset{s \to 0}{\mathrm{Lt}}\ sG(s)$

(c) $\underset{s \to \infty}{\mathrm{Lt}}\ sG(s)$

(d) none of these

40. The velocity error constant of a stable canonical feedback system is given by

(a) $\underset{s \to 0}{\mathrm{Lt}}\ G(s)$

(b) $\underset{s \to 0}{\mathrm{Lt}}\ sG(s)$

(c) $\underset{s \to 0}{\mathrm{Lt}}\ s^2 G(s)$

(d) none of these

41. The acceleration error constant of a stable feedback system is given by

(a) $\underset{s \to 0}{\mathrm{Lt}}\ sG(s)$

(b) $\underset{s \to 0}{\mathrm{Lt}}\ G(s)$

(c) $\underset{s \to 0}{\mathrm{Lt}}\ s^2 G(s)$

(d) none of these

42. A feedback control system has the transfer function given by

$$F(s) = \frac{8(s+2)(s+4)}{s^3(s+1)(s^2+5s+6)}$$

It is a

(a) type-6 system   (b) type-3 system

(c) type-2 system   (d) none of these

43. A control system is represented in a block schematic as shown in the figure. What is the type of the system?

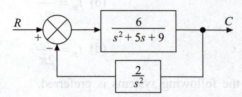

(a) Type-0   (b) Type-2

(c) Type-4   (d) None of these

44. A feedback control system has the transfer function

$$F(s) = \frac{K(s+2)}{s^2(s+1)(s^2+s+2)}$$

It is a

(a) second-order system   (b) first-order system

(c) fifth-order system   (d) none of these

45. The steady-state response of a system is dependent

(a) only on system poles

(b) only on the inputs applied

(c) both on the system poles and the inputs applied

(d) none of these

46. The type of a system indicates the number of integrations in the

(a) open-loop transfer function   (b) forward path transfer function

(c) closed-loop transfer function   (d) none of these

47. As type of system is increased

(a) more errors are eliminated   (b) more errors are introduced

(c) there is no effect on errors   (d) none of these

48. As type of system is increased

(a) stabilization becomes more difficult   (b) stabilization becomes very easy

(c) there is no effect on stability   (d) none of these

49. The roots of the characteristic equation are the same as the poles of the
    (a) closed-loop transfer function
    (b) open-loop transfer function
    (c) forward path transfer function
    (d) none of these

50. The effect of increase in the forward path gain of a control system on the damping ratio is that the damping ratio is
    (a) increased
    (b) reduced
    (c) not effected
    (d) made zero

51. Due to an increase in the forward path gain of a control system, the steady-state error is
    (a) reduced
    (b) increased
    (c) not effected
    (d) made infinite

52. Due to an increase in the forward path gain of a control system, the maximum overshoot is
    (a) reduced
    (b) increased
    (c) not effected
    (d) eliminated

53. Due to derivative control, the steady-state error is
    (a) reduced
    (b) increased
    (c) not effected
    (d) made zero

54. Due to derivative control, the rise time is
    (a) reduced
    (b) increased
    (c) not effected
    (d) made zero

55. Due to integral control, the order of a control system is
    (a) increased
    (b) decreased
    (c) not effected
    (d) none of these

PROBLEMS

4.1 The closed-loop transfer functions of certain second-order unity feedback control systems are given below. Determine the type of damping in the system.

(a) $\dfrac{C(s)}{R(s)} = \dfrac{9}{s^2 + 4s + 9}$

(b) $\dfrac{C(s)}{R(s)} = \dfrac{4}{s^2 + 6s + 4}$

(c) $\dfrac{C(s)}{R(s)} = \dfrac{3}{s^2 + 2s + 1}$

(d) $\dfrac{C(s)}{R(s)} = \dfrac{2}{s^2 + 2}$

4.2 A second-order system has a damping ratio of 0.7 and its natural frequency of oscillation is 12 radians per second. Determine the damped frequency of oscillation, the rise time, peak time, peak overshoot and settling time. Also determine the closed-loop transfer function.

4.3 The open-loop transfer function of a unity feedback system is

$$G(s) = \frac{10}{s(s+4)}$$

Determine the nature of response of the closed-loop system for a unit-step input. Also determine the rise time, peak time, peak overshoot and settling time.

4.4 Determine the unit-step response of the system shown in Figure P4.1.

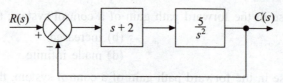

Figure P4.1

4.5 Consider the system shown in Figure P4.2, where $\xi = 0.5$ and $\omega_n = 4$ rad/s. Find the damped frequency of oscillation ω_d, rise time t_r, peak time t_p, peak overshoot M_p and settling time t_s.

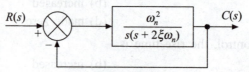

Figure P4.2

4.6 Measurements conducted on a servomechanism show the system response to be

$$c(t) = 1 + 0.5e^{-30t} - 1.5e^{-10t}$$

when subjected to a unit-step input.

(a) Obtain the expression for the closed-loop transfer function.

(b) Determine the undamped natural frequency and the damping ratio of the system.

4.7 The open-loop transfer function of a unity feedback system is given by

$$G(s) = \frac{K}{s(Ts+1)}$$

where K and T are positive constants. By what factor should the amplifier gain K be reduced so that the peak overshoot of unit-step response of the system is reduced from 60% to 30%.

4.8 A closed-loop control system is represented by the differential equation

$$\frac{d^2c}{dt^2} + 6\frac{dc}{dt} = 20e$$

where $e = r - c$ is the error signal. Determine the undamped natural frequency, damping ratio, and percentage maximum overshoot for a unit-step input.

4.9 A unity feedback control system has an open-loop transfer function

$$G(s) = \frac{4}{s(s+2)}$$

Determine the rise time, peak time, peak overshoot and the settling time when a step displacement of 15° is given to the system.

4.10 Determine the values of K and T of the closed-loop system shown in Figure P4.3 so that the maximum overshoot in unit-step response is 20% and the peak time is 1.5 s. Assume that $J = 1$ kg-m^2.

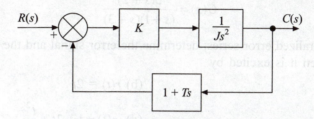

Figure P4.3

4.11 A unity feedback system is characterized by the open-loop transfer function

$$G(s) = \frac{1}{s(0.4s+1)(0.15s+1)}$$

Determine the steady-state errors for unit-step, unit-ramp and unit-acceleration inputs.

4.12 The open-loop transfer function of a unity feedback control system is given by

$$G(s) = \frac{20}{s(s+2)(s+5)}$$

Find the steady-state error when it is subjected to the input, $r(t) = 5 + 3t + 2t^2$.

4.13 A unity feedback system has

$$G(s) = \frac{10}{s(s+2)}$$

Find the generalized error coefficients and the steady-state error, for $r(t) = t$

4.14 For a unity feedback system having an open-loop transfer function

$$G(s) = \frac{K(s+2)(s+3)}{s^2(s^2+8s+15)}$$

Determine (a) type of system, (b) error constants K_p, K_v and K_a and (c) steady-state error for unit step, unit-ramp and unit-parabolic inputs.

4.15 Find the position, velocity and acceleration error constants for the following unity feedback systems having the forward path transfer function $G(s)$ as

(a) $G(s) = \dfrac{25}{(1 + 0.1s)(1 + 0.6s)}$

(b) $G(s) = \dfrac{20}{s(1 + 0.1s)(1 + 0.5s)}$

(c) $G(s) = \dfrac{50}{s^2(s^2 + 8s + 10)}$

(d) $G(s) = \dfrac{25}{s^3(s^2 + 5s + 4)}$

4.16 The open-loop transfer function of a unity feedback control system is

$$G(s) = \frac{5(s + 2)}{(s + 1)(s + 3)}$$

Using the generalized error series, determine the error signal and the steady-state error of the system when it is excited by

(a) $r(t) = 1$

(b) $r(t) = 2t$

(c) $r(t) = \dfrac{t^2}{2}$

(d) $r(t) = 1 + 2t + \dfrac{t^2}{2}$

MATLAB PROGRAMS

PROGRAM 4.1

Matlab program for unit step response curve of a second-order system for different Zeta values.

```
%Unit step response curves of second-order systems
clc;clear all;close all;
w=10;
for l=[0 0.2 0.4 1.0 1.5]
%t=0:0.1:50;
num = [w.^2] ;
den= [1 2*l*w w.^2] ;
t=0:0.01:2;
step(num,den, t)
hold on;
end
xlabel('Time in secs')
ylabel('Amplitude')
title( ' unit step response curves of Second-order systems' )
legend('Zeta= 0','Zeta= 0.2','Zeta= 0.4','Zeta= 1.0','Zeta= 1.5')
```

Output:

Unit step response curves of second-order systems

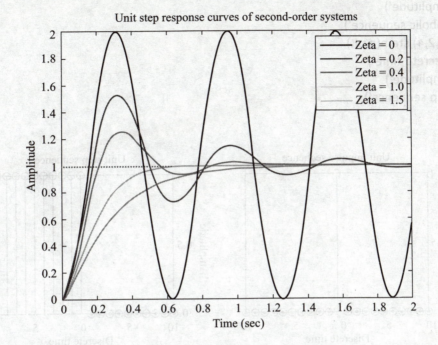

PROGRAM 4.2

Matlab program for plotting standard test signals - uint step, unit ramp, unit impulse and unit parabolic

```
% standard test signals
clc;clear all;close all;
n=-10:1:10;
I=[zeros(1,10) 1 zeros(1,10)];
U=[zeros(1,10) ones(1,11)];
n1=0:1:10;
P=3*(n1.^2)/2;
R=n1;
subplot(2,2,1),stem(n,I)
xlabel('Discrete time')
ylabel('Amplitude')
title('unit Impulse sequence')
subplot(2,2,2),stem(n,U)
xlabel('Discrete time')
ylabel('Amplitude')
title('Unit step sequence')
subplot(2,2,3),stem(n1,P)
```

```
xlabel('Discrete time')
ylabel('Amplitude')
title('parabolic sequence')
subplot(2,2,4),stem(n1,R)
xlabel('Discrete time')
ylabel('Amplitude')
title('Ramp sequence')
```

Output:

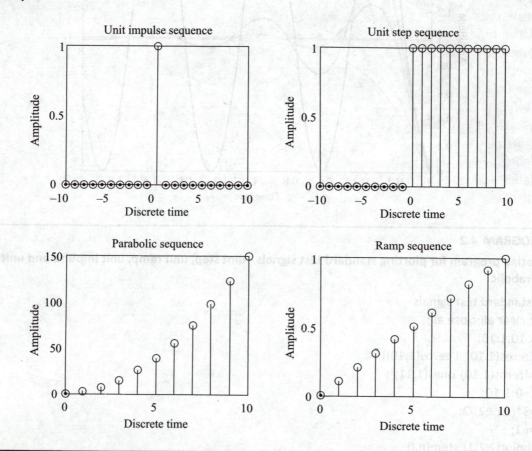

PROGRAM 4.3

Matlab program for finding step, ramp, parabolic input response for a closed-loop transfer

function $G(s) = \dfrac{3}{s(s+4)}$

```
%step, ramp, parabolic input to the closed loop transfer function
clc;clear all;close all;
g1=3;
```

```
g2=conv([1 0],[1 4]);
g=tf(g1,g2);
h=1;
c=feedback(g,1);
step(c)
t=0:0.001:10;
u=t;
[y,x]=lsim(c,u,t);
figure;plot(t,y,t,u)
xlabel('time in sec')
ylabel('Amplitude')
title('Closed loop response for ramp input')
legend('actual signal','desired signal')
u1=0.5*t.^2;
[y1,x1]=lsim(c,u1,t);
figure;plot(t,y1,t,u1)
xlabel('time in sec')
ylabel('Amplitude')
title('Closed loop response for parabolic input')
legend('actual signal','desired signal')
```

Output:

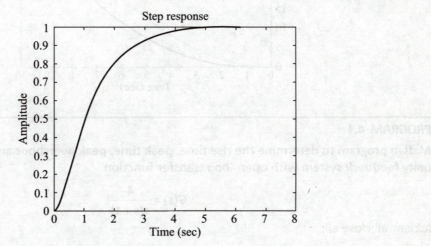

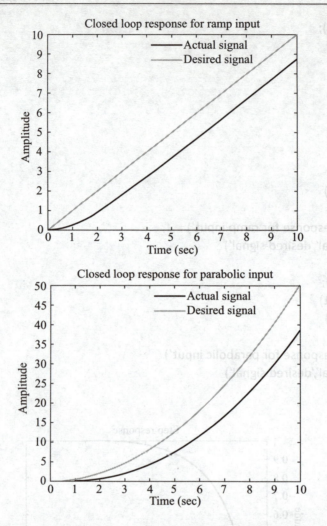

PROGRAM 4.4

Matlab program to determine the rise time, peak time, peak overshoot and settling time of a unity feedback system with open-loop transfer function

$$G(s) = \frac{4}{s(s+1)}$$

```
lc;clear all;close all;
g1=4;
g2=conv([1 0],[1 1]);
g=tf(g1,g2);
h=1;
c=feedback(g,1);
[num,den] = tfdata(c);
```

```
a=num{1};
b=den{1};
omegan = sqrt(b(3));
zeta = b(2) / (2*omegan);
Tsa = 4/ (zeta*omegan);
Tpa = pi/ (omegan*sqrt(1-zeta^2));
theta=atan((sqrt(1-zeta^2)/zeta));
Tra=(pi-theta)/(omegan*sqrt(1-zeta^2));
Mp = exp(-zeta*pi/ sqrt(1-zeta^2))*100;
fprintf('the value of Zeta is %f \n',zeta)
fprintf('the value of Omegan is %f \n',omegan)
fprintf('the value of Settling time is %f in seconds \n',Tsa)
fprintf('the value of Peak time is %f in seconds \n',Tpa)
fprintf('the value of Raise time is %f in seconds \n',Tra)
fprintf('the value of peakover shoot is %f in percentage \n',Mp)
```

Output:

the value of Zeta is 0.250000
the value of Omegan is 2.000000
the value of Settling time is 8.000000 in seconds
the value of Peak time is 1.622311 in seconds
the value of Raise time is 0.941639 in seconds
the value of peakover shoot is 44.434423 in percentage

PROGRAM 4.5

Matlab program to find the transfer function of a second order system with damping ratio = 0.25 and undamped natural frequency = 2

```
% Program to obtain Transfer function
clc;close all;clear all;
wn=2;
dampingratio=0.25;
[num1,den]=ord2(wn,dampingratio);
num=wn^2;
G=tf(num,den);
disp('Transfer function of second order system is');
G
```

Output:

Transfer function of second order system is
Transfer function:

$$\frac{4}{s^2 + s + 4}$$

PROGRAM 4.6

Matlab program to find the unit step response of a unity feedback control system with

$$G(s) = \frac{10}{s(s+3)} \text{ and } H(s) = 0.1s + 1.$$

```
% Unit step response of a given system
clc; clear all ;close all;
g1=10;
g2=conv([1 0],[1 3]);
G=tf(g1,g2);
g3=[0.1 1];
H=tf(g3,1);
c=feedback(G,H);
[num,den] = tfdata(c);
a=num{1};
b=den{1};
T1=tf(a,b);
step(T1)
```

Output:

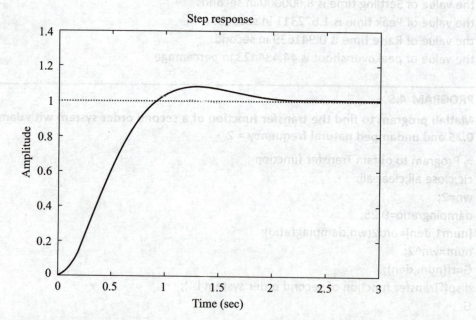

5

Routh Stability Criterion

5.1 INTRODUCTION

When a linear control system is subjected to both inputs and initial conditions, the total response is given by

total response = zero-state response + zero-input response

1. *Zero-state response*: The zero-state response is due to the input only; all the initial conditions of the system are zero.
2. *Zero-input response*: The zero-input response is due to initial conditions only; all the inputs are zero.

Roughly speaking, stability in a system implies that small changes in the system input, in initial conditions, or in system parameters do not result in large changes in system output. Stability is a very important characteristic of the transient performance of a system. An unstable system is a useless system. So almost every working system is designed to be stable. Within the boundaries of parameter variations permitted by stability considerations, we can then seek to improve the system performance.

The following two notions of system stability are to be satisfied for a linear time-invariant system to be stable:

1. When the system is excited by a bounded input, the output is bounded. This concept is called *bounded-input bounded-output stability* (BIBO stability).
2. When no input is applied, the output tends towards zero irrespective of the initial conditions. This stability is called *asymptotic stability*.

The notion of BIBO stability concerns a system under the influence of input. The notion of asymptotic stability generally concerns a free system relative to its transient behaviour.

When a system is excited by an unbounded input and produces an unbounded output nothing can be said about its stability. But if it is excited by a bounded input and produces an unbounded response, it is unstable. The output is unbounded does not mean that the output goes

283

to infinity. Actually the output of an unstable system may increase to a certain extent, and then the system may break down or become nonlinear after the output exceeds a certain magnitude so that the linear mathematical model no longer applies.

For linear time-invariant systems, the two notions of stability are essentially equivalent. Thus, if a system is BIBO stable, it must also be zero-input or asymptotically stable. Linear systems have only one equilibrium state. If a linear system is stable for one set of initial conditions, it will be stable for any other set of initial conditions. Also, if it is stable for one bounded input, it will be stable for any other bounded input. In fact, the stability of a linear system depends only on the parameters of the system and not on the input or driving function of the system. On the other hand, nonlinear systems may have multiple equilibrium states and other anomalies. So for nonlinear systems, the concept of stability is difficult even to define, and there is no clear-cut correspondence between the two notions of stability defined earlier. A nonlinear system may be stable for one set of initial conditions, but may become unstable for another set of initial conditions. It may be stable for one bounded input but may become unstable for another bounded input. No generalized techniques are available to determine the stability of nonlinear systems, but simple and powerful techniques are available to determine the stability of linear systems.

5.2 BOUNDED-INPUT BOUNDED-OUTPUT (BIBO) STABILITY

Let $r(t)$, $c(t)$, and $g(t)$ be the input, output, and impulse response of a linear time-invariant system. They are related in s-domain as

$$C(s) = R(s) \cdot G(s)$$

The convolution integral relating $r(t)$, $c(t)$, and $g(t)$ is

$$c(t) = \int_0^\infty r(t - \tau) g(\tau) \, d\tau$$

Taking the absolute value on both sides of the above equation, we get

$$|c(t)| = \left| \int_0^\infty r(t - \tau) g(\tau) \, d\tau \right|$$

Since the absolute value of an integral is less than or equal to the integral of the absolute value

$$|c(t)| \leq \int_0^\infty |r(t - \tau) g(\tau)| \, d\tau$$

$$\leq \int_0^\infty |g(\tau)| \, |r(t - \tau)| \, d\tau$$

The BIBO stability condition is satisfied if for every bounded input ($|r(t)| \leq M_1 < \infty$), the output is bounded ($|c(t)| \leq M_2 < \infty$).

Therefore, for a bounded input, the bounded output condition is

$$|c(t)| \le M_1 \int_0^\infty |g(\tau)|\, d\tau \le M_2$$

Thus the notion of BIBO stability is satisfied if the impulse response $g(t)$ is absolutely integrable, i.e.

$$\int_0^\infty |g(\tau)|\, d\tau$$

is finite. That is, the area under the absolute-value curve of the impulse response $g(t)$ evaluated from $t = 0$ to $t = \infty$ must be finite.

The nature of the impulse response $g(t)$ is dependent on the poles of the transfer function $G(s)$ which are the roots of the characteristic equation. These roots may be both real and complex conjugate and may have multiplicity of various orders. If any of the roots of the characteristic equation is in the right-half of the s-plane, then the transient response increases monotonically with time or oscillates with increasing amplitude. If there are non-repeated roots of the characteristic equation on the imaginary axis, the response oscillates with constant amplitude. If there is a single root at the origin, the output is of constant amplitude. If there are repeated roots of the characteristic equation on the imaginary axis, the response oscillates with increasing amplitude. If there are repeated roots at the origin of the s-plane, the output increases without bound. The impulse response of various terms of the closed-loop transfer function $M(s)$ corresponding to different pole locations is shown in Table 5.1. So the following general conclusions can be drawn regarding system stability.

Table 5.1 Response terms contributed by various types of roots

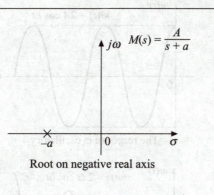

Root on negative real axis

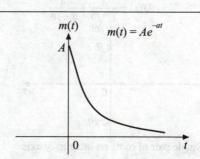

Response is exponentially decreasing

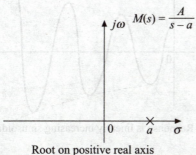

Root on positive real axis

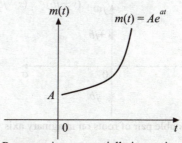

Response is exponentially increasing

(Contd.)

Table 5.1 Response terms contributed by various types of roots (contd.)

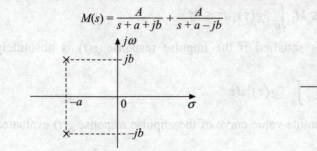

Complex conjugate roots on the
left-half of the s-plane

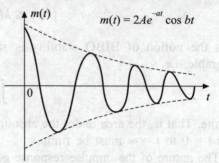

$$m(t) = 2Ae^{-at} \cos bt$$

Response is damped oscillatory

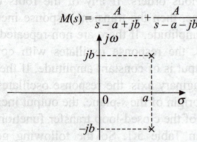

Complex conjugate roots on the
right-half of the s-plane

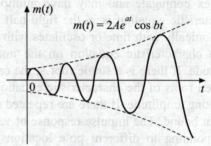

$$m(t) = 2Ae^{at} \cos bt$$

The response is exponentially
increasing sinusoidal

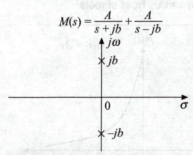

Single pair of roots on imaginary axis

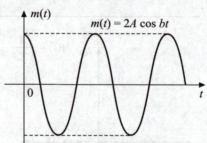

$$m(t) = 2A \cos bt$$

The response is oscillatory

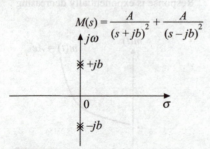

Double pair of roots on imaginary axis

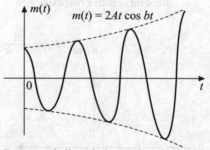

$$m(t) = 2At \cos bt$$

Response is linearly increasing sinusoidal

(Contd.)

Table 5.1 Response terms contributed by various types of roots (contd.)

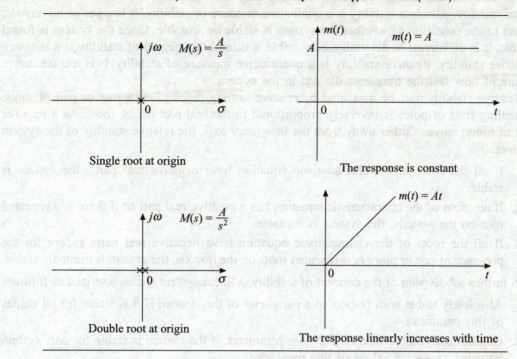

Single root at origin	The response is constant
Double root at origin	The response linearly increases with time

1. If all the roots of the characteristic equation have negative real parts, then the impulse response is bounded and eventually decreases to zero. Therefore, $\int_0^\infty |g(\tau)|\, d\tau$ is finite and the system is bounded-input, bounded-output stable.

2. If any root of the characteristic equation has a positive real part, $g(t)$ is unbounded and $\int_0^\infty |g(\tau)|\, d\tau$ is infinite. The system is therefore unstable.

3. If the characteristic equation has repeated roots on the $j\omega$-axis, $g(t)$ is unbounded and $\int_0^\infty |g(\tau)|\, d\tau$ is infinite. The system is therefore unstable.

4. If one or more non-repeated roots of the characteristic equation are on the $j\omega$-axis, then $g(t)$ is bounded but $\int_0^\infty |g(\tau)|\, d\tau$ is infinite. The system is therefore unstable.

There are a few exceptions to the normal definition of stability. A pole at the origin corresponds to an integrator. A pair of conjugate poles on the imaginary axis corresponds to a sinusoidal oscillator. Both the integrator and the sinusoidal oscillator are useful devices. The response in both cases is bounded unless the input has a pole matching one of the system poles on the $j\omega$-axis. So depending on the final response, such a system may be treated as acceptable or non-acceptable. These systems are also called marginally or limitedly stable systems.

For analysis and design purposes, stability may be classified as *absolute stability* and *relative stability*. Absolute stability is a qualitative measure of stability. It is a yes or no answer. It refers to the condition of whether the system is stable or unstable. Once the system is found to stable, it is of interest to determine how stable it is, and this degree of stability is a measure of relative stability. Relative stability is a quantitative measure of stability. It is a quantitative measure of how fast the transients die out in the system.

Relative stability may be measured by relative settling times of each root or pair of roots. The settling time of poles is inversely proportional to the real part of the roots. As a root (or a pair of roots) moves farther away from the imaginary axis, the relative stability of the system improves.

1. If all the roots of the characteristic equation have negative real parts, the system is stable.

2. If any root of the characteristic equation has a positive real part or if there is a repeated root on the $j\omega$-axis, the system is unstable.

3. If all the roots of the characteristic equation have negative real parts except for the presence of one or more non-repeated roots on the $j\omega$-axis, the system is limitedly stable.

In further subdivision of the concept of stability, a linear system is characterized as follows:

1. Absolutely stable with respect to a parameter of the system, if it is stable for all values of this parameter.

2. Conditionally stable with respect to a parameter, if the system is stable for only certain bounded ranges of values of this parameter.

From the above discussion, we can observe that the stability of a system can be determined by determining the roots of the characteristic equation. Unfortunately, no general formula in algebraic form is available to determine the roots of the characteristic equations of third- and higher-order systems. Even though various numerical methods are available to determine the roots of the characteristic equation, they are quite cumbersome even for third-order systems. So, many simple graphical and algebraic criteria have been developed to determine the roots of the characteristic equation. These criteria answer the question, whether a system be stable or not, in 'yes' or 'no' form.

5.3 NECESSARY CONDITIONS FOR STABILITY

The necessary (but not sufficient) conditions for stability of a linear time-invariant, single-input single-output system described by the characteristic equation

$$q(s) = a_0 s^n + a_1 s^{n-1} + \cdots + a_{n-1}s + a_n = 0; \; a_0 > 0$$

is that

1. All the coefficients of its characteristic equation be real and have the same sign.

2. None of the coefficients should be zero.

So certain conclusions regarding the stability of a system can be drawn by merely inspecting the coefficients of its characteristic equation in polynomial form. However, these conditions are not sufficient, because it is quite possible that an equation with all its coefficients non-zero and of the same sign may not have all the roots in the left-half of the s-plane.

Consider an nth order characteristic equation given as follows:

$$a_0 s^n + a_1 s^{n-1} + a_2 s^{n-2} + \cdots + a_{n-1} s + a_n = 0$$

Let the roots of this nth order characteristic equation be $s = r_1, r_2, \ldots, r_n$. These roots are functions of coefficients $a_0, a_1, a_2, \ldots, a_{n-1}, a_n$.

Consider a second-order polynomial:

$$a_0 s^2 + a_1 s + a_2 = a_0 \left(s^2 + \frac{a_1}{a_0} s + \frac{a_2}{a_0} \right)$$

$$= a_0 (s - r_1)(s - r_2)$$

$$= a_0 s^2 - a_0 (r_1 + r_2) s + a_0 r_1 r_2$$

Consider a third-order polynomial:

$$a_0 s^3 + a_1 s^2 + a_2 s + a_3 = a_0 \left(s^3 + \frac{a_1}{a_0} s^2 + \frac{a_2}{a_0} s + \frac{a_3}{a_0} \right)$$

$$= a_0 (s - r_1)(s - r_2)(s - r_3)$$

$$= a_0 s^3 - a_0 (r_1 + r_2 + r_3) s^2 + a_0 (r_1 r_2 + r_2 r_3 + r_3 r_1) s - a_0 r_1 r_2 r_3$$

On extending this expansion to the nth order polynomial, we get

$$a_0 s^n + a_1 s^{n-1} + a_2 s^{n-2} + \cdots + a_{n-1} s + a_n$$

$$= a_0 s^n - a_0 \text{ (sum of all the roots)} s^{n-1}$$
$$+ a_0 \text{ (sum of the products of 2 roots taken at time)} s^{n-2}$$
$$- a_0 \text{ (sum of the products of 3 roots taken at a time)} s^{n-3}$$
$$+ \cdots + a_0 (-1)^n \text{ (product of all the } n \text{ roots)}$$

If all the roots of a polynomial are real and are in the left-half of the s-plane, then all r_i's in the above equations are real and negative. Therefore all polynomial coefficients are positive. If at least one root is in the right-half of the s-plane, then some of the coefficients will be negative. Also, it can be observed that if all the roots are in the left-half of the s-plane, no coefficient can be zero.

For example, consider the characteristic polynomial with all positive coefficients

$$s^3 + s^2 + 2s + 8 = 0$$

The characteristic polynomial can be written as

$$s^3 + s^2 + 2s + 8 = (s + 2) \left(s - \frac{1}{2} + j \frac{\sqrt{15}}{2} \right) \left(s - \frac{1}{2} - j \frac{\sqrt{15}}{2} \right)$$

The coefficients of this polynomial are all positive, but two roots are in the right-half of the s-plane and so the system is unstable.

Another example is

$$s^3 + s^2 + 10s + 48 = (s + 3)(s - 1 + j4)(s - 1 - j4)$$

All the coefficients of this polynomial are positive but two roots are in the right-half of the s-plane and so the system is unstable.

One or more coefficients of the characteristic equation can be zero or negative only if

1. One or more roots have positive real parts or / and
2. One or more roots are at the origin or / and
3. One or more pairs of conjugate roots are on the imaginary axis.

It can therefore be concluded that the absence or negativeness of any of the coefficients of the characteristic equation (with $a_0 > 0$) indicates that the system is either unstable or atmost limitedly stable.

1. The positiveness of the coefficients of the characteristic equation ensures the negativeness of real roots as well as the negativeness of real parts of the complex roots of systems of first and second order. So it becomes the necessary and sufficient condition for stability of first- and second-order systems.
2. For third- and higher-order systems, the positiveness of the coefficients of the characteristic equation ensures the negativeness of real roots, but does not ensure the negativeness of the real parts of the complex roots. Therefore, it cannot be a sufficient condition for stability of third- and higher-order systems.

So in case of third- and higher-order systems, the system may be unstable even if all the coefficients are positive and none is missing. So to analyze the stability, first the characteristic equation is examined for necessary conditions. If one or more coefficients are zero or negative, it can be concluded that the system is unstable. Only if all the coefficients are positive (or all are negative) the possibility of stable system exists and one should proceed further to examine the sufficient conditions of stability.

Example 5.1 Investigate whether the following systems represented by the characteristic equations are stable or not.

(a) $s^5 + 4s^4 + s^2 + s + 2 = 0$
(b) $5s^4 - 2s^3 + 3s^2 + 2s + 16 = 0$
(c) $12s^3 - s + 10 = 0$
(d) $s^4 + 2s^3 + 5s^2 + s = 0$

Solution:

(a) In the given characteristic equation

$$s^5 + 4s^4 + s^2 + s + 2 = 0$$

the s^3 term is missing, that is, the coefficient of s^3 is zero, and so, the necessary condition for stability is not satisfied. So the system is unstable. There is no need to formulate the Routh table to check for stability.

(b) In the given characteristic equation

$$5s^4 - 2s^3 + 3s^2 + 2s + 16 = 0$$

the coefficient of s^3 is negative, and hence the necessary condition for stability is not satisfied. So the system is unstable. There is no need to formulate the Routh table to check for stability.

(c) In the given characteristic equation

$$12s^3 - s + 10 = 0$$

the s^2 term is missing and the coefficient of s is negative. So the necessary condition for stability is not satisfied. Hence the system is unstable, and there is no need to formulate the Routh table.

(d) In the given characteristic equation

$$s^4 + 2s^3 + 5s^2 + s = 0$$

the constant term is missing. So the necessary condition for stability is not satisfied. Hence the system is unstable, and there is no need to formulate the Routh table.

Example 5.2   Without using the Routh criterion, determine if the following systems are asymptotically stable, marginally stable, or unstable. In each case the closed-loop system transfer function is given.

(a) $M(s) = \dfrac{10(s+2)}{s^3 + 3s^2 + 5s}$

(b) $M(s) = \dfrac{s-1}{(s+5)(s^2+2)}$

(c) $M(s) = \dfrac{K}{s^2 + 5s + 5}$

(d) $M(s) = \dfrac{100(s-1)}{(s+5)(s^2 + 2s + 2)}$

(e) $M(s) = \dfrac{100}{s^3 - 2s^2 - 3s + 10}$

(f) $M(s) = \dfrac{10(s+12.5)}{s^6 + 4s^4 + 5s^2 + 2}$

Solution: To determine the stability of the system, determine the roots of the characteristic equation, that is, the poles of the closed-loop system transfer function.

(a) The characteristic equation is

$$s^3 + 3s^2 + 5s = 0$$

i.e.
$$s(s^2 + 3s + 5) = 0$$

i.e.
$$s\left(s+1.5 + j\sqrt{\frac{11}{4}}\right)\left(s+1.5 - j\sqrt{\frac{11}{4}}\right) = 0$$

So the closed-loop poles are at $s = 0$, $s = -1.5 + j\sqrt{\dfrac{11}{4}}$ and $s = -1.5 - j\sqrt{\dfrac{11}{4}}$.

Two poles of the closed-loop system are in the left-half of the s-plane and one pole is at the origin. So the system is marginally stable.

(b) The characteristic equation is

$$(s + 5)(s^2 + 2) = 0$$

i.e. $$(s + 5)(s + j\sqrt{2})(s - j\sqrt{2}) = 0$$

The poles are at

$$s = -5, s = -j\sqrt{2}, s = j\sqrt{2}$$

There is one pair of conjugate poles of the system on the imaginary axis of the *s*-plane and no pole in the right-half of the *s*-plane and so, the system is marginally stable.

(c) The characteristic equation is

$$s^2 + 5s + 5 = 0$$

i.e. $$(s + 3.168)(s + 1.382) = 0$$

So the poles are at $s = -3.618$ and $s = -1.382$.

All the poles of the closed-loop system are in the left-half of the *s*-plane, and so the system is asymptotically stable.

(d) The characteristic equation is

$$(s + 5)(s^2 + 2s + 2) = 0$$

i.e. $$(s + 5)(s + 1 + j1)(s + 1 - j1) = 0$$

So the closed-loop poles are at $s = -5$, $s = -1 - j1$ and $s = -1 + j1$.

All the closed-loop poles are in the left-half of the *s*-plane. So the system is asymptotically stable.

(e) The characteristic equation is

$$s^3 - 2s^2 - 3s + 10 = 0$$

i.e. $$(s + 2)(s^2 - 4s + 5) = 0$$

i.e. $$(s + 2)(s - 2 - j1)(s - 2 + j1) = 0$$

The poles of the closed-loop system transfer function are at, $s = -2$, $s = 2 + j1$ and $s = 2 - j1$, i.e. there is one root of the characteristic equation in the left-half of the *s*-plane and one pair of complex conjugate roots in the right-half of the *s*-plane. So the system is unstable. Also we can say that, since some of the coefficients of the characteristic equation are negative, it does not satisfy the necessary condition for stability. Hence, the system is unstable.

(f) The characteristic equation is

$$s^6 + 4s^4 + 5s^2 + 2 = 0$$

i.e. $$(s^2 + 1)(s^4 + 3s^2 + 2) = 0$$

i.e. $$(s^2 + 1)(s^2 + 1)(s^2 + 2) = 0$$

The poles of the closed-loop system are at $s = \pm j1$, $s = \pm j1$ and $s = \pm j\sqrt{2}$.

There are pairs of repeated poles of the system on the imaginary axis at $s = \pm j1$, and so the system is unstable.

5.4 ROUTH STABILITY CRITERION

The Routh stability criterion is based on formulating an array (or table) called the *Routh array* (or Routh table) using the coefficients of the characteristic equation. The first row of the array consists of the first, third, fifth, etc. coefficients and the second row consists of the second, fourth, sixth, etc., coefficients, all counting from the highest-order terms. The remaining rows are completed by the numbers obtained by the indicated operations below for an eighth-order system.

$$q(s) = a_0 s^8 + a_1 s^7 + a_2 s^6 + a_3 s^5 + a_4 s^4 + a_5 s^3 + a_6 s^2 + a_7 s^1 + a_8 = 0$$

Routh array

s^8	a_0	a_2	a_4	a_6 $\qquad a_8$
s^7	a_1	a_3	a_5	a_7
s^6	$\dfrac{a_1 \times a_2 - a_0 \times a_3}{a_1} = b_1$	$\dfrac{a_1 \times a_4 - a_0 \times a_5}{a_1} = b_2$	$\dfrac{a_1 \times a_6 - a_0 \times a_7}{a_1} = b_3$	$\dfrac{a_1 \times a_8 - a_0 \times 0}{a_1} = a_8$
s^5	$\dfrac{b_1 \times a_3 - a_1 \times b_2}{b_1} = c_1$	$\dfrac{b_1 \times a_5 - a_1 \times b_3}{b_1} = c_2$	$\dfrac{b_1 \times a_7 - a_1 \times a_8}{b_1} = c_3$	0
s^4	$\dfrac{c_1 \times b_2 - b_1 \times c_2}{c_1} = d_1$	$\dfrac{c_1 \times b_3 - b_1 \times c_3}{c_1} = d_2$	$\dfrac{c_1 \times a_8 - b_1 \times 0}{c_1} = a_8$	0
s^3	$\dfrac{d_1 \times c_2 - c_1 \times d_2}{d_1} = e_1$	$\dfrac{d_1 \times c_3 - c_1 \times a_8}{d_1} = e_2$	0	
s^2	$\dfrac{e_1 \times d_2 - d_1 \times e_2}{e_1} = f_1$	$\dfrac{e_1 \times a_8 - d_1 \times 0}{e_1} = a_8$		
s^1	$\dfrac{f_1 \times e_2 - e_1 \times a_8}{f_1} = g_1$	0		
s^0	$\dfrac{g_1 \times a_8 - f_1 \times 0}{g_1} = a_8$			

The column of s's on the left side is used for identification purposes. The reference column keeps track of the calculations, and the last row of the Routh table should always be the s^0 row.

In the process of generating the Routh array, the missing terms are regarded as zero. Also all the elements of any row can be divided by a positive constant during the process to simplify the computational work.

Once the Routh tabulation is completed, the next step in the application of the Routh criterion is to investigate the signs of the elements in the first column of the Routh array. The Routh stability criterion is: "For a system to be stable, it is necessary and sufficient that each term of the first column of the Routh array of its characteristic equation be positive if $a_0 > 0$. If this condition is not met, the system is unstable and the number of sign changes of the terms of the first column of the Routh array correspond to the number of roots of the characteristic equation in the right-half of the s-plane."

5.5   DIFFICULTIES IN THE FORMULATION OF THE ROUTH TABLE

In applying the Routh stability criterion, occasionally the following difficulties may arise causing the breakdown of Routh's test.

5.5.1   Difficulty 1

The first element in any row of the Routh array is zero while the rest of the row has at least one non-zero element.

Because of this zero element, the elements in the next row become infinite and Routh's test breaks down. This difficulty can be overcome by using any one of the following two methods.

1. Replace the first zero element by a small positive number ϵ and proceed with the formulation of the rest of the Routh array. Then examine the signs of the elements in the first column of the completed Routh array as $\epsilon \rightarrow 0$. The number of sign changes in the elements of the first column of the Routh array indicates the number of roots of the characteristic equation in the right-half of the s-plane. Even if there are no sign changes, the system is unstable and there are roots on the imaginary axis.

2. Obtain a modified characteristic equation in z, by replacing s in the original characteristic equation by $1/z$ and form the Routh array in z. The number of z roots with positive real parts (i.e. in the right-half of the z-plane) are the same as the number of s-roots with positive real parts.

5.5.2   Difficulty 2

All the elements in any one row of the Routh array are zero.

This condition indicates that there are symmetrically located roots in the s-plane (pair of real roots with opposite signs *and/or* pair of conjugate roots on the imaginary axis *and/or* complex conjugate roots forming quadrates in the s-plane). Because of this row of zeros, all the elements of the subsequent rows also become zero and the Routh's test breaks down. To overcome this difficulty, form an auxiliary polynomial by using the coefficients of the row just above the row of zeros in the Routh array. This polynomial gives the number and location of root pairs of the characteristic equation which are symmetrically located in the s-plane. The order of the auxiliary polynomial is always even. The roots of the auxiliary equation also satisfy the original equation.

Replace the row of zeros in the Routh array by a row of coefficients of the polynomial generated by taking the first derivative of the auxiliary polynomial and proceed with the formulation of the Routh array.

Look for the signs of the elements in the first column of the Routh array. The number of sign changes indicate the number of roots of the characteristic equation in the right-half of the s-plane. Even if there are no sign changes, the system is unstable only. It indicates that there are no roots of the characteristic equation in the right-half of the s-plane, but there are pairs of roots on the imaginary axis of the s-plane. The system may be limitedly stable if the poles on the $j\omega$-axis are not multiple.

In fact whenever difficulty 1 or difficulty 2 arises, it can immediately be concluded that the system is unstable. There is no need to complete the Routh table to determine the stability. The Routh table should be completed only if the location of the roots is to be determined.

The Routh stability criterion is an algebraic method to determine the stability of linear control systems. Being an algebraic method, it is very simple. There is no need to solve for the roots. Information about stability of control systems can be obtained directly from the coefficients of the characteristic equation. The limitations are as follows:

1. It is valid if and only if the characteristic equation is algebraic with real coefficients. If anyone of the coefficients is complex, or if the equation is not algebraic, such as containing exponential functions or sinusoidal functions of s, the Routh criterion simply cannot be applied.

2. Another limitation of the Routh criterion is that, it is valid only for the determination of the roots of the characteristic equation with respect to the left-half or right-half of the s-plane. The stability boundary is the $j\omega$-axis of the s-plane. The criterion cannot be applied to any other stability boundaries in a complex plane such as the unit circle in the z-plane, which is the stability boundary of discrete-data systems.

3. It gives information only on the absolute stability of a system. Determination of relative stability by repeated application of the Routh criterion by shifting the origin of the s-plane is quite cumbersome. It does not suggest how to improve the relative stability or how to stabilize an unstable system.

4. It can tell how many roots of the characteristic equation are in the right-half of the s-plane, but it cannot give any information about their exact location. Also it cannot tell whether the roots are real or complex.

5. This stability criterion applies to polynomials with only a finite number of terms.

Example 5.3   The characteristic equation of a servo system is given by

$$b_0 s^4 + b_1 s^3 + b_2 s^2 + b_3 s + b_4 = 0$$

Determine the conditions which must be satisfied by the coefficients of the characteristic equation for the system to be stable.

Solution: Form the Routh table as shown below.

s^4	b_0	b_2	b_4
s^3	b_1	b_3	
s^2	$\dfrac{b_1 b_2 - b_0 b_3}{b_1}$	$\dfrac{b_1 b_4 - b_0 \times 0}{b_1} = b_4$	
s^1	$\dfrac{(b_1 b_2 - b_0 b_3) b_3 - b_1^2 b_4}{b_1 b_2 - b_0 b_3}$		
s^0	b_4		

For stability, all the elements in the first column of the Routh array must be positive. So, the conditions that must be satisfied for stability of the given system are as follows:

$$b_1 > 0, \ b_1 b_2 - b_0 b_3 > 0, \ (b_1 b_2 - b_0 b_3) b_3 - b_1^2 b_4 > 0, \ b_4 > 0$$

Example 5.4 By means of the Routh criterion, determine the stability of the systems represented by the following characteristic equations. For systems found to be unstable, determine the number of roots of the characteristic equation in the right-half of the s-plane.

  (a) $s^5 + s^4 + 24s^3 + 48s^2 - 25s - 5 = 0$
  (b) $s^4 + 2s^3 + 10s^2 + 8s + 3 = 0$
  (c) $s^4 + 4s^3 + s^2 + 8s + 1 = 0$
  (d) $s^5 + s^4 + 6s^3 + 12s^2 + 18s + 6 = 0$
  (e) $s^6 + 2s^5 + 8s^4 + 15s^3 + 20s^2 + 16s + 16 = 0$

Solution:
(a) In the given characteristic equation

$$s^5 + s^4 + 24s^3 + 48s^2 - 25s - 5 = 0$$

the coefficient of s and the constant term are negative. Hence the necessary condition for stability is not satisfied and so the system is unstable. There is no need to formulate the Routh table to check for stability. However, to determine the location of the roots in the s-plane, formulate the Routh table as shown below.

s^5	1	24	-25
s^4	1	48	-5
s^3	$\dfrac{1 \times 24 - 1 \times 48}{1} = -24$	$\dfrac{1 \times (-25) - 1 \times (-5)}{1} = -20$	
s^2	$\dfrac{-24 \times 48 - 1 \times (-20)}{-24} = 47.16$	$\dfrac{-24 \times (-5) - 1 \times 0}{-24} = -5$	
s^1	$\dfrac{47.16 \times (-20) - (-24) \times (-5)}{47.16} = -22.54$		
s^0	$\dfrac{-22.54 \times (-5) - 47.16 \times 0}{-22.54} = -5$		

There are three sign changes (s^4 row to s^3 row, s^3 row to s^2 row and s^2 row to s^1 row) in the elements of the first column of the Routh array. Hence, there are three roots of the characteristic equation in the right-half of the s-plane.

(b) $s^4 + 2s^3 + 10s^2 + 8s + 3 = 0$

The Routh table is formed as follows:

s^4	1	10	3
s^3	2	8	
s^2	$\dfrac{2 \times 10 - 1 \times 8}{2} = 6$	$\dfrac{2 \times 3 - 1 \times 0}{2} = 3$	
s^1	$\dfrac{6 \times 8 - 2 \times 3}{6} = 7$	$\dfrac{6 \times 0 - 2 \times 0}{6} = 0$	
s^0	$\dfrac{7 \times 3 - 6 \times 0}{7} = 3$		

All the elements in the first column of the Routh array are positive. So the system is stable.

(c) $s^4 + 4s^3 + s^2 + 8s + 1 = 0$

The Routh table is formed as follows:

$$
\begin{array}{lll}
s^4 & 1 & 1 \\
s^3 & 4 & 8 \\
s^2 & \dfrac{4\times1-1\times8}{4}=-1 & \dfrac{4\times1-1\times0}{4}=1 \\
s^1 & \dfrac{-1\times8-4\times1}{-1}=12 & \dfrac{-1\times0-4\times0}{-1}=0 \\
s^0 & \dfrac{12\times1-(-1)\times0}{12}=1 &
\end{array}
$$

There are two sign changes in the elements of the first column of the Routh array. Hence there are two roots of the characteristic equation in the right-half of the s-plane. Hence the system is unstable.

(d) $s^5 + s^4 + 6s^3 + 12s^2 + 18s + 6 = 0$

The Routh table is formed as follows:

$$
\begin{array}{llll}
s^5 & 1 & 6 & 18 \\
s^4 & 1 & 12 & 6 \\
s^3 & \dfrac{1\times6-1\times12}{1}=-6 & \dfrac{1\times18-1\times6}{1}=12 & 0 \\
s^2 & \dfrac{-6\times12-1\times12}{-6}=14 & \dfrac{-6\times6-1\times0}{-6}=6 & \\
s^1 & \dfrac{14\times12-(-6)\times6}{14}=14.57 & 0 & \\
s^0 & \dfrac{14.57\times6-14\times0}{14.57}=6 & &
\end{array}
$$

There are two sign changes in the elements of the first column of the Routh array. Hence there are two roots of the characteristic equation in the right-half of the s-plane. Hence the system is unstable.

(e) $s^6 + 2s^5 + 8s^4 + 15s^3 + 20s^2 + 16s + 16 = 0$

The Routh table is formed as follows:

$$
\begin{array}{lllll}
s^6 & 1 & 8 & 20 & 16 \\
s^5 & 2 & 15 & 16 & \\
s^4 & \dfrac{2\times8-1\times15}{2}=0.5 & \dfrac{2\times20-1\times16}{2}=12 & \dfrac{2\times16-1\times0}{2}=16 &
\end{array}
$$

$$s^3 \qquad \frac{0.5 \times 15 - 2 \times 12}{0.5} = -33 \qquad\qquad \frac{0.5 \times 16 - 2 \times 16}{0.5} = -48$$

$$s^2 \qquad \frac{-33 \times 12 - 0.5 \times (-48)}{-33} = 11.27 \qquad \frac{-33 \times 16 - 0.5 \times 0}{-33} = 16$$

$$s^1 \qquad \frac{11.27 \times (-48) - (-33) \times 16}{11.27} = -1.16 \qquad 0$$

$$s^0 \qquad \frac{-1.16 \times 16 - 11.27 \times 0}{-1.16} = 16$$

There are four sign changes in the elements of the first column of the Routh array. Hence there are four roots of the characteristic equation in the right-half of the s-plane. So the system is unstable.

Example 5.5   Is the system shown in Figure 5.1 stable or not?

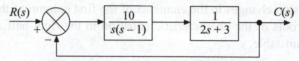

Figure 5.1   Example 5.5: Block diagram.

Solution: For the given system

$$G(s) = \frac{10}{s(s-1)(2s+3)} \quad \text{and} \quad H(s) = 1$$

The characteristic equation is

$$1 + G(s)\,H(s) = 0$$

i.e.
$$1 + \frac{10}{s(s-1)(2s+3)} = 0$$

i.e.
$$s(s-1)(2s+3) + 10 = 0$$

i.e.
$$2s^3 + s^2 - 3s + 10 = 0$$

In the characteristic equation, the coefficient of s is negative. So the system is unstable, because the necessary condition for stability is not satisfied.

To determine the location of the roots, formulate the Routh table as shown below.

$$s^3 \qquad\qquad 2 \qquad\qquad\qquad\qquad\qquad\qquad -3$$

$$s^2 \qquad\qquad 1 \qquad\qquad\qquad\qquad\qquad\qquad 10$$

$$s^1 \qquad \frac{1 \times (-3) - 2 \times 10}{1} = -23 \qquad\qquad 0$$

$$s^0 \qquad \frac{-23 \times 10 - 1 \times 0}{-23} = 10$$

There are two sign changes in the elements of the first column of the Routh array. Hence there are two roots of the characteristic equation in the right-half of the *s*-plane.

Example 5.6 By means of the Routh criterion, determine the stability of the systems represented by the following characteristic equations. For systems found to be unstable, determine the number of roots of the characteristic equation in the right-half of the *s*-plane.

(a) $s^4 + 2s^3 + 10s^2 + 20s + 5 = 0$

(b) $s^6 + 2s^5 + s^4 + 2s^3 + 3s^2 + 4s + 5 = 0$

(c) $s^5 + s^4 + 2s^3 + 3s^2 + 3s + 5 = 0$

Solution:

(a) $s^4 + 2s^3 + 10s^2 + 20s + 5 = 0$

The Routh table is formed as follows:

s^4	1	10	5
s^3	2	20	
s^2	$\dfrac{2\times10-1\times20}{2}=0$	$\dfrac{2\times5-1\times0}{2}=5$	
s^1			
s^0			

The first element in the s^2 row is zero, whereas there is one non-zero element in the same row. So Routh's test fails (difficulty 1 arises). So the system is unstable. To find the number of roots in the right-half of the *s*-plane, replace the first zero element by a small positive number $\in$ and proceed with the Routh array formation.

s^4	1	10	5
s^3	2	20	
s^2	$\in$	5	
s^1	$\dfrac{\in\times20-2\times5}{\in}$	0	
s^0	5		

As $\in \rightarrow 0$, there are two sign changes in the elements of the first column of the Routh array, one from the s^2 row to the s^1 row and another one from the s^1 row to the s^0 row. Hence there are two roots of the characteristic equation in the right-half of the *s*-plane, and the system is unstable.

Alternative method: Put $s = \dfrac{1}{z}$ in the characteristic equation and transform it into the *z*-plane and formulate the Routh table. So the characteristic equation in the *z*-plane is

$$\left(\frac{1}{z}\right)^4 + 2\left(\frac{1}{z}\right)^3 + 10\left(\frac{1}{z}\right)^2 + 20\left(\frac{1}{z}\right) + 5 = 0$$

i.e.
$$5z^4 + 20z^3 + 10z^2 + 2z + 1 = 0$$

z^4	5	10	1
z^3	20	2	
z^2	$\dfrac{20 \times 10 - 5 \times 2}{20} = 9.5$	$\dfrac{20 \times 1 - 5 \times 0}{20} = 1$	
z^1	$\dfrac{9.5 \times 2 - 20 \times 1}{9.5} = -0.105$	0	
z^0	$\dfrac{-0.105 \times 1 - 9.5 \times 0}{-0.105} = 1$		

There are two sign changes in the elements of the first column of the Routh array. One from the z^2 row to the z^1 row (from +ve to –ve) and another one from the z^1 row to the z^0 row (from –ve to +ve). Hence there are two roots of the characteristic equation in the right-half of the s-plane and the system is unstable.

(b) $s^6 + 2s^5 + s^4 + 2s^3 + 3s^2 + 4s + 5 = 0$

The Routh table is formed as follows:

s^6	1	1	3	5
s^5	2	2	4	
s^4	$\dfrac{2 \times 1 - 1 \times 2}{2} = 0$	$\dfrac{2 \times 3 - 1 \times 4}{2} = 1$	$\dfrac{2 \times 5 - 1 \times 0}{2} = 5$	
s^3	∞			
s^2				
s^1				
s^0				

The first element in the s^4 row is zero, whereas there are some non-zero elements in the same row (i.e., difficulty 1 arises). So the system is unstable. To find the location of the roots, replace the first zero element by a small positive number ϵ and proceed with the formulation of the Routh table.

s^6	1	1	3	5
s^5	2	2	4	
s^4	ϵ	1	5	
s^3	$\dfrac{\epsilon \times 2 - 2 \times 1}{\epsilon}$	$\dfrac{4\epsilon - 10}{\epsilon}$		
s^2	$\dfrac{\dfrac{2\epsilon - 2}{\epsilon} \times 1 - \dfrac{\epsilon(4\epsilon - 10)}{\epsilon}}{\dfrac{2\epsilon - 2}{\epsilon}} = \dfrac{-4\epsilon^2 + 12\epsilon - 2}{\epsilon}$	5		

$$s^1 \qquad \frac{\left(\dfrac{-4\,\epsilon^2+12\,\epsilon-2}{\epsilon}\right)\left(\dfrac{4\,\epsilon-10}{\epsilon}\right)-\left(\dfrac{2\,\epsilon-2}{\epsilon}\right)\times 5}{\dfrac{-4\,\epsilon^2+12\,\epsilon-2}{\epsilon}} \qquad\qquad 0$$

$$s^0 \qquad 5$$

As $\epsilon \to 0$, there are two sign changes in the elements of the first column of the Routh array (s^4 row to s^3 row and s^1 row to s^0 row). That means, there are two roots of the characteristic equation in the right-half of the s-plane. So the system is unstable.

Alternative method: Replace s in the characteristic equation by $1/z$ and transform the problem in the s-plane to the z-plane. The characteristic equation in the z-plane is

$$q(z)=\left(\frac{1}{z}\right)^6+2\left(\frac{1}{z}\right)^5+\left(\frac{1}{z}\right)^4+2\left(\frac{1}{z}\right)^3+3\left(\frac{1}{z}\right)^2+4\left(\frac{1}{z}\right)+5=0$$

i.e. $\qquad q(z) = 5z^6 + 4z^5 + 3z^4 + 2z^3 + z^2 + 2z + 1 = 0$

z^6	5			3		1	1
z^5	4			2		2	
z^4	$\dfrac{4\times3-5\times2}{4}=0.5$			$\dfrac{4\times1-5\times2}{4}=-1.5$		$\dfrac{4\times1-5\times0}{4}=1$	
z^3	$\dfrac{0.5\times2-4\times(-1.5)}{0.5}=14$			$\dfrac{0.5\times2-4\times1}{0.5}=-6$			
z^2	$\dfrac{14\times(-1.5)-0.5\times(-6)}{14}=-1.285$			$\dfrac{14\times1-0.5\times0}{14}=1$			
z^1	$\dfrac{-1.285\times(-6)-14\times1}{-1.285}=4.88$			0			
z^0	$\dfrac{4.88\times1-(-1.285)\times0}{4.88}=1$						

There are two sign changes in the elements of the first column of the Routh table. This indicates that there are two roots of the characteristic equation in the right-half of the s-plane. So the system is unstable.

(c) $s^5 + s^4 + 2s^3 + 2s^2 + 3s + 5 = 0$

The Routh table is formed as follows:

s^5	1	2	3
s^4	1	2	5
s^3	$\dfrac{1\times2-1\times2}{1}=0$	$\dfrac{1\times3-1\times5}{1}=-2$	0
s^2			
s^1			
s^0			

The first element in the s^3 row is zero, whereas there is one non-zero element in that row (i.e., difficulty 1 arises). So the system is unstable. To determine the location of the roots, complete the formulation of the Routh table by replacing the first zero element by a small positive number ϵ.

The modified Routh table is as follows:

s^5	1	2	3
s^4	1	2	5
s^3	ϵ	-2	0
s^2	$\dfrac{\epsilon\times2-1\times(-2)}{\epsilon}=\dfrac{2\epsilon+2}{\epsilon}$	$\dfrac{\epsilon\times5-1\times0}{\epsilon}=5$	
s^1	$\dfrac{\dfrac{(2\epsilon+2)\times(-2)}{\epsilon}-\epsilon\times5}{\dfrac{2\epsilon+2}{\epsilon}}=\dfrac{-(5\epsilon^2+4\epsilon+4)}{2\epsilon+2}$		
s^0	5		

As $\epsilon \to 0$, there are two sign changes in the elements of the first column of the modified Routh table (s^2 row to s^1 row and from s^1 row to s^0 row). So there are two roots of the characteristic equation in the right-half of the s-plane and so the system is unstable.

Alternative method: Transform the characteristic equation in the s-plane into the z-plane by replacing s by $1/z$ and apply Routh's test. So the characteristic equation in the z-plane is

$$\left(\frac{1}{z}\right)^5+\left(\frac{1}{z}\right)^4+2\left(\frac{1}{z}\right)^3+2\left(\frac{1}{z}\right)^2+3\left(\frac{1}{z}\right)+5=0$$

i.e.
$$5z^5 + 3z^4 + 2z^3 + 2z^2 + z + 1 = 0$$

z^5	5	2	1
z^4	3	2	1
z^3	$\dfrac{3\times2-5\times2}{3}=-1.33$	$\dfrac{3\times1-5\times1}{3}=-0.66$	0
z^2	$\dfrac{-1.33\times2-3\times(-0.66)}{-1.33}=0.5$	$\dfrac{-1.33\times1-3\times0}{-1.33}=1$	
z^1	$\dfrac{0.5\times(-0.66)-(-1.33)\times1}{0.5}=2$		
z^0	$\dfrac{2\times1-0.5\times0}{2}=1$		

There are two sign changes in the elements of the first column of the Routh table. So, there are two roots of the characteristic equation in z in the right-half of the z-plane. Correspondingly there are two roots of the original characteristic equation in s in the right-half of the s-plane. So the system is unstable.

Example 5.7 By means of the Routh criterion, determine the stability of the systems represented by the following characteristic equations. For systems found to be unstable, determine the number of roots of the characteristic equation in the right-half of the s-plane.

(a) $s^6 + 3s^5 + 5s^4 + 9s^3 + 8s^2 + 6s + 4 = 0$
(b) $s^5 + 4s^4 + 8s^3 + 8s^2 + 7s + 4 = 0$
(c) $s^6 + s^5 - 2s^4 - 3s^3 - 7s^2 - 4s - 4 = 0$

Solution:

(a) $s^6 + 3s^5 + 5s^4 + 9s^3 + 8s^2 + 6s + 4 = 0$

The Routh table is formed as follows:

s^6	1	5	8	4
s^5	3	9	6	
s^4	$\frac{3\times5-1\times9}{3}=2$	$\frac{3\times8-1\times6}{3}=6$	$\frac{3\times4-1\times0}{3}=4$	
s^3	$\frac{2\times9-3\times6}{2}=0$	$\frac{2\times6-3\times4}{2}=0$		
s^2				
s^1				
s^0				

All the elements in the s^3 row are zeros. So Routh's test fails (difficulty 2 arises). The system is unstable. To complete the Routh table, form an auxiliary equation

$$A(s) = 2s^4 + 6s^2 + 4 = 0$$

using the coefficients of the s^4 row (i.e. the row just above the row of zeros). Take the first derivative of the auxiliary equation

$$\frac{dA(s)}{ds} = 0 = \frac{d}{ds}(2s^4 + 6s^2 + 4) = 8s^3 + 12s = 0$$

i.e. $2s^3 + 3s = 0$

Replace the row of zeros by the elements of the first derivative of the auxiliary equation and proceed with the formulation of the Routh table as shown below.

s^6	1	5	8	4
s^5	3	9	6	
s^4	2	6	4	
s^3	2	3	0	

$$s^2 \qquad \frac{2 \times 6 - 2 \times 3}{2} = 3 \qquad \qquad \frac{2 \times 4 - 2 \times 0}{2} = 4 \qquad \qquad 0$$

$$s^1 \qquad \frac{3 \times 3 - 2 \times 4}{3} = 0.333 \qquad \qquad 0$$

$$s^0 \qquad \frac{0.333 \times 4 - 3 \times 0}{0.333} = 4$$

Looking at the new Routh array, all the elements in the first column of the Routh array are positive, which indicates that there are no roots of the characteristic equation in the right-half of the *s*-plane. Still the system is unstable due to the existence of the row of zeros, which means that there must be roots on the imaginary axis of the *s*-plane. To determine the roots on the imaginary axis, solve the auxiliary equation $2s^4 + s^2 + 4 = 0$. To determine the other roots, divide the original characteristic equation by the auxiliary equation as shown below.

$$
\begin{array}{r}
\frac{s^2}{2} + \frac{3s}{2} + 1 \\[4pt]
2s^4 + 6s^2 + 4 \enclose{longdiv}{s^6 + 3s^5 + 5s^4 + 9s^3 + 8s^2 + 6s + 4} \\[2pt]
\underline{s^6 \qquad\quad + 3s^4 \qquad\quad + 2s^2} \\[2pt]
3s^5 + 2s^4 + 9s^3 + 6s^2 + 6s + 4 \\[2pt]
\underline{3s^5 \qquad\quad + 9s^3 \qquad\quad + 6s} \\[2pt]
2s^4 \qquad + 6s^2 \qquad\quad + 4 \\[2pt]
\underline{2s^4 \qquad + 6s^2 \qquad\quad + 4}
\end{array}
$$

$$\therefore \quad s^6 + 3s^5 + 5s^4 + 9s^3 + 6s^2 + 6s + 4$$

$$= (2s^4 + 6s^2 + 4) \left(\frac{s^2}{2} + \frac{3s}{2} + 1 \right) = (s^4 + 3s^2 + 2)(s^2 + 3s + 2)$$

$$s^2 + 3s + 2 = 0$$

i.e. $\qquad (s + 1)(s + 2) = 0$

$\therefore \qquad\qquad\qquad s = -1 \quad \text{or} \quad s = -2$

$$s^4 + 3s^2 + 2 = 0$$

i.e. $\qquad (s^2 + 1)(s^2 + 2) = 0$

$\therefore \qquad\qquad\qquad s^2 = -1, \; s^2 = -2$

$\therefore \qquad\qquad\qquad s = \pm j1 \quad \text{or} \quad s = \pm j\sqrt{2}$

There are two pairs of non-repeated roots on the imaginary axis. So the system oscillates and it is marginally stable (unstable).

(b) $s^5 + 4s^4 + 8s^3 + 8s^2 + 7s + 4 = 0$

The Routh table is formed as follows:

s^5	1	8	7
s^4	4	8	4
s^4	1	2	1
s^3	$\dfrac{1 \times 8 - 1 \times 2}{1} = 6$	$\dfrac{1 \times 7 - 1 \times 1}{1} = 6$	
s^2	$\dfrac{6 \times 2 - 1 \times 6}{6} = 1$	$\dfrac{6 \times 1 - 1 \times 0}{6} = 1$	
s^1	$\dfrac{1 \times 6 - 6 \times 1}{1} = 0$	0	
s^0			

All the elements in the s^1 row are zeros (i.e. difficulty 2 arises). So the system is unstable. To find the number of roots lying in the right-half of the s-plane, form an auxiliary equation $A(s)$ using the coefficients of the s^2 row (i.e., the row above the row of zeros). Therefore,

$$A(s) = s^2 + 1 = 0$$

Take the first derivative of the auxiliary equation

$$\frac{dA(s)}{ds} = \frac{d}{ds}(s^2 + 1) = 2s + 0 = 0$$

Replace the row of zeros by the elements of the first derivative of the auxiliary equation and proceed with the formulation of the Routh table as shown below.

s^5	1	8	7
s^4	1	2	1
s^3	6	6	0
s^2	1	1	
s^1	2	0	
s^0	1		

All the elements in the first column of the revised Routh array are positive which indicates that there are no roots of the characteristic equation in the right-half of the s-plane. Still the system is unstable. So there must be roots on the imaginary axis of the s-plane. The roots on the imaginary axis may be found by solving the auxiliary equation.

$$s^2 + 1 = 0$$

i.e.

$$s^2 = -1$$

or

$$s = \pm j1$$

To find the other roots, factorize the characteristic equation

$$s^5 + 4s^4 + 8s^3 + 8s^2 + 7s + 4 = (s^2 + 1)(s^3 + 4s^2 + 7s + 4)$$

$$= (s^2 + 1)(s + 1)(s^2 + 3s + 4)$$

$$= (s^2 + 1)(s + 1)\left(s + 1.5 + j\sqrt{\frac{7}{4}}\right)\left(s + 1.5 - j\sqrt{\frac{7}{4}}\right)$$

Alternative method: In fact, the moment difficulty 2 arises (i.e., a row of zeros exists), we can conclude that the system is unstable. The roots on the imaginary axis can be obtained by solving the auxiliary equation, i.e.

$$s^2 + 1 = 0$$

The characteristic equation is divided by the auxiliary equation

$$
\begin{array}{r}
s^3 + 4s^2 + 7s + 4 \\
s^2 + 1 \overline{\smash{\big)}\ s^5 + 4s^4 + 8s^3 + 8s^2 + 7s + 4} \\
\underline{s^5 \qquad\quad + s^3} \\
4s^4 + 7s^3 + 8s^2 + 7s + 4 \\
\underline{4s^4 \qquad\quad + 4s^2} \\
7s^3 + 4s^2 + 7s + 4 \\
\underline{7s^3 \qquad\quad + 7s} \\
+ 4s^2 \qquad + 4 \\
\underline{+ 4s^2 \qquad + 4} \\
0
\end{array}
$$

i.e. $\quad s^5 + 4s^4 + 8s^3 + 8s^2 + 7s + 4 = (s^2 + 1)(s^3 + 4s^2 + 7s + 4)$

Apply Routh's test on $s^3 + 4s^2 + 7s + 4 = 0$ to check the location of the other roots.

s^3	1	7
s^2	4	4
s^1	6	0
s^0	4	

There is no change in the signs of the elements of the first column of the Routh array. Hence there is no root of the revised characteristic equation in the right-half of the s-plane. Since there is one pair of poles on the imaginary axis, the system is marginally stable.

(c) In the given characteristic equation

$$s^6 + s^5 - 2s^4 - 3s^3 - 7s^2 - 4s - 4 = 0$$

the coefficients of s^4, s^3, s^2, s and constant term are negative. Hence the necessary condition for stability is not satisfied, and so the system is unstable. There is no need to formulate the Routh table to test for stability. However, to determine the location of the roots of the characteristic equation in the s-plane, the Routh table is formulated as follows:

s^6	1	-2	-7	-4
s^5	1	-3	-4	
s^4	$\dfrac{1\times(-2)-1\times(-3)}{1}=1$	$\dfrac{1\times(-7)-1\times(-4)}{1}=-3$	-4	
s^3	$\dfrac{1\times(-3)-1\times(-3)}{1}=0$	$\dfrac{1\times(-4)-1\times(-4)}{1}=0$		
s^2				
s^1				
s^0				

There is a row of zeros (all the elements of s^3 row are zeros), i.e. difficulty 2 arises, which indicates that there are symmetrically located roots in the s-plane.

The auxiliary equation is

$$A(s) = s^4 - 3s^2 - 4 = 0$$

i.e. $\qquad\qquad\qquad A(s) = (s^2 - 4)(s^2 + 1) = 0$

i.e. $\qquad\qquad\qquad A(s) = (s + 2)(s - 2)(s + j)(s - j)$

That is, there is a pair of conjugate roots on the imaginary axis, and there is a pair of symmetrically located roots on the real axis.

To determine the other roots, factorize the characteristic equation

$$s^6 + s^5 - 2s^4 - 3s^3 - 7s^2 - 4s - 4 = (s^4 - 3s^2 - 4)\,(s^2 + s + 1)$$

$$s^2 + s + 1 = (s + 0.5 + j\sqrt{0.75}\,)(s + 0.5 - j\sqrt{0.75}\,)$$

Therefore, the roots of the characteristic equation are $s = +j1$, $s = -j1$, $s = +2$, $s = -2$, $s = -0.5 + j\sqrt{0.75}$ and $s = -0.5 - j\sqrt{0.75}$.

Example 5.8 Using the Routh criterion, check whether the system represented by the following characteristic equation is stable or not. Comment on the location of the roots. Determine the frequency of sustained oscillations if any.

$$s^4 + 2s^3 + 6s^2 + 8s + 8 = 0$$

Solution: The Routh table is formulated as follows:

s^4	1	6	8
s^3	2	8	

$$s^2 \qquad \frac{2\times6-1\times8}{2}=2 \qquad\qquad \frac{2\times8-1\times0}{2}=8$$

$$s^1 \qquad \frac{2\times8-2\times8}{2}=0 \qquad\qquad 0$$

$$s^0$$

All the elements in the s^1 row are zeros (i.e., difficulty 2 arises). That means, there are symmetrically located roots of the characteristic equation with respect to the origin of the s-plane. So the system is unstable.

To determine the location of the roots, form the auxiliary equation $A(s)$ by using the coefficients of the row just above the row of zeros, i.e.

$$A(s) = 2s^2 + 8 = 0$$

Take the first derivative of the auxiliary equation, i.e.

$$\frac{dA(s)}{ds} = 4s + 0 = 0$$

Replace the row of zeros with the coefficients of the first derivative of the auxiliary equation and complete the formation of the Routh table:

s^4	1	6	8
s^3	2	8	
s^2	2	8	
s^1	4	0	
s^0	8		

There are no sign changes in the elements of the first column of the Routh array and hence there are no roots of the characteristic equation in the right-half of the s-plane. Since the system is unstable, there must be roots on the imaginary axis of the s-plane which can be determined by solving the auxiliary equation

$$2s^2 + 8 = 0$$

i.e.

$$s^2 + 4 = 0$$

or

$$s = \pm j2$$

This shows that there is a pair of roots at $s = \pm j2$, and so the system oscillates and the frequency of sustained oscillations is $\omega = 2$ rad/s.

To determine the other two roots, factorize the characteristic equation

$$s^4 + 2s^3 + 6s^2 + 8s + 8 = (s^2 + 4)(s^2 + 2s + 2) = 0$$

$$s^2 + 2s + 2 = (s + 1 + j1)(s + 1 - j1)$$

The other two roots are a pair of complex conjugate roots in the left-half of the s-plane.

5.6 APPLICATION OF THE ROUTH STABILITY CRITERION TO LINEAR FEEDBACK SYSTEMS

The Routh stability criterion is frequently used for the determination of the condition of stability of linear feedback systems. We can determine the range of values of K for stability, the critical value of K, and the frequency of sustained oscillations also.

Example 5.9 Determine the range of values of K for the system to be stable.

(a) $s^3 + 3Ks^2 + (K + 2) s + 4 = 0$
(b) $s^4 + 4s^3 + 13s^2 + 36s + K = 0$
(c) $s^4 + 20Ks^3 + 5s^2 + 10s + 15 = 0$

Solution:

(a) The Routh table for the characteristic equation

$$s^3 + 3Ks^2 + (K + 2)s + 4 = 0$$

is formulated as follows:

s^3	1	$K + 2$
s^2	$3K$	4
s^1	$\dfrac{3K(K+2)-1\times 4}{3K}$	0
s^0	4	

For stability, all the elements in the first column of the Routh array must be positive. Therefore, from the s^2 row

$$3K > 0, \text{ i.e. } K > 0$$

and from the s^1 row

$$3K^2 + 6K - 4 > 0$$

i.e.

$$K > \frac{-6 \pm \sqrt{6^2 - 4(3)(-4)}}{2 \times 3}$$

i.e.

$$K > \frac{-6 \pm 9.16}{6} = -2.52 \text{ and } 0.526$$

i.e. $K > 0.526$ and $K > -2.52$

Therefore, the dominant condition is $K > 0.526$.

Since the open-loop gain K must be positive, the range of values of K for stability is

$$\infty > K > 0.526$$

(b) The Routh table for the characteristic equation

$$s^4 + 4s^3 + 13s^2 + 36s + K = 0$$

is formulated as follows:

s^4	1	13	K
s^3	4	36	

s^2	$\dfrac{4 \times 13 - 1 \times 36}{4} = 4$	$\dfrac{4 \times K - 1 \times 0}{4} = K$
s^1	$\dfrac{4 \times 36 - 4 \times K}{4} = 36 - K$	0
s^0	$\dfrac{(36 - K)K - 4 \times 0}{36 - K} = K$	

For stability, all the elements in the first column of the Routh array must be positive. Therefore, from the s^0 row

$$K > 0$$

and from the s^1 row

$$36 - K > 0$$

i.e.

$$K < 36$$

Since the open-loop gain K must be positive, the range of values of K for stability is

$$0 < K < 36$$

(c) The Routh table for the characteristic equation

$$s^4 + 20Ks^3 + 5s^2 + 10s + 15 = 0$$

is formed as follows:

s^4	1	5	15
s^3	$20K$	10	
s^2	$\dfrac{20K \times 5 - 1 \times 10}{20K}$	$\dfrac{20K \times 15 - 1 \times 0}{20K} = 15$	
s^1	$\dfrac{\dfrac{(100K - 10) \times 10}{20K} - 20K \times 15}{\dfrac{100K - 10}{20K}} = \dfrac{100K - 10 - 600K^2}{10K - 1}$		
s^0	15		

For stability, all the elements in the first column of the Routh array must be positive. Therefore, from the s^3 row,

$$20K > 0$$

i.e.

$$K > 0$$

From the s^2 row

$$100K > 10$$

i.e.

$$K > 0.1$$

From the s^1 row K must be complex.

Since K must be a real positive number, the third condition cannot be satisfied. So the system is always unstable.

Example 5.10 The characteristic equation of a feedback control system is given by

$$s^4 + 20s^3 + 15s^2 + 2s + K = 0$$

(a) Determine the range of values of K for the system to be stable.

(b) Can the system be marginally stable? If so, find the required value of K and the frequency of sustained oscillations.

Solution:

(a) The Routh table for the given characteristic equation is formed as follows:

s^4	1	15	K
s^3	20	2	
s^2	$\dfrac{20 \times 15 - 1 \times 2}{20} = 14.9$	$\dfrac{20 \times K - 1 \times 0}{20} = K$	
s^1	$\dfrac{14.9 \times 2 - 20 \times K}{14.9}$	0	
s^0	K		

For the system to be stable, all the elements in the first column of the Routh array must be positive. Therefore, from the s^0 row

$$K > 0$$

and from the s^1 row

$$2 \times 14.9 - 20K > 0$$

i.e.
$$K < 1.49$$

So the range of values of K for stability is $0 < K < 1.49$.

(b) Yes, the system can be marginally stable, for the marginal value of K, i.e. for $2 \times 14.9 - 20K = 0$, i.e. for $K = 1.49$. To obtain the frequency of sustained oscillations, substitute this critical value of K in the auxiliary equation formed by using the coefficients of the row just above the row which gives the critical value of K and solve it, i.e.

i.e.
$$A(s) = 14.9s^2 + K = 0$$

i.e.
$$14.9s^2 + 1.49 = 0$$

∴
$$s = \pm j\sqrt{\frac{1.49}{14.9}} = \pm j\sqrt{0.1} = \pm j0.316$$

Therefore, the frequency of sustained oscillations is 0.316 rad/s.

Example 5.11 A unity feedback system has the following open-loop transfer function:

$$G(s) = \frac{Ks(3s+1)}{s^2 + 2s + 3}$$

Discuss the stability of the system in terms of the parameter K.

Solution: Given

$$G(s) = \frac{Ks(3s+1)}{s^2 + 2s + 3}, H(s) = 1$$

The characteristic equation is

$$1 + G(s)\ H(s) = 0$$

i.e.

$$1 + \frac{Ks(3s+1)}{s^2 + 2s + 3} = 0$$

i.e.

$$s^2 + 2s + 3 + 3Ks^2 + Ks = 0$$

i.e.

$$s^2(3K+1) + s(K+2) + 3 = 0$$

This is a second-order system. For the second-order system to be stable, it is sufficient that all the coefficients of the characteristic equation must be real and positive. Therefore,

$$3K + 1 > 0$$

i.e.

$$K > -1/3$$

and

$$K + 2 > 0$$

i.e.

$$K > -2$$

Since K the open-loop gain is positive, the system is stable for all positive values of K.

Example 5.12 The open-loop transfer function of a closed-loop system with unity feedback is

$$G(s) = \frac{K}{(s+2)(s+4)(s^2 + 6s + 25)}$$

By applying the Routh criterion, discuss the stability of the closed-loop system as a function of K. Determine the values of K which will cause sustained oscillations in the closed-loop system. What are the corresponding oscillation frequencies?

Solution: Given

$$G(s) = \frac{K}{(s+2)(s+4)(s^2 + 6s + 25)}, H(s) = 1$$

The characteristic equation is

$$1 + G(s)H(s) = 1 + \frac{K}{(s+2)(s+4)(s^2 + 6s + 25)} = 0$$

i.e. $$(s + 2)(s + 4)(s^2 + 6s + 25) + K = 0$$

i.e. $$s^4 + 12s^3 + 69s^2 + 198s + (200 + K) = 0$$

The Routh table is formulated as follows:

s^4	1	69	$200 + K$
s^3	12	198	
s^2	$\dfrac{12 \times 69 - 1 \times 198}{12} = 52.5$	$\dfrac{12 \times (200 + K) - 1 \times 0}{12} = 200 + K$	
s^1	$\dfrac{52.5 \times 198 - 12(200 + K)}{52.5}$		
s^0	$200 + K$		

For the system to be stable, all the elements in the first column of the Routh array must be positive:

From the s^0 row

$$200 + K > 0$$

i.e. $$K > -200$$

From the s^1 row

$$52.5 \times 198 - 12(200 + K) > 0$$

i.e. $$K < 666.25$$

So the range of values of K for stability is $0 < K < 666.25$.

The value of K which causes sustained oscillations in the closed-loop system is obtained from the equation.

$$52.5 \times 198 - 12(200 + K) = 0$$

Therefore, the critical value of

$$K = \frac{52.5 \times 198 - 12 \times 200}{12} = 666.25$$

To find the corresponding frequency of oscillations, form an auxiliary equation by using the coefficients of the row (s^2 row) just above the row from which the critical value of K is obtained (s^1 row), substitute the critical value of K in that and solve it, i.e.

$$A(s) = 52.5s^2 + (200 + K) = 0$$

i.e. $$52.5s^2 + 200 + 666.25 = 0$$

i.e. $$s^2 = \frac{-866.25}{52.5} = -16.5$$

∴ $$s = \pm j4.006$$

So the frequency of sustained oscillations is $\omega = 4.06$ rad/s.

Example 5.13   A system oscillates with frequency ω if it has poles at $s = \pm j\omega$ and no poles in the right-half of the s-plane. Determine the values of K and a so that the system shown in Figure 5.2 oscillates at a frequency of 2 rad/s.

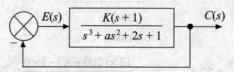

Figure 5.2   Example 5.13: Block diagram.

Solution: For the given system,

$$G(s) = \frac{K(s+1)}{s^3 + as^2 + 2s + 1}, H(s) = 1$$

Therefore, the characteristic equation is

$$1 + G(s)H(s) = 0$$

i.e.

$$s^3 + as^2 + (2 + K)s + (1 + K) = 0$$

The Routh table is formulated as follows:

s^3	1		$2 + K$
s^2	a		$1 + K$
s^1	$\dfrac{a(2+K) - 1(1+K)}{a}$		0
s^0	$1 + K$		

For stability, all the elements in the first column of the Routh array must be positive.
From the s^0 row,

$$1 + K > 0$$

i.e.

$$K > -1$$

From the s^1 row,

$$\frac{a(2+K) - 1(1+K)}{a} > 0$$

From the s^2 row,

$$a > 0$$

But for the system to oscillate

$$a(2 + K) - (1 + K) = 0$$

i.e.

$$a = \frac{1 + K}{2 + K} \tag{i}$$

To obtain the frequency of oscillations, form the auxiliary equation using the elements of the s^2 row, i.e.

$$A(s) = as^2 + (1 + K) = 0$$

Given the frequency of oscillation, $\omega = 2$ rad/s.

$$A(s) = a(-\omega^2) + 1 + K = 0$$

i.e. $\qquad\qquad -4a = -(1 + K)$

or $\qquad\qquad\qquad a = \dfrac{1 + K}{4}$ $\qquad\qquad\qquad\qquad\qquad\qquad$ (ii)

Equating the two values of a from Eqs. (i) and (ii),

$$a = \frac{1+K}{4} = \frac{1+K}{2+K}$$

$\therefore \qquad\qquad\qquad 2 + K = 4$

or $\qquad\qquad\qquad K = 4 - 2 = 2$

$\therefore \qquad\qquad a = \dfrac{1+K}{2+K} = \dfrac{1+2}{2+2} = 0.75$

So the values of K and a so that the system oscillates at a frequency of 2 rad/s is $K = 2$ and $a = 0.75$.

Example 5.14 A feedback system has an open-loop transfer function

$$G(s)H(s) = \frac{Ke^{-s}}{s(s^2 + 5s + 9)}$$

Determine by use of the Routh criterion, the maximum value of K for the closed-loop system to be stable.

[*Hint:* For low frequencies $e^{-s} \approx (1 - s)$]

Solution: The characteristic equation of the system is

$$1 + G(s)H(s) = 0$$

i.e. $\qquad\qquad 1 + \dfrac{K(1-s)}{s(s^2 + 5s + 9)} = 0$

$$s^3 + 5s^2 + (9 - K)s + K = 0$$

Forming the Routh array, we have

s^3	1	$9 - K$
s^2	5	K
s^1	$\dfrac{5 \times (9-K) - 1 \times K}{5}$	0
s^0	K	

For the system to be stable, all the elements in the first column of the Routh array must be positive:

From the s^0 row

$$K > 0$$

From the s^1 row

$$5(9 - K) - 1 \times K > 0$$

i.e.

$$45 - 6K > 0$$

i.e.

$$K < \frac{45}{6} = 7.5$$

So, the range of values of K for stability is $0 < K < 7.5$.

The maximum value of K for the closed-loop system to be stable is $K = 7.5$.

Example 5.15   The output of a control system is related to its input by

$$[s^4 + 5s^3 + 3s^2 + (3 + K)s + K] C(s) = K(s + 2) R(s)$$

where K represents the positive gain of the amplifier.

(a) With $K = 8$, and a step input, will the output response be stable?

(b) Determine the limiting positive value that K can have for a stable output response.

Solution:

(a) The closed-loop transfer function is

$$\frac{C(s)}{R(s)} = \frac{K(s + 2)}{s^4 + 5s^3 + 3s^2 + (3 + K)s + K}$$

The characteristic equation is

$$s^4 + 5s^3 + 3s^2 + (3 + K)s + K = 0$$

Therefore, with $K = 8$, the characteristic equation is

$$s^4 + 5s^3 + 3s^2 + 11s + 8 = 0$$

The Routh array is formulated as follows:

s^4	1	3	8
s^3	5	11	
s^2	$\dfrac{5 \times 3 - 1 \times 11}{5} = 0.8$	$\dfrac{5 \times 8 - 1 \times 0}{5} = 8$	
s^1	$\dfrac{0.8 \times 11 - 5 \times 8}{0.8} = -39$	0	
s^0	$\dfrac{-39 \times 8 - 0.8 \times 0}{-39} = 8$		

There are two sign changes in the elements of the first column of the Routh array which indicates that there are two roots of the characteristic equation for $K = 8$ in the right-half of the s-plane. So the output response of the system will be unstable.

(b) $s^4 + 5s^3 + 3s^2 + (3 + K)s + K = 0$

To determine the limiting positive value that K can have for a stable output response, the Routh table for the given characteristic equation is formulated as follows:

$$
\begin{array}{llll}
s^4 & 1 & 3 & K \\
s^3 & 5 & 3 + K & \\
s^2 & \dfrac{5 \times 3 - 1 \times (3 + K)}{5} = \dfrac{12 - K}{5} & K & \\
s^1 & \dfrac{\left(\dfrac{12 - K}{5}\right)(3 + K) - 5 \times K}{\dfrac{12 - K}{5}} = \dfrac{36 - 16K - K^2}{12 - K} & & \\
s^0 & K & &
\end{array}
$$

For stable output response, all the elements in the first column of the Routh table must be positive. Therefore, for stability

$$K > 0$$

$$\frac{12 - K}{5} > 0$$

i.e.

$$K < 12$$

and

$$\frac{36 - 16K - K^2}{12 - K} > 0$$

i.e.

$$K < 2$$

Therefore, the range of values of K for stability is $0 < K < 2$.
The limiting positive value that K can have for a stable output response is $K = 2$.

Example 5.16 A unity feedback control system has an open-loop transfer function consisting of two poles, two zeros and a variable gain K. The zeros are located at -2 and -1 and the poles at -0.1 and 1.

Using the Routh stability criterion, determine the range of values of K for which the closed-loop system has 0, 1 or 2 poles in the right-half of the s-plane.

Solution: Given

$$G(s) = \frac{K(s+1)(s+2)}{(s+0.1)(s-1)} \quad \text{and} \quad H(s) = 1$$

The characteristic equation is

$$1 + G(s)\,H(s) = 0$$

i.e.

$$1 + \frac{K(s+1)(s+2)}{(s+0.1)(s-1)} = 0$$

i.e.

$$(s + 0.1)(s - 1) + K(s + 1)(s + 2) = 0$$

i.e.

$$(1 + K)s^2 + (3K - 0.9)s + (2K - 0.1) = 0$$

The Routh array is formulated as follows:

s^2	$1 + K$	$2K - 0.1$
s^1	$3K - 0.9$	0
s^0	$2K - 0.1$	

For no pole to lie in the right-half of the *s*-plane (i.e., for the system to be stable), all the terms in the first column of the Routh array must be positive.

$$K + 1 > 0$$

or

$$K > -1$$

$$3K - 0.9 > 0$$

or

$$K > 0.3$$

$$2K - 0.1 > 0$$

or

$$K > 0.05$$

So the condition for no pole to lie in the right-half of the *s*-plane is $K > 0.3$.

For one pole to lie in the right-half of the *s*-plane, there must be one change of sign in the elements of the first column. For that, the first element in the last row must be negative, and the first element in the second row can also be negative. Therefore,

$$K < 0.05$$

For two poles to lie in the right-half of the *s*-plane, there must be two changes of sign in the elements of the first column. For that, the first element in the second row must be negative and the first elements in the first and third rows must be positive, i.e.

$$0.05 < K < 0.3$$

Example 5.17 The block diagram of a closed-loop control system is shown in Figure 5.3.

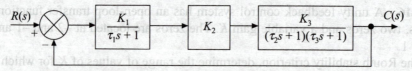

Figure 5.3 Example 5.17: Block diagram.

(a) Determine the limiting value of forward gain K (= $K_1 K_2 K_3$) for the system to be stable, if

$$\tau_1 = 0.2 \text{ s}, \ \tau_2 = 1 \text{s and } \tau_3 = 0.4 \text{s}$$

(b) Calculate the gain K for the system to be stable with a settling time of 4s based on dominant poles.

(c) With K as in part (b), find all the roots of the characteristic equation.

Solution:

(a) For the given system,

$$G(s) = \frac{K_1 K_2 K_3}{(1 + \tau_1 s)(1 + \tau_2 s)(1 + \tau_3 s)}$$

$$= \frac{K}{(1 + 0.2s)(1 + s)(1 + 0.4s)} \quad \text{and} \quad H(s) = 1$$

Therefore, the characteristic equation of the system is

$$1 + G(s)H(s) = 0$$

i.e.
$$1 + \frac{K}{(1 + 0.2s)(1 + s)(1 + 0.4s)} = 0$$

i.e.
$$(1 + 0.2s)(1 + s)(1 + 0.4s) + K = 0$$

i.e.
$$s^3 + 8.5s^2 + 20s + 12.5(1 + K) = 0$$

The Routh table is formed as follows:

s^3	1	20
s^2	8.5	12.5 (1 + K)
s^1	$\dfrac{8.5 \times 20 - 1 \times 12.5(1+K)}{8.5} = \dfrac{157.5 - 12.5K}{8.5}$	
s^0	12.5 (1 + K)	

For stability, all the elements in the first column must be positive:

$$12.5 (1 + K) > 0$$

i.e.
$$K > -1$$

$$157.5 - 12.5K > 0$$

i.e.
$$K < \frac{157.5}{12.5} = 12.6$$

Therefore, the range of values of K for stability is $0 < K < 12.6$.
The limiting value of forward gain K for the system to be stable, if $\tau_1 = 0.2$ s, $\tau_2 = 1$ s and $\tau_3 = 0.4$ s is $K = 12.6$.

(b) Settling time

$$t_s = \frac{4}{\xi \omega_n} = 4 \text{ s}$$

$$\therefore \qquad \xi \omega_n = \frac{4}{4} = 1$$

Thus, the real part of the dominant root (or complex root) pair should be -1 or more. To ascertain this and to find the corresponding value of K, putting $s = z-1$ in the characteristic equation, we get

$$(z - 1)^3 + 8.5 (z - 1)^2 + 20 (z - 1) + 12.5 (1 + K) = 0$$

i.e. $$z^3 + 5.5 z^2 + 6z + 12.5 K = 0$$

The Routh array for the characteristic equation is formulated as follows:

z^3	1	6
z^2	5.5	$12.5K$
z^1	$\dfrac{5.5 \times 6 - 1 \times 12.5 K}{5.5}$	0
z^0	$12.5K$	

For the limiting value of K

$$\frac{5.5 \times 6 - 1 \times 12.5 K}{5.5} = 0$$

i.e. $$K = \frac{5.5 \times 6}{12.5} = 2.64$$

For this value of gain K, we can find the imaginary part of the dominant roots from the auxiliary equation

$$5.5s^2 + 12.5K = 0$$

i.e. $$5.5s^2 + 12.5 \times 2.64 = 0$$

$\therefore$ $$s = \sqrt{\frac{-12.5 \times 2.64}{5.5}} = \pm j2.45$$

(c) From part (b) we have

$$\xi \omega_n = 1$$

$\therefore$ $$\omega_n^2 = (1)^2 + (2.45)^2 = 7$$

Therefore, the dominant roots are given by the factor

$$(s^2 + 2\xi\omega_n s + \omega_n^2) = (s^2 + 2s + 7)$$

The third root is obtained by dividing the characteristic equation with $K = 2.64$ by this factor.

The characteristic equation with $K = 2.64$ is

$$s^3 + 8.5s^2 + 20s + 12.5 (1 + 2.64) = 0$$

i.e. $$s^3 + 8.5s^2 + 20s + 45.5 = 0$$

$$s + 6.5$$

$$s^2 + 2s + 7 \overline{\smash{\big)}\ s^3 + 8.5s^2 + 20s + 45.5}$$

$$\underline{s^3 + 2s^2 + 7s}$$

$$6.5s^2 + 13s + 45.5$$

$$\underline{6.5s^2 + 13s + 45.5}$$

$$0$$

Thus, the roots of the characteristic equation (for $K = 2.64$) are $s_1 = -1 - j\,2.45$, $s_2 = -1 + j2.45$ and $s_3 = -6.5$.

Example 5.18 The characteristic equation of a control system is

$$s^4 + Ks^3 + 2s^2 + s + 3 = 0$$

Show that for no value of K the system is stable.

Solution: The Routh array is formulated as follows:

s^4	1	2	3
s^3	K	1	
s^2	$\dfrac{K \times 2 - 1 \times 1}{K} = \dfrac{2K - 1}{K}$	$\dfrac{K \times 3 - 1 \times 0}{K} = 3$	
s^1	$\dfrac{\left(\dfrac{2K-1}{K}\right) \times 1 - K \times 3}{\dfrac{2K-1}{K}} = \dfrac{-3K^2 + 2K - 1}{K}$	0	
s^0	3		

For stability, all the elements in the first column of the Routh array must be positive, i.e.

(i) $K > 0$

(ii) $\dfrac{2K - 1}{K} > 0$

i.e. $K > 0.5$

(iii) $-3K^2 + 2K - 1 > 0$

The equation $-3K^2 + 2K - 1 = 0$ has two imaginary roots. Thus, the three conditions for K cannot be fulfilled simultaneously. Therefore, there is no value of K for which the above system is stable.

Example 5.19 Find the range of K for the system with the closed-loop transfer function

$$\frac{C(s)}{R(s)} = \frac{K}{s[(s+2)(s+3)(s+4) + K]}$$

to be stable.

Solution: The characteristic equation of the system is given by

$$s[(s + 2)(s + 3)(s + 4) + K] = 0$$

i.e.

$$s^4 + 9s^3 + 26s^2 + (24 + 3K)s = 0$$

One of the coefficients of the characteristic equation (the constant term) is missing. So the necessary condition for stability is not satisfied. So the system cannot be stable for any value of K.

Example 5.20 A unity feedback control system is characterized by the open-loop transfer function

$$G(s) = \frac{K(s + 13)}{s(s + 3)(s + 7)}$$

Using the Routh criterion

(a) Calculate the range of values of K for the system to be stable.

(b) What is the marginal value of K for stability? Determine the frequency of oscillations if any.

(c) Check if for $K = 1$, all the roots of the characteristic equation of the above system have the damping factor greater than 0.5.

Solution:

(a) The characteristic equation of the system is

$$1 + G(s)H(s) = 0$$

i.e.

$$1 + \frac{K(s + 13)}{s(s + 3)(s + 7)} = 0$$

i.e.

$$s(s + 3)(s + 7) + K(s + 13) = 0$$

i.e.

$$s^3 + 10s^2 + (21 + K)s + 13K = 0$$

The Routh table is formulated as follows:

$$s^3 \qquad 1 \qquad\qquad\qquad\qquad 21 + K$$

$$s^2 \qquad 10 \qquad\qquad\qquad\qquad 13K$$

$$s^1 \qquad \frac{10 \times (21 + K) - 1 \times 13K}{10} = \frac{210 - 3K}{10}$$

$$s^0 \qquad 13K$$

For the system to be stable, all the elements in the first column of the Routh array must be positive.

From the s^0 row,

$$13K > 0$$

i.e.

$$K > 0$$

From the s^1 row,

$$210 - 3K > 0$$

i.e.
$$3K < 210$$

or
$$K < 70$$

Hence the range of values of K for stability of the system is $0 < K < 70$.

(b) The marginal value of K for stability is $K = 70$.

The frequency of sustained oscillations is given by the solution of the auxiliary equation formed by using the coefficients of the row just above the row from which the marginal value of K is determined.

$$10s^2 + 13K = 0$$

i.e.
$$10s^2 + 13 \times 70 = 0$$

i.e.
$$s = \pm j\sqrt{\frac{70 \times 13}{10}} = \pm j9.53$$

Therefore, the frequency of sustained oscillations is $\omega = 9.53$ rad/s.

(c) Putting $K = 1$ in the equation $s^3 + 10s^2 + (21 + K)s + 13K = 0$, the characteristic equation is

$$s^3 + 10s^2 + 22s + 13 = 0$$

Factorizing the above equation

$$(s + 1)(s^2 + 9s + 13) = 0$$

i.e.
$$(s + 1)(s + 4.5 + j5.38)(s + 4.5 - j5.38) = 0$$

Therefore, the roots of the characteristic equation are $s = -1$, $s = -4.5 - j5.38$, and $s = -4.5 + j5.38$.

Now for root at $s = -1$, $\theta = 0°$, and so the damping factor $\xi = \cos \theta = \cos 0° = 1$. For roots at $s = -4.5 \pm j5.38$,

$$\theta = \tan^{-1} \frac{5.38}{4.5} = 50.08°$$

Therefore, the damping factor $\xi = \cos \theta = \cos 50.08° = 0.64$.

Thus the damping factors for the roots are 1 and 0.64 both greater than 0.5. That means, all the roots of the characteristic equation of the above system have damping factor greater than 0.5.

The damping factor associated with $s^2 + 9s + 13$ can be determined by comparing it with the standard equation $s^2 + 2\xi\omega_n s + \omega_n^2 = 0$. Therefore,

$$\omega_n^2 = 13$$

or
$$\omega_n = \sqrt{13} = 3.6$$

$$2\xi\omega_n = 9$$

or
$$\xi = \frac{9}{2 \times 3.6} = 1.25$$

Example 5.21 The characteristic equation of a system in differential equation form is

$$\ddot{x} - (K + 2)\dot{x} + (2K + 10)x = 0$$

(a) Find the values of K for which the system is (i) stable, (ii) limitedly stable and (iii) unstable.

(b) For stable case, for what values of K is the system (i) underdamped and (ii) overdamped?

Solution: Taking the Laplace transform of the given characteristic equation

$$\ddot{x} - (K + 2)\dot{x} + (2K + 10)x = 0$$

the characteristic equation in s-domain is

$$s^2 X(s) - (K + 2)sX(s) + (2K + 10)X(s) = 0$$

i.e.
$$s^2 - (K + 2)s + (2K + 10) = 0$$

The Routh table is formed as follows:

s^2	1	$2K + 10$
s^1	$-(K + 2)$	0
s^0	$2K+10$	0

(a) (i) For the system to be stable, the conditions are

$$-(K + 2) > 0$$

i.e. $\qquad\qquad K < -2$

and $\qquad\qquad 2K + 10 > 0$

i.e. $\qquad\qquad K > -5$

Therefore, for stability

$$-5 < K < -2$$

(ii) For the system to be limitedly stable

$$-(K + 2) = 0$$

i.e. $\qquad\qquad K = -2$

and $\qquad\qquad (2K + 10) = 0$

i.e. $\qquad\qquad K = -5$

(iii) For the system to be unstable

$$-(K + 2) < 0$$

i.e. $\qquad\qquad K > -2$

and $\qquad\qquad 2K + 10 < 0$

i.e. $\qquad\qquad K < -5$

(b) The roots of the characteristic equation are expressed as

$$s_1, s_2 = \frac{(K+2) \pm \sqrt{(K+2)^2 - 4(2K+10)}}{2}$$

For critically damped case

$$(K+2)^2 - 4(2K+10) = 0$$

or $$K = 8.32 \quad \text{or} \quad -4.32$$

As per the stability condition of part (a) $K = 8.32$ is unstable. So for critical damping $K = -4.32$

   (i) Underdamped case $-2 > K > -4.32$
   (ii) Overdamped case $-4.32 > K > -5$

5.7   RELATIVE STABILITY ANALYSIS

Once a system is found to be stable, the relative stability of the system can be determined quantitatively by finding the settling time of the dominant roots of the characteristic equation. Since the settling time is inversely proportional to the real part of the dominant roots, the relative stability can be specified by requiring that all the roots of the characteristic equation be more negative than a certain value, i.e. all the roots must lie to the left of $s = -s_1(s_1 > 0)$. The characteristic equation of the system under study is then modified by shifting the origin of the s-plane to $s = -\sigma_1$ by the substitution $s = z - \sigma_1$. If the new characteristic equation in z satisfies the Routh criterion, it implies that all the roots of the original characteristic equation are more negative than $-\sigma_1$. Figure 5.4 shows the relative stability for various root locations in the s-plane.

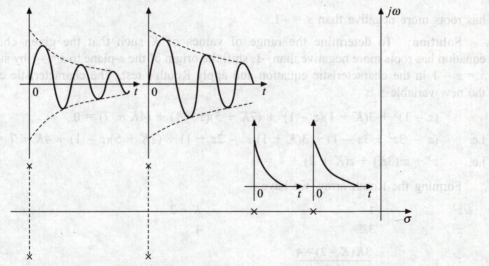

Figure 5.4   Relative stability for various root locations in the s-plane.

Example 5.22   Check whether all the roots of the equation

$$s^3 + 5s^2 + 25s + 30 = 0$$

have real parts more negative than –1 or not.

Solution: To check whether all the roots of the given characteristic equation have real parts more negative than –1 or not, shift the origin of the *s*-plane to $s = -1$ by substituting $s = z - 1$ in the characteristic equation.

The characteristic equation in terms of the new variable *z* is

$$(z - 1)^3 + 5(z - 1)^2 + 25(z - 1) + 30 = 0$$

i.e. $(z^3 - 3z^2 + 3z - 1) + 5(z^2 - 2z + 1) + 25(z - 1) + 30 = 0$

i.e. $z^3 + 2z^2 + 18z + 9 = 0$

Forming the Routh array, we have

z^3	1	18
z^2	2	9
z^1	$\dfrac{2 \times 18 - 1 \times 9}{2} = 13.5$	
z^0	9	

All the elements in the first column of the Routh array are positive. This indicates that all the roots of the characteristic equation in *z*, lie in the left-half of the *z*-plane, which implies that all the roots of the original characteristic equation in *s*, lie to the left of $s = -1$ in the *s*-plane, i.e. all the roots of the characteristic equation in *s* have real parts more negative than –1.

Example 5.23   Determine the range of values of $K(K > 0)$ such that the characteristic equation

$$s^3 + 3(K + 1)s^2 + (7K + 5)s + (4K + 7) = 0$$

has roots more negative than $s = -1$.

Solution: To determine the range of values of *K* such that the given characteristic equation has roots more negative than –1, shift the origin of the *s*-plane to $s = -1$ by substituting, $s = z - 1$ in the characteristic equation and apply Routh's test. The characteristic equation in the new variable *z* is

$$(z - 1)^3 + 3(K + 1)(z - 1)^2 + (7K + 5)(z - 1) + (4K + 7) = 0$$

i.e. $(z^3 - 3z^2 + 3z - 1) + 3(K + 1)(z^2 - 2z + 1) + (7K + 5)(z - 1) + 4K + 7 = 0$

i.e. $z^3 + z^2(3K) + z(K + 2) + 4 = 0$

Forming the Routh array, we have

z^3	1	$K + 2$
z^2	$3K$	4
z^1	$\dfrac{3K(K + 2) - 4}{3K}$	
z^0	4	

For the system to be stable, all the elements in the first column of the Routh array must be positive:

From the z^2 row

$$3K > 0$$

i.e.

$$K > 0$$

From the z^1 row

$$3K^2 + 6K - 4 > 0$$

i.e.

$$K > 0.527$$

The range of values of K, for the roots of the characteristic equation to have real parts more negative than -1 is $0.527 < K < \infty$.

Example 5.24 Determine if the pole nearest to the imaginary axis is at least -0.75 away from the imaginary axis, for the system given by the characteristic equation

$$s^4 + 5s^3 + 10s^2 + 10s + 4 = 0$$

Solution: To find whether the pole nearest to the imaginary axis is at least -0.75 away from the imaginary axis, shift the origin of the s-plane to $s = -0.75$ by substituting $s = z - 0.75$ in the characteristic equation and apply Routh's test for the modified characteristic equation in the z-plane.

The modified characteristic equation is

$$(z - 0.75)^4 + 5(z - 0.75)^3 + 10(z - 0.75)^2 + 10(z - 0.75) + 4 = 0$$

i.e.

$$(z^2 - 1.5z + 0.562)^2 + 5(z^3 - 2.25z^2 + 1.687z - 0.42) + 10(z^2 - 1.5z + 0.562)$$
$$+ 10(z - 0.75) + 4 = 0$$

i.e.

$$z^4 - 2z^3 + 11.24z^2 - 5z - 7.043 = 0$$

Since some of the coefficients of this characteristic equation are negative, it can be concluded that some of its roots are in the right-half of the z–plane, i.e. to the right of $s = -0.75$ in the s-plane. Hence the pole nearest to the origin is less than -0.75 away from the imaginary axis. To find the number of poles to the right of $s = -0.75$, formulate the Routh table as shown below.

z^4	1	11.24	-7.043
z^3	-2	-5	
z^2	$\dfrac{-2 \times 11.24 - 1 \times (-5)}{-2} = 8.74$	-7.043	
z^1	$\dfrac{8.74 \times (-5) - (-2) \times (-7.043)}{8.74} = -6.6$	0	
z^0	-7.043		

Looking at the elements of the first column, there are three sign changes. Hence there are three roots of the characteristic equation having real parts less negative than -0.75.

Example 5.25 Determine whether the largest time constant of the characteristic equation given below is greater than, less than or equal to 1.0 second.

$$s^3 + 4s^2 + 6s + 4 = 0$$

Solution: The time constant associated with the characteristic equation is

$$\tau = 1/\xi\omega_n = 1 \text{ s}$$

$$\therefore \qquad \xi\omega_n = 1$$

So we have to determine whether the roots of the characteristic equation have real parts greater than, less than, or equal to -1. For this, put $s = z - 1$ and transform the characteristic equation in the s-plane into a characteristic equation in the z-plane and apply the Routh method. The new characteristic equation in z is

$$(z - 1)^3 + 4(z - 1)^2 + 6(z - 1) + 4 = 0$$

i.e. $\qquad z^3 - 3z^2 + 3z - 1 + 4z^2 - 8z + 4 + 6z - 6 + 4 = 0$

i.e. $\qquad z^3 + z^2 + z + 1 = 0$

The Routh table is formulated as follows:

z^3	1	1
z^2	1	1
z^1	$\dfrac{1 \times 1 - 1 \times 1}{1} = 0$	0
z^0		

All the elements in the z^1 row are zeros (i.e., difficulty 2 arises). Replace the z^1 row of zeros by the coefficients of the first derivative of the auxiliary equation formed by using the coefficients of the z^2 row. Therefore,

$$\therefore \qquad A(z) = z^2 + 1 = 0$$

$$\frac{dA(z)}{dz} = 2z = 0$$

The modified Routh table is given as follows:

z^3	1	1
z^2	1	1
z^1	2	0
z^0	1	

Looking at the modified Routh table, all the elements in the first column of the Routh array are of the same sign. So there are no roots of this modified characteristic equation to the right of $s = -1$ (i.e., to the right of $z = 0$). Since there is a row of zeros, the roots are on the imaginary axis at $s = -1$. In fact the roots are at $s = -1 + j1$ and $s = -1 - j1$. So the largest time constant of the characteristic equation is equal to 1 second.

SHORT QUESTIONS AND ANSWERS

1. What does the term 'stability of a control system' imply?

A. The term 'stability of a control system' implies that small changes in the system input, in initial conditions, or in system parameters do not result in large changes in system output.

2. What are the two notions of system stability to be satisfied for a linear time-invariant system to be stable?

A. The two notions of system stability to be satisfied for a linear time-invariant system to be stable are

(a) When the system is excited by a bounded input, the output is bounded.

(b) In the absence of the input, the output tends to zero irrespective of the initial conditions.

3. What do you mean by Bounded-input Bounded-output (BIBO) stability?

A. BIBO stability means that the output of the system will be bounded for a bounded input.

4. What is the requirement for BIBO stability?

A. The requirement for BIBO stability is that the impulse response of the system must be absolutely integrable, i.e. $\int_0^\infty g(\tau)\,d\tau$ must be finite.

5. What do you mean by asymptotic stability?

A. Zero input stability is called the asymptotic stability. A system is said to be asymptotically stable if in the absence of any input, the output tends to zero irrespective of the initial conditions.

6. What do you mean by zero-state response?

A. The zero-state response means the response, i.e. the output of the system due to inputs only. All the initial conditions of the system are zero.

7. What do you mean by zero-input response?

A. The zero-input response means the response, i.e. the output of the system due to initial conditions only. The inputs to the system are zero.

8. Compare the stability considerations of linear and nonlinear systems.

A. For linear time-invariant systems, the two notions of stability, i.e. the BIBO stability and the asymptotic stability are essentially equivalent. For linear systems, there is only one equilibrium state, whereas for nonlinear systems, there can be many equilibrium states. If a linear system is stable for one bounded input, it will be stable for any other bounded input. A free stable linear system will be stable for any bounded input. For a free stable nonlinear system, there is no guarantee that the output will be bounded for a particular bounded input. A nonlinear system may be stable for a particular bounded input, but may become unstable for another bounded input. Many generalized techniques are available for the determination of stability of linear systems. No general method is available for the determination of stability of nonlinear systems.

9. What is impulse response of a system?

A. The impulse response of a system is the output of the system when it is excited by a unit-impulse signal. The impulse response of a system is also defined as the inverse Laplace transform of the system transfer function.

10. On what does the impulse response $g(t)$ depend?

A. The impulse response $g(t)$ of a system depends on the system transfer function.

11. What type of response terms results when there is a single root at the origin or non-multiple root pairs on the $j\omega$-axis?

A. When there is a single root at the origin or non-multiple root pairs on the $j\omega$-axis, the response term may be of constant amplitude or oscillations of constant amplitude.

$\int_0^\infty g(\tau)\,d\tau = \infty$. So the system is unstable. It may be called marginally stable.

12. What type of response terms results when there are multiple roots at the origin or multiple root pairs on the $j\omega$-axis?

A. When there are multiple roots at the origin or multiple root pairs on the imaginary axis, the response term may increase linearly with respect to time, or may be sinusoidal oscillations whose magnitude rises linearly.

$\int_0^\infty g(\tau)\,d\tau = \infty$. So the system is unstable.

13. What type of response terms results when the roots are in the right-half of the s-plane?

A. When the roots are in the right-half of the s-plane, the response terms increase without bound.

$\int_0^\infty g(\tau)\,d\tau = \infty$. So the system is unstable.

14. What type of response terms results when all the roots are in the left-half of the s-plane?

A. When all the roots are in the left-half of the s-plane, the response terms decay with time.

$\int_0^\infty g(\tau)\,d\tau = $ finite. So the system is BIBO stable.

15. What do you mean by a marginally or limitedly stable system?

A. A marginally or limitedly stable system is a system with non-repeated poles at the origin or / and on the imaginary axis. The system is neither stable nor unstable. Its output is of constant amplitude or oscillations of constant amplitude.

16. When do you say that the system is absolutely stable with respect to a parameter of the system?

A. A system is said to be absolutely stable with respect to a parameter of the system provided it is stable for all values of that parameter.

17. When do you say that the system is conditionally stable with respect to a parameter of the system?

A. A system is said to be conditionally stable with respect to a parameter of the system, if it is stable only for certain bounded ranges of values of that parameter.

18. Distinguish between absolute stability and relative stability.

A. Absolute stability is a qualitative measure of stability. It is a 'yes' or 'no' answer. It tells whether the system is stable or not. It cannot tell how much stable or how much unstable the system is. Relative stability is a quantitative measure of stability. It tells how much stable or unstable the system is. If the roots of the characteristic equation are nearer to origin in the left-half of the *s*-plane, the system is relatively less stable. If the roots are far away in the left-half of the *s*-plane, then the system is relatively more stable.

19. How are the roots of the characteristic equation related to stability?

A. If all the roots of the characteristic equation have only negative real parts, i.e. if all of them are in the left-half of the *s*-plane, the impulse response is bounded and eventually tends to zero. So the system is stable. If any root of the characteristic equation has a positive real part, the impulse response is unbounded and tends to ∞ as t tends to ∞. So the system is unstable.

Even if roots are on the imaginary axis, the system is unstable.

20. What is the relation between stability and coefficients of the characteristic polynomial?

A. If one or more coefficients of the characteristic polynomial are negative or zero, then some of the roots lie in the right-half of the *s*-plane or on the imaginary axis and hence the system is unstable. If all the coefficients of the characteristic equation are real and positive and no missing term is there, then there is a possibility for the system to be stable.

21. What are the necessary conditions for the stability of control systems?

A. The necessary conditions for the stability of control systems are as follows:

(a) All the coefficients of the characteristic equation must be real and positive.
(b) None of the coefficients can be missing.

22. Where must the roots of the characteristic equation lie for the system to be stable?

A. For a system to be stable, all the roots of the characteristic equation must lie only in the left-half of the *s*-plane.

23. Where must the roots of the characteristic equation lie for the system to be unstable?

A. For a system to be unstable, atleast one root of the characteristic equation must lie in the right-half of the *s*-plane, or if they lie on the imaginary axis, they must be repeated.

24. Where must the roots of the characteristic equation lie for the system to be marginally or limitedly stable?

A. For the system to be marginally or limitedly stable, only non-repeated roots of the characteristic equation must lie on the imaginary axis and no root should lie in the right half of the *s*-plane.

25. What is the necessary and sufficient condition for stability using the Routh method?

A. The necessary and sufficient condition for stability of a system using the Routh method is that, each term of the first column of the Routh array of its characteristic equation be positive if $a_0 > 0$. If this condition is not met, the system will be unstable and the number of sign changes of the terms of the first column of the Routh array corresponds to the number of roots of the characteristic equation in the right-half of the *s*-plane.

26. What conclusion can be drawn if the first element of any row of a Routh array is zero when that row has at least one non-zero element?

A. If the first element in any row of a Routh array is zero, when that row has at least one non-zero element, it can be concluded that the corresponding system is unstable. It indicates that there are roots either in the right-half of the *s*-plane or on the imaginary axis.

27. What conclusion can be made if there is a row of all zeros in the Routh array?

A. If there is a row of all zeros in the Routh array, it can be concluded that the corresponding system is unstable. It indicates that there are symmetrically located roots in the *s*-plane with respect to its origin (pair of real roots with opposite signs and / or pair(s) of conjugate roots on the imaginary axis and / or complex conjugate roots forming quadrates in the *s*-plane).

28. What is an auxiliary polynomial? What is its order?

A. The polynomial whose coefficients are the elements of the row just above the row of zeros in the Routh array is called an auxiliary polynomial. The order of the auxiliary polynomial is always even. It is a factor of the characteristic equation.

29. What information does the auxiliary polynomial give?

A. The auxiliary polynomial gives the number and location of root pairs of the characteristic equation which are symmetrically located in the *s*-plane.

30. What conclusion can be drawn about the stability of a system whenever difficulty 1 or difficulty 2 arises?

A. Whenever difficulty 1 or difficulty 2 arises, it can be immediately concluded that the system is unstable.

31. What is quadrantal symmetry?

A. Quadrantal symmetry means there are symmetrical roots in all four quadrants. This happens when we have complex conjugate roots forming the quadrates in the *s*-plane.

32. What is difficulty 1 in Routh method? What does it indicate? How is it overcome?

A. Difficulty 1 in the Routh method is that, the first element in any row of the Routh array is zero while the rest of the row has at least one non-zero element. It indicates that the system is unstable due to the presence of poles either on the imaginary axis or in the right half of *s*-plane. Whenever difficulty 1 arises, all the elements in the next row become infinite and Routh's test fails. Only to find the number of roots in the right-half of the *s*-plane, one should proceed with the formulation of the Routh array.

Difficulty 1 is overcome by replacing the first element '0' by a small positive number ϵ and proceeding with the formulation of the Routh array; or replacing s in the characteristic equation by $1/z$ and forming the Routh table on the modified characteristic equation in z.

33. What is difficulty 2 in the Routh method? What does it indicate? How is it overcome?

A. Difficulty 2 in Routh method is that, all the elements in any row of the Routh array are zero. It indicates that the system is unstable due to the presence of symmetrically located roots with respect to the origin of the s-plane. Only to find the location of the roots one should proceed with the formulation of the Routh array.

Difficulty 2 may be overcome by replacing the row of zeros by the coefficients of the first derivative of the auxiliary equation formed by using the coefficients of the row just above the row of zeros and proceeding with the formulation of the Routh array.

34. What are the advantages and drawbacks of the Routh stability criterion?

A. The Routh stability criterion is an algebraic method to test the stability of control systems. It is very simple because only the coefficients of the characteristic equation are to be manipulated to determine the stability of a system. It can be used to determine the condition for stability of linear feedback systems, but the drawbacks are as follows:

(a) For systems of order more than 6 or 7, it becomes cumbersome.

(b) It cannot be applied if the coefficients of the characteristic equation are complex.

(c) It is useful to find out only the absolute stability of a system.

(d) It is very cumbersome to obtain the relative stability of a system using this method. It has to be repeatedly applied to determine the relative stability.

(e) For an unstable system, it can tell only how many roots of the characteristic equation are in the right-half of the s-plane, but it cannot give the exact location of the roots. Also it cannot tell whether the roots are real or complex.

35. How can you determine the relative stability of a system by using the Routh stability criterion?

A. The relative stability of a system can be determined quantitatively by finding the settling time of the dominant roots of its characteristic equation. The settling time is inversely proportional to the real part of the dominant roots. So the relative stability can be specified by requiring that all the roots of the characteristic equation be more negative than a certain value, i.e. all the roots must lie to the left of the lines $s = -s_1(s_1 > 0)$. Modify the given characteristic equation by shifting the origin of the s-plane to $s = -\sigma$ by substituting $s = z - \sigma$ and apply the Routh criterion on the new characteristic equation. If the criterion is satisfied, it implies that all the roots of the original characteristic equation are more negative than $-\sigma$.

36. What does the presence of negative terms during the formulation of the Routh array mean?

A. The presence of negative terms during the formulation of the Routh array means that the characteristic equation has one or more roots in the right-half of the s-plane and hence the system is unstable.

REVIEW QUESTIONS

1. State and explain the Routh stability criterion.
2. Show that the BIBO stability is satisfied if the impulse response $g(t)$ is absolutely integrable.
3. What are the difficulties that may be encountered in the formulation of the Routh array? What do they indicate? How are they overcome?
4. Explain how relative stability of a system can be determined using the Routh criterion.

FILL IN THE BLANKS

1. The two notions of stability are essentially equivalent in _____ systems.
2. A free stable _____ system will be stable for any bounded input.
3. For a free stable _____ system, there is no guarantee that the output will be bounded for a particular bounded input.
4. A linear time-invariant system is stable, if the following two notions of system stability are satisfied:
   (a) _____.
   (b) _____.
5. Roughly speaking stability in a system implies that small changes in _____, _____, and _____ do not result in large changes in system output.
6. Stability is a _____ term, whereas relative stability is a _____ term.
7. If all the roots of the characteristic equation have _____, then the impulse response is bounded and the system is stable.
8. If any root of the characteristic equation has a _____, the impulse response is unbounded and the system is unstable.
9. The settling time of poles is _____ proportional to the real part of the poles.
10. A system is said to be absolutely stable with respect to a parameter of the system, if it is stable for _____.
11. A system is said to be conditionally stable with respect to a parameter of the system, if it is stable for _____.
12. The necessary as well as sufficient condition for the stability of _____ and _____ order systems is that all the coefficients of the characteristic equation be real and positive.
13. Stability is a very important characteristic of the _____ response of the system.
14. Whenever difficulty 1 or difficulty 2 arises in the formulation of the Routh array, it can be concluded that the system is _____.

15. All the elements in any row of the Routh array are zero indicates that there are _____ located roots of the characteristic equation in the s-plane.

16. The Routh stability criterion can be applied only if all the coefficients of the characteristic equation are _____. It cannot be applied when the coefficients are _____.

17. The number of sign changes in the elements of the first column of the Routh array indicates the number of roots of the characteristic equation in the _____ of the s-plane.

18. The Routh stability criterion gives information about only _____ stability of a system but fails to indicate the _____ stability of a system.

OBJECTIVE TYPE QUESTIONS

1. If the system has non repeated poles on the $j\omega$ axis, the system is
   (a) stable
   (b) unstable
   (c) marginally stable
   (d) conditionally stable

2. If the system has multiple poles on the $j\omega$ axis, the system is
   (a) stable
   (b) unstable
   (c) marginally stable
   (d) conditionally stable

3. If the system has $G(s) = \dfrac{1}{s(1 + 4s)}$, the system is

   (a) stable
   (b) unstable
   (c) marginally stable
   (d) conditionally stable

4. Integrators are
   (a) stable
   (b) unstable
   (c) marginally stable
   (d) conditionally stable

5. Sinusoidal oscillators are
   (a) stable
   (b) unstable
   (c) marginally stable
   (d) conditionally stable

6. When a system is excited by an unbounded input and produces an unbounded output,
   (a) the system is stable
   (b) the system is unstable
   (c) the system is conditionally stable
   (d) nothing can be said about stability

7. Marginally stable systems have some roots with real parts equal to zero, but none with
   (a) positive real parts
   (b) negative real parts
   (c) zero real part
   (d) none of these

8. If all the roots of the characteristic equation have negative real parts, then the system is
   (a) stable
   (b) unstable
   (c) conditionally stable
   (d) marginally stable

9. The Routh stability criterion for testing the stability of systems is
   (a) an algebraic method   (b) a graphical method
   (c) combination of (a) and (b)   (d) none of these

10. For the application of Routh's test, all the coefficients of the characteristic equation must be
    (a) real   (b) imaginary
    (c) complex   (d) none of these

11. The number of sign changes in the elements of the first column of the Routh array denotes
    (a) the number of zeros of the closed-loop system in the RHP
    (b) the number of poles of the closed-loop system in the RHP
    (c) the number of open-loop zeros in RHP
    (d) the number of open-loop poles in RHP

12. In the formulation of the Routh array, when ever difficulty 1 or difficulty 2 arises, it can be concluded that the system is
    (a) unstable   (b) conditionally stable
    (c) marginally stable   (d) stable

13. $G(s) = \dfrac{e^{-2s}}{s(s+4)}$. The system with this transfer function is operated in closed-loop with unity feedback. The closed-loop system is
    (a) stable   (b) unstable
    (c) marginally stable   (d) conditionally stable

14. The closed-loop transfer function of a system is $\dfrac{C(s)}{R(s)} = \dfrac{s-2}{(s+1)(s+3)(s+4)}$. The system is
    (a) stable   (b) unstable
    (c) marginally stable   (d) conditionally stable

15. The closed-loop transfer function of a system is $\dfrac{C(s)}{R(s)} = \dfrac{K(s+1)}{1+s+2s^2-3s^3+s^4}$. This system is
    (a) stable   (b) unstable
    (c) marginally stable   (d) conditionally stable

16. The terms in the first column of the Routh array of the characteristic equation of certain system are 2, 1, 8, −7, 2, 6. The number of roots of the characteristic equation in the right-half of the s-plane is equal to
    (a) 2   (b) 3
    (c) 1   (d) none of these

17. The terms in the first column of the Routh array of the characteristic equation of a certain system are 5, 7, 4, 3, −2. The number of roots of the characteristic equation in the right-half of the s-plane is equal to

(a) 2   (b) 1

(c) 3   (d) none of these

18. The terms in the first column of the Routh array of the characteristic equation of a certain system are 4, 7, 6, −5, −4, −3. The number of roots of the characteristic equation in the right-half of the s-plane is equal to

(a) 2   (b) 1

(c) 3   (d) none of these

19. The open-loop transfer function of a closed-loop system is $G(s) = \dfrac{K}{s(s+2)(s+4)}$. The range of values of K for stable operation is

(a) $0 < K < 48$ (b) $0 < K < 24$

(c) $0 < K < 36$ (d) none of these

20. The characteristic equation of a unity feedback system is given by $s^3 + s^2 + 2s + 2 = 0$.

(a) The system has one pole in the RH of the s-plane.

(b) The system has two poles in the RH of the s-plane.

(c) The system is asymptotically stable.

(d) The system exhibits oscillatory response.

21. A closed-loop control system has the following characteristic equation

$$s^3 + 8Ks^2 + (K+4)s + 20 = 0$$

where K is the open-loop gain of the system. The condition for marginal stability is

(a) $K = 0$ (b) $K = 2$

(c) $K = 0.55$ (d) $K = -4.55$

22. The open-loop transfer function of a control system is given by $G(s) = \dfrac{K(s+8)}{s(s+4)(s+a)}$.

The smallest possible value of a for which the system is stable in the closed-loop for all positive values of K is

(a) 0   (b) 4

(c) 8   (d) 12

23. The open-loop transfer function of a unity negative feedback control system is given by

$G(s) = \dfrac{K(s+4)}{(s+2)(s-6)}$. For $K > 4$, the stability characteristics of the open-loop and closed-loop configurations of the system are, respectively

(a) stable and stable   (b) unstable and stable

(c) stable and unstable   (d) unstable and unstable

24. The characteristic equation $1 + G(s)H(s) = 0$ of a system is given by

$$s^4 + 8s^3 + 12s^2 + 8s + K = 0$$

For the system to remain stable, the value of gain K should be

(a) zero   (b) $0 < K < 11$

(c) >11   (d) positive

25. The open-loop transfer function of a unity feedback control system is

$$G(s)H(s) = \frac{22.5}{s(s+2)(s+T)}$$

where T is a variable parameter. The closed-loop system will be stable for all values of

(a) $T > 0$ (b) $0 < T < 0.25$

(c) $T > 2.5$ (d) $2.5 < T < 5$

26. The open-loop transfer function of a unity negative feedback control system is given by

$$G(s) = \frac{5(s+1)}{s^2(s+2)}$$

The stability characteristics of the open-loop and closed-loop configurations are respectively

(a) stable and stable   (b) unstable and stable

(c) stable and unstable   (d) unstable and unstable

PROBLEMS

5.1 Test for stability and determine the location of the roots of the characteristic equations given as follows:

(a) $s^6 + s^5 - 2s^4 - 3s^3 - 7s^2 - 4s - 4 = 0$

(b) $s^5 + 2s^4 + 24s^3 + 48s^2 - 25s - 50 = 0$

(c) $s^4 + 6s^3 + 23s^2 + 40s + 50 = 0$

(d) $s^4 + 2s^3 + s^2 + 4s + 2 = 0$

(e) $s^5 + s^4 + 3s^3 + 9s^2 + 16s + 10 = 0$

(f) $s^4 + 8s^3 + 18s^2 + 16s + 5 = 0$

(g) $s^7 + 5s^6 + 9s^5 + 9s^4 + 4s^3 + 20s^2 + 36s + 36 = 0$

(h) $s^6 + s^5 + 3s^4 + 3s^3 + 3s^2 + 2s + 1 = 0$

(i) $s^5 + 2s^4 + 2s^3 + 4s^2 + 11s + 10 = 0$

(j) $s^7 + 9s^6 + 24s^5 + 24s^4 + 24s^3 + 24s^2 + 23s + 15 = 0$

(k) $s^6 + 2s^5 + 8s^4 + 12s^3 + 20s^2 + 16s + 16 = 0$

5.2 The characteristic equations for certain feedback control systems are given below. In each case

(a) Determine the range of values of K for the system to be stable

(b) Can the system be marginally stable?

If so, find the required value of K and the frequency of sustained oscillations.

(i) $s^3 + 2Ks^2 + (K + 2)s + 4 = 0$

(ii) $s^4 + 8s^3 + 24s^2 + 32s + K = 0$

    (iii) $s^4 + 25s^3 + 15s^2 + 20s + K = 0$

    (iv) $s^4 + Ks^3 + 2s^2 + (K + 1)s + 10 = 0$

    (v) $s^3 + (K + 2)s^2 + 2Ks + 10 = 0$

    (vi) $s^3 + 20s^2 + 5s + 10K = 0$

    (vii) $s^4 + Ks^3 + 5s^2 + 10s + 10K = 0$

    (viii) $s^4 + 125s^3 + s^2 + 5s + K = 0$

5.3 The open-loop transfer function of a unity feedback control system is given by

$$G(s)H(s) = \frac{K}{s(s+1)(3s+1)(2s+1)}$$

Determine the range of values of K for which the system is stable. Also determine the value of K for sustained oscillations and the frequency of the oscillations.

5.4 The open-loop transfer function of a feedback control system is given by

$$G(s)H(s) = \frac{K}{s(s+4)(s^2 + 2s + 2)}$$

    (a) Using the Routh criterion, determine the range of values of K for which the system is stable.

    (b) If a zero at $s = -4$ is added to the forward path transfer function, how is the stability affected?

5.5 For a system with $G(s) = \dfrac{K}{s(s^2 + s + 1)(s + 2)}$ and $H(s) = 1$, determine the range of K for

stability. Also determine the marginal value of K and the frequency of sustained oscillations.

5.6 Determine whether all the roots of the following characteristic equation

$$s^3 + 6s^2 + 10s + 12.4 = 0$$

have real parts more negative than -1 or not.

5.7 Use the Routh criterion to check the stability of a system given by the characteristic equation

$$2s^6 + s^5 + 2s^4 + s^3 + 3s^2 + 5s + 6 = 0$$

5.8 Determine the range of values of K for stability of a unity feedback system whose open-loop transfer function is

$$G(s) = \frac{K}{s(s+1)(s+2)}$$

5.9 The open-loop transfer function of a feedback control system is given by

$$G(s)H(s) = \frac{K}{s(s+1)(s+4)}$$

(a) Using the Routh criterion, determine the range of values of K for which the system will be stable.

(b) If a zero at $s = -1$ is added to the forward path transfer function, determine the range of K for stability.

5.10   The output of a control system is related to its input by

$$[s^4 + 2s^3 + 2s^2 + (3 + K)s + K] \, C(s) = K(s + 3) \, R(s)$$

(a) With $K = 8$ and a step input, will the output response be stable?

(b) Determine the limiting positive value that K can have for a stable output response.

5.11   The open-loop transfer function of a unity feedback system is

$$G(s) = \frac{K}{s(1 + 0.4s)(1 + 0.25s)}$$

Find the restriction on K so that the closed-loop system is absolutely stable.

5.12   Find the range of values of K for the system represented by the following characteristic equation to be stable. What is the marginal value of K and what is the frequency of sustained oscillation?

$$q(s) = s^4 + 22s^3 + 10s^2 + 2s + K = 0$$

5.13   Determine the range of K such that the unity feedback system with an open-loop transfer function

$$G(s) = \frac{K}{s(s^2 + s + 1)(s + 4)}$$

is stable.

5.14   Find the condition for stability for the systems whose characteristic equations are given below.

(a) $s^4 + 20s^3 + 224s^2 + 1240s + 2400 + K = 0$

(b) $s^3 + (6K + 0.5)s^2 + 4Ks + 50 = 0$

In each case, determine the value of K which will cause sustained oscillations and the frequency of the oscillations.

5.15   The open-loop transfer function of a unity feedback control system is given by

$$G(s) = \frac{K(1 + 2s)}{s^2(s + 2)(s + 5)}$$

Determine the range of values of K for stability. Also determine the marginal value of K for stability and the frequency of sustained oscillations.

5.16   Find the range of K such that the unity feedback system with the following open-loop transfer function will remain stable.

$$G(s) = \frac{K(s + 2)}{s^2(s + 5)}$$

5.17 Determine the maximum value of gain K for stability of the system given by the open-loop transfer function

$$G(s)H(s) = \frac{Ke^{-sT}}{s(s+1)}$$

5.18 The open-loop transfer function of a closed-loop system with unity feedback is given by

$$G(s) = \frac{K(s+2)}{(s+1)(s-1)}$$

Comment on the stability of the system. If a zero is added at $s = -1$, comment on the stability.

5.19 Find the maximum value of K for which the system given by

$$G(s)H(s) = \frac{Ke^{-3s}}{s}$$

is stable.

MATLAB PROGRAMS

PROGRAM 5.1

Matlab program for determining the stability of the system with characteristic equation $s^6 + 2s^5 + s^4 + 2s^3 + 3s^2 + 4s + 5 = 0$ by using Routh criterion.

```
clc;clear all;close all;
r=[1 2 1 2 3 4 5]; % co-efficients of charateristic equation
m=length(r);
n=round(m/2);
q=1; k=0;
for p = 1:length(r)
  if rem(p,2)==0
    c_even(k)=r(p);
  else
    c_odd(q)=r(p);
    k=k+1;
    q=q+1;
  end
end
a=zeros(m,n);
if m/2 ~= round(m/2)
  c_even(n)=0;
```

```
end
a(1,:)=c_odd;
a(2,:)=c_even;
if a(2,1)==0
  a(2,1)=0.01;
end
for i=3:m
  for j=1:n-1
    x=a(i-1,1);
    if x==0
      x=0.01;
    end
    a(i,j)=((a(i-1,1)*a(i-2,j+1))-(a(i-2,1)*a(i-1,j+1)))/x;
  end
  if a(i,:)==0
    order=(m-i+1);
    c=0;   d=1;
    for j=1:n-1
      a(i,j)=(order-c)*(a(i-1,d));
      d=d+1;    c=c+2;
    end
  end
  if a(i,1)==0
    a(i,1)=0.01;
  end
end
Right_poles=0;
for i=1:m-1
  if sign(a(i,1))*sign(a(i+1,1))==-1
    Right_poles=Right_poles+1;
  end
end
fprintf('\n Routh-Hurwitz Table:\n')
a
fprintf('\n Number Of Right Poles =%2.0f\n',Right_poles)
if Right_poles>0
  disp('The system is un-stable')
else
  disp('The system is stable')
end
```

Output:

Routh-Hurwitz Table:

a =

1.0000	1.0000	3.0000	5.0000
2.0000	2.0000	4.0000	0
0.0100	1.0000	5.0000	0
−198.0000	−996.0000	0	0
0.9497	5.0000	0	0
46.4378	0	0	0
5.0000	0	0	0

Number of Right Poles = 2

The system is un-stable.

PROGRAM 5.2

Matalab program for determining the stability of the system with characteristic equation

$s^5 + s^4 + 24s^3 + 48s^2 - 25s - 5 = 0$ **by using Routh criterion**

```
clc;clear all;close all;
r=[1 1 24 48 -25 -5]; % co-efficients of charateristic equation
m=length(r);
n=round(m/2);
q=1;
k=0;
for p = 1:length(r)
  if rem(p,2)==0
    c_even(k)=r(p);
  else
    c_odd(q)=r(p);
    k=k+1;
    q=q+1;
  end
end
a=zeros(m,n);
if m/2 ~= round(m/2)
  c_even(n)=0;
end
a(1,:)=c_odd;
a(2,:)=c_even;
if a(2,1)==0
  a(2,1)=0.01;
end
```

```
for i=3:m
  for j=1:n-1
      x=a(i-1,1);
      if x==0
        x=0.01;
      end
      a(i,j)=((a(i-1,1)*a(i-2,j+1))-(a(i-2,1)*a(i-1,j+1)))/x;
  end
  if a(i,:)==0
    order=(m-i+1);
    c=0;      d=1;
    for j=1:n-1
      a(i,j)=(order-c)*(a(i-1,d));
      d=d+1;   c=c+2;
    end
  end
  if a(i,1)==0
    a(i,1)=0.01;
  end
end
Right_poles=0;
for i=1:m-1
  if sign(a(i,1))*sign(a(i+1,1))==-1
    Right_poles=Right_poles+1;
  end
end
fprintf('\n Routh-Hurwitz Table:\n')
a
fprintf('\n Number Of Right Poles =%2.0f\n',Right_poles)
if Right_poles>0
  disp('The system is un-stable')
else
  disp('The system is stable')
end
```

Output:

Routh-Hurwitz Table:

a =

1.0000	24.0000	−25.0000
1.0000	48.0000	−5.0000
−24.0000	−20.0000	0
47.1667	−5.0000	0

−22.5442	0	0
−5.0000	0	0

Number of Right Poles = 3
The system is un-stable.

PROGRAM 5.3

Matalab program for determining the stability of the system with characteristic equation
$s^6 + 2s^5 + s^4 + 2s^3 + 3s^2 + 4s + 5 = 0$ **by using Routh criterion**

```
clc;clear all;close all;
D=[1 2 8 15 20 16 16];%input charecteristic coefficients
l=length (D);
disp('                         ')
disp('————————————————————')
disp('Roots of characteristic equation is:')
roots(D)
% ————————Begin of Building array————————————
if mod(l,2)==0
  m=zeros(l,l/2);
  [cols,rows]=size(m);
  for i=1:rows
    m(1,i)=D(1,(2*i)-1);
    m(2,i)=D(1,(2*i));
  end
else
  m=zeros(l,(l+1)/2);
  [cols,rows]=size(m);
  for i=1:rows
    m(1,i)=D(1,(2*i)-1);
  end
  for i=1:((l-1)/2)
    m(2,i)=D(1,(2*i));
  end
end
for j=3:cols
  if m(j-1,1)==0
    m(j-1,1)=0.001;
  end
  for i=1:rows-1
    m(j,i)=(-1/m(j-1,1))*det([m(j-2,1) m(j-2,i+1);m(j-1,1) m(j-1,i+1)]);
  end
end
```

```
disp('————The Routh-Hurwitz array is:————'),m
% Checking for sign change
Temp=sign(m);a=0;
for j=1:cols
    a=a+Temp(j,1);
end
if a==cols
    disp('          ----> System is Stable <----')
else
    disp('          ----> System is Unstable <----')
end
```

Output:

Roots of characteristic equation is:

ans =

```
0.1776 + 2.3520i
0.1776 - 2.3520i
-1.2224 + 0.8169i
-1.2224 - 0.8169i
0.0447 + 1.1526i
0.0447 - 1.1526i
```

------------The Routh-Hurwitz array is:------------

m =

1.0000	8.0000	20.0000	16.0000
2.0000	15.0000	16.0000	0
0.5000	12.0000	16.0000	0
-33.0000	-48.0000	0	0
11.2727	16.0000	0	0
-1.1613	0	0	0
16.0000	0	0	0

---->System is unstable <----

PROGRAM 5.4:

Matalab program for determining the stability of the system with characteristic equation $s^5 + s^4 + 24s^3 + 48s^2 - 2^-s - 5 = 0$ by using Routh criterion

```
function RSC=routh(poly,epsilon);
clc;clear all;close all;
poly=[1 1 24 48 -25 -5];
dim=size(poly);
coe=dim(2);
RSC=zeros(coe,ceil(coe/2));
```

```
for i=1:coe,
    RSC(2-rem(i,2),ceil(i/2))=poly(i);
end
r=coe-2;
index=zeros(r,1);
for i=1:r,
    index(r-i+1)=ceil(i/2);
end
for i=3:coe,
    for j=1:index(i-2),
        RSC(i,j)=-det([RSC(i-2,1) RSC(i-2,j+1);RSC(i-1,1) RSC(i-1,j+1)])/RSC(i-1,1);
    end
end
% Checking for sign change
Temp=sign(RSC);
a=0;
for i=1:dim
    a=a+Temp(i,1);
end
if a==dim
    disp('        ----> System is Stable <----')
else
    disp('        ----> System is Unstable <----')
end
disp('The constructed routh array is');
```

Output:

The constructed routh array is

ans =

1	1	3	5
2	2	4	0
0	1	5	0
−Inf	−Inf	0	0
NaN	NaN	0	0
NaN	0	0	0
NaN	0	0	0

---->System is unstable<----

PROGRAM 5.5

Matalab program for determining the stability of the system with characteristic equation $s^6 + 2s^5 + s^4 + 2s^3 + 3s^2 + 4s + 5 = 0$ by using Routh criterion.

```
function RSC=routh(poly,epsilon);
clc;clear all;close all;
poly=[1 2 1 2 3 4 5];
dim=size(poly);
coe=dim(2);
RSC=zeros(coe,ceil(coe/2));
for i=1:coe,
    RSC(2-rem(i,2),ceil(i/2))=poly(i);
end
r=coe-2;
index=zeros(r,1);
for i=1:r,
    index(r-i+1)=ceil(i/2);
end
for i=3:coe,
    for j=1:index(i-2),
        RSC(i,j)=-det([RSC(i-2,1) RSC(i-2,j+1);RSC(i-1,1) RSC(i-1,j+1)])/RSC(i-1,1);
    end
end
% Checking for sign change
Temp=sign(RSC);
a=0;
for i=1:dim
    a=a+Temp(i,1);
end
if a==dim
    disp('          ----> System is Stable <----')
else
    disp('          ----> System is Unstable <----')
end
 disp('The constructed routh array is');
```

Output:

The constructed routh array is

ans =

1	1	3	5
2	2	4	0
0	1	5	0
−Inf	−Inf	0	0
NaN	NaN	0	0
NaN	0	0	0
NaN	0	0	0

---->System is unstable---->

Root Locus Technique

6.1 INTRODUCTION

We have seen earlier that it is possible to adjust the location of the closed-loop poles of the system by varying the loop gain. Since the nature of the transient response is closely related to the location of the closed-loop poles, it is very important to know how they move in the s-plane as the gain or some other parameter is varied. Furthermore, since for economy in manufacture, it is necessary to allow some tolerance in the values of the parameters, it is desirable to determine the movement of the poles with small changes in parameters.

The root locus is the locus of the roots of the characteristic equation of a closed-loop system in the s-plane as a given system parameter (usually the open-loop gain K) is varied from 0 to ∞. The root locus technique was introduced by W.R. Evans in 1948.

The root locus is a powerful method of analysis and design for stability and transient response of the control systems. It brings into focus the complete dynamic response of the system and further being a graphical technique, an approximate root locus sketch can be made quickly. It gives information about the absolute stability as well as the relative stability of a system. It clearly shows the ranges of stability, ranges of instability and the conditions that cause a system to break into oscillations. It can be used to solve higher-order algebraic equations. The value of K for a particular root location and the roots for a particular K can be determined using root locus. It can be used to describe qualitatively the performance of a system as various parameters are changed, for example the effect of varying gain upon overshoot, settling time, and peak time can be vividly displayed.

In designing a linear control system, the root locus method is very useful since it indicates the manner in which the open-loop poles and zeros should be modified so that the response meets the system performance specifications.

6.2 ROOT LOCUS CONCEPTS

To understand the concepts underlying the root locus technique, consider the simple second-order system shown in Figure 6.1. The open-loop transfer function of this system is

$$G(s) = \frac{K}{s(s+b)}$$

where K and b are constants.

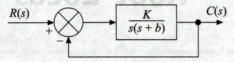

Figure 6.1 A second-order system.

The open-loop transfer function has two poles; one at the origin $s = 0$, and the other at $s = -b$. The closed-loop transfer function of this system is

$$\frac{C(s)}{R(s)} = \frac{G(s)}{1 + G(s)H(s)} = \frac{\dfrac{K}{s(s+b)}}{1 + \dfrac{K}{s(s+b)} \cdot 1} = \frac{K}{s^2 + bs + K}$$

The characteristic equation of the system is

$$s^2 + bs + K = 0$$

This second-order system is always stable for all positive values of b and K, but its dynamic behaviour is controlled by the roots of the characteristic equation and hence in turn by the magnitudes of b and K, since the roots are given by

$$s_1, s_2 = -\frac{b}{2} \pm \sqrt{\left(\frac{b}{2}\right)^2 - K} \qquad (6.1)$$

From Eq. (6.1), we can observe that the roots of the characteristic equation change as any one of the system parameters (b or K) varies. Consider that b is a constant and K is a variable. As the open-loop gain K is varied from zero to infinity, the two roots (s_1, s_2) describe a loci in the s-plane.

The root locations for various values of K are as follows:

1. $0 < K < \dfrac{b^2}{4}$, the roots are real and distinct. When $K = 0$, the two roots are $s_1 = 0$ and $s_2 = -b$, i.e. they coincide with the open-loop poles of the system.

2. $K = \dfrac{b^2}{4}$, the roots are real and equal in value, i.e. $s_1 = s_2 = -\dfrac{b}{2}$.

3. $\dfrac{b^2}{4} < K < \infty$, the roots are complex conjugate with real part $= -\dfrac{b}{2}$, i.e. unvarying real part.

The root locus with varying K is plotted in Figure 6.2. These loci give the following information about the system behaviour.

1. The root locus plot has two branches starting at the two open-loop poles ($s = 0$, and $s = -b$) for $K = 0$.

2. As K is increased from 0 to $b^2/4$, the roots move towards the point $(-b/2, 0)$ from opposite directions. Both the roots are real, negative, and unequal. They lie on the negative real axis which corresponds to an overdamped system. For $K = b^2/4$, the two roots meet at $s = -b/2$. So the roots are real, negative and equal. This corresponds to a critically-damped system. As K is increased further ($K > b^2/4$), the roots break away from the real axis, become complex conjugate and since the real part of both the roots remain fixed at $-b/2$, the roots move along the line $\sigma = -b/2$ and the system becomes underdamped.

3. For $K > b^2/4$, the real parts of the roots are fixed. Therefore, the settling time is nearly constant.

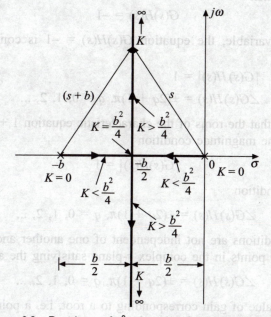

Figure 6.2 Root locus of $s^2 + bs + K = 0$ as a function of K.

The root locus shown in Figure 6.2 has been drawn by the direct solution of the characteristic equation. This procedure becomes tedious for third- and higher-order systems. Evans developed a graphical technique by using which the root locus can be constructed easily for third- and higher-order systems.

Consider the single-loop feedback system shown in Figure 6.3.

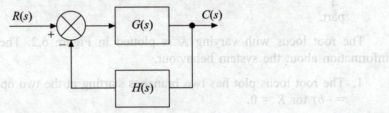

Figure 6.3 Single-loop feedback system.

Its closed-loop transfer function is

$$\frac{C(s)}{R(s)} = \frac{G(s)}{1 + G(s)H(s)}$$

The characteristic equation is

$$1 + G(s)H(s) = 0$$

The roots of the characteristic equation (i.e., the poles of the closed-loop system) occur only for those values of s for which

$$G(s)H(s) = -1$$

Since s is a complex variable, the equation $G(s)H(s) = -1$ is converted into two Evans conditions:

$$|G(s)H(s)| = 1$$

and

$$\angle G(s)H(s) = \pm(2q + 1)\pi, \; q = 0, 1, 2, \ldots$$

These conditions imply that the roots of the characteristic equation $1 + G(s)H(s) = 0$ are those values of s for which the magnitude condition

$$|G(s)H(s)| = 1$$

and the phase angle condition

$$\angle G(s)H(s) = \pm(2q + 1)\pi, \; q = 0, 1, 2, \ldots$$

are satisfied. These conditions are not independent of one another and one implies the other. Therefore, a plot of the points in the complex s-plane satisfying the angle criterion

$$\angle G(s)H(s) = \pm(2q + 1)\pi, \; q = 0, 1, 2, \ldots$$

is the root locus. The value of gain corresponding to a root, i.e. a point on the root locus can be determined from the magnitude criterion

$$|G(s)H(s)| = 1$$

The root locus can be quickly drawn by checking the angle criterion at various points of the s-plane.

Consider for example the feedback system of Figure 6.3 with

$$G(s) = \frac{K(s+a)}{s(s+b)}, H(s) = 1$$

Its characteristic equation is

$$1 + G(s)H(s) = 1 + G(s) = 0$$

The open-loop transfer function $G(s)H(s)$ has two poles at $s = 0$ and $s = -b$ and a zero at $s = -a$ as shown in Figure 6.4. The angle criterion for the root locus is

$$\angle G(s)H(s) = \angle \frac{(s+a)}{s(s+b)} = \pm(2q+1)\pi, q = 0, 1, 2, \ldots \tag{6.2}$$

With $s = \sigma + j\omega$, Eq. (6.2) becomes

$$\angle \frac{(s+a)}{s(s+b)} = \angle \frac{\sigma + j\omega + a}{(\sigma + j\omega)(\sigma + j\omega + b)}$$

Therefore,

$$\tan^{-1}\frac{\omega}{\sigma+a} - \tan^{-1}\frac{\omega}{\sigma} - \tan^{-1}\frac{\omega}{\sigma+b} = -\pi$$

or

$$\tan^{-1}\frac{\omega}{\sigma} + \tan^{-1}\frac{\omega}{\sigma+b} = \pi + \tan^{-1}\frac{\omega}{\sigma+a} \tag{6.3}$$

Taking tan on both sides of Eq. (6.3), we get

$$\frac{\dfrac{\omega}{\sigma}+\dfrac{\omega}{\sigma+b}}{1-\dfrac{\omega}{\sigma}\cdot\dfrac{\omega}{\sigma+b}} = \frac{\tan\pi + \dfrac{\omega}{\sigma+a}}{1-(\tan\pi)\left(\dfrac{\omega}{\sigma+a}\right)} = \frac{\omega}{\sigma+a}$$

i.e.

$$\frac{\omega(\sigma+b)+\omega\sigma}{\sigma(\sigma+b)-\omega^2} = \frac{\omega}{\sigma+a}$$

i.e.

$$\frac{2\sigma+b}{\sigma^2+\sigma b-\omega^2} = \frac{1}{\sigma+a}$$

i.e.

$$2\sigma^2 + 2\sigma a + \sigma b + ab = \sigma^2 + \sigma b - \omega^2$$

i.e.

$$\sigma^2 + 2\sigma a + \omega^2 = -ab$$

i.e.

$$(\sigma+a)^2 + \omega^2 = a^2 - ab = \left(\sqrt{a^2-ab}\right)^2 \tag{6.4}$$

Equation (6.4) is the equation for root locus in the s-plane. It is a circle centred at $(-a, 0)$, i.e. at the zero of the open-loop transfer function and radius $\left(\sqrt{a^2-ab}\right)$. The root locus is drawn in Figure 6.4.

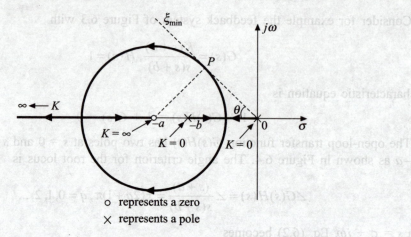

o represents a zero
× represents a pole

Figure 6.4   Root locus plot of a system with $G(s)H(s) = \dfrac{K(s+a)}{s(s+b)}$.

6.3   CONSTRUCTION OF ROOT LOCI

For the basic feedback system shown in Figure 6.3, the characteristic equation is

$$1 + G(s)H(s) = 0$$

The open-loop transfer function $G(s)H(s)$ is in factored form.

Let

$$G(s)H(s) = \frac{K(s+z_1)(s+z_2)...}{(s+p_1)(s+p_2)...} = \frac{K\prod_{i=1}^{m}(s+z_i)}{\prod_{j=1}^{n}(s+p_j)}$$

$$G(s)H(s) = -1$$

$$\therefore \qquad |G(s)H(s)| = 1$$

and

$$\angle G(s)H(s) = \pm(2q+1)\pi$$

$$\therefore \qquad \frac{K\prod_{i=1}^{m}(s+z_i)}{\prod_{j=1}^{n}(s+p_j)} = 1$$

or

$$K = \frac{\prod_{j=1}^{n}(s+p_j)}{\prod_{i=1}^{m}(s+z_i)}$$

$$\sum_{i=1}^{m}\angle(s+z_i) - \sum_{j=1}^{n}\angle(s+p_j) = \pm(2q+1)\pi; \quad q = 0, 1, 2, ...$$

An exact method of drawing the root locus is to locate a number of points in the s-plane where the phase angle criterion is satisfied and to draw a smooth curve passing through those points. The value of K at any point s_0 on the root locus can be found out by using the magnitude criterion.

$$K = \frac{\prod_{j=1}^{n}(s_0 + p_j)}{\prod_{i=1}^{m}(s_0 + z_i)}$$

i.e. $$K = \frac{\text{product of phasor lengths from } s_0 \text{ to the open-loop poles}}{\text{product of phasor lengths from } s_0 \text{ to the open-loop zeros}}$$

An approximate sketch of the root locus can be obtained by following certain rules called the rules for the construction of the root locus. This approximate root locus sketch is very useful in visualizing the effects of variation of system gain K, the effects of shifting pole-zero locations and bringing in a new set of poles and zeros.

6.4 RULES FOR THE CONSTRUCTION OF THE ROOT LOCUS

Rule 1. The root locus is symmetrical about the real axis.

The poles and zeros of any physically realizable closed-loop system are either real or complex conjugate or combinations of both, i.e. the pole-zero location is symmetrical with respect to the real axis of the s-plane. So the root locus must be symmetrical with respect to the real axis of the s-plane.

Rule 2. At the open-loop poles, $K = 0$ and at the open-loop zeros, $K = \infty$.

As the open-loop gain K is varied from zero to infinity, each branch of the root locus originates from an open-loop pole where $K = 0$ and terminates on an open-loop zero or zero at infinity where $K = \infty$. The number of branches of root locus terminating on infinity equals the number of open-loop poles minus zeros.

The open-loop transfer function of the system is

$$G(s)H(s) = \frac{K(s + z_1)(s + z_2)...}{(s + p_1)(s + p_2)...} = \frac{K \prod_{i=1}^{m}(s + z_i)}{\prod_{j=1}^{n}(s + p_j)}$$

Therefore the characteristic equation is

$$1 + G(s)H(s) = 0$$

i.e. $$\prod_{j=1}^{n}(s + p_j) + K \prod_{i=1}^{m}(s + z_i) = 0 \qquad (6.5)$$

When $K = 0$, Eq. (6.5) has roots at $s = -p_j (j = 1, 2,..., n)$ which are the open-loop poles. The root locus branches therefore start at the open-loop poles.

The characteristic equation can also be written as

$$\frac{1}{K} \prod_{j=1}^{n}(s + p_j) + \prod_{i=1}^{m}(s + z_i) = 0 \qquad (6.6)$$

When $K = \infty$, the first term of Eq. (6.6) becomes zero and the roots are located at $s = -z_i (i = 1, 2, ..., m)$ which are the given zeros of the system. Therefore, m branches of the root locus terminate on the open-loop zeros.

In case $n > m$, the open-loop transfer function has $(n - m)$ zeros at infinity and $(n - m)$ branches of the root locus terminate on these zeros.

Rule 3. *Segments of the real axis having an odd number of real axis open-loop poles and zeros to their right are parts of the root locus.*

Each pole and zero on the real axis to the right of any point on the real axis contribute an angle of 180° with respect to that point and each pole and zero on the real axis to the left of any point on the real axis contribute an angle of 0° with respect to that point. The net angle contribution of a complex conjugate pole or a zero is always zero. Figure 6.5 shows the angle contributions for a point on the real axis.

For the root locus to exist at any point in the s-plane the phase angle condition, i.e. $\angle G(s)H(s) = \pm(2q + 1)\pi$ must be satisfied. This condition can be satisfied at any point on the real axis only if the total number of open-loop poles and zeros to the right of that point is odd.

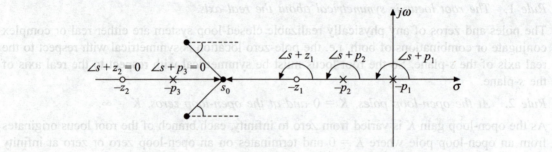

Figure 6.5 Angle contributions for a point on the real axis.

Example 6.1 Consider the system with the following open-loop transfer function:

$$G(s)H(s) = \frac{K(s + 3)(s + 4)}{(s + 1)(s + 5)(s + 6)}$$

Draw a root locus plot for it.

Solution: Using the above three rules, the root locus plot can be drawn as shown in Figure 6.6.

1. All the open-loop poles and zeros are on the real axis. So the root locus will be symmetrical with respect to the real axis.

2. There are three branches of the root locus (equal to the number of open-loop poles). These root locus branches start at the open-loop poles $s = -1$, $s = -5$, and $s = -6$ where $K = 0$.

   As K increases, the root locus branches leave the open-loop poles and go to the open-loop zeros. Two branches terminate on the two open-loop zeros ($s = -3$, $s = -4$) and the third one terminates on infinity.

3. The real axis segments between $s = -1$ and $s = -3$, $s = -4$ and $s = -5$, and $s = -6$ and $s = -\infty$ lie on the root locus (shown by thick lines in Figure 6.6).

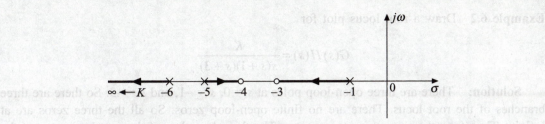

Figure 6.6   Example 6.1: Root locus on the real axis.

Rule 4.   The (n − m) branches of the root locus which go to infinity travel along straight line asymptotes whose angles are given by

$$\theta_q = \pm \frac{(2q+1)\pi}{n-m}; q = 0, 1, 2, ..., (n - m - 1)$$

Consider any point on a branch of the root locus which is far away from the open-loop poles and zeros. The phasors drawn from such a point to all the open poles and zeros make the same angle θ to each open-loop pole and zero.

Therefore, at the point considered

$$\angle G(s)H(s) = -(n - m)\theta$$

For the root locus to exist at this point

$$-(n - m)\theta = \pm(2q + 1)\pi$$

Since the $(n - m)$ branches of the root locus go to the zeros at infinity, the angles of the asymptotes are

$$\theta_q = \frac{\pm(2q+1)\pi}{n-m}; q = 0, 1, 2, ..., (n - m - 1)$$

Rule 5.   The asymptotes cross the real axis at a point known as centroid determined by the relationship.

$$\text{Centroid} = -\sigma = \frac{\text{sum of real parts of poles} - \text{sum of real parts of zeros}}{\text{number of poles} - \text{number of zeros}}$$

Rule 6.   The breakaway points and break-in points (points at which multiple roots of the characteristic equation exist)of the root locus are the solutions of

$$\frac{dK}{ds} = 0$$

The breakaway point and break-in point may be real or complex.

Break angles: The root locus branches must approach or leave the breakaway point on the real axis at an angle of $\pm \dfrac{180°}{r}$ where r is the number of branches approaching or leaving the break point.

Example 6.2   Draw a root locus plot for

$$G(s)H(s) = \frac{K}{s(s+1)(s+3)}$$

Solution: There are three open-loop poles at $s = 0$, $s = -1$, and $s = -3$. So there are three branches of the root locus. There are no finite open-loop zeros. So all the three zeros are at infinity. Therefore, there are three asymptotes. The three branches of the root locus start at the open-loop poles $s = 0$, $s = -1$, and $s = -3$ where $K = 0$ and terminate at the open-loop zeros at infinity where $K = \infty$.

The three branches of the root locus go to the zeros at infinity along straight line asymptotes making angles of

$$\theta_q = \frac{(2q+1)\pi}{(3-0)}; q = 0, 1, 2$$

i.e. $\qquad \theta_0 = \frac{\pi}{3} = 60°, \theta_1 = \frac{3\pi}{3} = 180°, \theta_3 = \frac{5\pi}{3} = 300°$

with the real axis.

The point of intersection of the asymptotes on the real axis called *centroid* is given by

$$-\sigma = \frac{\text{sum of real parts of poles} - \text{sum of real parts of zeros}}{\text{number of poles} - \text{number of zeros}}$$

i.e. $\qquad -\sigma = \frac{(0-1-3)-(0)}{3-0} = -1.33$

The root locus exists on the real axis between $s = 0$ to $s = -1$ and from $s = -3$ to $-\infty$.

The break points are given by the solution of $\dfrac{dK}{ds} = 0$.

$$1 + G(s)H(s) = 0$$

$$\therefore \qquad |G(s)H(s)| = 1$$

i.e. $\qquad \left| \dfrac{K}{s(s+1)(s+3)} \right| = 1$

$$\therefore \qquad K = s(s+1)(s+3) = s^3 + 4s^2 + 3s$$

$$\frac{dK}{ds} = \frac{d}{ds}(s^3 + 4s^2 + 3s) = 3s^2 + 8s + 3 = 0$$

$$\therefore \qquad s = \frac{-8 \pm \sqrt{8^2 - 4 \times 3 \times 3}}{2 \times 3} = \frac{-8 \pm \sqrt{28}}{6} = -0.451 \text{ or } -2.28$$

Out of these two break points, $s = -0.451$ is the actual break point and $s = -2.28$ break point can be ignored as no root locus exists there.

The root locus for the open-loop transfer function

$$G(s)H(s) = \frac{K}{s(s+1)(s+3)}$$

is shown in Figure 6.7. The remaining part of the root locus is drawn based on the rules to be discussed later. Out of the three branches of the root locus, one is the real root locus branch. It starts at $s = -3$, travels along the negative real axis along the asymptote with 180° and ends at $s = -\infty$. The other two branches of the root locus start at $s = 0$ and $s = -1$, move in opposite directions on the negative real axis approaching each other, meet at point $s = -0.451$ called the breakaway point, breakaway from the real axis, enter the complex plane and then one branch moves to infinity along the 60° asymptote and the second one moves to infinity along the 300° asymptote. The branches which represent the complex roots are known as *complex root branches*.

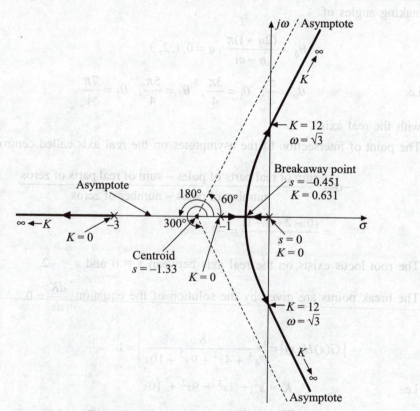

Figure 6.7 Example 6.2: Root locus plot.

Complex breakaway points: The application of the equation $\dfrac{dK}{ds} = 0$, for evaluation of complex breakaway points is illustrated in Example 6.3.

Example 6.3   Sketch the root locus of the open-loop transfer function given below.

$$G(s)H(s) = \frac{K}{s(s+2)(s^2+2s+5)}$$

Solution: The open-loop pole-zero configuration is shown in Figure 6.8. From the rules described so far, the following information concerning the root locus plot is obtained.

1. There are four open-loop poles. So there are four branches of the root locus originating at the open-loop poles $s = 0$, $s = -2$, $s = -1 + j2$, and $s = -1 - j2$, respectively where $K = 0$. Since there are no open-loop zeros in the finite region, all the four branches of the root locus terminate at the open-loop zeros at infinity where $K = \infty$.

2. The four branches of the root locus travel to the zeros at infinity along asymptotes making angles of

$$\theta_q = \frac{(2q+1)\pi}{n-m}, q = 0, 1, 2, 3$$

   i.e. $$\theta_0 = \frac{\pi}{4}, \quad \theta_1 = \frac{3\pi}{4}, \quad \theta_2 = \frac{5\pi}{4}, \quad \theta_3 = \frac{7\pi}{4}$$

   with the real axis.

3. The point of intersection of the asymptotes on the real axis called centroid is given by

$$-\sigma = \frac{\text{sum of real parts of poles} - \text{sum of real parts of zeros}}{\text{number of poles} - \text{number of zeros}}$$

$$= \frac{(0-2-1-1)}{4} = -1$$

4. The root locus exists on the real axis between $s = 0$ and $s = -2$.

5. The break points are given by the solution of the equation $\dfrac{dK}{ds} = 0$.

$$|G(s)H(s)| = \left| \frac{K}{s^4 + 4s^3 + 9s^2 + 10s} \right| = 1$$

   i.e. $$K = s^4 + 4s^3 + 9s^2 + 10s$$

   $\therefore$ $$\frac{dK}{ds} = (4s^3 + 12s^2 + 18s + 10) = 0$$

   i.e. $$(s+1)(s^2 + 2s + 2.5) = 0$$

   i.e. $$(s+1)(s+1+j1.225)(s+1-j1.225) = 0$$

Therefore, the break points are $s = -1$, $s = -1 - j1.225$ and $s = -1 + j1.225$.

All the three are valid break points. There is one real breakaway point and two complex breakaway points. The complete root locus is shown in Figure 6.8. The remaining calculations are based on the rules to be discussed hereafter.

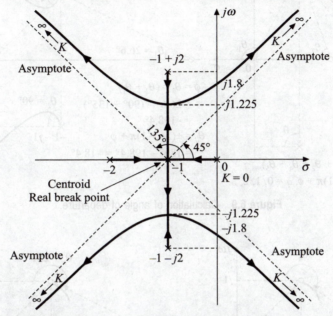

Figure 6.8 Example 6.3: Root locus plot with complex break points.

Rule 7. The angle of departure from an open-loop pole is given by

$$\theta_d = \pm(2q + 1)\pi + \phi; \quad q = 0, 1, 2, \ldots$$

where ϕ is the net angle contribution at this open-loop pole, of all other open-loop poles and zeros.

Similarly, *the angle of arrival at an open-loop zero is given by*

$$\theta_a = \pm(2q + 1)\pi - \phi; \quad q = 0, 1, 2, \ldots$$

where ϕ is the net angle contribution at this open-loop zero, of all other open-loop poles and zeros.

The angle of departure and the angle of arrival need to be calculated only when there are complex poles and zeros. The angle of departure from a real open-loop pole and the angle of arrival at a real open-loop zero is always equal to $0°$ or $180°$.

Figure 6.9 illustrates the calculation of angle of departure and Figure 6.10 illustrates the calculation of angle of arrival.

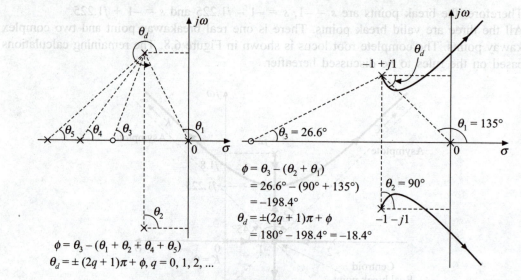

Figure 6.9 Calculation of angle of departure.

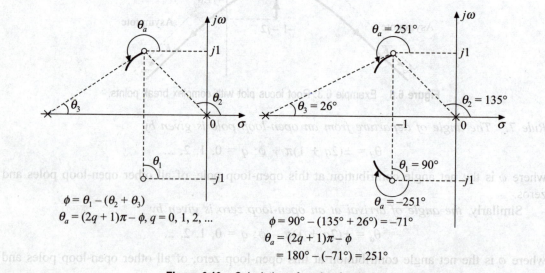

Figure 6.10 Calculation of angle of arrival.

Rule 8. *The point of intersection of the root locus branches with the imaginary axis and the critical value of K can be determined by use of the Routh criterion.*

This rule is simply an application of the Routh criterion discussed earlier. For illustration, consider the system in Example 6.2, i.e.

$$G(s)H(s) = \frac{K}{s(s+1)(s+3)}$$

Therefore, the characteristic equation of the system is given by

$$s^3 + 4s^2 + 3s + K = 0$$

Application of the Routh criterion to the above equation gives the following Routh array:

$$
\begin{array}{lll}
s^3 & 1 & 3 \\
s^2 & 4 & K \\
s^1 & \dfrac{12 - K}{4} & \\
s^0 & K &
\end{array}
$$

For all the roots of the characteristic equation to lie to the left of the imaginary axis, the following conditions should be satisfied:

$$K > 0$$

$$\frac{12 - K}{4} > 0$$

i.e.

$$K < 12$$

The critical value of K (which corresponds to location of roots on $j\omega$-axis) is given by

$$\frac{12 - K}{4} = 0$$

or

$$K = 12$$

The value of $K = 12$, makes all the coefficients of the s^1 row of the Routh array zero. For this value of K, the auxiliary equation formed from the coefficients of the s^2 row is given by

$$4s^2 + K = 0$$

For $K = 12$, the roots of the above equation lie on the $j\omega$-axis and are given by

$$4s^2 + 12 = 0$$

i.e.

$$s^2 = -3$$

or

$$s = \pm j\sqrt{3} = \pm j1.73$$

Thus, for the root locus plot shown in Figure 6.7, the branches intersect the $j\omega$-axis at $s = \pm j\sqrt{3}$ and the value of K corresponding to these roots is 12.

Alternative way: The point of intersection of the root locus branches with the imaginary axis and the critical value of K can also be obtained by letting $s = j\omega$ in the characteristic equation and equating the real part and imaginary part to zero, and solving for ω and K. The value of ω is the intersection point on the imaginary axis and K is the value of gain at the intersection point (i.e. the marginal value of K, i.e. K_m).

Considering the above example itself, the characteristic equation is

$$s^3 + 4s^2 + 3s + K = 0$$

Substituting $s = j\omega$ in the above equation, we get

$$(j\omega)^3 + 4(j\omega)^2 + 3(j\omega) + K = 0$$

i.e.
$$-j\omega^3 - 4\omega^2 + 3j\omega + K = 0$$

Equating the imaginary part to zero, we get

$$-j(\omega^3 - 3\omega) = 0$$

i.e.
$$\omega^2 - 3 = 0$$

or
$$\omega = \pm j\sqrt{3}$$

Equating the real part to zero, we get

$$K - 4\omega^2 = 0$$

$\therefore$
$$K = 4\omega^2 = 4 \times 3 = 12$$

The values of ω and K are the same as obtained earlier.

Rule 9.   *The value of the open-loop gain K at any point s_0 on the root locus is given by*

$$K = \frac{\text{product of lengths of vectors drawn from that point } s_0 \text{ to all the open-loop poles}}{\text{product of lengths of vectors drawn from that point } s_0 \text{ to all the open-loop zeros}}$$

The characteristic equation is given by

$$1 + G(s)H(s) = 0$$

$\therefore$
$$|G(s)H(s)| = 1$$

i.e.
$$\left| \frac{K(s + z_1)(s + z_2)...}{(s + p_1)(s + p_2)...} \right| = 1$$

$\therefore$
$$|K| = \frac{(s + p_1)(s + p_2)...}{(s + z_1)(s + z_2)...} = \frac{\prod_{j=1}^{n}(s + p_j)}{\prod_{i=1}^{m}(s + z_i)}$$

$$= \frac{\text{product of phasor lengths from } s_0 \text{ to open-loop poles}}{\text{product of phasor lengths from } s_0 \text{ to open-loop zeros}}$$

The rules described above are useful in determining the general configuration of the root locus and are summarized in Table 6.1.

Table 6.1 Rules for construction of root loci of $1 + G(s)H(s) = 0$, where the open-loop transfer function $G(s)H(s)$ is known in pole-zero form with n = number of open-loop poles and m = number of open-loop zeros.

S. No.	Rule
1.	The root locus is symmetrical about the real axis.
2.	Each branch of the root locus originates from an open-loop pole where $K = 0$, and terminates on an open-loop zero or on infinity where $K = \infty$. The number of branches of the root locus terminating on infinity is equal to $n - m$, i.e. the number of open-loop poles minus the number open-loop zeros.
3.	Segments of the real axis having an odd number of real axis open-loop poles plus zeros to their right are parts of the root locus.
4.	The $(n - m)$ root locus branches that tend to infinity do so along straight line asymptotes making angles with the real axis given by $$\theta_q = \frac{(2q+1)\pi}{n-m}; q = 0, 1, 2, ..., (n-m-1)$$
5.	The point of intersection of the asymptotes with the real axis called centroid is at $s = -\sigma$ where $$-\sigma = \frac{\text{sum of real parts of poles} - \text{sum of real parts of zeros}}{\text{number of poles} - \text{number of zeros}}$$
6.	The break points (breakaway and break-in points) of the root locus are determined from the roots of the equation $\dfrac{dK}{ds} = 0$. r branches of the root locus which meet at a point break away at an angle of $$\pm \frac{180°}{r}$$
7.	The angle of departure from an open-loop pole is given by $$\theta_d = \pm(2q + 1)\pi + \phi; q = 0, 1, 2, ...$$ where ϕ is the net angle contribution at the pole, of all other open-loop poles and zeros. Similarly, the angle of arrival at an open-loop zero is given by $$\theta_a = \pm(2q + 1)\pi - \phi; q = 0, 1, 2, ...$$ where ϕ is the net angle contribution at the zero, of all other open-loop poles and zeros.
8.	The point of intersection of the root locus branches with the imaginary axis and the critical value of K can be determined by use of the Routh criterion.
9.	The open-loop gain K in pole-zero form at any point s_0 on the root locus is given by $$K = \frac{\text{product of phasor lengths from } s_0 \text{ to open-loop poles}}{\text{product of phasor lengths from } s_0 \text{ to open-loop zeros}}$$

6.4.1 Determination of Roots for a Specified Open-Loop Gain

Along a particular root locus branch, a region is determined by trial and error such that the values of the open-loop gain (calculated by the magnitude criterion) at various points of the region are close to specified value. Further trial and error will then yield the root location.

The above procedure is repeated for each root locus branch.

6.4.2 Determination of Open-Loop Gain for a Specified Damping of Dominant Roots

The dominant poles are a pair of complex conjugate poles which decide the transient response of the system. In higher-order systems, the dominant poles are given by the poles which are very close to the origin, provided all other poles are lying far away from the dominant poles. The poles which are far away from the origin will have less effect on the transient response.

To fix a dominant pole on the root locus, draw a constant ξ line making an angle of $\theta = \cos^{-1} \xi$ with the negative real axis. The point of intersection of this line with the root locus will give the location of the dominant pole. The value of K corresponding to this dominant pole can be obtained from the magnitude condition.

6.5 EFFECT OF ADDING POLES AND ZEROS TO $G(s)H(s)$

The general problem of controller design in control systems may be treated as an investigation of the effects to the root loci when poles and zeros are added to the loop transfer function $G(s)H(s)$.

6.5.1 Addition of Poles to $G(s)H(s)$

Adding a pole to $G(s)H(s)$ has the effect of pushing the root loci towards the right half. The complex path of the root loci bends to the right, the angle of asymptotes reduces and the centroid is shifted to the left, and the system stability will be reduced. Even a system which was perfectly stable may become unstable as K increases.

In general, we can say that the addition of poles to $G(s)H(s)$ has the effect of moving the dominant portion of the root loci towards the right half of the s-plane. So the relative stability of the system is decreased by the addition of a pole.

6.5.2 Addition of Zeros to $G(s)H(s)$

Adding left-half plane zeros to the function $G(s)H(s)$ generally has the effect of moving and bending the root loci towards the left-half of the s-plane. So the relative stability of the system is improved by the addition of a zero.

Example 6.4   Sketch the root locus plot for the system given below with K as a variable parameter and show that the loci of complex roots are part of a circle with $(-1, 0)$ as centre and radius = $\sqrt{2}$. Is the system stable for all values of K? If not, determine the range of K for stable system operation. Find also the marginal value of K which causes sustained oscillations and the frequency of these oscillations. From the root locus plot, determine the value of K such that the resulting system has a settling time of 4 seconds. What are the corresponding values of the roots?

$$G(s)H(s) = \frac{K(s+1)}{s(s-1)}$$

Solution: For the given open-loop transfer function $G(s)H(s)$:

The open-loop poles are at $s = 0$, $s = 1$. Therefore, $n = 2$.

The open-loop zero is at $s = -1$. Therefore, $m = 1$.

Thus, the number of branches of root locus $n = 2$ and the number of asymptotes $n - m = 2 - 1 = 1$.

The complete root locus is drawn as shown in Figure 6.11, as per the rules given as follows:

1. All the open-loop poles and zeros are on the real axis only. Therefore, the root locus is symmetrical about the real axis.

2. The two branches of the root locus start at the open-loop poles $s = 0$ and $s = 1$, where $K = 0$, and terminate on the open-loop zeros at $s = -1$ and $s = \infty$, where $K = \infty$.

3. One branch of the root locus travels to the zero at infinity along a straight line asymptote drawn at an angle of

$$\theta_q = \frac{(2q+1)\pi}{n-m}, q = 0$$

That is, the angle of the asymptote is

$$\theta_0 = \frac{\pi}{1} = 180°$$

4. The point of intersection of the asymptotes on the real axis (centroid) is given by

$$-\sigma = \frac{\text{sum of real parts of poles} - \text{sum of real parts of zeros}}{\text{number of poles} - \text{number of zeros}} = \frac{(0+1)-(-1)}{2-1} = 2$$

5. The root locus exists on the real axis between $s = 1$ to $s = 0$ and to the left of $s = -1$.

6. The breakaway and break-in points are given by the solution of the equation $\dfrac{dK}{ds} = 0$.

Therefore, $\quad |G(s)H(s)| = \left| \dfrac{K(s+1)}{s(s-1)} \right| = 1$

$\therefore \quad\quad\quad K = \dfrac{s(s-1)}{(s+1)}$

i.e. $\quad\quad\quad \dfrac{dK}{ds} = \dfrac{d}{ds}\left[\dfrac{s(s-1)}{(s+1)} \right] = (s+1)(2s-1) - s(s-1)(1) = 0$

i.e. $\quad\quad\quad s^2 + 2s - 1 = 0$

Therefore, the break points are at

$$s = \frac{-2 \pm \sqrt{4+4}}{2} = -1 \pm \sqrt{2} = 0.414 \text{ and } -2.414$$

$s = 0.414$ is a breakaway point and $s = -2.414$ is a break-in point.

The break angles at $s = 0.414$ and at $s = -2.414$ are

$$\pm \frac{\pi}{r} = \pm \frac{180°}{2} = \pm 90°$$

7. There is no need to calculate the angle of departure and the angle of arrival, because the open-loop transfer function has no complex poles and zeros.

8. The point of intersection of the root locus with the imaginary axis and the critical value of K are determined by using the Routh criterion. The characteristic equation is

$$1 + G(s)H(s) = 0$$

i.e. $$1 + \frac{K(s+1)}{s(s-1)} = 0 \quad \text{i.e.} \quad s^2 + (K-1)s + K = 0$$

The Routh table is

s^2	1	K
s^1	$K-1$	
s^0	K	

For stability, all the elements in the first column of the Routh array must be positive. Therefore, $K > 0$ and $K - 1 > 0$, i.e. $K > 1$. So the system is not stable for all values of K. The marginal value of K for stability is

$$K_m = 1$$

The range of values of K for stable system operation is

$$1 < K < \infty$$

The frequency of the sustained oscillations is given by the solution of the auxiliary equation.

$$A(s) = s^2 + K = 0$$

i.e. $$s^2 + K_m = 0$$

i.e. $$s^2 + 1 = 0$$

i.e. $$s = \pm j1$$

Therefore, the root locus intersects the imaginary axis at $s = \pm j1$. Hence, the frequency of sustained oscillations is $\omega = 1$ rad/s.

Alternative way: The characteristic equation is

$$s^2 + (K - 1)s + K = 0$$

Substituting $s = j\omega$ in the characteristic equation, we have

$$(j\omega)^2 + (K - 1)j\omega + K = 0$$

i.e. $$-\omega^2 + K + j\omega(K - 1)$$

On equating the imaginary part to zero, we get

$$\omega(K - 1) = 0; \quad \omega \neq 0$$

$\therefore \qquad\qquad K = 1$

On equating the real part to zero, we get

$$-\omega^2 + K = 0$$

i.e. $\qquad\qquad \omega^2 = K$

$\therefore \qquad\qquad \omega = \sqrt{K} = 1 \text{ rad/s}$

The values of ω and K obtained are the same as got earlier.

The complete root locus sketch is shown in Figure 6.11. The root locus has two branches. One branch starts at $s = 1$ and travels to the left, the other one starts at $s = 0$ and travels to the right. Both meet at $s = 0.414$, break away, enter the complex plane and travel along the circle, meet and break-in on the real axis at $s = -2.414$ and afterwards one branch travels to the right on the real axis and ends at $s = -1$, and the other one travels to the left on the real axis along the asymptote at $180°$ and ends at $s = -\infty$.

To determine the value of K such that the resulting system has a settling time of 4 seconds, first locate the point on the negative real axis which gives the real part $(\xi\omega_n)$ of the complex pole which results in a settling time of 4 seconds.

$$t_s = \frac{4}{\xi\omega_n}$$

$\therefore \qquad\qquad \xi\omega_n = \frac{4}{t_s} = \frac{4}{4} = 1 \text{ s}$

With real part $= -\xi\omega_n$, locate the two complex poles and determine the value of K at those poles using the magnitude condition. From Figure 6.11 the roots are $s_1 = -1 + j1.414$ and $s_2 = -1 - j1.414$.

The value of K at $s = -1 + j1.414$ or at $s = -1 - j1.414$, i.e. for $t_s = 4\text{s}$ is

$$K = \frac{xy}{z} = \frac{2.45 \times 1.75}{1.44} = 2.977$$

To determine the loci of complex roots, apply the angle condition, i.e.

$$\angle G(s) = \angle \frac{K(s+1)}{s(s-1)} = \pm(2q+1)\pi$$

Substituting $s = \sigma + j\omega$ in the above equation,

$$\angle G(s) = \angle \frac{K[(\sigma + j\omega) + 1]}{(\sigma + j\omega)(\sigma + j\omega - 1)}$$

$$= \angle K + \angle \sigma + j\omega + 1 - \angle \sigma + j\omega - \angle \sigma + j\omega - 1 = \pm(2q + 1)\pi$$

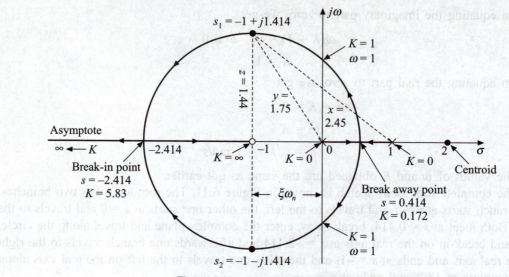

Figure 6.11   Example 6.4: Root locus.

$$\therefore \qquad \tan^{-1}\frac{\omega}{\sigma+1} - \tan\frac{\omega}{\sigma} - \tan^{-1}\frac{\omega}{\sigma-1} = -\pi$$

i.e.

$$\pi + \tan^{-1}\frac{\omega}{\sigma+1} = \tan^{-1}\frac{\omega}{\sigma} + \tan^{-1}\frac{\omega}{\sigma-1}$$

Taking tangent on both sides,

$$\frac{\tan\pi + \dfrac{\omega}{\sigma+1}}{1 - \tan\pi \cdot \dfrac{\omega}{\sigma+1}} = \frac{\dfrac{\omega}{\sigma} + \dfrac{\omega}{\sigma-1}}{1 - \dfrac{\omega}{\sigma}\cdot\dfrac{\omega}{\sigma-1}}$$

i.e.

$$\frac{\omega}{\sigma+1} = \frac{\omega(\sigma-1+\sigma)}{\sigma(\sigma-1)-\omega^2}$$

i.e.

$$\sigma(\sigma-1) - \omega^2 = (\sigma+1)(2\sigma-1)$$

i.e.

$$\sigma^2 - \sigma - \omega^2 = 2\sigma^2 + \sigma - 1$$

i.e.

$$\sigma^2 + 2\sigma + 1 + \omega^2 - 2 = 0$$

i.e.

$$(\sigma+1)^2 + \omega^2 = (\sqrt{2})^2$$

This shows that the loci of complex roots are part of a circle with center at (–1, 0) and radius = $\sqrt{2}$.

Example 6.5 Draw the complete root locus for

$$G(s)H(s) = \frac{K}{s(s+2)(s+4)}$$

From the root locus plot, find the range of values of K for which the system will have damped oscillatory response. Also, determine the value of K for a damping ratio of $\xi = 0.5$. With this value of K, find the closed-loop transfer function.

Solution: For the given open-loop transfer function $G(s)H(s)$:

The open-loop poles are at $s = 0$, $s = -2$ and $s = -4$. Therefore, $n = 3$.

There are no finite open-loop zeros. Therefore, $m = 0$.

So the number of branches of root locus $n = 3$ and the number of asymptotes $n - m = 3 - 0 = 3$.

The complete root locus is drawn as shown in Figure 6.12, as per the rules given below.

1. All the open-loop poles and zeros are on the real axis only. So the root locus will be symmetrical about the real axis.

2. The three branches of the root locus start at the open-loop poles $s = 0$, $s = -2$ and $s = -4$, where $K = 0$ and terminate at the zeros at infinity, where $K = \infty$.

3. There are three asymptotes, and the angles of the asymptotes are given by

$$\theta_q = \frac{(2q+1)\pi}{n-m}, q = 0, 1, 2$$

i.e. $$\theta_0 = \frac{\pi}{3}, \quad \theta_1 = \frac{3\pi}{3} = \pi, \quad \theta_2 = \frac{5\pi}{3}$$

4. The point of intersection of the asymptotes on the real axis (centroid) is given by

$$-\sigma = \frac{\text{sum of real parts of poles} - \text{sum of real parts of zeros}}{\text{number of poles} - \text{number of zeros}} = \frac{(0-2-4)-(0)}{3-0} = -2$$

5. The root locus exists on the real axis from $s = 0$ to $s = -2$ and to the left of $s = -4$.

6. The breakaway points are given by the solution of the equation $\dfrac{dK}{ds} = 0$.

$$|G(s)H(s)| = \left| \frac{K}{s(s+2)(s+4)} \right| = 1$$

$\therefore$ $$K = s(s+2)(s+4)$$

i.e. $$\frac{d}{ds}[s(s+2)(s+4)] = 0$$

$$\frac{d}{ds}(s^3 + 6s^2 + 8s) = 3s^2 + 12s + 8 = 0$$

i.e.
$$s = \frac{-12 \pm \sqrt{144 - 96}}{6} = -2 \pm \sqrt{\frac{48}{36}} = -2 \pm 1.15$$

Therefore, the break points are $s = -3.15$ and $s = -0.85$. Out of these two, $s = -0.85$ is the actual break point because the root locus exists there. $s = -3.15$ is not an actual break point because the root locus does not exist there, and so it can be ignored. The break angles at $s = -0.85$ are

$$\pm \frac{\pi}{r} = \pm \frac{180°}{2} = \pm 90°$$

7. There is no need to compute the angles of departure and arrival as there are no complex poles and zeros.

8. The point of intersection of the root locus with the imaginary axis, and the marginal value of K can be determined by applying the Routh criterion. The characteristic equation is

$$1 + G(s)H(s) = 1 + \frac{K}{s(s+2)(s+4)}$$

i.e.
$$s^3 + 6s^2 + 8s + K = 0$$

The Routh table is as follows:

s^3	1	8
s^2	6	K
s^1	$\dfrac{48 - K}{6}$	0
s^0	K	

For stability, all the elements in the first column of the Routh array must be positive. Therefore,

$$K > 0$$

and
$$48 - K > 0$$

i.e.
$$K < 48$$

Therefore, the range of values of K for stability is

$$0 < K < 48$$

The marginal value of K for stability is $K_m = 48$. The frequency of sustained oscillations is given by the solution of the auxiliary equation.

$$6s^2 + K = 0$$

i.e.
$$6s^2 + K_m = 0$$

i.e.
$$6s^2 + 48 = 0$$

∴
$$s^2 = -8$$

or
$$s = \pm j\sqrt{8} = \pm j2.828$$

Therefore, the frequency of sustained oscillations is $\omega = 2.828$ rad/s.

Alternative way: The characteristic equation is given by

$$s^3 + 6s^2 + 8s + K = 0$$

Substituting $s = j\omega$ in the above equation, we get

$$(j\omega)^3 + 6(j\omega)^2 + 8(j\omega) + K = 0$$

i.e.
$$-j\omega^3 - 6\omega^2 + j8\omega + K = 0$$

Equating the imaginary part to zero, we get

$$-\omega^3 + 8\omega = 0$$

∴
$$\omega^2 = 8$$

or
$$\omega = \sqrt{8} = 2.828 \text{ rad/s}$$

Equating the real part to zero, we get

$$K - 6\omega^2 = 0$$

∴
$$K = 6\omega^2 = 6 \times 8 = 48$$

The values of ω and K are the same as obtained earlier.

The complete root locus sketch is shown in Figure 6.12. The root locus has three branches. The branch starting at $s = -4$ travels to the left on the negative real axis and terminates at $s = -\infty$. The branch starting at $s = 0$ moves to the left, the branch starting at $s = -2$ moves to the right, both meet at $s = -0.85$ (break point) break away and enter the complex plane and cross the imaginary axis at $\omega = \pm 2.828$ with $K = 48$, cross over to the right-half of the s-plane and travel along the asymptotes at $60°$ and $300°$ and terminate at $s = \infty$.

For damped oscillatory response, the dominant poles must be complex conjugate of each other. The value of K at the break point can be determined by using the magnitude condition. So,

$$K \text{ (at break point)} = 0.85 \times 1.15 \times 3.15 = 3.08$$

The difference between the values of K at the break point and at the point of intersection of the root locus with the imaginary axis gives the range of K for which the system has damped oscillatory response. From the graph it is

$$3.08 < K < 48$$

To find the value of K for $\xi = 0.5$,

$$\theta = \cos^{-1} \xi = \cos^{-1} 0.5 = 60°$$

Draw a line making an angle of $\theta = 60°$ with respect to the negative real axis. Let it intersect the root locus at A. Since there are no open-loop zeros, the product of phasor lengths drawn from A to all the open-loop poles gives the value of K at A. Therefore, K for $\xi = 0.5$ is

$$K = xyz = 1.3 \times 1.8 \times 3.5 = 8.19$$

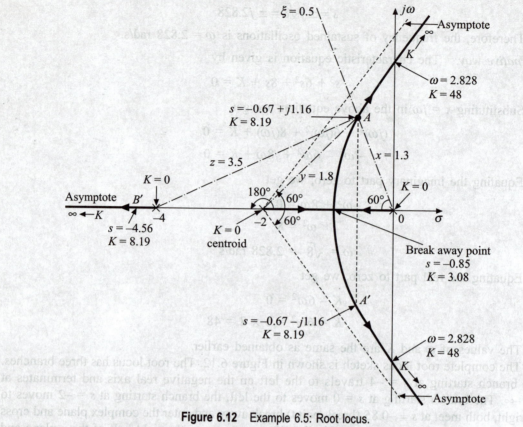

Figure 6.12 Example 6.5: Root locus.

To determine the closed-loop transfer function for $\xi = 0.5$, find K for $\xi = 0.5$ and locate the pair of complex poles at the point of intersection of constant ξ ($\xi = 0.5$) line with the root locus. From the root locus plot, it is $-0.67 + j1.16$. The second root is the conjugate of the first one. So it is $-0.67 - j1.16$. The third root will lie on the third branch of the root locus and can be determined by trial and error method (satisfying the magnitude condition). From the root locus plot it is $s = -4.56$ at B'. Therefore, the closed-loop transfer function is

$$\frac{C(s)}{R(s)} = \frac{8.19}{(s + 0.67 + j1.16)(s + 0.67 - j1.16)(s + 4.56)}$$

Example 6.6 A unity feedback system has an open-loop transfer function

$$G(s)H(s) = \frac{K}{s^2(s + 2)}$$

(a) By sketching a root locus plot, show that the system is unstable for all values of K.

(b) Add a zero at $s = -a$ ($0 \leq a < 2$) and show that the addition of a zero stabilizes the system.

(c) If $a = 1$, sketch the root locus plot. Find the value of K which gives the greatest damping ratio for the oscillatory mode. Find also the value of this damping ratio and the corresponding undamped natural frequency.

Solution:

(a) For the given open-loop transfer function $G(s)H(s)$:

The open-loop poles are at $s = 0$, $s = 0$ and $s = -2$. Therefore, $n = 3$.

There are no finite open-loop zeros. Therefore, $m = 0$.

So, the number of branches of root locus $= n = 3$ and the number of asymptotes $= n - m = 3 - 0 = 3$.

The complete root locus is drawn as shown in Figure 6.13, as per the rules given below.

1. All the open-loop poles and zeros are on the real axis itself. So the root locus will be symmetrical with respect to the real axis.

2. The three branches of the root locus start at the open-loop poles $s = 0$, $s = 0$ and $s = -2$, where $K = 0$ and terminate at the open-loop zeros $s = \infty$, $s = \infty$ and $s = \infty$, where $K = \infty$.

3. There are three asymptotes and the angles of the asymptotes are

$$\theta_q = \frac{(2q+1)\pi}{n-m}, \quad q = 0, 1, 2$$

i.e. $\qquad \theta_0 = \frac{\pi}{3}, \quad \theta_1 = \frac{3\pi}{3} = \pi, \quad \theta_2 = \frac{5\pi}{3}$

4. The point of intersection of the asymptotes on the real axis (centroid) is given by

$$-\sigma = \frac{\text{sum of real parts of poles} - \text{sum of real parts of zeros}}{\text{number of poles} - \text{number of zeros}} = \frac{(0+0-2)-(0)}{3-0} = -0.666$$

5. The root locus exists on the real axis to the left of $s = -2$.

6. The break points are given by the solution of $\dfrac{dK}{ds} = 0$.

$$|G(s)H(s)| = \left| \frac{K}{s^2(s+2)} \right| = 1$$

$\therefore \qquad K = s^2(s + 2)$

$$\frac{d}{ds}[s^2(s + 2)] = 3s^2 + 4s = 0$$

Therefore, the break points are at $s = 0$ and $s = -4/3$.

Out of these two, $s = 0$ is the actual break point. $s = -4/3$ is not an actual break point because the root locus does not exist at that point and hence can be ignored.

The break angles at $s = 0$ are

$$\pm \frac{\pi}{r} = \pm \frac{180°}{2} = \pm 90°$$

7. There are no complex poles and zeros. Therefore, there is no need to compute the angles of departure and arrival.

8. The point of intersection of the root locus with the imaginary axis and the critical value of K are obtained by using the Routh criterion. The characteristic equation is

$$1 + G(s)H(s) = 0$$

i.e.

$$1 + \frac{K}{s^2(s+2)} = s^3 + 2s^2 + K = 0$$

In the characteristic equation, the coefficient of $s = 0$. Hence, the necessary condition for stability is not satisfied and so the system is unstable for all values of K.

The complete root locus sketch is shown in Figure 6.13. There are three branches of the root locus. The branch starting at $s = -2$, travels to the left on the negative real axis and terminates at $s = -\infty$. The other two branches start at $s = 0$, break away at $s = 0$ itself and remain in the right-half of the s-plane only and terminate at $s = \infty$. So the system is always unstable.

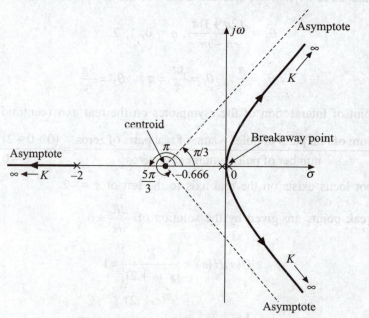

Figure 6.13   Example 6.6(a): Root locus.

(b) When a zero is added at $s = -a$ ($0 \le a < 2$), the open-loop transfer function is

$$G(s)H(s) = \frac{K(s+a)}{s^2(s+2)}$$

Therefore, $n = 3$, and $m = 1$ and $n - m = 3 - 1 = 2$.

Centroid will be

$$-\sigma = \frac{(-2)-(-a)}{3-1} = \frac{a-2}{2}$$

There are two asymptotes, and the asymptotic angles are

$$\theta_q = \frac{(2q+1)\pi}{n-m}, q = 0,1$$

$$\therefore \qquad \theta_0 = \frac{\pi}{2} \quad \text{and} \quad \theta_1 = \frac{3\pi}{2}$$

The root locus will now be as shown in Figure 6.14(a). Since the root locus now lies in the left-half of the s-plane for all positive values of K, we can conclude that the addition of a zero at $s = -a$, $(0 \leq a < 2)$ stabilizes the system.

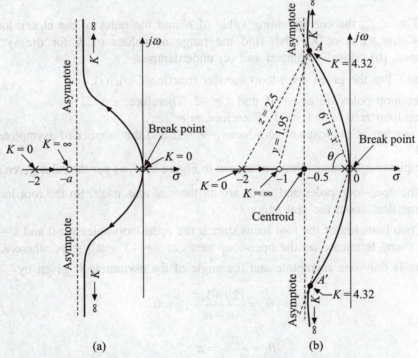

(a)	(b)

Figure 6.14 (a) Root locus (Example 6.6(b)) and, (b) root locus (Example 6.6(c)).

(c) If $a = 1$, the open-loop transfer function is

$$G(s)H(s) = \frac{K(s+1)}{s^2(s+2)}$$

The centroid is at $\dfrac{(-2)-(-1)}{3-1} = -0.5$

The root locus is now as shown in Figure 6.14(b). From Figure 6.14(b) we observe that the maximum value of damping ratio is 0.2 (cos θ, where θ is the minimum angle of the line tangential to the root locus). The distance from the origin to point A gives the undamped natural frequency. It is 1.9 rad/s. The value of K at point A is given by

$$K = \frac{xxz}{y} = \frac{1.9 \times 1.9 \times 2.5}{1.95} = 4.62$$

Therefore K at A = 4.62 and undamped natural frequency ω_n = 1.9 rad/s.

Example 6.7   Show that a part of the root locus of a system with

$$G(s)H(s) = \frac{K(s+3)}{s(s+2)}$$

is circular. Find ξ_{min}, the corresponding value of K and the poles of the closed-loop transfer function for this value of K. Also find the range of values of K for the system to be (a) overdamped, (b) critically damped and (c) underdamped.

Solution: For the given open-loop transfer function $G(s)H(s)$:

The open-loop poles are at $s = 0$, and $s = -2$. Therefore, $n = 2$.
The open-loop zero is at $s = -3$. Therefore, $m = 1$.
So, the number of branches of root locus = $n = 2$ and the number of asymptotes = $n - m$ = 2 – 1 = 1.
The complete root locus is drawn as shown in Figure 6.15, as per the rules given as follows:

1. All the open-loop poles and zeros are on the real axis itself. So the root locus will be symmetrical about the real axis.

2. The two branches of the root locus start at the open-loop poles $s = 0$ and $s = -2$, where $K = 0$ and terminate on the open-loop zeros at $s = -3$ and $s = \infty$, where $K = \infty$.

3. There is only one asymptote and the angle of the asymptote is given by

$$\theta_q = \frac{(2q+1)\pi}{n-m}, q = 0$$

i.e.

$$\theta_0 = \frac{\pi}{2-1} = \pi$$

4. The point of intersection of the asymptotes on the real axis (centroid) is given by

$$-\sigma = \frac{\text{sum of real parts of poles} - \text{sum of real parts of zeros}}{\text{number of poles} - \text{number of zeros}} = \frac{(-2)-(-3)}{2-1} = 1$$

5. The root locus lies on the real axis between $s = 0$ and $s = -2$ and to the left of $s = -3$.

6. The break points are given by the solution of the equation $\dfrac{dK}{ds} = 0$.

$$|G(s)H(s)| = \left|\dfrac{K(s+3)}{s(s+2)}\right| = 1$$

$\therefore$

$$K = \dfrac{s(s+2)}{s+3}$$

So,

$$\dfrac{d}{ds}\left[\dfrac{s(s+2)}{s+3}\right] = 0$$

i.e.

$$(s+3)(2s+2) - s(s+2)(1) = 0$$
$$2s^2 + 8s + 6 - s^2 - 2s = 0$$
$$s^2 + 6s + 6 = 0$$

Therefore, the break points are at

$$s = \dfrac{-6 \pm \sqrt{36-24}}{2} = -3 \pm \sqrt{3} = -1.29 \text{ and } -4.71$$

Both are actual break points. In fact $s = -1.29$ is a breakaway point and $s = -4.71$ is a break-in point.

The break angles at $s = -1.29$ and at $s = -4.71$ are

$$\pm\dfrac{\pi}{r} = \pm\dfrac{180°}{2} = \pm90°$$

7. There is no need to compute the angles of departure and arrival as there are no complex poles and zeros.
8. The root locus does not cross the imaginary axis at all. So there is no need to apply the Routh criterion. The system is stable for all positive values of K.

The complete root locus is shown in Figure 6.5. There are two branches of the root locus. The branch starting at $s = 0$ travels to the left and the branch starting at $s = -2$ travels to the right on the real axis, both of them will meet at $s = -1.29$, break away, enter the complex plane, travel along the circle, meet again on the real axis at $s = -4.71$, break-in and move in the opposite directions on the real axis. One terminates at $s = -3$ and the other one travels along the asymptotes at $180°$ and terminates at $s = -\infty$.

To find ξ_{min}, from the origin draw a line tangential to the circle. Let it meet the circle at A. Find the value of K at A using the magnitude condition.

$$K \text{ (at } A) = xy/z = 2.4 \times 1.4/1.75 = 1.92$$

From the graph, the pole at A for $K = 1.92$ is $-2 + j1.4$. Its complex conjugate is $s = -2 - j1.4$. Therefore, the closed-loop transfer function is

$$\dfrac{C(s)}{R(s)} = \dfrac{1.92}{(s+2+j1.4)(s+2-j1.4)}$$

The value of K at the breakaway point is $K = 0.573$ and the value of K at the break-in point is $K = 7.464$.

Therefore, the range of values of K for the system to be overdamped is

$$0 < K < 0.573$$

The values of K for critical damping are $K = 0.573$ and $K = 7.464$.
The range of values of K for the system to be underdamped is

$$0.573 < K < 7.464$$

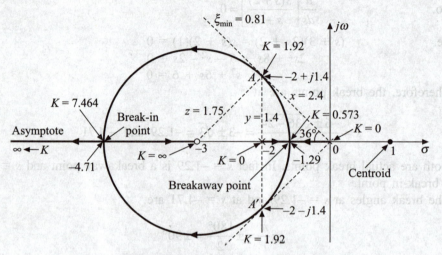

Figure 6.15   Example 6.7: Root locus.

To show that part of the root locus of the system is circular, apply the angle criteria, i.e.

$$\angle G(s)H(s) = \angle \frac{K(s+3)}{s(s+2)} = \pm(2q+1)\pi$$

$$\angle\sigma + j\omega + 3 - \angle\sigma + j\omega - \angle\sigma + j\omega + 2 = -\pi$$

$$\pi + \tan^{-1}\frac{\omega}{\sigma+3} = \tan^{-1}\frac{\omega}{\sigma} + \tan^{-1}\frac{\omega}{\sigma+2}$$

Taking the tangent on both sides of the above equation,

$$\frac{\dfrac{\omega}{\sigma} + \dfrac{\omega}{\sigma+2}}{1 - \dfrac{\omega}{\sigma}\cdot\dfrac{\omega}{\sigma+2}} = \frac{\tan\pi + \dfrac{\omega}{\sigma+3}}{1 - \tan\pi.\dfrac{\omega}{\sigma+3}}$$

$$\frac{\omega(\sigma+\sigma+2)}{\sigma(\sigma+2)-\omega^2} = \frac{\omega}{\sigma+3}$$

$$(\sigma + 3)(2\sigma + 2) = \sigma(\sigma + 2) - \omega^2$$

$$2\sigma^2 + 8\sigma + 6 = \sigma^2 + 2\sigma - \omega^2$$

$$\sigma^2 + 6\sigma + \omega^2 + 6 = 0$$

$$(\sigma + 3)^2 + \omega^2 = 3 = (\sqrt{3})^2$$

This is the equation of a circle with centre at $\sigma = -3$, $\omega = 0$ and radius $= \sqrt{3}$.

Example 6.8 Show that, the root loci for a control system with

$$G(s)H(s) = \frac{K(s^2 + 2s + 10)}{(s^2 + 6s + 10)}$$

are part of the circle centred at the origin with radius equal to $\sqrt{10}$. Determine the range of values of K for which the system is (a) overdamped, (b) critically damped and (c) underdamped.

Solution: $s^2 + 6s + 10 = 0$

$$\therefore \qquad s = \frac{-6 \pm \sqrt{36 - 40}}{2} = -3 \pm j1$$

$$s^2 + 2s + 10 = 0$$

$$\therefore \qquad s = \frac{-2 \pm \sqrt{4 - 40}}{2} = -1 \pm j3$$

So $\qquad G(s)H(s) = \dfrac{K(s + 1 + j3)(s + 1 - j3)}{(s + 3 + j1)(s + 3 - j1)}$

For the given open-loop transfer function $G(s)H(s)$:
The open-loop poles are at $s = -3 + j1$ and $s = -3 - j1$. Therefore, $n = 2$.
The open-loop zeros are at $s = -1 + j3$ and $s = -1 - j3$. Therefore, $m = 2$.
So the number of branches of root locus $= n = 2$ and the number of asymptotes $= n - m = 2 - 2 = 0$.
The complete root locus is drawn as shown in Figure 6.16, as per the rules given as follows:

1. Since the pole-zero configuration of the open-loop transfer function is symmetrical with respect to the real axis, the root locus will be symmetrical with respect to the real axis.

2. The two branches of the root locus start at the open-loop poles $s = -3 + j1$ and $s = -3 - j1$, where $K = 0$ and terminate at the open-loop zeros at $s = -1 + j3$ and $s = -1 - j3$ where $K = \infty$.

3. Since there are no asymptotes, there is no need to compute the angle of asymptotes.

4. Since there are no asymptotes, there is no need to compute the centroid.

5. The root locus does not exist on the real axis at all.

6. There are no break points. So no break angles.

7. The angles of departure and the angles of arrival can be computed from the graph by using the formula

$$\theta_d = \pm(2q + 1)\pi + \phi$$

where $\qquad \phi = \theta_3 + \theta_2 - \theta_1 = 223° + 115° - 90° = 248°$

$\therefore \qquad \theta_d = -180° + 248° = 68°$

and $\qquad \theta_a = \pm(2q + 1)\pi - \phi$

where $\qquad \phi = \theta_4 - \theta_5 - \theta_6 = 90° - 45° - 63° = -18°$

$\therefore \qquad \theta_a = 180° - (-18°) = 198°$

8. The root locus does not intersect the imaginary axis at all. So there is no need to formulate the Routh table.

The complete root locus is shown in Figure 6.16. There are two branches of the root locus. The root locus starting at the complex pole $s = -3 + j1$ departs at an angle of 68° travels along an arc of a circle and arrives at an angle of 198° and terminates on the complex zero $s = -1 + j3$. The root locus starting at the complex pole $-3 - j1$ departs at an angle of $-68°$ travels along an arc of a circle and arrives at an angle of $-198°$ and terminates at the complex zero $s = -1 - j3$.

The root locus does not lie on the real axis and there are no break points. So the system cannot be overdamped or critically damped. The range of values of K for which the system is underdamped is

$$K \text{ at } (-1 + j3) - K \text{ at } (-3 + j1) = \infty - 0 = \infty$$

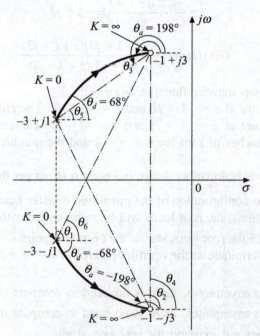

Figure 6.16 Example 6.8: Root locus.

To show that the root loci are arcs of a circle with radius $= \sqrt{10}$ and centred at the origin of the s-plane, apply the angle condition, i.e.

$$\angle G(s)H(s) = \angle K \frac{(s^2 + 2s + 10)}{s^2 + 6s + 10} = \pm(2q + 1)\pi$$

Putting $s = \sigma + j\omega$ in the above equation,

$$\angle G(s)H(s) = (\angle(\sigma + j\omega)^2 + 2(\sigma + j\omega) + 10) - (\angle(\sigma + j\omega)^2 + 6(\sigma + j\omega) + 10) = \pi$$

i.e. $(\angle\sigma^2 - \omega^2 + 2\sigma + 10 + j\omega(2\sigma + 2)) - (\angle(\sigma^2 - \omega^2 + 6\sigma + 10) + j\omega(2\sigma + 6)) = \pi$

i.e. $$\tan^{-1}\left[\frac{\omega(2\sigma + 2)}{\sigma^2 - \omega^2 + 2\sigma + 10}\right] - \tan^{-1}\left[\frac{\omega(2\sigma + 6)}{\sigma^2 - \omega^2 + 6\sigma + 10}\right] = \pi$$

Taking tangent on both sides of the equation,

$$\frac{\omega(2\sigma + 6)}{\sigma^2 - \omega^2 + 6\sigma + 10} = \frac{\omega(2\sigma + 2)}{\sigma^2 - \omega^2 + 2\sigma + 10}$$

Cross multiplying and simplifying the above equation,

$$4\sigma^2 + 4\omega^2 - 40 = 0$$

i.e. $$\sigma^2 + \omega^2 = 10$$

This is the equation of a circle centred at the origin of the s-plane with radius equal to $\sqrt{10}$. So the root loci are arcs of a circle with radius $= \sqrt{10}$ centred at the origin of the s-plane.

Example 6.9   Sketch the root locus for $0 < K < \infty$, for the system with the open-loop transfer function

$$G(s)H(s) = \frac{K}{s(s + 2)(s^2 + 2s + 2)}$$

Solution: For the given open-loop transfer function $G(s)H(s)$:

The open-loop poles are at $s = 0$, $s = -2$, $s = \dfrac{-2 \pm \sqrt{4 - 8}}{2} = -1 \pm j1$. Therefore, $n = 4$.

There are no finite open-loop zeros. Therefore, $m = 0$.

So the number of branches of root locus $= n = 4$ and the number of asymptotes $= n - m = 4 - 0 = 4$.

The complete root locus is drawn as shown in Figure 6.17, as per the rules given as follows:

1. Since the pole-zero configuration is symmetrical with respect to the real axis, the root locus will be symmetrical with respect to the real axis.

2. The four branches of the root locus originate at the open-loop poles $s = 0$, $s = -2$, $s = -1 + j1$ and $s = -1 - j1$, where $K = 0$ and terminate at the open-loop zeros at infinity, where $K = \infty$.

3. There are four asymptotes and the angles of the asymptotes are

$$\theta_q = \frac{(2q+1)\pi}{n-m}, \quad q = 0,1,2,3$$

i.e. $\qquad \theta_0 = \frac{\pi}{4}, \qquad \theta_1 = \frac{3\pi}{4}, \qquad \theta_2 = \frac{5\pi}{4}, \qquad \theta_3 = \frac{7\pi}{4}$

4. The point of intersection of the asymptotes on the real axis (centroid) is given by

$$-\sigma = \frac{\text{sum of real parts of poles} - \text{sum of real parts of zeros}}{\text{number of poles} - \text{number of zeros}} = \frac{(0-2-1-1)-(0)}{4-0} = -1$$

5. The root locus exists on the real axis from $s = 0$ to $s = -2$.

6. The break points are given by the solution of the equation $\dfrac{dK}{ds} = 0$.

$$|G(s)H(s)| = \left| \frac{K}{s(s+2)(s^2+2s+2)} \right| = 1$$

$\therefore \qquad\qquad K = s(s + 2)(s^2 + 2s + 2)$

So, $\qquad\qquad \dfrac{d}{ds}[s(s+2)(s^2+2s+2)]$

i.e. $\qquad\qquad \dfrac{d}{ds}(s^4 + 4s^3 + 6s^2 + 4s) = 0$

i.e. $\qquad\qquad 4s^3 + 12s^2 + 12s + 4 = 0$

i.e. $\qquad\qquad s^3 + 3s^2 + 3s + 1 = 0$

i.e. $\qquad\qquad (s + 1)^3 = 0$

Therefore, the break points are at $s = -1$, $s = -1$ and $s = -1$. All are the actual break points.

The break angles at $s = -1$ are

$$\pm\frac{\pi}{r} = \pm\frac{180°}{4} = \pm 45°$$

7. The angle of departure from the complex pole at $s = -1 + j1$ is

$$\theta_d = (2q + 1)\pi + \phi$$

where $\quad \phi = -(\theta_1 + \theta_2 + \theta_3) = -(135° + 90° + 45°) = -270°$

$$\therefore \qquad \theta_d = \pi - 270° = -90°$$

Hence the angle of departure from the complex pole at $s = -1 - j1$ is $\theta_d = +90°$.

8. The point of intersection of the root locus with the imaginary axis, and the critical value of K are obtained using the Routh criterion. The characteristic equation is

$$1 + G(s)H(s) = 0$$

i.e.
$$1 + \frac{K}{s(s+2)(s^2+2s+2)} = 0$$

i.e.
$$s^4 + 4s^3 + 6s^2 + 4s + K = 0$$

The Routh table is as follows:

s^4	1	6	K
s^3	4	4	
s^2	5	K	
s^1	$\dfrac{20-4K}{5}$	0	
s^0	K		

For stability, all the elements in the first column of the Routh array must be positive. Therefore,

$$K > 0$$

and
$$\frac{20-4K}{5} > 0$$

i.e.
$$K < 5$$

Therefore, the range of values of K for stability is $0 < K < 5$. The marginal value of K for stability is $K_m = 5$.

The point of intersection of the root locus with the imaginary axis (i.e. the frequency of sustained oscillations) is given by the solution of the auxiliary equation

$$5s^2 + K = 0$$

i.e.
$$5s^2 + K_m = 0$$

i.e.
$$5s^2 + 5 = 0$$

i.e.
$$s^2 + 1 = 0$$

or
$$s = \pm j1$$

Therefore, the frequency of sustained oscillations is $\omega = 1$ rad/s.
The complete root locus is shown in Figure 6.17.

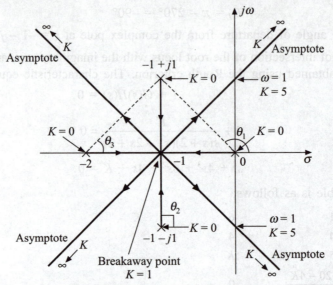

Figure 6.17 Example 6.9: Root locus.

Example 6.10 Sketch the root locus for the system with

$$G(s)H(s) = \frac{K(s^2 + 2s + 10)}{s^2(s + 2)}$$

Solution: For the given open-loop transfer function $G(s)H(s)$:
The open-loop poles are at $s = 0$, $s = 0$, and $s = -2$. Therefore, $n = 3$.

The open-loop zeros are at $s = \dfrac{-2 \pm \sqrt{4 - 40}}{2} = -1 \pm j3$. Therefore, $m = 2$.

So the number of branches of root locus $= n = 3$ and the number of asymptotes $= n - m$ $= 3 - 2 = 1$.

The complete root locus is drawn as shown in Figure 6.18, as per the rules given as follows:

1. Since the open-loop poles and zeros are symmetrical with respect to the real axis, the root locus will be symmetrical with respect to the real axis.

2. The three branches of the root locus start at the open-loop poles $s = 0$, $s = 0$ and $s = -2$, where $K = 0$ and terminate at the open-loop zeros $s = -1 + j3$, $s = -1 - j3$ and $s = \infty$, where $K = \infty$.

3. One branch of the root locus goes to the zero at infinity along an asymptote making an angle of $\theta_q = \dfrac{(2q + 1)\pi}{n - m}$, $q = 0$, i.e. $\theta_0 = \pi$.

4. The point of intersection of the asymptotes on the real axis (centroid) is given by

$$-\sigma = \frac{\text{sum of real parts of poles} - \text{sum of real parts of zeros}}{\text{number of poles} - \text{number of zeros}} = \frac{(-2) - (-1 - 1)}{3 - 2} = 0$$

5. The breakaway point is at the origin itself. The break angles at $s = 0$ are

$$\pm\frac{\pi}{r} = \pm\frac{180°}{2} = \pm90°$$

6. The root locus exists on the real axis to the left of $s = -2$.
7. The angle of arrival at the complex zero $-1 + j3$ is given by $\theta_a = \pm(2q + 1)\pi - \phi$ where, from the graph

$$\phi = \theta_3 - (\theta_1 + \theta_2 + \theta_4) = 90° - (108.4° + 108.4° + 71.6°) = -198.4°$$

$$\therefore \qquad \theta_a = -180° - (-198.4°) = 18.4°$$

The angle of arrival at the complex zero at $s = -1 - j3$ is $\theta_a = -18.4°$.

8. The point of intersection of the root locus with the imaginary axis, and the critical value of K are obtained using Routh criterion. The characteristic equation is

$$1 + G(s)H(s) = 0 = 1 + \frac{K(s^2 + 2s + 10)}{s^2(s + 2)}$$

i.e. $\qquad s^3 + (2 + K)s^2 + 2Ks + 10K = 0$

The Routh table is as follows:

s^3	1	$2K$
s^2	$2 + K$	$10K$
s^1	$\dfrac{2K^2 + 4K - 10K}{(2 + K)}$	
s^0	$10K$	

For stability all the elements in the first column of the Routh array must be positive. Therefore,

$$10K > 0$$

i.e. $\qquad\qquad K > 0$

$$2 + K > 0$$

i.e $\qquad\qquad K > -2$

$$2K^2 - 6K > 0$$

i.e. $\qquad\qquad K > 3$

So the range of values of K for stability is $3 < K < \infty$. The marginal value of K for stability is $K_m = 3$.

The frequency of oscillations is given by the solution of the auxiliary equation

$$(2 + K)s^2 + 10K = 0$$

i.e. $\qquad (2 + K_m)s^2 + 10K_m = 0$

i.e. $$(2 + 3)s^2 + 10 \times 3 = 0$$

i.e. $$s^2 = -30/5 = -6$$

∴ $$s = \pm j2.45$$

Therefore, the frequency of sustained oscillations is $\omega = 2.45$ rad/s. The complete root locus is shown in Figure 6.18.

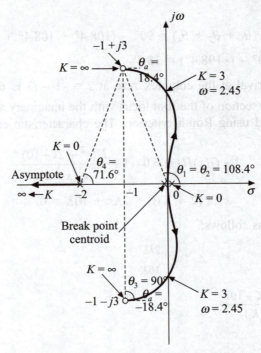

Figure 6.18 Example 6.10: Root locus.

Example 6.11 A unity feedback control system has an open-loop transfer function

$$G(s) = \frac{K(s + 4/3)}{s^2(s + 12)}$$

Sketch the complete root locus. Find the value of K for which all the roots are equal. What is the value of these roots?

Solution: For the given open-loop transfer function $G(s)H(s)$:

The open-loop poles are at $s = 0$, $s = 0$, $s = -12$. Therefore, $n = 3$.

The open-loop zero is at $s = -4/3$. Therefore, $m = 1$.

So the number of branches of root locus = $n = 3$ and the number of asymptotes = $n - m$ = $3 - 1 = 2$.

The complete root locus is drawn as shown in Figure 6.19, as per the rules given as follows:

1. Since the open-loop poles and zeros are symmetrical with respect to the real axis, the root locus will be symmetrical with respect to the real axis.

2. The three branches of the root locus originate at the open-loop poles $s = 0$, $s = 0$ and $s = -12$, where $K = 0$, and terminate at the open-loop zeros at $s = -4/3$, $s = \infty$ and $s = \infty$, where $K = \infty$.

3. The two branches of the root locus which tend to infinity do so along straight line asymptotes at angles of $\theta_q = \dfrac{(2q+1)\pi}{n-m}$, $q = 0, 1$, i.e. $\theta_0 = \dfrac{\pi}{2}$ and $\theta_1 = \dfrac{3\pi}{2}$.

4. The point of intersection of the asymptotes on the real axis (centroid) is given by

$$-\sigma = \frac{\text{sum of real parts of poles} - \text{sum of real parts of zeros}}{\text{number of poles} - \text{number of zeros}}$$

$$= \frac{(0 + 0 - 12) - (-4/3)}{3 - 1} = -16/3$$

5. The root locus exists on the real axis between $s = -4/3$ and $s = -12$.

6. The break points are given by the solution of $\dfrac{dK}{ds} = 0$.

$$|G(s)H(s)| = \left| \frac{K(s+4/3)}{s^2(s+12)} \right| = 1$$

$$\therefore \qquad K = \frac{s^2(s+12)}{s+4/3}$$

So

$$\frac{dK}{ds} = \frac{(s+4/3)(3s^2+24s) - s^2(s+12)}{(s+4/3)^2} = 0$$

$$3s^3 + 28s^2 + 32s - s^3 - 12s^2 = 0$$

$$2s^3 + 16s^2 + 32s = 0$$

$$s(s^2 + 8s + 16) = 0$$

$$s(s + 4)^2 = 0$$

Therefore, $s = 0$, $s = -4$ and $s = -4$ are the break points. All the three are actual break points.

7. There is no need to compute the angle of departure and arrival as there are no complex poles and zeros.

8. The root locus does not cross the imaginary axis, so there is no need to formulate the Routh array.

The equal roots are at $s = -4$

K at $s = -4$ is

$$K = \frac{4 \times 4 \times 8}{8/3} = 48$$

For $K = 48$, the three roots are $s = -4$, $s = -4$ and $s = -4$.
The complete root locus is shown in Figure 6.19.

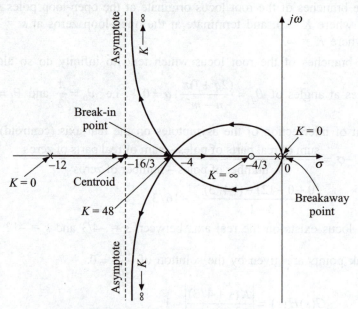

Figure 6.19 Example 6.11: Root locus.

Example 6.12 Sketch the root locus for the control system whose open-loop transfer function is

$$G(s)H(s) = \frac{Ke^{-s}}{s(s+2)}$$

Show that part of the root locus is a circle.

Solution: For low frequencies

$$e^{-s} \approx 1 - s$$

$\therefore$
$$G(s)H(s) = \frac{K(1-s)}{s(s+2)} = \frac{-K(s-1)}{s(s+2)}$$

Since $G(s)H(s)$ is –ve, the angle condition for the root locus to exist will be $\angle G(s)H(s) = \pm(2q)\pi$. So the root locus will exist at any point on the real axis, if the total number of poles and zeros to the right of that point is even. All other rules for construction of root locus will remain same.

For the given open-loop transfer function $G(s)H(s)$:

The open-loop poles are at $s = 0$, $s = -2$. Therefore, $n = 2$.

The only open-loop zero is at $s = 1$. Therefore, $m = 1$.

So the number of branches of the root locus $= n = 2$ and the number of asymptotes $= n - m = 2 - 1 = 1$.

The complete root locus is drawn as shown in Figure 6.20, as per the rules given as follows:

1. Since the open-loop pole-zero configuration is symmetrical with respect to the real axis, the root locus will be symmetrical with respect to the real axis.

2. The root locus starts at the open-loop poles $s = 0$ and $s = -2$, where $K = 0$ and terminates at the open-loop zeros $s = 1$ and $s = \infty$, where $K = \infty$.

3. One branch of the root locus goes to the zero at infinity along an asymptote making an angle of $\theta_q = \dfrac{2q\pi}{n-m}, q = 0$, i.e. $\theta_0 = 0°$ with respect to the real axis.

4. The point of intersection of the asymptotes on the real axis (centroid) is given by

$$-\sigma = \frac{\text{sum of real parts of poles} - \text{sum of real parts of zeros}}{\text{number of poles} - \text{number of zeros}} = \frac{(0-2)-(1)}{2-1} = -3$$

5. The root locus exists on the real axis from $s = -2$ to $s = 0$ and to the right of $s = 1$.

6. There are no complex poles and zeros, so there is no need to calculate the angle of departure and arrival.

7. The break points are given by the solution of $\dfrac{dK}{ds} = 0$.

$$|G(s)H(s)| = \left| \frac{K(1-s)}{s(s+2)} \right| = 1$$

$\therefore$
$$K = \frac{s(s+2)}{1-s}$$

$$\frac{dK}{ds} = \frac{d}{ds}\left[\frac{s(s+2)}{1-s} \right] = (1-s)(2s+2) - s(s+2)(-1) = 0$$

i.e. $\qquad 2s + 2 - 2s^2 - 2s + s^2 + 2s = 0$

i.e. $\qquad s^2 - 2s - 2 = 0$

Therefore, the break points are at

$$s = \frac{2 \pm \sqrt{4+8}}{2} = 1 \pm \sqrt{3} = 2.73 \text{ or } -0.73$$

$s = -0.73$ is a breakaway point and $s = 2.73$ is a break-in point.
The break angles at $s = -0.73$ and at $s = 2.73$ are

$$\pm\frac{\pi}{r} = \pm\frac{180°}{2} = \pm 90°$$

8. The frequency at the point of intersection of the root locus with the imaginary axis and the critical value of K are obtained by applying the Routh criterion. The characteristic equation is

$$1+G(s)H(s)=1+\frac{K(1-s)}{s(s+2)}=\frac{s^2+(2-K)s+K}{s(s+2)}=0$$

i.e.
$$s^2 + (2 - K)s + K = 0$$

The Routh table is given as follows:

s^2	1	K
s^1	$2 - K$	
s^0	K	

For stability all the elements in the first column of the Routh array must be positive. Therefore,

$$K > 0$$

and
$$2 - K > 0$$

i.e.
$$K < 2$$

The marginal value of K for stability is $K_m = 2$.

The frequency of oscillations is given by the solution of the auxiliary equation

$$s^2 + K = s^2 + K_m = 0$$

i.e.
$$s^2 + 2 = 0$$

∴
$$s^2 = -2$$

or
$$s = \pm j\sqrt{2}$$

Therefore, the frequency of sustained oscillations is $\omega = \sqrt{2} = 1.414$ rad/s.

The complete root locus is shown in Figure 6.20.

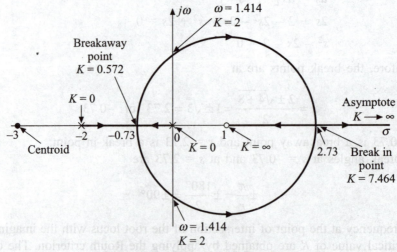

Figure 6.20 Example 6.12: Root locus.

To show that part of the root locus is a circle, apply the angle condition

$$\angle G(s)H(s) = \pm(2q)\pi$$

Putting $s = \sigma + j\omega$,

$$\angle G(s)H(s) = \angle\left[\frac{K(\sigma + j\omega - 1)}{(\sigma + j\omega)(\sigma + j\omega + 2)}\right] = 0$$

i.e.

$$\tan^{-1}\frac{\omega}{\sigma - 1} - \tan^{-1}\frac{\omega}{\sigma} - \tan^{-1}\frac{\omega}{\sigma + 2} = 0$$

∴

$$\tan^{-1}\frac{\omega}{\sigma - 1} = \tan^{-1}\frac{\omega}{\sigma} + \tan^{-1}\frac{\omega}{\sigma + 2}$$

Taking tangent on both sides

$$\frac{\omega}{\sigma - 1} = \frac{\dfrac{\omega}{\sigma} + \dfrac{\omega}{\sigma + 2}}{1 - \dfrac{\omega}{\sigma}\cdot\dfrac{\omega}{\sigma + 2}}$$

$$\frac{1}{\sigma - 1} = \frac{\sigma + 2 + \sigma}{\sigma(\sigma + 2) - \omega^2}$$

i.e.

$$\sigma^2 + 2\sigma - \omega^2 = 2\sigma^2 - 2\sigma + 2\sigma - 2$$

$$\sigma^2 - 2\sigma - 2 + \omega^2 = 0$$

$$(\sigma - 1)^2 + \omega^2 = 3 = (\sqrt{3})^2$$

This is the equation of a circle centred at (1, 0), with radius $= \sqrt{3}$.

Example 6.13   For a unity feedback system, the open-loop transfer function is given by

$$G(s) = \frac{K}{s(s + 2)(s^2 + 6s + 25)}$$

(a) Sketch the root locus for $0 < K < \infty$.
(b) At what value of K, the system becomes unstable.
(c) At this point of instability, determine the frequency of oscillation of the system.

Solution:
(a) For the given open-loop transfer function $G(s)H(s)$

The open-loop poles are at $s = 0$, $s = -2$ and $s = \dfrac{-6 \pm \sqrt{36 - 100}}{2} = -3 \pm j4$.

Therefore, $n = 4$.
There are no open-loop zeros. Therefore, $m = 0$.
So the number of branches of root locus $= n = 4$ and the number of asymptotes $= n - m$
$= 4 - 0 = 4$.

The complete root locus is drawn as shown in Figure 6.21, as per the rules given as follows:

1. Since the open-loop poles and zeros are symmetrical with respect to the real axis, the root locus will be symmetrical with respect to the real axis.

2. The four branches of the root locus originate at the open-loop poles $s = 0$, $s = -2$, $s = -3 + j4$, and $s = -3 - j4$, where $K = 0$ and terminate at the open-loop zeros at $s = \infty$, $s = \infty$, $s = \infty$, and $s = \infty$, where $K = \infty$.

3. The four branches of the root locus go to the zeros at infinity along asymptotes making angles of

$$\theta_q = \frac{(2q+1)\pi}{n-m}, \ q = 0, 1, 2, 3$$

i.e.
$$\theta_0 = \frac{\pi}{4}, \quad \theta_1 = \frac{3\pi}{4}, \quad \theta_2 = \frac{5\pi}{4}, \quad \theta_3 = \frac{7\pi}{4}$$

4. The point of intersection of the asymptotes on the real axis (centroid) is given by

$$-\sigma = \frac{\text{sum of real parts of poles} - \text{sum of real parts of zeros}}{\text{number of poles} - \text{number of zeros}} = \frac{(0 - 2 - 3 - 3) - (0)}{4} = -2.$$

5. The root locus exists on the real axis from $s = 0$ to $s = -2$.

6. The break points are given by the solution of $\dfrac{dK}{ds} = 0$.

$$|G(s)H(s)| = \left| \frac{K}{s(s+2)(s^2 + 6s + 25)} \right| = 1$$

∴
$$K = s(s + 2)(s^2 + 6s + 25) = s^4 + 8s^3 + 37s^2 + 50s$$

$$\frac{dK}{ds} = \frac{d}{ds}(s^4 + 8s^3 + 37s^2 + 50s) = 0$$

i.e.
$$4s^3 + 24s^2 + 74s + 50 = 0$$

$$s^3 + 6s^2 + 18.5s + 12.5 = 0$$

$$(s + 0.9)(s - 2.55 + j2.7)(s - 2.55 - j2.7) = 0$$

Therefore, $s = -0.9$, $s = 2.55 - j2.7$ and $s = 2.55 + j2.7$ are the break points.
Out of these three only $s = -0.9$ is the actual break point. The other two can be ignored as no root locus exists there.
The break angles at $s = -0.9$ are

$$\pm \frac{\pi}{r} = \pm \frac{180°}{2} = \pm 90°$$

7. The angle of departure from the complex pole at $s = -3 + j4$ is given by

$$\theta_d = \pm(2q + 1)\pi + \phi$$

where $\phi = -(\theta_1 + \theta_2 + \theta_3) = -(127° + 105° + 90°) = -322°$

$\therefore$ $\theta_d = 180° - 322° = -142°$

The angle of departure from the complex pole at $s = -3 - j4$ is $\theta_d = -(-142°) = 142°$.

8. The point of intersection of the root locus with the imaginary axis and the critical value of K can be obtained using the Routh criterion. The characteristic equation is

$$1 + G(s)H(s) = 1 + \frac{K}{s(s + 2)(s^2 + 6s + 25)} = s(s + 2)(s^2 + 6s + 25) + K = 0$$

i.e. $s^4 + 6s^3 + 10s^2 + 8s + K = 0$

The Routh table is as follows

s^4	1	10	K
s^3	6	8	
s^2	$\dfrac{60-8}{6} = 8.66$	K	
s^1	$\dfrac{208-18K}{26}$		
s^0	K		

For the system to be stable all the elements in the first column of the Routh array must be positive. Therefore,

$$K > 0$$

and $$\frac{208 - 18K}{26} > 0$$

i.e. $$18K < 208$$

$\therefore$ $$K < \frac{208}{18} = 11.55$$

The range of values of K for stability is $0 < K < 11.55$. The marginal value of K for stability is $K_m = 11.55$.

(b) The value of K at which the system becomes unstable is $K = 11.55$.

(c) The frequency of oscillations at the point of instability is given by the solution of the auxiliary equation

$$\frac{52}{6}s^2 + K = 0$$

i.e. $$\frac{52}{6}s^2 + K_m = 0$$

i.e. $$\frac{52}{6}s^2 + 11.55 = 0$$

i.e. $$s^2 = \frac{-6 \times 11.55}{52} = -\frac{69.30}{52} = -1.3$$

$$\therefore \qquad s = \pm j\sqrt{1.3} = \pm j1.16$$

Therefore, the frequency of sustained oscillations is $\omega = 1.16$ rad/s.

The complete root locus is drawn as shown in Figure 6.21.

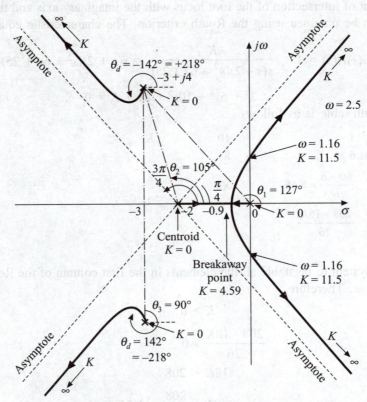

Figure 6.21 Example 6.13: Root locus.

Example 6.14 The characteristic equation of a feedback control system is

$$s^4 + 3s^3 + 12s^2 + (K - 16)s + K = 0$$

Sketch the root locus plot for $0 < K < \infty$ and show that the system is conditionally stable (stable only for a range of gain K). Determine the range of gain for which the system is stable.

Solution: The characteristic equation is

$$s^4 + 3s^3 + 12s^2 + (K - 16)s + K = 0$$

To sketch the root locus, we require the open-loop transfer function $G(s)H(s)$

$$1 + G(s)H(s) = s^4 + 3s^3 + 12s^2 - 16s + Ks + K$$

$$= s(s^3 + 3s^2 + 12s - 16) + K(s + 1) = 0$$

i.e.
$$1 + \frac{K(s+1)}{s(s^3 + 3s^2 + 12s - 16)} = 1 + \frac{K(s+1)}{s(s-1)(s^2 + 4s + 16)} = 0$$

$$\therefore \qquad G(s)H(s) = \frac{K(s+1)}{s(s-1)(s^2+4s+16)} = \frac{K(s+1)}{s(s-1)(s+2+j3.42)(s+2-j3.42)}$$

For the obtained open-loop transfer function $G(s)H(s)$:

The open-loop poles are at $s = 0$, $s = 1$, $s = -2 + j3.42$, $s = -2 - j3.42$. Therefore, $n = 4$.

The open-loop zero is at $s = -1$. Therefore, $m = 1$.

Hence the number of branches of root locus $= n = 4$ and the number of asymptotes $= n - m = 4 - 1 = 3$.

The complete root locus is drawn as shown in Figure 6.22, as per the rules given below.

1. Since the pole-zero configuration is symmetrical with respect to the real axis, the root locus will be symmetrical with respect to the real axis.

2. The four branches of the root locus originate at the open-loop poles $s = 0$, $s = 1$, $s = -2 + j3.42$, and $s = -2 - j3.42$, where $K = 0$ and terminate at the open-loop zeros at $s = 1$, $s = \infty$, $s = \infty$, and $s = \infty$, where $K = \infty$.

3. Three branches of the root locus go to the zeros at infinity along asymptotes making angles of $\theta_q = \dfrac{(2q+1)\pi}{n-m}$, $q = 0, 1, 2$ with the real axis, i.e.

$$\theta_0 = \frac{\pi}{3}, \quad \theta_1 = \pi, \quad \theta_2 = \frac{5\pi}{3}$$

4. The point of intersection of the asymptotes on the real axis (centroid) is given by

$$-\sigma = \frac{\text{sum of real parts of poles} - \text{sum of real parts of zeros}}{\text{number of poles} - \text{number of zeros}} = \frac{(0-2-2+1)-(-1)}{4-1} = -0.66$$

5. The root locus exists on the real axis from $s = 1$ to $s = 0$ and to the left of $s = -1$.

6. The breakaway points are given by the solution of $\dfrac{dK}{ds} = 0$.

$$\left| G(s)H(s) \right| = \left| \frac{K(s+1)}{s(s-1)(s^2+4s+16)} \right| = 1$$

$$\therefore \qquad K = \frac{s(s-1)(s^2+4s+16)}{s+1}$$

i.e. $\qquad \dfrac{dK}{ds} = (s+1)\dfrac{d}{ds}(s^4+3s^3+12s^2-16s) - (s^4+3s^3+12s^2-16s)\dfrac{d}{ds}(s+1) = 0$

i.e. $\qquad (s+1)(4s^3+9s^2+24s-16) - s^4 - 3s^3 - 12s^2 + 16s = 0$

$$4s^4 + 13s^3 + 33s^2 + 8s - 16 - s^4 - 3s^3 - 12s^2 + 16s = 0$$

$$3s^4 + 10s^3 + 21s^2 + 24s - 16 = 0$$

Therefore, $s = 0.45$ and $s = -2.26$ are the actual break points. Out of these, $s = 0.45$ is the breakaway point and $s = -2.26$ is the break-in point.

The break angles at $s = 0.45$ and $s = -2.26$ are

$$\pm \frac{\pi}{r} = \pm \frac{180°}{2} = \pm 90°$$

7. The angle of departure of the root locus from the open-loop pole at $s = -2 + j3.42$ is

$$\theta_d = (2q + 1)\pi + \phi, \text{ where } \phi = \theta_4 - (\theta_1 + \theta_2 + \theta_3)$$

$$= 106.29° - (131.25° + 120.31° + 90°) = -235.27°$$

Therefore, the angle of departure of the root locus from the open-loop pole at $s = -2 - j3.42$ is $\theta_d = 180° - 235.27° = -55.27°$.

8. The point of intersection of the root locus with the $j\omega$-axis and the critical value of K can be obtained using the Routh criterion. The characteristic equation is

$$s^4 + 3s^3 + 12s^2 + (K - 16)s + K = 0$$

The Routh table is as follows:

s^4	1	12	K
s^3	3	$K - 16$	
s^2	$\dfrac{36 - K + 16}{3}$	K	
s^1	$\dfrac{\dfrac{(52 - K)}{3}(K - 16) - 3K}{\dfrac{52 - K}{3}}$		
s^0	K		

For stability, all the elements in the first column of the Routh array must be positive. Therefore,

$$K > 0$$

$$52 - K > 0$$

i.e. $\qquad K < 52$

and $\qquad 52K + 16K - K^2 - 832 - 9K > 0$

i.e. $\qquad K^2 - 59K + 832 < 0$

∴ $\qquad K > 23.3 \text{ and } K < 35.7$

So the system is conditionally stable, and the range of values of K for stability is $23.3 < K < 35.7$. The corresponding oscillation frequencies are 1.55 rad/s and 2.6 rad/s, respectively.

The complete root locus is shown in Figure 6.22.

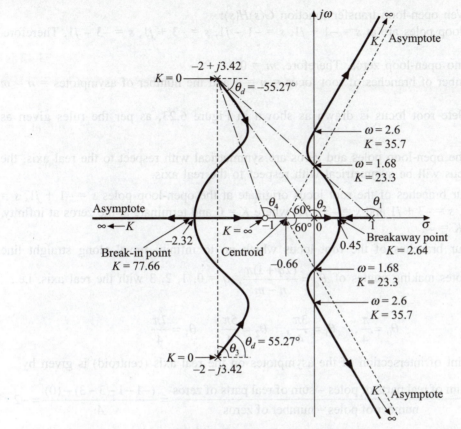

Figure 6.22   Example 6.14: Root locus.

Example 6.15   Draw the complete root locus of the system with the open-loop transfer function

$$G(s)H(s) = \frac{K}{(s^2 + 2s + 2)(s^2 + 6s + 10)}$$

Solution: The roots of $s^2 + 2s + 2 = 0$ are

$$s = \frac{-2 \pm \sqrt{4-8}}{2} = -1 \pm j1$$

The roots of $s^2 + 6s + 10 = 0$ are

$$s = \frac{-6 \pm \sqrt{36-40}}{2} = -3 \pm j1$$

$$G(s)H(s) = \frac{K}{(s^2 + 2s + 2)(s^2 + 6s + 10)} = \frac{K}{(s+1+j1)(s+1-j1)(s+3+j1)(s+3-j1)}$$

For the given open-loop transfer function $G(s)H(s)$:

The open-loop poles are at $s = -1 + j1$, $s = -1 - j1$, $s = -3 + j1$, $s = -3 - j1$. Therefore, $n = 4$.

There are no open-loop zeros. Therefore, $m = 0$.

So the number of branches of root locus $= n = 4$ and the number of asymptotes $= n - m = 4 - 0 = 4$.

The complete root locus is drawn as shown in Figure 6.23, as per the rules given as follows:

1. Since the open-loop poles and zeros are symmetrical with respect to the real axis, the root locus will be symmetrical with respect to the real axis.

2. The four branches of the root locus originate at the open-loop poles $s = -1 + j1$, $s = -1 - j1$, $s = -3 + j1$ and $s = -3 - j1$, where $K = 0$ and terminate at the zeros at infinity, where $K = \infty$.

3. The four branches of the root locus which go to infinity travel along straight line asymptotes making angles of $\theta_q = \dfrac{(2q + 1)\pi}{n - m}$, $q = 0, 1, 2, 3$ with the real axis, i.e.,

$$\theta_0 = \frac{\pi}{4}, \quad \theta_1 = \frac{3\pi}{4}, \quad \theta_2 = \frac{5\pi}{4}, \quad \theta_3 = \frac{7\pi}{4}$$

4. The point of intersection of the asymptotes on the real axis (centroid) is given by

$$-\sigma = \frac{\text{sum of real parts of poles} - \text{sum of real parts of zeros}}{\text{number of poles} - \text{number of zeros}} = \frac{(-1-1-3-3)-(0)}{4} = -2$$

5. The root locus does not exist on the real axis at all.

6. There are no break points. So no break angles.

7. The angle of departure from the complex pole at $s = -1 + j1$ is

$$\theta_d = \pm(2q + 1)\pi + \phi$$

where $\qquad \phi = (\theta_1 + \theta_2 + \theta_3) = -(90° + 45° + 0) = -135°$.

Therefore, $\qquad \theta_d = 180° - 135° = 45°$

The angle of departure from the complex pole at $s = -1 - j1$ is therefore $-45°$.

The angle of departure from the complex pole at $s = -3 + j1$ is

$$\theta_d = \pm(2q + 1)\pi + \phi$$

where $\qquad \phi = -(\theta_4 + \theta_5 + \theta_6)$

$$= -(135° + 90° + 180°) = -405°$$

$\therefore \qquad \theta_d = 180° - 405° = -225° = +135°$

The angle of departure form the complex pole at $s = -3 - j1$ is therefore $+225°$.

8. The points of intersection of the root locus with the imaginary axis and the critical value of K are obtained using the Routh criterion. The characteristic equation is

$$1 + G(s)H(s) = 0$$

$\therefore$

$$1 + \frac{K}{(s^2 + 2s + 2)(s^2 + 6s + 10)} = 0$$

i.e.

$$s^4 + 8s^3 + 24s^2 + 32s + 20 + K = 0$$

The Routh table is as follows:

s^4	1	24	$20 + K$
s^3	8	32	
s^2	20	$20 + K$	
s^1	$\dfrac{480 - 8K}{20}$	0	
s^0	$20 + K$		

For stability, all the elements in the first column of the Routh array must be positive. Therefore,

$$20 + K > 0$$

i.e.

$$K > -20$$

and

$$480 - 8K > 0$$

i.e.

$$K < 60$$

Therefore, the range of values of K for stability is $0 < K < 60$. The marginal value of K for stability is $K_m = 60$.

The frequency of sustained oscillations is given by the solution of the auxiliary equation

$$20s^2 + 20 + K = 0$$

i.e.

$$20s^2 + 20 + K_m = 0$$

i.e.

$$20s^2 + 20 + 60 = 0$$

i.e.

$$20s^2 + 80 = 0$$

i.e

$$s^2 = -4$$

or

$$s = \pm j2$$

or

$$\omega = 2 \text{ rad/s}$$

Therefore, the frequency of sustained oscillations is $\omega = 2$ rad/s.

The complete root locus is drawn as shown in Figure 6.23.

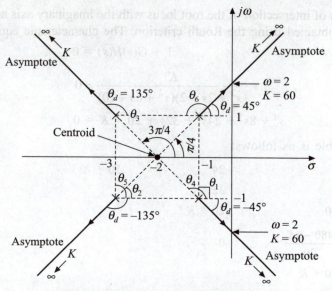

Figure 6.23 Example 6.15: Root locus.

Example 6.16 The open-loop transfer function of a feedback system is

$$G(s)H(s) = \frac{K}{s(s+4)(s^2+4s+20)}$$

Draw the complete root locus.

Solution: $s^2 + 4s + 20 = 0$

$$\therefore \qquad s = \frac{-4 \pm \sqrt{16-80}}{2} = -2 \pm j4$$

For the given open-loop transfer function $G(s)H(s)$:
The open-loop poles are at $s = 0$, $s = -4$, $s = -2 + j4$, $s = -2 - j4$. Therefore, $n = 4$.
There are no open-loop zeros. Therefore, $m = 0$.
Hence the number of branches of root locus = $n = 4$ and the number of asymptotes = $n - m$ = $4 - 0 = 4$.

The complete root locus is drawn as shown in Figure 6.24, as per the rules given as follows:

1. Since the open-loop poles and zeros are symmetrical with respect to the real axis, the root locus will be symmetrical with respect to the real axis.

2. The four branches of the root locus originate at the open-loop poles $s = 0$, $s = -4$, $s = -2 + j4$, and $s = -2 - j4$, where $K = 0$ and terminate at the open-loop zeros at infinity, where $K = \infty$.

3. Since there are no finite zeros, all the four branches of the root locus go to the zeros at infinity along straight line asymptotes, whose angles with the real axis are given by

$$\theta_q = \frac{(2q+1)\pi}{n-m}, \quad q = 0, 1, 2, 3$$

∴

$$\theta_0 = \frac{\pi}{4}, \quad \theta_1 = \frac{3\pi}{4}, \quad \theta_2 = \frac{5\pi}{4}, \quad \theta_3 = \frac{7\pi}{4}$$

4. The point of intersection of the asymptotes on the real axis (centroid) is given by

$$-\sigma = \frac{\text{sum of real parts of poles} - \text{sum of real parts of zeros}}{\text{number of poles} - \text{number of zeros}} = \frac{(0-4-2-2)-(0)}{4-0} = -2$$

5. The root locus exists on the real axis from $s = 0$ to $s = -4$.

6. The break points are given by the solution of $\dfrac{dK}{ds} = 0$.

$$|G(s)H(s)| = \left| \frac{K}{s(s+4)(s^2+4s+20)} \right| = 1$$

∴

$$K = s(s+4)(s^2+4s+20)$$

$$\frac{dK}{ds} = -(4s^3+24s^2+72s+80) = 0$$

i.e.

$$s^3 + 6s^2 + 18s + 20 = 0$$

$$(s+2)(s^2+4s+10) = 0$$

i.e.

$$(s+2)(s+2+j2.45)(s+2-j2.45) = 0$$

There is one breakaway point on the real axis at $s = -2$, and there are two complex conjugate breakaway points at $s = -2 \pm j2.45$.
The break angles at these break points are

$$\pm\frac{\pi}{r} = \pm\frac{180°}{2} = \pm 90°$$

7. The angle of departure from the complex pole $s = -2 + j4$ is given by

$$\theta_d = \pm(2q+1)\pi + \phi$$

where

$$\phi = -(\theta_1 + \theta_2 + \theta_3) = -(117° + 90° + 63°) = -270°$$

∴

$$\theta_d = 180° - 270° = -90°$$

Because of symmetry, the angle of departure from the complex pole at $s = -2 - j4$ is $+90°$.

8. The point of intersection of the root locus with the imaginary axis and the marginal value of K can be determined by use of the Routh criterion. The characteristic equation of the system is

$$1 + \frac{K}{s(s+4)(s^2+4s+20)} = 0$$

i.e $\qquad s(s+4)(s^2+4s+20) + K = 0$

i.e $\qquad s^4 + 8s^3 + 36s^2 + 80s + K = 0$

The Routh table is as follows:

s^4	1	36	K
s^3	8	80	
s^3	1	10	
s^2	26	K	
s^1	$\dfrac{260-K}{26}$		
s^0	K		

For stability, all the elements in the first column of the Routh array must be positive. Therefore,

$$K > 0$$

and $\qquad \dfrac{260-K}{26} > 0$

i.e. $\qquad K < 260$

So the range of values of K for stability is $0 < K < 260$. The marginal value of K for stability is $K_m = 260$. For $K = 260$, the roots lie on the imaginary axis.

The frequency of sustained oscillations is obtained by the solution of the auxiliary equation

$$A(s) = 26s^2 + K = 0$$

i.e. $\qquad 26s^2 + K_m = 0$

i.e. $\qquad 26s^2 + 260 = 0$

$\therefore \qquad s^2 = -10$

or $\qquad s = \pm j\sqrt{10}$

$\therefore \qquad \omega = \sqrt{10}$ rad/s

Thus, for the root locus plot shown in Figure 6.23, the branches intersect the $j\omega$-axis at $s = \pm j\sqrt{10}$ and the value of K corresponding to these roots is 260.

The complete root locus is drawn as shown in Figure 6.24.

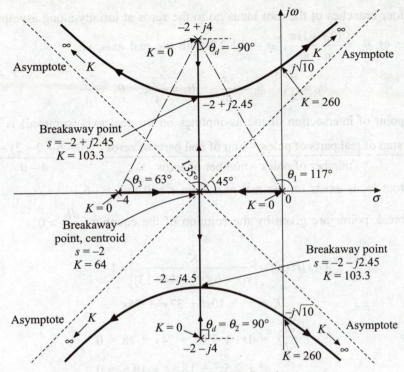

Figure 6.24 Example 6.16: Root locus.

Example 6.17 Draw the complete root locus for the system with

$$G(s)H(s) = \frac{K}{s(s+6)(s^2+4s+13)}$$

Solution: For the given open-loop transfer function $G(s)H(s)$:

The open-loop poles are at $s = 0$, $s = -6$, $s = \dfrac{-4 \pm \sqrt{16-52}}{2} = -2 \pm j3$. Therefore, $n = 4$.

There are no open-loop zeros. Therefore, $m = 0$.

Hence the number of branches of root locus = $n = 4$ and the number of asymptotes = $n - m = 4 - 0 = 4$.

The complete root locus is drawn as shown in Figure 6.25, as per the rules given as follows:

1. The root locus will be symmetrical about the real axis because the pole-zero location is symmetrical with respect to the real axis.

2. The four branches of the root locus start at the open-loop poles $s = 0$, $s = -6$, $s = -2 + j3$ and $s = -2 - j3$, where $K = 0$ and terminate at the open-loop zeros at infinity, where $K = \infty$.

3. The four branches of the root locus go to the zeros at infinity along asymptotes making angles of $\theta_q = \dfrac{(2q+1)\pi}{n-m}$, $q = 0,1,2,3$ with the real axis, i.e.

$$\theta_0 = \frac{\pi}{4}, \quad \theta_1 = \frac{3\pi}{4}, \quad \theta_2 = \frac{5\pi}{4}, \quad \theta_3 = \frac{7\pi}{4}$$

4. The point of intersection of the asymptotes on the real axis (centroid) is given by

$$-\sigma = \frac{\text{sum of real parts of poles} - \text{sum of real parts of zeros}}{\text{number of poles} - \text{number of zeros}} = \frac{(0-6-2-2)-(0)}{4-0} = -2.5$$

5. The root locus exists on the real axis from $s = 0$ to $s = -6$.

6. The break points are given by the solution of the equation $\dfrac{dK}{ds} = 0$.

$$|G(s)H(s)| = \left| \frac{K}{s(s+6)(s^2+4s+13)} \right| = 1$$

∴
$$K = s^4 + 10s^3 + 37s^2 + 78s$$

$$\frac{dK}{ds} = 4s^3 + 30s^2 + 74s + 78 = 0$$

i.e.
$$s^3 + 7.5s^2 + 18.5s + 19.5 = 0$$

i.e.
$$(s + 4.1)(s + 1.7 + j2.72)(s + 1.7 - j2.72) = 0$$

Therefore, the break points are $s = -4.1$, $s = -1.7 + j2.72$ and $s = -1.7 - j2.72$.

Out of these three break points, the actual break point is $s = -4.1$, because this point lies on the root locus. The other two are not actual break points, because the root locus does not exist there. They can be ignored.

The break angles at $s = -4.1$ are

$$\pm \frac{\pi}{r} = \pm \frac{180°}{2} = \pm 90°$$

7. The angle of departure of the root locus branch from the pole at $s = -2 + j3$ is given by

$$\theta_d = \pm(2q + 1)\pi + \phi$$

where
$$\phi = -(\theta_1 + \theta_2 + \theta_3) = -(122° + 90° + 38°) = -250°$$

∴
$$\theta_d = \pi - 250° = -70°$$

Therefore, the angle of departure of the root locus branch from the pole at $s = -2 - j3$ is $\theta_d = +70°$.

8. The point of intersection of the root locus with the imaginary axis and the critical value of K are obtained using the Routh criterion. The characteristic equation is

$$1 + G(s)H(s) = 0$$

i.e.
$$1 + \frac{K}{s(s+6)(s^2+4s+13)} = 0$$

i.e.
$$s^4 + 10s^3 + 37s^2 + 78s + K = 0$$

The Routh table is as follows:

s^4	1	37	K
s^3	10	78	
s^2	$\dfrac{370-78}{10} = 29.2$	K	
s^1	$\dfrac{29.2 \times 78 - 10K}{29.2}$		
s^0	K		

For stability, all the elements in the first column of the Routh array must be positive.
Therefore
$$K > 0$$
and
$$29.2 \times 78 - 10K > 0$$
i.e.
$$K < \frac{29.2 \times 78}{10} = 227.76$$

So the range of values of K for stability is $0 < K < 227.76$.

The marginal value of K for stability is $K_m = 227.76$. For $K > 227.76$, the system has two closed-loop poles in the right half of the s-plane and is thus unstable.

For that value of K, the frequency of sustained oscillations is given by the solution of the auxiliary equation

$$29.2s^2 + K = 0$$

i.e.
$$29.2s^2 + K_m = 0$$

i.e.
$$29.2s^2 + 227.76 = 0$$

∴
$$s^2 = -\frac{227.76}{29.2} = -7.8$$

or
$$s = \pm j2.8$$

∴
$$\omega = 2.8 \text{ rad/s}$$

Hence the frequency of sustained oscillations is $\omega = 2.8$ rad/s.

The complete root locus is drawn as shown in Figure 6.25.

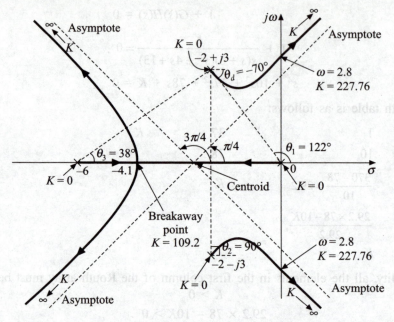

Figure 6.25 Example 6.17: Root locus.

Example 6.18 Obtain the open-loop transfer functions for the systems whose characteristic equations are given below.

(a) $s^2 + s(2 + K) + 4K = 0$

(b) $s^2 + (2 + K)s + (2K + 2) = 0$

(c) $s^3 + 3s^2 + (K + 2)s + 5K = 0$

(d) $s^3 + s^2 + (K + 2)s + 3K = 0$

(e) $s^4 + 6s^3 + 9s^2 + K(s^2 + 4s + 5) = 0$

(f) $s^2 + 2s + 2 + K = 0$

(g) $s^3 - 2s + K(s + 4)(s + 1) = 0$

(h) $s^3 + 2s^2 + 2s + K(s^2 - 1)(s + 2) = 0$

(i) $s(s^2 - 1) + K(s + 2)(s + 0.5) = 0$

(j) $s^4 + 2s^3 + 2s^2 + 2Ks + 5K = 0$

Solution:

(a) The characteristic equations is

$$1 + G(s)H(s) = s^2 + s(2 + K) + 4K = 0$$

$$s^2 + s(2 + K) + 4K = s^2 + 2s + K(s + 4) = 1 + \frac{K(s + 4)}{s(s + 2)} = 0$$

Therefore, the open-loop transfer function is

$$G(s)H(s) = \frac{K(s + 4)}{s(s + 2)}$$

(b) The characteristic equations is

$$1 + G(s)H(s) = s^2 + (2 + K)s + (2K + 2) = 0$$

$$s^2 + (2 + K)s + (2K + 2) = s^2 + 2s + 2 + K(s + 2)$$

$$= 1 + \frac{K(s + 2)}{s^2 + 2s + 2} = 1 + \frac{K(s + 2)}{(s + 1 + j1)(s + 1 - j1)} = 0$$

Therefore, the open-loop transfer function is

$$G(s)H(s) = \frac{K(s+2)}{(s+1+j1)(s+1-j1)}$$

(c) The characteristic equations is

$$1 + G(s)H(s) = s^3 + 3s^2 + (K+2)s + 5K = 0$$

$$s^3 + 3s^2 + s(K+2) + 5K = s^3 + 3s^2 + 2s + K(s+5)$$

$$= 1 + \frac{K(s+5)}{s(s^2+3s+2)} = 1 + \frac{K(s+5)}{s(s+1)(s+2)} = 0$$

Therefore, the open-loop transfer function is

$$G(s)H(s) = \frac{K(s+5)}{s(s+1)(s+2)}$$

(d) The characteristic equations is

$$1 + G(s)H(s) = s^3 + s^2 + (K+2)s + 3K = 0$$

$$s^3 + s^2 + (K+2)s + 3K = s^3 + s^2 + 2s + Ks + 3K = s^3 + s^2 + 2s + K(s+3) = 0$$

$$= 1 + \frac{K(s+3)}{s(s^2+s+2)} = 1 + \frac{K(s+3)}{s(s+0.5+j1.32)(s+0.5-j1.32)} = 0$$

Therefore, the open-loop transfer function is

$$G(s)H(s) = \frac{K(s+3)}{s(s+0.5+j1.32)(s+0.5-j1.32)}$$

(e) The characteristic equations is

$$1 + G(s)H(s) = s^4 + 6s^3 + 9s^2 + K(s^2+4s+5) = 0$$

$$= 1 + \frac{K(s^2+4s+5)}{s^4+6s^3+9s^2} = 1 + \frac{K(s+2+j1)(s+2-j1)}{s^2(s+3)^2} = 0$$

Therefore, the open-loop transfer function is

$$G(s)H(s) = \frac{K(s+2+j1)(s+2-j1)}{s^2(s+3)^2}$$

(f) The characteristic equations is

$$1 + G(s)H(s) = s^2 + 2s + 2 + K = s^2 + 2s + 2 + K = 0$$

$$= 1 + \frac{K}{s^2+2s+2} = 1 + \frac{K}{(s+1+j1)(s+1-j1)} = 0$$

Therefore, the open-loop transfer function is

$$G(s)H(s) = \frac{K}{(s+1+j1)(s+1-j1)}$$

(g) The characteristic equations is

$$1 + G(s)H(s) = s^3 - 2s + K(s + 4)(s + 1) = 0$$

$$s(s^2 - 2) + K(s + 1)(s + 4) = 0$$

i.e.

$$1 + \frac{K(s+1)(s+4)}{s(s^2-2)} = 1 + \frac{K(s+1)(s+4)}{s(s+\sqrt{2})(s-\sqrt{2})} = 0$$

Therefore, the open-loop transfer function is

$$G(s)H(s) = \frac{K(s+1)(s+4)}{s(s+\sqrt{2})(s-\sqrt{2})}$$

(h) The characteristic equations is

$$1 + G(s)H(s) = s^3 + 2s^2 + 2s + K\,(s^2 - 1)(s + 2) = 0$$

i.e.

$$s(s^2 + 2s + 2) + K(s + 1)(s - 1)(s + 2) = 0$$

i.e.

$$1 + \frac{K(s+1)(s-1)(s+2)}{s(s^2+2s+2)} = 1 + \frac{K(s+1)(s-1)(s+2)}{s(s+1+j1)(s+1-j1)} = 0$$

Therefore, the open-loop transfer function is

$$G(s)H(s) = \frac{K(s+1)(s-1)(s+2)}{s(s+1+j1)(s+1-j1)}$$

(i) The characteristic equations is

$$1 + G(s)H(s) = s(s^2 - 1) + K(s + 2)(s + 0.5) = 0$$

i.e.

$$1 + \frac{K(s+0.5)(s+2)}{s(s+1)(s-1)} = 0$$

Therefore, the open-loop transfer function is

$$G(s)H(s) = \frac{K(s+0.5)(s+2)}{s(s+1)(s-1)}$$

(j) The characteristic equations is

$$1 + G(s)H(s) = s^4 + 2s^3 + 2s^2 + 2Ks + 5K = 0$$

i.e.

$$s^4 + 2s^3 + 2s^2 + K(2s + 5) = 0$$

i.e.

$$1 + \frac{K(2s+5)}{s^4+2s^3+2s^2} = 1 + \frac{K_1(s+2.5)}{s^2(s+1+j1)(s+1-j1)} = 0$$

Therefore, the open-loop transfer function is

$$G(s)H(s) = \frac{K_1(s+2.5)}{s^2(s+1+j1)(s+1-j1)}$$

SHORT QUESTIONS AND ANSWERS

1. Who introduced the root locus technique?

A. W.R. Evans introduced the root locus technique.

2. Define the root locus.

A. The root locus is defined as the locus (i.e. the path taken by) of the roots of the characteristic equation, when one of the system parameters (usually the open-loop gain K) is varied from 0 to ∞.

3. What are the applications of the root locus?

A. The applications of the root locus are:

   (a) The root locus can be used to solve higher-order algebraic equations.

   (b) It can be used to determine the absolute stability as well as the relative stability of a system.

   (c) The roots corresponding to a particular value of the system parameter can be obtained from the root locus.

   (d) The value of open-loop gain K for any root location can be obtained from the root locus.

   (e) It can be used for the design of control systems.

   (f) It gives information about the transient response of a system.

4. What are the advantages of the root locus?

A. The advantages of the root locus are as follows:

   (a) It can be used to determine the absolute stability as well as the relative stability of control systems.

   (b) Being a graphical technique, an approximate root locus can be drawn quickly by following the rules for the construction of the root locus.

   (c) It is a time-domain technique.

   (d) The transient response of a system can be determined from its root locus.

   (e) Higher-order algebraic equations can be solved using the root locus.

   (f) It provides a measure of sensitivity of roots to the variation in the parameter being considered.

   (g) It brings into focus the complete dynamic response of the system.

   (h) It can be used for design and compensation of control systems.

5. For which systems the root locus is applicable?

A. The root locus technique is applicable for single as well as multi-loop systems.

6. What are the conditions to be satisfied for the root locus to exist at any point in the s-plane?

A. For the root locus to exist at any point in the s-plane, the magnitude and phase angle conditions, i.e. $|G(s)H(s)| = 1$ and $\angle G(s)H(s) = \pm(2q + 1)\pi$, $q = 0, 1, 2, ...$ must be satisfied at that point.

7. Are the magnitude and phase conditions to be satisfied independent of each other?

A. No. The magnitude and phase conditions to be satisfied are not independent of each other and one implies the other.

8. What is the exact method of drawing the root locus?

A. The exact method of drawing the root locus is to locate a number of points in the *s*-plane where magnitude and phase conditions of the root locus are satisfied and to draw a smooth curve passing through those points.

9. Which parameter is usually varied in drawing the root locus?

A. In drawing the root locus, usually the open-loop gain K is varied from 0 to ∞.

10. Where does the root locus start?

A. The root locus always starts at the open-loop poles where $K = 0$.

11. Where does the root locus terminate?

A. The root locus always terminates at the open-loop zeros or the zeros at infinity, where $K = \infty$.

12. How many branches of the root locus terminate at infinity?

A. The number of branches of the root locus terminating on ∞ is equal to the number of open-loop poles minus the number of open-loop zeros, i.e. $(n - m)$.

13. How does the root locus travel to the zero at infinity?

A. The root locus travels to the zero at infinity along an asymptote.

14. What is an asymptote?

A. An asymptote is a straight line along which the root locus is expected to travel to reach the zero at infinity.

15. How many branches of the root locus will be there for a given system?

A. The number of branches of the root locus for a given system is equal to the number of open-loop poles of the system.

16. How many asymptotes will be there in the root locus for a given system?

A. The number of asymptotes in the root locus for a given system is equal to the number of open-loop poles minus the number of open-loop zeros.

17. Where do the asymptotes intersect on the real axis?

A. The asymptotes intersect at the centroid on the real axis.

18. What do you mean by a centroid? How is it calculated?

A. The centroid is the point of intersection of the asymptotes on the real axis.
The centroid is given by

$$-\sigma = \frac{\text{sum of real parts of poles} - \text{sum of real parts of zeros}}{\text{number of poles} - \text{number of zeros}}$$

19. With respect to which axis, the angles of the asymptotes are measured?

A. The angles of the asymptotes are measured with respect to the real axis.

20. At which point on the real axis the asymptotic angles are measured, and how do you calculate the angles of asymptotes?

A. The asymptotic angles are measured at the centroid and are given by

$$\theta_q = \pm\frac{(2q+1)\pi}{n-m}, q = 0, 1, 2, ..., n-m-1$$

21. What is the condition to be satisfied for the root locus to exist at any point on the real axis?

A. The condition to be satisfied for the root locus to exist at any point on the real axis is that, the total number of open-loop poles plus zeros to the right of that point must be odd.

22. What do you mean by (a) breakaway point and (b) break-in point? Where can they occur? How can they be determined?

A. The breakaway or break-in points are the points in the *s*-plane where multiple roots of the characteristic equation exist. The break-in point is a point on the real axis at which roots from the complex plane enter the real axis. The breakaway point is a point either on the real axis or in the complex plane where two or more roots meet, break away and go into the complex plane. To find the breakaway or break-in points, form an equation for *K* from the characteristic equation and differentiate the equation of *K* with respect to *s*. Then find the roots of the equation $\frac{dK}{ds} = 0$. The roots of $\frac{dK}{ds} = 0$ are the breakaway or break-in points.

23. What do you mean by the break angle? How is it determined?

A. The break angle is the angle at which the root locus branches travel immediately after breaking away.

24. What do you mean by the angle of departure? When is it to be determined? How do you determine it?

A. The angle of departure is the angle at which the root locus departs from a complex pole. It has to be determined only when there are complex poles in the system open-loop transfer function. For all real poles, the angles of departure are either 0° or 180°. So no need to calculate them. The angle of departure from a complex pole is given by

$$\theta_d = \pm(2q + 1)\pi + \phi, q = 0, 1, 2, ...$$

where ϕ is the net angle contribution made at that pole by all other open-loop poles and zeros.

25. What do you mean by the angle of arrival? When is it to be determined? How do you determine it?

A. The angle of arrival is the angle at which the root locus arrives at a complex zero. For all real zeros, the angles of arrival are either 0° or 180°. So no need to calculate them. The angle of arrival at a complex zero is given by

$$\theta_a = \pm(2q + 1)\pi - \phi, \quad q = 0, 1, 2, \ldots$$

where ϕ is the net angle contribution made at that zero by all other open-loop poles and zeros.

26. How do you determine the point of intersection of the root locus with the imaginary axis and the critical value of K?

A. The point of intersection of the root locus with the imaginary axis and the critical value of K can be determined using the Routh criterion. The point of intersection of the root locus with the imaginary axis and the critical value of K can also be determined by letting $s = j\omega$ in the characteristic equation and separating the real and imaginary parts. These two equations are equated to zero and solved for ω and K. The value of ω gives the point where the root locus crosses the imaginary axis and the value of K is the gain corresponding to the crossing point, i.e. the marginal value of K.

27. How do you determine the value of K at any point on the root locus?

A. The value of the open-loop gain K at any point s_0 on the root locus is given by

$$K = \frac{\text{product of phasor lengths from } s_0 \text{ to open-loop poles}}{\text{product of phasor lengths from } s_0 \text{ to open-loop zeros}}$$

28. What are dominant poles?

A. The dominant poles are the poles which are very near to the origin. They dominate or decide the transient response of a higher-order system.

29. How do you determine ξ_{min} from the root locus?

A. To determine ξ_{min} form the root locus, draw a constant ξ line from the origin tangential to the circle representing the root locus. The cosine of the angle made by that line with respect to the negative real axis gives ξ_{min}.

30. How do you determine the value of K for a given damping ratio from the root locus plot?

A. To determine the value of K for a given damping ratio from the root locus plot, draw a constant ξ line making an angle of $\theta = \cos^{-1} \xi$ with the negative real axis. At the point of intersection of this line with the root locus plot, apply the magnitude condition and determine the value of K.

31. How do you determine the closed-loop transfer function for a given value of K from the root locus plot?

A. To determine the closed-loop transfer function from the root locus for a given value of K, locate by trial and error the point on each root locus branch where the magnitude condition is satisfied. Each one of those points give the corresponding root of the characteristic equation, that is the closed-loop pole. Since K is already known at that point, the closed-loop transfer function can be written as

$$\frac{C(s)}{R(s)} = \frac{K}{\text{pole terms}}$$

32. What is the effect of adding poles to $G(s)H(s)$ on the root locus?

A. Adding a pole to $G(s)H(s)$ has the effect of pushing the root loci toward the right half. The complex path of the root loci bends to the right, the angle of asymptotes reduces and the centroid is shifted to the left and the system stability is reduced. Even a system which was perfectly stable may become unstable as K increases.

In general, we can say that the addition of poles to $G(s)H(s)$ has the effect of moving the dominant portion of the root loci towards the right-half of the s-plane. So the relative stability of the system is decreased by the addition of a pole.

33. What is the effect of adding zeros to $G(s)H(s)$ on the root locus?

A. Adding left-half plane zeros to the function $G(s)H(s)$ generally has the effect of moving and bending the root loci towards the left-half of the s-plane. So the relative stability of the system is improved by the addition of a zero.

REVIEW QUESTIONS

1. Write short notes on root locus.
2. Write the properties of the root locus.

FILL IN THE BLANKS

1. The root locus technique was introduced by _____.
2. The root locus can be used to solve higher-order _____ equations.
3. The root locus is a powerful technique as it brings into focus the complete _____ of the system.
4. The magnitude and phase conditions are not _____ of each other and one _____ the other.
5. For any point s_0 in the s-plane to lie on the root locus, the phase angle condition to be satisfied at that point is _____.
6. For any point s_0 in the s-plane to lie on the root locus, the magnitude condition to be satisfied is _____.
7. A plot of points in the complex s-plane satisfying the angle criterion $\angle G(s)H(s) = \pm(2q + 1)\pi$; $q = 0, 1, 2 \ldots$, is the _____.
8. The root locus can give information about _____ stability as well as _____ stability of a control system.
9. The root locus is _____ about the real axis.
10. In drawing the root locus, usually _____ is increased from 0 to ∞.

11. As K is increased from 0 to ∞, each branch of the root locus originates at _____ where _____ and terminates on an _____ or a _____ where _____.

12. The number of branches of the root locus terminating on infinity is equal to _____.

13. The number of asymptotes in a root locus plot is equal to _____.

14. For any point on the real axis to lie on the root locus, the total number of open-loop poles and open-loop zeros to the right of that point must be _____.

15. An asymptote is a _____ along which the root locus is supposed to travel to reach the zero at infinity.

16. The point of intersection of asymptotes on the real axis is called _____ and is given by _____.

17. The points in the s-plane where multiple roots of the characteristic equation exist are called _____.

18. The breakaway point can be either _____ or _____.

19. The break points are given by the solution of _____.

20. For all real poles and zeros, the angles of departure and arrival are either _____ or _____.

21. The angle of departure from a complex pole is given by $\theta_d =$ _____ where ϕ is the _____.

22. The angle of arrival at a complex zero is given by $\theta_a =$ _____ where ϕ is the _____.

23. The value of K at any point s_0 on the root locus is given by $K =$ _____.

24. The point of intersection of the root locus with the imaginary axis and the critical value of K can be determined using _____.

25. Dominant poles are the poles which are _____.

OBJECTIVE TYPE QUESTIONS

1. The root locus is
   (a) an algebraic method
   (b) a graphical method
   (c) combination of both
   (d) none of these

2. The root locus is a
   (a) time-domain approach
   (b) frequency domain approach
   (c) combination of both
   (d) none of these

3. The root locus can be applied to
   (a) only linear systems
   (b) only nonlinear systems
   (c) both linear and nonlinear systems
   (d) none of these

4. The root locus can be used to determine
   (a) the absolute stability of a system
   (b) the relative stability of a system
   (c) both absolute and relative stabilities of a system
   (d) none of these

5. The root locus always starts at the
   (a) open-loop poles   (b) open-loop zeros
   (c) closed-loop poles   (d) closed-loop zeros

6. The root locus always terminates on the
   (a) open-loop zeros   (b) closed-loop zeros
   (c) roots of the characteristic equation   (d) none of these

7. The root locus gives the locus of
   (a) open-loop poles   (b) closed-loop poles
   (c) both open-loop and closed-loop poles   (d) none of these

8. An open-loop transfer function has 4 poles and 1 zero. The number of branches of root locus is
   (a) 4   (b) 1
   (c) 5   (d) 3

9. The open-loop transfer function of a system is $G(s)H(s) = \dfrac{K(s+2)}{s(s+3)(s+4)}$. Its centroid is at $s =$
   (a) −2.5   (b) −4
   (c) −4.5   (d) 0

10. The open-loop transfer function of a control system has 5 poles and 3 zeros. The number of asymptotes is equal to
    (a) 5   (b) 3
    (c) 2   (d) 8

11. Asymptotes can intersect
    (a) only on the negative real axis   (b) only on the positive real axis
    (c) any where on the real axis   (d) none of these

12. Angles of asymptotes are measured at the centroid with respect to
    (a) negative real axis   (b) positive real axis
    (c) imaginary axis   (d) none of these

13. Break points can be
    (a) only real   (b) only complex
    (c) real or complex (d) none of these

14. The open-loop transfer function of a system is $G(s)H(s) = \dfrac{K(s+4)}{s(s+2)}$. Its break points are

(a) −1.18 and −6.82

(b) −2 and −4

(c) −1.82 and 6.82

(d) none of these

15. The angle of departure from a real pole is always

(a) 0°

(b) 180°

(c) either 0° or 180°

(d) to be calculated for each problem

16. The angle of arrival at a real zero is always

(a) 0°

(b) 180°

(c) either 0° or 180°

(d) to be calculated for each problem

17. The root locus can be used to solve higher-order

(a) differential equations

(b) algebraic equations

(c) differential equations as well as algebraic equations

(d) none of these

18. The roots of the characteristic equation are the same as

(a) open-loop poles

(b) open-loop zeros

(c) closed-loop poles

(d) closed-loop zeros

PROBLEMS

6.1 Draw the complete root locus for the system with an open-loop transfer function

$$G(s)H(s) = \frac{K(s+4)}{s(s+2)}$$

Show that part of the root locus is a circle. Find ξ_{min} and the value of K for that ξ_{min}. Also find the roots of the characteristic equation for that value of K. Determine the range of values of K for which the system is (a) overdamped, (b) underdamped and (c) critically damped.

6.2 Draw the complete root locus for the system with

$$G(s)H(s) = \frac{K(s+2)}{s^2 + 2s + 2}$$

Show that part of the root locus is a circle.

6.3 Draw the complete root locus for the system with

$$G(s)H(s) = \frac{K(s+5)}{s(s+1)(s+2)}$$

Determine the value of K for $\xi = 0.5$. For that value of K obtain the closed-loop transfer function. Determine the range of values of K for which the second order system is (a) overdamped, (b) critically damped and (c) underdamped.

6.4 Draw the complete root locus for the system described by

$$G(s)H(s) = \frac{K(s+3)}{s(s^2+s+2)}$$

6.5 Draw the complete root locus for the system with

$$G(s)H(s) = \frac{K}{s^2+2s+2}$$

6.6 Draw the complete root locus for the system with

$$G(s)H(s) = \frac{K(s^2+4s+5)}{s^2(s^2+6s+9)}$$

6.7 Draw the complete root locus for the system with

$$G(s)H(s) = \frac{K(s+1)(s+4)}{s(s^2-2)}$$

6.8 Draw the complete root locus for the system with

$$G(s)H(s) = \frac{K(s^2-1)(s+2)}{s(s^2+2s+2)}$$

6.9 Draw the complete root locus for a system with

$$G(s)H(s) = \frac{K(s+0.5)(s+2)}{s(s+1)(s-1)}$$

6.10 Draw the complete root locus for a system with

$$G(s)H(s) = \frac{2K(s+5)}{s^2(s^2+2s+2)}$$

6.11 Draw the complete root locus for a system with

$$G(s)H(s) = \frac{K(s+12)}{s^2(s+20)}$$

6.12 Sketch the root locus for the system with

$$G(s)H(s) = \frac{K}{s(s^2+6s+13)}$$

6.13 Sketch the root locus for the system with

$$G(s)H(s) = \frac{K(s+2)(s+3)}{(s+1)(s-1)}$$

Show that part of the root locus is a circle.

6.14 Sketch the root locus of the unity feedback system with open-loop transfer function

$$G(s) = \frac{K(s+2)}{(s+1)^2}$$

Show that part of the root locus is a circle. Find ξ_{min} and the corresponding value of K. Also find the transfer function for this ξ_{min}. Determine the range of values of K for which the system is (a) overdamped, (b) critically damped and (c) underdamped.

6.15 A unity feedback control system has an open-loop transfer function

$$G(s) = \frac{K}{s(s^2 + 4s + 13)}$$

Sketch the complete root locus of the system.

6.16 Sketch the root locus for the control system with

$$G(s)H(s) = \frac{K(s+4)}{s^2 + 4s + 8}$$

Show that part of the root locus is a circle.

6.17 Sketch the root locus of the open-loop transfer function

$$G(s)H(s) = \frac{K(s^2 + 6s + 25)}{s(s+1)(s+2)}$$

as K varies from zero to infinity.

[**Note:** The Root Locus plots for the above 17 problems obtained using Matlab programs are given below.]

MATLAB PROGRAMS

PROGRAM 6.1

Matlab program for complete root locus for the system with open-loop transfer function

$$G(s)H(s) = \frac{K(s+4)}{s(s+2)}$$

```
clc
clear all
close all
a=tf([1 4],1)
b=poly([0 -2])
c=tf(b,1)
d=a/c
rlocus(d)
axis equal;
axis([-10 2 -4.5 4.5])
```

Output:

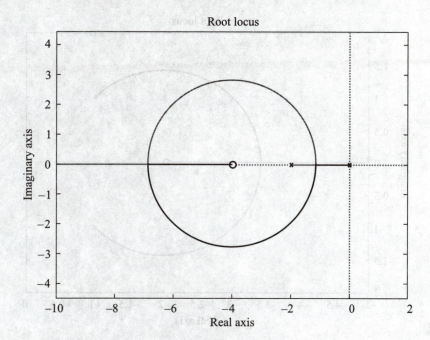

PROGRAM 6.2

Matlab program for complete root locus for the system with open-loop transfer function

$$G(s)H(s) = \frac{K(s+2)}{s^2 + 2s + 2}$$

```
clc
clear all
close all
a=tf([1 2],1);
c=tf([1 2 2],1);
d=a/c;
rlocus(d)
axis equal;
axis([-5 0 -2 2])
```

Output:

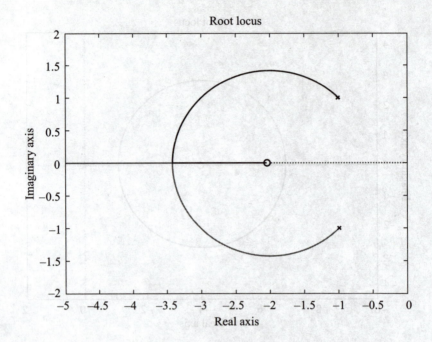

PROGRAM 6.3

Matlab program for complete root locus for the system with open-loop transfer function

$$G(s)H(s) = \frac{K(s+5)}{s(s+1)(s+2)}$$

```
clc
clear all
close all
a=tf([1 5],1);
b=poly([0 -1 -2]);
c=tf(b,1);
d=a/c;
rlocus(d)
axis equal;
axis([-8 4 -4.5 4.5])
```

Output:

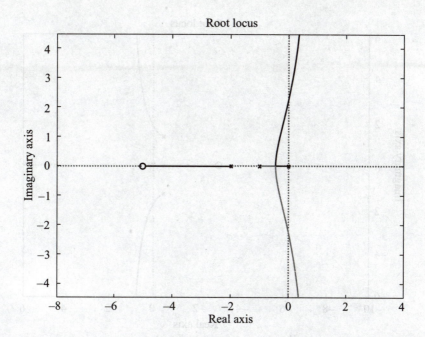

PROGRAM 6.4

Matlab program for complete root locus for the system with open-loop transfer function

$$G(s)H(s) = \frac{K(s+3)}{s(s^2 + s + 2)}$$

```
clc
clear all
close all
a=tf([1 3],1)
c=tf([1 1 2 0],1)
d=a/c
rlocus(d)
axis equal;
axis([-10 6 6 6])
```

Output:

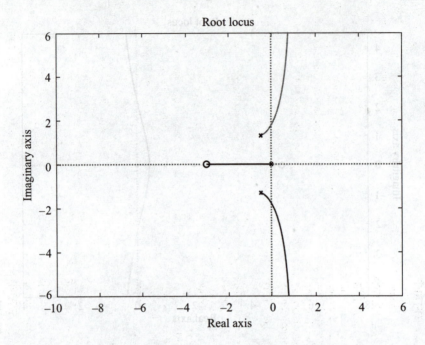

PROGRAM 6.5

Matlab program for complete root locus for the system with open-loop transfer function

$$G(s)H(s) = \frac{K}{s^2 + 2s + 2}$$

```
clc
clear all
close all
c=tf(1,[1 2 2])
rlocus(c)
axis equal;
axis([-6 2 -3  3])
```

Output:

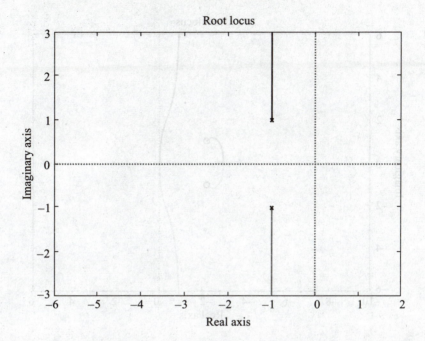

Root locus

PROGRAM 6.6

Matlab program for complete root locus for the system with open-loop transfer function

$$G(s)H(s) = \frac{K(s^2 + 4s + 5)}{s^2(s^2 + 6s + 9)}$$

```
clc
clear all
close all
a=tf(1,[1 6 9])
b=poly([0 0])
c=tf(1,b)
x=tf([1 4 5],1)
d=a*c*x
rlocus(d)
axis equal;
axis([-10 6 -6 6])
```

Output:

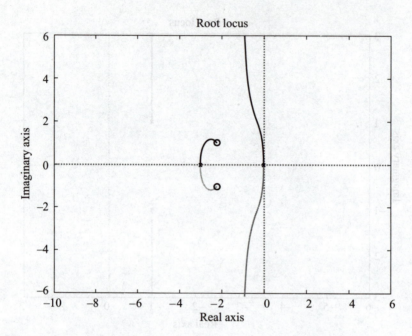

Root locus

PROGRAM 6.7

Matlab program for complete root locus for the system with open-loop transfer function

$$G(s)H(s) = \frac{K(s+1)(s+4)}{s(s^2-2)}$$

```
clc
clear all
close all
x=poly([-1 -4])
a=tf(x,1)
b=poly([0 -sqrt(2) sqrt(2)])
c=tf(b,1)
d=a/c
rlocus(d)
axis equal;
axis([-12 4 -6 6])
```

Output:

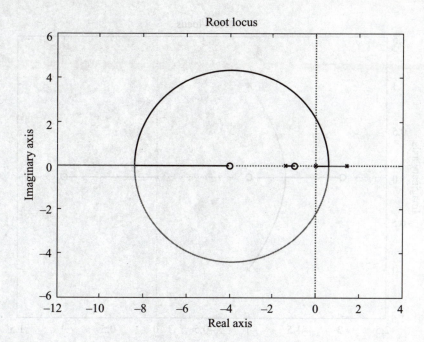

PROGRAM 6.8

Matlab program for complete root locus for the system with open-loop transfer function

$$G(s)H(s) = \frac{K(s^2 - 1)(s + 2)}{s(s^2 + 2s + 2)}$$

```
clc
clear all
close all
x=poly([1 -1 -2])
a=tf(x,1)
y=tf(1,[1 2 2])
b=poly([0])
c=tf(1,b)
d=a*y*c
rlocus(d)
axis equal;
```

Output:

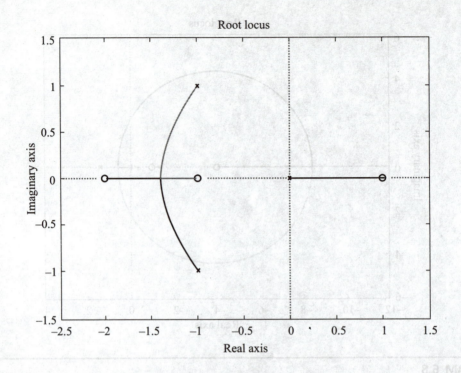

Root locus

PROGRAM 6.9

Matlab program for complete root locus for the system with open-loop transfer function

$$G(s)H(s) = \frac{K(s+0.5)(s+2)}{s(s+1)(s-1)}$$

```
clc
clear all
close all
x=poly([-0.5 -2])
a=tf(x,1)
b=poly([0 -1 1])
c=tf(b,1)
d=a/c
rlocus(d)
axis equal;
axis([-6 2 -3 3])
```

Output:

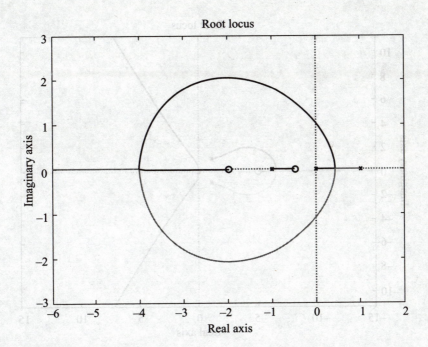

Root locus

PROGRAM 6.10

Matlab program for complete root locus for the system with open-loop transfer function

$$G(s)H(s) = \frac{2K(s+5)}{s^2(s^2+2s+2)}$$

```
clc
clear all
close all
x=poly([-5])
a=tf(x,1)
y=tf(1,[1 2 2])
b=poly([0 0])
c=tf(1,b)
d=2*a*y*c
rlocus(d)
axis equal;
axis([-15 15 -11.25 11.25])
```

Output:

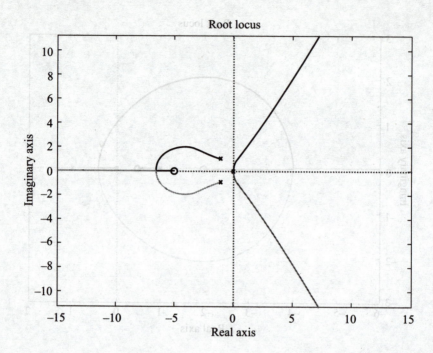

Root locus

PROGRAM 6.11

Matlab program for complete root locus for the system with open-loop transfer function

$$G(s)H(s) = \frac{K(s+12)}{s^2(s+20)}$$

```
clc
clear all
close all
a=tf([1 12],1)
b=poly([0 0 -20])
c=tf(b,1)
d=a/c
rlocus(d)
axis equal;
axis([-40 20 -22.5 22.5])
```

Output:

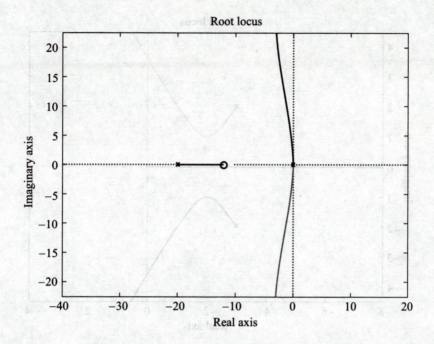

PROGRAM 6.12

Matlab program for complete root locus for the system with open-loop transfer function

$$G(s)H(s) = \frac{K}{s(s^2 + 6s + 13)}$$

```
clc
clear all
close all
a=tf(1,[1 6 13 0])
b=poly([0])
c=tf(1,b)
d=a*c
rlocus(a)
axis equal;
axis([-8 4 -4.5 4.5])
```

Output:

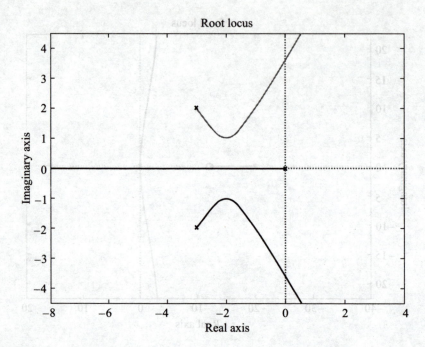

Root locus

PROGRAM 6.13

Matlab program for complete root locus for the system with open-loop transfer function

$$G(s)H(s) = \frac{K(s+2)(s+3)}{(s+1)(s-1)}$$

```
clc
clear all
close all
x=poly([-2 -3])
a=tf(x,1)
b=poly([-1 1])
c=tf(b,1)
d=a/c
rlocus(d)
axis equal;
axis([-3.5 0.5 -1.5 1.5])
```

Output:

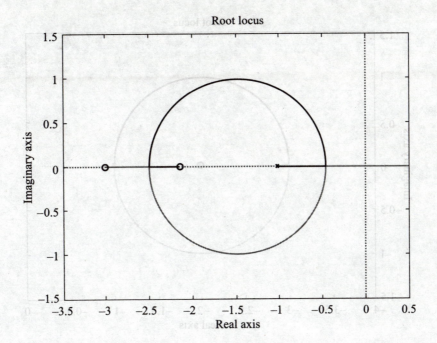

Root locus

PROGRAM 6.14

Matlab program for complete root locus of the unity feedback system with open-loop transfer function

$$G(s) = \frac{K(s+2)}{(s+1)^2}$$

```
clc
clear all
close all
a=tf([1 2],1);
c=tf([1 2 1],1);
d=a/c;
rlocus(d)
axis equal;
axis([-4 0 -1.5 1.5])
```

Output:

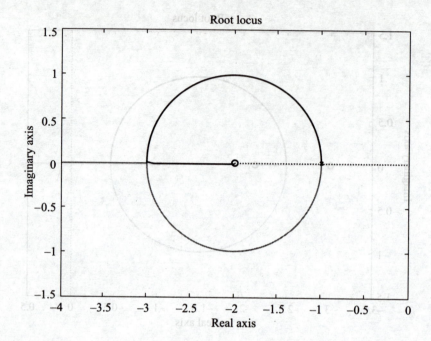

PROGRAM 6.15

Matlab program for complete root locus for the system with open-loop transfer function

$$G(s)\,H(s) = \frac{K}{s(s^2 + 4s + 13)}$$

```
clc
clear all
close all
y=tf(1,[1 4 13])
b=poly([0])
c=tf(1,b)
d=y*c
rlocus(d)
axis equal;
axis([-15 15 -11.25 11.25])
```

Output:

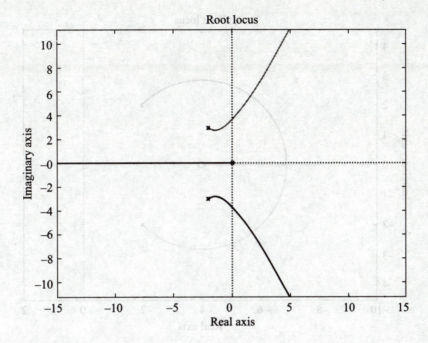

Root locus

PROGRAM 6.16

Matlab program for complete root locus for the system with open-loop transfer function

$$G(s)\,H(s) = \frac{K(s+4)}{s^2 + 4s + 8}$$

```
clc
clear all
close all
a=tf([1 4],1);
c=tf([1 4 8],1);
d=a/c;
rlocus(d)
axis equal;
axis([-10 2 -4.5 4.5])
```

Output:

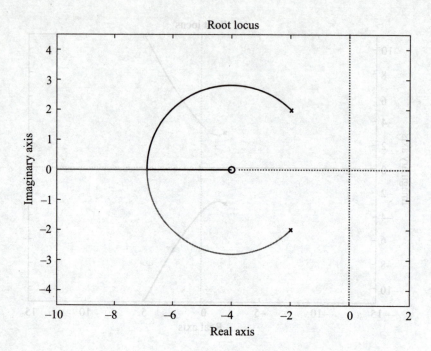

Root locus

PROGRAM 6.17

Matlab program for complete root locus for the system with open-loop transfer function

$$G(s)\,H(s) = \frac{K(s^2 + 6s + 25)}{s(s+1)(s+2)}$$

```
clc
clear all
close all
a=tf([1 6 25],1)
b=poly([0 -1 -2])
c=tf(b,1)
d=a/c
rlocus(d)
axis equal;
```

Output:

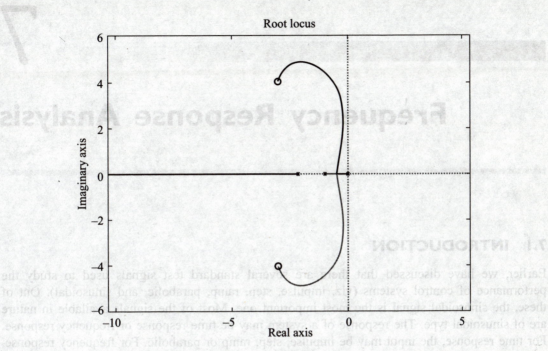

Root locus

7

Frequency Response Analysis

7.1 INTRODUCTION

Earlier, we have discussed that there are several standard test signals used to study the performance of control systems (viz. impulse, step, ramp, parabolic, and sinusoidal). Out of these, the sinusoidal signal is the most important one. Most of the signals available in nature are of sinusoidal type. The response of a system may be time response or frequency response. For time response, the input may be impulse, step, ramp or parabolic. For frequency response, the input must be sinusoidal. Consider a linear system, with a sinusoidal input.

$$r(t) = A \sin \omega t$$

Under steady-state, the system output as well as the signals at all other points in the system are sinusoidal. The steady-state out may be written as

$$c(t) = B \sin (\omega t + \phi)$$

The magnitude and phase relationship between the sinusoidal input and the steady-state output of a system is termed the *frequency response*. In linear time-invariant systems, the frequency response is independent of the amplitude and phase of the input signal.

The frequency response test on a system or a component is normally performed by keeping the amplitude A fixed and determining B and ϕ for a suitable range of frequencies.

The advantages of frequency response analysis are as follows:

1. Signal generators and precise measuring instruments are readily available for various ranges of frequencies and amplitudes.

2. The ease and accuracy of measurements is another advantage of the frequency response method.

3. Wherever it is not possible to obtain the form of the transfer function of a system through analytical techniques, the necessary information to compute its transfer function can be extracted by performing the frequency response test on the system. The step

response test can also be performed easily, but the extraction of transfer function from the step response data is quite a laborious procedure.

4. The design and parameter adjustment of the open-loop transfer function of a system for a specified closed-loop performance is carried out some what more easily in frequency-domain (i.e. through frequency response) than in time-domain (i.e. through time response).

5. The effects of noise disturbance and parameter variations are relatively easy to visualize and assess through frequency response.

6. If necessary, the transient response of a system can be obtained from its frequency response through the Fourier integral. This correlation between time and frequency response is quite tedious to compute except for first- and second-order systems. Usually, for the sake of simplicity and ease of analysis, the correlation between frequency and time response of a second-order system is employed as an approximation to higher-order systems as well. Through the use of this approximate correlation, a satisfactory transient response for higher-order systems can be achieved by the adjustment of their frequency response.

The drawbacks of frequency response method are as follows:

1. For systems with very large time constants, the frequency response test is cumbersome to perform, as the time required for the output to reach the steady-state for each frequency of the test signal is excessively long. Therefore, the frequency response test is not recommended for systems with very large time constants.

2. The frequency response test obviously cannot be performed on non-interruptable systems. Under such circumstances, a single shot test (step or impulse) is more convenient even though the computation of the transfer function from it gets involved.

An interesting and revealing comparison of frequency and time-domain approaches is based on the relative stability studies of feedback systems. The Routh stability criterion is a time-domain approach, which establishes with relative ease the stability of a system, but its adoption to determine the relative stability is involved and requires repeated application of the criterion. The root locus method is a very powerful time-domain approach as it reveals not only stability, but also the actual time response of the system. On the other hand, the Nyquist criterion is a powerful frequency-domain method of extracting the information regarding stability as well as relative stability of a system without the need to evaluate the roots of the characteristic equation.

The frequency response is easily evaluated from the sinusoidal transfer function which can be obtained simply by replacing s with $j\omega$ in the system transfer function $T(s)$. The transfer function $T(j\omega)$ thus obtained, is a complex function of frequency and has both magnitude and phase angle. These characteristics are conveniently represented by graphical plots.

7.2 CORRELATION BETWEEN TIME AND FREQUENCY RESPONSE

The correlation between time and frequency response has an explicit form only for systems of first- and second-order.

7.2.1 Second-Order Systems

The standard form of the transfer function of a second-order system shown in Figure 7.1 is

$$\frac{C(s)}{R(s)} = \frac{\omega_n^2}{s^2 + 2\xi\omega_n s + \omega_n^2}$$

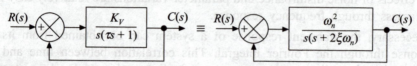

Figure 7.1   A second-order system.

The sinusoidal transfer function of the system is

$$\frac{C}{R}(j\omega) = T(j\omega) = \frac{\omega_n^2}{(j\omega)^2 + 2\xi\omega_n(j\omega) + \omega_n^2} \qquad (7.1)$$

Dividing the numerator and denominator of Eq. (7.1) by ω_n^2, we get

$$T(j\omega) = \frac{1}{1 - (\omega/\omega_n)^2 + j2\xi\omega/\omega_n} \qquad (7.2)$$

Putting $(\omega/\omega_n) = u$ in Eq. (7.2), where u is the normalized driving signal frequency, we get

$$T(j\omega) = \frac{1}{1 - u^2 + j2\xi u} \qquad (7.3)$$

$$\therefore \quad |T(j\omega)| = M = \frac{1}{\sqrt{(1-u^2)^2 + (2\xi u)^2}} \qquad (7.4)$$

and

$$\angle T(j\omega) = \phi = -\tan^{-1}\frac{2\xi u}{1-u^2} \qquad (7.5)$$

The steady-state output of the system for a sinusoidal input of unit magnitude and variable frequency ω is given by

$$c(t) = \frac{1}{\sqrt{(1-u^2)^2 + (2\xi u)^2}} \sin\left(\omega t - \tan^{-1}\frac{2\xi u}{1-u^2}\right)$$

From the equations of M and ϕ [Eqs. (7.4) and (7.5)], it is seen that when

$$u = 0, \qquad M = 1 \qquad \text{and} \qquad \phi = 0$$
$$u = 1, \qquad M = (1/2\xi) \qquad \text{and} \qquad \phi = -90°$$
$$u \to \infty, \qquad M \to 0 \qquad \text{and} \qquad \phi = -\pi$$

The magnitude and phase angle characteristic for normalized frequency u for certain values of ξ are shown in Figure 7.2(a) and Figure 7.2(b), respectively.

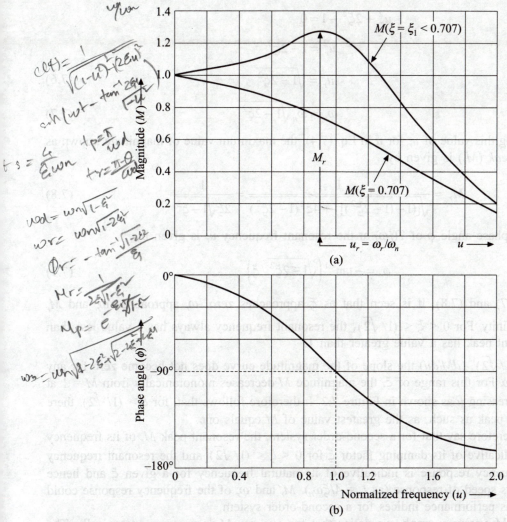

Figure 7.2 (a) Frequency response magnitude characteristic and (b) frequency response phase characteristic.

The frequency, where M has a peak value, is known as the *resonant frequency*. At this frequency, the slope of the magnitude curve is zero. Let ω_r be the resonant frequency and $u_r = (\omega_r/\omega_n)$ be the normalized resonant frequency. Then,

$$\frac{dM}{du}\bigg|_{u_r} = -\frac{1}{2} \cdot \frac{2(1-u_r^2)(-2u_r) + 8\xi^2 u_r}{[(1-u_r^2)^2 + (2\xi u_r)^2]^{3/2}} = 0$$

which gives

$$(1 - u_r^2)(-u_r) + 2\xi^2 u_r = 0$$

i.e.

$$u_r^2 + 2\xi^2 - 1 = 0$$

i.e.

$$u_r^2 = 1 - 2\xi^2$$

∴

$$u_r = \sqrt{1 - 2\xi^2} \quad natural\ freq \tag{7.6}$$

or

$$\omega_r = \omega_n \sqrt{1 - 2\xi^2} \tag{7.7}$$

Substituting this value of u_r for u in Eq. (7.4), the maximum value of magnitude known as the *resonant peak* (M_r) is given by

$$M_r = \frac{1}{\sqrt{[(1 - (1 - 2\xi^2)]^2 + 4\xi^2(1 - 2\xi^2)}} = \frac{1}{2\xi\sqrt{1 - \xi^2}} \tag{7.8}$$

Similarly, the phase angle ϕ of $T(j\omega)$ at the resonant frequency u_r is given by

$$\phi_r = -\tan^{-1}\left(\sqrt{1 - 2\xi^2}/\xi\right) \tag{7.9}$$

From Eqs. (7.7) and (7.8), it is seen that as ξ approaches zero, ω_r approaches ω_n and M_r approaches infinity. For $0 < \xi < (1/\sqrt{2})$, the resonant frequency always has a value less than ω_n and resonant peak has a value greater than 1.

For $\xi > (1/\sqrt{2})$, (dM/du) the slope of the magnitude curve does not become zero for any real value of ω. For this range of ξ, the magnitude M decreases monotonically from $M = 1$ at $u = 0$ with increasing u as shown in Figure 7.2. It therefore follows that, for $\xi > (1/\sqrt{2})$, there is no resonant peak as such, as the greatest value of M equals one.

We can therefore say that for a second-order system, the resonant peak M_r of its frequency response is indicative of its damping factor ξ for $0 < \xi < (1/\sqrt{2})$ and the resonant frequency ω_r of the frequency response is indicative of its natural frequency for a given ξ and hence indicative of its speed of response (as $t_s = 4/\xi\omega_n$). M_r and ω_r of the frequency response could thus be used as performance indices for a second-order system.

From the M_r versus u graph, we notice that for $\omega > \omega_r$, M decreases monotonically. The frequency at which M has a value of $(1/\sqrt{2})$ is of special significance and is called the cut-off frequency ω_c. The signal frequencies above cut-off are greatly attenuated in passing through a system.

For feedback control systems, the range of frequencies over which M is equal to or greater than $(1/\sqrt{2})$ is defined as bandwidth ω_b. Control systems being low-pass filters (at zero frequency, $M = 1$), the bandwidth ω_b is equal to the cut-off frequency.

In general, the bandwidth of a control system indicates the noise filtering characteristics of the system. Also bandwidth gives a measure of the transient response properties.

Expression for bandwidth: Typical magnitude versus frequency characteristic of a feedback control system is shown in Figure 7.3. At the cut-off frequency ($M = 1/\sqrt{2}$),

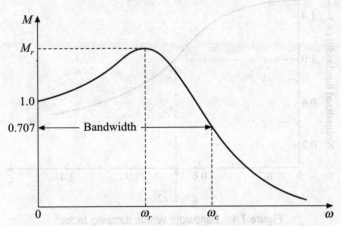

Figure 7.3 Typical magnification curve of a feedback control system.

$$M = \frac{1}{\sqrt{(1 - u_b^2)^2 + (2\xi u_b)^2}} = \frac{1}{\sqrt{2}}$$

or

$$u_b^4 - 2(1 - 2\xi^2)u_b^2 - 1 = 0$$

$\therefore$

$$u_b^2 = \frac{2(1 - 2\xi^2) \pm \sqrt{[2(1 - 2\xi^2)^2]^2 + 4}}{2}$$

$$= 1 - 2\xi^2 \pm \sqrt{1 + 4\xi^4 - 4\xi^2 + 1}$$

or

$$u_b = \sqrt{1 - 2\xi^2 + \sqrt{2 - 4\xi^2 + 4\xi^4}} \qquad (7.10)$$

As the bandwidth must be a positive real quantity, the negative sign in quadratic solution and the negative sign in taking the square root have been discarded.

Notice that the normalized bandwidth is a function of ξ only. The normalized bandwidth u_b versus damping ratio ξ plot is shown in Figure 7.4.

The denormalized bandwidth is given by

$$\omega_b = \omega_n \left[1 - 2\xi^2 + \sqrt{2 - 4\xi^2 + 4\xi^4}\right]^{1/2} \qquad (7.11)$$

Now considering the step response of the system, the expressions for the damped frequency of oscillation ω_d and peak overshoot M_p for $0 \le \xi \le 1$ are as follows:

$$\omega_d = \omega_n \sqrt{1 - \xi^2}$$

and

$$M_p = e^{-\pi\xi/\sqrt{1-\xi^2}}$$

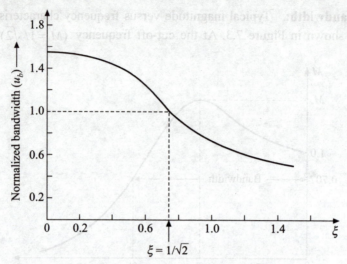

Figure 7.4 Bandwidth versus damping factor.

M_r, the resonant peak of the frequency response, and M_p, the peak overshoot of the step response for a second-order system are plotted in Figure 7.5 for various values of ξ.

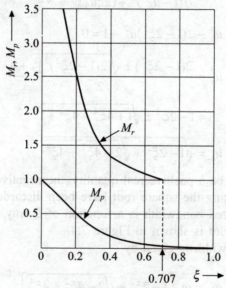

Figure 7.5 M_r, M_p versus ξ.

The comparison of M_r and M_p plots shows that for $0 < \xi < (1/\sqrt{2})$, the two performance indices are correlated as both are functions of the same damping factor ξ only. It means that a system with a given value of M_r of its frequency response must exhibit a corresponding value of M_p if subjected to a step input. For $\xi > (1/\sqrt{2})$, the resonant peak M_r does not exist and the correlation breaks down. For $\xi > (1/\sqrt{2})$, the step response oscillations are well damped and M_p is hardly perceptible.

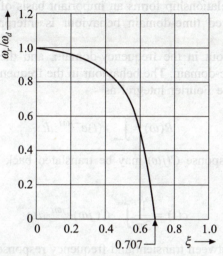

Figure 7.6 Correlation between ω_r and ω_d.

Similarly, the comparison of expressions for the resonant frequency ω_r of frequency response and the damped frequency of oscillations ω_d of step response reveals that there exists a definite correlation between them. The ratio of these two expressions is

$$\omega_r / \omega_d = \sqrt{(1 - 2\xi^2)/(1 - \xi^2)}$$

which is also a function of ξ and is plotted in Figure 7.6.

It is further observed from the expression for ω_b [i.e. Eq. (7.11)] that the bandwidth, a frequency-domain concept, is indicative of the undamped natural frequency ω_n of a system for a given ξ and therefore indicative of speed of response ($t_s = 4/\xi\omega_n$) a time-domain concept.

In time-domain, relative stability is measured by parameters such as maximum overshoot and damping ratio. In frequency-domain, the resonant peak M_r can be used to indicate relative stability.

Bandwidth and rise time are inversely proportional to each other. Therefore, the larger the bandwidth is, the faster the system will respond.

Increasing ω_n increases bandwidth, and decreases the rise time t_r, i.e. bandwidth is directly proportional to ω_n and t_r is inversely proportional to ω_n.

Increasing ξ decreases bandwidth and increases t_r. Bandwidth and M_r are directly proportional to each other.

M_r depends only on ξ. Larger values of M_r correspond to larger values of maximum overshoot in the step response. M_p also depends only on ξ.

The general effect of adding a zero to the forward path transfer function is to increase the bandwidth of the closed-loop system.

The effect of adding a pole to the forward path transfer function is to make the closed-loop system less stable, while decreasing the bandwidth.

7.2.2 Higher-Order Systems

In general, the transient response and frequency response of linear systems are related through the Fourier integral. This relationship forms an important basis of most design procedures and criteria. Usually, the desired time-domain behaviour is interpreted in terms of frequency response characteristics.

The design is carried out in the frequency-domain, and the frequency response is then translated back into the time-domain. The behaviour in the frequency-domain of a given driving function $r(t)$ is given by the Fourier integral as

$$R(\omega) = \int_{-\infty}^{\infty} r(t)e^{-j\omega t}\, dt$$

Similarly, the frequency response $C(j\omega)$ may be translated back into the time-domain by the inverse Fourier integral as

$$c(t) = \frac{1}{2\pi} \int_{-\infty}^{\infty} C(j\omega)e^{j\omega t}\, d\omega$$

However, the correlation between transient and frequency response through the Fourier integral is highly laborious to compute. So second-order correlations can be used for higher-order systems as well. Whenever a higher-order system has a transfer function which is dominated by a pair of complex conjugate poles, it can be approximated by a second-order system whose poles are the dominant poles of the higher-order system. When such an approximation is possible, all the time-domain and frequency-domain correlations of a second-order system become valid for use in higher-order systems. The design based on these correlations proceeds much faster though it is not exact.

Example 7.1 (a) Consider the feedback system shown in Figure 7.7. Find the values of K and b to satisfy the following frequency-domain specifications: $M_r = 1.1$, $\omega_r = 12$ rad/s. (b) For the values of K and b determined in part (a), calculate the settling time and bandwidth of the system.

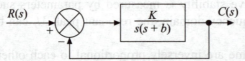

$$R(s) \longrightarrow \bigotimes \xrightarrow{} \boxed{\frac{K}{s(s+b)}} \longrightarrow C(s)$$

Figure 7.7 Example 7.1: Feedback system.

Solution: The closed-loop transfer function of the system shown in Figure 7.7 is

$$\frac{C(s)}{R(s)} = \frac{\dfrac{K}{s(s+b)}}{1 + \dfrac{K}{s(s+b)}} = \frac{K}{s^2 + bs + K}$$

Comparing it with the standard form of the closed-loop transfer function of a second-order system

$$\frac{K}{s^2 + bs + K} = \frac{\omega_n^2}{s^2 + 2\xi\omega_n s + \omega_n^2}$$

We have

$$\omega_n^2 = K$$

or

$$\omega_n = \sqrt{K}$$

$$2\xi\omega_n = b$$

or

$$\xi = \frac{b}{2\omega_n} = \frac{b}{2\sqrt{K}}$$

i.e.

$$\xi^2 = \frac{b^2}{4K}$$

We know

$$M_r = \frac{1}{2\xi\sqrt{1-\xi^2}} = 1.1$$

$\therefore$

$$1.1^2 = \frac{1}{4\xi^2(1-\xi^2)} = \frac{1}{\dfrac{4b^2}{4K}\left(1 - \dfrac{b^2}{4K}\right)} = \frac{1}{\dfrac{b^2}{K}\left[1 - \dfrac{b^2}{4K}\right]}$$

and

$$\omega_r = \omega_n\sqrt{1 - 2\xi^2} = 12$$

$\therefore$

$$12^2 = \omega_n^2(1 - 2\xi^2) = K\left(1 - 2\frac{b^2}{4K}\right)$$

or

$$144 = K - \frac{b^2}{2}$$

i.e.

$$b^2 = 2K - 288 \qquad\qquad\qquad (i)$$

$$1.21 = \frac{1}{\dfrac{b^2}{K}\left(1 - \dfrac{b^2}{4K}\right)}$$

i.e.

$$\frac{b^2}{K}\left(\frac{4K - b^2}{4K}\right) = \frac{1}{1.21}$$

$\therefore$

$$b^2(4K - b^2) = \frac{4K^2}{1.21} = 3.305K^2 \qquad\qquad\qquad (ii)$$

Substituting Eq. (i) in Eq. (ii), we get

i.e. $\qquad (2K - 288)(4K - 2K + 288) = 3.305K^2$

i.e. $\qquad (2K - 288)(2K + 288) = 3.305K^2$

i.e. $\qquad 4K^2 - 288^2 = 3.305K^2$

i.e. $\qquad 0.695K^2 = 288^2$

or $\qquad K^2 = 288^2/0.695 = (288/0.833)^2$

or $\qquad K = 345.7$

Therefore, $\qquad b = \sqrt{2K - 288} = \sqrt{2 \times 345.7 - 288} = 20.08$

$$\omega_n = \sqrt{K} = \sqrt{345.7} = 18.593 \text{ rad/s}$$

$$\xi = \frac{b}{2\sqrt{K}} = \frac{20.08}{2 \times 18.593} = 0.54$$

Settling time

$$t_s = \frac{4}{\xi\omega_n} = \frac{4}{0.54 \times 18.593} = \frac{4}{10.04} = 0.398 \text{ s (for 2\% criterion)}$$

$$t_s = \frac{3}{\xi\omega_n} = \frac{3}{0.54 \times 18.593} = \frac{3}{10.04} = 0.298 \text{ s (for 5\% criterion)}$$

The bandwidth

$$\omega_b = \omega_n \left[1 - 2\xi^2 + \sqrt{(2 - 4\xi^2 + 4\xi^4)} \right]^{1/2}$$

$$= 18.593 \left[1 - 2 \times 0.54^2 + \sqrt{2 - 4 \times 0.54^2 + 4 \times 0.54^4} \right]^{1/2}$$

$$= 22.068 \text{ rad/s}$$

The result is

(a) For $M_r = 1.1$, $\omega_r = 12$ rad/s, $K = 345.7$ and $b = 20.08$

(b) For $K = 345.7$, $b = 20.08$, $t_s = 0.398$ s or 0.298 s and BW $= 22.068$ rad/s

Example 7.2   A unit-step response test conducted on a second-order system yielded peak overshoot $M_p = 0.12$, and peak time $t_p = 0.2$ s. Obtain the corresponding frequency response indices (M_r, ω_r, ω_b) for the system.

Solution: The peak overshoot M_p is given by

$$M_p = e^{-\pi\xi/\sqrt{1-\xi^2}}$$

Taking natural logarithm on both sides,

$$\ln M_p = -\pi\xi/\sqrt{1-\xi^2}$$

Squaring both sides, we get

$$(\ln M_p)^2 = \pi^2 \xi^2 / 1 - \xi^2$$

On cross multiplying, we get

$$(1 - \xi^2)(\ln M_p)^2 = \pi^2 \xi^2$$

i.e.

$$\xi^2[\pi^2 + (\ln M_p)^2] = (\ln M_p)^2$$

∴

$$\xi^2 = \frac{[\ln M_p]^2}{\pi^2 + (\ln M_p)^2}$$

For $M_p = 0.12$,

$$\ln M_p = -2.12$$

or

$$(\ln M_p)^2 = 4.494$$

∴

$$\xi^2 = \frac{4.494}{9.869 + 4.494} = 0.3128$$

∴

$$\xi = \sqrt{0.3128} = 0.559$$

Therefore, resonant peak

$$M_r = \frac{1}{2\xi\sqrt{1-\xi^2}} = \frac{1}{2 \times 0.559\sqrt{1-0.559^2}} = 1.079$$

Given, the peak time

$$t_p = \frac{\pi}{\omega_d} = \frac{\pi}{\omega_n\sqrt{1-\xi^2}}$$

∴

$$\omega_n = \frac{\pi}{t_p\sqrt{1-\xi^2}}$$

The undamped natural frequency

$$\omega_n = \frac{\pi}{0.2\sqrt{1-0.559^2}} = 17.78 \text{ rad/s}$$

The resonant frequency

$$\omega_r = \omega_n\sqrt{1-2\xi^2} = 17.78\sqrt{1-2 \times 0.559^2} = 10.88 \text{ rad/s}$$

The bandwidth ω_b is given by

$$\omega_b = \omega_n\sqrt{1-2\xi^2 + \sqrt{2-4\xi^2+4\xi^4}}$$

$$= 17.78\sqrt{1 - 2 \times 0.559^2 + \sqrt{2 - 4 \times 0.559^2 - 4 \times 0.559^4}} = 21.36 \text{ rad/s}$$

The result is $M_r = 1.079$, $\omega_r = 10.88$ rad/s, and BW = 21.36 rad/s.

7.3 POLAR PLOTS

The sinusoidal transfer function $G(j\omega)$ is a complex function and is given by

$$G(j\omega) = Re[G(j\omega)] + jIm[G(j\omega)]$$

or
$$G(j\omega) = |G(j\omega)| \angle G(j\omega) = M\angle\phi \qquad (7.12)$$

From Eq. (7.12), it is seen that $G(j\omega)$ may be represented as a phasor of magnitude M and phase angle ϕ (measured positively in the counter clockwise direction). As the input frequency ω is varied from 0 to ∞, the magnitude M and phase angle ϕ change and hence the tip of the phasor $G(j\omega)$ traces a locus in the complex plane. The locus traced by the tip of the phasor $G(j\omega)$ as the frequency ω is varied from 0 to ∞ is known as *polar plot*.

As an example, consider a simple *RC* filter shown in Figure 7.8.

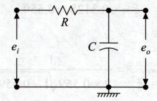

Figure 7.8 *RC filter circuit.*

$$\frac{E_o(s)}{E_i(s)} = G(s) = \frac{1/Cs}{R + \dfrac{1}{Cs}} = \frac{1}{1 + RCs} = \frac{1}{1 + Ts}$$

where $RC = T$.

Therefore, the sinusoidal transfer function is

$$G(j\omega) = \frac{1}{1 + j\omega T}$$

$$= \frac{1}{\sqrt{(1 + \omega^2 T^2)}} \angle - \tan^{-1} \omega T = M\angle\phi$$

The polar plot of $G(j\omega)$ as in the above equation is drawn in Figure 7.9(a).

When $\omega = 0$; $M = 1$ and $\phi = 0$. Therefore, the phasor at $\omega = 0$ has unit length and lies along the positive real axis. As ω increases, M decreases and phase angle increases negatively.

When $\omega = 1/T$; $M = 1/\sqrt{2}$ and $\phi = -45°$. As $\omega \to \infty$, M becomes zero and ϕ is $-90°$. This is represented by a phasor of zero length directed along the $-90°$ axis in the complex plane. In fact the locus of $G(j\omega)$ (polar plot) can be shown to be a semicircle.

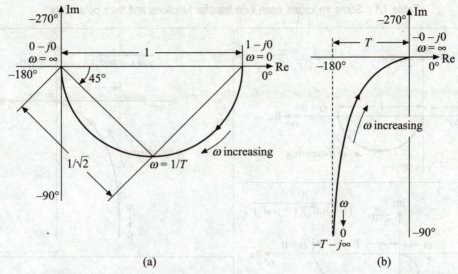

Figure 7.9 (a) Polar plot of $1/(1 + j\omega T)$ and (b) polar plot of $1/j\omega(1 + j\omega T)$.

In fact, the polar plots can be drawn very easily by rationalizing the sinusoidal transfer function, writing the real and imaginary parts, and finding the points $G(j0)$ and $G(j\infty)$, and drawing a smooth curve joining those points.

Consider now the transfer function

$$G(s) = \frac{1}{s(1 + Ts)}$$

The sinusoidal transfer function is

$$G(j\omega) = \frac{1}{j\omega(1 + j\omega T)}$$

Rationalizing,

$$G(j\omega) = \frac{1 - j\omega T}{j\omega(1 + j\omega T)(1 - j\omega T)} = \frac{-T}{1 + \omega^2 T^2} - j\frac{1}{\omega(1 + \omega^2 T^2)}$$

$$\underset{\omega \to 0}{\text{Lt}}\ G(j\omega) = G(j0) = -T - j\infty$$

$$\underset{\omega \to \infty}{\text{Lt}}\ G(j\omega) = G(j\infty) = -0 - j0$$

The shape of the polar plot of this transfer function is shown in Figure 7.9(b). The plot is asymptotic to the vertical line passing through the point $(-T, 0)$.

The major advantage of the polar plot lies in stability study of systems. Nyquist related the stability of a system to the form of these plots. Because of his work, polar plots are commonly referred to as Nyquist plots. The general shapes of the polar plots of some important open-loop transfer functions are shown in Table 7.1.

Table 7.1 Some important open-loop transfer functions and their polar plots.

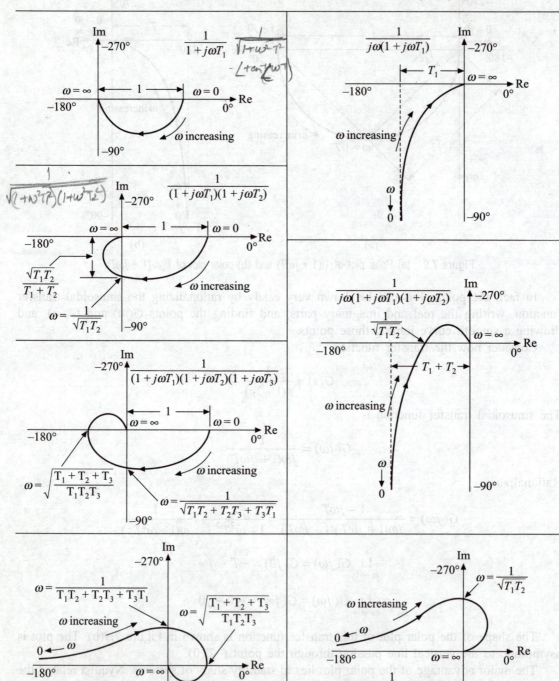

From the polar plots of Table 7.1, the following observations can be made.

1. Addition of a non-zero pole to a transfer function results in further rotation of the polar plot through an angle of $-90°$ as $\omega \to \infty$.
2. Addition of a pole at the origin to a transfer function rotates the polar plot at zero and infinite frequencies by a further angle of $-90°$.

The effect of addition of a zero to a transfer function is to rotate the high frequency portion of the polar plot by $90°$ in the counter clockwise direction.

7.3.1 Inverse Polar Plots

The inverse polar plot of $G(j\omega)$ is a graph of $1/G(j\omega)$ as a function of ω. For example, for the *RC* filter shown in Figure 7.8,

$$\frac{1}{G(j\omega)} = G^{-1}(j\omega) = 1 + j\omega T = \sqrt{(1+\omega^2 T^2)} \angle \tan^{-1} \omega T$$

The corresponding inverse polar plot is shown in Figure 7.10.

Inverse polar plots are valuable in stability study of non-unity feedback systems. They are also useful in applying the magnitude criterion.

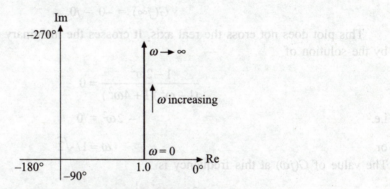

Figure 7.10 Inverse polar plot of $G(s) = 1/(1 + Ts)$.

Example 7.3 Sketch the polar plots of the transfer functions given below. Determine whether these plots cross the real axis. If so, determine the frequency at which the plots cross the real axis and the corresponding magnitude $|G(j\omega)|$.

(a) $G(s) = \dfrac{1}{(1+s)(1+2s)}$

(b) $G(s) = \dfrac{1+3s}{s(1+s)(1+2s)}$

(c) $G(s) = \dfrac{1}{s(1+s)(1+2s)}$

(d) $G(s) = \dfrac{1}{s^2(1+s)(1+2s)}$

(e) $G(s) = \dfrac{(1+0.2s)(1+0.025s)}{s^3(1+0.005s)(1+0.001s)}$

Solution: (a) Given

$$G(s) = \frac{1}{(1+s)(1+2s)}$$

The sinusoidal transfer function is

$$G(j\omega) = \frac{1}{(1+j\omega)(1+j2\omega)}$$

Rationalizing,

$$G(j\omega) = \frac{(1-j\omega)(1-j2\omega)}{(1+j\omega)(1-j\omega)(1+j2\omega)(1-j2\omega)}$$

$$= \frac{(1-2\omega^2) - j3\omega}{(1+\omega^2)(1+4\omega^2)}$$

$$= \frac{1-2\omega^2}{(1+\omega^2)(1+4\omega^2)} - j\frac{3\omega}{(1+\omega^2)(1+4\omega^2)} = 0$$

When $\omega = 0$,

$$G(j0) = 1 - j0$$

When $\omega = \infty$,

$$G(j\infty) = -0 - j0$$

This plot does not cross the real axis. It crosses the imaginary axis at the frequency given by the solution of

$$\frac{1-2\omega^2}{(1+\omega^2)(1+4\omega^2)} = 0$$

i.e.

$$1 - 2\omega^2 = 0$$

or

$$\omega = 1/\sqrt{2}$$

The value of $G(j\omega)$ at this frequency is

$$- j\frac{3\omega}{(1+\omega^2)(1+4\omega^2)}\bigg|_{\omega=1/\sqrt{2}} = -j\sqrt{2}/3 = - j0.471$$

Based on the above information, an approximate polar plot is traced as shown in Figure 7.11.

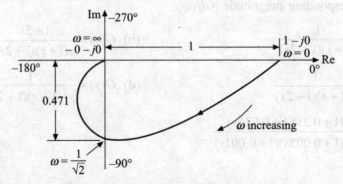

Figure 7.11   Example 7.3(a): Polar plot.

(b) Given

$$G(s) = \frac{1+4s}{s(1+s)(1+2s)}$$

The sinusoidal transfer function is

$$G(j\omega) = \frac{1+j4\omega}{j\omega(1+j\omega)(1+j2\omega)}$$

Rationalizing

$$G(j\omega) = \frac{(1+j4\omega)(1-j\omega)(1-j2\omega)}{j\omega(1+j\omega)(1-j\omega)(1+j2\omega)(1-j2\omega)}$$

$$= \frac{(1+j4\omega)(1-2\omega^2-j3\omega)}{j\omega(1+\omega^2)(1+4\omega^2)}$$

$$= \frac{(1+10\omega^2)+j\omega(1-8\omega^2)}{j\omega(1+\omega^2)(1+4\omega^2)}$$

$$= \frac{1-8\omega^2}{(1+\omega^2)(1+4\omega^2)} - j\frac{1+10\omega^2}{\omega(1+\omega^2)(1+4\omega^2)}$$

for imy part = 0
ω = -ve
(not
pssbl).

When $\omega = 0$,

$$G(j0) = 1 - j\infty$$

When $\omega = \infty$,

$$G(j\infty) = -0 - j0$$

The polar plot does not cross the real axis. It crosses the imaginary axis at a frequency given by the solution of

$$\frac{1-8\omega^2}{(1+\omega^2)(1+4\omega^2)} = 0$$

i.e.

$$1 - 8\omega^2 = 0$$

or

$$\omega = \frac{1}{\sqrt{8}}$$

The value of $G(j\omega)$ at that frequency is

$$-j\frac{1+10\omega^2}{\omega(1+\omega^2)(1+4\omega^2)}\Bigg|_{\omega=\frac{1}{\sqrt{8}}} = -j3.75$$

Based on the above information, an approximate polar plot is drawn as shown in Figure 7.12.

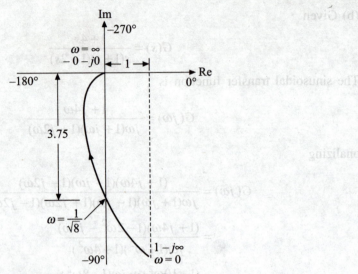

Figure 7.12 Example 7.3(b): Polar plot.

(c) Given

$$G(s) = \frac{1}{s(1+s)(1+2s)}$$

The sinusoidal transfer function is

$$G(j\omega) = \frac{1}{j\omega(1+j\omega)(1+j2\omega)}$$

Rationalizing,

$$G(j\omega) = \frac{(1-j\omega)(1-j2\omega)}{j\omega(1+j\omega)(1-j\omega)(1+j2\omega)(1-j2\omega)}$$

$$= \frac{(1-2\omega^2) - j3\omega}{j\omega(1+\omega^2)(1+4\omega^2)}$$

$$= \frac{-3}{(1+\omega^2)(1+4\omega^2)} - j\frac{1-2\omega^2}{\omega(1+\omega^2)(1+4\omega^2)}$$

When $\omega = 0$,

$$G(j0) = -3 - j\infty$$

When $\omega = \infty$,

$$G(j\infty) = -0 + j0$$

The frequency at which the polar plot crosses the real axis is given by the solution of

$$\frac{1-2\omega^2}{\omega(1+\omega^2)(1+4\omega^2)} = 0$$

i.e. $$1 - 2\omega^2 = 0$$

$$\therefore \qquad \omega = \frac{1}{\sqrt{2}}$$

The value of $G(j\omega)$ at this frequency is

$$\frac{-3}{(1+\omega^2)(1+4\omega^2)}\bigg|_{\omega=\frac{1}{\sqrt{2}}} = \frac{-3}{\left(1+\frac{1}{2}\right)\left(1+4\times\frac{1}{2}\right)} = -0.666$$

Based on the above information, an approximate polar plot is drawn as shown in Figure 7.13.

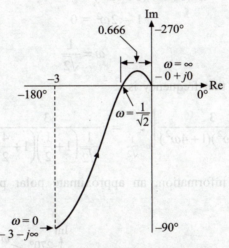

Figure 7.13 Example 7.3(c): Polar plot.

(d) Given

$$G(s) = \frac{1}{s^2(1+s)(1+2s)}$$

The sinusoidal transfer function is

$$G(j\omega) = \frac{1}{(j\omega)^2(1+j\omega)(1+j2\omega)}$$

Rationalizing,

$$G(j\omega) = \frac{(1-j\omega)(1-j2\omega)}{-\omega^2(1+j\omega)(1-j\omega)(1+j2\omega)(1-j2\omega)}$$

$$= \frac{(1-2\omega^2)-j3\omega}{-\omega^2(1+\omega^2)(1+4\omega^2)}$$

$$= -\frac{(1-2\omega^2)}{\omega^2(1+\omega^2)(1+4\omega^2)} + j\frac{3}{\omega(1+\omega^2)(1+4\omega^2)}$$

When $\omega = 0$,

$$G(j0) = -\infty + j\infty$$

When $\omega = \infty$,

$$G(j\infty) = 0 + j0$$

The polar plot does not cross the real axis. It crosses the imaginary axis at a frequency given by the solution of

$$\frac{-(1-2\omega^2)}{\omega^2(1+\omega^2)(1+4\omega^2)} = 0$$

i.e.

$$1 - 2\omega^2 = 0$$

∴

$$\omega = \frac{1}{\sqrt{2}}$$

The value of $G(j\omega)$ at that frequency is

$$j\frac{3}{\omega(1+\omega^2)(1+4\omega^2)}\bigg|_{\omega=\frac{1}{\sqrt{2}}} = j\frac{3}{\frac{1}{\sqrt{2}}\left(1+\frac{1}{2}\right)\left(1+\frac{4}{2}\right)} = j0.94$$

Based on the above information, an approximate polar plot is drawn as shown in Figure 7.14.

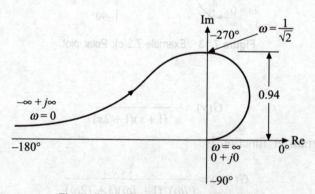

Figure 7.14   Example 7.3(d): Polar plot.

(e) Given

$$G(s) = \frac{(1+0.2s)(1+0.025s)}{s^3(1+0.005s)(1+0.001s)}$$

The sinusoidal transfer function is

$$G(j\omega) = \frac{(1 + j0.2\omega)(1 + j0.025\omega)}{(j\omega)^3 (1 + j0.005\omega)(1 + j0.001\omega)}$$

Rationalizing,

$$G(j\omega) = \frac{(1 + j0.2\omega)(1 + j0.025\omega)(1 - j0.005\omega)(1 + j0.001\omega)}{-j\omega^3 (1 + j0.005\omega)(1 - j0.005\omega)(1 + j0.001\omega)(1 - j0.001\omega)}$$

$$= \frac{(1 - 0.005\omega^2 + j0.225\omega)(1 - 0.000005\omega^2 + j0.006\omega)}{-j\omega^3 (1 + 0.000025\omega^2)(1 + 0.000001\omega^2)}$$

$$= -\frac{0.225(1 - 0.000005\omega^2) - 0.006(1 - 0.005\omega^2)}{\omega^2 (1 + 0.000025\omega^2)(1 + 0.000001\omega^2)}$$

$$+ j\frac{[(1 - 0.005\omega^2)(1 - 0.000005\omega^2) - 0.00135\omega^2]}{\omega^3 (1 + 0.000025\omega^2)(1 + 0.000001\omega^2)}$$

When $\omega = 0$,

$$G(j0) = -\infty + j\infty$$

When $\omega = \infty$,

$$G(j\infty) = -0 + j0$$

The polar plot does not cross the real axis.

Based on the above information, an approximate polar plot is drawn as shown in Figure 7.15.

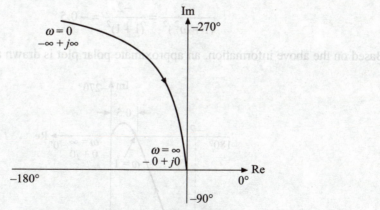

Figure 7.15 Example 7.3(e): Polar plot.

Example 7.4 Sketch the direct polar plot for a unity feedback system with open-loop transfer function

$$G(s) = \frac{1}{s(1 + s)^2}$$

Also find the frequency at which $|G(j\omega)| = 1$ and the corresponding phase angle $\angle G(j\omega)$.

Solution: The sinusoidal transfer function is

$$G(j\omega) = \frac{1}{j\omega(1+j\omega)^2} = \frac{1}{j\omega} \cdot \frac{1}{1+j\omega} \cdot \frac{1}{1+j\omega}$$

$$= \frac{(1-j\omega)(1-j\omega)}{j\omega(1+j\omega)(1-j\omega)(1+j\omega)(1-j\omega)}$$

$$= \frac{(1-\omega^2)-j2\omega}{j\omega(1+\omega^2)(1+\omega^2)} = -\frac{2}{(1+\omega^2)^2} - j\frac{(1-\omega^2)}{\omega(1+\omega^2)^2}$$

For $\omega = 0$,

$$G(j0) = -2 - j\infty$$

For $\omega = \infty$,

$$G(j\infty) = -0 + j0$$

The frequency at which the polar plot crosses the real axis is obtained by equating the imaginary part of $G(j\omega)$ to zero, i.e.

$$\frac{-(1-\omega^2)}{\omega(1+\omega^2)^2} = 0$$

i.e.

$$1 - \omega^2 = 0$$

or

$$\omega = 1 \text{ rad/s}$$

At this frequency, the value of $G(j\omega)$ is

$$\frac{-2}{(1+\omega^2)^2} = \frac{-2}{(1+1)^2} = -0.5$$

Based on the above information, an approximate polar plot is drawn as shown in Figure 7.16.

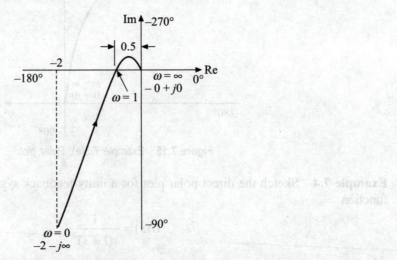

Figure 7.16 Example 7.4: Polar plot.

7.4 BODE PLOTS

Bode plots, also called logarithmic plots, are in two parts. One is the logarithm of the magnitude of a sinusoidal transfer function $G(j\omega)H(j\omega)$ expressed in dB (decibels) versus ω and the second one is phase angle in degrees versus ω both plotted on the log scale. One advantage of Bode plots is that since logarithmic representation is used, multiplication and division of magnitudes can be converted into addition and subtraction respectively. Both high frequency and low frequency portions can be represented on the same graph because a wide range of frequencies can be represented on the same plot. These plots are plotted on a semi-log sheet where the linear scale on y-axis is used to represent magnitude in dB or phase angle in degrees, and the logarithmic scale on x-axis is used for frequency. Another advantage of Bode plots is an approximate plot using straight line asymptotes can be drawn very quickly and easily and corrections can be made later to obtain an accurate plot. Both absolute stability and relative stability of a system can be determined using Bode plots. Bode plots are very useful in the design of control systems. Wherever it is not possible to obtain the transfer function of a system analytically, it can be determined from its magnitude Bode plot after conducting a frequency response test on the system and drawing the magnitude Bode plot.

The logarithmic scale used for frequency in Bode plots has some interesting properties. First, we observe that the logarithmic scale is nonlinear, and we cannot locate the point $\omega = 0$ on the log scale, since $\log 0 = -\infty$. In Bode diagrams, frequency ratios are expressed in terms of octaves or decades. An octave is a frequency band from ω_1 to $2\omega_1$, where ω_1 is any frequency value. A decade is the frequency band from ω_1 to $10\omega_1$, where ω_1 is any frequency. On the logarithmic scale of semi-log paper, any frequency ratio can be represented by the same horizontal distance. For example, the horizontal distance from $\omega = 1$ to $\omega = 10$ is equal to that from $\omega = 3$ to $\omega = 30$.

To express magnitude of $G(j\omega)H(j\omega)$ in dB take $20 \log |G(j\omega)H(j\omega)|$.

7.4.1 Basic Factors of $G(j\omega)H(j\omega)$

As stated earlier, the main advantage in using the logarithmic plot is the relative ease of plotting frequency response curves. The basic factors that very frequently occur in an arbitrary transfer function $G(j\omega)H(j\omega)$ are as follows:

1. Gain K
2. Pole at the origin (integral factor) $1/(j\omega)$
3. Multiple poles at the origin $1/(j\omega)^n$
4. Zero at the origin (derivative factor) $j\omega$
5. Multiple zeros at the origin $(j\omega)^n$
6. Factors of the form $K/(j\omega)^r$
7. First-order pole on the real axis $1/(1 + j\omega T)$
8. Multiple poles on the real axis $1/(1 + j\omega T)^n$
9. First-order zero on the real axis $(1 + j\omega T)$
10. Multiple zeros on the real axis $(1 + j\omega T)^n$
11. Quadratic poles $1/[1 + 2\xi(j\omega/\omega_n) + (j\omega/\omega_n)^2]$
12. Quadratic zeros $[1 + 2\xi(j\omega/\omega_n) + (j\omega/\omega_n)^2]$

Once we become familiar with the logarithmic plots of these basic factors, it is possible to utilize them in constructing a composite logarithmic plot for any general form of $G(j\omega)H(j\omega)$ by sketching the curves for each factor and adding individual curves graphically, because adding the logarithms of the gains corresponds to multiplying them together.

The gain K: A number greater than unity has a positive value in dB, while a number smaller than unity has a negative value. The log magnitude curve for a constant gain K is a horizontal straight line at the magnitude of 20 log K dB. The phase angle of the gain K is zero. So the phase plot is a straight line at 0°. The effect of varying the gain K in the transfer function is that it raises or lowers the log magnitude curve of the transfer function by the corresponding constant amount, but it has no effect on the phase curve. Figure 7.17 shows the Bode plot of constant gain K.

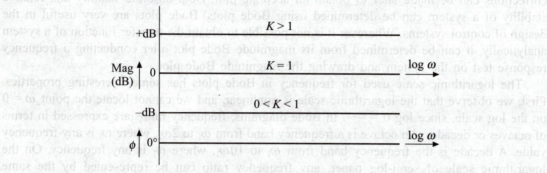

Figure 7.17   Bode plot of constant gain K.

Pole at the origin (integral factor) $\dfrac{1}{j\omega}$:   The logarithmic magnitude of $1/j\omega$ in dB is

$$20 \log |1/j\omega| = -20 \log \omega \text{ dB}$$

For $\omega = 1$,

$$|1/j\omega| = -20 \log 1 = 0 \text{ dB}$$

For $\omega = 0.1$,

$$|1/j\omega| = -20 \log 0.1 = +20 \log 10 = +20 \text{ dB}$$

For $\omega = 10$,

$$|1/j\omega| = -20 \log 10 = -20 \text{ dB}$$

So, if the magnitude of $-20 \log \omega$ dB is plotted against ω on a logarithmic scale, it is a straight line with a slope of -20 dB/decade, passing through the 0 dB line at $\omega = 1$ rad/s (because $-20 \log 1 = 0$ dB). The phase angle of $1/j\omega$ is constant and equal to $-90°$. Figure 7.18(a) shows the Bode plot of $1/j\omega$.

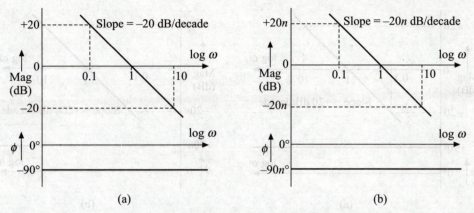

Figure 7.18 (a) Bode plot of pole at the origin $1/j\omega$ and (b) Bode plot of multiple poles at the origin $1/(j\omega)^n$.

Multiple poles at the origin $\dfrac{1}{(j\omega)^n}$:   The log magnitude of $1/(j\omega)^n$ in dB is

$$20 \log |1/(j\omega)^n| = -20 \log \omega^n = -20n \log \omega$$

For $\omega = 1$,

$$|1/(j\omega)^n| = -20n \log 1 = 0 \text{ dB}$$

For $\omega = 0.1$,

$$|1/(j\omega)^n| = -20\,n \log 0.1 = 20n \log 10 = +20n \text{ dB}$$

For $\omega = 10$,

$$|1/(j\omega)^n| = -20n \log 10 = -20n \text{ dB}$$

So the magnitude plot of $1/(j\omega)^n$ is a straight line with a slope of $-20n$ dB/decade passing through the 0 dB line at $\omega = 1$ rad/s. The phase angle of $1/(j\omega)^n$ is constant and is equal to $-90° \, n$. Figure 7.18(b) shows the Bode plot of multiple poles at the origin.

Zero at the origin (derivative factor) $j\omega$:   The log magnitude of $j\omega$ in dB is

$$20 \log | j\omega | = 20 \log \omega \text{ dB}$$

For $\omega = 1$,

$$| j\omega | = 20 \log 1 = 0 \text{ dB}$$

For $\omega = 0.1$,

$$| j\omega | = 20 \log 0.1 = -20 \log 10 = -20 \text{ dB}$$

For $\omega = 10$,

$$| j\omega | = 20 \log 10 = +20 \text{ dB}$$

So the log magnitude curve of $20 \log \omega$ dB plotted against ω on a logarithmic scale is a straight line with a slope of $+20$ dB/decade passing through the 0 dB line at $\omega = 1$ rad/s. The phase angle of $j\omega$ is constant and equal to $+90°$. Figure 7.19(a) shows the Bode plot of zero at the origin.

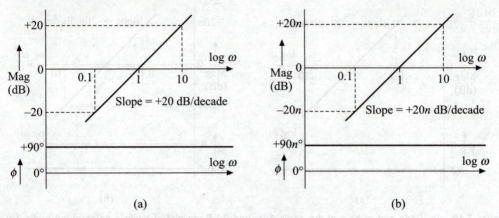

Figure 7.19 (a) Bode plot of zero at the origin $j\omega$ and (b) Bode plot of multiple zeros at the origin $(j\omega)^n$.

Multiple zeros at the origin $(j\omega)^n$: The log magnitude of $(j\omega)^n$ in dB is

$$20 \log | (j\omega)^n | = 20n \log \omega$$

For $\omega = 1$,

$$| (j\omega)^n | = 20n \log 1 = 0 \text{ dB}$$

For $\omega = 0.1$,

$$| (j\omega)^n | = 20n \log 0.1 = -20n \log 10 = -20n \text{ dB}$$

For $\omega = 10$,

$$| (j\omega)^n | = 20n \log 10 = +20n \text{ dB}$$

So the magnitude plot of $(j\omega)^n$ is a straight line with a slope of $+20n$ dB/decade passing through the 0 dB line at $\omega = 1$ rad/s.

The phase angle of $(j\omega)^n$ is constant and is equal to $90°n$. Figure 7.19(b) shows the Bode plot of multiple zeros at the origin.

Factors of the form $\dfrac{K}{(j\omega)^r}$ **:** The log magnitude of this factor is

$$20 \log | K/(j\omega)^r | = -20r \log \omega + 20 \log K$$

For $\omega = 1$,

$$| K/(j\omega)^r | = -20r \log 1 + 20 \log K = 20 \log K \text{ dB}$$

For $\omega = 0.1$,

$$| K/(j\omega)^r | = -20r \log 0.1 + 20 \log K = 20r + 20 \log K \text{ dB}$$

For $\omega = 10$,

$$| K/(j\omega)^r | = -20r \log 10 + 20 \log K = -20r + 20 \log K \text{ dB}$$

So the magnitude plot of $K/(j\omega)^r$ is a straight line with a slope of $-20r$ dB/decade and having a magnitude of 20 log K dB when log $\omega = 0$, i.e. at $\omega = 1$ as shown in Figure 7.20. Further, the plot has a value of 0 dB at the frequency of

$$20r \log \omega = 20 \log K$$

or

$$\omega = (K)^{1/r}$$

The angle contribution of the factor K is zero and that of $1/(j\omega)^r$ is $-90°r$ at any frequency. The phase diagram is simply a horizontal line at an angle of $-90°r$. Figure 7.20 shows the Bode plot of the pole factor $K/(j\omega)^r$.

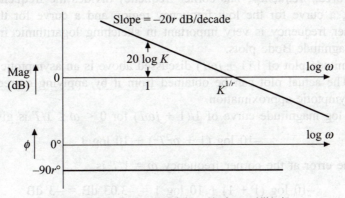

Figure 7.20 Bode plot of the pole factor $K/(j\omega)^r$.

Pole on the real axis $\dfrac{1}{1 + j\omega T}$: The log magnitude of this factor is

$$20 \log |1/(1 + j\omega T)| = 20 \log 1/\sqrt{(1 + \omega^2 T^2)} = 20 \log (1 + \omega^2 T^2)^{-1/2}$$

$$= -10 \log (1 + \omega^2 T^2)$$

For low frequencies $\left(\omega << \dfrac{1}{T}\right)$, the log magnitude may be expressed as

$$20 \log |1/(1 + j\omega T)| = -10 \log 1 = 0 \text{ dB}$$

Thus, the log magnitude curve at low frequencies is the constant 0 dB line.

For high frequencies $\left(\omega >> \dfrac{1}{T}\right)$, the log magnitude is approximated as

$$20 \log |1/(1 + j\omega T)| = -10 \log \omega^2 T^2 = -20 \log \omega T$$

$$= -20 \log \omega - 20 \log T$$

This is an approximate expression for the high frequency range.

At $\omega = 1/T$, the log magnitude equals 0 dB; at $\omega = 10/T$, the log magnitude is –20 dB. Thus, the log magnitude decreases by 20 dB for every decade of ω. Thus for $\omega > 1/T$, the log magnitude curve is a straight line with a slope of –20 dB/decade.

Though the above two straight line approximations hold good for $\omega \ll 1/T$ and $\omega \gg 1/T$ respectively, with some loss of accuracy these could be extended for frequencies $\omega \le 1/T$ and $\omega \ge 1/T$. Therefore, the log magnitude versus log frequency curve of $1/(1 + j\omega T)$ can be approximated by two straight line asymptotes, one a straight line at 0 dB for the frequency range $0 < \omega < 1/T$ and the other a straight line with a slope of –20 dB/decade for the frequency range $1/T < \omega < \infty$. The frequency $\omega = 1/T$ at which the two asymptotes meet is called the *corner frequency* or the *break frequency*. The corner frequency divides the frequency response curve into two regions, a curve for the low frequency region and a curve for the high frequency region. The corner frequency is very important in sketching logarithmic frequency response curves, that is magnitude Bode plots.

The log magnitude plot of $1/(1 + j\omega T)$ discussed above is an asymptotic approximation of the actual plot. The actual plot can be obtained from it by applying correction for the error introduced by asymptotic approximation.

The error in log magnitude curve of $1/(1 + j\omega T)$ for $0 < \omega \le 1/T$ is given by

$$-10 \log (1 + \omega^2 T^2) + 10 \log 1$$

Therefore, the error at the corner frequency $\omega = 1/T$ is

$$-10 \log (1 + 1) + 10 \log 1 = -3.03 \text{ dB} = -3 \text{ dB}$$

The error at half the corner frequency, i.e. at $\omega = 1/2T$ is

$$-10 \log (1 + 1/4) + 10 \log 1 = -0.97 \text{ dB} = -1 \text{ dB}$$

For $1/T \le \omega < \infty$, the error in magnitude is given by

$$-10 \log (1 + \omega^2 T^2) + 20 \log \omega T$$

Therefore, the error at the corner frequency $\omega = 1/T$ is

$$-10 \log (1 + 1) + 20 \log 1 = -3.03 \text{ dB} = -3 \text{ dB}$$

The error at double the corner frequency, i.e. at $\omega = 2/T$ is

$$-10 \log (1 + 4) + 20 \log 2 = -0.97 \text{ dB} = -1 \text{ dB}$$

Thus, the error at one octave below or above the corner frequency is approximately equal to –1 dB. Similarly, the error at one decade below or above the corner frequency is approximately –0.04 dB.

Since the asymptotes are quite easy to draw, an approximate Bode plot can be drawn using asymptotes and a sufficiently accurate log magnitude plot is obtained by correcting the asymptotic plot by –3 dB at the corner frequency and by –1 dB one octave below and one octave above the corner frequency, and then drawing a smooth curve through these three points approaching the low frequency and high frequency asymptotes as shown in Figure 7.21.

Note that varying the time constant T shifts the corner frequency to the left or to the right, but the shape of the log magnitude and the phase angle curves remain the same. The transfer function $1/(1 + j\omega T)$ has the characteristics of a low-pass filter.

The phase angle ϕ of the factor $1/(1 + j\omega T)$ is

$$\phi = -\tan^{-1} \omega T$$

At the corner frequency,

$$\phi = -\tan^{-1} (T/T) = -45°$$

At zero frequency, $\phi = 0°$, and at infinite frequency $\phi = -90°$.
At half the corner frequency, i.e. at $\omega = 1/2T$,

$$\phi = -\tan^{-1} (T/2T) = -26.6°$$

At 1/10th of the corner frequency, i.e at $\omega = 1/10T$,

$$\phi = -\tan^{-1} (T/10T) = -5.7°$$

At double the corner frequency, i.e. at $\omega = 2/T$,

$$\phi = -\tan^{-1} (2T/T) = -63.4°$$

At 10 times the corner frequency, i.e. at $\omega = 10/T$,

$$\phi = -\tan^{-1} (10T/T) = -84.3°$$

An accurate smooth phase curve can be drawn passing through these points. Figure 7.21 shows the Bode plot of the factor $1/(1 + j\omega T)$.

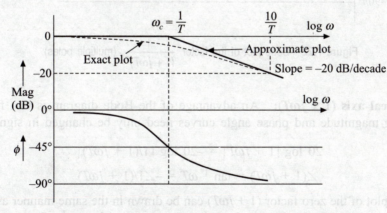

Figure 7.21   Bode plot of the factor $\dfrac{1}{1+j\omega T}$ (simple pole).

Multiple poles on the real axis $\dfrac{1}{(1 + j\omega T)^n}$: The log magnitude of this factor is

$$20 \log |1/(1 + j\omega T)^n| = 20 \log [1 + \omega^2 T^2]^{-n/2} = -10n \log (1 + \omega^2 T^2)$$

For $\omega < 1/T$,

$$|1/(1 + j\omega T)^n| = -10n \log 1 = 0 \text{ dB}$$

For $\omega > 1/T$,

$$|1/(1 + j\omega T)^n| = -20n \log \omega T$$

So the magnitude plot of $1/(1 + j\omega T)^n$ can be approximated by two straight lines, one is the straight line at 0 dB for the frequency range $0 < \omega < 1/T$ and the other is a straight line with a slope of $-20n$ dB/decade for the frequency range $1/T < \omega < \infty$.

The corner frequency $\omega_c = 1/T$ and error at the corner frequency is $-3n$ dB. The phase angle of the factor $1/(1 + j\omega T)^n$ varies from $0°$ to $-90°n$ as ω is varied from 0 to ∞. The phase plot is a curve through $-45°n$ at ω_c. Figure 7.22 shows the Bode plot of factor $1/(1 + j\omega T)^n$.

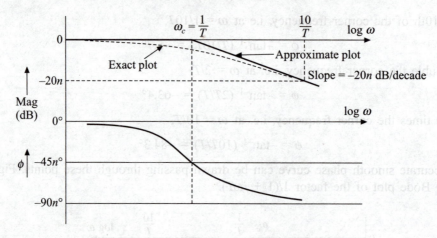

Figure 7.22 Bode plot of the factor $\dfrac{1}{(1 + j\omega T)^n}$ (multiple poles).

Zero on the real axis $(1 + j\omega T)$: An advantage of the Bode diagram is that for reciprocal factors, the log magnitude and phase angle curves need only be changed in sign, since

$$20 \log |1 + j\omega T| = -20 \log |1/(1 + j\omega T)|$$

and

$$\angle(1 + j\omega T) = \tan^{-1} \omega T = -\angle 1/(1 + j\omega T)$$

The Bode plot of the zero factor $(1 + j\omega T)$ can be drawn in the same manner as for the pole factor but with a slope of $+20$ dB/decade and a phase angle of $+\tan^{-1} \omega T$.

So the magnitude plot of the zero $(1 + j\omega T)$ can be approximated by two straight lines, one is a straight line at 0 dB for the frequency range $0 < \omega < 1/T$ and the other is a straight line with slope $+20$ dB/decade for the frequency range $1/T < \omega < \infty$. The two straight lines are the asymptotes of the exact curve. The corner frequency is $\omega_c = 1/T$. The phase angle of $(1 + j\omega T)$ varies from 0 to $+90°$ as ω is varied from 0 to ∞. At the corner frequency, phase angle = $45°$. Figure 7.23 shows the Bode plot of the factor $(1 + j\omega T)$.

The dB corrections will be $+3$ dB at the corner frequency and $+1$ dB at half and double the corner frequencies.

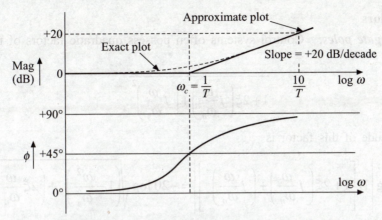

Figure 7.23 Bode plot of the factor $(1 + j\omega T)$ (simple zero).

Multiple Zeros on the real axis $(1 + j\omega T)^n$: The log magnitude of this factor is

$$20 \log |(1 + j\omega T)^n| = 20 \log \left(\sqrt{1 + \omega^2 T^2}\right)^n = 10n \log (1 + \omega^2 T^2)$$

For $\omega < 1/T$,

$$|(1 + j\omega T)^n| = 10n \log 1 = 0 \text{ dB}$$

For $\omega > 1/T$,

$$|(1 + j\omega T)^n| = 20n \log \omega T$$

So the magnitude plot of $(1 + j\omega T)^n$ can be approximated by two straight lines, one is a straight line at 0 dB for the frequency range $0 < \omega < 1/T$ and the other is a straight line with a slope of $+20n$ dB/decade for the frequency range $1/T < \omega < \infty$. The corner frequency $\omega_c = 1/T$ and error at the corner frequency is $+3n$ dB.

The phase angle of the factor $(1 + j\omega T)^n$ varies from $0°$ to $+90°n$ as ω is varied from 0 to ∞. The phase plot is a curve passing through $+45°n$ at ω_c. Figure 7.24 shows the Bode plot of the factor $(1 + j\omega T)^n$.

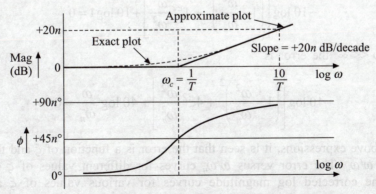

Figure 7.24 Bode plot of the factor $(1 + j\omega T)^n$ (multiple zeros).

Quadratic factors

Complex conjugate poles: Control systems often possess quadratic factors of the form

$$\frac{1}{1+2\xi\left(j\dfrac{\omega}{\omega_n}\right)+\left(j\dfrac{\omega}{\omega_n}\right)^2}$$

The log magnitude of this factor is

$$20\log\left|1\Big/\left[1+2\xi\left(j\frac{\omega}{\omega_n}\right)+\left(j\frac{\omega}{\omega_n}\right)^2\right]\right|=-20\log\sqrt{\left(1-\frac{\omega^2}{\omega_n^2}\right)^2+\left(2\xi\frac{\omega}{\omega_n}\right)^2}$$

For low frequencies such that $\omega \ll \omega_n$, the log magnitude becomes

$$-20\log 1 = 0\ \text{dB}$$

The low frequency asymptote is thus a horizontal line at 0 dB. For high frequencies such that $\omega \gg \omega_n$, the log magnitude becomes

$$-20\log\frac{\omega^2}{\omega_n^2}=-40\log\frac{\omega}{\omega_n}\ \text{dB}$$

The high frequency asymptote is a straight line having the slope -40 dB/decade.

The high frequency asymptote intersects the low frequency asymptote at $\omega = \omega_n$ on the 0 dB line. This frequency ω_n is called the corner frequency. These two asymptotes are independent of the value of ξ. Near the corner frequency $\omega = \omega_n$, a resonant peak occurs. The damping ratio ξ determines the magnitude of this resonant peak.

The error between the actual magnitude and the asymptotic approximation is given as follows:

For $0 < \omega \ll \omega_n$, the error is

$$-10\log\left[\left(1-\frac{\omega^2}{\omega_n^2}\right)^2+4\xi^2\frac{\omega^2}{\omega_n^2}\right]+10\log 1 = 0$$

and for $\omega_n < \omega \ll \infty$, the error is

$$-10\log\left[\left(1-\frac{\omega^2}{\omega_n^2}\right)^2+4\xi^2\frac{\omega^2}{\omega_n^2}\right]+40\log\frac{\omega}{\omega_n}=0$$

From the above expressions, it is seen that the error is a function of ξ and the normalized frequency $u = \omega/\omega_n$. The error versus ω/ω_n curves for different values of ξ are plotted in Figure 7.26. The corrected log magnitude curves for various values of ξ are shown in Figure 7.25.

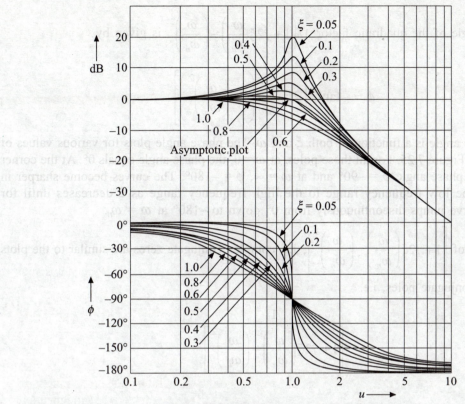

Figure 7.25 Bode plot of $1/(1 + j2\xi u - u^2)$.

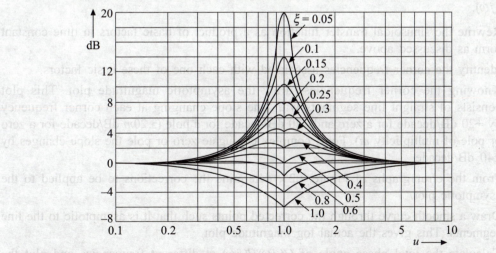

Figure 7.26 Error in dB vs normalized frequency for asymptotic Bode plot of $1/(1 + j2\xi u - u^2)$.

The phase angle of the quadratic factor $1/\left[1 + j2\xi\dfrac{\omega}{\omega_n} - \left(\dfrac{\omega}{\omega_n}\right)^2\right]$ is given by

$$\phi = -\tan^{-1}\left[2\xi\frac{\omega}{\omega_n}\bigg/\left(1 - \left(\frac{\omega}{\omega_n}\right)^2\right)\right]$$

The phase angle is a function of both ξ and ω. The phase angle plots for various values of ξ are given in Figure 7.25. For all those poles, at $\omega = 0$, the phase angle equals $0°$. At the corner frequency the phase angle $\phi = -90°$ and at $\omega = \infty$, $\phi = -180°$. The curves become sharper in going from the low frequency range to the high frequency range as ξ decreases until for $\xi = 0$, the curve jumps discontinuously from $0°$ down to $-180°$ at $\omega = \omega_n$.

The plots of $\left[1 + j2\xi\left(\dfrac{\omega}{\omega_n}\right) - \left(\dfrac{\omega}{\omega_n}\right)^2\right]$, i.e. complex conjugate zeros are similar to the plots of complex conjugate poles, i.e.

$$\frac{1}{\left[1 + j2\xi\left(\dfrac{\omega}{\omega_n}\right) - \left(\dfrac{\omega}{\omega_n}\right)^2\right]}$$

7.4.2   General Procedure for Constructing Bode Plots

The following steps are generally involved in constructing the Bode plot for a given $G(j\omega)H(j\omega)$.

1. Rewrite the sinusoidal transfer function as a product of basic factors in time constant form as discussed above.

2. Identify the corner frequencies associated with each one of these basic factors.

3. Knowing the corner frequencies, draw the asymptotic magnitude plot. This plot consists of straight line segments with line slope changing at each corner frequency by +20 dB/decade for a zero and −20 dB/decade for a pole ($\pm 20m$ dB/decade for a zero or pole of multiplicity m). For a complex conjugate zero or pole the slope changes by ± 40 dB/decade.

4. From the error graphs of Figure 7.25, determine the corrections to be applied to the asymptotic plot.

5. Draw a smooth curve through the corrected points such that it is asymptotic to the line segments. This gives the actual log magnitude plot.

6. Calculate the total phase angle of $G(j\omega)H(j\omega)$ at different frequencies and plot the resultant phase plot.

To illustrate the technique, let us draw the Bode plot for the transfer function

$$G(s)H(s) = \frac{54(s+4)}{s(s+1)(s^2+1.8s+36)}$$

The given transfer function is in pole-zero form. Converting it into time constant form, we have

$$G(s)H(s) = \frac{54 \times 4(1+s/4)}{s(s+1) \times 36 \times (1+1.8s/36+s^2/36)} = \frac{6(1+s/4)}{s(1+s)[1+0.3(s/6)+(s/6)^2]}$$

Therefore, the sinusoidal transfer function in time constant form is given by

$$G(j\omega)H(j\omega) = \frac{6(1+j\omega/4)}{j\omega(1+j\omega)[1+j0.3(\omega/6)-(\omega/6)^2]}$$

The corresponding magnitude and phase characteristics of each factor of the transfer function are given in Table 7.2.

Table 7.2 Asymptotic approximation table for construction of the Bode plot for

$$G(j\omega)H(j\omega) = \frac{6(1+j\omega/4)}{j\omega(1+j\omega)[1+j0.3(\omega/6)-(\omega/6)^2]}$$

Factor	Corner frequency	Asymptotic log-magnitude characteristic	Phase angle characteristic
$\dfrac{6}{j\omega}$	None	Straight line with a slope of -20 dB/decade passing through the $20 \log 6 = 15.56$ dB point at $\omega = 1$.	Constant $-90°$.
$\dfrac{1}{1+j\omega}$	$\omega_1 = 1$	For $\omega < \omega_1 = 1$, it is a straight line of 0 dB. For $\omega > \omega_1 = 1$, it is a straight line with a slope of -20 dB/decade.	Phase angle varies from 0 to $-90°$. At $\omega = \omega_1 = 1$, $\phi = -45°$.
$1 + j\omega/4$	$\omega_2 = 4$	For $\omega < \omega_2 = 4$, it is a straight line of 0 dB. For $\omega > \omega_2 = 4$, it is a straight line with a slope of $+20$ dB/decade.	Phase angle varies from 0 to $+90°$. At $\omega = \omega_2 = 4$, $\phi = -45°$.
$\dfrac{1}{1+j0.3\left(\dfrac{\omega}{6}\right)-\left(\dfrac{\omega}{6}\right)^2}$	$\omega_3 = 6$ $\xi = 0.15$	For $\omega < \omega_3 = 6$, it is a straight line of 0 dB. For $\omega > \omega_3 = 6$, it is a straight line with a slope of -40 dB/decade.	Phase angle varies from 0 to $-180°$. At $\omega = \omega_3 = 6$, $\phi = -90°$.

The resultant magnitude plot is drawn in Figure 7.27, as discussed below.

1. We start with the factor $(6/j\omega)$ corresponding to the pole at the origin. Its log magnitude plot is the asymptote 1, a straight line having a slope of -20 dB/decade and passing through the point $20 \log 6 = 15.66$ dB at $\omega = 1$. This will be the resultant plot up to the next corner frequency $\omega_1 = 1$.

2. Let us now add to the asymptote 1, the plot of the factor $1/1+j\omega$ corresponding to the lowest corner frequency $\omega = \omega_1 = 1$. Since this factor contributes 0 dB for $\omega \leq \omega_1 = 1$, the resultant plot up to $\omega = 1$ is the same as that of the asymptote 1. For $\omega > \omega_1 = 1$, this factor contributes -20 dB/decade such that the resultant plot of these two factors is the asymptote 2 of slope $(-20$ dB$) + (-20$ dB$) = -40$ dB/decade. This will be the resultant plot from $\omega_1 = 1$ up to the next corner frequency $\omega_2 = 4$.

3. Let us now add to the asymptote 2, the plot of the factor $(1 + j\omega/4)$ corresponding to the next corner frequency $\omega = \omega_2 = 4$. Since this factor contributes 0 dB for $\omega \leq \omega_2 = 4$, the resultant plot up to $\omega = 4$ is the same as that of the asymptote 2. For $\omega > \omega_2 = 4$, this factor contributes $+20$ dB/decade such that the resultant plot of these factors is the asymptote 3 with a slope $(-40$ dB$) + (20$ dB$) = -20$ dB/decade. This will be the resultant plot from $\omega = \omega_2 = 4$ to the next corner frequency $\omega = \omega_3 = 6$.

4. For $\omega > \omega_3 = 6$, the magnitude plot of $\dfrac{1}{1 + j0.3(\omega/6) - (\omega/6)^2}$ comes into effect and is to be added. This factor gives rise to a straight line of -40 dB/decade for $\omega > \omega_3 = 6$, which when added to the asymptote 3 results in the asymptote 4 having a slope of $(-20$ dB$) + (-40$ dB$) = -60$ dB/decade for $\omega > \omega_3 = 6$. Since there is no other factor this resultant plot continues from $\omega = \omega_3 = 6$ to $\omega = \infty$.

To the asymptotic plot thus obtained, corrections are to be made to get the actual plot. dB corrections are made at each corner frequency and twice and half its values. Corrections contributed by adjoining corner frequencies are to be added algebraically.

The resultant phase angle is

$$\phi = \angle \frac{6(1 + j\omega/4)}{j\omega(1 + j\omega)[1 + j0.3(\omega/6) - (\omega/6)^2]}$$

i.e.

$$\phi = -90° - \tan^{-1}\omega - \tan^{-1}\frac{0.3\omega/6}{1 - (\omega/6)^2} + \tan^{-1}(\omega/4)$$

The resultant phase at various frequencies is calculated and a smooth curve is drawn passing through those points.

$$\omega = 1, \qquad \phi = -90° - 45° - 2.94° + 14.03° = -123.91°$$
$$\omega = 4, \qquad \phi = -90° - 76° - 19.8° + 45° = -140.8°$$
$$\omega = 5, \qquad \phi = -90° - 79° - 39.3° + 51.3° = -157°$$
$$\omega = 5.5, \qquad \phi = -90° - 79.7° - 60° + 54° = -176°$$
$$\omega = 6, \qquad \phi = -90° - 80.5° - 90° + 56.3° = -204.2°$$
$$\omega = 8, \qquad \phi = -90° - 82.87° - 117° + 63.4° = -226.47°$$

The resultant phase plot is shown in Figure 7.27.

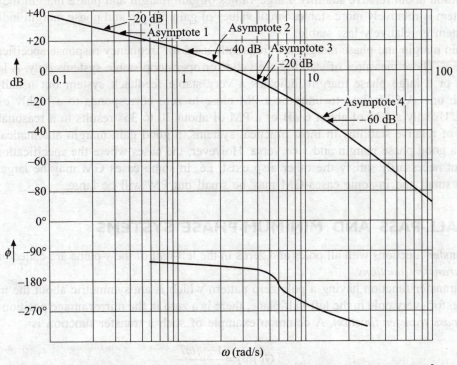

Figure 7.27 Bode plot for $G(j\omega)H(j\omega) = 6(1 + j\omega/4)/[j\omega(1 + j\omega)(1 + j0.3(\omega/6) - (\omega/6)^2)]$.

Once the magnitude and phase Bode plots are drawn, we can determine the absolute and relative stabilities of the system from these plots.

Gain crossover frequency: The gain crossover frequency ω_g is defined as the frequency at which the resultant magnitude is 0 dB, i.e. the gain crossover frequency is defined as the frequency at which $|G(j\omega)H(j\omega)| = 1$.

Phase crossover frequency: The phase crossover frequency ω_p is defined as the frequency at which the resultant phase is $-180°$, i.e. the phase crossover frequency is defined as the frequency at which $\angle G(j\omega)H(j\omega) = -180°$.

Gain margin: Gain margin (GM) is a measure of relative stability of a system. It is defined as the amount of additional gain that should be added at the phase crossover frequency to bring the system to the verge of instability. Gain margin is always positive for stable control systems.

Phase margin: Phase margin (PM) is also a measure of relative stability of a system. It is defined as the amount of additional phase lag that should be added at the gain crossover frequency to bring the system to the verge of instability. Phase margin is always positive for stable control systems.

Both gain margin and phase margin can be positive or negative. For a system to be stable, its gain margin and phase margin both must be positive. For an unstable system, both gain margin and phase margin will be negative. The values of gain margin and phase margin give information about relative stability. Large values of gain margin and phase margin indicate that the system is relatively more stable. Small values of gain margin and phase margin indicate that the system is relatively less stable.

Gain margin and phase margin are frequently used for frequency response specifications by designers. These measures of stability are valid for open-loop stable systems only. A large gain margin or a large phase margin indicates a very stable feedback system but usually a very sluggish one. A GM close to unity or a PM close to zero corresponds to a highly oscillatory system. Usually a GM of about 6 dB or a PM of about 30 to 35° results in a reasonably good degree of relative stability. In most practical systems, a good gain margin automatically guarantees a good phase margin and vice versa. However, the cases where the specification on one does not necessarily satisfy the other also exist, i.e. in some cases GM may be large but PM will be small and in some cases GM may be small but PM will be large.

7.5 ALL-PASS AND MINIMUM-PHASE SYSTEMS

The transfer functions with all poles and zeros in the left-half of the *s*-plane are called *minimum-phase transfer functions*.

A transfer function having a pole-zero pattern which is antisymmetric about the imaginary axis, i.e. for every pole in the left-half plane, there is a zero in the mirror image position is called an *all-pass transfer function*. A common example of such a transfer function is

$$G(j\omega) = \frac{1 - j\omega T}{1 + j\omega T}$$

which has a pole-zero configuration shown in Figure 7.28(c). It has a magnitude of unity at all frequencies. Hence it is called an all-pass transfer function. Its phase angle $(-2\tan^{-1}\omega T)$ varies from 0° to $-180°$ as ω is increased from 0 to ∞. The property of unit magnitude at all frequencies applies to all transfer functions with an antisymmetric pole zero pattern. Physical systems with this property are called *all-pass systems*.

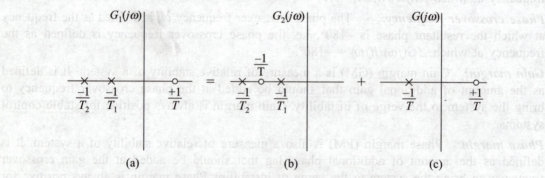

Figure 7.28 Pole-zero patterns for (a) nonminimum-phase function,
(b) minimum-phase function and (c) all-pass function.

Consider the case of the transfer function having poles in the left-half of the s-plane and zeros in both the left- and right-half of the s-plane. Poles are not permitted to lie in the right-half of the s-plane, because such a system would be unstable. A transfer function which has one or more zeros in the right-half of the s-plane is known as *nonminimum-phase transfer function*. A nonminimum-phase transfer function can be treated as a combination of a minimum-phase transfer function and an all-pass transfer function.

Consider, for example the nonminimum-phase transfer function

$$G_1(j\omega) = \frac{1 - j\omega T}{(1 + j\omega T_1)(1 + j\omega T_2)}$$

whose pole zero pattern is shown in Figure 7.28(a).

This transfer function may be rewritten as

$$G_1(j\omega) = \left[\frac{1 + j\omega T}{(1 + j\omega T_1)(1 + j\omega T_2)}\right]\left[\frac{1 - j\omega T}{1 + j\omega T}\right]$$

$$= G_2(j\omega)G(j\omega)$$

That is, as a product of minimum-phase transfer function ($G_2(j\omega)$ has all its poles and zeros only in the left-half of the s-plane) and an all-pass transfer function ($G(j\omega)$ has pole-zero pattern antisymmetric with respect to $j\omega$ axis). It is evident that $G_1(j\omega)$ and $G_2(j\omega)$ have identical curves of magnitude versus frequency, but their phase versus frequency curves are different as shown in Figure 7.29, with $G_2(j\omega)$ having a smaller range of phase angle than $G_1(j\omega)$. It means that for $G_1(j\omega)$, there is no unique relationship between magnitude and phase, as it is always possible to alter the phase curve without affecting the associated magnitude curve by the addition of an all-pass transfer function.

In general, if a transfer function has any zeros in the right-half of the s-plane, it is possible to extract them one by one by associating them with all-pass transfer function in a manner shown in Figure 7.28. Each time this is done, the magnitude curve remains unaltered, but the phase lag is reduced, until eventually we are left with a function which contains no zeros in the right-half of the s-plane. Such a transfer function has the least (minimum) phase angle range for a magnitude curve and is called a minimum-phase function. Typical phase angle characteristics of minimum and nonminimum-phase transfer functions are shown in Figure 7.29.

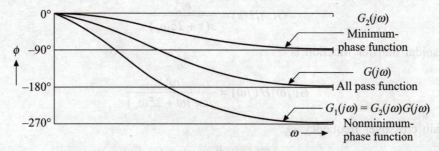

Figure 7.29 Phase angle characteristics of minimum-phase and nonminimum-phase transfer functions.

For control systems, elements with nonminimum-phase transfer functions are avoided as far as possible, because the larger the phase lags present in the system, the more complex are its stabilization problems.

A common example of a nonminimum-phase element is transportation lag which has the transfer function

$$G(j\omega) = e^{-j\omega T}$$

$$= 1\angle{-\omega T} \text{ rad} = 1\angle{-57.3} \ \omega T°$$

The phase angle characteristics of transportation lag are shown in Figure 7.30(a) and Figure (b).

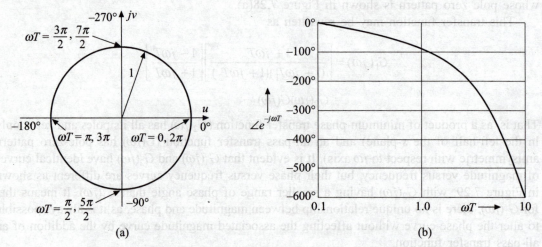

Figure 7.30 Phase angle characteristics of $e^{-j\omega T}$.

7.5.1 Correlation between Phase Margin and Damping Ratio of a Second-Order Underdamped System

The open-loop transfer function of a standard second-order system is given by

$$G(s)H(s) = \frac{\omega_n^2}{s(s + 2\xi\omega_n)}$$

The sinusoidal transfer function is

$$G(j\omega)H(j\omega) = \frac{\omega_n^2}{j\omega(j\omega + 2\xi\omega_n)}$$

At the gain crossover frequency ω_g,

$$|G(j\omega_g)H(j\omega_g)| = 1$$

$$\therefore \qquad \frac{\omega_n^2}{\omega_g \sqrt{\omega_g^2 + 4\xi^2 \omega_n^2}} = 1$$

Squaring both sides and cross multiplying,

$$\omega_n^4 = \omega_g^2 (\omega_g^2 + 4\xi^2 \omega_n^2) = \omega_g^4 + 4\xi^2 \omega_n^2 \omega_g^2$$

i.e. $\qquad \omega_g^4 + 4\xi^2 \omega_n^2 \omega_g^2 - \omega_n^4 = 0$

i.e. $\qquad (\omega_g / \omega_n)^4 + 4\xi^2 (\omega_g / \omega_n)^2 - 1 = 0$

$$\therefore \qquad \left(\frac{\omega_g}{\omega_n}\right)^2 = \frac{-4\xi^2 \pm \sqrt{(4\xi^2)^2 + 4}}{2} = -2\xi^2 \pm \sqrt{4\xi^4 + 1}$$

or $\qquad \dfrac{\omega_g}{\omega_n} = \sqrt{\left(\sqrt{4\xi^4 + 1} - 2\xi^2\right)}$

The phase margin of the system is given by

$$\phi = -90° - \tan^{-1} (\omega_g / 2\xi\omega_n) + 180°$$

$$= 90° - \tan^{-1} \left\{ \frac{1}{2\xi} \left[(4\xi^4 + 1)^{1/2} - 2\xi^2 \right]^{1/2} \right\}$$

$$= \tan^{-1} \left\{ 2\xi \left[\frac{1}{(4\xi^4 + 1)^{1/2} - 2\xi^2} \right]^{1/2} \right\}$$

For $\xi \le 0.7$, a reasonably good linear approximation between ξ and ϕ is

$$\xi = 0.01\phi$$

where ϕ is in degrees.

7.6 COMPUTATION OF GAIN MARGIN AND PHASE MARGIN

GM and PM may be computed by the use of various plots—direct polar plot, inverse polar plot, Bode plot, the log magnitude versus phase plot. In relatively simple cases, GM and PM may be computed directly.

7.6.1 Determination of Gain Margin and Phase Margin from Bode Plot

On the Bode plot: Gain crossover frequency is defined as the frequency at which the resultant magnitude plot crosses the 0 dB line and phase crossover frequency is defined as the frequency at which the resultant phase plot crosses the −180° line.

The difference between the zero dB line and the resultant magnitude plot at the phase crossover frequency gives the gain margin, i.e.

GM = 0 − (resultant magnitude in dB at the phase crossover frequency)

GM is the negative of the magnitude of $G(j\omega)H(j\omega)$ in dB at the phase crossover frequency.

If the resultant magnitude plot is below the 0 dB line at the phase crossover frequency, the gain margin is positive and the system is stable. If the resultant magnitude plot is above the 0 dB line at the phase crossover frequency, the gain margin is negative and the system is unstable.

The difference between the resultant phase plot and the −180° line at the gain crossover frequency gives the phase margin, i.e.

PM = resultant phase in degrees at the gain crossover frequency −(−180°)

i.e.　　PM = ϕ + 180°

where $\phi = \angle G(j\omega)H(j\omega)$ at the gain crossover frequency.

If the resultant phase plot is above the −180° line at the gain crossover frequency, the PM is positive and the system is stable. If the resultant phase plot is below the −180° line at the gain crossover frequency, the phase margin is negative and the system is unstable. Figure 7.31 shows the determination of gain margin and phase margin from the Bode plot.

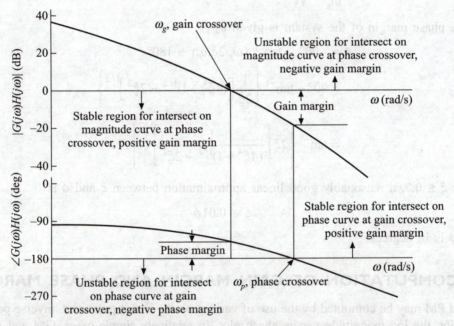

Figure 7.31　Determination of gain margin and phase margin on the Bode plot.

7.6.2　Relative Stability Related to the Slope of the Log Magnitude Curve of the Bode Plot

In addition to GM, PM and M_r as relative stability measures, the slope of the magnitude curve of the Bode plot of the loop transfer function at the gain crossover also gives qualitative indication of the relative stability of a closed-loop system. In general, the steeper the slope of the magnitude curve, the more negative the phase. Thus, if the gain crossover is at a point where the slope of the magnitude curve is steep, it is likely that the phase margin will be small or negative.

7.6.3 Advantages and Disadvantages of the Bode Plot Compared to the Nyquist Plot

Advantages: The following are the advantages of the Bode plot compared to the Nyquist plot.

   1. An approximate Bode plot can be drawn very quickly.
   2. Gain crossover frequency, phase crossover frequency, gain margin and phase margin are more easily determined on the Bode plot than from the Nyquist plot.
   3. For design purposes, the affects of adding controllers and their parameters are more easily visualized on the Bode plot than on the Nyquist plot.

Disadvantages: Absolute and relative stability of only nonminimum-phase systems can be determined from the Bode plot.

   The following observations can be made on system stability with respect to the properties of the Bode plot.

   1. The gain margin is positive and the system is stable if the magnitude $T(j\omega)$ at the phase crossover is negative in dB, i.e. the gain margin is measured below the 0 dB axis. If the gain margin is measured above the 0 dB axis, the gain margin is negative and the system is unstable.
   2. The phase margin is positive and the system is stable if the phase of $T(j\omega)$ is greater than $-180°$ at the gain crossover, i.e. the phase margin is measured above the $-180°$ axis. If the phase margin is measured below the $-180°$ axis, the phase margin is negative and the system is unstable.

7.6.4 Gain Adjustment in Bode Plot

In the open-loop transfer function $G(j\omega)H(j\omega)$, the constant K contributes only magnitude. Hence by changing the value of K, the system gain can be adjusted to meet the desired specifications. The desired specifications are gain margin GM, phase margin PM, phase crossover frequency ω_p and gain crossover frequency ω_g. In a system transfer function, if the value of K is required to be estimated to satisfy a desired specification, then draw the Bode plot of the system with $K = 1$. The constant K can add 20 log K to every point of the magnitude plot and due to this addition, the magnitude plot will shift vertically up or down. Hence shift the magnitude plot vertically up or down to meet the desired specification. Equate the vertical distance by which the magnitude plot is shifted to 20 log K and solve for K.

   Let X be the change in dB (X is positive if the plot is shifted up and vice versa).
   Now

$$20 \log K = X$$

or

$$\log K = \frac{X}{20}$$

∴

$$K = 10^{X/20}$$

While calculating phase angles, the following points should be remembered.

$$\angle a + jb = \tan^{-1} b/a \qquad\qquad \angle -a + jb = \pi - \tan^{-1} b/a$$

$$\angle -a - jb = \pi + \tan^{-1} b/a \qquad\qquad \angle a - jb = -\tan^{-1} b/a$$

7.7 EXPERIMENTAL DETERMINATION OF TRANSFER FUNCTIONS

Sometimes it is very difficult to obtain the transfer function of a system analytically. In such cases, the frequency response test can be conducted on the system and based on the experimentally obtained frequency response data, the magnitude and phase Bode plots can be drawn. The system transfer function within a certain degree of accuracy can then be obtained by fitting an asymptotic log magnitude plot to the experimental data as per the procedure outlined as follows:

1. The experimental data is used to plot the exact log magnitude and phase angle versus frequency curves on a semi-log graph sheet.

2. Asymptotes are then drawn on the log magnitude curve keeping in view the fact that the slopes of the asymptotes must be multiples of ± 20 dB/decade. The corner frequencies are so adjusted that the dB value at the corner frequency on the asymptotic plot differs from the actual magnitude plot by an amount which is in close agreement with the dB correction of the kind of factor revealed.

3. If the slope of the asymptotic log magnitude curve obtained in step 2 changes by $-20n$ dB/decade at $\omega = \omega_1$, it indicates that the factor $1/[1 + j(\omega/\omega_1)]^n$ exists in the transfer function.

4. If the slope changes by $+20n$ dB/decade at $\omega = \omega_2$, it indicates the presence of the factor $[1 + j(\omega/\omega_2)]^n$ in the transfer function.

5. If the slope changes by -40 dB/decade at $\omega = \omega_3$, it indicates that either a double pole $(n = 2)$ or a pair of complex conjugate poles are present in the transfer function. If the error at the corner frequency between the asymptotic plot and the actual plot is about -6 dB, then a factor of the form $1/[1 + j(\omega/\omega_3)]^2$ is present and if the error is positive, then a quadratic factor of the form $1/[1 + j2\xi(\omega/\omega_3) + (j\omega/\omega_3)^2]$ is present. The corresponding value of ξ is obtained with the help of the error graph of Figure 7.26.

6. In the low frequency range, the plot is dominated by a factor of the form $K/(j\omega)^r$. In most practical systems r equals 0,1 or 2.

   (a) If the low frequency asymptote is a horizontal line at X dB, it indicates that the transfer function represents a type-0 system with a gain K given by

   $$20 \log K = X$$

   i.e.
   $$\log K = \frac{X}{20}$$

   or
   $$K = \log^{-1}\left(\frac{X}{20}\right)$$

(b) If the low frequency asymptote has a slope of –20 dB/decade, it indicates the presence of a factor of the form $K/j\omega$ in the transfer function (type-1 system). The frequency at which the asymptote (extended if necessary) intersects the 0 dB line numerically represents the value of K. Also the asymptote (extended if necessary) has a gain of 20 log K at $\omega = 1$.

(c) If the low frequency asymptote has a slope of –40 dB/decade, then the transfer function has a factor of the form $K/(j\omega)^2$ (type-2 system). The frequency at which this asymptote (extended if necessary) intersects the 0 dB line is numerically equal to $\sqrt{K}$. Also the asymptote (extended if necessary) has a gain of 20 log K at $\omega = 1$.

After obtaining the transfer function from the log magnitude curve, the phase angle curve is constructed from it and is then compared with the one obtained experimentally. If the two curves are in fair agreement and if the phase angles of both the curves at very high frequencies tend to –90° $(q - p)$ where p and q are degrees of the numerator and denominator polynomials respectively of the transfer function, then the transfer function is of minimum-phase type. If the computed phase angle is 180° less negative than the one obtained experimentally, then the transfer function is of nonminimum-phase type and one of the zeros of the transfer function lies in the right half s-plane.

7.8 LOG MAGNITUDE VERSUS PHASE PLOTS

An alternative to polar plots and Bode plots in frequency-response representation is the log magnitude versus phase plot. It is a plot of magnitude in dB versus phase angle in degrees with frequency ω as the running parameter. It has certain advantages for analysis and design in the frequency-domain. The gain and phase crossovers and the gain and phase margins can be clearly indicated on the magnitude versus phase plot. So the relative stability of a closed-loop control system can be determined quickly. Another advantage of using the magnitude versus phase plot is that for unity feedback systems, closed-loop system parameters such as M_r, ω_r, and BW can all be determined from the plot with the help of the constant M loci. To draw the log magnitude versus phase plot for any system transfer function, first the magnitude and phase Bode plots are drawn and then by reading the values of the log magnitude and phase angle at different frequencies from these plots, the log magnitude versus phase angle plot is constructed with frequencies of various points indicated thereon.

The gain phase plot of $T(s) = 10/[s(1 + 0.2s)(1 + 0.02s)]$ is shown in Figure 7.32. In the log magnitude versus phase plot:

1. The critical point is the intersect of the 0 dB axis and the –180° axis.

2. The phase crossover is where the locus intersects the –180° axis.

3. The gain crossover is where the locus intersects the 0 dB axis.

4. The gain margin is the vertical distance in dB measured from the phase crossover to the critical point.

5. The phase margin is the horizontal distance in degrees measured from the gain crossover to the critical point.

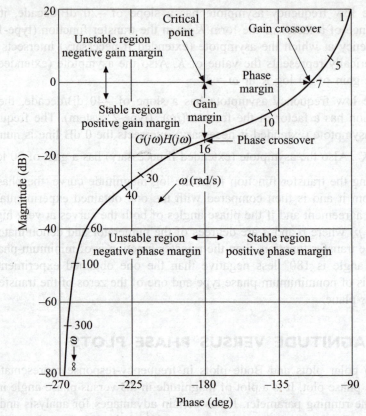

Figure 7.32 Gain phase plot of $G(s)H(s) = 10/[s(1 + 0.2s)(1 + 0.02s)]$.

7.9 CLOSED-LOOP FREQUENCY-RESPONSE

The closed-loop frequency-response analysis enables us to use the second-order correlations between frequency response and time response to predict approximately the time response of feedback systems. Design in time-domain is tedious. So with the help of these correlations, the time response specifications are first converted into a set of specifications in frequency-domain. The design and compensation is done in frequency-domain, and afterwards the frequency response is translated back to give an approximate time response. Usually the specifications in frequency-domain are given in the following terms.

7.9.1 Frequency-Domain Specifications

1. *Resonance peak M_r:* The resonance peak M_r is the maximum value of M, the magnitude of the closed-loop frequency response. A large resonance peak corresponds to a large overshoot in transient response.

2. *Resonant frequency ω_r:* The resonant frequency ω_r is the frequency at which the resonant peak M_r occurs. This is related to the frequency of oscillations in the step response and thus is indicative of the speed of transient response.

3. *Bandwidth ω_b:* The bandwidth is the range of frequencies for which the system gain is more than -3 dB. The bandwidth measures the ability of a feedback system to reproduce the input signal and also measures its noise rejection characteristics. It is also indicative of the rise time in transient response for a given damping factor. A large bandwidth corresponds to small rise time or fast response.

4. *Cut-off rate:* The cut-off rate is the slope of the log magnitude curve near the cut-off frequency. The cut-off rate indicates the ability of the system to distinguish the signal from noise.

5. *Gain margin and phase margin:* Gain margin and phase margin are measures of relative stability of a system and are related to the closeness of the closed-loop poles to the $j\omega$-axis.

Gain margin is defined as the margin between the actual gain and critical gain which causes sustained oscillations. It is the factor by which the system gain can be increased to drive it to the verge of instability.

Phase margin is defined as the amount of additional phase lag at the gain crossover frequency required to bring the system to the verge of instability.

For a stable system both GM and PM must be positive. Gain margin and phase margin are applicable only to open-loop stable systems.

The relation between damping ratio ξ and phase margin ϕ of a second-order system is

$$\xi \approx 0.01\phi$$

where ϕ is in degrees.

Example 7.5 Sketch the Bode plots showing the magnitude in dB and phase angle in degrees as a function of log frequency for the transfer function given below. Determine the gain crossover frequency, phase crossover frequency, gain margin and phase margin. Also determine the value of K and the corresponding phase margin for a gain crossover frequency of (a) 10 rad/s, (b) 50 rad/s, (c) 1 rad/s.

$$G(s)H(s) = \frac{2000}{s(s+2)(s+100)}$$

Solution: The sinusoidal transfer function is

$$G(j\omega)H(j\omega) = \frac{2000}{j\omega(j\omega+2)(j\omega+100)}$$

The sinusoidal transfer function in time constant form is

$$G(j\omega)H(j\omega) = \frac{2000}{j\omega(1+j\omega/2)2(1+j\omega/100)100} = \frac{10}{j\omega(1+j0.5\omega)(1+j0.01\omega)}$$

The factors of this transfer function in order of their occurrence as frequency increases are as follows:

1. Constant gain 10
2. Pole at the origin $1/j\omega$
3. Pole at $s = -2$, [factor $= 1/(1 + j0.5\omega)$], corner frequency $\omega_1 = 2$
4. Pole at $s = -100$, [factor $= 1/(1 + j0.01\omega)$], corner frequency $\omega_2 = 100$

The pertinent characteristics of each factor are given in Table 7.3.

Table 7.3 Example 7.5

Factor	Corner frequency	Asymptotic log magnitude characteristic	Phase angle characteristic
$\dfrac{10}{j\omega}$	none	Straight line of constant slope –20 dB/decade passing through the 20 log 10 = 20 dB point at $\omega = 1$.	Constant –90°.
$\dfrac{1}{1+j0.5\omega}$	$\omega_1 = 2$	Straight line of 0 dB for $\omega < \omega_1 = 2$. Straight line of slope –20 dB/decade for $\omega > \omega_1 = 2$.	Phase angle varies from 0 to –90°. Angle at $\omega = \omega_1 = 2$ is –45°.
$\dfrac{1}{1+j0.01\omega}$	$\omega_2 = 100$	Straight line of 0 dB for $\omega < \omega_2 = 100$. Straight line of –20 dB/decade for $\omega > \omega_2 = 100$.	Phase angle varies from 0 to –90°. Angle at $\omega = \omega_2 = 100$ is –45°.

The resultant magnitude plot: Up to the first corner frequency of $\omega_1 = 2$, the resultant magnitude plot is a straight line with a slope of –20 dB/decade passing through the 20 dB point at $\omega = 1$. For $\omega_1 = 2 < \omega < \omega_2 = 100$ it is a straight line with a slope of $(-20 \text{ dB}) + (-20 \text{ dB}) = -40$ dB/ decade. For $\omega > \omega_2 = 100$ it is a straight line with a slope of $(-40 \text{ dB}) + (-20 \text{ dB}) = -60$ dB/decade.

The error corrections are –3 dB at $\omega = 2$ and $\omega = 100$, –1 dB at $\omega = 1$ and $\omega = 4$, at $\omega = 50$ and $\omega = 200$.

The resultant phase is

$$\phi = \angle 1/j\omega + \angle 1/(1 + j0.5\omega) + \angle 1/(1 + j0.01\omega)$$

i.e.

$$\phi = -90° - \tan^{-1} 0.5\omega - \tan^{-1} 0.01\omega$$

At $\omega = 0.1$, $\phi = -90° - 2.86° - 0.05° = -92.91°$

At $\omega = 0.5$, $\phi = -90° - 14.03° - 0.28° = -104.3°$

At $\omega = 1$, $\phi = -90° - 26.6° - 0.57° = -117.2°$

At $\omega = 5$, $\phi = -90° - 68.19° - 2.86° = -161.05°$

At $\omega = 10$, $\phi = -90° - 78.69° - 5.7° = -174.4°$

At $\omega = 50$, $\phi = -90° - 87.7° - 26.6° = -204.3°$

At $\omega = 100$, $\phi = -90° - 88.85° - 45° = -223.85°$

Based on the above information, the magnitude and phase Bode plots are drawn as shown in Figure 7.33.

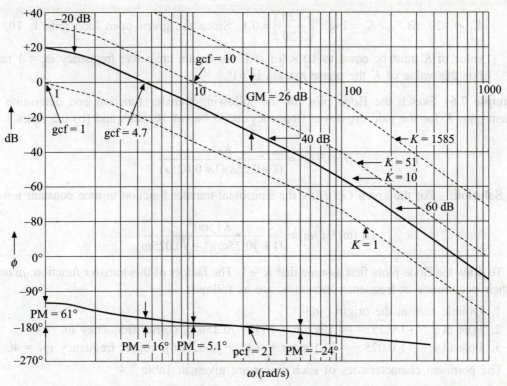

Figure 7.33   Example 7.5: Bode plot for $G(j\omega)H(j\omega) = 10/[j\omega(1 + j0.5\omega)(1 + j0.01\omega)]$.

1. From the frequency response plots of Figure 7.33, for $K = 10$:
   - the gain crossover frequency (gcf) = 4.7 rad/s   the phase margin is 16°
   - the phase crossover frequency (pcf) = 21 rad/s   the gain margin is 26 dB

2. From the Bode plot we observe that at $\omega = 10$ rad/s, the resultant magnitude is −14.2 dB. For it to become the gain cross over frequency, the resultant magnitude plot must be raised by +14.2 dB. ∴ The open loop gain is to be multiplied by K_1 such that 20 log $K_1 = 14.2$ dB. ∴ $K_1 = $ log^{-1} (14.2/20) = 5.1. Since the given open loop gain is 10, the value of K must be equal to $10 \times 5.1 = 51$, for a gain crossover frequency of $\omega_g = 10$ rad/s. For this value of K, the phase margin is 5.1°.

3. From the Bode plot we observe that at $\omega = 50$ rad/s, the resultant magnitude is −44 dB. For it to become the gain cross over frequency, the resultant magnitude plot must be raised by +44 dB. ∴ The open loop gain is to be multiplied by K_1 such that 20 log K_1 = 44 dB. ∴ $K_1 = $ log^{-1} (44/20) = 158.5. Since the given open loop gain is 10, the

value of K must be equal to $10 \times 158.5 = 1585$, for a gain crossover frequency $\omega_g = 50$ rad/s. For this value of K, the phase margin is $-24°$.

4. From the Bode plot we observe that at $\omega = 1$ rad/s, the resultant magnitude is $+20$ dB. For it to become the gain cross over frequency, the resultant magnitude plot must be lowered by -20 dB. $\therefore$ The open loop gain is to be multiplied by K_1 such that $20 \log$

$$K_1 = -20 \text{ dB}. \therefore K_1 = \log^{-1}\left(-\frac{20}{20}\right) = 0.1. \text{ Since the given open loop gain is 10, the}$$

value of K must be equal to $10 \times 0.1 = 1$, for a gain crossover frequency $\omega_g = 1$ rad/s. For this value of K the phase margin is $61°$.

Example 7.6 Sketch the Bode plot for the following transfer function and determine the system gain K for the gain crossover frequency ω_g to be (a) 10 rad/s and (b) 0.5 rad/s.

$$G(s)H(s) = \frac{Ks^2}{(1 + 0.25s)(1 + 0.025s)}$$

Solution: For the given $G(s)H(s)$, the sinusoidal transfer function in time constant form is

$$G(j\omega)H(j\omega) = \frac{K(j\omega)^2}{(1 + j0.25\omega)(1 + j0.025\omega)}$$

To draw the Bode plots first assume that $K = 1$. The factors of this transfer function, in order of their occurrence as frequency increases, are as follows:

1. Double zero at the origin $(j\omega)^2$
2. Pole at $s = -1/0.25 = -4$ [factor $= 1/(1 + j0.25\omega)$], corner frequency $\omega_1 = 4$
3. Pole at $s = -1/0.025 = -40$ [factor $= 1/(1 + j0.025\omega)$], corner frequency $\omega_2 = 40$

The pertinent characteristics of each factor are given in Table 7.4.

Table 7.4 Example 7.6

Factor	Corner frequency	Asymptotic log magnitude characteristic	Phase angle characteristic
$(j\omega)^2$	None	Straight line of constant slope $+40$ dB/decade, passing through the 0 dB line at $\omega = 1$.	Constant $+180°$.
$\dfrac{1}{1 + j0.25\omega}$	$\omega_1 = 4$	Straight line of 0 dB for $\omega < \omega_1 = 4$, straight line of slope -20 dB/decade for $\omega > \omega_1 = 4$.	Phase angle varies from 0 to $-90°$. Angle at $\omega = \omega_1 = 4$ is $-45°$.
$\dfrac{1}{1 + j0.025\omega}$	$\omega_2 = 40$	Straight line of 0 dB for $\omega < \omega_2 = 40$, straight line of slope -20 dB/decade for $\omega > \omega_2 = 40$.	Phase angle varies from 0 to $-90°$. Angle at $\omega = \omega_2 = 40$ is $-45°$.

The resultant magnitude plot: Up to the first corner frequency of $\omega_1 = 4$, the resultant magnitude plot is a straight line with a slope of $+40$ dB/decade, passing through the 0 dB line at $\omega = 1$. For $\omega_1 = 4 < \omega < \omega_2 = 40$, it is a straight line with a slope of $(+40 \text{ dB}) + (-20 \text{ dB}) = +20$ dB/decade. For $\omega > \omega_2 = 40$, it is a straight line with a slope of $(+20 \text{ dB}) + (-20 \text{ dB}) = 0$ dB/decade, i.e. it is a straight line parallel to the 0 dB line.

The error corrections to be made are -3 dB at $\omega = 4$ and $\omega = 40$, -1 dB at $\omega = 2$ and $\omega = 8$, and at $\omega = 20$ and $\omega = 80$.

The resultant phase angle is

$$\angle G(j\omega) = \angle(j\omega)^2 + \angle 1/(1 + j0.25\omega) + \angle 1/(1 + j0.025\omega)$$

i.e. $\qquad\qquad \phi = 180° - \tan^{-1} 0.25\omega - \tan^{-1} 0.025\omega$

At $\omega = 0.1$, $\qquad \phi = 180° - 1.43° - 0.143° = 178.42°$

At $\omega = 1$, $\qquad \phi = 180° - 14.03° - 1.43° = 164.54°$

At $\omega = 5$, $\qquad \phi = 180° - 51.34° - 7.12° = 121.54°$

At $\omega = 10$, $\qquad \phi = 180° - 68.20° - 14.03° = 97.68°$

At $\omega = 50$, $\qquad \phi = 180° - 85.42° - 51.34° = 43.24°$

At $\omega = 100$, $\qquad \phi = 180° - 87.7° - 68.2° = 24.1°$

At $\omega = 1000$, $\qquad \phi = 180° - 89.7° - 87.7° = 2.6°$

Based on the above information, the resultant magnitude and phase plots are drawn as shown in Figure 7.34. From the Bode plot it can be observed that with $K = 1$, the gain crossover frequency is $\omega = 1$ rad/s. At $\omega = 10$, the resultant magnitude is 30 dB. For $\omega = 10$ to become the gain crossover frequency, the resultant magnitude plot must pass through the 0 dB line at this point. So the gain is to be reduced by 30 dB. Therefore,

$$20 \log K = -30$$

i.e. $\qquad\qquad\qquad \log K = -1.5$

or $\qquad\qquad\qquad K = \log^{-1}(-1.5) = 0.031$

If the gain crossover frequency is to be $\omega_g = 0.5$ rad/s, from the graph we can observe that the resultant magnitude curve should be shifted up by 12 dB. So the value of K should be selected such that

$$20 \log K = 12$$

i.e. $\qquad\qquad\qquad \log K = \frac{12}{20} = 0.6$

or $\qquad\qquad\qquad K = 4$

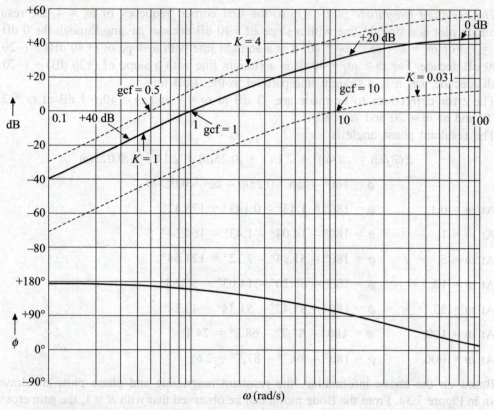

Figure 7.34   Example 7.6: Bode plots for $G(j\omega)H(j\omega) = K(j\omega)^2/[(1 + j0.25\omega)(1 + j0.025\omega)]$.

Example 7.7   Sketch the Bode plots for the following transfer function and determine the system gain K for the gain crossover frequency to be 2 rad/s.

(a) What is the PM for this value of K?

(b) What is the value of K for the gain crossover frequency to be 5 rad/s. For this value of K, what is the PM?

$$G(s)H(s) = \frac{Ke^{-0.1s}}{s(1+s)(1+0.1s)}$$

Solution: For the given $G(s)H(s)$, the sinusoidal transfer function is

$$G(j\omega)H(j\omega) = \frac{Ke^{-j0.1\omega}}{j\omega(1+ j\omega)(1+ j0.1\omega)}$$

Draw the Bode plot taking $K = 1$ and from the Bode plot, calculate the value of K for gain crossover frequency to be 2 rad/s.

The affect of the time delay T_d is to add a phase equal to $-\omega T_d \times \dfrac{180°}{\pi}$ along the curve.

The factor $e^{-j\omega T_d}$ corresponds to time delay.

The factors of this transfer function, in order of their occurrence as frequency increases, are as follows:

1. $e^{-j0.1\omega}$
2. Pole at the origin ($1/j\omega$)
3. Pole at $s = -1$, [factor $= 1/(1 + j\omega)$], corner frequency $\omega_1 = 1$
4. Pole at $s = -10$, [factor $= 1/(1 + j0.1\omega)$], corner frequency $\omega_2 = 10$

The pertinent characteristics of each factor are given in Table 7.5.

Table 7.5   Example 7.7

Factor	Corner frequency	Asymptotic log magnitude characteristic	Phase angle characteristic
$e^{-j0.1\omega}$	None	0 dB at all frequencies.	$\angle -57.3 \times \omega \times 0.1$ $= \angle -5.73\omega°$.
$\dfrac{1}{j\omega}$	None	Straight line of constant slope -20 dB/decade passing through the 0 dB line at $\omega = 1$ rad/s.	Constant $-90°$.
$\dfrac{1}{1 + j\omega}$	$\omega_1 = 1$	Straight line of 0 dB for $\omega < \omega_1 = 1$, straight line of -20 dB/decade for $\omega > \omega_1 = 1$.	Phase angle varies from 0 to $-90°$. Angle at $\omega = \omega_1 = 1$ is $-45°$.
$\dfrac{1}{1 + j0.1\omega}$	$\omega_2 = 10$	Straight line of 0 dB for $\omega < \omega_2 = 10$, straight line of -20 dB/decade for $\omega > \omega_2$.	Phase angle varies from 0 to $-90°$. Angle at $\omega = \omega_2 = 10$ is $-45°$.

The resultant magnitude plot: Up to the first corner frequency of $\omega_1 = 1$, the resultant magnitude plot is a straight line with a slope of -20 dB/decade, passing through the 0 dB line at $\omega = 1$. For $\omega_1 = 1 < \omega < \omega_2 = 10$, it is a straight line with a slope of $(-20$ dB$) + (-20$ dB$)$ $= -40$ dB/decade. For $\omega > \omega_2 = 10$, it is a straight line with a slope of $(-40$ dB$) + (-20$ dB$)$ $= -60$ dB/decade.

The error corrections to be made are -3 dB at $\omega = 1$ and $\omega = 10$ and -1 dB at $\omega = 0.5$ and $\omega = 2$, and at $\omega = 5$ and $\omega = 20$.

The resultant phase angle is

$$\phi = \angle e^{-j0.1\omega} + \angle 1/j\omega + \angle 1/(1 + j\omega) + \angle 1/(1 + j0.1\omega)$$

i.e. $$\phi = -90° - \tan^{-1}\omega - \tan^{-1}0.1\omega - 5.7\omega$$

At $\omega = 0.1$, $\phi = -90° - 5.7° - 0.57° - 0.57° = -96.84°$

At $\omega = 1$, $\phi = -90° - 45° - 5.7° - 5.7° = -146.4°$

At $\omega = 2$, $\phi = -90° - 63.4° - 11.3° - 11.4° = -176.1°$

At $\omega = 5$, $\phi = -90° - 78.7° - 26.6° - 28.5° = -223.8°$

At $\omega = 10$, $\phi = -90° - 84.28° - 45° - 57° = -276.3°$

Based on the above information, the resultant magnitude and phase plots are plotted as shown in Figure 7.35. From the Bode plots, we observe that with $K = 1$, the gain crossover frequency $\omega_g = 0.9$ rad/s, and the phase margin PM = 33.6°.

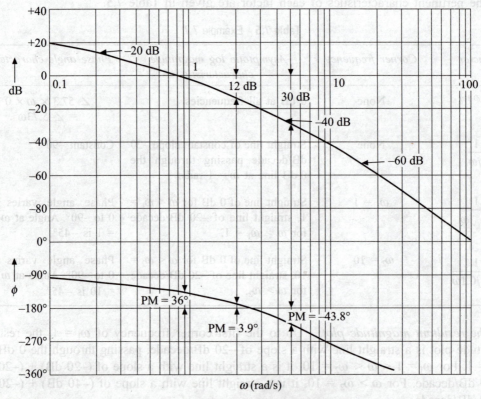

Figure 7.35   Example 7.7: Bode plots for $G(j\omega)H(j\omega) = Ke^{-j0.1\omega}/[j\omega(1 + j\omega)(1 + j0.1\omega)]$.

For the gain crossover frequency to be $\omega = 2$ rad/s, the resultant magnitude plot must pass through the 0 dB line at $\omega = 2$. But from the Bode plot, at $\omega = 2$, the resultant magnitude is -12 dB. So the magnitude is to be raised by 12 dB. This can be done by choosing the open-loop gain K such that

$$20 \log K = 12 \text{ dB}$$

or
$$\log K = 12/20 = 0.6$$

or
$$K = 4$$

For $K = 4$ the phase margin is 3.9°.

For the gain crossover frequency to be 5 rad/s, the resultant magnitude plot must pass through the 0 dB line at $\omega = 5$. But from the Bode plot at $\omega = 5$, the resultant magnitude is −30 dB. So the magnitude is to be raised by 30 dB. This can be done by choosing the open-loop gain K such that

$$20 \log K = 30 \text{ dB}$$

or
$$\log K = \frac{30}{20} = 1.5$$

or
$$K = \log^{-1} 1.5 = 31.5$$

For $K = 31.5$ the phase margin is −43.8° and the system is unstable.

Example 7.8 Sketch the Bode plot for the following transfer function and determine the system gain crossover frequency, phase crossover frequency, gain margin and phase margin. Also determine the value of K for a phase margin of 45°.

$$G(s)H(s) = \frac{80(s+5)}{s^2(s+50)}$$

Solution: For the given $G(s)H(s)$, the sinusoidal transfer function is

$$G(j\omega)H(j\omega) = \frac{80(j\omega + 5)}{(j\omega)^2(j\omega + 50)}$$

The sinusoidal transfer function in time constant form is

$$G(j\omega)H(j\omega) = \frac{80(1 + j\omega/5)5}{(j\omega)^2(1 + j\omega/50)50} = \frac{8(1 + j0.2\omega)}{(j\omega)^2(1 + j0.02\omega)}$$

The factors of this transfer function, in order of their occurrence as frequency increases are as follows:

1. Factor $8/(j\omega)^2$
2. Zero at $s = -5$, (factor $1 + j0.2\omega$), corner frequency $\omega_1 = 5$
3. Pole at $s = -50$, (factor $1/(1 + j0.02\omega)$), corner frequency $\omega_2 = 50$

The pertinent characteristics of each factor are given in Table 7.6.

Table 7.6 Example 7.8

Factor	Corner frequency	Asymptotic log magnitude characteristic	Phase angle characteristic
$\dfrac{8}{(j\omega)^2}$	None	Straight line of constant slope -40 dB/decade passing through the $20 \log 8 = 18$ dB point at $\omega = 1$.	Constant $-180°$.
$1 + j0.2\omega$	$\omega_1 = 5$	Straight line of 0 dB for $\omega < \omega_1 = 5$, straight line of slope $+20$ dB/decade for $\omega > \omega_1 = 5$.	Phase angle varies from 0 to $+90°$. Angle at $\omega = \omega_1 = 5$ is $+45°$.
$\dfrac{1}{1 + j0.02\omega}$	$\omega_2 = 50$	Straight line of 0 dB for $\omega < \omega_2 = 50$, straight line of -20 dB/decade for $\omega > \omega_2 = 50$.	Phase angle varies from 0 to $-90°$. Angle at $\omega = \omega_2 = 50$ is $-45°$.

The resultant magnitude plot: Up to the first corner frequency $\omega_1 = 5$, the resultant magnitude plot is a straight line with a slope of -40 dB/decade passing through the $20 \log 8 = 18$ dB point at $\omega = 1$. For $\omega_1 = 5 < \omega < \omega_2 = 50$ it is a straight line with a slope of $(-40$ dB$) + (+20$ dB$) = -20$ dB/decade.

For $\omega > \omega_2 = 50$, it is a straight line with a slope of $(-20$ dB$) + (-20$ dB$) = -40$ dB/decade.

The error corrections to be made are $+3$ dB at $\omega = 5$, $+1$ dB at $\omega = 2.5$ and $\omega = 10$, -3 dB at $\omega = 50$ and -1 dB at $\omega = 25$ and $\omega = 100$.

The resultant phase angle is

$$\phi = \angle 8/(j\omega)^2 + \angle(1 + j0.2\omega) + \angle 1/(1 + j0.02\omega)$$

i.e.

$$\phi = -180° + \tan^{-1} 0.2\omega - \tan^{-1} 0.02\omega$$

At $\omega = 0.1$, $\phi = -180° + 11.3° - 1.14° = -169.84°$

At $\omega = 10$, $\phi = -180° + 63.43° - 11.3° = -127.87°$

At $\omega = 50$, $\phi = -180° + 84.28° - 45° = -140.72°$

At $\omega = 100$, $\phi = -180° + 87.13° - 63.43° = -156.3°$

At $\omega = 500$, $\phi = -180° + 89.42° - 87.13° = -177.71°$

At $\omega = 5000$, $\phi = -180° + 89.94° - 89.42° = -179.48°$

Based on the above information, the resultant magnitude and phase plots are plotted as shown in Figure 7.36. From the Bode plots, we observe that, the phase plot does not cross the $-180°$ line at all. Therefore, the phase crossover frequency $\omega_p = \infty$ and the gain margin GM $= \infty$.

gcf $= 3$ rad/s   PM $= 27°$

pcf $= \infty$ GM $= \infty$

To determine the value of K for a phase margin of 45°, locate the frequency at which the resultant phase is 45° − 180° = −135°. From the Bode plot it is $\omega = 7$. At this frequency of $\omega = 7$, the resultant magnitude is −12 dB. For a phase margin of 45°, this should be the gcf. So the gain must be increased by 12 dB. This can be done if $K = 4$.

$$[20 \log K = 12 \text{ dB}$$

$\therefore$
$$\log K = \frac{12}{20} = 0.6 \text{ dB}$$

$\therefore$
$$K = \log^{-1} 0.6 = 4]$$

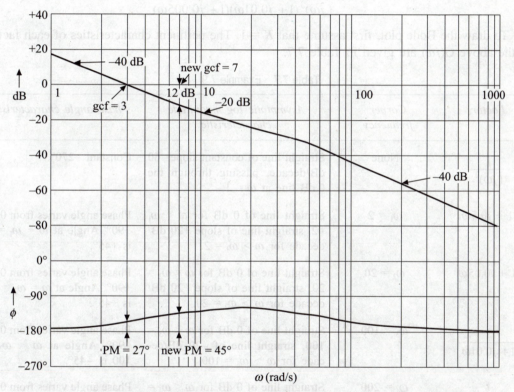

Figure 7.36 Example 7.8: Bode plot for $G(j\omega)H(j\omega) = 8(1 + j0.2\omega)/[(j\omega)^2(1 + j0.02\omega)]$.

Example 7.9 Draw the Bode plots for the system whose open-loop transfer function is

$$G(s)H(s) = \frac{500K(s+2)(s+20)}{s^3(s+100)(s+200)}$$

Determine the range of values of K for which the system is stable.

Solution: For the given $G(s)H(s)$, the sinusoidal transfer function is

$$G(j\omega)H(j\omega) = \frac{500K(j\omega+2)(j\omega+20)}{(j\omega)^3(j\omega+100)(j\omega+200)}$$

In time constant form

$$G(j\omega)H(j\omega) = \frac{500K(1+j0.5\omega)(1+j0.05\omega)2\times20}{(j\omega)^3(1+j0.01\omega)(1+j0.005\omega)100\times200}$$

$$= \frac{K(1+j0.5\omega)(1+j0.05\omega)}{(j\omega)^3(1+j0.01\omega)(1+j0.005\omega)}$$

To draw the Bode plot, first assume that $K = 1$. The pertinent characteristics of each factor of the above $G(j\omega)$ are given in Table 7.7.

Table 7.7   Example 7.9

Factor	Corner frequency	Asymptotic log magnitude characteristic	Phase angle characteristic
$\dfrac{1}{(j\omega)^3}$	None	Straight line of constant slope –60 dB/decade, passing through the 0 dB line at $\omega = 1$.	Constant –270°.
$1 + j0.5\omega$	$\omega_1 = 2$	Straight line of 0 dB for $\omega < \omega_1$ =2, straight line of slope +20 dB/decade for $\omega > \omega_1 = 2$.	Phase angle varies from 0 to +90°. Angle at $\omega = \omega_1 = 2$ is +45°.
$1 + j0.05\omega$	$\omega_2 = 20$	Straight line of 0 dB for $\omega < \omega_2 =$ 20, straight line of slope +20 dB/decade for $\omega > \omega_2 = 20$.	Phase angle varies from 0 to +90°. Angle at $\omega = \omega_2 = 20$ is +45°.
$\dfrac{1}{1+j0.01\omega}$	$\omega_3 = 100$	Straight line of 0 dB for $\omega < \omega_3 =$ 100, straight line of –20 dB/decade for $\omega > \omega_3 = 100$.	Phase angle varies from 0 to –90°. Angle at $\omega = \omega_3 =$ 100 is –45°.
$\dfrac{1}{1+j0.005\omega}$	$\omega_4 = 200$	Straight line of 0 dB for $\omega < \omega_4 =$ 200, straight line of –20 dB/decade for $\omega > \omega_4 = 200$.	Phase angle varies from 0 to –90°. Angle at $\omega = \omega_4 =$ 200 is –45°.

The resultant magnitude plot: Up to the first corner frequency of $\omega_1 = 2$, the resultant magnitude plot is a straight line with a slope of –60 dB/decade, passing through the 0 dB line at $\omega = 1$ rad/s. For $\omega_1 = 2 < \omega < \omega_2 = 20$, it is a straight line with a slope of (–60 dB) + (+20 dB) = –40 dB/decade. For $\omega_2 = 20 < \omega < \omega_3 = 100$, it is a straight line with a slope of (–40 dB) + (+20 dB) = –20 dB/decade. For $\omega_3 = 100 < \omega < \omega_4 = 200$, it is a straight line with a slope of (–20 dB) + (–20 dB) = –40dB/decade. For $\omega > \omega_4 = 200$, it is a straight line with a slope of (–40 dB) + (–20 dB) = –60dB/decade.

The error corrections to be made are +3 dB at $\omega = 2$ and $\omega = 20$, +1 dB at $\omega = 1$ and $\omega = 4$, and at $\omega = 10$ and $\omega = 40$, –3 dB at $\omega = 100$ and $\omega = 200$, –1 dB at $\omega = 50$ and $\omega = 200$, and at $\omega = 100$ and $\omega = 400$.

The resultant phase angle is

$$\phi = \angle 1/(j\omega)^3 + \angle(1 + j0.5\omega) + \angle(1 + j0.05\omega)$$
$$+ \angle 1/(1 + j0.01\omega) + \angle 1/(1 + j0.005\omega)$$

i.e. $\quad\quad \phi = -270° + \tan^{-1} 0.5\omega + \tan^{-1} 0.05\omega - \tan^{-1} 0.01\omega - \tan^{-1} 0.005\omega$

At $\omega = 1$, $\quad\quad \phi = -270° + 26.56° + 2.86° - 0.57° - 0.28° = -241.39°$

At $\omega = 5$, $\quad\quad \phi = -270° + 68.19° + 14.03° - 2.86° - 1.43° = -192.07°$

At $\omega = 10$, $\quad\quad \phi = -270° + 78.69° + 26.6° - 5.7° - 2.86° = -173.27°$

At $\omega = 50$, $\quad\quad \phi = -270° + 87.7° + 68.19° - 26.6° - 14.03° = -154.74°$

At $\omega = 100$, $\quad\quad \phi = -270° + 88.85° + 78.69° - 45° - 26.6° = -174.06°$

At $\omega = 500$, $\quad\quad \phi = -270° + 89.77° + 87.7° - 78.69° - 68.19° = -248.42°$

Based on the above information, the resultant magnitude and phase plots are drawn as shown in Figure 7.37. From the Bode plots we observe that for $K = 1$, the gain crossover frequency $\omega_g = 1$ rad/s and the phase margin is –61.4° and the system is unstable. The system is stable for frequencies between $\omega = 8$ rad/s to $\omega = 110$ rad/s. These are the two phase crossover frequencies. The phase characteristics between these two frequencies indicate, that if the gain crossover frequency lies in this range, the system would be stable. At $\omega = 8$ rad/s, the resultant magnitude = –42 dB. It can be the gain crossover frequency if 20 log $K = 42$ dB, i.e. $K = \log^{-1} 42/20 = \log^{-1} 2.1 = 125.9$. At $\omega = 110$ rad/s, resultant magnitude = –78 dB. It can be the gain crossover frequency if 20 log $K = 78$ dB, i.e. $K = \log^{-1} 78/20 = \log^{-1} 3.9 = 7943$. For values of K above and below this range, the phase of $G(j\omega)$ is less than –180°, and the system is unstable.

This example serves as a good example of the relation between relative stability and the slope of the magnitude curve at the gain crossover frequency. As observed from Figure 7.37, at both very low and very high frequencies, the slope of the magnitude curve is –60 dB/decade; if the gain crossover falls in either one of these two regions, the phase margin is negative and the system is unstable. In the two sections of the magnitude curve that has a slope of –40 dB/decade, the system is stable only if the gain crossover falls in small part of these regions, but even then the phase margin is small. If the gain crossover falls in the region in which the magnitude curve has a slope of –20 dB/decade, the system is stable.

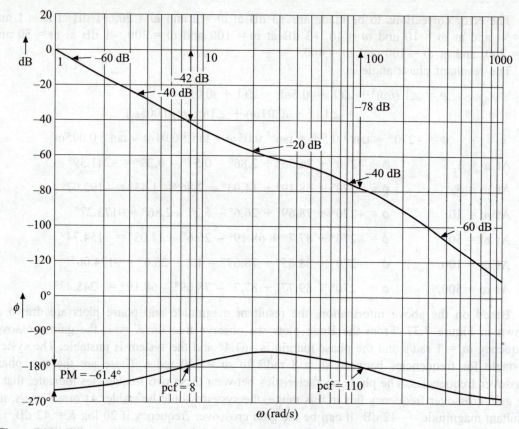

Figure 7.37 Example 7.9: Bode plot for $G(j\omega)H(j\omega) = K(1 + j0.5\omega)(1 + j0.05\omega)/[(j\omega)^3(1 + j0.01\omega)(1 + j0.005\omega)]$.

Example 7.10 A unity feedback system has a plant transfer function of

$$G(s)H(s) = \frac{K(s+4)}{(s-1)(s-2)}$$

(a) For $K = 8$, draw the Bode plots and find therefrom the phase margin and gain margin.

(b) What should be the value of K for a phase margin of 30° and what is the corresponding gain margin?

Solution: The sinusoidal transfer function is

$$G(j\omega)H(j\omega) = \frac{K(j\omega+4)}{(j\omega-1)(j\omega-2)}$$

The sinusoidal transfer function in time constant form is

$$G(j\omega)H(j\omega) = \frac{K \times 4(1 + j\omega/4)}{(-1)(1 - j\omega)(-2)(1 - j\omega/2)} = \frac{2K(1 + j0.25\omega)}{(1 - j\omega)(1 - j0.5\omega)} = \frac{K'(1 + j0.25\omega)}{(1 - j\omega)(1 - j0.5\omega)}$$

(a) For $K = 8$,

$$G(j\omega)H(j\omega) = \frac{16(1 + j0.25\omega)}{(1 - j\omega)(1 - j0.5\omega)}$$

The factors of the above transfer function and the characteristics of each factor are given in Table 7.8.

Table 7.8 Example 7.10

Factor	Corner frequency	Asymptotic log magnitude characteristic	Phase angle characteristic
16	None	Constant +24 dB	0°
$\dfrac{1}{1 - j\omega}$	$\omega_1 = 1$	Straight line of 0 dB for $\omega < \omega_1$ = 1, straight line of slope −20 dB/decade for $\omega > \omega_1 = 1$.	Phase angle varies from −180° to −90°. Angle at $\omega = \omega_1 = 1$ is −135°.
$\dfrac{1}{1 - j0.5\omega}$	$\omega_2 = 2$	Straight line of 0 dB for $\omega < \omega_2$ = 2, straight line of slope −20 dB/decade for $\omega > \omega_2 = 2$.	Phase angle varies from −180° to −90°. Angle at $\omega = \omega_2 = 2$ is −135°.
$1 + j0.25\omega$	$\omega_3 = 4$	Straight line of 0 dB for $\omega < \omega_3$ = 4, straight line of +20 dB/decade for $\omega > \omega_3 = 4$.	Phase angle varies from 0 to +90°. Angle at $\omega = \omega_3 = 4$ is +45°.

The resultant magnitude plot: At low frequencies (for $\omega < \omega_1 = 1$), the resultant magnitude plot is a straight line of +24 dB. From $\omega = \omega_1 = 1$ to $\omega = \omega_2 = 2$, it is a straight line with a slope of −20 dB/decade. For $\omega = \omega_2 = 2$ to $\omega = \omega_3 = 4$, it is a straight line with a slope of $(-20\ \text{dB}) + (-20\ \text{dB}) = -40\ \text{dB/decade}$. For $\omega > \omega_3 = 4$, it is a straight line with a slope of $(-40\ \text{dB}) + (+20\ \text{dB}) = -20\ \text{dB/decade}$.

The error corrections are −3 dB at $\omega = 1$ and $\omega = 2$, −1 dB at $\omega = 0.5$ and $\omega = 1$ and at $\omega = 1$ and $\omega = 4$. +3 dB at $\omega = 4$ and +1 dB at $\omega = 2$ and $\omega = 8$.

The resultant phase angle is

$$\phi = -\angle(-1 + j\omega) - \angle(-2 + j\omega) + \angle(4 + j\omega)$$

i.e.

$$\phi = -180° + \tan^{-1} \omega - 180° + \tan^{-1} \omega/2 + \tan^{-1} \omega/4$$

At $\omega = 0.1$, $\phi = -180° + 5.7° - 180° + 2.86° + 1.43° = -350.1°$

At $\omega = 0.5$, $\phi = -180° + 26.56° - 180° + 14.03° + 7.12° = -312.29°$

At $\omega = 1$, $\phi = -180° + 45° - 180° + 26.52° + 14.03° = -274.45°$

At $\omega = 2$, $\phi = -180° + 63.43° - 180° + 45° + 26.56° = -225.01°$

At $\omega = 4$,　　　$\phi = -180° + 75.96° - 180° + 63.43° + 45° = -175.61°$

At $\omega = 10$,　　$\phi = -180° + 84.2° - 180° + 78.69° + 68.1° = -129.01°$

At $\omega = 100$,　$\phi = -180° + 89.42° - 180° + 88.85° + 87.7° = -94.3°$

Based on the above information, the magnitude and phase Bode plots are drawn as shown in Figure 7.38. From them we can see that:

(a) For $K = 8$, PM = 45° corresponding to gain crossover frequency of $\omega_g = 8$, and GM = -8 dB for a phase crossover frequency of $\omega_p = 3.6$.

(b) For PM = 30°, gain crossover frequency must be $\omega_g = 6$. For $\omega = 6$ to become the gain crossover frequency, the gain should be reduced by 4 dB. Therefore,

$$K \text{ (new)} = 24 - 4 = 20 \text{ dB}$$

or　　　　　　　　　　　$$K = 10$$

When the gain is reduced by 4 dB, at the phase crossover frequency, gain = 4 dB. Therefore, new gain margin = -4 dB.

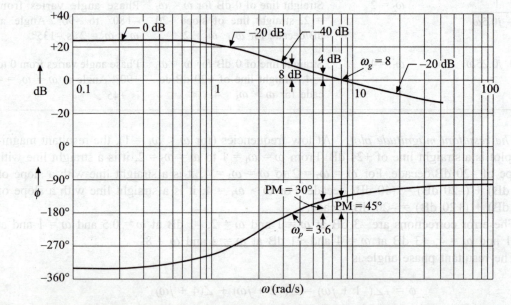

Figure 7.38　Example 7.10: Bode plots for $G(j\omega)H(j\omega) = K'(1 + j0.25\omega)/[(1 - j\omega)(1 - j0.5\omega)]$.

Example 7.11 The frequency response test data of certain elements plotted on the Bode diagrams and asymptotically approximated are shown in Figure 7.39. Find the transfer function of each element (elements are known to have minimum-phase characteristics).

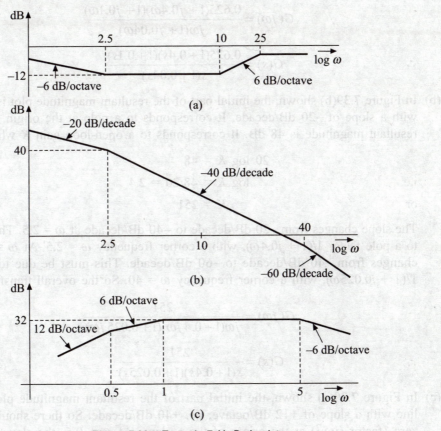

Figure 7.39   Example 7.11: Bode plots.

Solution:

(a) In Figure 7.39(a) shown, the initial part of the resultant magnitude plot has a slope of -6 dB/octave, i.e. -20 dB/decade. It corresponds to a pole at the origin (i.e. factor $1/j\omega$). It has a magnitude of -4 dB at $\omega = 1$. It corresponds to the open-loop gain K, where

$$20 \log K = -4$$

i.e. $$\log K = -4/20 = -0.2$$

or $$K = 0.625$$

At $\omega = 2.5$, slope changes from -20 dB/decade to zero. So a zero factor $(1 + j0.4\omega)$ with a corner frequency of $\omega = 2.5$ has to be added. At $\omega = 10$, the slope changes from 0 to $+6$ dB/octave. So a zero factor $(1 + j0.1\omega)$ with a corner frequency of $\omega = 10$ has to be added. At $\omega = 25$, the slope changes from +6 dB/octave to 0 dB/octave. So a pole factor $(1/1 + j0.4\omega)$ with a corner frequency of $\omega = 25$ is to be added. So the resultant transfer function is

$$G(j\omega) = \frac{0.625(1 + j0.4\omega)(1 + j0.1\omega)}{j\omega(1 + j0.04\omega)}$$

$$\therefore \qquad G(s) = \frac{0.625(1 + 0.4s)(1 + 0.1s)}{s(1 + 0.04s)}$$

(b) In Figure 7.39(b) shown, the initial part of the resultant magnitude plot is a straight line with a slope of –20 dB/decade. It corresponds to a pole at the origin. At $\omega = 1$, the resultant magnitude is 48 dB. It corresponds to a open-loop gain K where

$$20 \log K = 48$$

i.e. $$\log K = 48/20 = 2.4$$

or $$K = 251$$

The slope changes from –20 dB/decade to –40 dB/decade at $\omega = 2.5$. This must be due to a pole factor $1/(1 + j0.4\omega)$, with a corner frequency $\omega = 2.5$. At $\omega = 40$, the slope changes from –40 dB/decade to –60 dB/decade. This must be due to a pole factor $1/(1 + j0.025\omega)$, with a corner frequency $\omega = 40$. So the overall transfer function is

$$G(j\omega) = \frac{251}{j\omega(1 + 0.4\,j\omega)(1 + 0.025\,j\omega)}$$

$$\therefore \qquad G(s) = \frac{251}{s(1 + 0.4s)(1 + 0.025s)}$$

(c) In Figure 7.39(c) shown, the initial part of the resultant magnitude plot is a straight line with a slope of +12 dB/octave, i.e. +40 dB/decade. So there should be a double zero (factor $(j\omega)^2$) at the origin of the s-plane. At $\omega = 0.5$, the slope changes from +40 dB/decade to +20 dB/decade. So there must be a pole (factor $1/(1 + j2\omega)$, with a corner frequency $\omega = 0.5$. At $\omega = 1$, the slope changes from +6 dB/octave, i.e. +20 dB/decade to 0 dB/decade. So there must be a pole (factor $1/(1 + j\omega)$), with a corner frequency $\omega = 1$. At $\omega = 5$, the slope changes from 0 dB/decade to –20 dB/decade. So there must be a pole (factor $1/(1 + j0.2\omega)$), with a corner frequency $\omega = 5$. So the transfer function is

$$G(j\omega) = \frac{K(j\omega)^2}{(1 + j2\omega)(1 + j\omega)(1 + j0.2\omega)}$$

$$\therefore \qquad G(s) = \frac{Ks^2}{(1 + 2s)(1 + s)(1 + 0.2s)}$$

The value of K is determined like this.

For $0.5 < \omega < 1$, it is a straight line with a slope of +20 dB/decade having a magnitude of 32 dB at $\omega = 1$. It starts at $\omega = 0.5$. If it is extended up to $\omega = 5$, at $\omega = 5$ the magnitude will be 46 dB. So at $\omega = 0.5$, the magnitude must be 26 dB. Now for $\omega < 0.5$, it is a straight line with a slope of +40 dB/decade. Draw a line with a slope of +40 dB/decade, from $\omega = 0.05$ to $\omega = 0.5$; it has a magnitude of –2 dB at $\omega = 0.1$. Now if we draw a line with a slope of +40 dB/decade from $\omega = 0.1$ to $\omega = 1$, it will have a magnitude of 38 dB, at $\omega = 1$. Therefore,

$$20 \log K = 38$$

i.e. $$\log K = 38/20 = 1.9$$

$\therefore$ $$K = \log^{-1} 1.9 = 79.43$$

SHORT QUESTIONS AND ANSWERS

1. What do you mean by frequency response?

A. The magnitude and phase relationship between the sinusoidal input and the steady-state output of a system is called the frequency response.

2. How is the frequency response test conducted on a system?

A. The frequency response test on a system is normally conducted by keeping the amplitude of the input signal constant and determining the amplitude of the output and the phase shift between the input and the output of the system for various ranges of frequencies.

3. What are the advantages of frequency response analysis?

A. The advantages of frequency response analysis are as follows:

(a) The absolute and relative stability of a closed-loop control system can be estimated from the knowledge of the open-loop frequency response.

(b) Frequency response tests can be easily carried out on systems because of the ready availability of signal generators and precise measuring instruments.

(c) The ease and accuracy of measurements.

(d) Wherever it is not possible to obtain the transfer function of a system analytically, it can be determined experimentally by conducting frequency response tests.

(e) The design and parameter adjustment of the open-loop transfer function of a system for a specified closed-loop performance can be carried out easily.

(f) The effects of noise disturbance and parameter variations can be visualized easily.

(g) The transient response of a system can be obtained from its frequency response.

(h) It can be extended to certain nonlinear systems.

4. What are the limitations of frequency response analysis?

A. The limitations of frequency response analysis are as follows:

(a) For systems with large time constants, the frequency response test is cumbersome to perform.

(b) The frequency response test cannot be performed on non-interruptible systems.

5. What are frequency-domain specifications?

A. The frequency-domain specifications indicate the performance of the system in the frequency-domain. They are as follows:

1. Resonant peak M_r
2. Resonant frequency ω_r
3. Bandwidth ω_b
4. Cut-off rate
5. Gain margin GM
6. Phase margin PM (ϕ_{pm})

6. Define resonant peak.

A. The resonant peak M_r is defined as the maximum value M of the magnitude of the closed-loop frequency response.

7. Define resonant frequency.

A. The resonant frequency ω_r is defined as the frequency at which the resonant peak occurs.

8. Define bandwidth.

A. Bandwidth is defined as the range of frequencies for which the system gain is more than −3 dB.

9. Write a short note on the correlation between time and frequency responses.

A. A correlation exists between the time and frequency responses of first- and second-order systems. For a peak overshoot M_p in time-domain, there is a corresponding resonant peak M_r in the frequency-domain. For the damped frequency ω_d in the time-domain, there is a corresponding resonant frequency ω_r in the frequency-domain. All these specifications can be expressed in terms of ξ and ω_n.

$$M_p = e^{-\pi\xi/\sqrt{1-\xi^2}}$$

$$M_r = 1/2\xi\sqrt{1-\xi^2}$$

$$\omega_d = \omega_n\sqrt{1-\xi^2}$$

$$\omega_r = \omega_n\sqrt{1-2\xi^2}$$

For higher-order systems, there is no explicit correlation between time and frequency responses. But if the higher-order system has a pair of dominant complex conjugate poles, then it can be approximated by a second-order system and the correlation between time and frequency responses can be estimated.

10. The damping ratio and the undamped natural frequency of a second-order system are 0.4 and 6 rad/s respectively. Calculate the resonant peak M_r and resonant frequency ω_r.

A. Resonant peak

$$M_r = 1/2\xi\sqrt{1-\xi^2} = 1/2 \times 0.4\sqrt{1-0.4^2} = 1.365$$

Resonant frequency

$$\omega_r = \omega_n\sqrt{1 - 2\xi^2} = 6\sqrt{1 - 2 \times 0.4^2} = 4.947 \text{ rad/s}$$

11. What is the effect of adding a zero to the forward path transfer function?

A. The general effect of adding a zero to the forward path transfer function is to increase the bandwidth of the system.

12. What is the effect of adding a pole to the forward path transfer function?

A. The effect of adding a pole to the forward path transfer function is to make the closed-loop system less stable while decreasing the bandwidth.

13. How are bandwidth and rise time related?

A. Bandwidth ω_b and rise time t_r are inversely proportional to each other.

14. How are bandwidth and resonant peak related?

A. Bandwidth ω_b and resonant peak M_r are directly proportional to each other.

15. What do you mean by a polar plot?

A. The locus traced by the tip of the phasor $G(j\omega)$, as the frequency ω is varied from 0 to ∞ is known as polar plot, i.e. the polar plot of a sinusoidal transfer function $G(j\omega)$ is a plot of the magnitude of $G(j\omega)$ versus the phase angle of $G(j\omega)$ on polar or rectangular coordinates as ω is varied from 0 to ∞.

16. What is the advantage of polar plots?

A. An approximate polar plot can be drawn quickly and polar plots can be used for stability studies of control systems.

17. How do you draw a polar plot?

A. An approximate polar plot can be drawn very easily by rationalizing the sinusoidal transfer function, writing the real and imaginary parts and finding the points $G(j0)$ and $G(j\infty)$, and drawing a smooth curve joining those points.

18. What is the Bode plot?

A. The Bode plot, also called the logarithmic plot, is a frequency response plot of the transfer function of a system. It consists of two plots: magnitude plot and phase plot.
The magnitude plot is a graph between the magnitude of $G(j\omega)H(j\omega)$ expressed in dB and the frequency ω on the log scale. The phase plot is a graph between the phase angle of $G(j\omega)H(j\omega)$ in degrees and the frequency ω on the log scale.

19. What do you mean by an approximate Bode plot?

A. An approximate Bode plot is one which is drawn using straight line asymptotes. Slope changes only at the corner frequencies.

20. Define corner frequency.

A. The magnitude Bode plot can be approximated by straight line asymptotes. The frequency at which the low frequency and high frequency asymptotes meet is called the corner frequency. The slope of the magnitude plot changes at the corner frequencies.

21. What are the advantages of Bode plots?

A. The advantages of Bode plots are as follows:

(a) An approximate Bode plot using straight line asymptotes can be quickly and easily sketched and then corrections can be made to obtain the exact plot.

(b) Both absolute and relative stability of a system can be determined using Bode plots.

(c) Since the logarithmic scale is used, both low frequency and high frequency portions can be represented on the same sheet.

(d) Since the magnitude is expressed in dB, multiplication and division of magnitudes can be converted into addition and subtraction respectively.

(e) They can be used to analyze both open-loop and closed-loop systems.

22. What are the corrections to be made to the asymptotic magnitude plot?

A. The corrections to be made to an asymptotic magnitude plot are as follows:

(a) For simple poles, error at the corner frequency is –3 dB, and error at half and double the corner frequencies is –1 dB.

(b) For simple zero, error at the corner frequency is +3 dB, and error at half and double the corner frequency is +1 dB.

(c) For multiple poles and zeros, the errors get multiplied.

(d) For complex poles and zeros, error depends on ξ.

23. Define the cut-off rate.

A. The cut-off rate is defined as the slope of the log-magnitude curve near the cut-off frequency. The cut-off rate indicates the ability of the system to distinguish the signal from noise.

24. Define the gain crossover frequency.

A. The gain crossover frequency ω_g is defined as the frequency at which the resultant magnitude is zero dB, i.e. the gain crossover frequency is defined as the frequency at which $|G(j\omega)H(j\omega)| = 1$.

25. Define the phase crossover frequency.

A. The phase crossover frequency ω_p is defined as the frequency at which the resultant phase is $-180°$ i.e. the phase crossover frequency is defined as the frequency at which $\angle G(j\omega)H(j\omega) = -180°$.

26. Define gain margin.

A. Gain margin is defined as the margin between the actual gain and the critical gain which causes sustained oscillations.

Gain margin is also defined as the amount of additional gain that should be added at the phase crossover frequency to bring the system to the verge of instability.

Gain margin is also defined as the factor by which the system gain can be increased to drive the system to the verge of instability.

Gain margin is also defined as the reciprocal of the magnitude of the open-loop transfer function at the phase crossover frequency.

27. Define phase margin.

A. Phase margin ϕ_{pm} is defined as the amount of additional phase lag that should be added at the gain crossover frequency to bring the system to the verge of instability.

28. What does a large gain margin or a large phase margin indicate?

A. A large gain margin or a large phase margin indicate a very stable feedback system but usually a very sluggish one.

29. What does a gain margin close to unity or a phase margin close to zero indicate?

A. A gain margin close to unity or a phase margin close to zero indicate a highly oscillatory system.

30. What are the values of gain margin and phase margin usually required for reasonably good degree of relative stability?

A. Usually a gain margin of about 6 dB or a phase margin of about 30° to 35° results in a reasonably good degree of relative stability.

31. How do you determine the gain crossover frequency ω_g and phase crossover frequency ω_p from the Bode plot?

A. To determine the gain crossover frequency and phase crossover frequency from the Bode plots, first draw the magnitude and phase Bode plots. Locate the frequency at which the resultant magnitude plot crosses the zero dB line. This gives the gain cross-over frequency.

Locate the frequency at which the resultant phase plot crosses the −180° line. This gives the phase crossover frequency.

32. How do you determine the gain margin and phase margin of a system from its Bode plot?

A. To determine the gain margin and phase margin from the Bode plots, first draw the magnitude and phase Bode plots. Locate the gain and phase crossover frequencies. At the gain crossover frequency, the phase margin can be determined as

$$\text{phase margin} = \angle G(j\omega)H(j\omega) \text{ at the gain crossover frequency} + 180°$$

The negative of the resultant magnitude at the phase crossover frequency gives the gain margin.

33. What is the requirement of gain margin and phase margin for a stable system?

A. For a stable system, both gain margin and phase margin must be positive. Large values of gain margin and phase margin yield a relatively more stable system, but the system will be sluggish.

34. What is a minimum-phase system?

A. A minimum-phase system is a system whose transfer function is of minimum-phase type. A minimum-phase transfer function is a transfer function which has got all its poles and zeros only in the left half of the *s*-plane. Such a transfer function has the least (minimum) phase angle range for a magnitude curve.

35. What is an all-pass system?

A. An all-pass system is a system with all-pass transfer function. An all-pass transfer function is a transfer function having a pole-zero pattern which is antisymmetric about the imaginary axis (i.e. for every pole in the left half *s*-plane, there is a zero in the mirror image position with respect to imaginary axis). The magnitude of the all-pass transfer function is unity at all frequencies.

36. What is nonminimum-phase transfer function?

A. A transfer function which has one or more zeros in the right-half *s*-plane is known as nonminimum-phase transfer function. A nonminimum-phase transfer function can be treated as a combination of a minimum-phase transfer function and an all-pass transfer function.

37. What is log-magnitude versus phase plot? What are its advantages?

A. The log-magnitude versus phase plot is a plot of magnitude in dB versus phase angle in degrees with frequency ω as the running parameter. Its advantages are, the gain and phase crossovers, and the gain and phase margins can be clearly indicated on the magnitude versus phase plot. So the relative stability of a closed-loop control system can be determined quickly and the compensation can be carried out easily. Another advantage of using the magnitude versus phase plot is that for unity feedback systems, closed-loop system parameters such as M_r, ω_r and ω_b can all be determined from the plot with the help of the constant M loci.

REVIEW QUESTIONS

1. Write notes on correlation between time and frequency response of a second-order system.

2. Derive expressions for (a) M_r, (b) ω_r, (c) ω_b and (d) ϕ_{pm} of a second-order system.

3. Write notes on (a) polar plots and (b) Bode plots.

4. Write notes on minimum-phase and nonminimum-phase systems.

5. Write notes on log-magnitude versus phase plot.

FILL IN THE BLANKS

1. The magnitude and phase relationship between the ___Sin___ input and the _____ output of a system is called the frequency response.

2. The maximum value M of the closed-loop frequency response is called the _____.

3. The frequency at which the _____ occurs is called the resonant frequency.

4. The _____ is defined as the range of frequencies for which the system gain is more than −3 dB.

5. The *cut-off rate* is defined as the slope of the log magnitude curve near the cut-off frequency.

6. The general effect of adding a zero to the forward path transfer function is to *increase* the bandwidth of the closed-loop system.

7. The effect of adding a pole to the forward path transfer function is to make the closed-loop system *less* stable, while *lowering* the bandwidth.

8. Bandwidth and rise time are *inversely* proportional.

9. Bandwidth and resonant peak are *directly* proportional.

10. The larger the bandwidth is, the *faster* the system will respond.

11. Increasing ω_n *increases* the bandwidth and *lowers* the rise time.

12. t_r is _____ proportional to ω_n.

13. M_r and M_p depend only on ξ.

14. The locus traced by the tip of the phasor $G(j\omega)$ as the frequency ω is varied from 0 to ∞ is known as _____ plot.

15. The Bode plot is also called the _____ plot.

16. Bode plots are drawn on a _____ sheet.

17. An approximate Bode plot is one which is drawn using *st line asymptotes*

18. The frequency at which the low frequency and high frequency asymptotes of the Bode plot meet is called the _____.

19. The frequency at which $|G(j\omega)H(j\omega)| = 1$ is called the _____ frequency.

20. The frequency at which $\angle G(j\omega)H(j\omega) = -180°$ is called the _____ frequency.

21. The *phase margin* is defined as the amount of additional phase lag that should be added at the gain crossover frequency to bring the system to the verge of instability.

22. The amount of additional gain that should be added at the phase crossover frequency to bring the system to the verge of instability is called the *GM*.

23. Gain margin and phase margin must be *+ve* for a stable system.

24. Large values of gain margin and phase margin result in a *sluggish* system.

25. A transfer function which has all its poles and zeros only in the left-half of the s-plane is called a *min phase* transfer function.

26. An all-pass transfer function has a pole-zero pattern which is *antisymm* about the imaginary axis.

27. A transfer function which has one or more zeros in the right-half of the s-plane is known as a *non-min* transfer function.

28. A nonminimum-phase transfer function can be treated as a combination of a *min* transfer function and an *allpass* transfer function.

29. Absolute and relative stability of only *non-min* systems can be determined from the Bode plot.

OBJECTIVE TYPE QUESTIONS

1. Frequency response test is not recommended for systems with
   (a) very low time constants
   (b) with small time constants
   (c) with large time constants
   (d) any time constant

2. The frequency where M has a peak value is known as the
   (a) peak frequency
   (b) resonant frequency
   (c) normalized frequency
   (d) none of these

3. M_r does not exist for
   (a) $\xi = 0$
   (b) $\xi < 0.707$
   (c) $\xi > 0.707$
   (d) all values of ξ

4. The damping ratio ξ of a system is 0.5. The value of M_r is
   (a) 2.308
   (b) 1.54
   (c) 1.01
   (d) none of these

5. For a second-order system, $\omega_n = 8$ and $\xi = 0.5$. The value of ω_r in rad/s is
   (a) 4.657
   (b) 5.657
   (c) 6.657
   (d) none of these

6. The gain margin of a system is 0 dB. It represents a
   (a) stable system
   (b) unstable system
   (c) conditionally stable system
   (d) marginally stable system

7. The phase margin of a system is $0°$. It represents a
   (a) stable system
   (b) unstable system
   (c) conditionally stable system
   (d) marginally stable system

8. For a stable system
   (a) gain margin must be positive but phase margin can be positive or negative
   (b) phase margin must be positive but gain margin can be positive or negative
   (c) both gain margin and phase margin must be positive
   (d) one of them must be zero

9. For the pole factor $1/(s + 5)$, the corner frequency is
   (a) $\omega = 1/5$
   (b) $\omega = 5$
   (c) $\omega = -5$
   (d) $\omega = -1/5$

10. For a factor $1/(s + 4)^2$ at $\omega = 2$ rad/s, the asymptotic plot will have an error of
    (a) -6 dB
    (b) -2 dB
    (c) -4 dB
    (d) $+6$ dB

11. At the phase crossover frequency, $\omega = 5$ rad/s, $|G(j\omega)H(j\omega)| = 10$ dB. The system is
    (a) stable
    (b) unstable
    (c) conditionally stable
    (d) cannot be predicted

12. At the phase crossover frequency, $\omega = 10$ rad/s, $|G(j\omega)H(j\omega)| = -8$ dB. The system is
    (a) stable   (b) unstable
    (c) conditionally stable   (d) cannot be predicted

13. At the gain crossover frequency, $\omega = 6$ rad/s, $\angle G(j\omega)H(j\omega) = -150°$. The system is
    (a) stable   (b) unstable
    (c) conditionally stable   (d) cannot be predicted

14. At the gain crossover frequency, $\omega = 8$ rad/s, $\angle G(j\omega)H(j\omega) = -195°$. The system is
    (a) stable   (b) unstable
    (c) conditionally stable   (d) cannot be predicted

15. At the phase crossover frequency $\omega = 10$ rad/s, $|G(j\omega)H(j\omega)| = 15$ dB. Its gain margin is
    (a) 15 dB   (b) 0 dB
    (c) –15 dB   (d) cannot be predicted

16. At the phase crossover frequency $\omega = 7$ rad/s, $|G(j\omega)H(j\omega)| = -12$ dB. Its gain margin is
    (a) –12 dB   (b) +12 dB
    (c) 0 dB   (d) cannot be predicted

17. At the gain crossover frequency $\omega = 5$ rad/s, $\angle G(j\omega)H(j\omega) = -170°$. The phase margin is
    (a) –10°   (b) +10°
    (c) –170°   (d) +170°

18. At the gain crossover frequency $\omega = 12$ rad/s, $\angle G(j\omega)H(j\omega) = -195°$. The phase margin is
    (a) 15°   (b) –195°
    (c) –15°   (d) +195°

19. A transfer function which has all its poles and zeros only in the left-half of the s-plane is called
    (a) an all-pass transfer function   (b) a minimum-phase transfer function
    (c) a nonminimum-phase transfer function (d) none of these

20. A transfer function having a pole-zero pattern which is antisymmetric about the imaginary axis is called
    (a) an all-pass transfer function   (b) a minimum-phase transfer function
    (c) a nonminimum-phase transfer function (d) none of these

21. Large values of gain margin and phase margin result in
    (a) a fast system   (b) an unstable system
    (c) a sluggish system   (d) an underdamped system

22. At the phase crossover frequency
    (a) $\angle G(j\omega)H(j\omega) = 0°$ (b) $\angle G(j\omega)H(j\omega) = -180°$
    (c) $\angle G(j\omega)H(j\omega) = -90°$ (d) $\angle G(j\omega)H(j\omega) = +180°$

23. At the gain crossover frequency
    (a) $|G\ G(j\omega)H(j\omega)| = 0$ dB
    (b) $|G(j\omega)H(j\omega)| = 1$ dB
    (c) $|G(j\omega)H(j\omega)| = -20$ dB
    (d) $|G(j\omega)H(j\omega)| = 20$ dB

PROBLEMS

7.1 Consider the feedback system shown in Figure P7.1.

(a) Find the values of K and b to satisfy the following frequency-domain specifications: $M_r = 1.2$ and $\omega_r = 14$ rad/s.

(b) For the values of K and b determined in part (a) calculate the settling time and bandwidth of the system.

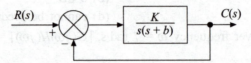

Figure P7.1

7.2 The unit-step response test conducted on a second-order system yielded $M_p = 0.2$ and $t_p = 0.3$ ms. Obtain the corresponding frequency response indices (M_r, ω_r, ω_b) for the system.

7.3 Sketch the polar plots of the transfer functions given below. Determine whether these plots cross the real axis. If so, determine the frequency at which the plots cross the real axis and the corresponding magnitude $|G(j\omega)|$.

(a) $G(s) = \dfrac{1}{(1+s)(1+4s)}$

(b) $G(s) = \dfrac{1}{s(1+s)(1+4s)}$

(c) $G(s) = \dfrac{1}{s^2(1+s)(1+4s)}$

(d) $G(s) = \dfrac{(1+0.1s)(1+0.2s)}{s^3(1+0.004s)(1+0.001s)}$

7.4 Sketch the magnitude and phase Bode plots. Determine the gain crossover frequency, phase crossover frequency, gain margin and phase margin of the system. Comment on the stability of the system.

(a) $G(s) = \dfrac{10}{s(1+0.5s)(1+0.05s)}$

(b) $G(s) = \dfrac{20(1+s)}{s^2(1+0.25s)(1+0.025s)}$

7.5 Sketch the Bode plots for the following transfer functions and determine in each case, the system gain K for the gain crossover frequency ω_g to be 10 rad/s. Comment on the stability of the system for $K = 1$.

(a) $G(s) = \dfrac{Ks^2}{(1+s)(1+0.1s)(1+0.01s)}$

(b) $G(s) = \dfrac{Ke^{-0.2s}}{s(1+s)(1+0.2s)}$

7.6 The frequency response test data of certain elements plotted on Bode diagrams and asymptotically approximated are shown in Figure P7.2. Find the transfer function of each element. (Elements are known to have minimum-phase characteristics.)

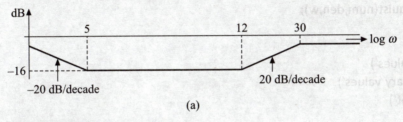

(a)

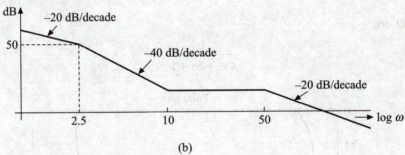

(b)

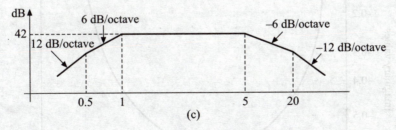

(c)

Figure P7.2

MATLAB PROGRAMS

PROGRAM 7.1
Matlab program for plotting the Polar plot for the transfer function

$$G(s) = \frac{1}{(1+s)(1+4s)}$$

```
% Polar plot
clc;clear all;close all;
w=0:0.01:40;
num=1;
den=conv([1 1],[4 1]);
G=tf(num,den)
[Re1,Im1]=nyquist(num,den,w);
plot(Re1,Im1)
grid on;
xlabel('Real values')
ylabel('Imaginary values')
title('polar plot')
```

Output:

Transfer function:

$$\frac{1}{4s^2 + 5s + 1}$$

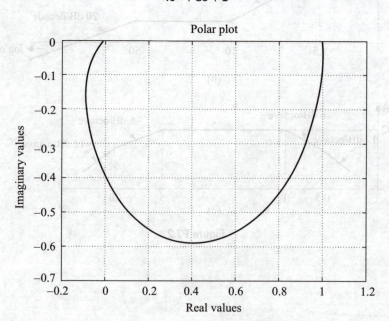

PROGRAM 7.2

Matlab program for plotting the Polar plot for the transfer function

$$G(s) = \frac{1}{s(1+s)(1+4s)}$$

```
%polar plot
clc;clear all;close all;
w=0:0.1:40;
num=[1];
den=conv(conv([1 1],[4 1]),[1 0]);
G=tf(num,den)
[Re,Im]=nyquist(num,den,w);
plot(Re,Im)
xlabel('Real values')
ylabel('Imaginary values')
title('polar plot')
grid on
```

Output:

Transfer function:

$$\frac{1}{4s^3 + 5s^2 + s}$$

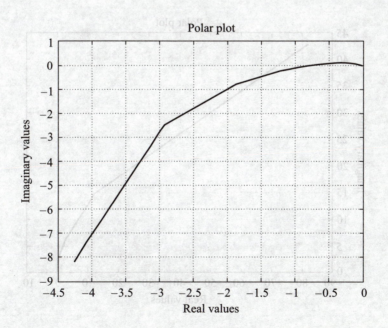

PROGRAM 7.3

Matlab program for plotting the Polar plot for the transfer function

$$G(s) = \frac{1}{s^2 (1 + s)(1 + 4s)}$$

```
%polar plot
clc;clear all;close all;
w=0:0.1:40;
num=[1];
den=conv(conv([1 1],[4 1]),[1 0 0]);
G=tf(num,den)
[Re1,Im1]=nyquist(num,den,w);
plot(Re1,Im1)
xlabel('Real values')
ylabel('Imaginary values')
title('polar plot')
grid on;
```

Output:

Transfer function:

$$\frac{1}{4s^4 + 5s^3 + s^2}$$

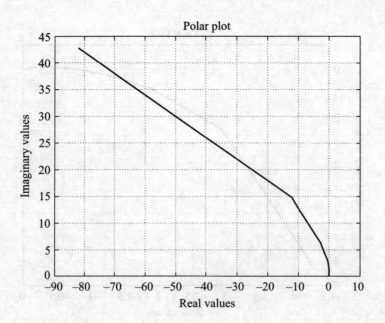

PROGRAM 7.4

Matlab program for plotting the Polar plot for the transfer function

$$G(s) = \frac{(1 + 0.1s)(1 + 0.2s)}{s^3(1 + 0.004s)(1 + 0.001s)}$$

```
%polar plot
clc;clear all;close all;
w=0:0.1:40;
num=conv([0.1 1],[0.2 1]);
den=conv(conv([0.004 1],[0.001 1]),[1 0 0 0]);
G=tf(num,den)
[Re1,lm1]=nyquist(num,den,w);
plot(Re1,lm1)
xlabel('Real values')
ylabel('Imaginary values')
title('polar plot')
grid on;
```

Output:

Transfer function:

$$\frac{0.02s^2 + 0.3s + 1}{4e - 006s^5 + 0.005s^4 + s^3}$$

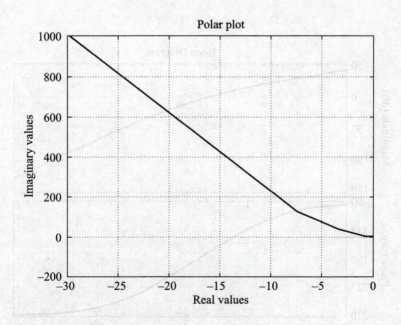

PROGRAM 7.5:

Matlab program for drawing the Bode plot for the transfer function

$$G(s) = \frac{10}{s(1+0.5s)(1+0.05s)}$$

```
% Frequency Response Analysis
% Bode plot
clc
clear all
close all
s=tf('s');
GH=10/(s*(1+0.5*s)*(1+0.05*s))
bode(GH)
grid on
[Gm, pm, wcp, wcg] = margin (GH);
disp('Gain Margin is')
disp(Gm)
disp('Phase Margin is')
disp(pm)
disp('Phase crossover frequency is')
disp(wcp)
disp('Gain crossover frequency is')
disp(wcg)
```

Output:

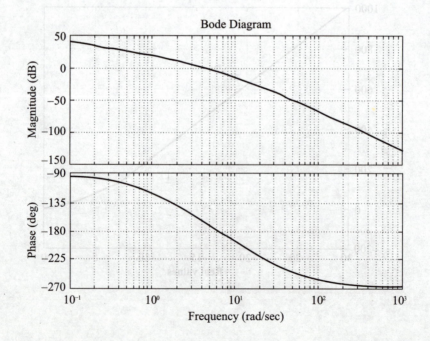

Gain Margin is
   2.2000
Phase Margin is
   13.5709
Phase crossover frequency is
   6.3246
Gain crossover frequency is
   4.2041

PROGRAM 7.6

Matlab program for drawing the Bode plot for the transfer function

$$G(s) = \frac{20(1+s)}{s^2(1+0.25s)(1+0.025s)}$$

```
% Frequency Response Analysis
% Bode plot
clc;clear all;close all;
s=tf('s');
GH=(20*(1+s))/((s^2)*(1+0.25*s)*(1+0.025*s))
bode(GH)
grid on;
[Gm, pm, wcp, wcg] = margin(GH);
disp('Gain Margin is')
disp(Gm)
disp('Phase Margin is')
disp(pm)
disp('Phase crossover frequency is')
disp(wcp)
disp('Gain crossover frequency is')
disp(wcg)
```

Output:

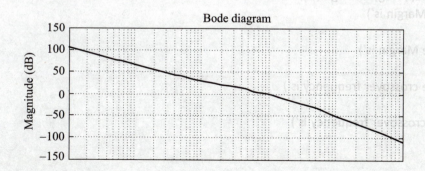

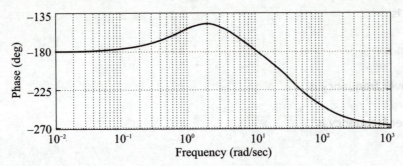

Gain Margin is
   1.5943
Phase Margin is
   6.6870
Phase crossover frequency is
   10.7680
Gain crossover frequency is
   8.4397

PROGRAM 7.7

Matlab program for drawing the Bode plot for the transfer function

$$G(s) = \frac{Ks^2}{(1+s)(1+0.1s)(1+0.01s)}$$

```
% Frequency Response Analysis
% Bode plot
clc;clear all;close all;
num=1*[1 0 0]
den=conv(conv([1 1],[0.1 1]),[0.01 1])
G=tf(num,den)
bode(G)
grid on;
[Gm, pm, wcp, wcg] = margin(G);
disp('Gain Margin is')
disp(Gm)
disp('Phase Margin is')
disp(pm)
disp('Phase crossover frequency is')
disp(wcp)
disp('Gain crossover frequency is')
disp(wcg)
```

Output:

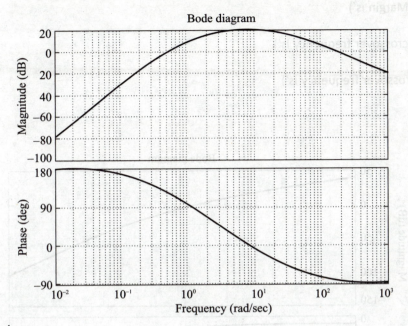

Bode diagram

Gain Margin is

Inf

Phase Margin is

60.0180

Phase crossover frequency is

0

Gain crossover frequency is

1.2796

PROGRAM 7.8

Matlab program for drawing the Bode plot for the transfer function

$$G(s) = \frac{Ke^{-0.2s}}{s(1+s)(1+0.2s)}$$

```
% Frequency Response Analysis
% Bode plot
clc;clear all;close all;
s=tf('s');
G=1*(exp(-0.2*s))/(s*(1+s)*(1+0.2*s));
bode(G)
grid on;
[Gm, pm, wcp, wcg] = margin(G);
disp('Gain Margin is')
```

```
disp(Gm)
disp('Phase Margin is')
disp(pm)
disp('Phase crossover frequency is')
disp(wcp)
disp('Gain crossover frequency is')
disp(wcg)
```

Output:

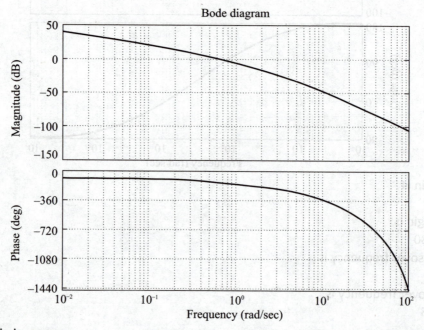

Gain Margin is
    2.8064
Phase Margin is
    34.2793
Phase crossover frequency is
    1.4949
Gain crossover frequency is
    0.7793

PROGRAM 7.9

Matlab program for plotting the Bode plot for the transfer function

$$G(s)\,H(s) = \frac{K(s+4)}{(s-1)\,(s-2)}$$

```
% Frequency Response Analysis
% Bode plot
clc;clear all;close all;
G=zpk([-4],[1 2],10);
margin(G)
grid on;
disp('Transfer function is');
G
```

Output:

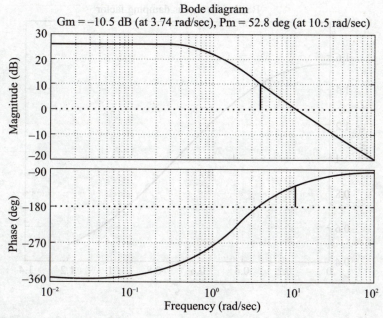

Transfer function is
Zero/pole/gain:

$$\frac{10(s+4)}{(s-1)(s-2)}$$

PROGRAM 7.10

Matlab program for Bandwidth versus damping factor of a second order system

```
% Frequency Response Analysis
% Bandwidth versus damping factor
clc;clear all;close all;
i=1;
for  zetai=0:sqrt(1/2)/100:1.2
    m(i)=sqrt((1-2*zetai.^2)+sqrt(4*zetai.^4-4*zetai.^2+2));
```

```
    zeta(i)=zetai;
    i=i+1;
end
plot(zeta,m)
xlabel('\zeta')
ylabel('BW/\omega_n')
title('Bandwidth Versus damping factor')
grid on;
```

Output:

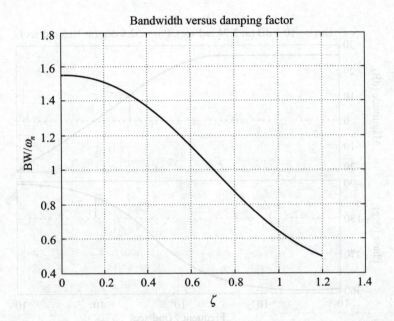

PROGRAM 7.11

Matlab program for error in dB vs normalized frequency for asymptotic Bode plot of

$$\frac{1}{1 + j2\xi u - u^2}$$

```
% Frequency Response Analysis
% Error in dB Vs normalized frequency for asympotic bode plot
clc;clear all;close all;

i=1;
zeta=[0.05 0.1 0.15 0.2 0.25 0.3 0.4 0.5 0.6 0.8 1.0];
for u=0:0.001:3
```

```
z=1;
m(z,i)=abs(1/(1+(j*2*zeta(z)*u)-(u^2)));z=z+1;
m(z,i)=abs(1/(1+(j*2*zeta(z)*u)-(u^2)));z=z+1;
m(z,i)=abs(1/(1+(j*2*zeta(z)*u)-(u^2)));z=z+1;
m(z,i)=abs(1/(1+(j*2*zeta(z)*u)-(u^2)));z=z+1;
m(z,i)=abs(1/(1+(j*2*zeta(z)*u)-(u^2)));z=z+1;
m(z,i)=abs(1/(1+(j*2*zeta(z)*u)-(u^2)));z=z+1;
m(z,i)=abs(1/(1+(j*2*zeta(z)*u)-(u^2)));z=z+1;
m(z,i)=abs(1/(1+(j*2*zeta(z)*u)-(u^2)));z=z+1;
m(z,i)=abs(1/(1+(j*2*zeta(z)*u)-(u^2)));z=z+1;
m(z,i)=abs(1/(1+(j*2*zeta(z)*u)-(u^2)));z=z+1;
m(z,i)=abs(1/(1+(j*2*zeta(z)*u)-(u^2)));z=z+1;
i=i+1;
end
u=0:0.001:3;
for i=1:length(zeta)
    plot(u,m(i,:));
    hold on
end
xlabel('\mu=\omega/\omega_n')
ylabel('|M(j\omega)|)')
grid on;
```

Output:

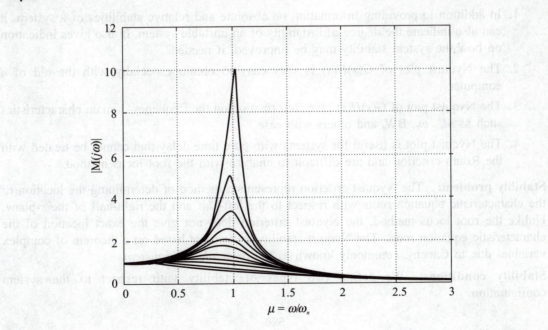

8

Nyquist Plot

8.1 INTRODUCTION

The Nyquist stability criterion relates the location of the roots of the characteristic equation to the open-loop frequency response of the system. In this, the computation of closed-loop poles is not necessary to determine the stability of the system and the stability study can be carried out graphically from the open-loop frequency response. Therefore, experimentally determined open-loop frequency response can be used directly for the study of stability, when the feedback path is closed.

The Nyquist criterion has the following features that make it an alternative method that is attractive for the analysis and design of control systems.

1. In addition to providing information on absolute and relative stabilities of a system, it can also indicate the degree of instability of an unstable system. It also gives indication on how the system stability may be improved, if needed.

2. The Nyquist plot of $G(s)H(s)$ is very easy to obtain especially with the aid of a computer.

3. The Nyquist plot of $G(s)H(s)$ gives information on the frequency-domain characteristics such as M_r, ω_r, BW, and others with ease.

4. The Nyquist plot is useful for systems with pure time delay that cannot be treated with the Routh criterion and are difficult to analyze with the root locus method.

Stability problem: The Nyquist criterion represents a method of determining the location of the characteristic equation roots with respect to the left-half and the right-half of the s-plane. Unlike the root locus method, the Nyquist criterion does not give the exact location of the characteristic equation roots. The Nyquist stability criterion is based on a theorem of complex variables due to Cauchy, commonly known as the *principle of argument*.

Stability conditions: We define two types of stability with respect to the system configuration.

526

***Open-loop stability*:**   A system is said to be open-loop stable if the poles of the loop transfer function $G(s)H(s)$ are all in the left-half of the s-plane. For a single loop system, this is equivalent to the system being stable when the loop is opened at any point.

***Closed-loop stability*:**   A system is said to be closed-loop stable, or simply stable, if the poles of the closed-loop transfer function, i.e., the zeros of $1 + G(s)H(s)$ are all in the left-half of the s-plane. Exceptions to the above definitions are systems with poles or zeros intentionally placed at $s = 0$.

8.2   PRINCIPLE OF ARGUMENT

Consider a function $q(s)$ that can be expressed as a quotient of two polynomials. Each polynomial may be assumed to be known in the form of product of linear factors indicated as follows:

$$q(s) = \frac{(s - \alpha_1)(s - \alpha_2)\ldots(s - \alpha_m)}{(s - \beta_1)(s - \beta_2)\ldots(s - \beta_n)} \tag{8.1}$$

Let s be a complex variable, represented by $s = \sigma + j\omega$ on the complex s-plane. Then the function $q(s)$ is also complex (being a dependent variable) and may be defined as $q(s) = u + jv$ and represented on the complex $q(s)$ plane with coordinates u and v. Equation (8.1) indicates that for every point s in the s-plane at which $q(s)$ is analytic [A function $q(s)$ is said to be analytic in the s-plane provided the function and all its derivatives exist. The points in the s-plane where the function (or its derivatives) does not exist are called singular points. The poles of a function are singular points.], we can find a corresponding point $q(s)$ in the $q(s)$-plane. Alternatively, it can be stated that the function $q(s)$ maps the points in the s-plane into the $q(s)$-plane. Since any number of points in the s-plane, can be mapped into the $q(s)$-plane, it follows that for a contour in the s-plane which does not go through any singular point, there corresponds a contour in the $q(s)$-plane as shown in Figure 8.1. The region to the right of the closed contour is considered enclosed by the contour when the contour is traversed in the clockwise direction. Thus the shaded area in Figure 8.1(a) is enclosed by the closed contour.

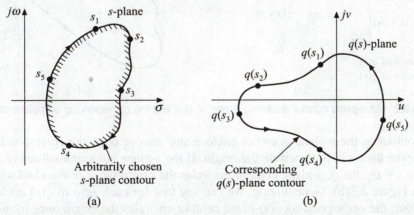

Figure 8.1   Arbitrarily chosen s-plane contour which does not go through singular points and the corresponding $q(s)$-plane contour.

While developing the Nyquist criterion, we are not interested in the exact shape of the $q(s)$-plane contour. An important fact that concerns us is the encirclement of the origin by the $q(s)$-plane contour. To investigate this, consider an s-plane contour shown in Figure 8.2(a) which encloses only one of the zeros of $q(s)$, say $s = \alpha_1$, while all the poles and remaining zeros are distributed in the s-plane outside the contour. As discussed above, for any non-singular point s in the s-plane contour, there corresponds a point $q(s)$ on the $q(s)$ plane contour. The point $q(s)$ is given by

$$|q(s)| = \frac{|s - \alpha_1||s - \alpha_2|\ldots}{|s - \beta_1||s - \beta_2|\ldots}$$

$$\angle q(s) = \angle(s - \alpha_1) + \angle(s - \alpha_2) + \ldots - \angle(s - \beta_1) - \angle(s - \beta_2) - \ldots$$

From Figure 8.2(a) it is found that as the point s follows the prescribed path (i.e. clockwise direction) on the s-plane contour, eventually returning to the starting point, the phasor $(s - \alpha_1)$ generates a net angle of -2π, while all other phasors generate zero net angles. Therefore, the $q(s)$-phasor undergoes a net phase change of -2π. This implies that the tip of the $q(s)$-phasor must describe a closed contour about the origin of the $q(s)$-plane in the clockwise direction. As said earlier, the exact shape of the closed contour in the $q(s)$-plane is not of interest to us, but it is sufficient for us to observe that this contour encircles the origin once.

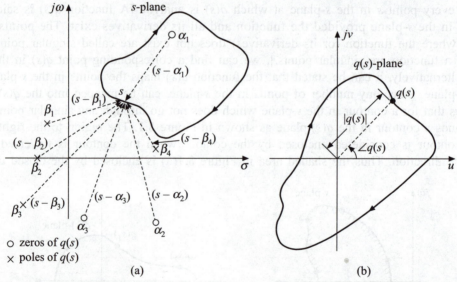

Figure 8.2 An s-plane contour enclosing a zero of $q(s)$ and the corresponding $q(s)$-plane contour.

If the contour in the s-plane does not enclose any zero or pole, the corresponding contour in the $q(s)$-plane then will not encircle the origin. If the s-plane contour encloses two zeros, say at $s = \alpha_1$ and $s = \alpha_2$, the $q(s)$-plane contour encircles the origin twice in the clockwise direction as shown in Figure 8.3(b). Generalizing, we can say that for each zero of $q(s)$ enclosed by the s-plane contour, the corresponding $q(s)$-plane contour encircles the origin once in the clockwise direction.

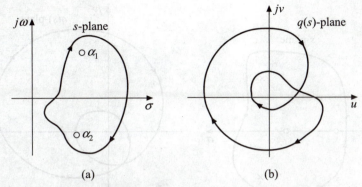

Figure 8.3 An s-plane contour enclosing two zeros of $q(s)$ and the corresponding $q(s)$-plane contour.

If the s-plane contour encloses a pole (at $s = \beta_1$) of $q(s)$, the phasor $(s - \beta_1)$ generates an angle of -2π as s traverses the prescribed path. Since the pole term $(s - \beta_1)$ is in the denominator of $q(s)$, the $q(s)$-plane contour experiences an angle change of $+2\pi$, which means one counterclockwise encirclement of the origin. This argument holds for all other poles of $q(s)$. If the s-plane contour encloses two poles say at $s = \beta_1$ and $s = \beta_2$, the $q(s)$-plane contour encircles the origin twice in the counterclockwise direction as shown in Figure 8.4.

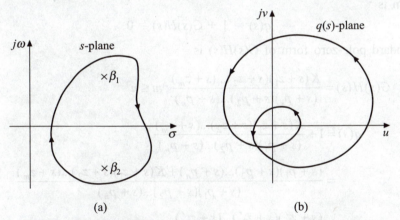

Figure 8.4 Mapping of the s-plane contour which encloses two poles.

Thus, if there are P poles and Z zeros of $q(s)$ enclosed by the s-plane contour, then the corresponding $q(s)$-plane contour must encircle the origin Z times in the clockwise direction and P times in the counterclockwise direction, resulting in a net encirclement of the origin, $(P - Z)$ times in the counterclockwise direction. For example, in case of two zeros and four poles enclosed by the s-plane contour, the net encirclement of the origin by the $q(s)$-plane contour is $2\pi (4 - 2) = 4\pi$ rad, i.e. two counterclockwise revolutions as shown in Figure 8.5(a) and Figure 8.5(b). This relation between the enclosure of poles and zeros of $q(s)$ by the s-plane contour and the encirclements of the origin by the $q(s)$-plane contour is commonly known as the *principle of argument.*

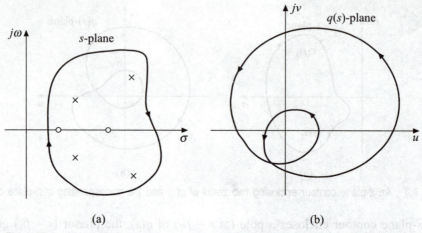

(a)   (b)

Figure 8.5 Mapping of the s-plane contour which encloses two zeros and four poles.

8.3 NYQUIST STABILITY CRITERION

Consider the single loop feedback system shown in Figure 8.6(a). The characteristic equation of the system is

$$q(s) = 1 + G(s)H(s) = 0$$

The standard pole-zero form of $G(s)H(s)$ is

$$G(s)H(s) = \frac{K(s+z_1)(s+z_2)...(s+z_m)}{(s+p_1)(s+p_2)...(s+p_n)}; m \le n$$

$$\therefore \qquad q(s) = 1 + \frac{K(s+z_1)(s+z_2)...(s+z_m)}{(s+p_1)(s+p_2)...(s+p_n)}$$

$$= \frac{(s+p_1)(s+p_2)...(s+p_n) + K(s+z_1)(s+z_2)...(s+z_m)}{(s+p_1)(s+p_2)...(s+p_n)}$$

$$= \frac{(s+z_1')(s+z_2')...(s+z_n')}{(s+p_1)(s+p_2)...(s+p_n)} \tag{8.2}$$

From Eq. (8.2), we observe that the zeros of $q(s)$ at $-z_1', -z_2', ..., -z_n'$ are the roots of the characteristic equation and the poles of $q(s)$ at $-p_1, -p_2, ..., -p_n$ are the same as the open-loop poles of the system. For the system to be stable, the roots of the characteristic equation and hence the zeros of $q(s)$ must lie in the left-half of the s-plane. Even if some of the open-loop poles lie in the right-half s-plane, all the zeros of $q(s)$, i.e. the closed-loop poles may lie in the left-half s-plane. This means that an open-loop unstable system may lead to a closed-loop stable operation.

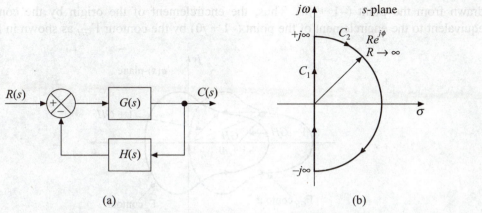

(a)　　　　　　　　　　　　　　(b)

Figure 8.6　(a) A feedback control system and (b) the Nyquist contour.

In order to investigate the presence of any zeros of $q(s) = 1 + G(s)H(s)$ in the right-half s-plane, let us choose a contour which completely encloses the right-half of the s-plane. Such a contour C, called the *Nyquist contour*, is shown in Figure 8.6(b). It is directed clockwise and comprises of an infinite line segment C_1 along the $j\omega$-axis and an arc C_2 of infinite radius.

Along C_1, $s = j\omega$ with ω varying from $-\infty$ to $+\infty$ and along C_2, $s = \underset{R \to \infty}{Re^{j\phi}}$ with ϕ varying from $+\pi/2$ to 0 to $-\pi/2$.

The Nyquist contour so defined encloses all the right-half s-plane zeros and poles of $q(s) = 1 + G(s)H(s)$. Let there be Z zeros and P poles of $q(s)$ in the right-half of the s-plane. As s moves along the Nyquist contour in the s-plane, a closed contour Γ_q is traversed in the $q(s)$-plane which encloses the origin,

$$N = P - Z$$

times in the counter-clockwise direction.

For the system to be stable, there should be no zeros of $q(s) = 1 + G(s)H(s)$ in the right-half of the s-plane, i.e. $Z = 0$. This condition is met if

$$N = P$$

that is, for a closed-loop system to be stable, the number of counter-clockwise encirclements of the origin of the $q(s)$-plane by the contour Γ_q should equal the number of the right-half s-plane poles of $q(s)$ which are the poles of the open-loop transfer function $G(s)H(s)$.

For open-loop stable systems (i.e. $P = 0$), the closed-loop system is stable if

$$N = P = 0$$

which means that the net encirclements of the origin of the $q(s)$-plane by the Γ_q contour should be zero.

It is easily observed that

$$G(s)H(s) = [1 + G(s)H(s)] - 1$$

It therefore follows that the contour Γ_{GH} of the open-loop transfer function $G(s)H(s)$ corresponding to the Nyquist contour in the s-plane is the same as the contour Γ_q of $1 + G(s)H(s)$

drawn from the point $(-1 + j0)$. Thus, the encirclement of the origin by the contour Γ_q is equivalent to the encirclement of the point $(-1 + j0)$ by the contour Γ_{GH} as shown in Figure 8.7.

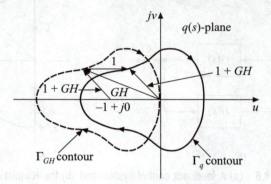

Figure 8.7 Γ_{GH} and Γ_q contours.

The Nyquist stability criterion may now be stated as follows:

If the contour Γ_{GH} of the open-loop transfer function $G(s)H(s)$ corresponding to the Nyquist contour in the s-plane encircles the point $(-1 + j0)$ in the counterclockwise direction as many times as the number of right-half s-plane poles of $G(s)H(s)$, the closed-loop system is stable.

In the commonly occurring case of the open-loop stable systems, the closed-loop system is stable if the contour Γ_{GH} of $G(s)H(s)$ does not encircle the $(-1 + j0)$ point, i.e. the net encirclement is zero.

The mapping of the Nyquist contour into the contour Γ_{GH} is carried out as follows:

1. The mapping of the imaginary axis is carried out by substitution of $s = j\omega$ in $G(s)H(s)$. This converts the mapping function into a frequency function of $G(j\omega)H(j\omega)$.

2. In physical systems ($m \le n$),

$$\underset{\substack{s \to Re^{j\phi} \\ R \to \infty}}{\text{Lt}} G(s)H(s) = \text{real constant (it is zero if } m < n)$$

Thus, the infinite arc of the Nyquist contour maps into a point on the real axis.

The complete contour Γ_{GH} is thus the polar plot of $G(j\omega)H(j\omega)$ with ω varying from $-\infty$ to ∞. This is usually called the Nyquist plot or locus of $G(s)H(s)$. The Nyquist plot is symmetrical about the real axis since $G^*(j\omega)H^*(j\omega) = G(-j\omega)H(-j\omega)$.

Example 8.1 Draw the Nyquist plot and comment on the stability of the system represented by

$$G(s)H(s) = \frac{K}{(1+T_1 s)(1+T_2 s)}$$

Solution: The open-loop sinusoidal transfer function is

$$G(j\omega)H(j\omega) = \frac{K}{(1+j\omega T_1)(1+j\omega T_2)}$$

Rationalizing,

$$G(j\omega)H(j\omega) = \frac{K(1 - j\omega T_1)(1 - j\omega T_2)}{(1 - j\omega T_1)(1 + j\omega T_1)(1 - j\omega T_2)(1 + j\omega T_2)}$$

$$= \frac{K[1 - \omega^2 T_1 T_2] - jK\omega(T_1 + T_2)}{(1 + \omega^2 T_1^2)(1 + \omega^2 T_2^2)} = \frac{K(1 - \omega^2 T_1 T_2)}{(1 + \omega^2 T_1^2)(1 + \omega^2 T_2^2)} - \frac{jK\omega(T_1 + T_2)}{(1 + \omega^2 T_1^2)(1 + \omega^2 T_2^2)}$$

Along the segment (C_1) of the Nyquist contour on the $j\omega$-axis, s varies from $-j\infty$ to $+j\infty$. At $\omega = -\infty$,

$$G(j\omega)H(j\omega) = \frac{K[1 - (-\infty)^2 T_1 T_2]}{[1 + (-\infty)^2 T_1^2][1 + (-\infty)^2 T_2^2]} - \frac{jK(-\infty)(T_1 + T_2)}{[1 + (-\infty)^2 T_1^2][1 + (-\infty)^2 T_2^2]} = -0 + j0$$

At $\omega = 0^-$,

$$G(j\omega)H(j\omega) = \frac{K[1 - (-0)^2 T_1 T_2]}{[1 + (-0)^2 T_1^2][1 + (-0)^2 T_2^2]} - \frac{jK(-0)(T_1 + T_2)}{[1 + (-0)^2 T_1^2][1 + (-0)^2 T_2^2]} = K + j0$$

At $\omega = 0^+$,

$$G(j\omega)H(j\omega) = \frac{K[1 - (+0)^2 T_1 T_2]}{[1 + (+0)^2 T_1^2][1 + (+0)^2 T_2^2]} - \frac{jK(+0)(T_1 + T_2)}{[1 + (+0)^2 T_1^2][1 + (+0)^2 T_2^2]} = K - j0$$

At $\omega = +\infty$,

$$G(j\omega)H(j\omega) = \frac{K[1 - (+\infty)^2 T_1 T_2]}{[1 + (+\infty)^2 T_1^2][1 + (+\infty)^2 T_2^2]} - \frac{jK(+\infty)(T_1 + T_2)}{[1 + (+\infty)^2 T_1^2][1 + (+\infty)^2 T_2^2]} = -0 - j0$$

So, we get four points to draw an approximate Nyquist plot.

The infinite semi-circular arc of the Nyquist contour (segment C_2) of Figure 8.8(a) is mapped like this.

Along the semi-circular arc,

$$s = Re^{j\phi} \atop R \to \infty$$

where ϕ varies from $\pi/2$ through $0°$ to $-\pi/2$. Therefore,

$$G(s)H(s) = \underset{R \to \infty}{\mathrm{Lt}} \frac{K}{(1 + Re^{j\phi}T_1)(1 + Re^{j\phi}T_2)}$$

$$= \underset{\substack{R \to \infty \\ \phi \to \frac{\pi}{2} \text{ to} -\frac{\pi}{2}}}{\mathrm{Lt}} \frac{K}{R^2 e^{j2\phi}T_1 T_2} = 0.e^{-j2\phi} = 0 \angle -2\phi$$

So the magnitude is zero and the phase varies from $-2 \times (\pi/2)$ to $-2 \times (-\pi/2)$, i.e. from $-180°$ to $+180°$. So the infinite semi-circular arc is mapped onto a point at the origin joining the $\omega = +\infty$ and $\omega = -\infty$ points in the $q(s)$-plane.

The point of intersection of the Nyquist plot with the imaginary axis is obtained by equating the real part of $G(j\omega)H(j\omega)$ to zero. Therefore,

$$\frac{K(1 - \omega^2 T_1 T_2)}{(1 + \omega^2 T_1^2)(1 + \omega^2 T_2^2)} = 0$$

$\therefore$ $$1 - \omega^2 T_1 T_2 = 0$$

or $$\omega = \frac{1}{\sqrt{T_1 T_2}}$$

The value of $G(j\omega)H(j\omega)$ at that point of intersection is obtained by substituting this value of $\omega = \dfrac{1}{\sqrt{T_1 T_2}}$ in the imaginary part, i.e.

$$G(j\omega)H(j\omega)\left(\text{at } \omega = \frac{1}{\sqrt{T_1 T_2}}\right) = -j\frac{K \cdot \dfrac{1}{\sqrt{T_1 T_2}}(T_1 + T_2)}{\left[1 + \left(\dfrac{1}{\sqrt{T_1 T_2}}\right)^2 T_1^2\right]\left[1 + \left(\dfrac{1}{\sqrt{T_1 T_2}}\right)^2 T_2^2\right]} = -j\frac{K\sqrt{T_1 T_2}}{T_1 + T_2}$$

Based on the above information, an approximate Nyquist plot is drawn as shown in Figure 8.8(b). From Figure 8.8(b), it can be observed that the Nyquist plot of $G(j\omega)H(j\omega)$ does not encircle the $(-1 + j0)$ point of $q(s)$ plane for any positive values of K, T_1 and T_2. Therefore, the system is stable for all positive values of K, T_1 and T_2.

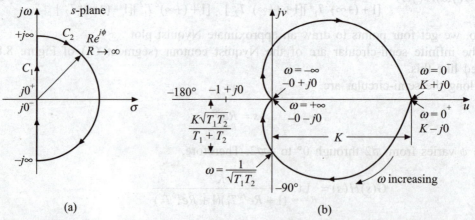

Figure 8.8   Example 8.1: (a) Nyquist contour and (b) the corresponding Nyquist plot of $K/(1 + T_1 s)(1 + T_2 s)$.

Example 8.2   Draw the Nyquist plot and assess the stability of the closed-loop system whose open-loop transfer function is

$$G(s)H(s) = \frac{(s + 4)}{(s + 1)(s - 1)}$$

Solution: From the transfer function of the open-loop system, we observe that there is one open-loop pole in the right-half of the *s*-plane. So the open-loop system is unstable. $P = 1$. So for the closed-loop system to be stable, the Nyquist plot of $G(s)H(s)$ must encircle the $(-1 + j0)$ point of $q(s)$ plane once in the counterclockwise direction.

$G(s)H(s)$ in sinusoidal form is

$$G(j\omega)H(j\omega) = \frac{j\omega + 4}{(j\omega + 1)(j\omega - 1)} = -\frac{4 + j\omega}{(1 + j\omega)(1 - j\omega)}$$

$$= -\frac{4 + j\omega}{1 + \omega^2} = -\frac{4}{1 + \omega^2} - j\frac{\omega}{1 + \omega^2}$$

Along the segment (C_1) of the Nyquist contour on the $j\omega$-axis, *s* varies from $-j\infty$ to $+j\infty$. At $\omega = -\infty$,

$$G(j\omega)H(j\omega) = \frac{-4}{[1 + (-\infty)^2]} - \frac{j(-\infty)}{[1 + (-\infty)^2]} = -0 + j0$$

At $\omega = 0^-$,

$$G(j\omega)H(j\omega) = \frac{-4}{[1 + (-0)^2]} - \frac{j(-0)}{[1 + (-0)^2]} = -4 + j0$$

At $\omega = 0^+$,

$$G(j\omega)H(j\omega) = \frac{-4}{[1 + (+0)^2]} - \frac{j(+0)}{[1 + (+0)^2]} = -4 - j0$$

At $\omega = +\infty$,

$$G(j\omega)H(j\omega) = \frac{-4}{[1 + (+\infty)^2]} - \frac{j(+\infty)}{[1 + (+\infty)^2]} = -0 - j0$$

So, we get four points to draw an approximate Nyquist plot.

Along the semicircular arc of the Nyquist contour $s = Re^{j\phi}$ (ϕ varying from $+90°$ through $R \to \infty$

$0°$ to $-90°$). So it is mapped into

$$G(s)H(s) = \underset{R \to \infty}{\text{Lt}} \frac{(Re^{j\phi} + 4)}{(Re^{j\phi} - 1)(Re^{j\phi} + 1)} = \underset{R \to \infty}{\text{Lt}} \frac{1}{Re^{j\phi}} = 0e^{-j\phi}$$

that is, the origin of the $G(s)H(s)$ plane. The $G(s)H(s)$ locus thus turns at the origin with zero radius from $-90°$ through $0°$ to $+90°$.

Based on the above information, an approximate Nyquist plot is drawn as shown in Figure 8.9(b). It indicates that the $(-1 + j0)$ point is encircled by this locus once in the counterclockwise direction. So the closed-loop system is stable.

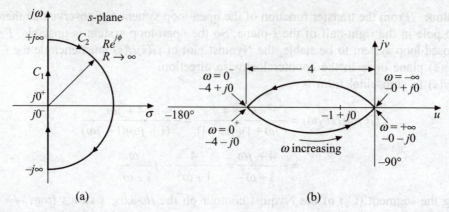

(a)   (b)

Figure 8.9 Example 8.2: (a) Nyquist contour and (b) the corresponding Nyquist plot for $G(s)H(s)$ = $(s + 4)/[(s +1)(s - 1)]$.

8.3.1 Open-Loop Poles on the $j\omega$–Axis

If the open-loop transfer function $G(s)H(s)$ and therefore the characteristic polynomial $1 + G(s)H(s)$ has any poles on the $j\omega$-axis, the Nyquist contour defined earlier [Figure 8.6(b)] cannot be used as such since the s-plane contour should not pass through a singularity of $1 + G(s)H(s)$. To investigate stability in such cases, the Nyquist contour must be modified so as to bypass any $j\omega$-axis poles. This is achieved by indenting the Nyquist contour around the $j\omega$-axis poles along a semicircle of radius $\in$, where $\in \rightarrow 0$ as shown in Figure 8.10.

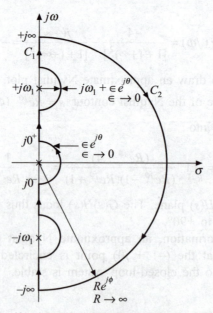

Figure 8.10 Nyquist contour indented for $j\omega$-axis open-loop poles.

Example 8.3 Draw the Nyquist plot and assess the stability of the closed-loop system whose open-loop transfer function is given by

$$G(s)H(s) = \frac{K}{s(2s+1)}$$

Solution: The given open-loop system has a pole at the origin. The Nyquist contour must therefore be indented to bypass the origin as shown in Figure 8.11(a).

The mapping of the Nyquist contour is carried out as follows.

The open-loop transfer function in sinusoidal form is

$$G(j\omega)H(j\omega) = \frac{K}{j\omega(2j\omega+1)} = \frac{K(1-j2\omega)}{j\omega(1+j2\omega)(1-j2\omega)}$$

$$= \frac{K(1-j2\omega)}{j\omega(1+4\omega^2)} = -\frac{2K}{1+4\omega^2} - j\frac{K}{\omega(1+4\omega^2)}$$

Along the segment (C_1) of the Nyquist contour on the $j\omega$-axis, s varies from $-j\infty$ to $+j\infty$. At $\omega = -\infty$,

$$G(j\omega)H(j\omega) = -0 + j0$$

At $\omega = 0^-$,

$$G(j\omega)H(j\omega) = -2K + j\infty$$

At $\omega = 0^+$,

$$G(j\omega)H(j\omega) = -2K - j\infty$$

At $\omega = +\infty$,

$$G(j\omega)H(j\omega) = -0 - j0$$

So we get four points to draw an approximate Nyquist plot.

The infinitesimally small semicircular indent around the pole at the origin of Figure 8.11(a) represented by $s = \epsilon e^{j\theta}$ (θ varying from $-\pi/2°$ through $0°$ to $+\pi/2°$) maps into

$$\underset{\epsilon \to 0}{\text{Lt}} \ [K/(\epsilon e^{j\theta})(2\epsilon e^{j\theta} + 1)] = \underset{\epsilon \to 0}{\text{Lt}} \ K/\epsilon e^{j\theta} = \underset{\epsilon \to 0}{\text{Lt}} \ (K/\epsilon)e^{-j\theta} = \infty e^{-j\theta}$$

$-\theta$ varies from $+90° \to 0° \to -90°$. Thus, the infinitesimal semi-circular indent around the origin of the s-plane maps into a semicircular arc of infinite radius in $G(s)H(s)$ plane extending from $+90°$ through $0°$ to $-90°$.

The infinite semicircular arc of the Nyquist contour (segment C_2) of Figure 8.11(a) represented by $s = Re^{j\phi}$ (ϕ varying from $+90°$ through $0°$ to $-90°$) is mapped into

$$\underset{R \to \infty}{\text{Lt}} \ [K/(Re^{j\phi})(2Re^{j\phi} + 1)] = \underset{R \to \infty}{\text{Lt}} \ K/(2R^2 e^{j2\phi}) = 0e^{-j2\phi}$$

that is, the origin of the $G(s)H(s)$ plane. The $G(s)H(s)$ locus thus turns at the origin with zero radius from $-180°$ through $0°$ to $+180°$.

Based on the above information, an approximate Nyquist plot is drawn as shown in Figure 8.11(b).

The given open-loop system has no poles in the right-half of the *s*-plane, i.e. $P = 0$. So as per the Nyquist stability criterion, for the closed-loop system to be stable, the Nyquist plot of $G(j\omega)H(j\omega)$ must not encircle the $(-1 + j0)$ point. Since the actual Nyquist plot in Figure 8.11(b) does not encircle the $(-1 + j0)$ point, the closed-loop system is always stable.

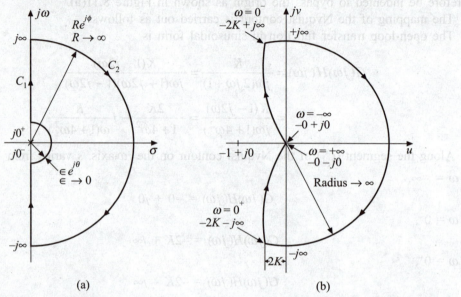

(a) (b)

Figure 8.11 Example 8.3: (a) Nyquist contour and (b) the corresponding Nyquist plot for $G(s)H(s)$ $= K/s(2s + 1)$.

Example 8.4 Draw the Nyquist plot and assess the stability of the closed-loop system whose open-loop transfer function is

$$G(s)H(s) = \frac{(6s+1)}{s^2(s+1)(3s+1)}$$

Solution: The given open-loop system has a double pole at the origin. The Nyquist contour is, therefore, indented to bypass the origin as shown in Figure 8.12(a). The mapping of the Nyquist contour is obtained as follows.

The given open-loop transfer function in sinusoidal form is

$$G(j\omega)H(j\omega) = \frac{(j6\omega+1)}{(j\omega)^2(j\omega+1)(j3\omega+1)} = \frac{(j6\omega+1)(1-j\omega)(1-j3\omega)}{-\omega^2(1+\omega^2)(1+9\omega^2)}$$

$$= \frac{[1+21\omega^2]}{-\omega^2(1+\omega^2)(1+9\omega^2)} - j\frac{(2-18\omega^2)}{\omega(1+\omega^2)(1+9\omega^2)}$$

Along the segment (C_1) of the Nyquist contour on the $j\omega$-axis, s varies from $-j\infty$ to $+j\infty$.
At $\omega = -\infty$,

$$G(j\omega)H(j\omega) = -0 - j0$$

At $\omega = 0^-$,

$$G(j\omega)H(j\omega) = -\infty + j\infty$$

At $\omega = 0^+$,

$$G(j\omega)H(j\omega) = -\infty - j\infty$$

At $\omega = +\infty$,

$$G(j\omega)H(j\omega) = -0 + j0$$

So, we get four points to draw an approximate Nyquist plot. The infinitesimally small semicircular arc of the Nyquist contour of Figure 8.12(a) represented by $s = \underset{\epsilon \to 0}{Lt} \, \epsilon e^{j\theta}$ (where θ varies from $-90°$ through $0°$ to $+90°$) is mapped into

$$\underset{\epsilon \to 0}{Lt} \left[\frac{6 \in e^{j\theta} + 1}{\epsilon^2 e^{j2\theta}(\in e^{j\theta} + 1)(3 \in e^{j\theta} + 1)} \right] = \underset{\epsilon \to 0}{Lt} \left(\frac{1}{\epsilon^2 e^{j2\theta}} \right) = \infty e^{-j2\theta}$$

$$= \infty \; (\angle 180° \to \angle 0° \to \angle -180°)$$

that is, into a semicircle of infinite radius extending from $+180°$ through $0°$ to $-180°$ as shown in Figure 8.12(b).

The infinite semicircle of the Nyquist contour of Figure 8.12(a) represented by $s = \underset{R \to \infty}{Lt} \, Re^{j\phi}$ (ϕ varies from $+90°$ through $0°$ to $-90°$) is mapped into

$$\underset{R \to \infty}{Lt} \left[\frac{6Re^{j\phi} + 1}{(R^2 e^{j2\phi})(Re^{j\phi} + 1)(3Re^{j\phi} + 1)} \right] = \underset{R \to \infty}{Lt} \frac{6Re^{j\phi}}{3R^4 e^{j4\phi}} = \underset{R \to \infty}{Lt} \frac{2}{R^3 e^{j3\phi}} = 0e^{-j3\phi}$$

$$= 0 \; (\angle -270° \to \angle 0° \to \angle +270°)$$

The point of intersection of the Nyquist plot on the real axis is obtained by equating the imaginary part to zero, i.e.

$$\frac{(2 - 18\omega^2)}{-\omega(1 + \omega^2)(1 + 9\omega^2)} = 0$$

i.e.

$$2 - 18\omega^2 = 0$$

or

$$\omega^2 = 1/9$$

or

$$\omega = 1/3 \text{ rad/s}$$

The value of $G(j\omega)H(j\omega)$ at $\omega = 1/3$ is obtained by substituting this value of ω in the real part of $G(j\omega)H(j\omega)$, i.e.

$$\frac{1+21\omega^2}{-\omega^2(1+\omega^2)(1+9\omega^2)} = \frac{1+21/9}{(-1/9)(1+1/9)(1+9/9)} = \frac{30/9}{10 \times 2/9 \times 9} = -13.5$$

So, the Nyquist plot crosses the real axis at -13.5.

Based on the above information, an approximate Nyquist plot drawn for the Nyquist path shown in Figure 8.12(a) is shown in Figure 8.12(b). From this plot we can observe that, the Nyquist plot of $G(s)H(s)$ encircles the $(-1 + j0)$ point twice in the clockwise direction. Therefore, $N = -2$. The given open-loop transfer function $G(s)H(s)$ has no poles in the right-half of the s-plane. So, $P = 0$. Thus, $-2 = 0 - Z$ or $Z = 2$. Hence two zeros of $q(s)$ lie in the right-half of the s-plane. So the closed-loop system is unstable.

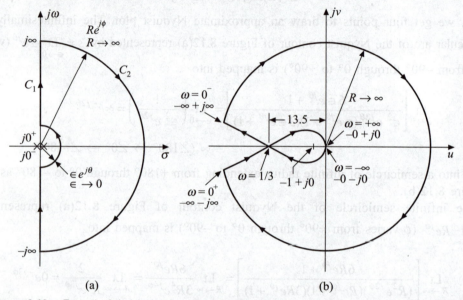

Figure 8.12   Example 8.4: (a) Nyquist contour and (b) the corresponding Nyquist plot for $G(s)H(s)$ = $(6s + 1)/s^2(s + 1)(3s + 1)$.

Example 8.5   Sketch the Nyquist plot and comment on the stability of the closed-loop system whose open-loop transfer function is

$$G(s)H(s) = \frac{K(s+3)}{s(s-1)}$$

Solution: The given open-loop transfer function has one pole in the right-half of the s-plane. So, $P = 1$. For the closed-loop system to be stable, the Nyquist plot must encircle the $(-1 + j0)$ point of the $q(s)$-plane once in the counterclockwise direction. $G(s)H(s)$ has one pole at the origin. The Nyquist contour is therefore indented to bypass the origin.

The given open-loop transfer function in sinusoidal form is

$$G(j\omega)H(j\omega) = \frac{K(j\omega + 3)}{j\omega(j\omega - 1)} = \frac{K(3 + j\omega)(1 + j\omega)}{-j\omega(1 - j\omega)(1 + j\omega)}$$

$$= \frac{K[(3 - \omega^2) + j4\omega]}{-j\omega(1 + \omega^2)} = -\frac{4K}{1 + \omega^2} + j\frac{K(3 - \omega^2)}{\omega(1 + \omega^2)}$$

Along the segment (C_1) of the Nyquist contour on the $j\omega$-axis, s varies from $-j\infty$ to $+j\infty$. At $\omega = -\infty$,

$$G(j\omega)H(j\omega) = -0 + j0$$

At $\omega = 0^-$,

$$G(j\omega)H(j\omega) = -4K - j\infty$$

At $\omega = 0^+$,

$$G(j\omega)H(j\omega) = -4K + j\infty$$

At $\omega = +\infty$,

$$G(j\omega)H(j\omega) = -0 - j0$$

So, we get four points to draw an approximate Nyquist plot. The semicircular indent around the pole at the origin of the Nyquist contour of Figure 8.13(a) represented by $s = \underset{\epsilon \to 0}{\in e^{j\theta}}$ (θ varying from $-90°$ through $0°$ to $+90°$) maps into

$$\underset{\epsilon \to 0}{Lt} \frac{K(\in e^{j\theta} + 3)}{\in e^{j\theta}(\in e^{j\theta} - 1)} = \underset{\epsilon \to 0}{Lt} \frac{-3K}{\in e^{j\theta}} = -\infty e^{-j\theta} = \infty e^{-j(180° + \theta)}$$

$$= \infty\angle -90° \to \infty\angle -180° \to \infty\angle -270°$$

This is an infinite semicircular arc in the left-half of the $G(s)H(s)$ plane with clockwise direction as in Figure 8.13(b).

The infinite semicircular arc of the Nyquist contour (segment C_2) of Figure 8.13(a) represented by $s = \underset{R \to \infty}{Re^{j\phi}}$ (ϕ varying from $+90°$ through $0°$ to $-90°$) is mapped into

$$\underset{R \to \infty}{Lt} \frac{K(Re^{j\phi} + 3)}{Re^{j\phi}(Re^{j\phi} - 1)} = \underset{R \to \infty}{Lt} \frac{K}{R}e^{-j\phi} = 0e^{-j\phi}$$

$$= 0\angle -90° \to \angle 0° \to \angle +90°$$

The map turns around the origin from $\angle -90° \to \angle 0° \to \angle +90°$ as sketched in Figure 8.13(b).

The point of intersection of the Nyquist plot with the real axis is obtained by equating the imaginary part of $G(j\omega)H(j\omega)$ to zero, i.e.

$$\frac{K(3 - \omega^2)}{\omega(1 + \omega^2)} = 0$$

i.e. $$\omega^2 = 3$$

or $$\omega = \pm\sqrt{3}$$

The value of $G(j\omega)H(j\omega)$ at that point is obtained by substituting this value of ω in the real part of $G(j\omega)H(j\omega)$, i.e.

$$-\frac{4K}{1 + \omega^2} = \frac{-4K}{1 + 3} = -K$$

Based on the above information, an approximate Nyquist plot is drawn as shown in Figure 8.13(b).

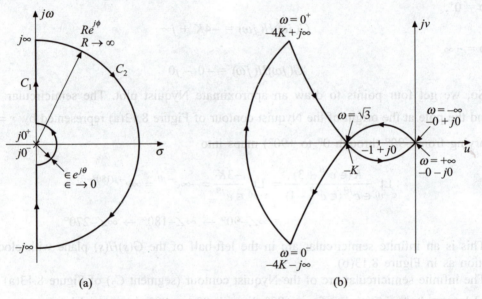

Figure 8.13   Example 8.5: (a) Nyquist contour and (b) the corresponding Nyquist plot for $G(s)H(s)$ = $K(s + 3)/s(s - 1)$.

Conclusions on stability: For $K > 1$

The Nyquist plot encircles the $(-1 + j0)$ point once in the counterclockwise direction, i.e. $N = 1$.

The open-loop transfer function has $P = 1$. Then

$$N = P - Z$$
$$1 = 1 - Z$$
$$\therefore \qquad Z = 0$$

Thus the system is stable.

For $K < 1$, we can see that the $(-1 + j0)$ point will lie beyond $-K$, the crossing point of the plot. So, the Nyquist plot encircles the $-1 + j0$ point once in the clockwise direction and hence

$$N = -1, \ P = 1$$

$$N = P - Z$$

∴

$$-1 = P - Z$$

or

$$Z = P + 1 = 1 + 1 = 2$$

The closed-loop system is unstable as two roots of its characteristic equation are in the right-half of the *s*-plane.

Example 8.6 Sketch the Nyquist plot and comment on the stability of the closed-loop system whose open-loop transfer function is

$$G(s)H(s) = \frac{K(s-4)}{(s+1)^2}$$

Solution: The given open-loop system has one zero in the right-half of the *s*-plane. The sinusoidal transfer function is

$$G(j\omega)H(j\omega) = \frac{K(j\omega - 4)}{(j\omega + 1)^2} = \frac{K(j\omega - 4)(1 - j\omega)^2}{(1 + j\omega)^2(1 - j\omega)^2} = \frac{K(6\omega^2 - 4)}{(1 + \omega^2)^2} + j\frac{K\omega(9 - \omega^2)}{(1 + \omega^2)^2}$$

Along the segment (C_1) of the Nyquist contour on the $j\omega$-axis, *s* varies from $-j\infty$ to $+j\infty$.

At $\omega = -\infty$,

$$G(j\omega)H(j\omega) = 0 + j0$$

At $\omega = 0^-$,

$$G(j\omega)H(j\omega) = -4K - j0$$

At $\omega = 0^+$,

$$G(j\omega)H(j\omega) = -4K + j0$$

At $\omega = +\infty$,

$$G(j\omega)H(j\omega) = 0 - j0$$

So, we get four points to draw an approximate Nyquist plot. The infinite semicircular arc of the Nyquist contour (segment C_2) of Figure 8.14(a) represented by $s = \underset{R \to \infty}{Re^{j\phi}}$ (ϕ varying from $+90°$ through $0°$ to $-90°$) is mapped into

$$\underset{R \to \infty}{Lt} \frac{K(Re^{j\phi} - 4)}{(Re^{j\phi} + 1)^2} = \underset{R \to \infty}{Lt} \frac{K}{Re^{j\phi}} = 0e^{-j\phi}$$

$$= 0\angle{-90°} \to \angle 0° \to \angle{+90°}$$

The map turns around the origin from $\angle{-90°} \to \angle 0° \to \angle{+90°}$ as sketched in Figure 8.14(b). The point of intersection of the Nyquist plot on the real axis is obtained by equating the imaginary part to zero, i.e.

$$\frac{K\omega(9 - \omega^2)}{(1 + \omega^2)^2} = 0$$

i.e.

$$\omega^2 = 9$$

or

$$\omega = \pm 3 \text{ rad/s}$$

The value of $G(j\omega)H(j\omega)$ at this point is obtained by substituting this value of ω in the real part of $G(j\omega)H(j\omega)$. Therefore,

$$\frac{K(6\omega^2 - 4)}{(1 + \omega^2)^2} = \frac{K(6 \times 9 - 4)}{(1 + 9)^2} = \frac{K}{2}$$

Based on the above information, an approximate Nyquist plot is drawn as shown in Figure 8.14(b). Examination of this plot reveals that for $\dfrac{K}{2} < -1$ or $K > \dfrac{1}{4}$, i.e. for $K < -2$ or

$K > \dfrac{1}{4}$

$$N = -1, P = 0$$
$$N = P - Z$$
$$-1 = 0 - Z$$

or

$$Z = 1$$

The system is therefore unstable for $K < -2$ or $K > \dfrac{1}{4}$. It should be stable for $K > -2$ and

$K < \dfrac{1}{4}$ i.e. for $-2 < K < \dfrac{1}{4}$, when $N = 0$, $P = 0$ and therefore $Z = 0$.

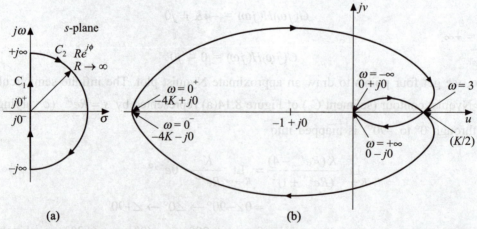

Figure 8.14 Example 8.6: (a) Nyquist contour and (b) the corresponding Nyquist plot for $G(s)H(s)$ = $K(s - 4)/(s + 1)^2$.

Example 8.7 Sketch the Nyquist plot and there from assess the stability of the closed-loop system whose open-loop transfer function is

$$G(s)H(s) = \frac{K(s+4)}{s^2(s+1)}$$

Solution: The given open-loop system has no poles in the right half of the s-plane. i.e. $P = 0$. So for the closed-loop system to be stable, the Nyquist plot must not encircle the $(-1 + j0)$ point of the $q(s)$-plane.

The given open-loop transfer function in sinusoidal form is

$$G(j\omega)H(j\omega) = \frac{K(j\omega+4)}{(j\omega)^2(j\omega+1)} = \frac{K(4+j\omega)(1-j\omega)}{-\omega^2(1+j\omega)(1-j\omega)}$$

$$= \frac{K[(4+\omega^2)-j3\omega]}{-\omega^2(1+\omega^2)} = -\frac{K(4+\omega^2)}{\omega^2(1+\omega^2)} + j\frac{3K}{\omega(1+\omega^2)}$$

Along the segment (C_1) of the Nyquist contour on the $j\omega$-axis, s varies from $-j\infty$ to $+j\infty$. At $\omega = -\infty$,

$$G(j\omega)H(j\omega) = -0 - j0$$

At $\omega = 0^-$,

$$G(j\omega)H(j\omega) = -\infty - j\infty$$

At $\omega = 0^+$,

$$G(j\omega)H(j\omega) = -\infty + j\infty$$

At $\omega = +\infty$,

$$G(j\omega)H(j\omega) = -0 + j0$$

So, we get four points to draw an approximate Nyquist plot. The semicircular indent around the pole at the origin of the Nyquist contour of Figure 8.15(a) represented by $s = \underset{\in\to0}{\in e^{j\theta}}$ (θ varying from $-90°$ through $0°$ to $+90°$) is mapped into

$$\underset{\in\to0}{Lt}\frac{K(\in e^{j\theta}+4)}{(\in e^{j\theta})^2(\in e^{j\theta}+1)} = \underset{\in\to0}{Lt}\frac{4K}{\in^2 e^{j2\theta}} = \infty e^{-j2\theta}$$

$$= \infty\angle+180° \to \angle0° \to \angle-180°$$

It is an infinite circular arc with clockwise directions. The infinite semicircular arc of the Nyquist contour (segment C_2) of Figure 8.15(a) represented by $s = \underset{R\to\infty}{Re^{j\phi}}$ (ϕ varying from $+90°$ through $0°$ to $-90°$) is mapped into

$$\underset{R\to\infty}{Lt}\frac{K(Re^{j\phi}+4)}{(Re^{j\phi})^2(Re^{j\phi}+1)} = \underset{R\to\infty}{Lt}\frac{K}{R^2 e^{j2\phi}} = 0e^{-j2\phi}$$

$$= 0\angle-180° \to \angle0° \to \angle+180°$$

The map turns around the origin from $\angle-180° \to \angle0° \to \angle+180°$ as sketched in Figure 8.14(b). Looking at the imaginary part of $G(j\omega)H(j\omega)$, we observe that the Nyquist plot intersects the real axis at $\omega = \infty$.

The point of intersection of the Nyquist plot on the real axis is obtained by setting the imaginary part to zero, i.e.

$$\frac{3\omega K}{\omega^2(1+\omega^2)} = 0$$

∴ $\omega = 0$

The value of the real part at this frequency is obtained by substituting this value of ω in the real part of $G(j\omega)H(j\omega)$, i.e.

$$-\frac{K(4+\omega^2)}{\omega^2(1+\omega^2)} = -\infty$$

Based on the above information, an approximate Nyquist plot is drawn as shown in Figure 8.15(b). It can be concluded that the system is unstable, as the Nyquist plot encircles the $(-1+j0)$ point twice in the clockwise direction.

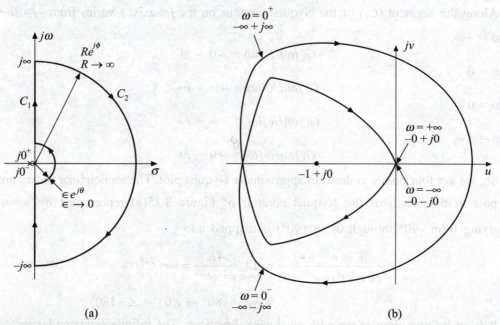

Figure 8.15 Example 8.7: (a) Nyquist contour and (b) the corresponding Nyquist plot for $G(s)H(s)$ = $K(s+4)/s^2(s+1)$.

Example 8.8 Sketch the Nyquist plot and therefrom determine the stability of the closed-loop system whose open-loop transfer function is given by

$$G(s)H(s) = \frac{K}{s(s^2+s+2)}$$

Solution: The given open-loop system has no poles in the right-half of s-plane. So, $P = 0$. For the closed-loop system to be stable, the Nyquist plot must not encircle the $(-1+j0)$ point of the $q(s)$ plane.

The given open-loop transfer function in sinusoidal form is

$$G(j\omega)H(j\omega) = \frac{K}{j\omega[(j\omega)^2 + j\omega + 2]} = \frac{K}{j\omega[(2 - \omega^2) + j\omega]}$$

$$= \frac{K[(2 - \omega^2) - j\omega]}{j\omega[(2 - \omega^2) + j\omega][(2 - \omega^2) - j\omega]}$$

$$= \frac{K[(2 - \omega^2) - j\omega]}{j\omega[(2 - \omega^2)^2 + \omega^2]} = -\frac{K}{(2 - \omega^2)^2 + \omega^2} - j\frac{K(2 - \omega^2)}{\omega[(2 - \omega^2)^2 + \omega^2]}$$

Along the segment (C_1) of the Nyquist contour on the $j\omega$-axis, s varies from $-j\infty$ to $+j\infty$.

At $\omega = -\infty$,

$$G(j\omega)H(j\omega) = -0 - j0$$

At $\omega = 0^-$,

$$G(j\omega)H(j\omega) = -(K/4) + j\infty$$

At $\omega = 0^+$,

$$G(j\omega)H(j\omega) = -(K/4) - j\infty$$

At $\omega = +\infty$,

$$G(j\omega)H(j\omega) = -0 + j0$$

So, we get four points to draw an approximate Nyquist plot.

The semicircular indent around the pole at the origin of the Nyquist contour of Figure 8.16(a) represented by $s = \epsilon e^{j\theta}$ (θ varying from $-90°$ through $0°$ to $+90°$) maps into $\epsilon \to 0$

$$\underset{\epsilon \to 0}{\text{Lt}} \frac{K}{\epsilon e^{j\theta}[(\epsilon e^{j\theta})^2 + (\epsilon e^{j\theta}) + 2]} = \underset{\epsilon \to 0}{\text{Lt}} \frac{K}{2 \epsilon e^{j\theta}} = \infty e^{-j\theta}$$

$$= \infty \angle + 90° \to \angle 0° \to \angle - 90°$$

It is an infinite circular arc with clockwise directions.

The infinite semicircular arc of the Nyquist contour (segment C_2) of Figure 8.16(a) represented by $s = Re^{j\phi}$ (ϕ varying from $+90°$ through $0°$ to $-90°$) is mapped into $R \to \infty$

$$\underset{R \to \infty}{\text{Lt}} \frac{K}{Re^{j\phi}[(Re^{j\phi})^2 + Re^{j\phi} + 2]} = \underset{R \to \infty}{\text{Lt}} \frac{K}{R^3 e^{j3\phi}} = 0e^{-j3\phi}$$

$$= 0\angle -270° \to \angle 0° \to \angle +270°$$

The map turns around the origin from $\angle -270° \to \angle 0° \to \angle +270°$ as sketched in Figure 8.16(b).

The point of intersection of the Nyquist plot with the real axis is obtained by equating the imaginary part of $G(j\omega)H(j\omega)$ to zero, i.e.

$$-\frac{K(2-\omega^2)}{\omega[(2-\omega^2)^2+\omega^2]}=0$$

i.e.
$$\omega^2 = 2$$

or
$$\omega = \sqrt{2}$$

The value of $G(j\omega)H(j\omega)$ at that point is obtained by substituting this value of ω in the real part of $G(j\omega)H(j\omega)$, i.e.

$$-\frac{K}{(2-\omega^2)^2+\omega^2}\bigg|_{\omega^2=2}=\frac{-K}{2}$$

Based on the above information, an approximate Nyquist plot is drawn as shown in Figure 8.16(b). It crosses the real axis at $\omega = \pm\sqrt{2}$ with an intercept of $-K/2$.

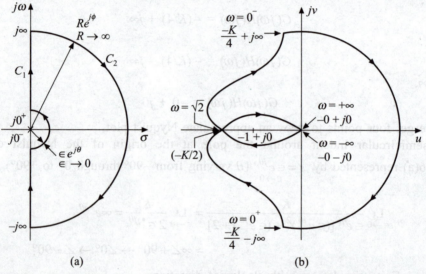

| (a) | (b) |

Figure 8.16   Example 8.8: (a) Nyquist contour and (b) the corresponding Nyquist plot for $G(s)H(s)$ = $K/s(s^2 + s + 2)$.

From the Nyquist plot

For
$$K/2 > 1$$

i.e. for
$$K > 2$$

the Nyquist plot encircles the $(-1 + j0)$ point twice in the clockwise direction.

$$N = P - Z$$
$$-2 = 0 - Z$$

or
$$Z = 2$$

So the system is unstable. For $K < 2$, the system will be stable.

8.4 NYQUIST STABILITY CRITERION APPLIED TO INVERSE POLAR PLOTS

Sometimes it is more convenient to work with the inverse function $1/G(j\omega)H(j\omega)$ rather than the direct function $G(j\omega)H(j\omega)$. The Nyquist stability criterion for direct polar plots can be extended for use to inverse polar plots after minor modifications.

Consider the open-loop transfer function in standard form

$$G(s)H(s) = \frac{K(s+z_1)(s+z_2)...(s+z_m)}{(s+p_1)(s+p_2)...(s+p_n)}; \; m \le n$$

For the system to be stable, none of the roots of the characteristic equation

$$q(s) = 1 + G(s)H(s) = 1 + \frac{K(s+z_1)(s+z_2)...(s+z_m)}{(s+p_1)(s+p_2)...(s+p_n)}$$

$$= \frac{K(s+z_1')(s+z_2')...(s+z_m')}{(s+p_1)(s+p_2)...(s+p_n)} \tag{8.3}$$

should lie in the right half s-plane or on the $j\omega$-axis.

Dividing Eq. (8.3) by $G(s)H(s)$, we get

$$q'(s) = \frac{1}{G(s)H(s)} + 1 = \frac{K(s+z_1')(s+z_2')...(s+z_m')}{(s+z_1)(s+z_2)...(s+z_m)} \tag{8.4}$$

From Eq. (8.4) it is seen that the zeros of $q'(s)$ are the same as the zeros of $q(s)$, which are the roots of the characteristic equation, i.e. the poles of the closed-loop system. It can be further seen that the poles of $q(s)$ are the same as poles of $G(s)H(s)$, while poles of $q'(s)$ are the same as the poles of $1/G(s)H(s)$ or the zeros of $G(s)H(s)$.

It can therefore be concluded that if $1/G(s)H(s)$ has P right-half s-plane poles and the characteristic equation has Z right-half s-plane zeros, the locus of $1/G(s)H(s)$ encircles the point $(-1 + j0)$, N times in counterclockwise direction.

$$N = P - Z$$

Since for stability, there should not be any zeros of the characteristic equation in the right-half s-plane, i.e. $Z = 0$, the Nyquist stability criterion for inverse polar plots can be stated as follows:

If the Nyquist plot of $1/G(s)H(s)$, corresponding to the Nyquist contour in the s-plane, encircles the point $(-1 + j0)$ as many times as are the number of right half s-plane poles of $1/G(s)H(s)$, the closed-loop system is stable. In the special case where $1/G(s)H(s)$ has no poles in the right-half s-plane, the closed-loop system is stable provided the net encirclement of $(-1 + j0)$ point by the Nyquist plot of $1/G(s)H(s)$ is zero.

Example 8.9 Draw the inverse polar plot for a feedback system with an open-loop transfer function

$$G(s)H(s) = K/s(1 + Ts)$$

Solution:

$$\frac{1}{G(s)H(s)} = \frac{s(1+Ts)}{K}$$

Therefore, the sinusoidal transfer function is

$$\frac{1}{G(j\omega)H(j\omega)} = \frac{(j\omega)(1+j\omega T)}{K} = \frac{-\omega^2 T + j\omega}{K}$$

Along the segment (C_1) of the Nyquist contour on the $j\omega$-axis, s varies from $-j\infty$ to $+j\infty$. At $\omega = -\infty$,

$$1/G(j\omega)H(j\omega) = -\infty - j\infty$$

At $\omega = 0^-$,

$$1/G(j\omega)H(j\omega) = -0 - j0$$

At $\omega = 0^+$,

$$1/G(j\omega)H(j\omega) = -0 + j0$$

At $\omega = +\infty$,

$$1/G(j\omega)H(j\omega) = -\infty + j\infty$$

So we get four points to draw an approximate Nyquist plot.

The semicircular indent around the origin of the Nyquist contour of Figure 8.17(a) represented by $s = \underset{\epsilon \to 0}{\mathrm{Lt}}\ \epsilon e^{j\theta}$; where θ varies from $-90°$ through $0°$ to $+90°$, is mapped into $1/G(s)H(s)$ plane as

$$\underset{\epsilon \to 0}{\mathrm{Lt}} \left[\frac{\epsilon e^{j\theta}(\epsilon e^{j\theta} + 1)}{K} \right] = \underset{\epsilon \to 0}{\mathrm{Lt}} \frac{\epsilon e^{j\theta}}{K} = 0e^{j\theta}$$

which is a point at the origin with θ varying from $+\pi/2 \to 0° \to -\pi/2$.

The infinite semicircular arc of the Nyquist contour (segment C_2) of Figure 8.17(a) represented by $s = \underset{R \to \infty}{\mathrm{Lt}}\ Re^{j\phi}$; where ϕ varies from $+90°$ through $0°$ to $-90°$, is mapped into the $1/G(s)H(s)$ plane as

$$\underset{R \to \infty}{\mathrm{Lt}} \left[\frac{Re^{j\phi}(Re^{j\phi} + 1)}{K} \right] = \underset{R \to \infty}{\mathrm{Lt}} \frac{R^2 e^{j2\phi}}{K} = \infty\ e^{j2\phi}$$

which is a circle of infinite radius with phase angle varying from $+180° \to 0° \to -180°$.

The inverse polar plot of $G(s)H(s) = K/s(1 + Ts)$ obtained from the above steps is shown in Figures 8.17(b). It is observed that $(-1 + j0)$ point is not encircled by $1/G(s)H(s)$ locus. Since $1/G(s)H(s) = s(1 + Ts)/K$ has no poles in the right-half s-plane, the system is stable.

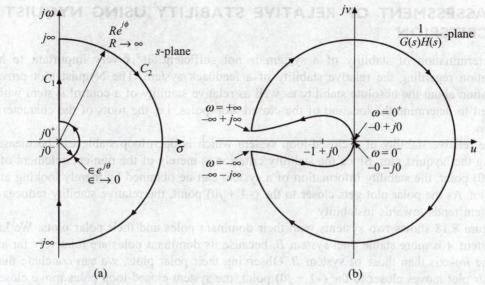

Figure 8.17 Example 8.9: (a) The Nyquist contour and (b) the corresponding Nyquist plot for $1/G(s)H(s) = s(sT + 1)/K$.

8.5 EFFECTS OF ADDITION OF POLES AND ZEROS TO *G(s)H(s)* ON THE SHAPE OF NYQUIST PLOT

8.5.1 Addition of Poles at *s* = 0

Since adding a pole at $s = 0$ is equivalent to dividing $G(s)H(s)$ by $j\omega$, the phase of $G(j\omega)H(j\omega)$ is reduced by 90° at both zero and infinite frequencies, i.e. the addition of a pole at the origin to a loop transfer function rotates the Nyquist plot at zero and infinite frequencies by a further angle of –90°. In addition, the magnitude of $G(j\omega)H(j\omega)$ at $\omega = 0$ becomes infinite.

The conclusion is that the addition of poles at $s = 0$ to a loop transfer function will affect the stability of the closed-loop system adversely. A system that has a loop transfer function with more than one pole at $s = 0$ (type-2 or higher) is likely to be unstable or difficult to stabilize.

8.5.2 Addition of Finite Non-zero Poles

Addition of a non-zero pole to the loop transfer function shifts the phase of the Nyquist plot by –90° at $\omega = \infty$, i.e. it results in further rotation of the polar plot through an angle of –90° as $\omega \to \infty$. The stability is adversely affected.

8.5.3 Addition of a Zero

The effect of addition of a zero to the loop transfer function is to rotate the high frequency portion of the Nyquist plot by 90° in the counterclockwise direction without effecting the value at $\omega = 0$. So it has the effect of reducing the overshoot and the general effect of stabilization.

8.6 ASSESSMENT OF RELATIVE STABILITY USING NYQUIST CRITERION

Just determination of stability of a system is not sufficient. It is very important to have information regarding the relative stability of a feedback system. The Nyquist plot provides information about the absolute stability as well as relative stability of a control system without any need to determine the location of the closed-loop poles, i.e. the roots of the characteristic equation.

The relative stability of a closed-loop system which is open-loop stable can be measured by using the Nyquist plot. Since the stability criterion is merely of the non-encirclement of the $(-1 + j0)$ point, the stability information of a system can be obtained by merely looking at the polar plot. As the polar plot gets closer to the $(-1 + j0)$ point, the relative stability reduces and the system tends towards instability.

Figure 8.18 shows two systems with their dominant poles and their polar plots. We know that system A is more stable than system B, because its dominant poles are relatively far away from the $j\omega$-axis than those of system B. Observing their polar plots, we can conclude that as the polar plot moves closer to the $(-1 + j0)$ point, the system closed-loop poles move closer to the $j\omega$-axis, and hence the system becomes relatively less stable and vice versa.

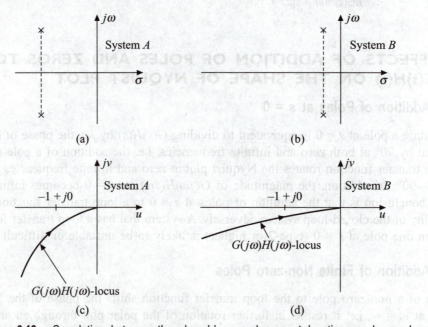

Figure 8.18 Correlation between the closed-loop s-plane root locations and open-loop frequency response curves.

Figure 8.19 shows the polar plot of $G(s)H(s) = 1/s(1 + T_1s)(1 + T_2s)$. It crosses the negative real axis at a frequency $\omega = \omega_2$ with an intercept of a. Let the unit circle centered at origin (obviously it passess through the $(-1 + j0)$ point) intersect this polar plot ($G(j\omega)H(j\omega)$ locus) at a frequency $\omega = \omega_1$. Let the phasor $G(j\omega_1)H(j\omega_1)$ make an angle of ϕ with the negative real axis measured positively in the counter-clockwise direction. It can be observed from Figure 8.19 that as the $G(j\omega)H(j\omega)$ locus moves closer to the $(-1 + j0)$ point, the relative stability reduces. Simultaneously, the value of the intercept a approaches unity and ϕ tends to zero. The relative stability could thus be measured in terms of the intercept a or the angle ϕ. These concepts are used to define gain margin (GM) and phase margin (PM) as practical measures of relative stability. It should also be noted that the concepts of GM and PM are applicable only to open-loop stable systems. Of course most of the practical systems lie in this category only.

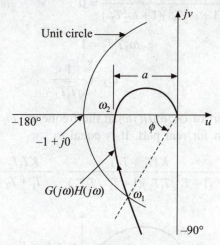

Figure 8.19 Polar plot of $G(s)H(s) = 1/s(1 + T_1s)(1 + T_2s)$.

8.6.1   Gain Margin and Phase Margin

Consider a feedback system with the open-loop transfer function

$$G(s)H(s) = \frac{K}{s(1 + T_1s)(1 + T_2s)}$$

Let us investigate the stability of the system for various values of K.
The sinusoidal transfer function is

$$G(j\omega)H(j\omega) = \frac{K}{j\omega(1 + j\omega T_1)(1 + j\omega T_2)}$$

$$= -\frac{K(T_1 + T_2)}{(1 + \omega^2 T_1^2)(1 + \omega^2 T_2^2)} - j\frac{K(1 - \omega^2 T_1 T_2)}{\omega(1 + \omega^2 T_1^2)(1 + \omega^2 T_2^2)}$$

At $\omega = 0$,

$$G(j\omega)H(j\omega) = -K(T_1 + T_2) - j\infty$$

At $\omega = \infty$,

$$G(j\omega)H(j\omega) = -0 + j0$$

In fact, the real and imaginary parts of $G(j\omega)H(j\omega)$ at various frequencies can be computed in addition to the above two points and a polar plot passing through all those points can be drawn as shown in Figure 8.20. The polar plots for $K = K_1, K_2, K_3$ are shown in Figure 8.20. The point of intersection of the polar plot with the negative real axis can be determined by setting the imaginary part of $G(j\omega)H(j\omega) = 0$. Let ω_2 be the frequency at the point of intersection. Therefore,

$$\frac{K(1 - \omega_2^2 T_1 T_2)}{\omega_2(1 + \omega_2^2 T_1^2)(1 + \omega_2^2 T_2^2)} = 0$$

i.e.

$$\omega_2^2 T_1 T_2 = 1$$

$\therefore$

$$\omega_2 = \frac{1}{\sqrt{T_1 T_2}}$$

The magnitude of real part of $G(j\omega)H(j\omega)$ at the frequency ω_2 is given by substituting this value of ω_2 in the expression for real part. It is equal to

$$-\frac{K(T_1 + T_2)}{(1 + T_1^2/T_1 T_2)(1 + T_2^2/T_1 T_2)} = -\frac{KT_1 T_2}{T_1 + T_2}$$

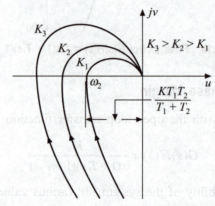

Figure 8.20 The polar plots of $G(s)H(s) = K/s(1 + T_1 s)(1 + T_2 s)$ for various values of gain K.

From Figure 8.20 it is seen that for the system to be stable

$$\frac{KT_1 T_2}{T_1 + T_2} < 1$$

or

$$K < \frac{T_1 + T_2}{T_1 T_2}$$

When the gain K is less than $(T_1 + T_2)/T_1 T_2$, the critical point $(-1 + j0)$ is not encircled by $G(j\omega)H(j\omega)$ plot and the system is stable. When $K = (T_1 + T_2)/T_1 T_2$, the plot passess through the critical point $(-1 + j0)$ which indicates that the system has roots on the $j\omega$-axis and the system is limitedly stable. When K is further increased so as to be greater than $(T_1 + T_2)/T_1 T_2$, the $G(j\omega)H(j\omega)$ plot encircles the critical point $(-1 + j0)$ and hence the system is unstable. The margin between the actual gain and the critical gain which causes sustained oscillations is a measure of relative stability and is called the *gain margin*.

Gain margin: Gain margin is defined as the factor by which the system gain can be increased to drive it to the verge of instability.

In Figure 8.19, we can see that at $\omega = \omega_2$, the phase angle $\angle G(j\omega)H(j\omega) = +180°$ and magnitude $|G(j\omega)H(j\omega)| = a$. If the gain of the system is increased by a factor $1/a$, then $\left|G(j\omega)H(j\omega)\right|_{\omega = \omega_2}$ becomes $a(1/a) = 1$ and hence the $G(j\omega)H(j\omega)$ plot will pass through the point $(-1 + j0)$, driving the system to the verge of instability. Therefore, the gain margin may be defined as the reciprocal of the magnitude at the frequency at which the phase angle becomes $-180°$. The frequency at which the phase angle is $-180°$ is called the *phase crossover frequency*.

With reference to Figure 8.19, we have

$$GM = 1/a$$

where
$$a = \left|G(j\omega)H(j\omega)\right|_{\omega = \omega_2}$$

In dB, the increase in gain for $G(j\omega)H(j\omega)$ plot to pass through $(-1 + j0)$ point is given by

$$GM = -20 \log a \text{ dB}$$

Since a is less than 1 for stable systems, $\log a$ is negative and hence GM is positive.

Phase margin: The frequency at which $|G(j\omega)H(j\omega)| = 1$ is called the gain crossover frequency. It is given by the intersection of the $G(j\omega)H(j\omega)$ plot and the unit circle centred at the origin as shown in Figure 8.19. At this frequency $\omega = \omega_1$, the phase angle $\angle G(j\omega_1)H(j\omega_1)$ $= (-180° + \phi)$. If an additional phase lag equal to ϕ is introduced at the gain crossover frequency, the phase angle $\angle G(j\omega_1)H(j\omega_1)$ will become $-180°$, while the magnitude remains unity. The $G(j\omega)H(j\omega)$ plot will then pass through the $(-1 + j0)$ point, driving the system to the verge of instability. This additional phase lag ϕ is known as the phase margin ϕ_{pm} (PM).

The phase margin is therefore defined as the amount of additional phase lag at the gain crossover frequency required to bring the system to the verge of instability. The phase margin is measured positively in the counterclockwise direction from the negative real axis. The phase margin is always positive for stable feedback systems.

The value of phase margin for any system can be computed from:

phase margin $\phi_{pm} = \angle G(j\omega)H(j\omega)$ at the gain crossover frequency $+180°$

For a system to be stable, both its GM and PM must be positive. In most practical systems, a good GM ensures a good PM and vice versa. However, the cases of systems with a good GM but a poor PM and systems with a good PM but a poor GM also exist as shown in Figures 8.21 and 8.22.

In second-order systems, GM always remains fixed at infinite value as the plot always reaches the real axis at the origin, while the PM reduces continuously with increasing system gain as shown in Figure 8.23.

In such cases PM is the correct measure of relative stability. Usually it is the phase margin which is specified as a measure of system performance in design.

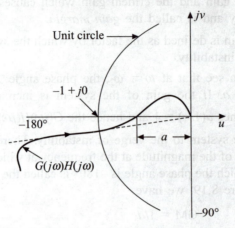

Figure 8.21   Polar plot of a system with good GM and poor PM.

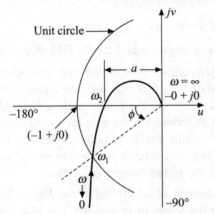

Figure 8.22   Polar plot of a system with good PM and poor GM.

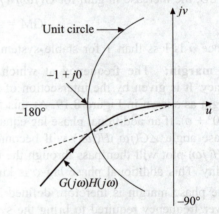

Figure 8.23   Polar plot of a second-order system with GM always equal to infinity while PM reduces continuously with increasing gain.

Example 8.10   Determine the gain crossover frequency ω_g, phase crossover frequency ω_p, gain margin GM and phase margin ϕ_{pm} of a system with open-loop transfer function

$$G(s) = \frac{1}{s(1+s)(1+2s)}$$

Comment on the stability of the system.

Solution: *Determination of phase crossover frequency ω_p and gain margin*: For the given $G(s)$, the sinusoidal transfer function is

$$G(j\omega) = \frac{1}{j\omega(1+j\omega)(1+j2\omega)} = \frac{1}{j\omega(1-2\omega^2+j3\omega)} = \frac{1}{-3\omega^2+j\omega(1-2\omega^2)}$$

At the phase crossover frequency ω_p, the imaginary part of the $G(j\omega)$ is zero. Hence put $\omega = \omega_p$ in the imaginary part and equate it to zero to solve for ω_p. Therefore,

$$\omega_p(1-2\omega_p^2) = 0$$

Since $$\omega_p \neq 0,$$

i.e. $$1 - 2\omega_p^2 = 0$$

$$\omega_p^2 = 1/2$$

or $$\omega_p = 1/\sqrt{2} = 0.707 \text{ rad/s}$$

The gain margin is defined as the reciprocal of the magnitude of $G(j\omega)$ at the phase crossover frequency. Therefore,

$$\text{GM} = \frac{1}{|G(j\omega)|_{\omega=\omega_p}} = \frac{1}{|1/(-3\omega^2)|_{\omega=\omega_p}} = 3\omega_p^2 = 3 \times 0.707^2 = 1.5$$

$$\therefore \qquad \text{GM in dB} = 20 \log \text{GM} = 20 \log 1.5 = 3.5 \text{ dB}$$

Determination of gain crossover frequency and phase margin: For the given $G(s)$,

$$G(j\omega) = \frac{1}{j\omega(1+j\omega)(1+j2\omega)} = \frac{1}{[\omega\angle 90°][\sqrt{(1+\omega^2)}\angle\tan^{-1}\omega][\sqrt{(1+4\omega^2)}\angle\tan^{-1}2\omega]}$$

$$\therefore \qquad |G(j\omega)| = 1/\omega\sqrt{1+\omega^2} \cdot \sqrt{1+4\omega^2}$$

$$\angle G(j\omega) = -90° - \tan^{-1}\omega - \tan^{-1}2\omega$$

At the gain crossover frequency ω_g, the magnitude of $G(j\omega)$ is unity. Therefore, at $\omega = \omega_g$

$$|G(j\omega)| = 1/\omega_g\sqrt{1+\omega_g^2} \cdot \sqrt{1+4\omega_g^2} = 1$$

Solving the above equation for ω_g will be tedious. Hence, by trial and error we can find the root of the above equation.
When $\omega = 1$,

$$|G(j\omega)| = \frac{1}{\omega\sqrt{1+\omega^2}\sqrt{1+4\omega^2}} = \frac{1}{1\sqrt{1+1}\sqrt{1+4}} = 0.3$$

When $\omega = 0.5$,

$$|G(j\omega)| = \frac{1}{0.5\sqrt{1+0.5^2}\sqrt{1+4\times0.5^2}} = 1.26$$

From the above two calculations, we can conclude that the unity magnitude will occur for a frequency between 0.5 and 1.0.

When $\omega = 0.6$,

$$|G(j\omega)| = \frac{1}{0.6\sqrt{1+0.6^2}\sqrt{1+4\times0.6^2}} = 0.915$$

When $\omega = 0.57$,

$$|G(j\omega)| = \frac{1}{0.57\sqrt{1+0.57^2}\sqrt{1+4\times0.57^2}} = 1.005$$

Let $\omega = 0.57$ be the gain crossover frequency, since for this value of ω, the magnitude of $G(j\omega)$ is approximately equal to one. Therefore, gain crossover frequency $\omega_g = 0.57$ rad/s.

Let the phase of $G(j\omega)$ at ω_g be ϕ_g.

At $\omega = \omega_g = 0.57$,

$$\phi_g = -90° - \tan^{-1}\omega - \tan^{-1}2\omega$$

$$= -90° - \tan^{-1}0.57 - \tan^{-1}2\times0.57 = -168°$$

Therefore, phase margin

$$\phi_{pm}\ (PM) = 180° + \phi_g = 180° - 168° = 12°$$

Since the GM and PM are positive, the system is stable.

Example 8.11 The open-loop transfer function of a system is

$$G(s) = \frac{K}{s(1+0.1s)(1+s)}$$

(a) Determine the value of K so that the gain margin is 6 dB.
(b) Determine the value of K so that the phase margin is 40°.

Solution:

(a) *Determination of K for specified gain margin:* Given that

$$G(s) = \frac{K}{s(1+0.1s)(1+s)}$$

Putting $s = j\omega$, the sinusoidal transfer function is

$$G(j\omega) = \frac{K}{j\omega(1+j0.1\omega)(1+j\omega)}$$

$$= \frac{K}{j\omega(1+j1.1\omega - 0.1\omega^2)} = \frac{K}{-1.1\omega^2 + j\omega(1-0.1\omega^2)}$$

At the phase crossover frequency ω_p, the imaginary part is zero. Hence, put $\omega = \omega_p$ in the imaginary part, equate it to zero and solve for ω_p.

At $\omega = \omega_p$,

$$\omega_p (1 - 0.1\omega_p^2) = 0$$

$$\omega_p \neq 0$$

$\therefore$
$$1 - 0.1\omega_p^2 = 0$$

or
$$\omega_p^2 = 1/0.1 = 10$$

or
$$\omega_p = \sqrt{10} = 3.162 \text{ rad/s}$$

$$\left| G(j\omega) \right|_{\omega=\omega_p} = \left| \frac{K}{-1.1\omega^2} \right|_{\omega=\omega_p} = \frac{K}{1.1 \times 10} = 0.0909K$$

Given that GM = 6 dB. Therefore,

$$20 \log \text{GM} = 6 \text{ dB}$$

or
$$\log \text{GM} = 6/20 = 0.3$$

$\therefore$
$$\text{GM} = 10^{0.3} = 1.9953$$

Since gain margin is the reciprocal of the gain at the phase crossover frequency,

$$\text{GM} = \frac{1}{\left| G(j\omega) \right|_{\omega=\omega_p}}$$

$$1.9953 = \frac{1}{0.0909K}$$

or
$$K = \frac{1}{0.0909 \times 1.9953} = 5.513$$

(b) *Determination of K for specified phase margin:* The sinusoidal transfer function of the given system is

$$G(j\omega) = \frac{K}{j\omega(1 + j0.1\omega)(1 + j\omega)}$$

$$= \frac{K}{[\omega\angle 90°][\sqrt{1 + 0.01\omega^2} \angle \tan^{-1} 0.1\omega][\sqrt{1 + \omega^2} \angle \tan^{-1} \omega]}$$

$\therefore$
$$\left| G(j\omega) \right| = \frac{K}{\omega\sqrt{1 + 0.01\omega^2} \sqrt{1 + \omega^2}}$$

$$\angle G(j\omega) = -90° - \tan^{-1} 0.1\omega - \tan^{-1} \omega$$

Let ω_g be the gain crossover frequency and let ϕ_g be the resultant phase at the gain crossover frequency.

At $\omega = \omega_g$,

$$\phi_g = \angle G(j\omega)\big|_{\omega=\omega_g} = -90° - \tan^{-1} 0.1\omega_g - \tan^{-1} \omega_g$$

By the definition of phase margin,

$$\phi_{pm} \text{ (PM)} = 180° + \phi_g$$

The required PM is 40°. Therefore,

$$40° = 180° - 90° - \tan^{-1} 0.1\omega_g - \tan^{-1} \omega_g$$

∴　　　$\tan^{-1} 0.1\omega_g + \tan^{-1} \omega_g = 180° - 90° - 40° = 50°$

On taking the tan on either side, we get

$$\frac{0.1\omega_g + \omega_g}{1 - 0.1\omega_g \times \omega_g} = \tan 50° = 1.192$$

i.e.　　　$1.1\omega_g = 1.192(1 - 0.1\omega_g^2)$

i.e.　　　$0.1192\omega_g^2 + 1.1\omega_g - 1.192 = 0$

i.e.　　　$\omega_g^2 + 9.228\omega_g - 10 = 0$

∴　　　$\omega_g = \dfrac{-9.228 \pm \sqrt{9.228^2 + 40}}{2} = \dfrac{-9.228 \pm 11.187}{2}$

On taking positive value, we get

$$\omega_g = \frac{-9.228 + 11.187}{2} = 0.98 \text{ rad/s}$$

At $\omega = \omega_g$, $|G(j\omega)| = 1$

$$|G(j\omega)|_{\omega=\omega_g} = \frac{K}{\omega_g\sqrt{1+0.1\omega_g^2}\sqrt{1+\omega_g^2}} = 1$$

∴　　　$K = \omega_g\sqrt{1+0.1\omega_g^2}\sqrt{1+\omega_g^2} = 0.98\sqrt{1+0.1\times0.98^2}\sqrt{1+0.98^2} = 1.378$

The result is for a GM of 6 dB, $K = 5.513$ and for a PM of 40°, $K = 1.378$.

Example 8.12　The open-loop transfer function of a unity feedback system is

$$G(s) = \frac{K}{s(1+0.2s)(1+0.05s)}$$

(a) Determine the value of K so that GM is 20 dB.
(b) Determine the value of K so that PM is 40°.

Solution:

(a) *Determination of K for a gain margin of* 20 dB:　For the given $G(s)$, the sinusoidal transfer function is

$$G(j\omega) = \frac{K}{j\omega(1 + j0.2\omega)(1 + j0.05\omega)}$$

$$= \frac{K}{-0.25\omega^2 + j\omega(1 - 0.01\omega^2)}$$

At the phase crossover frequency ω_p, the $G(j\omega)$ is real and so equate the imaginary part to zero and solve for ω_p. Therefore,

$$\omega_p(1 - 0.01\omega_p^2) = 0$$

Since $\omega_p \neq 0$,

$$1 - 0.01\omega_p^2 = 0$$

or

$$\omega_p^2 = 1/0.01 = 100$$

or

$$\omega_p = 10 \text{ rad/s}$$

The Nyquist plot intersects the real axis at a point where $G(j\omega)$ is real.

$$|G(j\omega)|_{\omega=\omega_p} = \frac{K}{0.25\omega_p^2} = \frac{K}{0.25 \times 100} = \frac{K}{25} = 0.04K$$

Given that GM = 20 dB, i.e.

$$20 \log GM = 20 \text{ dB}$$

$$\therefore \qquad GM = 10$$

$$a = 1/GM = \frac{1}{10} = 0.1$$

$$0.04K = a = 0.1$$

or

$$K = 0.1/0.04 = 2.5$$

(b) *Determination of K for a phase margin of 40°:* Let $\omega = \omega_g$ be the gain crossover frequency. Then for a PM of 40°,

$$-90° - \tan^{-1} 0.2\omega_g - \tan^{-1} 0.05\omega_g + 180° = 40°$$

$$\therefore \qquad \tan^{-1} 0.2\omega_g + \tan^{-1} 0.05\omega_g = 180° - 90° - 40° = 50°$$

Taking the tan on both sides,

$$\frac{0.2\omega_g + 0.05\omega_g}{1 - 0.2\omega_g \times 0.05\omega_g} = \tan 50° = 1.2$$

i.e.

$$\frac{0.25\omega_g}{1 - 0.01\omega_g^2} = 1.2$$

i.e.
$$0.012\omega_g^2 + 0.25\omega_g - 1.2 = 0$$

∴
$$\omega_g = \frac{-0.25 \pm \sqrt{0.25^2 + 4 \times 0.012 \times 1.2}}{2 \times 0.012}$$

Solving for positive value of ω_g, we get $\omega_g = 4$ rad/s.
Hence

$$|G(j\omega)|_{\omega=\omega_g} = \frac{K}{\omega_g\sqrt{(1+(0.2\omega_g)^2)}\sqrt{(1+(0.05\omega_g)^2)}} = 1$$

which gives $K = 5.2$.

This method of determining GM and PM and also the values of K for specified GM and PM easily without drawing the Nyquist plot is possible only for first- and second-order systems and for those third-order systems which have one open-loop pole at origin and no open-loop zeros.

Determination of GM *and* PM *by drawing the Nyquist plot:* Given

$$G(j\omega) = \frac{K}{j\omega(1 + j0.2\omega)(1 + j0.05\omega)}$$

For $K = 1$,

$$|G(j\omega)| = \frac{1}{\omega\sqrt{[1+(0.2\omega)^2}\sqrt{1+(0.05\omega)^2}}$$

$$\angle G(j\omega) = -90° - \tan^{-1}0.2\omega - \tan^{-1}0.05\omega$$

The values of $|G(j\omega)|$ and $\angle G(j\omega)$ at various frequencies are given in Table 8.1.

Table 8.1 Example 8.12

Frequency	$\omega = 0$	$\omega = 1$	$\omega = 5$	$\omega = 10$	$\omega = 20$	$\omega = 100$
Magnitude	∞	0.9794	0.126	0.04	0.0085	0.00009793
Phase angle	−90°	−114.162°	−149.03°	−180°	−210.96°	−255.82°

The Nyquist plot of $G(j\omega)$ based on the above table for $K = 1$ is shown in Figure 8.24. From this plot it is found that

$$a = 0.04$$

∴
$$1/a = 1/0.04 = 25$$

$$\text{GM} = 20 \log(1/a) = 20 \log 25 = 28 \text{ dB}$$

A unit circle centred at the origin will intersect the Nyquist plot at A. OA makes an angle of 76° with the negative real axis. So the phase margin ϕ_{pm} (PM) is 76°.

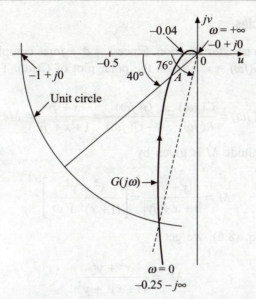

Figure 8.24 Example 8.12: Nyquist plot of $G(s) = 1/s(1 + 0.2s)(1 + 0.05s)$.

We can use the Nyquist plot for adjustment of system gain for specified GM or PM.

1. For a GM of 20 dB, the Nyquist plot should intersect the real axis at $-a$ where

$$20 \log (1/a) = 20$$

or

$$a = 0.1$$

This is achieved if the system gain is increased by a factor of $0.1/0.04 = 2.5$. Thus $K = 2.5$.

2. A PM of 40° is obtained, if the system gain K is increased such that point A is shifted to location A' in Figure 8.24. This is achieved if the system gain is increased by a factor of

$$\frac{OA'}{OA} = \frac{1}{0.191} = 5.24$$

Thus

$$K = 5.24$$

8.7 CONSTANT *M* AND *N* CIRCLES

In frequency-domain, the figures of merit of a system are resonant peak M_r, the maximum value of M and resonant frequency ω_r, the frequency at which resonant peak occurs. Eventhough they can be evaluated from the closed-loop frequency response, it is a time-consuming process. These values can be determined directly from the open-loop frequency response by using graphical techniques. These graphical techniques require constant M and constant N contours drawn in the complex plane. So, there is no need to determine the complete closed-loop frequency response, and the values of M_r and ω_r can be determined easily by using the open-loop frequency response and the constant M and N contours.

8.7.1 Constant *M* Circles

Let $G(s)$ be the open-loop transfer function. Since $s = \sigma + j\omega$ is complex, $G(s)$ is also complex.

Consider any point $G(j\omega) = x + jy$ on the polar plot of $G(j\omega)$. The closed-loop frequency response is

$$T(j\omega) = \frac{C(j\omega)}{R(j\omega)} = \frac{G(j\omega)}{1 + G(j\omega)} = \frac{x + jy}{1 + x + jy} = Me^{j\alpha} \tag{8.5}$$

From Eq. (8.5), the magnitude M is given by

$$M = \frac{|x + jy|}{|1 + x + jy|} = \left[\frac{x^2 + y^2}{(1 + x)^2 + y^2} \right]^{1/2} \tag{8.6}$$

Squaring both sides of Eq. (8.6), we get

$$M^2 = \frac{x^2 + y^2}{(1 + x)^2 + y^2} \tag{8.7}$$

Crossmultiplying and rearranging Eq. (8.7), we get

$$M^2(1 + x^2 + 2x + y^2) = x^2 + y^2$$

i.e.
$$y^2[M^2 - 1] + x^2(M^2 - 1) + 2xM^2 + M^2 = 0$$

i.e.
$$y^2 + \left[x^2 + 2x\frac{M^2}{M^2 - 1} + \left(\frac{M^2}{M^2 - 1} \right)^2 \right] = -\frac{M^2}{M^2 - 1} + \left(\frac{M^2}{M^2 - 1} \right)^2 = \left(\frac{M}{M^2 - 1} \right)^2$$

i.e.
$$[y]^2 + \left[x + \frac{M^2}{M^2 - 1} \right]^2 = \left[\frac{M}{M^2 - 1} \right]^2 \tag{8.8}$$

Equation (8.8) is the equation of a circle with centre at

$$x_0 = -\frac{M^2}{M^2 - 1}; \ y_0 = 0$$

and with radius

$$r_0 = \frac{M}{M^2 - 1}$$

Using the above information, constant M circles for various values of M can be drawn.

To determine the values of M_r and ω_r, superimpose the $G(j\omega)H(j\omega)$ plot on the constant M circles. The constant M circle tangential to the $G(j\omega)H(j\omega)$ plot gives the maximum value of M, i.e. M_r. The frequency at the tangential point gives the value of ω_r. Figure 8.25 shows three constant M circles and $G(j\omega)$ plot. Since M_2 circle is tangent to the $G(j\omega)$ plot at $\omega = \omega_2$, the maximum value of M is M_2, i.e. $M_r = M_2$ and $\omega_r = \omega_2$.

A family of constant M circles for different values of M is constructed in Figure 8.25.

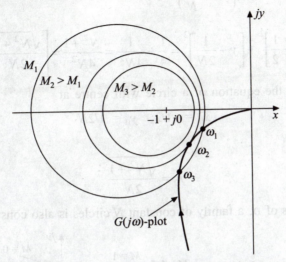

Figure 8.25 Constant-M circles and $G(j\omega)$-plot.

8.7.2 Constant N Circles

The closed-loop frequency response corresponding to any point $G(j\omega) = x + jy$ on the polar plot of $G(j\omega)$ is

$$T(j\omega) = \frac{C(j\omega)}{R(j\omega)} = \frac{G(j\omega)}{1 + G(j\omega)} = \frac{x + jy}{1 + x + jy} = Me^{j\alpha} \qquad (8.9)$$

The phase angle of $T(j\omega)$ is given by

$$\angle T(j\omega) = \alpha = \angle \left(\frac{x + jy}{1 + x + jy} \right)$$

$$= \tan^{-1} \frac{y}{x} - \tan^{-1} \frac{y}{1 + x} \qquad (8.10)$$

Taking the tangent on both sides of Eq. (8.10), we get

$$\tan \alpha = \frac{\dfrac{y}{x} - \dfrac{y}{1+x}}{1 + \dfrac{y}{x} \cdot \dfrac{y}{1+x}} = \frac{y}{x^2 + x + y^2} = N \qquad (8.11)$$

For a constant value of α, $N = \tan \alpha$ is also constant.

Crossmultiplying and rearranging Eq. (8.11), we get

$$y = x^2 N + xN + y^2 N$$

i.e.
$$(x^2 + x) + \left(y^2 - \frac{y}{N}\right) = 0$$

i.e.
$$\left[x + \frac{1}{2}\right]^2 + \left[y - \frac{1}{2N}\right]^2 = \frac{1}{4} + \frac{1}{4N^2} = \frac{N^2 + 1}{4N^2} = \left[\frac{\sqrt{N^2 + 1}}{2N}\right]^2 \qquad (8.12)$$

Equation (8.12) is the equation of a circle with centre at

$$x_0 = -1/2; \quad y_0 = 1/2N$$

and with radius

$$r_0 = \frac{\sqrt{N^2 + 1}}{2N}$$

For different values of α, a family of constant N circles is also constructed in Figure 8.26.

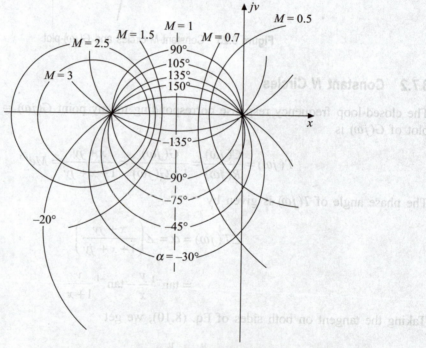

Figure 8.26 Constant-M and constant-N circles.

Since Eq. (8.12) for a circle is satisfied for $x = 0$, $y = 0$, and for $x = -1$, $y = 0$, all the constant N circles pass through the origin and $(-1 + j0)$ point regardless of the value of N.

Given the open-loop transfer function of a system $G(s)$, to obtain the closed-loop frequency response, first draw the polar plot of $G(s)$, superimpose it on the constant M and N circles, read the values of the magnitude M and phase angle α at various values of frequencies and with the data thus obtained plot the closed-loop frequency response curves, i.e. magnitude versus frequency and phase angle versus frequency curves.

8.8 THE NICHOLS CHART

We have seen earlier that the constant M and constant N contours on the polar plots are circles. Since it is easier to construct a Bode plot than a polar plot, it is preferable to have constant M and constant N contours constructed on logarithmic gain and phase coordinates. N.B. Nichols transformed the constant M and N circles to log magnitude and phase angle coordinates and the resulting chart is known as the *Nichols chart*.

Constant M and constant N contours repeat for every 360° interval and there is a symmetry at every 180° interval. Figure 8.27 shows a typical Nichols chart.

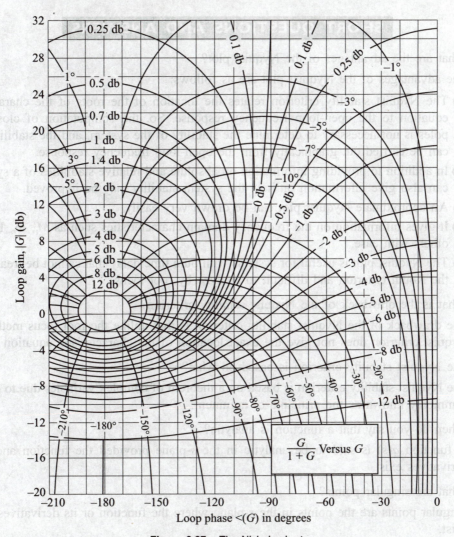

Figure 8.27 The Nichols chart.

The Nichols chart is very useful for determining the closed-loop frequency response from that of the open-loop. This is accomplished by superimposing the log magnitude versus phase angle plot of $G(j\omega)$ on the Nichols chart. The intersections of the log magnitude versus phase angle plot and constant M and N contours give the magnitude M and phase angle α of the closed-loop frequency response at different frequency points.

The determination of the value of open-loop gain K for specified M_r or GM or PM can be very conveniently carried on the Nichols chart. The closed-loop frequency response and bandwidth can be easily obtained from the Nichols chart.

SHORT QUESTIONS AND ANSWERS

1. What are the advantages of the Nyquist plot?

A. The advantages of the Nyquist plot are as follows:

(a) The Nyquist stability criterion relates the location of the roots of the characteristic equation to the open-loop frequency response. So, the computation of closed-loop poles is not necessary to determine the stability of the system, and the stability study can be carried out graphically from the open-loop frequency response.

(b) In addition to providing information on absolute and relative stabilities of a system, it can also give information on how the system stability may be improved.

(c) An approximate Nyquist plot can be drawn very easily.

(d) It gives information on the frequency-domain characteristics such as M_r, ω_r, BW, and others with ease.

(e) The Nyquist plot is useful for systems with pure time delay that cannot be treated with the Routh criterion and difficult to analyze by root locus.

2. What is the drawback of the Nyquist stability criterion?

A. The drawback of the Nyquist stability criterion is that unlike the root locus method, the Nyquist criterion does not give the exact location of the characteristic equation roots.

3. The Nyquist stability criterion is based on what?

A. The Nyquist stability criterion is based on a theorem of complex variables due to Cauchy, commonly known as the principle of argument.

4. When do you say that a function is analytic?

A. A function $q(s)$ is said to be analytic in the s-plane provided the function and all its derivatives exist.

5. What are singular points?

A. Singular points are the points in the s-plane where the function or its derivatives do not exist.

6. What do you mean by a region being enclosed?

A. A point or a region is said to be enclosed by a closed contour, if the point or region lies to the right of the path of traversal when the contour is traversed in the clockwise direction.

7. When do you say that a point or region is encircled?

A. A point or region is said to be encircled by a closed contour if it lies inside the closed path.

8. What is the principle of argument?

A. If there are P poles and Z zeros of $q(s)$ enclosed by the s-plane contour, then the corresponding $q(s)$-plane contour must encircle the origin of the $q(s)$-plane Z times in the clockwise direction and P times in the counterclockwise direction, resulting in a net encirclement of the origin, $(P\text{-}Z)$ times in the counterclockwise direction. This relation between the enclosure of poles and zeros of $q(s)$ by the s-plane contour and the encirclements of the origin by the $q(s)$-plane contour is commonly known as the principle of argument.

9. State the Nyquist stability criterion.

A. The Nyquist stability criterion states that if the contour Γ_{GH} of the open-loop transfer function $G(s)H(s)$ corresponding to the Nyquist contour in the s-plane encircles the point $(-1 + j0)$ in the counterclockwise direction as many times as the number of right half s-plane poles of $G(s)H(s)$, the closed-loop system is stable.

In the commonly occurring case of open-loop stable systems, the closed-loop system is stable if the contour Γ_{GH} of $G(s)H(s)$ does not encircle the $(-1 + j0)$ point, i.e. the net encirclement is zero.

10. The Nyquist plot is symmetrical about which axis?

A. The Nyquist plot is symmetrical about the real axis.

11. Why does the infinite arc of the Nyquist contour map into a point on the real axis of $q(s)$-plane?

A. In physical systems, usually $m < n$. Therefore, $G(s)H(s)$ for $\underset{R\to\infty}{s = Re^{j\phi}} = 0$.

Therefore, the infinite arc of Nyquist contour maps into a point on the real axis.

12. The infinitesimal semicircular indent at the origin of s-plane is mapped into what in $q(s)$-plane?

A. The infinitesimal semicircular indent around the origin of the s-plane maps into a semi-circular arc of infinite radius in $q(s)$-plane extending from $+90°$ through $0°$ to $-90°$.

13. What is the effect of addition of a pole at $s = 0$ to $G(s)H(s)$ on the Nyquist plot?

A. The addition of a pole at the origin to the loop transfer function rotates the Nyquist plot at zero and infinite frequencies by a further angle of $-90°$. In addition, the magnitude of $G(j\omega)H(j\omega)$ at $\omega = 0$ becomes infinite. The stability is adversely affected.

14. What is the effect of addition of a non zero pole to $G(s)H(s)$, on the Nyquist plot?

A. The addition of a non zero pole to the loop transfer function shifts the phase of the Nyquist plot by $-90°$ at $\omega = \infty$. The stability is adversely affected.

15. What is the effect of addition of a zero to $G(s)H(s)$ on the Nyquist plot?

A. The effect of addition of a zero to the loop transfer function is to rotate the high frequency portion of the Nyquist plot by 90° in the counterclockwise direction without affecting the value at $\omega = 0$. So, it has the affect of reducing the overshoot and the general affect of stabilization.

16. As the polar plot gets closer to the $(-1 + j0)$ point, what happens to stability?

A. As the polar plot gets closer to the $(-1 + j0)$ point, the relative stability reduces and the system tends towards instability.

17. In second-order systems how much is the gain margin?

A. In second-order systems, gain margin always remains fixed at infinite value.

18. In frequency-domain, what are the figures of merit of a system?

A. In frequency-domain, the figures of merit of a system are: resonance peak M_r, and resonant frequency ω_r.

19. To which systems, the concepts of gain margin and phase margin are valid?

A. The concepts of gain margin and phase margin are valid only for open-loop stable systems.

20. What are constant M circles?

A. The magnitude M of a closed-loop transfer function with unity feedback will be in the form of a circle in complex plane for each constant value of M. The family of these circles is called M circles.

21. What are constant N circles?

A. Let $N = \tan \alpha$, where α is the phase of the closed-loop transfer function with unity feedback. For each constant value of N, a circle can be drawn in the complex plane. The family of these circles is called N circles.

22. What is the advantage of constant M and N circles?

A. The advantage of constant M and N circles is that the closed-loop frequency response specifications can be determined directly from the open-loop frequency response using M and N circles.

23. How closed-loop frequency response is determined from open-loop frequency response using M and N circles?

A. The $G(j\omega)H(j\omega)$ locus i.e. the polar plot of the open-loop system is sketched on the standard M and N circles chart. The M circle to which the $G(j\omega)H(j\omega)$ locus is tangential is located. The value of M of that constant M circle gives the magnitude of the closed-loop system. The meeting point of the $G(j\omega)H(j\omega)$ locus with the N circle gives the value of phase of the closed-loop system.

24. What is Nichols chart?

A. The Nichols chart consists of constant M and N contours superimposed on ordinary graph. Along each constant M contour, the magnitude of the closed-loop system, M will be constant. Along each constant N contour, the phase angle α of the closed-loop system will be constant. The ordinary graph consists of magnitude in dB marked on *y*-axis and phase angle in degrees marked on *x*-axis. The Nichols chart is used to find the closed-loop frequency response from the open-loop frequency response.

25. How is the closed-loop frequency response determined from the open-loop frequency response using Nichols chart?

A. The $G(j\omega)H(j\omega)$ locus, i.e. the polar plot is sketched on the standard Nichols chart. The meeting point of $G(j\omega)H(j\omega)$ locus with constant M circle gives the magnitude of the closed-loop system and the meeting point with N circle gives the phase of the closed-loop system.

26. What are the advantages of the Nichols chart?

A. The advantages of Nichols chart are as follows:

1. It is used to find the closed-loop frequency response from the open-loop frequency response.
2. The gain of the system can be adjusted to satisfy the given specifications.
3. The frequency-domain specifications can be determined from Nichols chart.

REVIEW QUESTIONS

1. State and explain the Nyquist stability criterion.
2. Explain the following terms: enclosure, encirclement, principle of argument.
3. Write notes on constant M and N circles. Show that their loci are circles.
4. Write notes on Nichols chart.

FILL IN THE BLANKS

1. The Nyquist stability criterion relates the _____ to the open-loop frequency response.
2. The Nyquist stability criterion provides information on _____ stability as well as _____ stability of a system.
3. The Nyquist stability criterion does not give the *location* of the characteristic equation roots.
4. The Nyquist stability criterion is based on the *princ. of arg.*
5. A point is said to be enclosed by a closed contour if it lies _____ of the path of traversal.
6. The relation between the enclosure of poles and zeros of $q(s)$ by the *s*-plane contour and the encirclements of the origin by the $q(s)$ plane contour is commonly known as the

princ. of arg.

7. The Nyquist plot is symmetrical about the _____.

8. The points in the s-plane where the function or its derivatives do not exist are called *singular*.

9. A function is said to be *analytic* in the s-plane provided the function and all its derivatives exist at all points in the s-plane.

10. The infinitesimal semicircular indent at the origin of s-plane maps into a circle of *∞ rad.* in the $q(s)$ plane.

11. Addition of a pole at origin or a finite pole to $G(s)H(s)$ adversely affects the *stability* of a system.

12. Addition of a zero to $G(s)H(s)$ *improves* the stability of a system.

13. As the polar plot gets closer to the $(-1 + j0)$ point, the _____ reduces and the system tends towards _____.

14. Gain margin is the *reciprocal* between the actual gain and the critical gain.

15. Gain margin may be defined as the _____ of the magnitude of $G(s)H(s)$ at the phase crossover frequency.

16. In second-order systems, the gain margin is _____.

17. _____ and _____ are figures of merit in frequency-domain.

18. The damping ratio of a second-order system is 0.35. Its phase margin is approximately _____.

19. The phase margin of a second-order system is 25°. Its damping ratio is approximately _____.

20. The polar plot of a system intersects the negative real axis at $-a = -0.1$. The gain margin is _____.

21. The gain margin of a system has to be 30 dB. The polar plot of the system must intersect the negative real axis at $-a =$ _____.

22. The polar plot of a system passess through the $-1 + j0$ point of the $q(s)$-plane. The response is _____.

23. The polar plot of a system passess through the $-1 + j0$ point of the $q(s)$-plane. The gain margin of the system is _____ dB.

24. The polar plot of a system passess through the $-1 + j0$ point of the $q(s)$-plane. The phase margin of the system is _____.

25. A circular path along which the magnitude is constant is called a _____ circle.

26. A circular path along which the phase angle is constant is called a _____ circle.

27. The advantage of constant M and N circles is _____ response can be determined from the _____ response using them.

28. A Nichols chart consists of _____ superimposed on ordinary graph.

29. A Nichols chart is used to find the _____ response from the _____ response.

30. The _____ domain specifications can be determined from the Nichols chart.

OBJECTIVE TYPE QUESTIONS

1. A point lying inside the closed contour is said to be
   - (a) enclosed by it
   - (b) encircled by it
   - (c) closed by it
   - (d) none of these

2. A point or region lying to the right of the path of traversal when the closed contour is traversed in the clockwise direction is said to be
   - (a) enclosed by it
   - (b) encircled by it
   - (c) closed by it
   - (d) none of these

3. In $q(s)$-plane the Nyquist plot is symmetrical about the
   - (a) imaginary axis
   - (b) real axis
   - (c) origin
   - (d) none of these

4. The points in the s-plane where the function does not exist are called
   - (a) analytic points
   - (b) singular points
   - (c) non-existent points
   - (d) none of these

5. If the s-plane contour encloses 3 zeros and 2 poles of $q(s)$, the corresponding $q(s)$ plane contour will encircle the origin of $q(s)$ plane
   - (a) once in clockwise direction
   - (b) once in counterclockwise direction
   - (c) thrice in clockwise direction
   - (d) twice in counterclockwise direction

6. If the s-plane contour encloses 3 poles and 2 zeros of $q(s)$, the corresponding $q(s)$ plane contour will encircle the origin of $q(s)$ plane
   - (a) once in clockwise direction
   - (b) once in counterclockwise direction
   - (c) thrice in clockwise direction
   - (d) twice in counterclockwise direction

7. If the s-plane contour encloses 2 zeros and 2 poles of $q(s)$, the corresponding $q(s)$ plane contour will encircle the origin of $q(s)$ plane
   - (a) twice in clockwise direction
   - (b) twice in counterclockwise direction
   - (c) zero times
   - (d) four times

8. The Nyquist plot intersects the real axis at $-a = -2$, the gain margin is
   - (a) 2
   - (b) 1/2
   - (c) –2
   - (d) cannot be estimated

9. The Nyquist plot intersects the real axis at $-a = -0.02$, the gain margin is
   - (a) –0.02
   - (b) +0.02
   - (c) 50
   - d) cannot be estimated

10. The phase margin of a system is 40°. The damping ratio of the system ξ is approximately
    - (a) 0.04
    - (b) 0.4
    - (c) 4
    - (d) cannot be estimated

11. For a GM of 20 dB, the Nyquist plot should intersect the real axis at $-a$ where a =
    (a) 0.1   (b) 1
    (c) 10   (d) 20

12. The polar plot touches the negative real axis only at the origin. The gain margin is
    (a) 0   (b) ∞
    (c) negative   (d) finite positive value

13. The damping ratio of a second-order system is 0.2. Its phase margin is approximately
    (a) 0.4°   (b) 2°
    (c) 20°   (d) 40°

14. The open-loop transfer function of a second-order system is $G(s)H(s) = 20/(s + 1)(s + 10)$. Its gain margin is
    (a) 0 dB   (b) 20 dB
    (c) ∞ dB   (d) 2 dB

15. A polar plot intersects the unit circle at $(-1 + j0)$. The gain margin of the system is
    (a) –1 dB   (b) 0 dB
    (c) ∞ dB   (d) cannot be estimated

16. A polar plot crosses the real axis at $(-1 + j0)$ point. The phase margin of the system is
    (a) –1°   (b) 0°
    (c) –180°   (d) +180°

17. A polar plot intersects the unit circle at a point making an angle of $-45°$ with the negative real axis. The phase margin of the system is
    (a) –45°   (b) 45°
    (c) –180° – 45°   (d) –180° + 45°

18. All the constant N circles pass through
    (a) only origin   (b) only $(-1 + j0)$ point
    (c) both origin and $(-1 + j0)$ point   (d) none of these

19. As the polar plot gets closer to the $(-1 + j0)$ point, the stability of the system is
    (a) improved   (b) reduced
    (c) not affected   (d) none of these

20. In second-order systems, the gain margin is a constant at
    (a) zero value   (b) finite value
    (c) infinite value   (d) none of these

21. Because of the addition of a pole to $G(s)H(s)$, the stability of the system is
    (a) improved   (b) reduced
    (c) not affected   (d) none of these

22. Because of the addition of a zero to $G(s)H(s)$, the stability of the system is
    (a) improved   (b) reduced
    (c) not affected   (d) none of these

23. The parameter which is constant along the constant M circles is
    (a) frequency
    (b) phase angle
    (c) magnitude
    (d) open-loop gain

24. The parameter which is constant along the constant N circles is
    (a) frequency
    (b) phase angle
    (c) magnitude
    (d) open-loop gain

25. The Nichols chart can be used to determine
    (a) transient response
    (b) time response
    (c) closed-loop frequency response
    (d) open-loop frequency response

PROBLEMS

8.1 By using the Nyquist stability criterion, determine whether the closed-loop systems having the following open-loop transfer functions are stable or not. If not, how many closed-loop poles lie in the right half s-plane?

(a) $G(s)H(s) = \dfrac{1}{s^2 + 100}$

(b) $G(s)H(s) = \dfrac{1}{s(1+s)(1+4s)}$

(c) $G(s)H(s) = \dfrac{1}{s^2(1+2s)(1+8s)}$

8.2 Sketch the Nyquist plot for a system with the open-loop transfer function given below and assess the stability of the system.

$$G(s)H(s) = \frac{K(1+0.5s)(1+2s)}{(1+16s)(s-2)}$$

8.3 Draw the Nyquist plot and assess the stability of the closed-loop system whose open-loop transfer function is

$$G(s)H(s) = \frac{s+6}{(s+2)(s+2)}$$

8.4 Sketch the Nyquist plot and comment on the stability of the closed-loop system whose open-loop transfer function is

$$G(s)H(s) = \frac{K(s+4)}{s(s-2)}$$

8.5 Sketch the Nyquist plot and assess the stability of the closed-loop system whose open-loop transfer function is

$$G(s)H(s) = \frac{K(s-6)}{(s+2)^2}$$

8.6 Sketch the Nyquist plot and there from assess the stability of the closed-loop system whose open-loop transfer function is

$$G(s)H(s) = \frac{K(s+6)}{s^2(s+2)}$$

8.7 Sketch the Nyquist plot and determine there from the stability of the following feedback control system with

$$G(s)H(s) = \frac{K}{s(s^2 + 2s + 6)}$$

8.8 Sketch the inverse polar plot and there from assess the stability of a control system with an open-loop transfer function

$$G(s)H(s) = \frac{K}{s(1+2s)}$$

8.9 The open-loop transfer function of a unity feedback system is

$$G(s)H(s) = \frac{K}{s(1+0.5s)(1+0.02s)}$$

(a) Determine the value of K so that GM is 20 dB.
(b) Determine the value of K so that PM is 30°.

8.10 Determine the gain crossover frequency, phase crossover frequency, gain margin, and phase margin of a system with the open-loop transfer function, and comment on the stability of the system.

$$G(s)H(s) = \frac{1}{s(1+s)(1+4s)}$$

[**Note:** The Nyquist plots for the above problems 8.1 to 8.8 obtained using Matlab Programs are given below.]

MATLAB PROGRAMS

PROGRAM 8.1

Matlab program for Nyquist plot for the open-loop transfer function

$$G(s)H(s) = \frac{1}{s^2 + 100}$$

```
% Nyquist plot
clc;clear all;close all;
s=tf('s');
GH=1/(s^2+100)
nyquist(GH)
grid on;
```

Output:

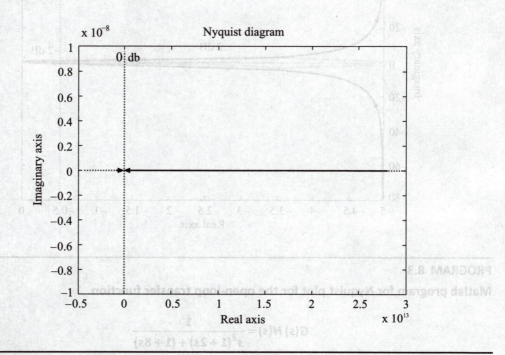

Nyquist diagram

PROGRAM 8.2

Matlab program for Nyquist plot for the open-loop transfer function

$$G(s)\,H(s) = \frac{1}{s(1+s) + (1+4s)}$$

```
% Nyquist plot
clc;clear all;close all;
s=tf('s');
GH=1/(s*(1+s)*(1+4*s))
nyquist(GH)
grid on;
```

Output:

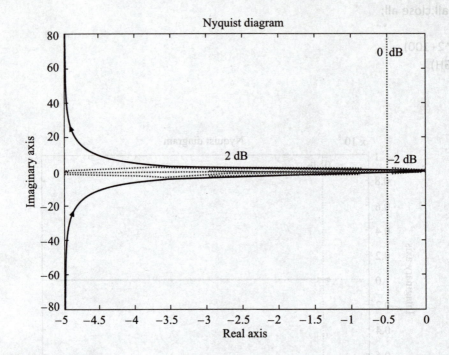

Nyquist diagram

PROGRAM 8.3

Matlab program for Nyquist plot for the open-loop transfer function

$$G(s)\,H(s) = \frac{1}{s^2(1+2s)+(1+8s)}$$

```
% Nyquist plot
clc;clear all;close all;
s=tf('s');
GH=1/((s^2)*(1+2*s)*(1+8*s))
nyquist(GH)
grid on;
```

Output:

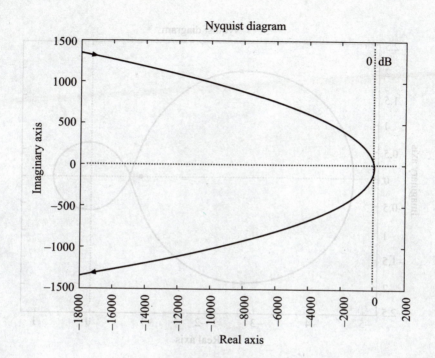

PROGRAM 8.4

Matlab program for Nyquist plot for the open-loop transfer function

$$G(s)\,H(s) = \frac{K(1+0.5s)\,(1+2s)}{(1+16s)+(s-2)}$$

```
% Nyquist plot
clc;clear all;close all;
K=10;
s=tf('s');
GH=(K*(1+0.5*s)*(1+2*s))/((1+16*s)*(s-2))
nyquist(GH)
axis equal;
```

Output:

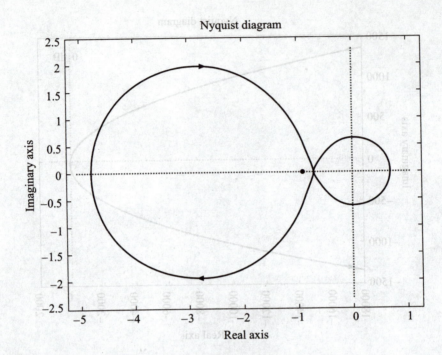

Nyquist diagram

PROGRAM 8.5

Matlab program for Nyquist plot for the open-loop transfer function

$$G(s)\,H(s) = \frac{s+6}{(s+2)\,(s+2)}$$

```
% Nyquist plot
clc;clear all;close all;
s=tf('s');
GH=(s+6)/((s+2)*(s+2))
nyquist(GH)
%grid on;
```

Output:

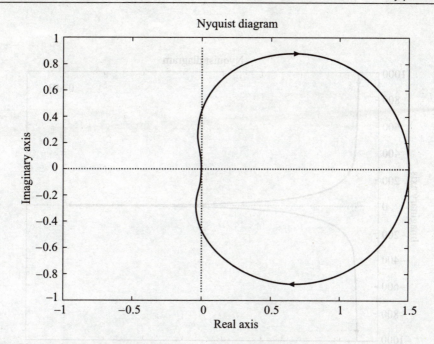

Nyquist diagram

PROGRAM 8.6

Matlab program for Nyquist plot for the open-loop transfer function

$$G(s)\,H(s) = \frac{K\,(s+4)}{s\,(s-2)}$$

```
% Nyquist plot
clc;clear all;close all;
s=tf('s');
K=50;
GH=(K*(s+4))/(s*(s-2))
nyquist(GH)
grid on;
```

Output:

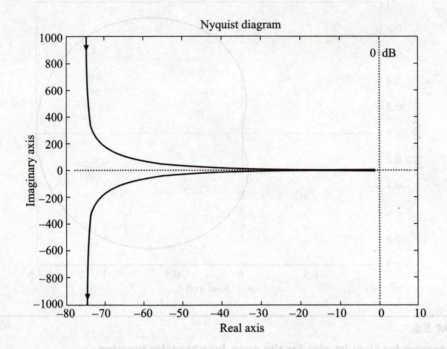

PROGRAM 8.7

Matlab program for Nyquist plot for the open-loop transfer function

$$G(s)\,H(s) = \frac{K(s-6)}{(s+2)^2}$$

```
% Nyquist plot
clc;clear all;close all;
s=tf('s');
K=10;
GH=(K*(s-6))/((s+2)^2)
nyquist(GH)
%grid on;
```

Output:

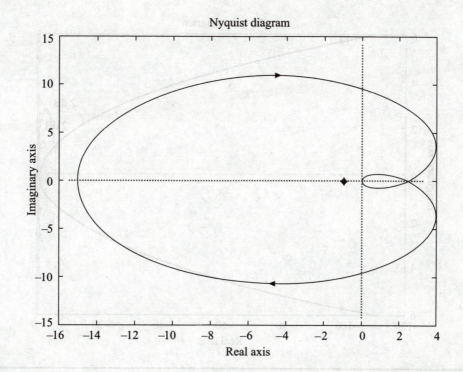

Nyquist diagram

PROGRAM 8.8

Matlab program for Nyquist plot for the open-loop transfer function

$$G(s)\,H(s) = \frac{K(s+6)}{s^2(s+2)}$$

```
% Nyquist plot
clc;clear all;close all;
s=tf('s');
K=1;
GH=(K*(s+6))/((s+2)*(s^2))
nyquist(GH)
grid on;
```

Output:

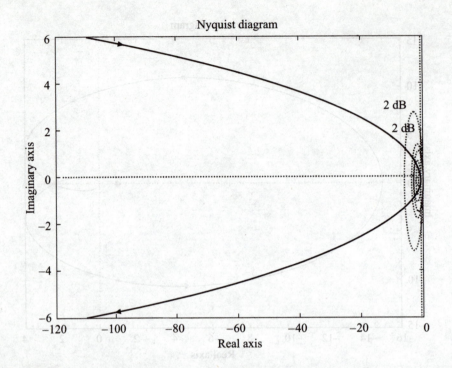

Nyquist diagram

PROGRAM 8.9

Matlab program for Nyquist plot for the open-loop transfer function

$$G(s)\,H(s) = \frac{K}{s(s^2 + 2s + 6)}$$

```
% Nyquist plot
clc;clear all;close all;
s=tf('s');
K=50;
GH=K/(s*(s^2+2*s+6))
nyquist(GH)
%grid on;
```

Output:

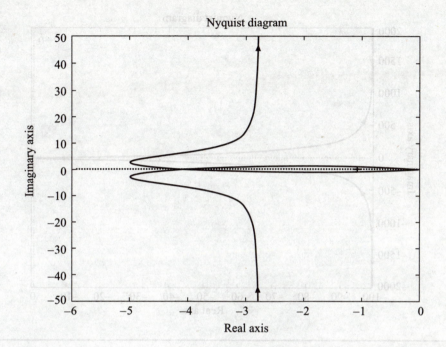

Nyquist diagram

PROGRAM 8.10

Matlab program for Nyquist plot for the open-loop transfer function

$$G(s)\,H(s) = \frac{K}{s(1+2s)}$$

```
% Nyquist plot
clc;clear all;close all;
s=tf('s');
K=50;
GH=K/(s*(1+2*s))
nyquist(GH)
grid on;
```

Output:

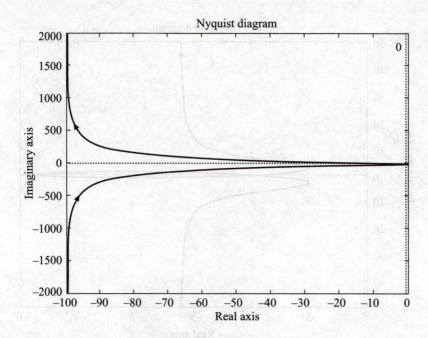

Nyquist diagram

PROGRAM 8.11

Matlab program for Nyquist plot for the open-loop transfer function

$$G(s)\,H(s) = \frac{K}{s(1+0.5s)\,(1+0.02s)}$$

```
% Nyquist plot
clc;clear all;close all;
K=10;
s=tf('s');
GH=K/(s*(1+0.5*s)*(1+0.02*s))
nyquist(GH)
[Gm, pm, wcp, wcg] = margin (GH);
disp('Gain Margin is')
disp(Gm)
disp('Phase Margin is')
disp(pm)
disp('Phase crossover frequency is')
disp(wcp)
disp('Gain crossover frequency is')
disp(wcg)
%grid on;
```

Output:

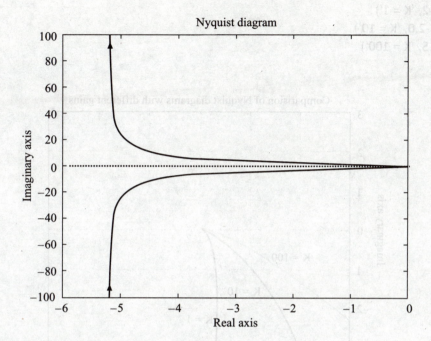

Nyquist diagram

PROGRAM 8.12

Matlab program for comparision of Nyquist plots for different gains K to the open-loop transfer function

$$G(s)\,H(s) = \frac{K(s+3)}{(s^3 + 8s + 7s)}$$

```
% nyquist plot
% comparision of nyquist plots for different gains K
clc;clear all;close all;
num = [1 3];
den = [1 8 7 0];
w = 0.1:0.1:100;
[re1, im1, w] = nyquist(num, den, w);
[re2, im2, w] = nyquist(10*num, den, w);
[re3,im3,w] = nyquist(100*num, den, w);
plot(re1, im1, re2, im2, re3, im3)
v = [-3 3 -3 3]; axis(v)
grid on;
title('comparision of Nyquist diagrams with different gains')
xlabel('Real axis')
```

ylabel('Imaginary axis')
text(-0.2, -2, 'K = 1')
text(-1.5, -2.0, 'K = 10')
text(-2, -1.5, 'K = 100')

Output:

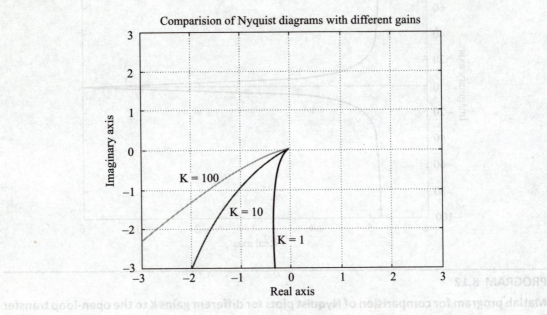

Comparision of Nyquist diagrams with different gains

Compensation

9.1 INTRODUCTION

Compensators are corrective sub-systems introduced into the system to compensate for the deficiency in the performance of the plant. So given a plant and a set of specifications, suitable compensators are to be designed so that the overall system will meet the given specifications.

Proper selection of performance specifications is the most important step in the design of compensators. The desired behaviour of a system is specified in terms of transient response measures and the steady-state error. The steady-state error of a system is usually specified in terms of error constants K_p, K_v and K_a for specific inputs, i.e. for step, ramp and parabolic inputs, but the transient response measures of relative stability and speed of response may be specified in time or frequency-domain or even in both. In time-domain, the measure of relative stability is damping ratio ξ or peak overshoot M_p, while the speed of response is measured in terms of rise time, settling time or undamped natural frequency. On the other hand, in frequency-domain, the measure of relative stability is resonant peak M_r or phase margin ϕ_{pm} while the measure of speed of response is resonant frequency ω_r or bandwidth ω_b.

Once a set of performance specifications have been selected, the next step is to choose the compensator. Usually electrical compensators are preferred, eventhough mechanical, pneumatic, hydraulic or other types can be used. The compensation may be cascade or series compensation (in this, the compensator transfer function is placed in series with the plant transfer function) or feedback or parallel compensation (in this, the compensator transfer function is placed in the feedback path) as shown in Figure 9.1 (a) and Figure (b).

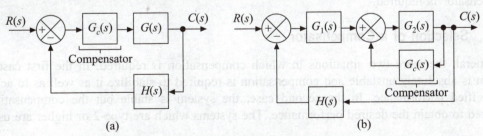

Figure 9.1 (a) Cascade compensation and (b) feedback compensation.

9.2 TYPES OF COMPENSATORS

Basically there are three types of compensators:

1. Lead compensator
2. Lag compensator
3. Lag-lead compensator

The compensator having a transfer function of the form

$$G_c(s) = \frac{s+z_c}{s+p_c} = \frac{s+1/\tau}{s+1/\alpha\tau}; \alpha = \frac{z_c}{p_c} < 1, \tau > 0$$

is known as a *lead compensator*. For this, the pole is located to the left of a zero.

A lead compensator speeds up the transient response and increases the margin of stability of a system. It also helps to increase the system error constant though to a limited range.

The compensator having a transfer function of the form

$$G_c(s) = \frac{s+z_c}{s+p_c} = \frac{s+1/\tau}{s+1/\beta\tau}; \beta = \frac{z_c}{p_c} > 1, \tau > 0$$

is known as a *lag compensator*. For this, the pole is located to the right of a zero, i.e. nearer to the origin than zero.

A lag compensator improves the steady-state behaviour of a system, while nearly preserving its transient response. This compensation scheme therefore is found useful in systems having satisfactory transient response but unsatisfactory steady-state response.

The compensator having a transfer function of the form

$$G_c(s) = \left(\frac{s+z_{c1}}{s+p_{c1}}\right)\left(\frac{s+z_{c2}}{s+p_{c2}}\right) = \left(\frac{s+1/\tau_1}{s+1/\alpha\tau_1}\right)\left(\frac{s+1/\tau_2}{s+1/\beta\tau_2}\right); \beta > 1, \alpha < 1, \tau_1 > 0, \tau_2 > 0$$

is known as a *lag-lead compensator*. It is a combination of a lag compensator and a lead compensator connected in series.

The lead compensator is suitable for systems having unsatisfactory transient response, but it provides only a limited improvement in steady-state response. If the steady-state behaviour is highly unsatisfactory, the lead compensator may not be the right choice. On the other hand for systems with satisfactory transient response but unsatisfactory steady-state response, the lag compensator is preferred.

When both the transient and steady-state responses required improvement, a lag-lead compensator is required.

9.2.1 Selection of a Compensator

In general, there are two situations in which compensation is required. In the first case, the system is absolutely unstable and compensation is required to stabilize it as well as to achieve a specified performance. In the second case, the system is stable but the compensation is required to obtain the desired performance. The systems which are type-2 or higher are usually absolutely unstable. For these types of systems, clearly lead compensation is required because only the lead compensator increases the margin of stability. In the type-1 and type-0 systems, stable operation is always possible, if the gain is sufficiently reduced. In such cases, any of the three compensators, viz. lag, lead and lag-lead may be used to obtain the desired performance.

9.3 REALIZATION OF BASIC COMPENSATORS

The compensators discussed earlier, i.e. the lag compensator, the lead compensator and the lag-lead compensator may be realized by many types of components like electrical, mechanical, pneumatic, hydraulic, etc. The choice of the type of components to be used depends upon the system structure. Realization by electrical components is quite common in many control systems. So, we discuss here electric network realization of basic compensators and their frequency characteristics.

9.3.1 Lead Compensator

The pole-zero representation of the lead compensator is shown in Figure 9.2. It has a zero at $s = -1/\tau$ and a pole at $s = -1/\alpha\tau$ with the zero closer to the origin than the pole. The general form of the lead compensator is

$$G_c(s) = \frac{s + z_c}{s + p_c} = \frac{(s + 1/\tau)}{(s + 1/\alpha\tau)}; \quad \alpha = z_c/p_c < 1, \tau > 0$$

$$= \alpha\left(\frac{1 + \tau s}{1 + \alpha\tau s}\right)$$

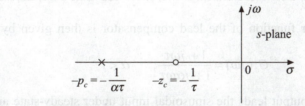

Figure 9.2 The pole-zero plot of lead compensator.

The lead compensator mentioned above can be realized by an electric lead network shown in Figure 9.3(a). Assuming the impedance of the source to be zero and the output load impedance to be infinite, the transfer function of the lead network is

$$\frac{E_o(s)}{E_i(s)} = \frac{R_2}{R_2 + R_1 \parallel \dfrac{1}{Cs}} = \frac{R_2}{R_2 + \dfrac{R_1/Cs}{R_1 + 1/Cs}} = \frac{s + 1/R_1C}{s + \dfrac{1}{\left[R_2/(R_1 + R_2)\right]R_1C}}$$

Defining

$$\tau = R_1 C \text{ and } \alpha = \frac{R_2}{(R_1 + R_2)} < 1$$

$$\frac{E_o(s)}{E_i(s)} = \frac{s + 1/\tau}{s + 1/\alpha\tau}$$

In the compensator design, the three network components R_1, R_2 and C are to be determined from the two lead compensator parameters α and τ.

The sinusoidal transfer function of the lead network is

$$G_c(j\omega) = \alpha\left(\frac{1 + j\omega\tau}{1 + j\omega\alpha\tau}\right); \quad \alpha < 1$$

At zero frequency, the network has a gain of $\alpha < 1$, or an attenuation of $1/\alpha$. The dc attenuation of the network can be compensated by cascading it with an amplifier of gain $A = 1/\alpha$. So the lead compensator may be treated as a combination of a network and an amplifier as shown in Figure 9.3(b).

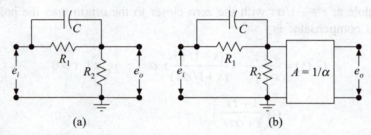

(a)   (b)

Figure 9.3 (a) Electric lead network and (b) phase-lead network with amplifier.

The sinusoidal transfer function of the lead compensator is then given by

$$G_c(j\omega) = \frac{1 + j\omega\tau}{1 + j\alpha\omega\tau}; \quad \alpha < 1$$

Since $\alpha < 1$, the network output leads the sinusoidal input under steady-state and hence this is called a lead compensator.

The Bode diagram of the lead compensator is shown in Figure 9.4.

The phase-lead of the above compensator at any frequency ω is given by

$$\phi = \tan^{-1}\omega\tau - \tan^{-1}\alpha\omega\tau$$

or

$$\tan\phi = \frac{\omega\tau - \alpha\omega\tau}{1 + \omega\tau \cdot \alpha\omega\tau} = \frac{\omega\tau(1 - \alpha)}{1 + \alpha\omega^2\tau^2}$$

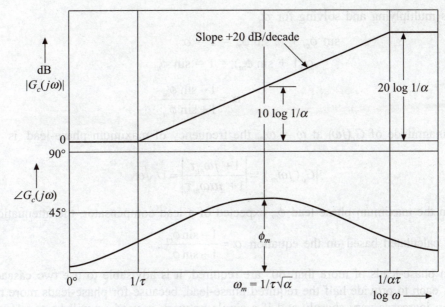

Figure 9.4 Bode plot of phase-lead network with amplifier of gain $A = 1/\alpha$.

The frequency at which maximum phase-lead occurs ω_m is given by the solution of $\dfrac{d\phi}{d\omega} = 0$, i.e.

$$\frac{d}{d\omega}\left(\frac{\omega\tau(1-\alpha)}{1+\alpha\omega^2\tau^2}\right) = 0$$

i.e.

$$(1 + \alpha\omega^2\tau^2)(1 - \alpha)\tau - \omega\tau(1 - \alpha)(2\alpha\omega\tau^2) = 0$$

or

$$\omega = \frac{1}{\sqrt{\alpha}\tau}$$

i.e.

$$\omega_m = \frac{1}{\tau\sqrt{\alpha}} = \sqrt{(1/\tau)(1/\alpha\tau)}$$

So, ω_m is the geometric mean of the two corner frequencies of the compensator. At $\omega = \omega_m$, the maximum phase-lead ϕ_m is given by

$$\tan\phi_m = \frac{\omega_m\tau(1-\alpha)}{1+\alpha\omega_m^{\,2}\tau^2} = \frac{\dfrac{1}{\tau\sqrt{\alpha}}\cdot\tau\cdot(1-\alpha)}{1+\alpha\cdot\dfrac{1}{\tau^2\alpha}\cdot\tau^2} = (1-\alpha)/2\sqrt{\alpha}$$

or

$$\sin\phi_m = \frac{1-\alpha}{1+\alpha}$$

Cross multiplying and solving for α,

$$\sin \phi_m + \alpha \sin \phi_m = 1 - \alpha$$

$$\alpha(1 + \sin \phi_m) = 1 - \sin \phi_m$$

i.e.

$$\alpha = \frac{1 - \sin \phi_m}{1 + \sin \phi_m}$$

The magnitude of $G_c(j\omega)$ at $\omega = \omega_m$, the frequency of maximum phase-lead, is

$$\left| G_c(j\omega_m) \right| = \left| \frac{1 + j\omega_m \tau}{1 + j\alpha\omega_m \tau} \right| = 1/\sqrt{\alpha}$$

Given the maximum phase-lead ϕ_m expected of a lead compensator, the attenuation factor α can be calculated based on the equation $\alpha = \dfrac{1 - \sin \phi_m}{1 + \sin \phi_m}$.

When phase-leads of more than 60° are required, it is advisable to use two cascaded lead networks, each to provide half the required phase-lead, because for phase-leads more than 60°, attenuation increases very sharply and if a single network is used, α will be too low.

The choice of α is also governed by the inherent noise in control systems. The nature of this noise is that, the noise signal frequencies are higher than control signal frequencies. In a lead network, the high frequency noise signals are amplified by a factor $1/\alpha > 1$, while the low frequency control signals undergo unit amplification. Thus, the signal to noise ratio at the output of the lead compensator is poorer than at its input. To prevent the signal/noise ratio at the output from deteriorating excessively, the value of α should not be less than 0.07. A common choice is $\alpha = 0.1$.

9.3.2   Lag Compensator

The pole-zero representation of the lag compensator is shown in Figure 9.5(a). It has a pole at $-1/\beta\tau$ and a zero at $-1/\tau$ with the pole located nearer to the origin on the negative real axis. The general form of the transfer function of the lag compensator is

$$G_c(s) = \frac{(s + z_c)}{(s + p_c)} = \frac{s + 1/\tau}{s + 1/\beta\tau}; \quad \beta = \frac{z_c}{p_c} > 1, \quad \tau > 0$$

The electric phase-lag network is shown in Figure 9.5(b). The transfer function of the lag compensator is

$$\frac{E_o(s)}{E_i(s)} = \frac{R_2 + 1/Cs}{R_1 + R_2 + 1/Cs} = \frac{1}{\dfrac{R_1 + R_2}{R_2}} \left[\frac{s + (1/R_2 C)}{s + \dfrac{1}{\left(\dfrac{R_1 + R_2}{R_2}\right) R_2 C}} \right]$$

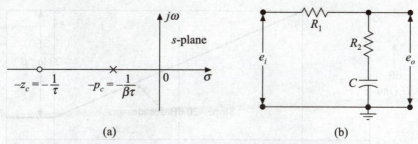

Figure 9.5 (a) The pole-zero plot of lag compensator and (b) electric lag network.

Comparing this transfer function with $G_c(s)$, we get

$$\tau = R_2C, \qquad \beta = (R_1 + R_2)/R_2 > 1$$

Therefore, the transfer function of the network becomes

$$G_c(s) = \frac{1}{\beta}\left(\frac{s+1/\tau}{s+1/\beta\tau}\right) = \frac{1}{\beta}\left(\frac{s+z_c}{s+p_c}\right); \quad \beta = z_c/p_c > 1$$

$$= \frac{1+\tau s}{1+\beta\tau s}$$

The sinusoidal transfer function of the lag network is given by

$$G_c(j\omega) = \frac{1+j\omega\tau}{1+j\beta\omega\tau}$$

Since $\beta > 1$, the steady-state output has a lagging phase angle with respect to the sinusoidal input and hence the name lag network. The Bode diagram of the lag network is drawn in Figure 9.6. The maximum phase-lag ϕ_m and the corresponding frequency ω_m are given by

$$\omega_m = \sqrt{\frac{1}{\tau}\cdot\frac{1}{\beta\tau}}$$

$$\phi_m = \sin^{-1}\left(\frac{1-\beta}{1+\beta}\right)$$

From Figure 9.6, we can see that the lag network has a dc gain of unity while it offers a high frequency gain of $1/\beta$. Since $\beta > 1$, it means that the high frequency noise is attenuated in passing through the network whereby the signal to noise ratio is improved, in contrast to the lead network. A typical choice of β is 10.

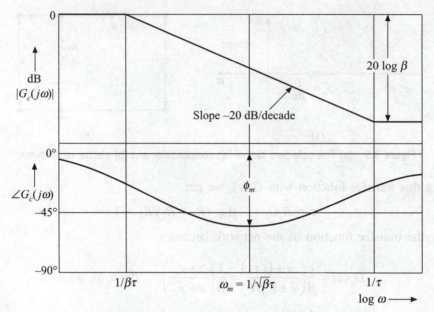

Figure 9.6 Bode plot of phase-lag network.

9.3.3 Lag-Lead Compensator

The lag-lead compensator is a combination of a lag compensator and a lead compensator. The lag-section has one real pole and one real zero with the pole to the right of the zero. The lead-section also has one real pole and one real zero but the zero is to the right of the pole. The pole-zero representation of the lag-lead compensator is shown in Figure 9.7(a). The general form of this compensator is

$$G_c(s) = \underbrace{\left(\frac{s+1/\tau_1}{s+1/\beta\tau_1}\right)}_{\text{Lag section}}\underbrace{\left(\frac{s+1/\tau_2}{s+1/\alpha\tau_2}\right)}_{\text{Lead section}}; \quad \beta > 1, \alpha < 1, \tau_1 > 0, \tau_2 > 0$$

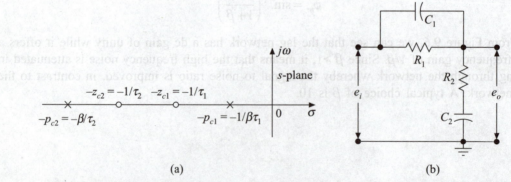

(a) (b)

Figure 9.7 (a) The pole-zero plot of lag-lead compensator and (b) electric lag-lead network.

This equation for $G_c(s)$ can be realized by a single electric lag-lead network shown in Figure 9.7(b). From this figure, the transfer function of the lag-lead network is given by

$$\frac{E_o(s)}{E_i(s)} = \frac{R_2 + 1/C_2 s}{R_2 + 1/C_2 s + \dfrac{R_1/C_1 s}{R_1 + 1/C_1 s}} = \frac{(R_2 C_2 s + 1)/C_2 s}{\dfrac{R_2 C_2 s + 1}{C_2 s} + \dfrac{R_1}{R_1 C_1 s + 1}}$$

$$= \frac{(R_2 C_2 s + 1)(R_1 C_1 s + 1)}{R_1 C_1 s + 1 + R_1 R_2 C_1 C_2 s^2 + R_2 C_2 s + R_1 C_2 s}$$

$$= \frac{\left(s + \dfrac{1}{R_1 C_1}\right)\left(s + \dfrac{1}{R_2 C_2}\right) R_1 C_1 R_2 C_2}{R_1 R_2 C_1 C_2 \left[s^2 + \left(\dfrac{1}{R_1 C_1} + \dfrac{1}{R_2 C_2} + \dfrac{1}{R_2 C_1}\right) s + \dfrac{1}{R_1 R_2 C_1 C_2}\right]}$$

Comparing the above two equations for $G_c(s)$ and $E_o(s)/E_i(s)$, we have

$$R_1 C_1 = \tau_1$$

$$R_2 C_2 = \tau_2$$

$$R_1 R_2 C_1 C_2 = \alpha\beta\tau_1\tau_2$$

$$\frac{1}{R_1 C_1} + \frac{1}{R_2 C_1} + \frac{1}{R_2 C_2} = \frac{1}{\beta\tau_1} + \frac{1}{\alpha\tau_2}$$

From the above equations it is found that

$$\alpha\beta = 1$$

It means that a single lag-lead network does not permit us an independent choice of α and β. Keeping this in view, the transfer function of a lag-lead compensator may be written as

$$G_c(s) = \frac{(s + 1/\tau_1)(s + 1/\tau_2)}{(s + 1/\beta\tau_1)(s + \beta/\tau_2)}; \quad \beta > 1$$

$$= \left(\frac{s + z_{c1}}{s + p_{c1}}\right)\left(\frac{s + z_{c2}}{s + p_{c2}}\right); \quad \beta = z_{c1}/p_{c1} = p_{c2}/z_{c2} > 1$$

where $\tau_1 = R_1 C_1$, $\tau_2 = R_2 C_2$ and $\beta > 1$ such that

$$\frac{1}{R_1 C_1} + \frac{1}{R_2 C_1} + \frac{1}{R_2 C_2} = \frac{1}{\beta\tau_1} + \frac{\beta}{\tau_2}$$

The sinusoidal transfer function of a lag-lead compensator is given by

$$G_c(j\omega) = \frac{(1 + j\omega\tau_1)(1 + j\omega\tau_2)}{(1 + j\omega\beta\tau_1)(1 + j\omega\tau_2/\beta)}$$

The corresponding Bode plot is shown in Figure 9.8.

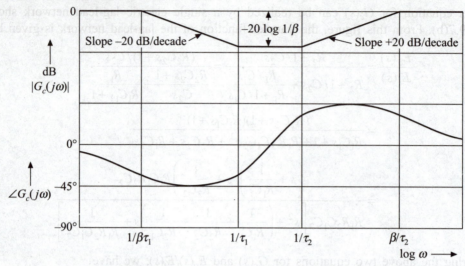

Figure 9.8 Bode plot of lag-lead network.

9.4 CASCADE COMPENSATION IN FREQUENCY-DOMAIN

Compensation design can be carried out in time-domain or frequency-domain. The specifications in time-domain are generally given in the following form:

1. Damping ratio ξ
2. Peak overshoot M_p—indicative of the relative stability
3. Undamped natural frequency ω_n
4. Rise time t_r or settling time t_s—indicative of speed of response
5. Error constant e_{ss}—indicative of steady-state error

Frequency-domain specifications are generally given in the following form.

1. Phase margin ϕ_{pm} or resonant peak M_r—indicative of relative stability
2. Bandwidth ω_b or resonant frequency ω_r—indicative of rise time and settling time
3. Error constant indicative of steady-state error

The design in time-domain is carried out using the root locus and the design in frequency-domain is carried out using the Nyquist plots, Bode plots, or Nichols chart. Design in time-domain is tedious. So, usually the given time-domain specifications are first converted into frequency-domain specifications using second-order correlations between time and frequency responses, the design and compensation is carried out in frequency-domain and then the results are converted back into time-domain. These correlations are valid approximations for higher-order systems.

The time response is checked with these specifications and if required, the complete design process may be repeated.

The correlations discussed earlier are as follows:

$$M_r = \frac{1}{2\xi\sqrt{1-\xi^2}}$$

$$\omega_r = \omega_n \sqrt{1 - 2\xi^2}$$

$$\phi_{pm} = \tan^{-1}\left\{ 2\xi / \left[\sqrt{(1+4\xi^4)} - 2\xi^2 \right]^{1/2} \right\}$$

$$\omega_b = \omega_n \left[1 - 2\xi^2 + \sqrt{(2 - 4\xi^2 + 4\xi^4)} \right]^{1/2}$$

The specifications in terms of M_r and ω_r are convenient for compensation using the Nyquist plots. When phase margin is specified, the Bode plots are more convenient. Gain crossover frequency ω_g can be used as a rough measure of bandwidth ω_b. When the Nichols charts are used any type of specification can be handled.

The advantages of frequency-domain compensation are as follows:

1. Simplicity in analysis and design
2. Ease in experimental determination of frequency response for real systems

The disadvantage of frequency-domain compensation is that direct control on system performance is lost.

Eventhough frequency-domain compensation can be carried out using the Nyquist plots, Bode plots or Nichols chart, the compensation is normally carried out by using the Bode plots because of the following:

1. The Bode plots are easier to draw and modify.
2. The gain adjustment can be conveniently carried out using the Bode plots.
3. The error constants are always clearly in evidence when the Bode plots are used. Of course the Nichols charts can be used to check the values of M_r, ω_n, and ω_b wherever necessary.

9.4.1 Lead Compensation

The lead compensator is basically a high-pass filter. The design procedure for a lead compensator given below is quite general and applies to any type and order of a system.

Step 1. Adjust the system error constant to the desired value. Determine the open-loop gain K required to satisfy the specified error constant.

Step 2. Using this value of K draw the magnitude and phase Bode plots and determine the phase margin ϕ_{pm1} and gain crossover frequency ω_{g1} of the uncompensated system. If the phase margin of the uncompensated system ϕ_{pm1} is not satisfactory, proceed with the following steps to design a lead compensator.

Step 3. Determine the phase-lead ϕ_l required using the relation

$$\phi_l = \phi_s - \phi_{pm1} + \epsilon$$

where ϕ_s is the required (specified) phase margin, ϕ_{pm1} is the phase margin of the fixed part of the system (i.e. the uncompensated system); and $\in$ is a margin of safety. (It is required by the fact that the gain crossover frequency will increase due to compensation and so the phase margin of the fixed part of the system reduces at the new gain crossover frequency. The value of $\in$ may be guessed as $\in = 5°$ if the slope of the magnitude plot of the uncompensated system in the region near the gain crossover frequency is -40 dB/decade and it may be guessed as $15°$ to $20°$ if the slope is -60 dB/decade.)

Step 4. Let $\phi_m = \phi_l$ and determine the α parameter of the network using the formula

$$\alpha = \frac{1 - \sin \phi_m}{1 + \sin \phi_m}$$

If the required ϕ_m is more than $60°$, it is recommended to use two identical networks each contributing a maximum lead of $\phi_l/2$.

(It is because in order to provide a phase-lead of ϕ_l at the new gain crossover frequency ω_{g2} with the largest value of α, the frequency of maximum phase-lead ω_m of the network must be made to coincide with ω_{g2}. Thus we get $\omega_{g2} = \omega_m$.)

Step 5. Calculate the dB-gain $10 \log (1/\alpha)$. Locate the frequency at which the uncompensated system has a gain of $-10 \log (1/\alpha)$. This is the frequency $\omega_{g2} = \omega_m$ of the compensated system.

(Once α is determined, it is necessary only to determine the value of τ to complete the design in principle. This is accomplished by placing the corner frequencies of the phase-lead controller, $1/\alpha\tau$ and $1/\tau$ on either side of new gain crossover frequency ω_{g2} such that ϕ_m is located at the new gain crossover frequency ω_m. It is known that the high frequency gain of the phase-lead controller is $20 \log (1/\alpha)$ dB. Thus the new gain crossover frequency ω_m, which is the geometric mean of $1/\alpha\tau$ and $1/\tau$ is selected as the frequency at which the magnitude of the uncompensated system $G(j\omega)$ is $-10 \log (1/\alpha)$ dB, so that adding the controller gain of $10 \log (1/\alpha)$ dB to this makes the magnitude curve go through 0 dB at ω_m.)

Step 6. Compute the two corner frequencies of the network as

$$\omega_1 = 1/\tau = \omega_m \sqrt{\alpha}; \ \omega_2 = 1/\alpha\tau = \omega_m/\sqrt{\alpha}$$

With those values of ω_1 and ω_2, the design is complete and the lead compensator transfer function can be written as

$$G_c(s) = \frac{1 + \tau s}{1 + \alpha \tau s}$$

Step 7. Draw the magnitude and phase Bode plots of the compensated system and check the resulting phase margin and gain crossover frequency (it is a rough measure of bandwidth of the system). If the phase margin is still low, raise the value of $\in$ and repeat from step 3 above.

Step 8. Check any additional specifications on system performance, e.g. bandwidth. Redesign for another choice of crossover frequency ω_{g2} till this specification is met.

Effects of phase-lead compensation: The following are the effects of phase-lead compensation:

1. The phase-lead controller adds a zero and a pole, with the zero to the right of the pole, to the forward path transfer function. The general effect is to add more damping to the closed-loop system. The rise and settling times are reduced in general.

2. The phase of the forward path transfer function in the vicinity of the gain crossover frequency is increased. This improves the phase margin of the closed-loop system.

3. The slope of the magnitude curve of the Bode plot of the forward path transfer function is reduced at the gain cross frequency. This usually corresponds to an improvement in the relative stability of the system in the form of improved gain and phase margins.

4. The bandwidth of the closed-loop system is increased. This corresponds to faster time response.

5. The steady-state error of the system is not affected.

Limitations of single-stage phase-lead control: The following are the limitations of single-stage phase-lead control:

1. If the original system is unstable or has low stability margin, the additional phase-lead required to realize a certain desired phase margin may be excessive. This may require very small value of α and may result in large BW.

2. If the original system is unstable or has a low stability margin, the phase curve of the Bode plot of the forward path transfer function has a steep negative slope at the gain crossover frequency and the single-stage phase-lead control is ineffective. It requires an amplifier with large gain which will be costly.

3. The maximum phase-lead available from a single lead network is less than 60°. Thus, if a phase-lead of more than 60° is required, a multistage controller may be used.

Example 9.1 Design a lead compensator for a unity feedback system with an open-loop transfer function

$$G_f(s) = \frac{K}{s(s+1)}$$

For the specifications of $K_v = 10 \text{ s}^{-1}$ and $\phi_m = 35°$.

Solution: The specification on K_v is met by choosing $K = 10$.

The given open-loop transfer function in sinusoidal time constant form is

$$G_f(j\omega) = \frac{10}{j\omega(1 + j\omega)}$$

The Bode plots of the system with $K_v = 10$ are drawn in Figure 9.9. The phase margin of the uncompensated system is 16°. Since a lead compensator is to be designed, the phase-lead required at the new gain crossover frequency is given by

$$\phi_l = 35° - 16° + 5° = 24° = \phi_m$$

The attenuation factor

$$\alpha = \frac{1 - \sin \phi_m}{1 + \sin \phi_m} = \frac{1 - \sin 24°}{1 + \sin 24°} = \frac{1 - 0.4067}{1 + 0.4067} = 0.4217$$

The magnitude contribution of the compensating network at ω_m is

$$10 \log (1/\alpha) = 10 \log (1/0.4217) = 3.75 \text{ dB}$$

Therefore, the frequency at which the uncompensated system has a magnitude of -3.75 dB becomes the new crossover frequency $\omega_{g2} = \omega_m$ when the lead network is added. From the Bode plot of Figure 9.9, we find

$$\omega_{g2} = 4 \text{ rad/s}$$

Lower corner frequency of the network,

$$\omega_1 = \frac{1}{\tau} = \omega_m \sqrt{\alpha} = 4\sqrt{0.4217} = 2.60 \text{ rad/s}$$

Upper corner frequency of the network,

$$\omega_2 = \frac{1}{\alpha \tau} = \frac{\omega_m}{\sqrt{\alpha}} = \frac{4}{\sqrt{0.4217}} = 6.16 \text{ rad/s}$$

The transfer function of the lead network (with amplifier) therefore becomes

$$G_c(s) = \frac{1 + \tau s}{1 + \alpha \tau s} = \frac{1 + (1/2.60)s}{1 + (1/6.16)s} = \frac{1 + 0.385s}{1 + 0.162s}$$

The amplification necessary to cancel the lead network attenuation is

$$A = \frac{1}{\alpha} = \frac{1}{0.4217} = 2.37$$

The open-loop transfer function of the lead compensated system is

$$G(s) = G_f(s)G_c(s) = \frac{10(1 + 0.385s)}{s(1 + s)(1 + 0.162s)}$$

The magnitude and phase Bode plots of the compensated system are drawn as shown in Figure 9.9.

From the plots, the new gain crossover frequency is 4 rad/s and the corresponding phase margin is 38° which satisfies the requirement of $\phi_{pm} = 35°$.

From the Bode plots of the compensated system, we can observe that

1. The crossover frequency is increased.
2. The high frequency end of the log magnitude plot has been raised up by a gain of 20 log $(1/\alpha)$ dB.

Since the gain crossover frequency is a rough measure of the bandwidth of the system, it can be concluded that, the lead compensation results in an increase in bandwidth of the system which automatically results in an improvement in speed of response of the system. The actual value of the bandwidth can be determined by transferring the data from the Bode plots on to the Nichols chart. Too large a bandwidth is also not desirable because the high frequency noise signals will also be included.

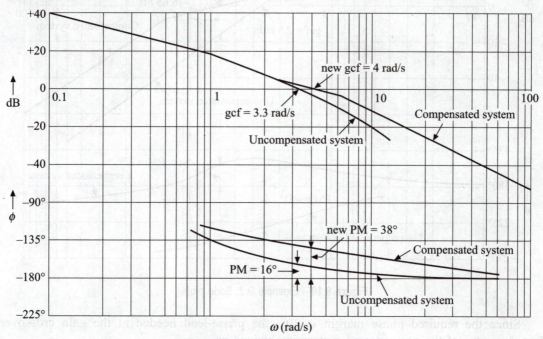

Figure 9.9 Example 9.1: Bode plots.

Example 9.2 Design a lead compensator for the system with an open-loop transfer function

$$G_f(s) = \frac{K}{s^2(1+0.1s)}$$

for the specifications of $K_a = 10$ and $\phi_{pm} = 30°$.

Solution: The specification on K_a is met by choosing $K = 10$. So the given open-loop transfer function in sinusoidal time constant form is

$$G_f(j\omega) = \frac{K}{(j\omega)^2(1+j0.1\omega)} = \frac{10}{(j\omega)^2(1+j0.1\omega)}$$

The magnitude and phase Bode plots of the above system are drawn as shown in Figure 9.10. From these plots, it can be seen that the gain crossover frequency is $\omega_{g1} = 2.6$ rad/s, and the phase margin is $\phi_{pm1} = -51°$. The uncompensated system is absolutely unstable.

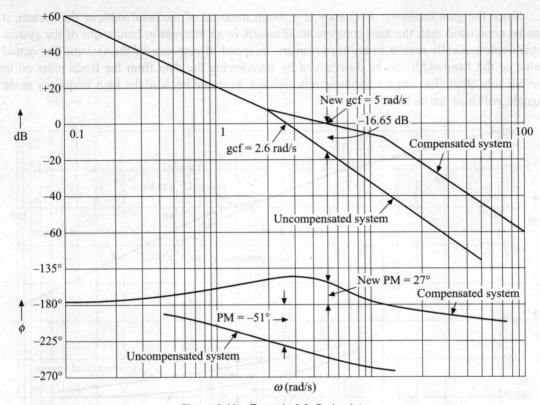

Figure 9.10 Example 9.2: Bode plots.

Since the required phase margin is 30°, the phase-lead needed at the gain crossover frequency ω_{g2} of the compensated system is obtained as

$$\phi_{pm2} = 30° - (-51°) + 15° = 96°$$

Here $\epsilon = 15°$ is the estimated reduction in the phase angle of fixed part of the transfer function since $\omega_{g2} > \omega_{g1}$. A large value of ϵ has been selected because $\angle G_f(s)$ is decreasing at a faster rate, since the final slope of the log magnitude curve is -60 dB/decade.

Since using a single lead network to give such a large phase-lead is not advisable, a double lead network is selected so that each section has to provide a maximum phase-lead of $96°/2 = 48°$. Therefore, $\phi_m = 48°$.

The attenuation factor of each lead section is

$$\alpha = \frac{1 - \sin 48°}{1 + \sin 48°} = 0.147$$

From the plot of the uncompensated system, we can see that the gain

$$2\left[-10 \log\left(\frac{1}{0.147}\right)\right] = -16.652 \text{ dB}$$

occurs at $\omega_{g2} = 5$ rad/s. This should be the gain crossover frequency of the compensated system. Choosing $\omega_m = \omega_{g2} = 5$ rad/s, the network corner frequencies are

$$\omega_1 = 1/\tau = \omega_m(\sqrt{\alpha}) = 5 \times 0.383 = 1.92 \text{ rad/s} \qquad \text{or} \qquad \tau = 1/1.92 = 0.52$$

$$\omega_2 = 1/\alpha\tau = \omega_m(1/\sqrt{\alpha}) = 5 \times 2.61 = 13.05 \text{ rad/s} \quad \text{or} \quad \alpha\tau = 1/13.05 = 0.076$$

Thus, the transfer function of each section of the double lead network (with the attenuation cancelled by an amplification $A = 1/\alpha = 1/0.147 = 6.8$) is

$$G_c(s) = \frac{1 + \tau s}{1 + \alpha\tau s} = \frac{1 + (1/1.92)s}{1 + (1/13.05)s} = \frac{1 + 0.52s}{1 + 0.076s}$$

The transfer function of the double lead network becomes

$$G_c(s) = \frac{(1 + 0.52s)^2}{(1 + 0.076s)^2}$$

The net additional amplifier gain required is $A^2 = 6.8^2 = 46.24$. Cascading this amplifier between the two sections of the lead network as shown in Figure 9.11 provides the isolation needed to prevent the second lead section from loading the first one.

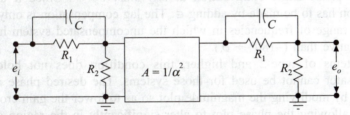

Figure 9.11 Double lead network.

The open-loop transfer function of the system compensated by the double lead network is given by

$$G(s) = G_f(s)G_c(s) = \frac{10(1 + 0.52s)^2}{s^2(1 + 0.5s)(1 + 0.076s)^2}$$

The Bode plots of the compensated system are drawn as shown in Figure 9.10. From the Bode plots, we can see that the phase margin at the new gain crossover frequency of $\omega_{g2} = 5$ rad/s is $+27°$. This indicates that the system has become stable but the desired phase margin is not fully achieved. This is because of the excessive lag of the fixed part of the system at the new gain crossover frequency. If this phase margin is not acceptable, then the compensator may be redesigned with a higher value of ϵ, say $\epsilon = 25°$.

9.4.2 Lag Compensator

From the frequency response plot of the lag network shown in Figure 9.6, it can be observed that the lag network acts like a low-pass filter attenuating high frequencies by $(-20 \log 1/\beta)$ dB.

Also it can be seen that the phase-lag mainly occurs within and around the two corner frequencies of the lag network and the maximum phase-lag occurs at the geometric mean of the two corner frequencies. It must be noted that any phase-lag is undesirable at the gain crossover frequency of the compensated system. Therefore, it is the attenuation characteristic of the lag network and not the phase characteristic which is used for compensation purposes.

The lag compensator design can be carried out as per the following steps:

Step 1. First adjust the error constant to the specified value. Determine the open-loop gain K necessary to satisfy the specified error constant.

Step 2. With this value of K, draw the magnitude and phase Bode plots and determine the phase margin ϕ_{pm1} and gain crossover frequency ω_{g1} of the uncompensated system. If the phase margin ϕ_{pm1} is not satisfactory, proceed with the following steps and design a lag compensator. Some times the phase margin may even be negative.

Step 3. Find the frequency ω_{g2} where the uncompensated system makes a phase margin contribution of

$$\phi_{pm2} = \phi_s + \epsilon$$

where ϕ_{pm2} is measured above the $-180°$ line. ϕ_s is the specified phase margin and $\epsilon = 5°$ to $15°$ is to correct for phase-lag contributed by the lag network at ω_{g2}. (Ideally the lag network phase angle contribution at ω_{g2} must be $0°$. Since it does not happen, correction has to be made by adding ϵ. The lag compensation is only possible if there exists a range of frequencies in which the uncompensated system has a phase angle less negative than $(-180° + \phi_s)$.

For systems of type-2 and higher, this condition does not hold good. So, lag compensator cannot be used for those systems. The desired phase margin has to be attained by modifying the magnitude plot so as to lower the gain crossover frequency without allowing the phase plot to alter significantly in the region of new crossover frequency. This can be easily achieved by a lag network wherein its high frequency attenuation $(-20 \log \beta)$ is utilized to lower the gain crossover frequency, while the two corner frequencies of the network are placed sufficiently lower than the desired gain crossover frequency so that the phase-lag contribution of the network at this crossover frequency is made sufficiently small.)

Step 4. Measure the gain of the uncompensated system at ω_{g2} and equate it to the required high frequency network attenuation $20 \log \beta$ and calculate the β parameter of the network. (This ensures that the gain of the compensated system is 0 dB at ω_{g2} and so gain crossover frequency of the compensated system is at ω_{g2}.)

Step 5. Since we want to utilize only the attenuation characteristic of the lag network and not its phase characteristic, choose the upper cut-off frequency $(\omega_2 = 1/\tau)$ of the lag network one octave to one decade below ω_{g2}, i.e.

$$\omega_2 = 1/\tau = \omega_{g2}/2 \text{ to } \omega_{g2}/10$$

so that the phase-lag contribution of the lag network at this frequency is negligible.

Step 6. With β and τ determined, the lag compensator design is complete. The transfer function of the lag compensator is

$$G_c(s) = \frac{(s + z_c)}{(s + p_c)} = \frac{s + 1/\tau}{s + 1/\beta\tau}$$

Step 7. Draw the magnitude and phase Bode plots of the compensated system and check the resulting phase margin.

Step 8. If there is any additional specification, check if it is satisfied. If the specifications are not met, redesign the compensator by choosing another value of τ.

Effects and limitations of phase-lag control: The effects and limitations of phase-lag control on the performance of control systems are as follows:

1. For a given forward path gain K, the magnitude of the forward path transfer function is attenuated near and above the gain crossover frequency, thus allowing improvement of the relative stability of the system. The additional attenuation at high frequencies improves the signal to noise ratio of the system.

2. The gain crossover frequency is decreased and thus the bandwidth of the system is reduced.

3. The rise and settling times of the system are usually longer since the bandwidth is usually decreased.

4. The system is more sensitive to parameter variations in the sense that the sensitivity function is greater than unity for all frequencies approximately greater than the bandwidth of the system.

Example 9.3 Compensate the system with the open-loop transfer function

$$G_f(s) = \frac{K}{s(s + 1)(s + 5)}$$

to meet the following specifications:
- Damping ratio $\xi = 0.3$
- Settling time $t_s = 12$ s
- Velocity error constant $K_v \geq 8$ s^{-1}

Solution: The given time-domain specifications are first converted into frequency-domain specifications by using the correlations between them.

$t_s = 3/(\xi\omega_n)$ for 5% tolerance band. Therefore,

$$\omega_n = \frac{3}{t_s\xi} = \frac{3}{12 \times 0.3} = 0.83 \text{ rad/s}$$

$$\therefore \quad \omega_b = \omega_n \left[1 - 2\xi^2 + \sqrt{(2 - 4\xi^2 + 4\xi^4)} \right]^{1/2}$$

$$= 0.83 \left[1 - 2(0.3)^2 + \sqrt{2 - 4(0.3)^2 + 4(0.3)^4} \right]^{1/2}$$

$$= 1.217 \text{ rad/s}$$

$$\phi_{pm} = \tan^{-1}\left\{2\xi/[\sqrt{(1+4\xi^4)}-2\xi^2]^{1/2}\right\}$$

$$= \tan^{-1}\left\{2\times0.3/[\sqrt{(1+4(0.3)^4)}-2\times0.3^2]^{1/2}\right\} = 33°$$

So the frequency-domain specifications are as follows:

$$\phi_{pm} = 33°; \quad \omega_b = 1.217 \text{ rad/s}; \quad K_v \geq 8 \text{ s}^{-1}$$

The open-loop transfer function of the uncompensated system may be written as

$$G_f(s) = \frac{K/5}{s(1+s)(1+0.2s)}$$

$$K_v = \underset{s\to0}{\text{Lt}}\ sG(s) = \frac{K}{5} = 8$$

$$\therefore \qquad\qquad K = 40$$

The specification K_v is met by choosing $K = 40$. Thus

$$G_f(j\omega) = \frac{8}{j\omega(1+j\omega)(1+j0.2\omega)}$$

The magnitude and phase Bode plots of $G_f(s)$ are drawn as shown in Figure 9.12. From these plots we observe that the gain crossover frequency $\omega_{g1} = 2.7$ rad/s and the phase margin is −8°. The uncompensated system is therefore unstable.

From the Bode plots we can observe that, neglecting the phase-lag contribution of the lag network, the specified phase margin of 33° is obtained, if the gain crossover frequency is 1 rad/s. Since this is fairly low, the upper cut-off frequency of the lag network cannot be taken far to its left in order to avoid large time constants. That means, the phase-lag contribution of the lag network at the new crossover frequency will be considerable and may be guessed as $\in = 10°$. The uncompensated system must therefore make a phase margin contribution of

$$\phi_2 = \phi_s + \in = 33° + 10° = 43°$$

at ω_{g2} which is found from the Bode plots of Figure 9.12 to be 0.8 rad/s.

Placing the upper corner frequency of the compensator two octaves below ω_{g2}, we have

$$\omega_2 = \frac{1}{\tau} = \frac{\omega_{g2}}{2^2} = \frac{0.8}{4} = 0.2 \text{ rad/s} \qquad \text{or} \qquad \tau = \frac{1}{0.2} = 5$$

To bring the log magnitude curve down to zero dB at ω_{g2}, the lag network must provide an attenuation of 18 dB. Therefore,

$$20 \log \beta = 18 \text{ dB}$$

or
$$\beta = 8$$

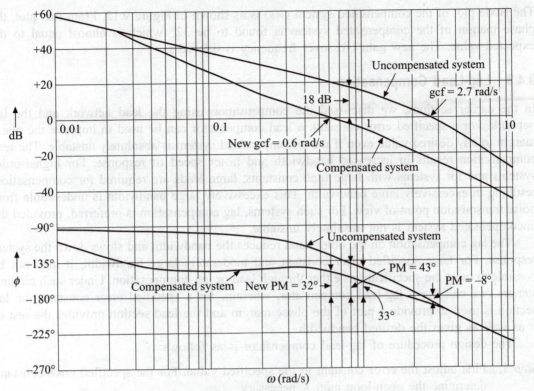

Figure 9.12 Example 9.3: Bode plots.

The lower corner frequency of the lag network is then fixed at

$$\omega_1 = \frac{1}{\beta\tau} = \frac{0.2}{8} = 0.025 \text{ rad/s} \quad \text{or} \quad \beta\tau = \frac{1}{0.025} = 40$$

The transfer function of the lag network is then

$$G_c(s) = \frac{1}{8}\left(\frac{s + 0.2}{s + 0.025}\right) = \frac{1 + \tau s}{1 + \beta\tau s} = \left(\frac{1 + 5s}{1 + 40s}\right)$$

Phase-lag introduced by the lag network at ω_{g2} is

$$\tan^{-1}(5\omega_{g2}) - \tan^{-1}(40\omega_{g2})$$

$$= 75.96° - 88° = -12°$$

So, it would have been appropriate to take $\epsilon = 12°$.

The open-loop transfer function of the compensated system becomes

$$G(s) = G_f(s)\, G_c(s) = \frac{8(1 + 5s)}{s(1 + s)(1 + 0.2s)(1 + 40s)}$$

The Bode plot of the compensated system $G(s)$ is as shown in Figure 9.12. From that plot, the phase margin of the compensated system is found to be 32° which is almost equal to the expected value. The new gain crossover frequency is 0.6 rad/s.

9.4.3   Lag-Lead Compensation

In the earlier sections, we discussed the compensation using the lead network and the lag network. For a specified error constant, a lead compensator can be used to improve the phase margin to any desired value even if the uncompensated system is absolutely unstable. The lead compensation results in increased bandwidth and faster speed of response. For higher-order systems and for systems with large time constants, large leads are required for compensation, resulting in excessively large bandwidth. This excessively large bandwidth is undesirable from noise transmission point of view. For such systems, lag compensation is preferred, provided the uncompensated system is not absolutely unstable.

The lag compensation on the other hand reduces the bandwidth and slows down the system response. For large specified error constant and moderately large bandwidth, it may not be possible to meet the specifications either through lead or lag compensation. Under such circumstances, we can use a lag-lead compensator, wherein, for a specified error constant, the lag section is used to provide a part of the phase margin and the lead section provides the rest of it as well as gives the desired bandwidth.

The design procedure of lag-lead compensator is as follows:

Step 1.   First adjust the error constant to the specified value. For the specified error constant, determine the open-loop gain K necessary.

Step 2.   Draw the magnitude and phase Bode plots of the uncompensated system with this value of K and determine the phase margin and gain crossover frequency.

Step 3.   First design the lag section to provide only partial compensation of phase margin. Choose the gain crossover frequency such that it is higher than the gain crossover frequency if the system was fully lag compensated.

Step 4.   Determine the value of β required such that the high frequency attenuation provided by the lag network is equal to the magnitude of the uncompensated system at this frequency.

Step 5.   Calculate the value of τ_1 such that the upper cut-off frequency of the lag network is two octaves below the gain crossover frequency.

Step 6.   Calculate the lower cut-off frequency

$$\omega_1 = 1/\beta\tau_1$$

So, the lag network design is complete. Find its transfer function. Draw the magnitude and phase Bode plots of the lag compensated system and determine the gain crossover frequency and the phase margin from them.

Step 7.   For the lead section design, independent value of α cannot be chosen. So select $\alpha = 1/\beta$ and calculate the maximum phase-lead provided by the lead section using the formula

$$\phi_m = \sin^{-1}\left[\frac{1-\alpha}{1+\alpha}\right] = \sin^{-1}\left[\frac{1-1/\beta}{1+1/\beta}\right]$$

Step 8. To fully utilize the lead effect, choose the compensated crossover frequency to coincide with ω_m. This is the frequency where the lag section compensated system has a gain of $-10 \log \beta$ dB. Read this from Bode plot. Then

$$\omega_m = 1/\tau_2 \sqrt{\alpha}$$

So calculate τ_2 and $\alpha\tau_2$ and write the lead compensator transfer function.

Step 9. Combine the transfer functions of the lag and lead sections to get the lag-lead compensator transfer function. Write the transfer function of the compensated system and draw the Bode plots for that transfer function and determine the phase margin. (The bandwidth of the compensated system can be found by drawing the log magnitude versus phase curve of the compensated system on the Nichols chart.)

Step 10. If the specifications are not met, redesign the system by modifying the values of β and τ.

Example 9.4 The open-loop transfer function of a unity feedback control system is given by

$$G_f(s) = \frac{K}{s(1+0.5s)(1+0.1s)}$$

Compensate the system to meet the following specifications:

- Velocity error constant $K_v \geq 25$ s^{-1}
- Phase margin $\phi_s \geq 60°$
- Bandwidth $\omega_b = 10$ rad/s

  Solution:

$$K_v = \underset{s\to 0}{\text{Lt}} \; sG(s) = K$$

$$\therefore \qquad K = K_v = 25$$

So the sinusoidal transfer function of the given system is

$$G_f(j\omega) = \frac{25}{(j\omega)(1+j0.1\omega)(1+j0.5\omega)}$$

The magnitude and phase Bode plots of $G_f(j\omega)$ are drawn as shown in Figure 9.13. From the Bode plots, it is seen that the uncompensated system has a gain crossover frequency of 6.5 rad/s ($\approx$ BW) and a phase margin of $-16°$. The uncompensated system is therefore unstable for the specified K_v. It can also be observed that the uncompensated system is conditionally stable, i.e. it is stable only for a certain range of values of K_v. So a lag-lead compensator is to be provided.

First let us select a lag compensator so that it partially compensates the requirement of phase margin. Let it provide a phase margin of $36°$ so that the new crossover frequency will be 2 rad/s. For this to become the crossover frequency, as seen from the Bode plot, the magnitude plot must be brought down by 18 dB. So the β parameter of the lag section is

$$20 \log \beta = 18$$

or

$$\beta = \log^{-1} 18/20 = 8$$

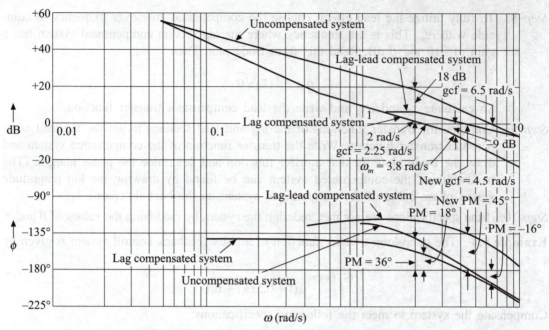

Figure 9.13 Example 9.4: Bode plots.

Let us now choose the upper cut-off frequency of lag section two octaves below this new gain crossover frequency of 2 rad/s. Therefore,

$$\omega_2 = \frac{1}{\tau} = \frac{gcf}{2^2} = \frac{2}{4} = 0.5$$

or
$$\tau = 2$$

The lower corner frequency of the lag network is then fixed at

$$\omega_1 = \frac{1}{\beta\tau} = \frac{1}{8 \times 2} = 0.0625 \text{ rad/s} \quad \text{or} \quad \beta\tau = 16$$

Therefore, the transfer function of the lag compensator is

$$G_{c1}(s) = \frac{1+\tau s}{1+\beta\tau s} = \frac{1+2s}{1+16s}$$

So, the lag section compensated system is

$$G_1(s) = G_f(s)\,G_{c1}(s) = \frac{25(1+2s)}{s(1+0.5s)(1+0.1s)(1+16s)}$$

The magnitude and phase Bode plots of the lag section compensated system are shown in Figure 9.13. From the plots, it can be seen that the lag section compensated system has a phase margin of 18° and a gain crossover frequency of 2.25 rad/s.

To design the lead section, select

$$\alpha = \frac{1}{\beta} = \frac{1}{8} = 0.125$$

The maximum lead that can be provided by the lead network is

$$\phi_m = \sin^{-1}\left(\frac{1-\alpha}{1+\alpha}\right) = \sin^{-1}\left(\frac{1-0.125}{1+0.125}\right) = 51.05°$$

To fully utilize the lead effect, choose the compensated crossover frequency to coincide with ω_m. So, ω_m is the frequency at which the lag section compensated system has a dB-gain of

$$-10 \log \frac{1}{\alpha} = -9 \text{ dB}$$

From the magnitude Bode plot of the lag compensated system, it can be observed that –9 dB magnitude occurs at $\omega_m = 3.8$ rad/s. Then the lower corner frequency of the lead network is

$$\omega_1 = \frac{1}{\tau_2} = \omega_m \sqrt{\alpha} = 3.8\sqrt{0.125} = 1.34 \text{ rad/s} \quad \text{or} \quad \tau_2 = \frac{1}{1.34} = 0.746$$

The upper corner frequency of the lead network is

$$\omega_2 = \frac{1}{\alpha\tau_2} = \omega_m/\sqrt{\alpha} = \frac{3.8}{\sqrt{0.125}} = 10.74 \text{ rad/s} \quad \text{or} \quad \alpha\tau_2 = \frac{1}{10.74} = 0.093$$

So, the transfer function of the lead network is

$$G_{c2}(s) = \frac{1+\tau_2 s}{1+\alpha\tau_2 s} = \frac{1+0.746s}{1+0.093s}$$

So, the transfer function of the lag-lead compensated system is

$$G(s) = G_f(s)G_{c1}(s)G_{c2}(s) = \frac{25(1+2s)(1+0.746s)}{s(1+0.5s)(1+0.1s)(1+16s)(1+0.093s)}$$

The magnitude and phase Bode plots of the lag-lead compensated system are shown in Figure 9.13. From the Bode plots we can see that the phase margin of the compensated system is 45° and the gain crossover frequency is 4.5 rad/s.

9.5 PID CONTROLLER

The proportional controller is a device that produces a control signal $u(t)$ which is proportional to the input error signal $e(t)$. The proportional controller amplifies the error signal by an amount K_p. Also, introduction of the controller on the system increases the loop gain by an amount K_p. The increase in loop gain improves the steady-state tracking accuracy, disturbance signal rejection and the relative stability and also makes the system less sensitive to parameter variations. But increasing the gain to very large values may lead to instability of the system. The drawback in proportional controller is that it leads to a constant steady-state error.

The integral controller is a device that produces a control signal $u(t)$ which is proportional to the integral of the error signal $e(t)$. The integral controller removes or reduces the steady-state error without the need for the manual reset. Hence, the integral controller is sometimes called *automatic reset*. The drawback in the integral controller is that it may lead to oscillatory response of increasing or decreasing amplitude which is undesirable and the system may become unstable.

The derivative controller is a device that produces a control signal $u(t)$ which is proportional to the derivative of the input error signal, i.e. the derivative control acts on rate of change of error and not on the actual error signal. The derivative control action is effective only during transient periods and so it does not produce corrective measures for any constant error. Hence the derivative controller is never used alone, but it is employed in association with proportional and integral controllers. The derivative controller does not affect the steady-state error directly but anticipates the error, initiates an early corrective action and tends to increase the stability of the system. While derivative control action has an advantage of being anticipatory, it has the disadvantage that it amplifies noise signals and may cause a saturation effect on the actuator. The derivative control is also called *rate control*.

A PID controller (Proportional plus Integral plus Derivative controller) produces an output signal consisting of three terms—one proportional to error signal, another one proportional to integral of error signal and the third one proportional to derivative of error signal.

The combination of proportional control action, integral control action and derivative control action is called *PID control action*. The combined action has the advantage of each of the three individual control actions.

The proportional controller stabilizes the gain but produces a steady-state error. The integral controller reduces or eliminates the steady-state error. The derivative controller reduces the rate of change of error.

PID controllers are commonly employed in process control industries. The determination of the proportional, integral and derivative constants of the controller called tuning in process control depends on the dynamic response of the plant.

Consider a PID controller

$$G_c(s) = K_p + \frac{K_i}{s} + K_d s = \frac{K_d s^2 + K_p s + K_i}{s}$$

For using the frequency response for PID controller design, write the transfer function in the form

$$G_c(s) = \frac{K_i \left[\dfrac{K_d}{K_i} s^2 + \dfrac{K_p}{K_i} s + 1 \right]}{s} = \frac{K_i (\tau_s + 1) \left(\dfrac{\tau}{\alpha} s + 1 \right)}{s}$$

where the controller constants are adjusted to yield two real zeros. The Bode plot of this $G_c(s)$ is drawn against $\omega\tau$ in Figure 9.14. It is seen from this figure that that Bode plot of a PID controller is very much similar to that of a lag-lead network as given in Figure 9.15. Compared to the lag-lead network, the PID controller has the superiority of having lag behaviour throughout the low frequency end and a lead behaviour throughout the high frequency end.

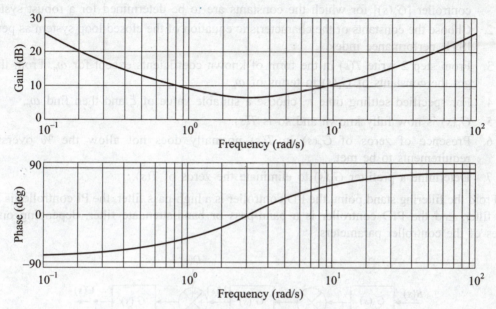

Figure 9.14 PID controller Bode plots.

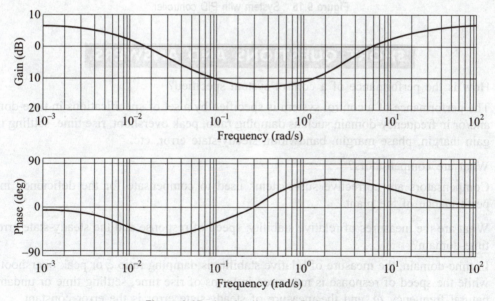

Figure 9.15 Lag-lead network Bode plots.

Design procedure: The design procedure for the system shown in Figure 9.16. consists of the following steps:

Step 1.   Find the closed loop transfer function $T(s)$ of the controlled system $G_f(s)$ and the PID controller $[G_c(s)]$ for which the constants are to be determined for a robust system.

Step 2.   Choose the constants of the characteristic equation of the closed loop system as per the ISTE performance index.

Step 3.   From step 2 write $T(s)$ in the form of known coefficients except for ω_n. From these, get the constants of $G_c(s)$ in terms of ω_n.

Step 4.   For specified settling time t_s, choose a suitable value of ξ and then find ω_n.

Step 5. $G_c(s)$ is now fully known and so is $T(s)$.

Step 6.   Presence of zeros of $G_c(s)$ in $T(s)$ normally does not allow the % overshoot requirements to be met.

Step 7.   Determine a prefilter $G_p(s)$ to eliminate the zeros of $T(s)$.

From the filtering stand point, the PD controller is a high-pass filter, the PI controller is low-pass filter, and the PID controller is a band-pass or band-attenuate filter, depending on the values of the controller parameters.

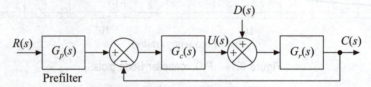

Figure 9.16   System with PID controller.

SHORT QUESTIONS AND ANSWERS

1. How is the performance of a control system specified?

A. The performance of a control system is specified by a set of specifications in time-domain and/or in frequency-domain such as damping ratio, peak overshoot, rise time, settling time, gain margin, phase margin, bandwidth, steady-state error, etc.

2. What are compensators?

A. Compensators are corrective sub-systems used to compensate for the deficiency in the performance of the plant.

3. What are the measures of relative stability, speed of response and the steady-state error in time-domain?

A. In time-domain, the measure of relative stability is damping ratio ξ or peak overshoot M_p, while the speed of response is measured in terms of rise time, settling time or undamped natural frequency ω_n and the measure of steady-state error is the error constant.

4. What are the measures of relative stability, speed of response and steady-state error in frequency-domain?

A. In frequency-domain, the measure of relative stability is resonant peak M_r or phase margin ϕ_{pm}, while the measure of speed of response is resonant frequency ω_r or bandwidth ω_b, and the measure of steady-state error is the error constant.

5. What are the two types of compensation?

A. The two types of compensation are (i) cascade or series compensation and (ii) feedback or parallel compensation. In series compensation, the compensator transfer function is placed in cascade with the plant transfer function and in parallel compensation, the compensator transfer function is placed in the feedback path.

6. What is a lead compensator? When is it preferred?

A. A compensator having a transfer function of the form

$$G_c(s) = \frac{s + z_c}{s + p_c} = \frac{s + 1/\tau}{s + 1/\alpha\tau}, \quad \alpha = \frac{z_c}{p_c} < 1, \tau > 0$$

is called a lead compensator. Its pole is located to the left of the zero. It is basically a high-pass filter. It increases the bandwidth of the system and the high frequencies are amplified by a factor of 20 log $(1/\alpha)$. It speeds up the transient response and increases the margin of stability of a system. It also helps to increase the system error constant though to a limited extent, i.e. it mainly improves the transient response of a system.

7. What is a lag compensator? When is it preferred?

A. A compensator having a transfer function of the form

$$G_c(s) = \frac{s + z_c}{s + p_c} = \frac{s + 1/\tau}{s + 1/\beta\tau}, \quad \beta = \frac{z_c}{p_c} > 1, \tau > 0$$

is called a lag compensator. Its pole is located to the right of the zero, i.e. nearer to the origin than the zero. It lowers the bandwidth of the system and the high frequency signals are attenuated by a factor of 20 log β.

8. What is a lag-lead compensator? When is it preferred?

A. A compensator having a transfer function of the form

$$G_c(s) = \left(\frac{s + z_{c1}}{s + p_{c1}}\right)\left(\frac{s + z_{c2}}{s + p_{c2}}\right) = \left(\frac{s + 1/\tau_1}{s + 1/\alpha\tau_1}\right)\left(\frac{s + 1/\tau_2}{s + 1/\beta\tau_2}\right), \quad \alpha < 1, \tau_1 > 0, \beta > 1, \tau_2 > 0$$

is called a lag-lead compensator. It is a cascade connection of a lag compensator and a lead compensator. When both the transient and steady-state responses require improvement, a lag-lead compensator is to be used.

9. When is compensation required? How is a compensator selected?

A. In general, there are two situations in which compensation is required. In the first case, the system is absolutely unstable and the compensation is required to stabilize it as well as to achieve a specified performance. In the second case, the system is stable, but the compensation is required to obtain the desired performance. The systems which are of type-2 or higher are usually absolutely unstable.

For type-2 or higher systems, only the lead compensator is required because only the lead compensator improves the margin of stability. In type-1 and type-0 systems, stable operation is always possible if the gain is sufficiently reduced. In such cases, any of the three compensators, viz. lead, lag, and lag-lead may be used to obtain the desired performance.

10. What is the basis for the selection of a particular compensator?

A. When mainly transient response is to be improved, a lead compensator is chosen. When steady-state response is to be improved, while nearly preserving the transient response, a lag compensator is chosen. When both the transient and steady-state responses are to be improved, a lag-lead compensator is chosen.

11. Which characteristic of the lag network is utilized for compensation?

A. The attenuation characteristic of the lag network is utilized for compensation purposes.

12. What are the advantages of frequency-domain methods of compensation?

A. The advantages of frequency-domain methods of compensation are: (i) simplicity in analysis and design and (ii) ease in experimental determination of frequency response for real systems.

13. What is the disadvantage of frequency-domain method of compensation?

A. The disadvantage of frequency-domain method of compensation is that in frequency-domain compensation, direct control on system time performance is lost.

14. Using which plots frequency-domain compensation can be carried out? Out of them which one is preferred and why?

A. The frequency-domain compensation may be carried out using the Nyquist plots, Bode plots, and Nichols chart. Out of them normally the Bode plots are preferred because they are easier to draw and modify. Also the gain adjustments can be conveniently carried out and also the error constants are always clearly in evidence in the Bode plots.

15. Which plot is preferred for particular frequency-domain specification?

A. If the specifications are in terms of M_r and ω_r, the Nyquist plot is preferred. If the specifications are in terms of phase margin ϕ_{pm} and bandwidth ω_b, Bode plots are preferred. The Nichols chart can handle any type of specification.

16. What is a rough measure of bandwidth?

A. The gain crossover frequency is a rough measure of bandwidth of a closed-loop system.

17. When is lag compensation possible?

A. Lag compensation is only possible if there exists a range of frequencies in which the uncompensated system has a phase angle less negative than $(-180° + \phi)$.

18. What is done if the specifications are given in time-domain?

A. When the specifications are given in time-domain, they are first translated into frequency-domain using the explicit correlations between the two domains for second-order system. Compensation is carried out in frequency-domain and the results are translated back into time-domain and the time response may be checked.

19. Why frequency domain compensation is normally carried out using the Bode plots?

A. Eventhough frequency-domain compensation can be carried out using the Nyquist plots, Bode plots or Nichols chart, the compensation is normally carried out by using the Bode plots because:

(a) The Bode plots are easier to draw and modify.

(b) The gain adjustment can be conveniently carried out using the Bode plots.

(c) The error constants are always clearly in evidence when the Bode plots are used.

20. What are the effects of phase-lead compensation?

A. The effects of phase-lead compensation are as follows:

(a) The phase-lead controller adds a zero and a pole, with the zero to the right of the pole, to the forward path transfer function. The general effect is to add more damping to the closed-loop system. The rise and settling times are reduced in general.

(b) The phase of the forward path transfer function in the vicinity of the gain crossover frequency is increased. This improves the phase margin of the closed-loop system.

(c) The slope of the magnitude curve of the Bode plot of the forward path transfer function is reduced at the gain cross frequency. This usually corresponds to an improvement in the relative stability of the system in the form of improved gain and phase margins.

(d) The bandwidth of the closed-loop system is increased. This corresponds to faster time response.

(e) The steady-state error of the system is not affected.

21. What are the limitations of single-stage phase-lead control?

A. The limitations of single-stage phase-lead control are as follows:

(a) If the original system is unstable or has low stability margin, the additional phase-lead required to realize a certain desired phase margin may be excessive. This may require very small value of α and may result in large BW.

(b) If the original system is unstable or has a low stability margin, the phase curve of the Bode plot of the forward path transfer function has a steep negative slope at the gain crossover frequency and the single-stage phase-lead control is ineffective. It requires an amplifier with large gain which will be costly.

(c) The maximum phase-lead available from a single lead network is less than 60°. Thus, if a phase-lead of more than 60° is required, a multistage controller may be used.

22. What are the effects and limitations of phase-lag control?

A. The effects and limitations of phase-lag control on the performance of control systems are as follows:

(a) For a given forward path gain K, the magnitude of the forward path transfer function is attenuated near and above the gain crossover frequency, thus allowing improvement of the relative stability of the system. The additional attenuation of high frequencies improves the signal to noise ratio of the system.

(b) The gain crossover frequency is decreased and thus the bandwidth of the system is reduced.

(c) The rise and settling times of the system are usually longer, since the bandwidth is usually decreased.

(d) The system is more sensitive to parameter variations in the sense that the sensitivity function is greater than unity for all frequencies approximately greater than the bandwidth of the system.

23. A lead compensator acts like which filter?

A. A lead compensator acts like a high-pass filter.

24. A lag compensator acts like which filter?

A. A lag compensator acts like a low-pass filter.

25. A lag-lead compensator acts like which filter?

A. A lag-lead compensator acts like a band-pass filter.

REVIEW QUESTIONS

1. Derive expression for the transfer function of a

    (a) lead compensator   (b) lag compensator   (c) lag-lead compensator

2. Write the procedure for the design of a lead compensator.

3. Write the procedure for the design of a lag compensator.

4. Write the procedure for the design of a lag-lead compensator.

5. Write notes on PID controller.

6. Write the procedure for the design of a PID controller.

FILL IN THE BLANKS

1. In time-domain, the measure of relative stability is ___ξ___ and ___Mp___.

2. In time-domain, the measure of speed of response is ___tr___, ___ts___ and ___Wn___.

3. In frequency-domain, the measure of relative stability is ___Mr___ and ___ϕpm___.

4. In frequency-domain, the measure of speed of response is ___Wr___ and ___ω_b___.

5. The two types of compensation are (i) ___series___ and (ii) ___parallel___.

6. Lead compensation is preferred when ___transient___ response is to be improved.

7. Lag compensation is preferred when ___steady state___ response is to be improved.

8. Lag-lead compensation is preferred when both the ___transient___ response and the ___steady state___ response are to be improved.

9. ___Lead___ compensator increases the bandwidth, while the ___lag___ compensator lowers the bandwidth.

10. For a lead compensator a ___zero___ is nearer to the origin.

11. For a lag compensator a _pole_ is nearer to the origin.

12. The _____ characteristic but not the _____ characteristic of the lag network is used for compensation.

13. The advantages of frequency-domain methods of compensation are (i) _____ and (ii) _____.

14. Frequency-domain compensation is carried out using the _____ or _____ or _____.

15. _Bode_ are preferred for frequency-domain compensation.

16. The Nyquist plots are preferred for compensation when the specifications are in terms of _____ and _____.

17. The Bode plots are preferred for compensation, when the specifications are in terms of _ϕ_{pm}_ and _ω_b_.

18. The _____ can handle any type of specification.

19. The _ogc_ is a rough measure of the bandwidth of a system.

20. Compensation in _freq._ domain is easier compared to compensation in _time_ domain.

21. With a lead compensator, maximum phase-lead occurs at the _geometric mean_ of the two corner frequencies.

22. The lead network acts as a _HP_ filter.

23. The lag network acts as a _LP_ filter.

24. The lag-lead network acts as a _bandpass_ filter.

25. When a lead compensator is used, the rise and settling times are _reduced_.

OBJECTIVE TYPE QUESTIONS

1. The compensator required to improve the transient response of a system is
   (a) lag   (b) lead
   (c) lag-lead   (d) none of these

2. The compensator required to improve the steady-state response of a system is
   (a) lag   (b) lead
   (c) lag-lead   (d) none of these

3. The compensator required to improve both the transient and the steady-state response of a system is
   (a) lag   (b) lead
   (c) lag-lead   (d) none of these

4. A rough measure of bandwidth of a system is
   (a) gain crossover frequency   (b) phase crossover frequency
   (c) resonant frequency   (d) undamped natural frequency

5. Rise time t_r and settling time t_s are measures of
   (a) relative stability
   (b) absolute stability
   (c) speed of response
   (d) steady-state error

6. Damping ratio ξ and peak overshoot M_p are measures of
   (a) relative stability
   (b) absolute stability
   (c) speed of response
   (d) steady-state error

7. Resonant peak M_r and phase margin ϕ_{pm} are measures of
   (a) relative stability
   (b) absolute stability
   (c) speed of response
   (d) steady-state error

8. Resonant frequency ω_r and bandwidth ω_b are measures of
   (a) relative stability
   (b) absolute stability
   (c) speed of response
   (d) steady-state error

9. Bandwidth is increased when the compensator used is
   (a) lag
   (b) lead
   (c) lag-lead
   (d) none of these

10. Bandwidth is reduced when the compensator used is
    (a) lag
    (b) lead
    (c) lag-lead
    (d) none of these

11. When the specifications are resonant peak M_r and resonant frequency ω_r, the plot used to design a compensator is
    (a) Nyquist plot
    (b) Bode plot
    (c) Nichols chart
    (d) none of these

12. When the specifications are phase margin ϕ_{pm} and bandwidth ω_b, the plot used to design a compensator is
    (a) Nyquist plot
    (b) Bode plot
    (c) Nichols chart
    (d) none of these

13. Any type of specification can be handled using
    (a) Nyquist plot
    (b) Bode plot
    (c) Nichols chart
    (d) none of these

PROBLEMS

9.1 The open-loop transfer function of a unity feedback system is

$$G(s) = \frac{K}{s(s+2)}$$

Design a suitable lead compensator to meet the following specifications:
- Velocity error constant $K_v = 12$ s^{-1}
- Phase margin $\phi_{pm} = 45°$

9.2 The open-loop transfer function of a type-2 unity feedback system is

$$G(s) = \frac{K}{s^2(1 + 0.2s)}$$

Design a suitable compensator to meet the following specifications:
- Acceleration error constant $K_a = 10$
- Phase margin $\phi_{pm} = 30°$

9.3 A unity feedback system has an open-loop transfer function

$$G(s) = \frac{K}{s(s + 1)(0.1s + 1)}$$

Design a phase-lag compensator for this system to meet the following specifications:
- Velocity error constant $K_v = 10$ s^{-1}
- Phase margin $\phi_{pm} = 35°$

Also compare the crossover frequencies of the uncompensated and compensated systems.

9.4 Consider a system with an open-loop transfer function

$$G(s) = \frac{K}{s(0.2s + 1)(0.1s + 1)}$$

Design a suitable lag-lead compensator to meet the following specifications:
- Velocity error constant $K_v = 25$ s^{-1}
- Phase margin $\phi_{pm} \geq 45°$
- Bandwidth $\omega_b = 10$ rad/s.

[**Note:** The Bode plots and the results for the above problems obtained using Matlab programs are given below.]

MATLAB PROGRAMS

PROGRAM 9.1

Matlab program for lead compensator for a unity feedback system with an open-loop transfer function

$$G(s) = \frac{K}{s(s + 2)} \text{ with } K_v = 12s^{-1} \text{ and } \phi_{pm} = 45°$$

```
% Lead compensator
clc;clear all;close all;
s=tf('s');
GH1=24/(s*(s+2));
```

```
bode(GH1)
grid on
[gm1, pm1, wcp1, wcg1] = margin(GH1);
disp('The gain margin of un-compensated system is')
disp(gm1)
disp('The Phase margin of un-compensated system is')
disp(pm1)
disp('The gain-crossover frequency of un-compensated system is')
disp(wcg1)
disp('The Phase-crossover frequency of un-compensated system is')
disp(wcp1)
GH2=(12*(1+0.285*s))/(s*(1+0.5*s)*(1+0.091*s));
hold on;
bode(GH2)
[gm2, pm2, wcp2, wcg2] = margin(GH2);
disp('The gain margin of compensated system is')
disp(gm2)
disp('The Phase margin of compensated system is')
disp(pm2)
disp('The gain-crossover frequency of compensated system is')
disp(wcg2)
disp('The Phase-crossover frequency of compensated system is')
disp(wcp2)
```

Output:

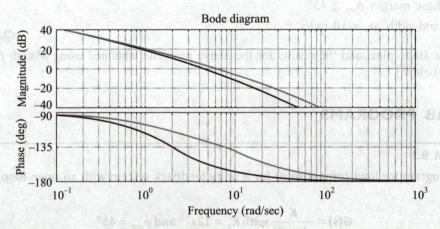

The gain margin of un-compensated system is
    Inf
The phase margin of un-compensated system is
    23.0552

The gain-crossover frequency of un-compensated system is
   4.6991
The phase-crossover frequency of un-compensated system is
   Inf
The gain margin of compensated system is
   Inf
The phase margin of compensated system is
   48.3394
The gain-crossover frequency of compensated system is
   6.4242
The phase-crossover frequency of compensated system is
   Inf

PROGRAM 9.2

Matlab program for lead compensator for a type-2 unity feedback system with an open-loop transfer function

$$G(s) = \frac{K}{s^2(1+0.2s)} \text{ with } K_a = 10 \text{ and } \phi_{pm} = 30°$$

```
% Lead compensator
clc;clear all;close all;
s=tf('s');
GH1=10/(s^2*(1+0.2*s));
bode(GH1)
grid on
[gm1, pm1, wcp1, wcg1] = margin(GH1)
disp('The gain margin of un-compensated system is')
disp(gm1)
disp('The Phase margin of un-compensated system is')
disp(pm1)
disp('The gain-crossover frequency of un-compensated system is')
disp(wcg1)
disp('The Phase-crossover frequency of un-compensated system is')
disp(wcp1)
GH2=(10*((1+0.397*s)^2))/(s^2*(1+0.2*s)*((1+0.0862*s)^2));
hold on;
bode(GH2)
[gm2, pm2, wcp2, wcg2] = margin(GH2)
disp('The gain margin of compensated system is')
disp(gm2)
disp('The Phase margin of compensated system is')
```

disp(pm2)

disp('The gain-crossover frequency of compensated system is')

disp(wcg2)

disp('The Phase-crossover frequency of compensated system is')

disp(wcp2)

Output:

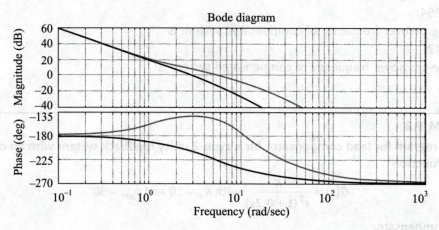

The gain margin of un-compensated system is

   0

The Phase margin of un-compensated system is

   −30.4220

The gain-crossover frequency of un-compensated system is

   2.9361

The Phase-crossover frequency of un-compensated system is

   0

The gain margin of compensated system is

   2.9359

The Phase margin of compensated system is

   31.2240

The gain-crossover frequency of compensated system is

   5.7031

The Phase-crossover frequency of compensated system is

   11.3504

PROGRAM 9.3

Matlab program for lag compensator for a unity feedback system with an open-loop transfer function

$$G(s) = \frac{K}{s(s+1)(0.1s+1)} \text{ with } K_v = 10s^{-1} \text{ and } \phi_{pm} = 35°$$

```
% Lag compensator
clc;clear all;close all;
s=tf('s');
GH1=10/(s*(s+1)*(1+0.1*s));
bode(GH1)
grid on
[gm1, pm1, wcp1, wcg1] = margin(GH1);
disp('The gain margin of un-compensated system is')
disp(gm1)
disp('The Phase margin of un-compensated system is')
disp(pm1)
disp('The gain-crossover frequency of un-compensated system is')
disp(wcg1)
disp('The Phase-crossover frequency of un-compensated system is')
disp(wcp1)
GH2=(10*(1+5*s))/(s*(1+s)*(1+0.1*s)*(1+50*s));
hold on;
bode(GH2)
[gm2, pm2, wcp2, wcg2] = margin(GH2);
disp('The gain margin of compensated system is')
disp(gm2)
disp('The Phase margin of compensated system is')
disp(pm2)
disp('The gain-crossover frequency of compensated system is')
disp(wcg2)
disp('The Phase-crossover frequency of compensated system is')
disp(wcp2)
```

Output:

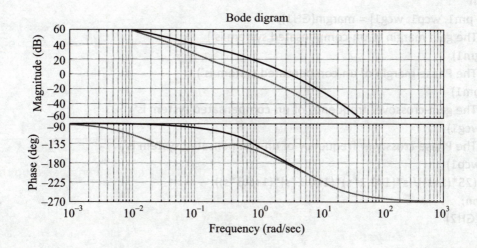

The gain margin of un-compensated system is
   1.1000
The Phase margin of un-compensated system is
   1.5763
The gain-crossover frequency of un-compensated system is
   3.0145
The Phase-crossover frequency of un-compensated system is
   3.1623
The gain margin of compensated system is
   8.8176
The Phase margin of compensated system is
   34.1255
The gain-crossover frequency of compensated system is
   0.8014
The Phase-crossover frequency of compensated system is
   2.8319

PROGRAM 9.4

Matlab program for lag-lead compensator for a unity feedback system with an open-loop transfer function

$$G(s) = \frac{K}{s(0.2s + 1)(0.1s + 1)} \text{ with } K_v = 25s^{-1} \text{ and } \phi_{pm} \geq 45° \text{ and } \omega_b = 10 \text{ rad/s}$$

```
% Lag-Lead Compensator
clc;clear all;close all;
s=tf('s');
GH1=25/(s*(1+0.2*s)*(1+0.1*s));
bode(GH1)
grid on
[gm1, pm1, wcp1, wcg1] = margin(GH1);
disp('The gain margin of un-compensated system is')
disp(gm1)
disp('The Phase margin of un-compensated system is')
disp(pm1)
disp('The gain-crossover frequency of un-compensated system is')
disp(wcg1)
disp('The Phase-crossover frequency of un-compensated system is')
disp(wcp1)
GH2=(25*(1+s))/(s*(1+0.2*s)*(1+0.1*s)*(1+5.3*s));
hold on;
bode(GH2)
```

```
[gm2, pm2, wcp2, wcg2] = margin(GH2);
disp('The gain margin of lag compensated system is')
disp(gm2)
disp('The Phase margin of lag compensated system is')
disp(pm2)
disp('The gain-crossover frequency of lag compensated system is')
disp(wcg2)
disp('The Phase-crossover frequency of lag compensated system is')
disp(wcp2)
GH3=(25*(1+s)*(1+0.46*s))(s*(1+0.2*s)*(1+0.1*s)*(1+5.3*s)*(1+0.086*s));
hold on;
bode(GH3)
[gm3, pm3, wcp3, wcg3] = margin(GH3);
disp('The gain margin of Lag-lead compensated system is')
disp(gm3)
disp('The Phase margin of Lag-lead compensated system is')
disp(pm3)
disp('The gain-crossover frequency of Lag-lead compensated system is')
disp(wcg3)
disp('The Phase-crossover frequency of Lag-lead compensated system is')
disp(wcp3)
```

Output:

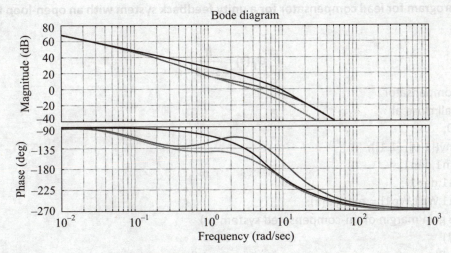

Bode diagram

The gain margin of un-compensated system is
    0.6000
The Phase margin of un-compensated system is
    −12.9919

The gain-crossover frequency of un-compensated system is
9.0101
The Phase-crossover frequency of un-compensated system is
7.0711
The gain margin of lag compensated system is
2.3994
The Phase margin of lag compensated system is
21.1175
The gain-crossover frequency of lag compensated system is
3.6863
The Phase-crossover frequency of lag compensated system is
6.1546
The gain margin of Lag-lead compensated system is
2.8476
The Phase margin of Lag-lead compensated system is
38.4206
The gain-crossover frequency of Lag-lead compensated system is
6.6621
The Phase-crossover frequency of Lag-lead compensated system is
12.4636

PROGRAM 9.5

Matlab program for lead compensator for a unity feedback system with an open-loop transfer function

$$G_f(s) = \frac{K}{s+1}$$

```
% Lead compensator
clc;clear all;close all
num1=10;
den1=conv([1 0], [1 1]);
bode(num1,den1)
a=tf(num1,den1);
[Gm1,Pm1,Wg1,Wp1] = margin(a);
disp('The gain margin of un-compensated system is')
disp(Gm1)
disp('The Phase margin of un-compensated system is')
disp(Pm1)
disp('The gain-crossover frequency of un-compensated system is')
disp(Wg1)
```

```
disp('The Phase-crossover frequency of un-compensated system is')
disp(Wp1)
grid on
hold on
num2=10*[0.385 1];
den2=conv([1 0],conv([1 1],[0.162 1]));
bode(num2,den2)
%legend('un-compensated','compensated')
b=tf(num2,den2);
[Gm2,Pm2,Wg2,Wp2] = margin(b);
disp('The gain margin of Compensated system is')
disp(Gm2)
disp('The Phase margin of Compensated system is')
disp(Pm2)
disp('The gain-crossover frequency of Compensated system is')
disp(Wg2)
disp('The Phase-crossover frequency of Compensated system is')
disp(Wp2)
```

Output:

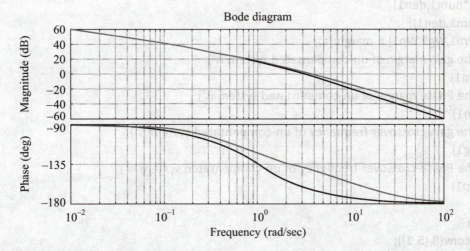

The gain margin of un-compensated system is

    Inf

The Phase margin of un-compensated system is

    17.9642

The gain-crossover frequency of un-compensated system is

    Inf

The Phase-crossover frequency of un-compensated system is

    3.0842

The gain margin of Compensated system is

Inf

The Phase margin of Compensated system is

38.6843

The gain-crossover frequency of Compensated system is

Inf

The Phase-crossover frequency of Compensated system is

3.8261

PROGRAM 9.6

Matlab program for lag compensator for a unity feedback system with an open-loop transfer function

$$G_f(s) = \frac{K}{s^2(s+1)(s+5)}$$

```
% Lag compensator
clc;clear all;close all;
k=40;
num1=1;
den1=conv([1 0],conv([1 1],[1 5]));
bode(k*num1,den1)
a=tf(num1,den1);
[Gm1,Pm1,Wg1,Wp1] = margin(a);
disp('The gain margin of un-compensated system is')
disp(Gm1)
disp('The Phase margin of un-compensated system is')
disp(Pm1)
disp('The gain-crossover frequency of un-compensated system is')
disp(Wg1)
disp('The Phase-crossover frequency of un-compensated system is')
disp(Wp1)
grid on
hold on
num2=conv(8,[5 1]);
den2=conv([1 0],conv([1 1],conv([0.2 1],[40 1])));
bode(num2,den2)
legend('un-compensated','compensated')
b=tf(num2,den2);
[Gm2,Pm2,Wg2,Wp2] = margin(b);
disp('The gain margin of Compensated system is')
disp(Gm2)
```

```
disp('The Phase margin of Compensated system is')
disp(Pm2)
disp('The Phase-crossover frequency of Compensated system is')
disp(Wg2)
disp('The Phase-crossover frequency of Compensated system is')
disp(Wp2)
```

Output:

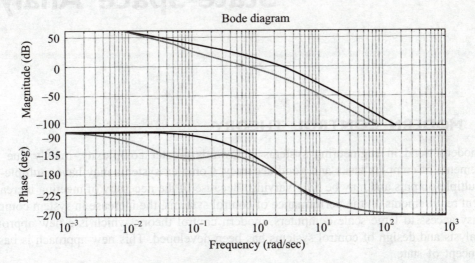

The gain margin of un-compensated system is
   30
The Phase margin of un-compensated system is
   76.6603
The gain-crossover frequency of un-compensated system is
   2.2361
The Phase-crossover frequency of un-compensated system is
   0.1961
The gain margin of Compensated system is
   4.7356
The Phase margin of Compensated system is
   30.1235
The Phase-crossover frequency of Compensated system is
   1.9876
The Phase-crossover frequency of Compensated system is
   0.7962

10

State-Space Analysis

10.1 MODERN CONTROL THEORY

The modern trend in engineering systems is towards greater complexity, mainly due to the requirements of complex tasks and good accuracy. Complex systems may have multiple-inputs and multiple-outputs and may be time-varying. Because of the necessity of meeting increasingly stringent requirements on the performance of control systems, the increase in system complexity and easy access to large scale computers, modern control theory, which is a new approach to the analysis and design of control systems has been developed. This new approach is based on the concept of state.

10.1.1 Modern Control Theory versus Conventional Control Theory

Basically there are two approaches to the analysis and design of control systems: the transfer function approach and the state variable approach. The transfer function approach is also called the conventional approach or the classical approach and the state variable approach is called the modern approach.

The transfer function approach has certain drawbacks. The transfer function approach is applicable only to linear time-invariant systems and there too, it is generally restricted to single-input-single-output systems. It is cumbersome for multi-input-multi-output systems. It is powerless for nonlinear systems and time-varying systems. The initial conditions are neglected. Eventhough this approach is conceptually simple and provides us with simple and powerful analysis and design techniques, the classical design methods are based on trial and error procedures and do not result in optimal and adaptive systems. They result only in acceptable systems, i.e. systems, which only satisfy the basic requirements, but not the best for the prescribed conditions. Since the transfer function gives only the input-output relationship of the system, in conventional control theory, only the input, output, and error signals are considered important. The input and output variables must be measurable. The design reveals only the system output for a given input and provides no information about the internal state of the system. The internal variables cannot be fed back. It is basically a frequency-domain approach. There may be situations where the output of a system is stable and yet some of the system elements may have a tendency to exceed their specified ratings. It may sometimes be necessary and advantageous to provide a feedback proportional to some of the internal variables of the system, rather than the output alone, for the purpose of stabilizing and improving the performance of a system.

On the other hand, the state variable approach is applicable to linear as well as nonlinear systems, time-invariant as well as time-varying systems, and single-input-single-output as well as multi-input-multi-output systems. Also all these can be modelled in a unified manner. It is basically a direct time-domain approach which provides a basis for modern control theory and is easily amenable to solution through a digital computer. Initial conditions are taken into account and optimal and adaptive systems can be designed. Also the state variables can be fed back. The state variables need not represent physical variables. They need not even be measurable and observable.

Eventhough the state variable approach has a number of advantages compared to the transfer function approach, the transfer function approach is still very much in use, because it provides the control engineer with a deep physical insight into the system and greatly aids in the preliminary system design. It provides simple and powerful analysis and design techniques like root locus and frequency response methods.

The transfer function formulation requires the Laplace transform for continuous-data control systems and z-transform for discrete-data control systems, but the state variable approach offers us a way to look at both the continuous-data systems and the discrete-data systems with the same formulation.

Although the state model of a system is not unique, the transfer function of a system is unique. All models of a system have the same number of elements in the state vector. This number is referred to as the *order of the system*. State variable approach can be used to solve higher order differential equations. An nth order differential equation can be converted into n first-order differential equations using state variable approach. The solution of n first-order differential equations is simpler compared to the solution of one nth order differential equation.

Table 10.1 summarizes the comparison of the transfer function approach and the state variable approach.

Table 10.1   Transfer function approach versus state variable approach.

Transfer function approach	*State variable approach*
1. The transfer function approach is also called the conventional approach or classical approach.	1. The state variable approach is called the modern approach.
2. It is based on the input-output relationship or transfer function.	2. It is based on the description of the system equations in terms of n first-order differential equations, which may be combined into first-order vector-matrix differential equations.
3. The transfer function approach is applicable only to linear time-invariant systems and there too, it is generally limited to single-input-single-output systems. It is cumbersome for multi-input-multi-output systems.	3. The state variable approach is applicable to linear as well as nonlinear, time-invariant as well as time-varying, single-input-single-output as well as multi-input-multi-output systems.
4. In this initial conditions are neglected.	4. In this initial conditions are considered.

(Contd.)

Table 10.1 Transfer function approach versus state variable approach (contd.)

Transfer function approach	*State variable approach*
5. Classical design methods are based on trial and error procedures and design using this approach yields only acceptable systems.	5. Design is not based on trial and error procedure. Design using this approach yields optimal systems.
6. It is basically a frequency-domain approach.	6. It is basically a time-domain approach.
7. Only input, output and error signals are considered important. The input and output variables must be measurable.	7. The state variables need not represent physical variables. They need not even be measurable and observable.
8. It requires Laplace transform for continuous-data control systems and *z*-transform for discrete-data control systems.	8. It formulates both the continuous-data control systems and the discrete-data control systems in the same way.
9. The internal variables cannot be fed back.	9. The state variables can be fed back.
10. The transfer function of a system is unique.	10. The state model of a system is not unique.

10.2 CONCEPTS OF STATE, STATE VARIABLES AND STATE MODEL

State: The state of a dynamic system is the smallest set of variables (called state variables) such that the knowledge of these variables at $t = t_0$, together with the knowledge of the inputs for $t \geq t_0$, completely determine the behaviour of the system for any time $t \geq t_0$.

The concept of state is not limited to physical systems. It is applicable to biological systems, economic systems, social systems, and others.

State variables: The state variables of a dynamic system are the smallest set of variables that determine the state of the dynamic system, i.e. the state variables are the minimal set of variables such that the knowledge of these variables at any initial time $t = t_0$, together with the knowledge of the inputs for $t \geq t_0$ is sufficient to completely determine the behaviour of the system for any time $t \geq t_0$. If atleast n variables $x_1, x_2, ..., x_n$ are needed to completely describe the behaviour of a dynamic system (so that once the input is given for $t \geq t_0$ and the initial state at $t = t_0$ is specified, the future of the system is completely specified), then those n variables are a set of state variables.

The state variables need not be physically measurable or observable quantities. Variables that do not represent physical quantities and those that are neither measurable nor observable can also be chosen as state variables. Such freedom in choosing state variables is an added advantage of the state-space methods.

State vector: If n state variables are needed to completely describe the behaviour of a given system, then these n state variables can be considered as the n components of a vector $\mathbf{x}(t)$. Such a vector is called a *state vector*. A state vector is thus a vector that determines uniquely the system state $\mathbf{x}(t)$ for any time $t \geq t_0$, once the state at $t = t_0$ is given and the input $\mathbf{u}(t)$ for $t \geq t_0$ is specified.

State-space: The n dimensional space whose coordinate axes consist of the x_1 axis, x_2 axis, ..., x_n axis, where x_1, x_2, ..., x_n are state variables is called the *state-space*. Any state can be represented by a point in the state-space.

10.2.1 State-Space Equations

In the state-space analysis, we are concerned with three types of variables that are involved in the modelling of dynamic systems: input variables, output variables, and state variables. The state-space representation for a given system is not unique, except that the number of state variables is the same for any of the different state-space representations of the same system.

The dynamic system must involve elements that memorize the values of the input for $t \geq t_0$. Since integrators in continuous-time control system serve as memory devices, the outputs of such integrators can be considered as the variables that define the internal state of the dynamic system. Thus, the outputs of the integrators serve as state variables. The number of state variables to completely define the dynamics of the system is equal to the number of integrators involved in the system.

In state variable formulation of a system, the state variables are usually represented by $x_1(t)$, $x_2(t),...,x_n(t)$, the inputs by $u_1(t)$, $u_2(t),..., u_m(t)$, and the outputs by $y_1(t)$, $y_2(t),..., y_p(t)$ assuming that the system has m inputs, p outputs and n state variables. For notational economy, the different variables may be represented in vector form by the input vector $\mathbf{u(t)}$ ($m \times 1$), output vector $\mathbf{y(t)}$ ($p \times 1$) and state vector $\mathbf{x(t)}$ ($n \times 1$). The state-space representation in block diagram form is shown in Figure 10.1, where broad arrows are used to represent vector quantities.

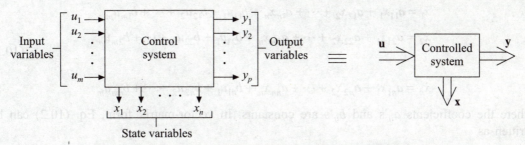

Figure 10.1 State-space representation of a system.

The state variable representation of a system can be arranged in the form of n-first-order differential equations.

$$\frac{dx_1}{dt} = \dot{x}_1 = f_1(x_1, x_2,...,x_n; u_1, u_2,...,u_m)$$

$$\frac{dx_2}{dt} = \dot{x}_2 = f_2(x_1, x_2,...,x_n; u_1, u_2,...,u_m)$$

$$\vdots \qquad \vdots \qquad \vdots \qquad \qquad (10.1)$$

$$\frac{dx_n}{dt} = \dot{x}_n = f_n(x_1, x_2,...,x_n; u_1, u_2,...,u_m)$$

Integration of Eq. (10.1) gives

$$x_i(t) = x_i(t_0) + \int_{t_0}^{t} f_i(x_1, x_2, ..., x_n; u_1, u_2, ..., u_m) \, dt \qquad i = 1, 2, ..., n$$

Thus, the n state variables and hence the state of the system can be determined uniquely at any $t > t_0$, if each state variable is known at $t = t_0$ and all the m control inputs are known throughout the interval t_0 to t.

The n differential equations may be written in vector matrix notation as

$$\dot{\mathbf{x}}(t) = \mathbf{f}(\mathbf{x}(t), \mathbf{u}(t))$$

for time-invariant systems, where $\mathbf{x}(t)$ is an $n \times 1$ state vector, $\mathbf{u}(t)$ is an $m \times 1$ input vector as already defined earlier and $\mathbf{f}$ is an $n \times 1$ function vector.

For time-varying systems, the function $\mathbf{f}$ is dependent on time as well and the vector equation may be written as

$$\dot{\mathbf{x}}(t) = \mathbf{f}(\mathbf{x}(t), \mathbf{u}(t), t)$$

10.2.2 State Model of Linear Time-invariant Systems

The state equations of a linear time-invariant system are a set of first-order differential equations, where each first derivative of the state variable is a linear combination of system states and inputs, i.e.

$$\dot{x}_1 = a_{11}x_1 + a_{12}x_2 + \cdots + a_{1n}x_n + b_{11}u_1 + b_{12}u_2 + \cdots + b_{1m}u_m$$
$$\dot{x}_2 = a_{21}x_1 + a_{22}x_2 + \cdots + a_{2n}x_n + b_{21}u_1 + b_{22}u_2 + \cdots + b_{2m}u_m$$
$$\vdots$$
$$\dot{x}_n = a_{n1}x_1 + a_{n2}x_2 + \cdots + a_{nn}x_n + b_{n1}u_1 + b_{n2}u_2 + \cdots + b_{nm}u_m$$

$$(10.2)$$

where the coefficients a_{ij}'s and b_{ij}'s are constants. In vector-matrix form, Eq. (10.2) can be written as

$$\dot{\mathbf{x}}(t) = \mathbf{A}\mathbf{x}(t) + \mathbf{B}\mathbf{u}(t)$$

where $\mathbf{x}(t)$ is an $n \times 1$ state vector, $\mathbf{u}(t)$ is a $m \times 1$ input vector, $\mathbf{A}$ is an $n \times n$ system matrix, and $\mathbf{B}$ is an $n \times m$ input matrix defined by

$$\mathbf{x}(t) = \begin{bmatrix} x_1(t) \\ x_2(t) \\ \vdots \\ x_n(t) \end{bmatrix}, \ \mathbf{u}(t) = \begin{bmatrix} u_1(t) \\ u_2(t) \\ \vdots \\ u_m(t) \end{bmatrix} \ \mathbf{A} = \begin{bmatrix} a_{11} & a_{12} & \cdots & a_{1n} \\ a_{21} & a_{22} & \cdots & a_{2n} \\ \vdots & & & \\ a_{n1} & a_{n2} & \cdots & a_{nn} \end{bmatrix}, \ \mathbf{B} = \begin{bmatrix} b_{11} & b_{12} & \cdots & b_{1m} \\ b_{21} & b_{22} & \cdots & b_{2m} \\ \vdots & & & \\ b_{n1} & b_{n2} & \cdots & b_{nm} \end{bmatrix}$$

Similarly, the output variables at time t are linear combination of the input and state variables at time t, i.e.

$$y_1(t) = c_{11}x_1(t) + c_{12}x_2(t) + \cdots + c_{1n}x_n(t) + d_{11}u_1(t) + d_{12}u_2(t) + \cdots + d_{1m}u_m(t)$$

$$\vdots \tag{10.3}$$

$$y_p(t) = c_{p1}x_1(t) + c_{p2}x_2(t) + \cdots + c_{pn}x_n(t) + d_{p1}u_1(t) + d_{p2}u_2(t) + \ldots + d_{pm}u_m(t)$$

where the coefficients c_{ij}'s and d_{ij}'s are constants. This set of equations [Eq. (10.3)] written in vector-matrix form is

$$\mathbf{y}(t) = \mathbf{C}\mathbf{x}(t) + \mathbf{D}\mathbf{u}(t)$$

where $\mathbf{y}(t)$ is a $p \times 1$ output vector, $\mathbf{C}$ is a $p \times n$ output matrix, and $\mathbf{D}$ is a $p \times m$ transmission matrix defined by

$$\mathbf{y}(t) = \begin{bmatrix} y_1(t) \\ y_2(t) \\ \vdots \\ y_p(t) \end{bmatrix}, \quad \mathbf{C} = \begin{bmatrix} c_{11} & c_{12} & \cdots & c_{1n} \\ c_{21} & c_{22} & \cdots & c_{2n} \\ \vdots & & & \\ c_{p1} & c_{p2} & \cdots & c_{pn} \end{bmatrix}, \quad \mathbf{D} = \begin{bmatrix} d_{11} & d_{12} & \cdots & d_{1m} \\ d_{21} & d_{22} & \cdots & d_{2m} \\ \vdots & & & \\ d_{p1} & d_{p2} & \cdots & d_{pm} \end{bmatrix}$$

The state model of linear time-invariant systems is thus given by the following equations

$$\dot{\mathbf{x}}(t) = \mathbf{A}\mathbf{x}(t) + \mathbf{B}\mathbf{u}(t) : \text{State equations}$$

$$\mathbf{y}(t) = \mathbf{C}\mathbf{x}(t) + \mathbf{D}\mathbf{u}(t) : \text{Output equations}$$

The block diagram representation of the state model is shown in Figure 10.2.

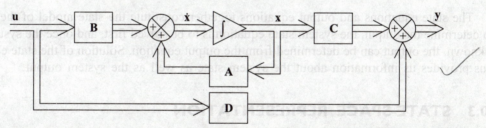

Figure 10.2 Block diagram representation of the state model of a linear multi-input-multi-output system.

10.2.3 State Model for Single-Input-Single-Output Linear Systems

The transfer function analysis deals mainly with single-input-single-output linear time-invariant systems. Here we link the transfer function approach with the state variable approach. If we let $m = 1$, and $p = 1$ in the state model of a multi-input-multi-output linear system, we obtain the following state model for a single-input-single-output linear system.

$$\dot{\mathbf{x}}(t) = \mathbf{A}\mathbf{x}(t) + \mathbf{B}u(t)$$

$$y(t) = \mathbf{C}\mathbf{x}(t) + du(t)$$

where $\mathbf{B}$ and $\mathbf{C}$ are now respectively $(n \times 1)$ and $(1 \times n)$ matrices, d is a constant and u is a scalar control variable. The block diagram representation of this state model is shown in Figure 10.3

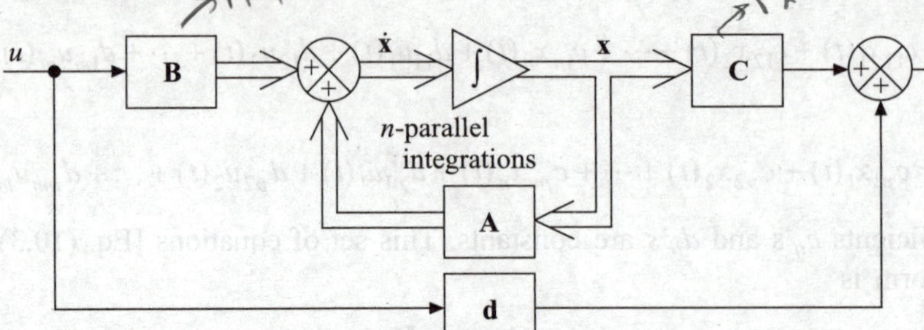

Figure 10.3   Block diagram representation of the state model of a linear single-input-single-output system.

So the state equations are

$$\dot{\mathbf{x}}(t) = f[\mathbf{x}(t), \mathbf{u}(t)]: \text{For time-invariant systems}$$

$$\dot{\mathbf{x}}(t) = f[\mathbf{x}(t), \mathbf{u}(t), t]: \text{For time-varying systems} \qquad (10.4)$$

In the above equation, the state vector $\mathbf{x}(t)$ determines a point (called the state point) in an n dimensional space called the state-space. The curve traced out by the state point from $t = t_0$ to $t = t_1$ in the direction of increasing time is known as the state trajectory. For the two dimensional cases, the state-space reduces to the state plane or phase plane.

To output vector $\mathbf{y}(t)$ can in general be expressed in terms of the state vector $\mathbf{x}(t)$ and the input $\mathbf{u}(t)$ as

$$\mathbf{y}(t) = g(\mathbf{x}(t), \mathbf{u}(t)) : \text{Time-invariant systems}$$

$$\mathbf{y}(t) = g(\mathbf{x}(t), \mathbf{u}(t), t) : \text{Time-varying systems} \qquad (10.5)$$

The state equations and output equations together constitute the state model of the system. To determine the output, the system state equation is to be solved first, and once the system state is known, the output can be determined from the output equation. Solution of the state equations thus provides us information about the system state as well as the system output.

10.3   STATE-SPACE REPRESENTATION

10.3.1   State-Space Representation Using Physical Variables

Consider the *RLC* circuit shown in Figure 10.4 The input is a voltage source $e(t)$. Let us say the input is applied at $t = t_0$. The desired output information is usually the voltages and currents associated with various elements of the network. This information at any time t can be obtained if the initial voltage across the capacitor $e_c(t_0)$ and the initial current through the inductor $i(t_0)$ are known in addition to the values of the input $e(t)$ applied for $t > t_0$. The voltage across the capacitor and the current through the inductor thus constitute a set of characterizing variables of the circuit. The initial state of the circuit is given by $e_c(t_0)$ and $i(t_0)$, and the state of the circuit at any time t is given by $e_c(t)$ and $i(t)$. The values of the characterizing variables at time t describe the state of the network at that time. These variables are therefore called state variables of the circuit.

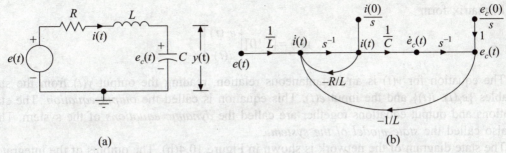

(a) (b)

Figure 10.4 (a) *RLC* network and (b) state diagram.

Circuit analysis usually requires setting up of dynamical equations (using Kirchoff's voltage and current laws) in terms of rates of change of capacitor voltages and inductor currents. The solution of these equations describes the state of the network at time t. Desired output information is then obtained from the state using algebraic relation.

For the circuit shown

$$Ri(t) + \frac{Ldi(t)}{dt} + e_c(t) = e(t) \tag{10.6}$$

and

$$\frac{Cde_c(t)}{dt} = i(t) \tag{10.7}$$

Rearrangement of Eqs. (10.6) and (10.7) gives the rates of change of capacitor voltage and inductor current.

$$\frac{de_c(t)}{dt} = \frac{1}{C}i(t) \tag{10.8}$$

$$\frac{di(t)}{dt} = \frac{1}{L}e(t) - \frac{R}{L}i(t) - \frac{1}{L}e_c(t) \tag{10.9}$$

In vector-matrix form, Eqs. (10.8) and (10.9) can be written as

$$\begin{bmatrix} \dfrac{de_c(t)}{dt} \\ \dfrac{di(t)}{dt} \end{bmatrix} = \begin{bmatrix} 0 & \dfrac{1}{C} \\ -\dfrac{1}{L} & -\dfrac{R}{L} \end{bmatrix} \begin{bmatrix} e_c(t) \\ i(t) \end{bmatrix} + \begin{bmatrix} 0 \\ \dfrac{1}{L} \end{bmatrix} e(t)$$

These equations give the rates of change of state variables (capacitor voltage $e(t)$ and inductor current $i(t)$) in terms of the state variables and the input. These equations are called the *state equations*.

The solution of these equations for given input $e(t)$ applied at $t = 0$ and given initial state $[e_c(0), i(0)]$ yields the state $[e_c(t), i(t)]$ for $t > 0$. If $y(t)$ shown in Figure 10.4(a) is the desired output information, we have the following algebraic relation to obtain $y(t)$.

$$y(t) = e_c(t)$$

In matrix form

$$y(t) = [1 \quad 0]\begin{bmatrix} e_c(t) \\ i(t) \end{bmatrix}$$

The equation for $y(t)$ is an instantaneous relation, reading the output $y(t)$ from the state variables $\{e_c(t), i(t)\}$ and the input $e(t)$. This equation is called the *output equation*. The state equations and output equations together are called the *dynamic equations* of the system. They are also called the *state model of the system*.

The state diagram of the network is shown in Figure 10.4(b). The outputs of the integrators are defined as the state variables. The transfer functions of the system are obtained by applying the signal flow graph gain formula to the state diagram when all the initial states are set to zero.

$$\frac{E_c(s)}{E(s)} = \frac{\dfrac{1}{L} \cdot s^{-1} \cdot \dfrac{1}{C} \cdot s^{-1}}{1 + \dfrac{R}{L} \cdot s^{-1} + \dfrac{1}{LC} s^{-2}} = \frac{1}{LCs^2 + RCs + 1}$$

$$\frac{I(s)}{E(s)} = \frac{\dfrac{1}{L} \cdot s^{-1}}{1 + \dfrac{R}{L} \cdot s^{-1} + \dfrac{1}{LC} s^{-2}} = \frac{Cs}{LCs^2 + RCs + 1}$$

Example 10.1 Obtain the state model of the network shown in Figure 10.5 assuming $R_1 = R_2 = 1 \ \Omega$, $C_1 = C_2 = 1$ F, and $L = 1$ H.

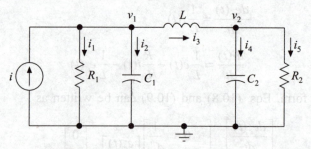

Figure 10.5 Example 10.1: Network.

Solution: The behaviour of the network shown in Figure 10.5 at any time t can be determined if the initial current through the inductor and the initial voltages across the capacitors together with the input i applied for $t > 0$ are known. So select the current through the inductor i_3, and the voltages across the capacitors C_1 and C_2, i.e. $v_1(t)$ and $v_2(t)$ as the state variables. To obtain the state equations, express the first derivatives of the state variables in terms of the input variable and the state variables.

Writing the KCL at node 1

$$i = i_1 + i_2 + i_3$$

i.e.
$$i = \frac{v_1}{R_1} + C_1 \frac{dv_1}{dt} + i_3$$

∴
$$\frac{dv_1}{dt} = \frac{-v_1}{R_1 C_1} - \frac{i_3}{C_1} + \frac{i}{C_1}$$

Writing the KCL at node 2

$$i_3 = i_4 + i_5$$

i.e.
$$i_3 = C_2 \frac{dv_2}{dt} + \frac{v_2}{R_2}$$

∴
$$\frac{dv_2}{dt} = \frac{-v_2}{R_2 C_2} + \frac{i_3}{C_2}$$

Writing KVL for the loop consisting of L

$$L \frac{di_3}{dt} + v_2 - v_1 = 0$$

∴
$$\frac{di_3}{dt} = \frac{v_1}{L} - \frac{v_2}{L}$$

If the current through the resister R_2 and the voltage across it are the outputs, the output equations are

$$y_1 = i_5 = \frac{v_2}{R_2} \qquad y_2 = i_5 R_2 = v_2$$

In vector-matrix form, the state model is

$$\begin{bmatrix} \dfrac{dv_1}{dt} \\ \dfrac{dv_2}{dt} \\ \dfrac{di_3}{dt} \end{bmatrix} = \begin{bmatrix} \dfrac{-1}{R_1 C_1} & 0 & \dfrac{-1}{C_1} \\ 0 & \dfrac{-1}{R_2 C_2} & \dfrac{1}{C_2} \\ \dfrac{1}{L} & \dfrac{-1}{L} & 0 \end{bmatrix} \begin{bmatrix} v_1 \\ v_2 \\ i_3 \end{bmatrix} + \begin{bmatrix} \dfrac{1}{C_1} \\ 0 \\ 0 \end{bmatrix} i \qquad \begin{bmatrix} i_5 \\ v_2 \end{bmatrix} = \begin{bmatrix} 0 & \dfrac{1}{R_2} & 0 \\ 0 & 1 & 0 \end{bmatrix} \begin{bmatrix} v_1 \\ v_2 \\ i_3 \end{bmatrix}$$

Substituting the values of components, the state model is

$$\begin{bmatrix} \dot{v}_1 \\ \dot{v}_2 \\ i_3 \end{bmatrix} = \begin{bmatrix} -1 & 0 & -1 \\ 0 & -1 & 1 \\ 1 & -1 & 0 \end{bmatrix} \begin{bmatrix} v_1 \\ v_2 \\ i_3 \end{bmatrix} + \begin{bmatrix} 1 \\ 0 \\ 0 \end{bmatrix} i \qquad \begin{bmatrix} i_5 \\ v_2 \end{bmatrix} = \begin{bmatrix} 0 & 1 & 0 \\ 0 & 1 & 0 \end{bmatrix} \begin{bmatrix} v_1 \\ v_2 \\ i_3 \end{bmatrix}$$

Example 10.2 Obtain the dynamic equations of the network shown in Figure 10.6. The current through R_2 is the output required.

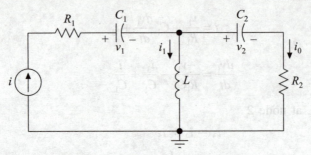

Figure 10.6   Example 10.2: Network.

Solution: In the network shown in Figure 10.6, the current though C_1 is the same as the source current. Therefore,

$$C_1 \frac{dv_1}{dt} = i$$

i.e.

$$\frac{dv_1}{dt} = \frac{1}{C_1} i$$

The current through C_2 is the difference between the source current and the current through the inductor, i.e.

$$C_2 \frac{dv_2}{dt} = i - i_1$$

∴

$$\frac{dv_2}{dt} = -\frac{1}{C_2} i_1 + \frac{1}{C_2} i$$

The voltage across the inductor is the same as the voltage across the combination of R_2 and C_2 i.e.

$$L \frac{di_1}{dt} = v_2 + R_2(i - i_1)$$

∴

$$\frac{di_1}{dt} = \frac{1}{L} v_2 - \frac{R_2}{L} i_1 + \frac{R_2}{L} i$$

The output variable, that is the current i_0 through the resistor R_2 is

$$i_0 = i - i_1$$

So, the dynamic equations in matrix form are as follows:

$$
\begin{bmatrix} \dfrac{dv_1}{dt} \\[2mm] \dfrac{dv_2}{dt} \\[2mm] \dfrac{di_1}{dt} \end{bmatrix}
=
\begin{bmatrix} 0 & 0 & 0 \\[2mm] 0 & 0 & \dfrac{-1}{C_2} \\[2mm] 0 & \dfrac{1}{L} & \dfrac{-R_2}{L} \end{bmatrix}
\begin{bmatrix} v_1 \\[2mm] v_2 \\[2mm] i_1 \end{bmatrix}
+
\begin{bmatrix} \dfrac{1}{C_1} \\[2mm] \dfrac{1}{C_2} \\[2mm] \dfrac{R_2}{L} \end{bmatrix} i
$$

$$i_0 = \begin{bmatrix} 0 & 0 & -1 \end{bmatrix} \begin{bmatrix} v_1 \\ v_2 \\ i_1 \end{bmatrix} + (1)i$$

The above matrix form gives the state model.

Example 10.3 Write the state variable formulation of the parallel *RLC* network shown in Figure 10.7. The current through the inductor and the voltage across the capacitor are the output variables.

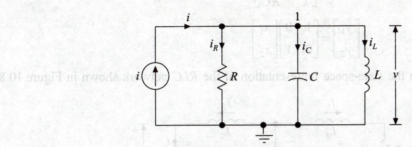

Figure 10.7 Example 10.3: Network.

Solution: In the network shown in Figure 10.7, choose the current through the inductor i_L and the voltage across the capacitor v as the state variables, and the current i_0 through L and the voltage v_0 across L as the output variable.

Writing the KCL at node 1

$$i = i_R + i_C + i_L = \frac{v}{R} + C\frac{dv}{dt} + i_L$$

i.e.

$$\frac{dv}{dt} = \frac{-1}{C}i_L - \frac{v}{RC} + \frac{1}{C}i$$

The voltage across the inductor is

$$v = L\frac{di_L}{dt}$$

i.e.

$$\frac{di_L}{dt} = \frac{v}{L}$$

Also,

$$i_o = i_L$$

and

$$v_o = v$$

Based on the above equations, the state model is

$$\begin{bmatrix} \dfrac{di_L}{dt} \\[2ex] \dfrac{dv}{dt} \end{bmatrix} = \begin{bmatrix} 0 & \dfrac{1}{L} \\[2ex] \dfrac{-1}{C} & \dfrac{-1}{RC} \end{bmatrix} \begin{bmatrix} i_L \\[1ex] v \end{bmatrix} + \begin{bmatrix} 0 \\[1ex] \dfrac{1}{C} \end{bmatrix} i$$

$$\begin{bmatrix} i_0 \\ v_0 \end{bmatrix} = \begin{bmatrix} 1 & 0 \\ 0 & 1 \end{bmatrix}\begin{bmatrix} i_L \\ v \end{bmatrix}$$

If the state variables are selected as i_L is x_1 and v is x_2, and the output i_0 is y_1 and v_0 is y_2 and the input current i is u, then the state model is

$$\begin{bmatrix} \dot{x}_1 \\ \dot{x}_2 \end{bmatrix} = \begin{bmatrix} 0 & \dfrac{1}{L} \\ \dfrac{-1}{C} & \dfrac{-1}{RC} \end{bmatrix}\begin{bmatrix} x_1 \\ x_2 \end{bmatrix} + \begin{bmatrix} 0 \\ \dfrac{1}{C} \end{bmatrix}u$$

$$\begin{bmatrix} y_1 \\ y_2 \end{bmatrix} = \begin{bmatrix} 1 & 0 \\ 0 & 1 \end{bmatrix}\begin{bmatrix} x_1 \\ x_2 \end{bmatrix}$$

Example 10.4   Obtain the state-space representation of the *RLC* network shown in Figure 10.8.

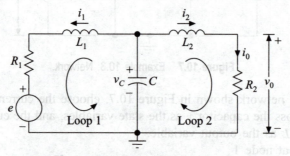

Figure 10.8   Example 10.4: Network.

Solution: The network shown in Figure 10.8 has three energy storage elements, a capacitor C and two inductors L_1 and L_2. History of the network is completely specified by the voltage across the capacitor and the currents through the inductors at $t = 0$. If we have a knowledge of initial conditions $i_1(0)$, $i_2(0)$, $v_c(0)$ and the input signal $e(t)$ for $t \geq 0$, then the behaviour of the network is completely specified for $t \geq 0$. However, if one (or more) of the initial conditions is not known, we are unable to determine the complete response of the network to a given input. Therefore, the initial conditions $i_1(0)$, $i_2(0)$, $v_c(0)$ together with the input signal $e(t)$ for $t \geq 0$ constitute the minimum information needed. Hence select the currents through the inductors $i_1(t)$ and $i_2(t)$ and the voltage across the capacitor $v_c(t)$ as the state variables. The output variables are the current through R_2, i.e. $i_0(t)$ and the voltage across R_2, i.e. $v_0(t)$ and the input variable is $e(t)$. Hence let

$$x_1(t) = i_1(t) \qquad\qquad y_1(t) = i_0(t)$$
$$x_2(t) = i_2(t) \qquad\qquad y_2(t) = v_0(t)$$
$$x_3(t) = v_c(t) \qquad\qquad u(t) = e(t)$$

The differential equations governing the behaviour of the *RLC* network are obtained by writing the KCL equation at the node and the KVL equations around the two loops.

Writing the KCL equation at the node

$$i_1 + i_2 + C\frac{dv_c}{dt} = 0$$

Writing KVL equation around loop 1

$$L_1\frac{di_1}{dt} + R_1 i_1 + e - v_c = 0$$

Writing KVL equation around loop 2

$$L_2\frac{di_2}{dt} + R_2 i_2 - v_c = 0$$

Expressing the first derivatives of the state variables $\dfrac{di_1}{dt}, \dfrac{di_2}{dt}$ and $\dfrac{dv_c}{dt}$ as linear combinations of the state variables i_1, i_2, v_c, and the input variable e, the state equations are

$$\frac{di_1}{dt} = \frac{-R_1}{L_1}i_1 + \frac{1}{L_1}v_c - \frac{1}{L_1}e$$

$$\frac{di_2}{dt} = \frac{-R_2}{L_2}i_2 + \frac{1}{L_2}v_c$$

$$\frac{dv_c}{dt} = \frac{-1}{C}i_1 - \frac{1}{C}i_2$$

and the output equations are

$$i_0(t) = i_2(t)$$

and

$$v_0(t) = i_2(t)\, R_2$$

In terms of the state variables and the outputs defined earlier, the state variable formulation in matrix form is

$$
\begin{bmatrix} \dfrac{di_1}{dt} \\[2mm] \dfrac{di_2}{dt} \\[2mm] \dfrac{dv_c}{dt} \end{bmatrix}
=
\begin{bmatrix} -\dfrac{R_1}{L_1} & 0 & \dfrac{1}{L_1} \\[2mm] 0 & -\dfrac{R_2}{L_2} & \dfrac{1}{L_2} \\[2mm] -\dfrac{1}{C} & -\dfrac{1}{C} & 0 \end{bmatrix}
\begin{bmatrix} i_1 \\ i_2 \\ v_c \end{bmatrix}
+
\begin{bmatrix} -\dfrac{1}{L_1} \\[2mm] 0 \\[2mm] 0 \end{bmatrix} e, \quad \text{i.e.} \quad
\begin{bmatrix} \dot{x}_1 \\ \dot{x}_2 \\ \dot{x}_3 \end{bmatrix}
=
\begin{bmatrix} -\dfrac{R_1}{L_1} & 0 & \dfrac{1}{L_1} \\[2mm] 0 & -\dfrac{R_2}{L_2} & \dfrac{1}{L_2} \\[2mm] -\dfrac{1}{C} & -\dfrac{1}{C} & 0 \end{bmatrix}
\begin{bmatrix} x_1 \\ x_2 \\ x_3 \end{bmatrix}
+
\begin{bmatrix} -\dfrac{1}{L_1} \\[2mm] 0 \\[2mm] 0 \end{bmatrix} u(t)
$$

$$
\begin{bmatrix} i_0 \\ v_0 \end{bmatrix}
=
\begin{bmatrix} 0 & 1 & 0 \\ 0 & R_2 & 0 \end{bmatrix}
\begin{bmatrix} i_1 \\ i_2 \\ v_c \end{bmatrix}
\quad \text{i.e.} \quad
\begin{bmatrix} y_1 \\ y_2 \end{bmatrix}
=
\begin{bmatrix} 0 & 1 & 0 \\ 0 & R_2 & 0 \end{bmatrix}
\begin{bmatrix} x_1 \\ x_2 \\ x_3 \end{bmatrix}
$$

The state diagram of the network of Figure 10.8 is shown in Figure 10.9. The transfer function between $I_1(s)$ and $E(s)$, $I_2(s)$ and $E(s)$, $V_c(s)$ and $E(s)$ are written from the state diagram after neglecting the initial conditions.

$$\frac{I_1(s)}{E(s)} = \frac{\left(-\dfrac{1}{L_1}s^{-1}\right)\left[1 + \dfrac{R_2}{L_2}s^{-1} + \dfrac{1}{L_2C}s^{-2}\right]}{\Delta} = \frac{-\dfrac{1}{L_1s}\left[1 + \dfrac{R_2}{L_2s} + \dfrac{1}{L_2Cs^2}\right]}{\Delta} = \frac{-\left(\dfrac{R_2Cs + L_2Cs^2 + 1}{L_1L_2Cs^3}\right)}{\Delta}$$

$$\frac{I_2(s)}{E(s)} = \frac{\left(-\dfrac{1}{L_1}\right)(s^{-1})\left(-\dfrac{1}{C}\right)(s^{-1})\left(\dfrac{1}{L_2}\right)(s^{-1})}{\Delta} = \frac{\dfrac{1}{L_1L_2Cs^3}}{\Delta}$$

$$\frac{V_c(s)}{E(s)} = \frac{\left(-\dfrac{1}{L_1}\right)(s^{-1})\left(-\dfrac{1}{C}\right)(s^{-1})\left(1 + \dfrac{R_2}{L_2}s^{-1}\right)}{\Delta} = \frac{\dfrac{1}{L_1Cs^2}\left(1 + \dfrac{R_2}{L_2s}\right)}{\Delta} = \frac{\dfrac{L_2s + R_2}{L_1L_2Cs^3}}{\Delta}$$

where

$$\Delta = 1 - \left[-\frac{R_1}{L_1s} - \frac{1}{L_1Cs^2} - \frac{R_2}{L_2s} - \frac{1}{L_2Cs^2}\right] + \left[\frac{R_1R_2}{L_1L_2s^2} + \frac{R_2}{L_1L_2Cs^3} + \frac{R_1}{L_1L_2Cs^3}\right]$$

$$= \frac{L_1L_2Cs^3 + (R_1L_2 + R_2L_1)Cs^2 + (R_1R_2C + L_1 + L_2)s + (R_1 + R_2)}{L_1L_2Cs^3}$$

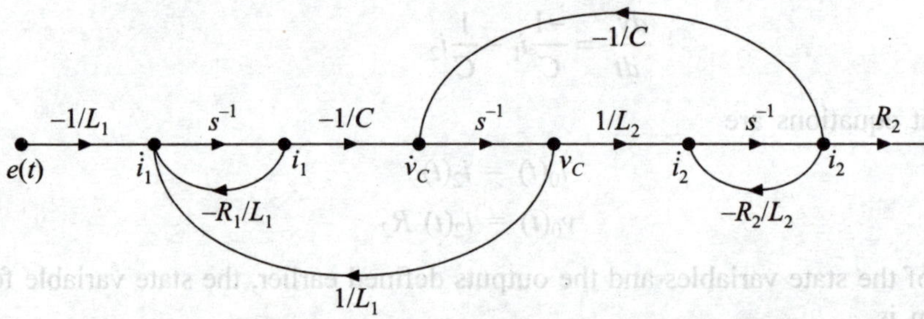

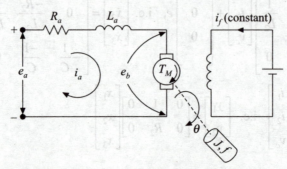

Figure 10.9 State diagram for network of Figure 10.8.

Example 10.5 Obtain the state variable representation of an armature-controlled DC motor (Figure 10.10).

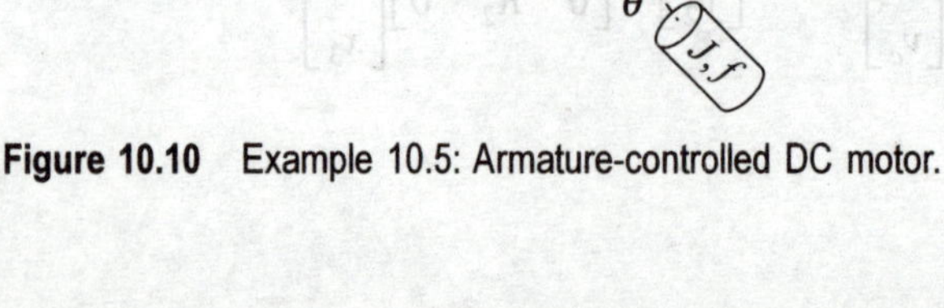

Figure 10.10 Example 10.5: Armature-controlled DC motor.

Solution: In chapter 2, we have written the equations governing the behaviour of an armature controlled DC motor shown in Figure 10.10 as

$$\phi = K_f i_f$$

$$T_M = K_T i_a$$

$$e_b = K_b \frac{d\theta}{dt} = K_b \omega$$

$$L_a \frac{di_a}{dt} + R_a i_a + e_b = e_a$$

and

$$J \frac{d^2\theta}{dt^2} + f \frac{d\theta}{dt} = T_M = K_T i_a$$

i.e.

$$J \frac{d\omega}{dt} + f\omega = T_M = K_T i_a$$

Selecting the armature current $i_a(t)$, the angular displacement of the shaft $\theta(t)$, and the angular velocity of the shaft $\omega(t)$ as the state variables and expressing the first derivative of the state variables in terms of the state variables $i_a(t)$, $\theta(t)$ and $\omega(t)$ and the input variable $e_a(t)$, the state equations are as follows:

$$\frac{di_a}{dt} = \frac{-R_a}{L_a} i_a - \frac{K_b}{L_a} \omega + \frac{1}{L_a} e_a$$

$$\frac{d\theta}{dt} = \omega$$

$$\frac{d\omega}{dt} = \frac{K_T}{J} i_a - \frac{f}{J} \omega$$

In matrix form they are:

$$
\begin{bmatrix} \dfrac{di_a}{dt} \\[2mm] \dfrac{d\theta}{dt} \\[2mm] \dfrac{d\omega}{dt} \end{bmatrix} =
\begin{bmatrix} -\dfrac{R_a}{L_a} & 0 & -\dfrac{K_b}{L_a} \\[2mm] 0 & 0 & 1 \\[2mm] \dfrac{K_T}{J} & 0 & -\dfrac{f}{J} \end{bmatrix}
\begin{bmatrix} i_a \\[2mm] \theta \\[2mm] \omega \end{bmatrix} +
\begin{bmatrix} \dfrac{1}{L_a} \\[2mm] 0 \\[2mm] 0 \end{bmatrix} e_a
$$

Taking the angular displacement as the output variable,

$$\theta = \begin{bmatrix} 0 & 1 & 0 \end{bmatrix} \begin{bmatrix} i_a \\ \theta \\ \omega \end{bmatrix}$$

Designating the state variables i_a, θ and ω as x_1, x_2 and x_3 respectively, and the output variable θ as $y(t)$, the state model is

$$\begin{bmatrix} \dot{x}_1 \\ \dot{x}_2 \\ \dot{x}_3 \end{bmatrix} = \begin{bmatrix} -\dfrac{R_a}{L_a} & 0 & -\dfrac{K_b}{L_a} \\ 0 & 0 & 1 \\ \dfrac{K_T}{J} & 0 & -\dfrac{f}{J} \end{bmatrix} \begin{bmatrix} x_1 \\ x_2 \\ x_3 \end{bmatrix} + \begin{bmatrix} \dfrac{1}{L_a} \\ 0 \\ 0 \end{bmatrix} e_a$$

$$y = \begin{bmatrix} 0 & 1 & 0 \end{bmatrix} \begin{bmatrix} x_1 \\ x_2 \\ x_3 \end{bmatrix}$$

Example 10.6 Obtain the state variable formulation of a field-controlled DC motor (Figure 10.11).

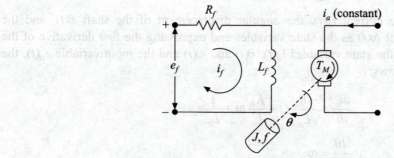

Figure 10.11 Example 10.6: Field-controlled DC motor.

Solution: In chapter 2, we have written the equations governing the behaviour of a field controlled DC motor shown in Figure 10.11 as

$$L_f \frac{di_f}{dt} + R_f i_f = e_f$$

i.e.

$$\frac{di_f}{dt} = -\frac{R_f}{L_f} i_f + \frac{e_f}{L_f}$$

$$\frac{d\theta}{dt} = \omega$$

and

$$\frac{J d^2\theta}{dt^2} + f\frac{d\theta}{dt} = T_M = K_T i_f$$

i.e.

$$J \frac{d\omega}{dt} + f\omega = K_T i_f$$

i.e.

$$\frac{d\omega}{dt} = -\frac{f}{J}\omega + \frac{K_T}{J}i_f$$

Selecting the field current i_f, the angular displacement θ, and the angular velocity ω as the state variables and designating them by x_1, x_2 and x_3 respectively and selecting the angular displacement $\theta(t)$ as the output variable and designating it by $y(t)$, and designating the input variable $e(t)$ by $u(t)$, the state variable formulation is

$$\begin{bmatrix} \dot{x}_1 \\ \dot{x}_2 \\ \dot{x}_3 \end{bmatrix} = \begin{bmatrix} -\dfrac{R_f}{L_f} & 0 & 0 \\ 0 & 0 & 1 \\ \dfrac{K_T}{J} & 0 & -\dfrac{f}{J} \end{bmatrix} \begin{bmatrix} x_1 \\ x_2 \\ x_3 \end{bmatrix} + \begin{bmatrix} \dfrac{1}{L_f} \\ 0 \\ 0 \end{bmatrix} u(t)$$

$$y = \begin{bmatrix} 0 & 1 & 0 \end{bmatrix} \begin{bmatrix} x_1 \\ x_2 \\ x_3 \end{bmatrix}$$

Example 10.7 Obtain a state model for the mechanical system shown in Figure 10.12(a).

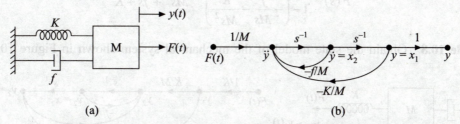

(a)   (b)

Figure 10.12 Example 10.7: (a) mechanical system and (b) state diagram.

Solution: The differential equation governing the behaviour of the given mechanical system is

$$F(t) = M\frac{d^2 y}{dt^2} + f\frac{dy}{dt} + Ky$$

∴

$$\frac{d^2 y}{dt^2} = -\frac{f}{M}\frac{dy}{dt} - \frac{K}{M}y + \frac{1}{M}F(t)$$

The state diagram of the system is constructed as shown in Figure 10.12(b). By defining the outputs of the integrators on the state diagram as state variables x_1 and x_2, the state equations are as follows:

$$\frac{dx_1}{dt} = x_2$$

$$\frac{dx_2}{dt} = -\frac{K}{M}x_1 - \frac{f}{M}x_2 + \frac{1}{M}F(t)$$

and the output equation is

$$y(t) = x_1(t)$$

In vector-matrix form, the state model is

$$\begin{bmatrix} \dot{x}_1 \\ \dot{x}_2 \end{bmatrix} = \begin{bmatrix} 0 & 1 \\ -\dfrac{K}{M} & -\dfrac{f}{M} \end{bmatrix} \begin{bmatrix} x_1 \\ x_2 \end{bmatrix} + \begin{bmatrix} 0 \\ \dfrac{1}{M} \end{bmatrix} F(t)$$

$$y = \begin{bmatrix} 1 & 0 \end{bmatrix} \begin{bmatrix} x_1 \\ x_2 \end{bmatrix}$$

From the state diagram, the transfer function of the system is

$$\frac{Y(s)}{F(s)} = \frac{\dfrac{1}{Ms^2}}{1 - \left(-\dfrac{f}{Ms} - \dfrac{K}{Ms^2}\right)} = \frac{1}{Ms^2 + fs + K}$$

Example 10.8 Obtain the state model of the mechanical system shown in Figure 10.13(a).

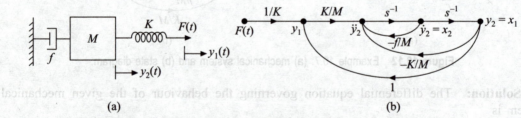

(a)   (b)

Figure 10.13 Example 10.8: (a) mechanical system and (b) state diagram.

Solution: The differential equations governing the behaviour of the given mechanical system are

$$F(t) = K[y_1(t) - y_2(t)]$$

$$M\frac{d^2 y_2(t)}{dt^2} + K(y_2(t) - y_1(t)) + f\frac{dy_2(t)}{dt} = 0$$

Let the output be $y_1(t)$. The equations are arranged as

$$\frac{d^2 y_2(t)}{dt^2} = \frac{K}{M}y_1(t) - \frac{K}{M}y_2(t) - \frac{f}{M}\frac{dy_2(t)}{dt}$$

and
$$y_1(t) = \frac{1}{K}F(t) + y_2(t)$$

Using the last two equations, the state diagram of the system is drawn as shown in Figure 10.13(b). The outputs of the integrators are taken as the state variables. So defining the state variables as $x_1(t) = y_2(t)$ and $x_2(t) = \dot{y}_2(t)$, the state equations and the output equation written directly from the state diagram are

$$\frac{dx_1(t)}{dt} = x_2(t)$$

$$\frac{dx_2(t)}{dt} = -\frac{f}{M}x_2(t) + \frac{1}{M}F(t)$$

and
$$y_1(t) = y_2(t) + \frac{1}{K}F(t)$$

So in vector-matrix form, the state model is

$$\begin{bmatrix} \dot{x}_1 \\ \dot{x}_2 \end{bmatrix} = \begin{bmatrix} 0 & 1 \\ 0 & -\dfrac{f}{M} \end{bmatrix} \begin{bmatrix} x_1 \\ x_2 \end{bmatrix} + \begin{bmatrix} 0 \\ \dfrac{1}{M} \end{bmatrix} F(t)$$

$$y = \begin{bmatrix} 1 & 0 \end{bmatrix} \begin{bmatrix} x_1 \\ x_2 \end{bmatrix} + \frac{1}{K}F(t)$$

The transfer functions of the system are obtained by applying the Mason's gain formula to the state diagram.

$$\frac{Y_2(s)}{F(s)} = \frac{\dfrac{1}{K} \cdot \dfrac{K}{M} . s^{-1} . s^{-1}}{1 - \left(-\dfrac{f}{M}s^{-1} - \dfrac{K}{M}s^{-2} + \dfrac{K}{M}s^{-2}\right)} = \frac{\dfrac{1}{Ms^2}}{1 + \dfrac{f}{Ms}} = \frac{1}{Ms^2 + fs}$$

$$\frac{Y_1(s)}{F(s)} = \frac{\dfrac{1}{K}\left(1 + \dfrac{f}{M}s^{-1} + \dfrac{K}{M}s^{-2}\right)}{1 - \left(-\dfrac{f}{M}s^{-1} - \dfrac{K}{M}s^{-2} + \dfrac{K}{M}s^{-2}\right)} = \frac{Ms^2 + fs + K}{Ks(Ms + f)}$$

Example 10.9 Consider the mechanical system shown in Figure 10.14. Choosing suitable state variables, construct a state model of the system.

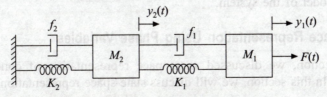

Figure 10.14 Example 10.9: Mechanical system.

Solution: Select the displacements y_1 and y_2 and their derivatives, i.e. velocities $\dot{y}_1$ and $\dot{y}_2$ as the state variables.

Let
$$x_1 = y_1$$
$$x_2 = \dot{y}_1$$
$$x_3 = y_2$$

and
$$x_4 = \dot{y}_2$$

Let
$$F(t) = u(t)$$

Therefore, $\dot{x}_1 = x_2$ and $\dot{x}_3 = x_4$. To obtain the first derivatives of x_2 and x_4, i.e. $\dot{x}_2$ and $\dot{x}_4$, write the differential equations describing the behaviour of the system. The equations governing the behaviour of the mechanical system are as follows:

$$F(t) = M_1\ddot{y}_1 + f_1(\dot{y}_1 - \dot{y}_2) + K_1(y_1 - y_2)$$

$$M_2\ddot{y}_2 + f_2\dot{y}_2 + K_2y_2 + f_1(\dot{y}_2 - \dot{y}_1) + K_1(y_2 - y_1) = 0$$

$$\dot{x}_2 = \ddot{y}_1 = \frac{F(t)}{M_1} - \frac{f_1x_2}{M_1} + \frac{f_1x_4}{M_1} - \frac{K_1x_1}{M_1} + \frac{K_1x_3}{M_1}$$

$$\dot{x}_4 = \ddot{y}_2 = -\frac{(f_1+f_2)x_4}{M_2} - \frac{(K_1+K_2)x_3}{M_2} + \frac{f_1x_2}{M_2} + \frac{K_1x_1}{M_2}$$

Therefore, the state equations and the output equations in matrix form are

$$\begin{bmatrix} \dot{x}_1 \\ \dot{x}_2 \\ \dot{x}_3 \\ \dot{x}_4 \end{bmatrix} = \begin{bmatrix} 0 & 1 & 0 & 0 \\ \dfrac{-K_1}{M_1} & \dfrac{-f_1}{M_1} & \dfrac{K_1}{M_1} & \dfrac{f_1}{M_1} \\ 0 & 0 & 0 & 1 \\ \dfrac{K_1}{M_2} & \dfrac{f_1}{M_2} & \dfrac{-(K_1+K_2)}{M_2} & \dfrac{-(f_1+f_2)}{M_2} \end{bmatrix} \begin{bmatrix} x_1 \\ x_2 \\ x_3 \\ x_4 \end{bmatrix} + \begin{bmatrix} 0 \\ \dfrac{1}{M_1} \\ 0 \\ 0 \end{bmatrix} u(t)$$

$$\begin{bmatrix} y_1 \\ y_2 \end{bmatrix} = \begin{bmatrix} 1 & 0 & 0 & 0 \\ 0 & 0 & 1 & 0 \end{bmatrix} \begin{bmatrix} x_1 \\ x_2 \\ x_3 \\ x_4 \end{bmatrix}$$

This is the state model of the system.

10.3.2 State-Space Representation Using Phase Variables

In the previous section, we discussed state-space representation of control systems using physical variables. In this section, we will discuss state-space representation of control systems using phase variables as state variables. The phase variables are defined as those particular state variables, which are obtained from one of the system variables and its derivatives. Normally, the system variable used is the system output and the remaining variables are then derivatives of the output. It is very easy to obtain the state model of a system using phase variables, but a disadvantage of phase variable formulation is that the phase variables in general are not physical variables of the system and therefore are not available for measurement and control purposes. Also it becomes difficult to take second or higher derivatives of output. In spite of these disadvantages, phase variables provide a powerful method of state variable formulation. A link between transfer function design approach and time-domain design approach is established through phase variables. The general form of an nth-order linear continuous-time system is

$$y^{(n)} + a_1 y^{(n-1)} + a_2 y^{(n-2)} + \ldots + a_n y = b_0 u^{(n)} + b_1 u^{(n-1)} + b_2 u^{(n-2)} + \ldots + b_n u$$

where for time-invariant systems, a_i's and b_j's are constants, n is an integer and $y^{(n)}$ means $d^n y/dt^n$.

The initial conditions are expressed in terms of $y(0)$, $y^{(1)}(0)$, $\ldots$, $y^{(n-1)}(0)$. For linear time-invariant systems, change of state does not depend on the initial time, but depends only on the length of the time for which the control force is applied. So assumption of zero initial conditions does not create any loss of generality. The transfer function representation of the differential equation is

$$T(s) = \frac{Y(s)}{U(s)} = \frac{b_0 s^n + b_1 s^{n-1} + \cdots + b_{n-1}s + b_n}{s^n + a_1 s^{n-1} + \cdots + a_{n-1}s + a_n}$$

State-space representation of an nth-order system in which the forcing function does not involve derivative terms: If the transfer function of the system has no zeros (i.e. the differential equation of the system has no derivatives of the input) the state model of the system can be obtained very easily as shown below.

Consider the transfer function,

$$T(s) = \frac{b}{s^n + a_1 s^{n-1} + \ldots + a_{n-1}s + a_n}$$

corresponding to the differential equation

$$y^{(n)} + a_1 y^{(n-1)} + a_2 y^{(n-2)} + \cdots + a_{n-1}y^{(1)} + a_n y = b$$

This is an nth-order system, so n state variables $x_1, x_2, \ldots, x_n$ are required. Let the first state variable be x_1 equal to the output variable y. Let the second state variable x_2 be equal to the first derivative of the output variable and so on, i.e.

$$x_1 = y$$
$$x_2 = \dot{y}$$
$$x_3 = \ddot{y}$$
$$\vdots$$
$$x_n = y^{(n-1)}$$

These equations can be reduced to a set of first-order differential equations given as follows:

$$\dot{x}_1 = x_2$$
$$\dot{x}_2 = x_3$$
$$\vdots$$
$$\dot{x}_{n-1} = x_n \qquad (10.10)$$
$$\dot{x}_n = -a_n x_1 - a_{n-1} x_2 - \cdots - a_1 x_n + bu$$

The last equation is obtained by equating the highest-order derivative term of the output in the differential equation to all other terms.

The above set of state equations [Eq. (10.10)] can be written in vector-matrix form as

$$
\begin{bmatrix} \dot{x}_1 \\ \dot{x}_2 \\ \vdots \\ \dot{x}_{n-1} \\ \dot{x}_n \end{bmatrix} = \begin{bmatrix} 0 & 1 & 0 & \cdots & 0 \\ 0 & 0 & 1 & \cdots & 0 \\ \vdots & & & & \vdots \\ 0 & 0 & 0 & \cdots & 1 \\ -a_n & -a_{n-1} & -a_{n-2} & \cdots & -a_1 \end{bmatrix} \begin{bmatrix} x_1 \\ x_2 \\ \vdots \\ x_{n-1} \\ x_n \end{bmatrix} + \begin{bmatrix} 0 \\ 0 \\ \vdots \\ 0 \\ b \end{bmatrix} u
$$

i.e. $$\dot{\mathbf{x}} = \mathbf{Ax} + \mathbf{Bu}$$

The matrix **A** has a very special form. It has all 1s in the upper off-diagonal. Its last row is comprised of the negative of the coefficients of the differential equation, and all other elements are zero. This form of matrix **A** is known as the *bush form* or the *companion form*. The matrix **B** has the speciality that all the elements in **B** except the last one are zero. In fact **A** and **B** and therefore the state equation can be written directly by inspection of the linear differential equation.

The output being $y = x_1$, the output equation is given by

$$
\mathbf{y} = \begin{bmatrix} 1 & 0 & 0 \end{bmatrix} \begin{bmatrix} x_1 \\ x_2 \\ \vdots \\ x_n \end{bmatrix}
$$

i.e. $$\mathbf{y}(t) = \mathbf{Cx}(t)$$

where $\mathbf{C} = [1, 0, \ldots, 0]$.

From the above, we can see that for the transfer functions with poles only, the derivation of the state model through the differential equations is quite straightforward. However, when a transfer function has zeros as well, the resulting differential equation contains terms which are derivates of the control force u and the method discussed above cannot be applied as such.

A block diagram representation of the state model for $\dot{\mathbf{x}} = \mathbf{Ax} + \mathbf{Bu}$ is shown in Figure 10.15.

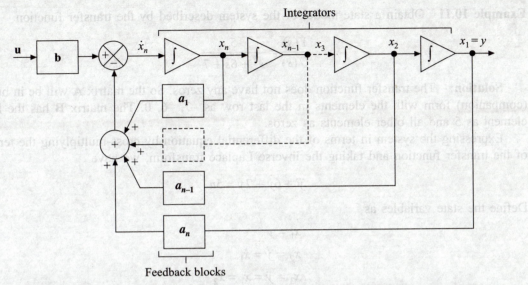

Figure 10.15 Block diagram representation of the state model for $\dot{x} = Ax + Bu$ and $y = CX$.

Example 10.10 Obtain a state model for the system described by

$$T(s) = \frac{Y(s)}{U(s)} = \frac{1}{s^3 + 6s^2 + 10s + 5}$$

Solution: The differential equation corresponding to the given transfer function is obtained by cross-multiplying and taking the inverse Laplace transform. So, we have

$$\dddot{y} + 6\ddot{y} + 10\dot{y} + 5y = u$$

Since the derivatives of the input are not present in the differential equation, phase variables can be selected as the state variables. Therefore,

$$x_1 = y \qquad \text{i.e.} \qquad y = x_1$$
$$x_2 = \dot{y} = \dot{x}_1 \qquad\qquad \dot{x}_1 = x_2$$
$$x_3 = \ddot{y} = \dot{x}_2 \qquad\qquad \dot{x}_2 = x_3$$
$$\dddot{y} = -6\ddot{y} - 10\dot{y} - 5y + u \qquad\qquad \dot{x}_3 = -5x_1 - 10x_2 - 6x_3 + u$$

Therefore, the state model is

$$\begin{bmatrix} \dot{x}_1 \\ \dot{x}_2 \\ \dot{x}_3 \end{bmatrix} = \begin{bmatrix} 0 & 1 & 0 \\ 0 & 0 & 1 \\ -5 & -10 & -6 \end{bmatrix} \begin{bmatrix} x_1 \\ x_2 \\ x_3 \end{bmatrix} + \begin{bmatrix} 0 \\ 0 \\ 1 \end{bmatrix} u$$

$$y = \begin{bmatrix} 1 & 0 & 0 \end{bmatrix} \begin{bmatrix} x_1 \\ x_2 \\ x_3 \end{bmatrix}$$

Example 10.11 Obtain a state model of the system described by the transfer function

$$\frac{Y(s)}{U(s)} = \frac{5}{s^3 + 6s + 7}$$

Solution: The transfer function does not have any zeros. So the matrix **A** will be in bush (companion) form with the elements in the last row as –7, –6, 0. The matrix **B** has the last element as 5 and all other elements as zeros.

Expressing the system in terms of the differential equation by cross-multiplying the terms of the transfer function and taking the inverse Laplace transform, we have

$$\dddot{y} + 6\dot{y} + 7y = 5u$$

Define the state variables as

$$x_1 = y$$
$$x_2 = \dot{y} = \dot{x}_1$$
$$x_3 = \ddot{y} = \ddot{x}_1 = \dot{x}_2$$

Equating the highest-order term $\dddot{y}$ to all other terms in the differential equation, we have

$$\dddot{y} = -6\dot{y} - 7y + 5u$$

i.e.

$$\dot{x}_3 = -6x_2 - 7x_1 + 5u$$

So, the first-order differential equations constituting the state equations are

$$\dot{x}_1 = x_2$$
$$\dot{x}_2 = x_3$$
$$\dot{x}_3 = -7x_1 - 6x_2 + 5u$$

The output equation is

$$y = x_1$$

The state model based on the above equations is

$$\begin{bmatrix} \dot{x}_1 \\ \dot{x}_2 \\ \dot{x}_3 \end{bmatrix} = \begin{bmatrix} 0 & 1 & 0 \\ 0 & 0 & 1 \\ -7 & -6 & 0 \end{bmatrix} \begin{bmatrix} x_1 \\ x_2 \\ x_3 \end{bmatrix} + \begin{bmatrix} 0 \\ 0 \\ 5 \end{bmatrix} u$$

$$y = \begin{bmatrix} 1 & 0 & 0 \end{bmatrix} \begin{bmatrix} x_1 \\ x_2 \\ x_3 \end{bmatrix}$$

State-space representation of an *n*th-order system in which the forcing function involves derivative terms: Consider an *n*th-order system represented by the differential equation

$$y^{(n)} + a_1 y^{(n-1)} + \ldots + a_{n-1} y^{(1)} + a_n y = b_0 u^{(n)} + b_1 u^{(n-1)} + \ldots + b_{n-1} u^{(1)} + b_n u$$

Its transfer function is

$$\frac{Y(s)}{U(s)} = \frac{b_0 s^n + b_1 s^{n-1} + \cdots + b_{n-1} s + b_n}{s^n + a_1 s^{n-1} + \cdots + a_{n-1} s + a_n}$$

Since the derivatives of the input are present in the differential equation, the output and its derivatives cannot be chosen as the state variables, i.e. phase variables cannot be selected as the state variables. The state model for the above equation may be obtained as follows.

Define the following *n* variables as a set of state variables:

$$x_1 = y - \beta_0 u$$
$$x_2 = \dot{x}_1 - \beta_1 u$$
$$x_3 = \dot{x}_2 - \beta_2 u$$
$$\vdots$$
$$x_{n-1} = \dot{x}_{n-2} - \beta_{n-2} u$$
$$x_n = \dot{x}_{n-1} - \beta_{n-1} u$$

[handwritten: $y = x_1 + \beta_0 u$; $\dot{x}_1 = x_2 + \beta_1 u$; $\dot{x}_2 = x_3 + \beta_2 u$; $\dot{x}_n = -a_n x_1 - a_{n-1} x_2 \cdots + \beta_n u$]

Therefore, the output equation is

$$y = x_1 + \beta_0 u$$

and the state equations are

$$\dot{x}_1 = x_2 + \beta_1 u$$
$$\dot{x}_2 = x_3 + \beta_2 u$$
$$\vdots$$
$$\dot{x}_{n-1} = x_n + \beta_{n-1} u$$
$$\dot{x}_n = -a_n x_1 - a_{n-1} x_2 - \cdots - a_1 x_n + \beta_n u$$

[handwritten: $\beta_0 = b_0$; $\beta_1 = b_1 - \beta_0 a_1$; $\beta_2 = b_2 - \beta_0 a_2 - \beta_1 a_1$]

where

$$\beta_0 = b_0$$
$$\beta_1 = b_1 - a_1 \beta_0$$
$$\beta_2 = b_2 - a_2 \beta_0 - a_1 \beta_1$$
$$\beta_3 = b_3 - a_3 \beta_0 - a_2 \beta_1 - a_1 \beta_2$$
$$\vdots$$
$$\beta_n = b_n - a_n \beta_0 - a_{n-1} \beta_1 - \cdots - a_2 \beta_{n-2} - a_1 \beta_{n-1}$$

In vector-matrix form, the state model is

$$
\begin{bmatrix} \dot{x}_1 \\ \dot{x}_2 \\ \vdots \\ \dot{x}_{n-1} \\ \dot{x}_n \end{bmatrix} = \begin{bmatrix} 0 & 1 & 0 & \cdots & 0 \\ 0 & 0 & 1 & \cdots & 0 \\ \vdots & & & & \\ 0 & 0 & 0 & \cdots & 1 \\ -a_n & -a_{n-1} & -a_{n-2} & \cdots & -a_1 \end{bmatrix} \begin{bmatrix} x_1 \\ x_2 \\ \vdots \\ x_{n-1} \\ x_n \end{bmatrix} + \begin{bmatrix} \beta_1 \\ \beta_2 \\ \vdots \\ \beta_{n-1} \\ \beta_n \end{bmatrix} u
$$

$$
y(t) = \begin{bmatrix} 1 & 0 & \cdots & 0 \end{bmatrix} \cdot \begin{bmatrix} x_1 \\ x_2 \\ \vdots \\ x_n \end{bmatrix} + \beta_0 u
$$

Example 10.12 Construct a state model for the system described by

$$
\ddot{y} + 7\dot{y} + 5y + 6\int_0^t y \,.\, dt = \dot{u} + 3u + 2\int_0^t u \, dt
$$

Solution: Differentiating the given integro-differential equation, we have

$$
\dddot{y} + 7\ddot{y} + 5\dot{y} + 6y = \ddot{u} + 3\dot{u} + 2u
$$

Comparing this with the standard third-order differential equation, we have

$$
\dddot{y} + a_1\ddot{y} + a_2\dot{y} + a_3 y = b_0\dddot{u} + b_1\ddot{u} + b_2\dot{u} + b_3 u
$$

$$
a_1 = 7, \ a_2 = 5, \ a_3 = 6 \quad \text{and} \quad b_0 = 0, \ b_1 = 1, \ b_2 = 3, \ b_3 = 2
$$

Therefore,

$$
\beta_0 = b_0 = 0
$$
$$
\beta_1 = b_1 - a_1\beta_0 = 1 - 7 \times 0 = 1
$$
$$
\beta_2 = b_2 - a_2\beta_0 - a_1\beta_1 = 3 - 5 \times 0 - 7 \times 1 = -4
$$
$$
\beta_3 = b_3 - a_3\beta_0 - a_2\beta_1 - a_1\beta_2 = 2 - 6 \times 0 - 5 \times 1 - 7 \times (-4) = 25
$$

The state variables are defined as

$$
x_1 = y - \beta_0 u
$$
$$
x_2 = \dot{x}_1 - \beta_1 u
$$
$$
x_3 = \dot{x}_2 - \beta_2 u
$$

Also $\dot{x}_3 = -a_3 x_1 - a_2 x_2 - a_1 x_3 + \beta_3 u$

The state and output equations are therefore

$$
y = x_1 + \beta_0 u
$$
$$
\dot{x}_1 = x_2 + \beta_1 u
$$
$$
\dot{x}_2 = x_3 + \beta_2 u
$$
$$
\dot{x}_3 = -6x_1 - 5x_2 - 7x_1 + 25u
$$

The state model in vector-matrix form is

$$\begin{bmatrix} \dot{x}_1 \\ \dot{x}_2 \\ \dot{x}_3 \end{bmatrix} = \begin{bmatrix} 0 & 1 & 0 \\ 0 & 0 & 1 \\ -6 & -5 & -7 \end{bmatrix} \begin{bmatrix} x_1 \\ x_2 \\ x_3 \end{bmatrix} + \begin{bmatrix} 1 \\ -4 \\ 25 \end{bmatrix} u$$

$$y = \begin{bmatrix} 1 & 0 & 0 \end{bmatrix} \begin{bmatrix} x_1 \\ x_2 \\ x_3 \end{bmatrix}$$

Example 10.13 The transfer function of a control system is given by

$$\frac{Y(s)}{U(s)} = \frac{s^2 + 3s + 4}{s^3 + 2s^2 + 3s + 2}$$

Obtain a state model.

Solution: The corresponding differential equation obtained by cross-multiplying and taking the inverse Laplace transform is

$$\dddot{y} + 2\ddot{y} + 3\dot{y} + 2y = \ddot{u} + 3\dot{u} + 4u$$

Comparing this differential equation with the standard differential equation of a third-order system, we have

$$\dddot{y} + a_1\ddot{y} + a_2\dot{y} + a_3 y = b_0\dddot{u} + b_1\ddot{u} + b_2\dot{u} + b_3 u$$

i.e. $a_1 = 2, \ a_2 = 3, \ a_3 = 2 \quad \text{and} \quad b_0 = 0, \ b_1 = 1, \ b_2 = 3, \ b_3 = 4$

Therefore,

$$\beta_0 = b_0 = 0$$
$$\beta_1 = b_1 - a_1\beta_0 = 1 - 2 \times 0 = 1$$
$$\beta_2 = b_2 - a_2\beta_0 - a_1\beta_1 = 3 - 3 \times 0 - 2 \times 1 = 1$$
$$\beta_3 = b_3 - a_3\beta_0 - a_2\beta_1 - a_1\beta_2 = 4 - 2 \times 0 - 3 \times 1 - 2 \times 1 = -1$$

The state variables are as follows: The state and output equations are as follows:

$$x_1 = y - \beta_0 u \qquad\qquad y = x_1 + \beta_0 u = x_1$$
$$x_2 = \dot{x}_1 - \beta_1 u \qquad\qquad \dot{x}_1 = x_2 + \beta_1 u = x_2 + u$$
$$x_3 = \dot{x}_2 - \beta_2 u \qquad\qquad \dot{x}_2 = x_3 + \beta_2 u = x_3 + u$$

Also $\dot{x}_3 = -a_3 x_1 - a_2 x_2 - a_1 x_3 + \beta_3 u \qquad \dot{x}_3 = -2x_1 - 3x_2 - 2x_3 - u$

Hence the state model is

$$\begin{bmatrix} \dot{x}_1 \\ \dot{x}_2 \\ \dot{x}_3 \end{bmatrix} = \begin{bmatrix} 0 & 1 & 0 \\ 0 & 0 & 1 \\ -2 & -3 & -2 \end{bmatrix} \begin{bmatrix} x_1 \\ x_2 \\ x_3 \end{bmatrix} + \begin{bmatrix} 1 \\ 1 \\ -1 \end{bmatrix} u$$

$$y = \begin{bmatrix} 1 & 0 & 0 \end{bmatrix} \begin{bmatrix} x_1 \\ x_2 \\ x_3 \end{bmatrix}$$

An alternative method using signal flow graphs is presented as follows:

Alternative way of obtaining the state model using signal flow graph when the transfer functions have poles and zeros: Let us consider an *n*th-order transfer function

$$T(s) = \frac{Y(s)}{U(s)} = \frac{b_0 s^n + b_1 s^{n-1} + \cdots + b_{n-1}s + b_n}{s^n + a_1 s^{n-1} + \cdots + a_{n-1}s + a_n}$$

Let the state variables be x_1, x_2, ..., x_n.

The signal flow graph must have *n* integrators. By dividing the numerator and denominator of $T(s)$ by s^n, the above transfer function may be rearranged as

$$T(s) = \frac{b_0 + b_1 s^{-1} + b_2 s^{-2} + \dots + b_{n-1}s^{-n+1} + b_n s^{-n}}{1 + a_1 s^{-1} + a_2 s^{-2} + \dots + a_{n-1}s^{-n+1} + a_n s^{-n}}$$

$$= \frac{b_0 + b_1 s^{-1} + b_2 s^{-2} + \dots + b_{n-1}s^{-n+1} + b_n s^{-n}}{1 - (-a_1 s^{-1} - a_2 s^{-2} - \dots - a_{n-1}s^{-n+1} - a_n s^{-n})}$$

Earlier we have seen that the transfer function and signal flow graph are related by Mason's gain formula:

$$T(s) = \sum_k \frac{M_k \Delta_k}{\Delta}$$

where M_k = the path gain of the *k*th forward path

Δ (Determinant of the signal flow graph)

= 1 − (sum of loop gains of all individual loops)

+ (sum of gain products of all possible combinations of two non touching loops)

− (sum of gain products of all possible combinations of three non touching loops) +...

Δ_k = the value of Δ for that part of the graph not touching the *k*th forward path.

Comparing the above expressions for $T(s)$, we observe that the signal flow graph for $T(s)$ may consist of

1. *n* feedback loops (touching each other) with gains $-a_1 s^{-1}$, $-a_2 s^{-2}$, ..., $-a_{n-1}s^{-n+1}$, $-a_n s^{-n}$
2. *n* + 1 forward paths which touch the loops and have gains b_0, $b_1 s^{-1}$, $b_2 s^{-2}$, ..., $b_{n-1}s^{-n+1}$, $b_n s^{-n}$

The signal flow graph configuration which satisfies the above requirements is shown in Figure 10.16.

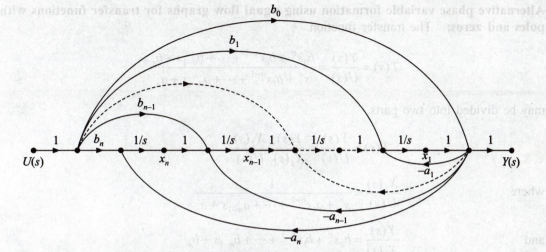

Figure 10.16 Signal flow graph for *n*th-order system with zeros.

Choosing the outputs of the integrators as the state variables and ordering the state variables x_1 to x_n from right to left, we have

$$y = x_1 + b_0 u$$
$$\dot{x}_1 = -a_1 x_1 + x_2 + (b_1 - a_1 b_0)u$$
$$\dot{x}_2 = -a_2 x_1 + x_3 + (b_2 - a_2 b_0)u$$
$$\vdots$$
$$\dot{x}_{n-1} = -a_{n-1} x_1 + x_n + (b_{n-1} - a_{n-1} b_0)u$$
$$\dot{x}_n = -a_n x_1 + (b_n - a_n b_0)u$$

In matrix form, the state model is

$$
\begin{bmatrix} \dot{x}_1 \\ \dot{x}_2 \\ \vdots \\ \dot{x}_{n-1} \\ \dot{x}_n \end{bmatrix} =
\begin{bmatrix} -a_1 & 1 & 0 & \cdots & 0 \\ -a_2 & 0 & 1 & \cdots & 0 \\ \vdots & & & & \\ -a_{n-1} & 0 & 0 & \cdots & 1 \\ -a_n & 0 & 0 & \cdots & 0 \end{bmatrix}
\begin{bmatrix} x_1 \\ x_2 \\ \vdots \\ x_{n-1} \\ x_n \end{bmatrix} +
\begin{bmatrix} b_1 - a_1 b_0 \\ b_2 - a_2 b_0 \\ \vdots \\ b_{n-1} - a_{n-1} b_0 \\ b_n - a_n b_0 \end{bmatrix} u
$$

$$
y = \begin{bmatrix} 1 & 0 & \cdots & 0 & 0 \end{bmatrix}
\begin{bmatrix} x_1 \\ x_2 \\ \vdots \\ x_{n-1} \\ x_n \end{bmatrix} + b_0 u
$$

Alternative phase variable formation using signal flow graphs for transfer functions with poles and zeros: The transfer function

$$T(s) = \frac{Y(s)}{U(s)} = \frac{b_0 s^n + b_1 s^{n-1} + \cdots + b_{n-1}s + b_n}{s^n + a_1 s^{n-1} + \cdots + a_{n-1}s + a_n}$$

may be divided into two parts.

$$T(s) = \frac{Y(s)}{U(s)} = \frac{Y(s)}{X_1(s)} \cdot \frac{X_1(s)}{U(s)}$$

where

$$\frac{X_1(s)}{U(s)} = \frac{1}{s^n + a_1 s^{n-1} + \cdots + a_{n-1}s + a_n}$$

and

$$\frac{Y(s)}{X_1(s)} = b_0 s^n + b_1 s^{n-1} + \cdots + b_{n-1}s + b_n$$

$U(s)$ → $\boxed{\dfrac{b_0 s^n + b_1 s^{n-1} + \ldots + b_{n-1}s + b_n}{s^n + a_1 s^{n-1} + \ldots + a_{n-1}s + a_n}}$ → $Y(s)$

$U(s)$ → $\boxed{\dfrac{1}{s^n + a_1 s^{n-1} + \ldots + a_{n-1}s + a_n}}$ → $X_1(s)$ → $\boxed{b_0 s^n + b_1 s^{n-1} + \ldots + b_{n-1}s + b_n}$ → $Y(s)$

The transfer function $\dfrac{X_1(s)}{U(s)}$ is without zeros and therefore its phase variable representation may be obtained as

$$\begin{bmatrix} \dot{x}_1 \\ \dot{x}_2 \\ \vdots \\ \dot{x}_{n-1} \\ \dot{x}_n \end{bmatrix} = \begin{bmatrix} 0 & 1 & 0 & \cdots & 0 \\ 0 & 0 & 1 & \cdots & 0 \\ \vdots & & & & \\ 0 & 0 & 0 & \cdots & 1 \\ -a_n & -a_{n-1} & -a_{n-2} & \cdots & -a_1 \end{bmatrix} \begin{bmatrix} x_1 \\ x_2 \\ \vdots \\ x_{n-1} \\ x_n \end{bmatrix} + \begin{bmatrix} 0 \\ 0 \\ \vdots \\ 0 \\ 1 \end{bmatrix} u$$

From the transfer function $\dfrac{Y(s)}{X_1(s)}$, we get

$$y = b_0 x_1^{(n)} + b_1 x_1^{(n-1)} + \cdots + b_{n-1} x_1^{(1)} + b_n x_1$$

$$= b_0(-a_n x_1 - a_{n-1} x_2 \cdots - a_1 x_n + u) + b_1 x_n + b_2 x_{n-1} + \cdots b_n x_1$$

$$= (b_n - a_n b_0)x_1 + (b_{n-1} - a_{n-1} b_0)x_2 + \cdots + (b_1 - a_1 b_0)x_n + b_0 u$$

The output equation can be written in vector-matrix form as

$$y = [(b_n - a_n b_0)\ (b_{n-1} - a_{n-1} b_0)\ \cdots\ (b_1 - a_1 b_0)] \begin{bmatrix} x_1 \\ x_2 \\ \vdots \\ x_n \end{bmatrix} + b_0 u$$

The signal flow graph corresponding to the above state model is drawn in Figure 10.17.

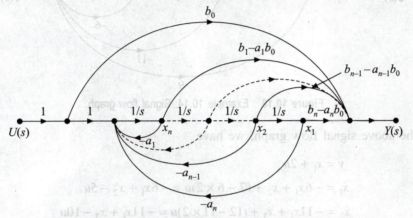

Figure 10.17 Alternative signal flow graph for *n*th-order system with zeros.

Example 10.14 Obtain a state model for the system described by

$$T(s) = \frac{Y(s)}{U(s)} = \frac{2s^3 + 7s^2 + 12s + 8}{s^3 + 6s^2 + 11s + 9}$$

Solution: The given transfer function is of third-order and hence 3 state variables x_1, x_2 and x_3 are identified. The transfer function can be written as

$$T(s) = \frac{Y(s)}{U(s)} = \frac{2 + 7s^{-1} + 12s^{-2} + 8s^{-3}}{1 - (-6s^{-1} - 11s^{-2} - 9s^{-3})}$$

So the corresponding signal flow graph will have three feedback loops with gains $-6s^{-1}$, $-11s^{-2}$ and $-9s^{-3}$ and four forward paths which touch the loops and have gains 2, $7s^{-1}$, $12s^{-2}$, and $8s^{-3}$.

A signal flow graph configuration which satisfies the above requirements is shown in Figure 10.18.

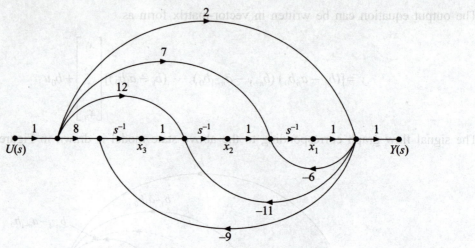

Figure 10.18 Example 10.14: Signal flow graph.

From the above signal flow graph, we have

$$y = x_1 + 2u$$

$$\dot{x}_1 = -6x_1 + x_2 + (7 - 6 \times 2)u = -6x_1 + x_2 - 5u$$

$$\dot{x}_2 = -11x_1 + x_3 + (12 - 11 \times 2)u = -11x_1 + x_3 - 10u$$

$$\dot{x}_3 = -9x_1 + (8 - 9 \times 2)u = -9x_1 - 10u$$

In matrix form, the state model is

$$\begin{bmatrix} \dot{x}_1 \\ \dot{x}_2 \\ \dot{x}_3 \end{bmatrix} = \begin{bmatrix} -6 & 1 & 0 \\ -11 & 0 & 1 \\ -9 & 0 & 0 \end{bmatrix} \begin{bmatrix} x_1 \\ x_2 \\ x_3 \end{bmatrix} + \begin{bmatrix} -5 \\ -10 \\ -10 \end{bmatrix} u$$

$$y = \begin{bmatrix} 1 & 0 & 0 \end{bmatrix} \begin{bmatrix} x_1 \\ x_2 \\ x_3 \end{bmatrix} + 2u$$

Alternative way: The given transfer function is divided into two parts

$$T(s) = \frac{Y(s)}{U(s)} = \frac{X_1(s)}{U(s)} \cdot \frac{Y(s)}{X_1(s)} = \frac{1}{s^3 + 6s^2 + 11s + 9}(2s^3 + 7s^2 + 12s + 8)$$

The first part

$$\frac{X_1(s)}{U(s)} = \frac{1}{s^3 + 6s^2 + 11s + 9}$$

is without zeros and therefore its phase variable representation is

$$\begin{bmatrix} \dot{x}_1 \\ \dot{x}_2 \\ \dot{x}_3 \end{bmatrix} = \begin{bmatrix} 0 & 1 & 0 \\ 0 & 0 & 1 \\ -9 & -11 & -6 \end{bmatrix} \begin{bmatrix} x_1 \\ x_2 \\ x_3 \end{bmatrix} + \begin{bmatrix} 0 \\ 0 \\ 1 \end{bmatrix} u$$

From the transfer function

$$\frac{Y(s)}{X_1(s)} = 2s^3 + 7s^2 + 12s + 8,$$

we get

$$y = 2\dddot{x}_1 + 7\ddot{x}_1 + 12\dot{x}_1 + 8x_1 = 2\dot{x}_3 + 7\dot{x}_2 + 12\dot{x}_1 + 8x_1$$

$$= 2(-9x_1 - 11x_2 - 6x_3 + u) + 7x_3 + 12x_2 + 8x_1$$

$$= -10x_1 - 10x_2 - 5x_3 + 2u$$

In vector-matrix form, the output equation is

$$y = \begin{bmatrix} -10 & -10 & -5 \end{bmatrix} \begin{bmatrix} x_1 \\ x_2 \\ x_3 \end{bmatrix} + 2u$$

The signal flow graph corresponding to the above state and output equations is drawn as shown in Figure 10.19.

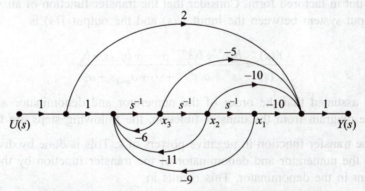

Figure 10.19 Example 10.14: Alternative signal flow graph.

10.4 DECOMPOSITION OF TRANSFER FUNCTIONS

We know that a linear system can be modeled by differential equations, transfer function, or dynamic equations. All these methods are closely related. The state diagram is a useful tool that not only can lead to the solution of the state equations but also serves as a vehicle of transformation from one form of description to the others. The block diagram of Figure 10.20

shows the relationship between the various ways of describing a linear system. The block diagram shows that starting for instance with the differential equation of a system, one can get to the solution by use of the transfer function method or the state equation method. The block diagram also shows that the majority of the relationships are bilateral, so a great deal of flexibility exists between the methods.

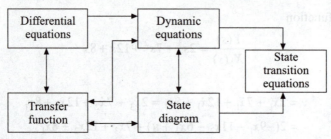

Figure 10.20 Block diagram showing the relationships among various methods of describing linear systems.

The process of going from the transfer function to the state diagram is called decomposition. In general there are three basic methods of decomposition of transfer functions: direct decomposition, cascade decomposition, and parallel decomposition. Each of these three schemes of decomposition has its own merits and is best suited for a particular purpose.

10.4.1 Direct Decomposition

First companion form: The direct decomposition is applied to an input-output transfer function that is not in factored form. Consider that the transfer function of an nth-order single-input-single-output system between the input $U(s)$ and the output $Y(s)$ is

$$\frac{Y(s)}{U(s)} = \frac{b_0 s^n + b_1 s^{n-1} + \cdots + b_{n-1}s + b_n}{s^n + a_1 s^{n-1} + \cdots + a_{n-1}s + a_n}$$

where we have assumed that the order of the numerator and denominator are the same. To construct a state diagram from the transfer function, the following steps are to be followed.

1. Express the transfer function in negative powers of s. This is done by dividing each term present in the numerator and denominator of the transfer function by the highest power of s present in the denominator. This results in

$$\frac{Y(s)}{U(s)} = \frac{b_0 + b_1 s^{-1} + b_2 s^{-2} + \cdots + b_{n-1}s^{-n+1} + b_n s^{-n}}{1 + a_1 s^{-1} + a_2 s^{-2} + \cdots + a_{n-1}s^{-n+1} + a_n s^{-n}} \qquad (10.11)$$

2. Multiply and divide the transfer function [Eq. (10.11)] by a dummy variable $X(s)$. This results in

$$\frac{Y(s)}{U(s)} = \frac{b_0 + b_1 s^{-1} + b_2 s^{-2} + \cdots + b_{n-1}s^{-n+1} + b_n s^{-n}}{1 + a_1 s^{-1} + a_2 s^{-2} + \cdots + a_{n-1}s^{-n+1} + a_n s^{-n}} \frac{X(s)}{X(s)} \qquad (10.12)$$

3. Equate the numerators and denominators on both sides of Eq. (10.12):

$$Y(s) = (b_0 + b_1 s^{-1} + \cdots + b_{n-1} s^{-n+1} + b_n s^{-n})X(s) \tag{10.13}$$

$$U(s) = (1 + a_1 s^{-1} + \cdots + a_{n-1} s^{-n+1} + a_n s^{-n})X(s) \tag{10.14}$$

4. Write the equations in cause-and-effect form. The equation for $Y(s)$ is already in cause-and-effect form. Write the equation for $U(s)$ in cause-and-effect form. Therefore,

$$X(s) = U(s) - a_1 s^{-1}X(s) - a_2 s^{-2}X(s) - \cdots - a_{n-1} s^{-n+1}X(s) - a_n s^{-n}X(s)$$

5. Construct the state diagram based on equations for $Y(s)$ and $X(s)$ as shown in Figure 10.21.

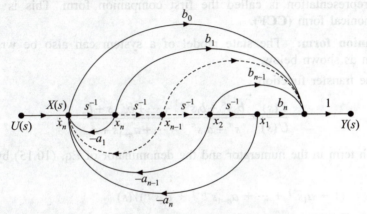

Figure 10.21 State diagram for direct decomposition (first companion form).

The state variables $x_1(t)$, $x_2(t)$, ..., $x_n(t)$ are defined as the outputs of the integrators and arranged in order from right to left on the state diagram. The state equations are obtained by expressing the first derivatives of the state variables in terms of the state variables and the input by applying signal flow graph gain formula.

From the state diagram, the dynamic equations are as follows:

$$\dot{x}_1(t) = x_2(t)$$
$$\dot{x}_2(t) = x_3(t)$$
$$\vdots$$
$$\dot{x}_{n-1}(t) = x_n(t)$$
$$\dot{x}_n(t) = -a_n x_1(t) - a_{n-1} x_2(t) - \cdots - a_1 x_n(t) + u(t)$$

and
$$y(t) = (b_n - a_n b_0)x_1(t) + (b_{n-1} - a_{n-1}b_0)x_2(t) + \cdots + (b_1 - a_1 b_0)x_n(t) + b_0 u(t)$$

Writing them in matrix form, the state model is

$$
\begin{bmatrix} \dot{x}_1(t) \\ \dot{x}_2(t) \\ \vdots \\ \dot{x}_{n-1}(t) \\ \dot{x}_n(t) \end{bmatrix}
=
\begin{bmatrix}
0 & 1 & 0 & \cdots & 0 \\
0 & 0 & 1 & \cdots & 0 \\
\vdots & & & & \vdots \\
0 & 0 & 0 & \cdots & 1 \\
-a_n & -a_{n-1} & -a_{n-2} & \cdots & -a_1
\end{bmatrix}
\begin{bmatrix} x_1(t) \\ x_2(t) \\ \vdots \\ x_{n-1}(t) \\ x_n(t) \end{bmatrix}
+
\begin{bmatrix} 0 \\ 0 \\ \vdots \\ 0 \\ 1 \end{bmatrix} u(t)
$$

$$y(t) = [(b_n - a_n b_0)\ (b_{n-1} - a_{n-1} b_0)\ \cdots\ (b_1 - a_1 b_0)] \begin{bmatrix} x_1(t) \\ x_2(t) \\ \vdots \\ x_n(t) \end{bmatrix} + b_0 u(t)$$

With usual notation, the state model is

$$\dot{x}(t) = Ax(t) + Bu(t)$$
$$y(t) = Cx(t) + Du(t)$$

This form of representation is called the first companion form. This is also called the controllable canonical form **(CCF)**.

Second companion form: The state model of a system can also be written in second companion form as shown below.

Consider the transfer function

$$\frac{Y(s)}{U(s)} = \frac{b_0 s^n + b_1 s^{n-1} + \cdots + b_{n-1} s + b_n}{s^n + a_1 s^{n-1} + \cdots + a_{n-1} s + a_n} \tag{10.15}$$

Multiplying each term in the numerator and the denominator of Eq. (10.15) by s^{-n} and cross-multiplying,

$$(1 + a_1 s^{-1} + \cdots + a_{n-1} s^{-n+1} + a_n s^{-n}) Y(s)$$
$$= (b_0 + b_1 s^{-1} + \cdots + b_{n-1} s^{-n+1} + b_n s^{-n}) U(s)$$

i.e.
$$Y(s) = (-a_1 s^{-1} - \cdots - a_{n-1} s^{-n+1} - a_n s^{-n}) Y(s)$$
$$+ (b_0 + b_1 s^{-1} + \cdots + b_{n-1} s^{-n+1} + b_n s^{-n}) U(s) \tag{10.16}$$

Figure 10.22 shows the state diagram form of Eq. (10.16). The outputs of the integrators are designated as the state variables. However, unlike the usual convention, the state variables are assigned in descending order from right to left.

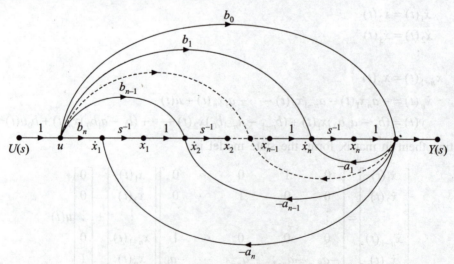

Figure 10.22 State diagram for second companion form.

From the state diagram of Figure 10.22, the dynamic equations of the system are as follows:

$$
\begin{bmatrix} \dot{x}_1(t) \\ \dot{x}_2(t) \\ \dot{x}_3(t) \\ \vdots \\ \dot{x}_n(t) \end{bmatrix} = \begin{bmatrix} 0 & 0 & 0 & -a_n \\ 1 & 0 & 0 & -a_{n-1} \\ 0 & 1 & 0 & -a_{n-2} \\ \vdots & & & \\ 0 & 0 & 1 & -a_1 \end{bmatrix} \begin{bmatrix} x_1(t) \\ x_2(t) \\ x_3(t) \\ \vdots \\ x_n(t) \end{bmatrix} + \begin{bmatrix} b_n - a_n b_0 \\ b_{n-1} - a_{n-1} b_0 \\ b_{n-2} - a_{n-2} b_0 \\ \vdots \\ b_1 - a_1 b_0 \end{bmatrix} u(t)
$$

$$
y(t) = [0 \quad 0 \quad \cdots \quad 1] x(t)
$$

This form of representation is called the observable canonical form **(OCF)**.

Example 10.15 Obtain two companion forms for the system whose input-output transfer function is

$$
\frac{Y(s)}{U(s)} = \frac{2s^2 + 3s + 1}{s^3 + 5s^2 + 6s + 7}
$$

Solution: *First companion form (direct decomposition method)*: The given transfer function is

$$
T(s) = \frac{Y(s)}{U(s)} = \frac{2s^2 + 3s + 1}{s^3 + 5s^2 + 6s + 7}
$$

Multiplication of each term in the numerator and denominator polynomials by s^{-3} gives

$$
\frac{Y(s)}{U(s)} = \frac{2s^{-1} + 3s^{-2} + s^{-3}}{1 + 5s^{-1} + 6s^{-2} + 7s^{-3}}
$$

Multiplying the numerator and the denominator polynomials by a dummy variable $X(s)$,

$$
\frac{Y(s)}{U(s)} = \frac{2s^{-1} + 3s^{-2} + s^{-3}}{1 + 5s^{-1} + 6s^{-2} + 7s^{-3}} \frac{X(s)}{X(s)}
$$

Equating the numerators and denominators on either side,

$$
Y(s) = 2s^{-1}X(s) + 3s^{-2}X(s) + s^{-3}X(s)
$$
$$
U(s) = X(s) + 5s^{-1}X(s) + 6s^{-2}X(s) + 7s^{-3}X(s)
$$

The equation for $Y(s)$ is already in cause-and-effect form. Writing the equation for $U(s)$ in cause-and-effect form

$$
X(s) = U(s) - 5s^{-1}X(s) - 6s^{-2}X(s) - 7s^{-3}X(s)
$$

The state diagram based on the above equations for $Y(s)$ and $U(s)$ is shown in Figure 10.23.

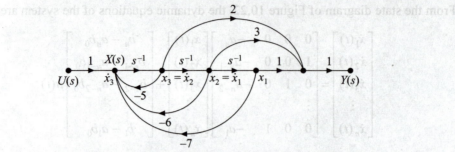

Figure 10.23 Example 10.15: State diagram (first companion form).

From the state diagram, the state equations are as follows:

$$\dot{x}_1 = x_2$$

$$\dot{x}_2 = x_3$$

$$\dot{x}_3 = -7x_1 - 6x_2 - 5x_3 + u$$

and the output equation is

$$y = x_1 + 3x_2 + 2x_3$$

The state model in matrix form is

$$\begin{bmatrix} \dot{x}_1 \\ \dot{x}_2 \\ \dot{x}_3 \end{bmatrix} = \begin{bmatrix} 0 & 1 & 0 \\ 0 & 0 & 1 \\ -7 & -6 & -5 \end{bmatrix} \begin{bmatrix} x_1 \\ x_2 \\ x_3 \end{bmatrix} + \begin{bmatrix} 0 \\ 0 \\ 1 \end{bmatrix} u$$

$$y = \begin{bmatrix} 1 & 3 & 2 \end{bmatrix} \begin{bmatrix} x_1 \\ x_2 \\ x_3 \end{bmatrix}$$

Second companion form: For the second companion form, the equation is expanded to

$$Y(s) = -(5s^{-1} + 6s^{-2} + 7s^{-3})Y(s) + (2s^{-1} + 3s^{-2} + s^{-3})U(s)$$

by multiplying each term in the numerator and the denominator of the given transfer function by s^{-3} and cross-multiplying.

The state diagram based on the above equation is shown in Figure 10.24.

Choosing the outputs of the integrators as the state variables, the state equations and output equations are as follows:

$$\dot{x}_1 = u - 7x_3$$

$$\dot{x}_2 = 3u - 6x_3 + x_1$$

$$\dot{x}_3 = 2u - 5x_3 + x_2$$

$$y = x_3$$

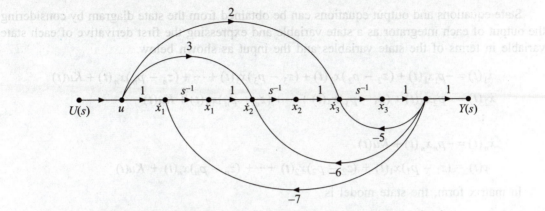

Figure 10.24 Example 10.15: State diagram (second companion form).

The state model in matrix form is

$$\begin{bmatrix} \dot{x}_1 \\ \dot{x}_2 \\ \dot{x}_3 \end{bmatrix} = \begin{bmatrix} 0 & 0 & -7 \\ 1 & 0 & -6 \\ 0 & 1 & -5 \end{bmatrix} \begin{bmatrix} x_1 \\ x_2 \\ x_3 \end{bmatrix} + \begin{bmatrix} 1 \\ 3 \\ 2 \end{bmatrix} u$$

$$y = \begin{bmatrix} 0 & 0 & 1 \end{bmatrix} \begin{bmatrix} x_1 \\ x_2 \\ x_3 \end{bmatrix}$$

10.4.2 Cascade Decomposition

Cascade decomposition is applied to transfer functions that are written as products of simple first- or second-order components.

Consider the following transfer function which is the product of n first-order transfer functions.

$$\frac{Y(s)}{U(s)} = K \left(\frac{s + z_1}{s + p_1} \right) \left(\frac{s + z_2}{s + p_2} \right) \cdots \left(\frac{s + z_n}{s + p_n} \right)$$

where $p_1, p_2, ..., p_n$ and $z_1, z_2, ..., z_n$ are all real constants. To obtain the state diagram, decompose each first-order transfer function by direct decomposition and connect all the state diagrams in cascade as shown in Figure 10.25.

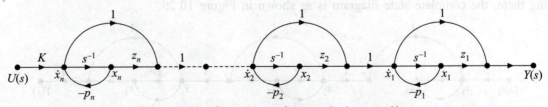

Figure 10.25 State diagram for cascade decomposition.

State equations and output equations can be obtained from the state diagram by considering the output of each integrator as a state variable and expressing the first derivative of each state variable in terms of the state variables and the input as shown below.

$$\dot{x}_1(t) = -p_1 x_1(t) + (z_2 - p_2)x_2(t) + (z_3 - p_3)x_3(t) + \cdots + (z_n - p_n)x_n(t) + Ku(t)$$

$$\dot{x}_2(t) = -p_2 x_2(t) + (z_3 - p_3)x_3(t) + \cdots + (z_n - p_n)x_n(t) + Ku(t)$$

$$\vdots$$

$$\dot{x}_n(t) = -p_n x_n(t) + Ku(t)$$

$$y(t) = (z_1 - p_1)x_1(t) + (z_2 - p_2)x_2(t) + \cdots + (z_n - p_n)x_n(t) + Ku(t)$$

In matrix form, the state model is

$$
\begin{bmatrix} \dot{x}_1(t) \\ \dot{x}_2(t) \\ \vdots \\ \dot{x}_n(t) \end{bmatrix}
=
\begin{bmatrix}
-p_1 & (z_2 - p_2) & (z_3 - p_3) & \cdots & (z_n - p_n) \\
0 & -p_2 & (z_3 - p_3) & \cdots & (z_n - p_n) \\
\vdots & & & & \vdots \\
0 & 0 & 0 & \cdots & -p_n
\end{bmatrix}
\begin{bmatrix} x_1(t) \\ x_2(t) \\ \vdots \\ x_n(t) \end{bmatrix}
+
\begin{bmatrix} K \\ K \\ \vdots \\ K \end{bmatrix} u(t)
$$

$$
y(t) = [(z_1 - p_1) \quad (z_2 - p_2) \quad \cdots \quad (z_n - p_n)]
\begin{bmatrix} x_1(t) \\ x_2(t) \\ x_3(t) \end{bmatrix} + Ku(t)
$$

The cascade decomposition has the advantage that the poles and zeros of the transfer function appear as isolated branch gains on the state diagram. This facilitates the study of the effects on the system when the poles and zeros are varied.

Example 10.16 Decompose the transfer function

$$\frac{Y(s)}{U(s)} = \frac{5(s^3 + 5s^2 + 6s)}{s^3 + 6s^2 + 9s + 4}$$

by cascade decomposition.

Solution: Factorizing the numerator and the denominator polynomials, the given transfer function can be written as

$$\frac{Y(s)}{U(s)} = 5\left(\frac{s}{s+1}\right)\left(\frac{s+2}{s+1}\right)\left(\frac{s+3}{s+4}\right)$$

Drawing the state diagram for each first-order transfer function independently and cascading them, the complete state diagram is as shown in Figure 10.26.

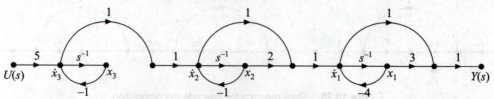

Figure 10.26 Example 10.16: State diagram.

Choosing the outputs of the integrators as the state variables, the state model is

$$\dot{x}_1 = (-4)x_1 + (2-1)x_2 + (0-1)x_3 + 5u = -4x_1 + x_2 - x_3 + 5u$$
$$\dot{x}_2 = (-1)x_2 + (0-1)x_3 + 5u = -x_2 - x_3 + 5u$$
$$\dot{x}_3 = (-1)x_3 + 5u = -x_3 + 5u$$
$$y = (3-4)x_1 + (2-1)x_2 + (0-1)x_3 + 5u = -x_1 + x_2 - x_3 + 5u$$

In matrix form, the state model is

$$\begin{bmatrix} \dot{x}_1 \\ \dot{x}_2 \\ \dot{x}_3 \end{bmatrix} = \begin{bmatrix} -4 & 1 & -1 \\ 0 & -1 & -1 \\ 0 & 0 & -1 \end{bmatrix} \begin{bmatrix} x_1 \\ x_2 \\ x_3 \end{bmatrix} + \begin{bmatrix} 5 \\ 5 \\ 5 \end{bmatrix} u$$

$$y = \begin{bmatrix} -1 & 1 & -1 \end{bmatrix} \begin{bmatrix} x_1 \\ x_2 \\ x_3 \end{bmatrix} + 5u$$

Example 10.17 Obtain a state model of the system described by the transfer function

$$\frac{Y(s)}{U(s)} = 6\left[\frac{s+3}{s+2}\right]\left[\frac{s+2.5}{s^2+4s+5}\right]$$

Solution: The state diagram of the system shown in Figure 10.27 will be the cascade of the state diagrams of the two sub systems.

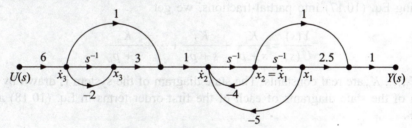

Figure 10.27 Example 10.17: State diagram.

From the state diagram, the state model is given by the following state and output equations:

$$\dot{x}_1 = x_2$$
$$\dot{x}_2 = -5x_1 - 4x_2 + x_3 + 6u$$
$$\dot{x}_3 = -2x_3 + 6u$$
$$y = 2.5x_1 + x_2$$

In matrix form, the state model is

$$\begin{bmatrix} \dot{x}_1 \\ \dot{x}_2 \\ \dot{x}_3 \end{bmatrix} = \begin{bmatrix} 0 & 1 & 0 \\ -5 & -4 & 1 \\ 0 & 0 & -2 \end{bmatrix} \begin{bmatrix} x_1 \\ x_2 \\ x_3 \end{bmatrix} + \begin{bmatrix} 0 \\ 6 \\ 6 \end{bmatrix} u$$

$$y = \begin{bmatrix} 2.5 & 1 & 0 \end{bmatrix} \begin{bmatrix} x_1 \\ x_2 \\ x_3 \end{bmatrix}$$

10.4.3 Parallel Decomposition

When the denominator of the transfer function is in factored form, the transfer function may be expanded by partial-fraction expansion. The resulting state diagram will consist of simple first- and second-order systems connected in parallel, which leads to state equations in canonical form or Jordan canonical form.

Consider an nth-order system represented by

$$\frac{Y(s)}{U(s)} = \frac{Q(s)}{(s + p_1)(s + p_2) \cdots (s + p_n)} \tag{10.17}$$

where $Q(s)$ is a polynomial of order less than n and $p_1, p_2, \ldots, p_n$ are real and distinct. Although analytically $p_1, p_2, \ldots, p_n$ may be complex, realistically complex numbers are difficult to implement on a computer.

Expanding Eq. (10.17) into partial-fractions, we get

$$\frac{Y(s)}{U(s)} = \frac{K_1}{s + p_1} + \frac{K_2}{s + p_2} + \cdots + \frac{K_n}{s + p_n} \tag{10.18}$$

where $K_1, K_2, \ldots, K_n$ are real constants. The state diagram of the system is drawn by the parallel combination of the state diagrams of each of the first-order terms in Eq. (10.18) as shown in Figure 10.28.

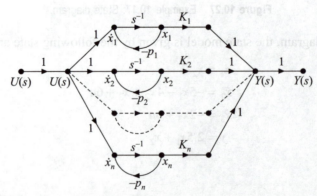

Figure 10.28 State diagram by parallel decomposition (only non-repeated poles).

Again selecting the outputs of the integrators as the state variables, the dynamic equations of the system in matrix form are as follows:

$$
\begin{bmatrix} \dot{x}_1(t) \\ \dot{x}_2(t) \\ \vdots \\ \dot{x}_n(t) \end{bmatrix} = \begin{bmatrix} -p_1 & 0 & \cdots & 0 \\ 0 & -p_2 & \cdots & 0 \\ \vdots & & & \vdots \\ 0 & 0 & \cdots & -p_n \end{bmatrix} \begin{bmatrix} x_1(t) \\ x_2(t) \\ \vdots \\ x_n(t) \end{bmatrix} + \begin{bmatrix} 1 \\ 1 \\ \vdots \\ 1 \end{bmatrix} u(t)
$$

$$
y(t) = [K_1 \quad K_2 \quad \cdots \quad K_n] \begin{bmatrix} x_1(t) \\ x_2(t) \\ \vdots \\ x_n(t) \end{bmatrix}
$$

The matrix **A** is in canonical form and the main diagonal elements are nothing but the eigenvalues of the matrix **A**. This form of representation is called the diagonal canonical form (**DCF**). It is also called the *normal form*. This form of state model plays an important role in control theory. It has unique decoupled nature due to the fact that, the n first-order differential equations are completely independent of each other. This decoupling feature greatly helps in the analysis of the system. The disadvantage of the canonical form is: the canonical variables like phase variables are not physical variables of the system.

If the transfer function has repeated poles, the **A** matrix will be in Jordan canonical form. Suppose the transfer function has three poles as $-p_1$, $-p_1$, $-p_1$, and two poles as $-p_2$, $-p_2$ and the remaining poles are distinct, then the partial-fraction expansion is

$$
\frac{Y(s)}{U(s)} = \frac{K_1}{(s+p_1)^3} + \frac{K_2}{(s+p_1)^2} + \frac{K_3}{s+p_1} + \frac{K_4}{(s+p_2)^2} + \frac{K_5}{s+p_2} + \cdots + \frac{K_n}{s+p_n}
$$

The corresponding state diagram is as shown in Figure 10.29.
Choosing the outputs of the integrators as the state variables, the state equations are

$$
\begin{bmatrix} \dot{x}_1(t) \\ \dot{x}_2(t) \\ \dot{x}_3(t) \\ \dot{x}_4(t) \\ \dot{x}_5(t) \\ \vdots \\ \dot{x}_n(t) \end{bmatrix} = \begin{bmatrix} -p_1 & 1 & 0 & 0 & 0 & \cdots & 0 \\ 0 & -p_1 & 1 & 0 & 0 & \cdots & 0 \\ 0 & 0 & -p_1 & 0 & 0 & \cdots & 0 \\ 0 & 0 & 0 & -p_2 & 1 & \cdots & 0 \\ 0 & 0 & 0 & 0 & -p_2 & \cdots & 0 \\ \vdots & & & & & & \vdots \\ 0 & 0 & 0 & 0 & 0 & \cdots & -p_n \end{bmatrix} \begin{bmatrix} x_1(t) \\ x_2(t) \\ x_3(t) \\ x_4(t) \\ x_5(t) \\ \vdots \\ x_n(t) \end{bmatrix} + \begin{bmatrix} 0 \\ 0 \\ 1 \\ 0 \\ 1 \\ \vdots \\ 1 \end{bmatrix} u(t)
$$

Observe the 3×3 and 2×2 Jordan blocks.
The output equation is same as that for DCF.

In the Jordan block, all the diagonal elements are the same (value of the repeated poles) and the elements just above the main diagonal are all 1s and all other elements are 0s. This form of representation is called the Jordan canonical form **(JCF)**.

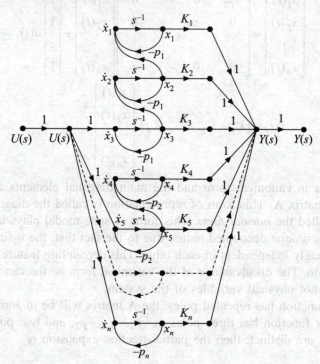

Figure 10.29 State diagram for parallel decomposition (repeated poles present).

Example 10.18 Decompose the transfer function given below by using parallel decomposition.

$$\frac{Y(s)}{U(s)} = \frac{s^3 + 7s^2 + 12s + 8}{s^3 + 6s^2 + 11s + 6}$$

Solution: The numerator and the denominator polynomials are of the same order. So, divide the numerator by the denominator to remove the constant term and then write in partial-fraction form. Therefore,

$$\frac{Y(s)}{U(s)} = 1 + \frac{s^2 + s + 2}{(s+1)(s+2)(s+3)}$$

The above transfer function can be written in terms of partial-fractions as

$$\frac{Y(s)}{U(s)} = 1 + \frac{1}{s+1} - \frac{4}{s+2} + \frac{4}{s+3}$$

The corresponding state diagram can be drawn as shown in Figure 10.30.

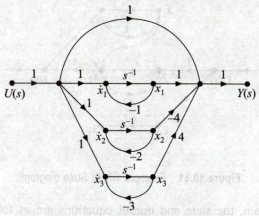

Figure 10.30 Example 10.18: State diagram.

Choosing the outputs of the integrators as the state variables, the state model is

$$\dot{x}_1 = -x_1 + u$$
$$\dot{x}_2 = -2x_2 + u$$
$$\dot{x}_3 = -3x_3 + u$$
$$y = x_1 - 4x_2 + 4x_3 + u$$

The state model in matrix form is as follows:

$$\begin{bmatrix} \dot{x}_1 \\ \dot{x}_2 \\ \dot{x}_3 \end{bmatrix} = \begin{bmatrix} -1 & 0 & 0 \\ 0 & -2 & 0 \\ 0 & 0 & -3 \end{bmatrix} \begin{bmatrix} x_1 \\ x_2 \\ x_3 \end{bmatrix} + \begin{bmatrix} 1 \\ 1 \\ 1 \end{bmatrix} u$$

$$y = \begin{bmatrix} 1 & -4 & 4 \end{bmatrix} \begin{bmatrix} x_1 \\ x_2 \\ x_3 \end{bmatrix} + u$$

Example 10.19 Obtain a state model of the system described by the transfer function given below by parallel decomposition.

$$\frac{Y(s)}{U(s)} = \frac{2s^2 + 6s + 5}{s^3 + 4s^2 + 5s + 2}$$

Solution: Writing the given transfer function in partial-fraction form,

$$\frac{Y(s)}{U(s)} = \frac{2s^2 + 6s + 5}{s^3 + 4s^2 + 5s + 2} = \frac{2s^2 + 6s + 5}{(s+1)^2(s+2)} = \frac{1}{(s+1)^2} + \frac{1}{s+1} + \frac{1}{s+2}$$

The state diagram based on these partial-fractions is as shown in Figure 10.31.

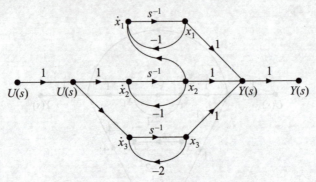

Figure 10.31 Example 10.19: State diagram.

From the state diagram, the state and output equations are as follows:

$$\dot{x}_1 = -x_1 + x_2$$
$$\dot{x}_2 = -x_2 + u$$
$$\dot{x}_3 = -2x_3 + u$$
$$y = x_1 + x_2 + x_3$$

As usual, choosing the outputs of the integrators as the state variables, the state model is as follows:

$$\begin{bmatrix} \dot{x}_1 \\ \dot{x}_2 \\ \dot{x}_3 \end{bmatrix} = \begin{bmatrix} -1 & 1 & 0 \\ 0 & -1 & 0 \\ 0 & 0 & -2 \end{bmatrix} \begin{bmatrix} x_1 \\ x_2 \\ x_3 \end{bmatrix} + \begin{bmatrix} 0 \\ 1 \\ 1 \end{bmatrix} u$$

$$y = \begin{bmatrix} 1 & 1 & 1 \end{bmatrix} \begin{bmatrix} x_1 \\ x_2 \\ x_3 \end{bmatrix}$$

When the overall transfer function has complex poles or zeros, the individual factors related to these poles or zeros should be in second-order form.

10.5 DIAGONALIZATION

In the previous sections, we observed that the state model of a system is not unique. Depending on the choice of the state variables, the same system can be represented using many state models. The state variables selected may be physical variables, phase variables, canonical variables or some other variables. From application point of view, the choice of physical variables as state variables for system representation is most useful, as these variables can be easily measured and used for control purposes. However, the corresponding state model in this case is generally not convenient for investigation of system properties and evaluation of time response. The phase variables in general are not physical variables of the system and therefore are not available for measurement and control purposes. The canonical state model wherein $\mathbf{A}$ is in diagonal form is the most suitable for this purpose. So we discuss here the techniques for transforming a general state model into a canonical one. These techniques are generally referred to as *diagonalization techniques*.

10.5.1 Similarity Transformation

Consider an nth-order multi-input-multi-output state model.

$$\dot{\mathbf{x}}(t) = \mathbf{A}\mathbf{x}(t) + \mathbf{B}\mathbf{u}(t)$$

$$\mathbf{y}(t) = \mathbf{C}\mathbf{x}(t) + \mathbf{D}\mathbf{u}(t)$$

We want to transform these dynamic equations into another set of equations of the same dimensions. Let us define a new state vector $\mathbf{z}(t)$ such that

$$\mathbf{x}(t) = \mathbf{P}\mathbf{z}(t)$$

where $\mathbf{P}$ is an $n \times n$ non-singular matrix. Under this transformation, the original state model reduces to

$$\mathbf{P}\dot{\mathbf{z}}(t) = \mathbf{A}\mathbf{P}\mathbf{z}(t) + \mathbf{B}\mathbf{u}(t)$$

i.e. $$\dot{\mathbf{z}}(t) = \mathbf{P}^{-1}\mathbf{A}\mathbf{P}\mathbf{z}(t) + \mathbf{P}^{-1}\mathbf{B}\mathbf{u}(t)$$

and $$\mathbf{y}(t) = \mathbf{C}\mathbf{P}\mathbf{z}(t) + \mathbf{D}\mathbf{u}(t)$$

i.e. $$\dot{\mathbf{z}}(t) = \bar{\mathbf{A}}\mathbf{z}(t) + \bar{\mathbf{B}}\mathbf{u}(t)$$

and $$\mathbf{y}(t) = \bar{\mathbf{C}}\mathbf{z}(t) + \bar{\mathbf{D}}\mathbf{u}(t)$$

where $$\bar{\mathbf{A}} = \mathbf{P}^{-1}\mathbf{A}\mathbf{P}$$

$$\bar{\mathbf{B}} = \mathbf{P}^{-1}\mathbf{B}$$

$$\bar{\mathbf{C}} = \mathbf{C}\mathbf{P}$$

and $$\bar{\mathbf{D}} = \mathbf{D}$$

The transformation described above is called a *similarity transformation* since in the transformed system, such properties as the characteristic equation, eigenvectors, eigenvalues, and transfer function are all preserved by the transformation. If the non-singular matrix $\mathbf{P}$ is chosen as the modal matrix $\mathbf{M}$, then the transformed state model will be a canonical state model and the matrix $\bar{\mathbf{A}}$ will be a diagonal matrix with the eigenvalues of $\mathbf{A}$ as its main diagonal elements.

We can show that the characteristic equation, eigenvalues and eigenvectors are invariant under a linear transformation.

Consider the state equation of a dynamic system

$$\dot{x}(t) = Ax(t) + Bu(t)$$

Its characteristic equation is given by

$$|sI - A| = 0$$

Under a linear transformation $x(t) = Pz(t)$, the state equations transform to

$$\dot{z}(t) = P^{-1}APz(t) + P^{-1}Bu(t)$$

Therefore, the new characteristic equation of the system is $|sI - \bar{A}| = 0$

$$|sI - \bar{A}| = |sI - P^{-1}AP| = |sP^{-1}P - P^{-1}AP|$$

Since the determinant of a product matrix is equal to the product of the determinants of the matrices

$$|sI - \bar{A}| = |P^{-1}||sI - A||P| = |sI - A||P^{-1}||P| = |sI - A|$$

This shows that the characteristic equation is preserved under the linear transformation which leads naturally to the same eigenvalues and eigenvectors.

We can also show that the transfer function matrix is also invariant under the linear transformation.

We know that for the original state model, the transfer function matrix is

$$G(s) = C[sI - A]^{-1}B + D$$

For the transformed state model, the transfer function matrix is

$$\bar{G}(s) = \bar{C}[sI - \bar{A}]^{-1}\bar{B} + \bar{D}$$

$$= CP[sI - P^{-1}AP]^{-1}P^{-1}B + D$$

$$= CPP^{-1}(sI - A)^{-1}PP^{-1}B + D$$

$$= C(sI - A)^{-1}B + D$$

Eigenvalues: The roots of the characteristic equation

$$|\lambda I - A| = 0$$

i.e.

$$\lambda^n + a_1\lambda^{n-1} + a_2\lambda^{n-2} + \cdots + a_n = 0$$

are often referred to as the eigenvalues of the matrix **A**. We know that the roots of the characteristic equation

$$|sI - A| = 0$$

i.e.

$$s^n + a_1s^{n-1} + a_2s^{n-2} + \cdots + a_n = 0$$

in terms of s are the same as the poles of the closed-loop transfer function. So it can be concluded that the eigenvalues of **A** and the poles of the closed-loop transfer function are the same. Hence all the conclusions established earlier on system stability based upon the location of transfer function poles (i.e. roots of the characteristic equation) are therefore valid for the eigenvalues of the state model. Thus a state model is stable if all its eigenvalues have negative real parts.

Some of the important properties of eigenvalues are as follows:

1. If the coefficients of **A** are all real, its eigenvalues are either real or in complex conjugate pairs.
2. The trace (sum of the main diagonal elements) of **A** is the sum of all the eigenvalues of **A**.
3. The eigenvalues of the transpose of **A**, i.e. of $\mathbf{A}^T$ are the same as the eigenvalues of **A**.
4. The eigenvalues of the inverse of **A**, i.e. of $\mathbf{A}^{-1}$ are the inverse of the eigenvalues of **A**.

Eigenvectors: Any non-zero vector p_i that satisfies the matrix equation

$$[\lambda_i \mathbf{I} - \mathbf{A}]p_i = 0$$

where λ_i, $i = 1, 2, \ldots, n$ denotes the ith eigenvalue of **A**, is called the *eigenvector* of **A** associated with the eigenvalue λ_i. If **A** has distinct eigenvalues, the eigenvectors can be obtained directly from the above equation by the solution of the set of n homogeneous equations written for different values of λ_i. The eigenvectors can also be obtained by determining the co-factors along a row of $[\lambda_i \mathbf{I} - \mathbf{A}]$, for $i = 1, 2, \ldots, n$ and transposing that row of co-factors. If all the co-factors along any row are zero, then the row which gives non zero co-factors is to be considered.

If **A** has multiple-order eigenvalues, then all the eigenvectors cannot be found by solving the equation $[\lambda_i \mathbf{I} - \mathbf{A}]p_i = 0$, or by finding the co-factors along rows of $[\lambda_i \mathbf{I} - \mathbf{A}]$.

If among the n eigenvalues of **A**, q ($< n$), are distinct, the eigenvectors that correspond to the q distinct eigenvalues can be determined in the usual manner from

$$[\lambda_i \mathbf{I} - \mathbf{A}]p_i = 0$$

where λ_i denotes the ith distinct eigenvalue, $i = 1, 2, \ldots, q$. Among the remaining high-order eigenvalues, if λ_j is of the mth order ($m \leq n - q$); the corresponding eigenvectors, called the generalized eigenvectors, can be determined from the following m vector equations.

$$(\lambda_j \mathbf{I} - \mathbf{A})p_{n-q+1} = 0$$
$$(\lambda_j \mathbf{I} - \mathbf{A})p_{n-q+2} = -p_{n-q+1}$$
$$(\lambda_j \mathbf{I} - \mathbf{A})p_{n-q+3} = -p_{n-q+2}$$
$$\vdots$$
$$(\lambda_j \mathbf{I} - \mathbf{A})p_{n-q+m} = -p_{n-q+m-1}$$

The generalized eigenvectors can also be determined using the method of co-factors.

If out of n eigenvalues of **A**, q are distinct, the q eigenvectors can be determined in the usual manner by finding the cofactors along any row of $[\lambda_i \mathbf{I} - \mathbf{A}]$, where λ_i denotes the ith distinct eigenvalue, $i = 1, 2, ..., q$. If the remaining $n - q$ eigenvalues are repeated, then the jth eigenvector can be determined by taking co-factors along any row of $[\lambda_j \mathbf{I} - \mathbf{A}]$. The remaining generalized eigenvectors can be determined by taking the derivatives of the co-factors forming the jth eigenvector $[\lambda_j \mathbf{I} - \mathbf{A}]$ as shown below.

$$\begin{bmatrix} C_{j1} \\ C_{j2} \\ \vdots \\ C_{jn} \end{bmatrix} \begin{bmatrix} \dfrac{1}{1!}\dfrac{d}{d\lambda_j}C_{j1} \\[2mm] \dfrac{1}{1!}\dfrac{d}{d\lambda_j}C_{j2} \\ \vdots \\ \dfrac{1}{1!}\dfrac{d}{d\lambda_j}C_{jn} \end{bmatrix} \begin{bmatrix} \dfrac{1}{2!}\dfrac{d^2}{d\lambda_j^2}C_{j1} \\[2mm] \dfrac{1}{2!}\dfrac{d^2}{d\lambda_j^2}C_{j2} \\ \vdots \\ \dfrac{1}{2!}\dfrac{d^2}{d\lambda_j^2}C_{jn} \end{bmatrix} \cdots \begin{bmatrix} \dfrac{1}{(q-1)!}\dfrac{d^{n-1}}{d\lambda_j^{n-1}}C_{j1} \\[2mm] \dfrac{1}{(q-1)!}\dfrac{d^{n-1}}{d\lambda_j^{n-1}}C_{j2} \\ \vdots \\ \dfrac{1}{(q-1)!}\dfrac{d^{n-1}}{d\lambda_j^{n-1}}C_{jn} \end{bmatrix}$$

The matrix formed by placing the eigenvectors together (column wise) is called the *modal matrix* $\mathbf{M}$. If the system matrix $\mathbf{A}$ is in companion form and if all its n eigenvalues are distinct, then the modal matrix will be a special matrix called the *Vander Monde matrix*.

$$\mathbf{V} = \begin{bmatrix} 1 & 1 & \cdots & 1 \\ \lambda_1 & \lambda_2 & \cdots & \lambda_n \\ \lambda_1^2 & \lambda_2^2 & \cdots & \lambda_n^2 \\ \vdots & & & \\ \lambda_1^{n-1} & \lambda_2^{n-1} & \cdots & \lambda_n^{n-1} \end{bmatrix}$$

If the system matrix $\mathbf{A}$ is in companion form and if only q of its n eigenvalues are distinct, and the remaining $n - q$ eigenvalues are repeated, then the modal matrix is the modified Vander Monde matrix.

$$\mathbf{V} = \begin{bmatrix} 1 & 1 & \cdots & 1 & 1 & 0 & 0 & \cdots \\ \lambda_1 & \lambda_2 & \cdots & \lambda_q & \lambda_{q+1} & 1 & 0 & \cdots \\ \lambda_1^2 & \lambda_2^2 & \cdots & \lambda_q^2 & \lambda_{q+1}^2 & 2\lambda_{q+1} & 1 & \cdots \\ \lambda_1^3 & \lambda_2^3 & \cdots & \lambda_q^3 & \lambda_{q+1}^3 & 3\lambda_{q+1}^2 & 3\lambda_{q+1} & \cdots \\ \vdots & & & & & & & \\ \lambda_1^{n-1} & \lambda_2^{n-1} & \cdots & \lambda_q^{n-1} & \lambda_{q+1}^{n-1} & \dfrac{d(\lambda_{q+1}^{n-1})}{d\lambda_{q+1}} & \dfrac{1}{2!}\dfrac{d^2(\lambda_{q+1}^{n-1})}{d\lambda_{q+1}^2} & \cdots \end{bmatrix}$$

Example 10.20   Diagonalize the system matrix given below.

(a) $\mathbf{A} = \begin{bmatrix} 0 & 1 & 0 \\ 0 & 0 & 1 \\ -6 & -11 & -6 \end{bmatrix}$ (b) $\mathbf{A} = \begin{bmatrix} 0 & 1 & 0 \\ 0 & 0 & 1 \\ -2 & -5 & -4 \end{bmatrix}$

Solution: (a) The eigenvalues of the system matrix $\mathbf{A}$ are the roots of the characteristic equation

$$|\lambda\mathbf{I} - \mathbf{A}| = \lambda\begin{bmatrix} 1 & 0 & 0 \\ 0 & 1 & 0 \\ 0 & 0 & 1 \end{bmatrix} - \begin{bmatrix} 0 & 1 & 0 \\ 0 & 0 & 1 \\ -6 & -11 & -6 \end{bmatrix} = \begin{bmatrix} \lambda & -1 & 0 \\ 0 & \lambda & -1 \\ 6 & 11 & \lambda+6 \end{bmatrix}$$

$$= \lambda^3 + 6\lambda^2 + 11\lambda + 6 = (\lambda+1)(\lambda+2)(\lambda+3) = 0$$

Therefore, the eigenvalues are $\lambda_1 = -1$, $\lambda_2 = -2$, $\lambda_3 = -3$.

To diagonalise the matrix $\mathbf{A}$, first find the modal matrix $\mathbf{M}$. The modal matrix can be determined by finding the eigenvectors, which are nothing but the co-factors along any row of $[\lambda_i\mathbf{I} - \mathbf{A}] = 0$, for $i = 1, 2, 3$.

$$[\lambda_1\mathbf{I} - \mathbf{A}] = \begin{bmatrix} \lambda_1 & -1 & 0 \\ 0 & \lambda_1 & -1 \\ 6 & 11 & \lambda_1+6 \end{bmatrix} = \begin{bmatrix} -1 & -1 & 0 \\ 0 & -1 & -1 \\ 6 & 11 & 5 \end{bmatrix}$$

The co-factors along the first row are $C_{11} = 6$, $C_{12} = -6$, $C_{13} = 6$.
Therefore, the eigenvector associated with $\lambda_1 = -1$ is

$$[6 \quad -6 \quad 6]^T = [1 \quad -1 \quad 1]^T$$

$$[\lambda_2\mathbf{I} - \mathbf{A}] = \begin{bmatrix} \lambda_2 & -1 & 0 \\ 0 & \lambda_2 & -1 \\ 6 & 11 & \lambda_2+6 \end{bmatrix} = \begin{bmatrix} -2 & -1 & 0 \\ 0 & -2 & -1 \\ 6 & 11 & 4 \end{bmatrix}$$

The co-factors along the first row are $C_{11} = 3$, $C_{12} = -6$, $C_{13} = 12$.
Therefore, the eigenvector associated with $\lambda_2 = -2$ is

$$[3 \quad -6 \quad 12]^T = [1 \quad -2 \quad 4]^T$$

$$[\lambda_3\mathbf{I} - \mathbf{A}] = \begin{bmatrix} \lambda_3 & -1 & 0 \\ 0 & \lambda_3 & -1 \\ 6 & 11 & \lambda_3+6 \end{bmatrix} = \begin{bmatrix} -3 & -1 & 0 \\ 0 & -3 & -1 \\ 6 & 11 & 3 \end{bmatrix}$$

The co-factors along the first row are $C_{11} = 2$, $C_{12} = -6$, $C_{13} = 18$.
Therefore, the eigenvector associated with $\lambda_3 = -3$ is

$$[2 \quad -6 \quad 18]^T = [1 \quad -3 \quad 9]^T$$

Hence, the modal matrix is

$$\mathbf{M} = \begin{bmatrix} 6 & 3 & 2 \\ -6 & -6 & -6 \\ 6 & 12 & 18 \end{bmatrix} = \begin{bmatrix} 1 & 1 & 1 \\ -1 & -2 & -3 \\ 1 & 4 & 9 \end{bmatrix}$$

Since the matrix **A** is in companion form, and has distinct eigenvalues, the modal matrix **M** can be written directly in Vander Monde form as

$$\mathbf{M} = \begin{bmatrix} 1 & 1 & 1 \\ \lambda_1 & \lambda_2 & \lambda_3 \\ \lambda_1^2 & \lambda_2^2 & \lambda_3^2 \end{bmatrix} = \begin{bmatrix} 1 & 1 & 1 \\ -1 & -2 & -3 \\ 1 & 4 & 9 \end{bmatrix}$$

The inverse of the modal matrix is

$$\mathbf{M}^{-1} = \frac{\text{adj}\,[\mathbf{M}]}{\Delta} = \frac{1}{-2} \begin{bmatrix} -6 & 6 & -2 \\ -5 & 8 & -3 \\ -1 & 2 & -1 \end{bmatrix}^T = \frac{1}{2} \begin{bmatrix} 6 & 5 & 1 \\ -6 & -8 & -2 \\ 2 & 3 & 1 \end{bmatrix}$$

The diagonal matrix is given by

$$\mathbf{M}^{-1}\mathbf{A}\mathbf{M} = \frac{1}{2} \begin{bmatrix} 6 & 5 & 1 \\ -6 & -8 & -2 \\ 2 & 3 & 1 \end{bmatrix} \begin{bmatrix} 0 & 1 & 0 \\ 0 & 0 & 1 \\ -6 & -11 & -6 \end{bmatrix} \begin{bmatrix} 1 & 1 & 1 \\ -1 & -2 & -3 \\ 1 & 4 & 9 \end{bmatrix} = \begin{bmatrix} -1 & 0 & 0 \\ 0 & -2 & 0 \\ 0 & 0 & -3 \end{bmatrix}$$

(b) To diagonalise the matrix **A**, first determine the eigenvalues of the matrix **A**.
The eigenvalues of the matrix **A** are nothing but the roots of the characteristic equation

$$|\lambda\mathbf{I} - \mathbf{A}| = \begin{bmatrix} \lambda & 0 & 0 \\ 0 & \lambda & 0 \\ 0 & 0 & \lambda \end{bmatrix} - \begin{bmatrix} 0 & 1 & 0 \\ 0 & 0 & 1 \\ -2 & -5 & -4 \end{bmatrix} = \begin{vmatrix} \lambda & -1 & 0 \\ 0 & \lambda & -1 \\ 2 & 5 & \lambda+4 \end{vmatrix}$$

$$= \lambda^3 + 4\lambda^2 + 5\lambda + 2 = (\lambda+1)(\lambda+1)(\lambda+2) = 0$$

Therefore, the eigenvalues of the matrix **A** are $\lambda_1 = -1$, $\lambda_2 = -1$, $\lambda_3 = -2$.

The eigenvector corresponding to the first eigenvalue $\lambda_1 = -1$ is obtained by taking the co-factors along the first row of

$$[\lambda_1\mathbf{I} - \mathbf{A}] = \begin{bmatrix} \lambda_1 & -1 & 0 \\ 0 & \lambda_1 & -1 \\ 2 & 5 & \lambda_1+4 \end{bmatrix} = \begin{bmatrix} -1 & -1 & 0 \\ 0 & -1 & -1 \\ 2 & 5 & 3 \end{bmatrix}$$

The co-factors along the first row are $C_{11} = 2$, $C_{12} = -2$, $C_{13} = 2$.

Therefore, the first eigenvector is

$$[2 \quad -2 \quad 2]^T = [1 \quad -1 \quad 1]^T$$

Since the eigenvalues are repeated, the second eigenvector (generalized eigenvector) can be obtained by differentiating the co-factors corresponding to the first row of $[\lambda_1 I - A] = 0$.

$$\begin{bmatrix} C_{21} \\ C_{22} \\ C_{23} \end{bmatrix} = \begin{bmatrix} \dfrac{dC_{11}}{d\lambda_1} \\ \dfrac{dC_{12}}{d\lambda_1} \\ \dfrac{dC_{13}}{d\lambda_1} \end{bmatrix} = \begin{bmatrix} \dfrac{d[\lambda_1(\lambda_1+4)+5]}{d\lambda_1} \\ \dfrac{d[-2]}{d\lambda_1} \\ \dfrac{d[-2\lambda_1]}{d\lambda_1} \end{bmatrix} = \begin{bmatrix} 2\lambda_1+4 \\ 0 \\ -2 \end{bmatrix} = \begin{bmatrix} 2 \\ 0 \\ -2 \end{bmatrix}$$

Therefore, the second eigenvector is $[1 \quad 0 \quad -1]^T$.

The third eigenvector corresponding to $\lambda_3 = -2$ is obtained by taking the co-factors along the first row of

$$[\lambda_3 I - A] = \begin{bmatrix} \lambda_3 & -1 & 0 \\ 0 & \lambda_3 & -1 \\ 2 & 5 & \lambda_3+4 \end{bmatrix} = \begin{bmatrix} -2 & -1 & 0 \\ 0 & -2 & -1 \\ 2 & 5 & 2 \end{bmatrix}$$

$$\therefore \qquad C_{31} = 1, \ C_{32} = -2, \ C_{33} = 4$$

Therefore, the third eigenvector is $[1 \quad -2 \quad 4]^T$.

The modal matrix based on the eigenvectors is

$$M = \begin{bmatrix} 1 & 1 & 1 \\ -1 & 0 & -2 \\ 1 & -1 & 4 \end{bmatrix}$$

The modal matrix obtained above is not in modified Vander Monde form.

$$M^{-1} = \frac{\text{adj}[M]}{\Delta} = \frac{1}{1}\begin{bmatrix} -2 & 2 & 1 \\ -5 & 3 & 2 \\ -2 & 1 & 1 \end{bmatrix}^T = \begin{bmatrix} -2 & -5 & -2 \\ 2 & 3 & 1 \\ 1 & 2 & 1 \end{bmatrix}$$

The diagonal matrix obtained using this modal matrix is

$$M^{-1}AM = \begin{bmatrix} -2 & -5 & -2 \\ 2 & 3 & 1 \\ 1 & 2 & 1 \end{bmatrix}\begin{bmatrix} 0 & 1 & 0 \\ 0 & 0 & 1 \\ -2 & -5 & -4 \end{bmatrix}\begin{bmatrix} 1 & 1 & 1 \\ -1 & 0 & -2 \\ 1 & -1 & 4 \end{bmatrix} = \begin{bmatrix} -1 & 1 & 0 \\ 0 & -1 & 0 \\ 0 & 0 & -2 \end{bmatrix}$$

Since the system matrix **A** is in companion form, the modal matrix **M** could have been written directly in modified Vander Monde form as

$$\mathbf{M} = \begin{bmatrix} 1 & \dfrac{d}{d\lambda_1}(1) & 1 \\[2mm] \lambda_1 & \dfrac{d}{d\lambda_1}(\lambda_1) & \lambda_2 \\[2mm] \lambda_1^2 & \dfrac{d}{d\lambda_1}(\lambda_1^2) & \lambda_2^2 \end{bmatrix} = \begin{bmatrix} 1 & 0 & 1 \\ \lambda_1 & 1 & \lambda_2 \\ \lambda_1^2 & 2\lambda_1 & \lambda_2^2 \end{bmatrix} = \begin{bmatrix} 1 & 0 & 1 \\ -1 & 1 & -2 \\ 1 & -2 & 4 \end{bmatrix}$$

This modal matrix is not the same as the one obtained earlier.

$$\mathbf{M}^{-1} = \frac{\text{adj } [\mathbf{M}]}{\Delta} = \frac{1}{1}\begin{bmatrix} 0 & 2 & 1 \\ -2 & 3 & 2 \\ -1 & 1 & 1 \end{bmatrix}^T = \begin{bmatrix} 0 & -2 & -1 \\ 2 & 3 & 1 \\ 1 & 2 & 1 \end{bmatrix}$$

The diagonal matrix is given by

$$\mathbf{M}^{-1}\mathbf{AM} = \begin{bmatrix} 0 & -2 & -1 \\ 2 & 3 & 1 \\ 1 & 2 & 1 \end{bmatrix}\begin{bmatrix} 0 & 1 & 0 \\ 0 & 0 & 1 \\ -2 & -5 & -4 \end{bmatrix}\begin{bmatrix} 1 & 0 & 1 \\ -1 & 1 & -2 \\ 1 & -2 & 4 \end{bmatrix} = \begin{bmatrix} -1 & 1 & 0 \\ 0 & -1 & 0 \\ 0 & 0 & -2 \end{bmatrix}$$

This shows that even though the modal matrix is not unique, the resultant diagonal matrix is unique.

Example 10.21   Obtain the modal matrix for the system matrix given below by determining the Eigenvectors using simultaneous equations.

(a) $\mathbf{A} = \begin{bmatrix} 0 & 1 & 0 \\ 0 & 0 & 1 \\ -6 & -11 & -6 \end{bmatrix}$ (b) $\mathbf{A} = \begin{bmatrix} 0 & 1 & 0 \\ 0 & 0 & 1 \\ -2 & -5 & -4 \end{bmatrix}$

Solution: (a) The eigenvalues of the given system matrix **A** are $\lambda_1 = -1$, $\lambda_2 = -2$ and $\lambda_3 = -3$. To obtain the modal matrix, determine the eigenvectors using simultaneous equations:

$$|\lambda_i \mathbf{I} - \mathbf{A}|p_i = \begin{bmatrix} \lambda_i & -1 & 0 \\ 0 & \lambda_i & -1 \\ 6 & 11 & \lambda_i + 6 \end{bmatrix}\begin{bmatrix} p_{i1} \\ p_{i2} \\ p_{i3} \end{bmatrix} = 0$$

To obtain the first eigenvector, solve the equation $|\lambda_1\mathbf{I} - \mathbf{A}|p_1 = 0$.

$$\begin{bmatrix} -1 & -1 & 0 \\ 0 & -1 & -1 \\ 6 & 11 & 5 \end{bmatrix}\begin{bmatrix} p_{11} \\ p_{12} \\ p_{13} \end{bmatrix} = 0$$

i.e.
$$-p_{11} - p_{12} = 0$$

∴
$$p_{11} = -p_{12}$$

Let
$$p_{11} = 1$$

∴
$$p_{12} = -1$$

$$-p_{12} - p_{13} = 0$$

∴
$$p_{13} = -p_{12}$$

∴
$$p_{13} = -(-1) = 1$$

$$6p_{11} + 11p_{12} + 5p_{13} = 0$$

Therefore, the first eigenvector is $[1 \quad -1 \quad 1]^T$.

The second eigenvector is determined by solving $|\lambda_2 \mathbf{I} - \mathbf{A}| p_2 = 0$, i.e.

$$\begin{bmatrix} -2 & -1 & 0 \\ 0 & -2 & -1 \\ 6 & 11 & 4 \end{bmatrix} \begin{bmatrix} p_{21} \\ p_{22} \\ p_{23} \end{bmatrix} = 0$$

$$-2p_{21} - p_{22} = 0$$

i.e.
$$p_{22} = -2p_{21}$$

Let
$$p_{21} = 1$$

∴
$$p_{22} = -2$$

$$-2p_{22} - p_{23} = 0$$

i.e.
$$p_{23} = -2p_{22}$$

∴
$$p_{23} = -2(-2) = 4$$

Therefore, the second eigenvector is $[1 \quad -2 \quad 4]^T$.

The third eigenvector is obtained by solving $|\lambda_3 \mathbf{I} - \mathbf{A}| p_3 = 0$, i.e.

$$\begin{bmatrix} -3 & -1 & 0 \\ 0 & -3 & -1 \\ 6 & 11 & 3 \end{bmatrix} \begin{bmatrix} p_{31} \\ p_{32} \\ p_{33} \end{bmatrix} = 0$$

$$-3p_{31} - p_{32} = 0$$

i.e.
$$p_{32} = -3p_{31}$$

Let
$$p_{31} = 1$$

∴
$$p_{32} = -3$$

$$-3p_{32} - p_{33} = 0$$

i.e.
$$p_{33} = -3p_{32}$$

∴
$$p_{33} = -3(-3) = 9$$

Therefore, the third eigenvector is $[1 \quad -3 \quad 9]^T$.

Therefore, the modal matrix is given by

$$M = \begin{bmatrix} 1 & 1 & 1 \\ -1 & -2 & -3 \\ 1 & 4 & 9 \end{bmatrix}$$

(b) The eigenvalues of **A** are the same as the roots of the characteristic equation

$$|\lambda I - A| = \begin{bmatrix} \lambda & 0 & 0 \\ 0 & \lambda & 0 \\ 0 & 0 & \lambda \end{bmatrix} - \begin{bmatrix} 0 & 1 & 0 \\ 0 & 0 & 1 \\ -2 & -5 & -4 \end{bmatrix} = \begin{vmatrix} \lambda & -1 & 0 \\ 0 & \lambda & -1 \\ 2 & 5 & \lambda+4 \end{vmatrix}$$

$$= \lambda^3 + 4\lambda^2 + 5\lambda + 2 = (\lambda + 1)(\lambda + 1)(\lambda + 2) = 0$$

Therefore, the eigenvalues are $\lambda_1 = -1$, $\lambda_2 = -1$, and $\lambda_3 = -2$.

There are repeated eigenvalues. The eigenvector corresponding to $\lambda_1 = -1$ is obtained as usual

$$\begin{bmatrix} \lambda_1 & -1 & 0 \\ 0 & \lambda_1 & -1 \\ 2 & 5 & \lambda_1+4 \end{bmatrix} \begin{bmatrix} p_{11} \\ p_{12} \\ p_{13} \end{bmatrix} = 0$$

i.e.

$$\begin{bmatrix} -1 & -1 & 0 \\ 0 & -1 & -1 \\ 2 & 5 & 3 \end{bmatrix} \begin{bmatrix} p_{11} \\ p_{12} \\ p_{13} \end{bmatrix} = 0$$

i.e.
$$-p_{11} - p_{12} = 0$$

i.e.
$$p_{12} = -p_{11}$$

Let
$$p_{11} = 1, \quad \text{then} \quad p_{12} = -1.$$

$$-p_{12} - p_{13} = 0$$

i.e.
$$p_{13} = -p_{12}$$

Since
$$p_{12} = -1, p_{13} = -(-1) = 1.$$

$$2p_{11} + 5p_{12} + 3p_{13} = 0$$

Therefore, the eigenvector associated with $\lambda_1 = -1$ is $\begin{bmatrix} 1 & -1 & 1 \end{bmatrix}^T$.

Since there are repeated eigenvalues, the eigenvector corresponding to the eigenvalue $\lambda_2 = -1$ is obtained as follows.

$$\begin{bmatrix} \lambda_2 & -1 & 0 \\ 0 & \lambda_2 & -1 \\ 2 & 5 & \lambda_2+4 \end{bmatrix} \begin{bmatrix} p_{21} \\ p_{22} \\ p_{23} \end{bmatrix} = - \begin{bmatrix} p_{11} \\ p_{12} \\ p_{13} \end{bmatrix}$$

i.e.
$$\begin{bmatrix} -1 & -1 & 0 \\ 0 & -1 & -1 \\ 2 & 5 & 3 \end{bmatrix} \begin{bmatrix} p_{21} \\ p_{22} \\ p_{23} \end{bmatrix} = -\begin{bmatrix} 1 \\ -1 \\ 1 \end{bmatrix} = \begin{bmatrix} -1 \\ 1 \\ -1 \end{bmatrix}$$

$$\therefore \qquad -p_{21} - p_{22} = -1$$

$$\therefore \qquad p_{22} = 1 - p_{21}$$

Let
$$p_{22} = 1, \quad \text{then} \quad p_{21} = 0.$$

$$-p_{22} - p_{23} = 1$$

i.e.
$$p_{23} = -1 - p_{22} = -1 - 1 = -2$$

Therefore, the second eigenvector is $[0 \quad 1 \quad -2]^T$.

$$[\lambda_3 \mathbf{I} - \mathbf{A}]p_3 = 0$$

i.e.
$$\begin{bmatrix} -2 & -1 & 0 \\ 0 & -2 & -1 \\ 2 & 5 & 2 \end{bmatrix} \begin{bmatrix} p_{31} \\ p_{32} \\ p_{33} \end{bmatrix} = 0$$

$$-2p_{31} - p_{32} = 0$$

$$\therefore \qquad p_{32} = -2p_{31}$$

Let
$$p_{31} = 1, \quad \text{then} \quad p_{32} = -2.$$

$$-2p_{32} - p_{33} = 0$$

$$\therefore \qquad p_{33} = -2p_{32}$$

Since
$$p_{32} = -2, \quad \text{then} \quad p_{33} = 4.$$

Therefore, eigenvector associated with $\lambda_3 = -3$ is $[1 \quad -2 \quad 4]^T$.
Hence the modal matrix

$$\mathbf{M} = \begin{bmatrix} 1 & 0 & 1 \\ -1 & 1 & -2 \\ 1 & -2 & 4 \end{bmatrix}$$

10.6 SOLUTION OF STATE EQUATIONS: STATE TRANSITION MATRIX AND STATE TRANSITION EQUATION

In the preceding sections, we discussed various state models used to represent a system. Here we shall discuss methods for the solution of state equations from which the system transient response can then be obtained.

To solve the homogeneous (unforced) state equation

$$\dot{x}(t) = Ax(t), \; x(0) = x_0$$

Consider a scalar case,

$$\frac{dx}{dt} = ax(t), \; x(0) = x_0$$

This equation has the solution

$$x(t) = e^{at}x_0$$

$$= \left(1 + at + \frac{a^2 t^2}{2!} + \frac{a^3 t^3}{3!} + \cdots\right)x_0$$

By analogy with the scalar case, the vector state equation has the solution

$$x(t) = \left(I + At + \frac{A^2 t^2}{2!} + \frac{A^3 t^3}{3!} + \cdots\right)x_0$$

Each of the terms inside the brackets is an $n \times n$ matrix and the entire term is called a matrix exponential, which may be written as

$$e^{At} = I + At + \frac{A^2 t^2}{2!} + \frac{A^3 t^3}{3!} + \cdots$$

The solution $x(t)$ can therefore be written as $x(t) = e^{At}x(0)$. This solution of homogeneous state equation shows that the initial state x_0 at $t = 0$, is driven to a state $x(t)$ at time t.

Since this transition in state is carried out by the matrix exponential e^{At}, e^{At} is known as the state transition matrix (STM) and is denoted by $\phi(t)$, i.e. $\phi(t) = e^{At}$.

Since the STM depends only on the system matrix A, it is also called the STM of A. In general, for linear time-invariant systems, if the initial time is $t = t_0$, the state transition matrix becomes

$$\phi(t - t_0) = e^{A(t - t_0)}$$

Since the STM depends only on the length of the time $(t - t_0)$ and not on the initial time t_0, the initial time is conveniently regarded as zero. Given the system matrix A, the STM can be computed by expanding e^{At} into a power series in t and then adding the corresponding elements in the matrix terms of the infinite series. This is practical only for simple cases.

Let us now consider the solution of the non-homogeneous state equation.

$$\dot{x}(t) = Ax(t) + Bu(t); \; x(0) = x_0$$

By writing this equation as

$$\dot{x}(t) - Ax(t) = Bu(t)$$

and pre-multiplying both sides of this equation by e^{-At}, we obtain

$$e^{-At}[\dot{\mathbf{x}}(t) - \mathbf{A}\mathbf{x}(t)] = \frac{d}{dt}[e^{-At}\mathbf{x}(t)] = e^{-At}\mathbf{B}\mathbf{u}(t)$$

Integrating this with respect to t between the limits 0 and t, gives

$$\int_0^t \frac{d}{dt}[e^{-At}\mathbf{x}(t)] = e^{-At}\mathbf{x}(t)\Big|_0^t = \int_0^t e^{-A\tau}\mathbf{B}\mathbf{u}(\tau)\,d\tau$$

i.e.
$$e^{-At}\mathbf{x}(t) - \mathbf{x}(0) = \int_0^t e^{-A\tau}\mathbf{B}\mathbf{u}(\tau)\,d\tau$$

Now pre-multiplying both sides by e^{At}

$$\mathbf{x}(t) = e^{At}\left[\mathbf{x}(0) + \int_0^t e^{-A\tau}\mathbf{B}\mathbf{u}(\tau)\,d\tau\right]$$

In terms of STM,

$$\mathbf{x}(t) = \phi(t)\mathbf{x}(0) + \int_0^t \phi(t - \tau)\mathbf{B}\mathbf{u}(\tau)\,d\tau$$

If the initial time is t_0 instead of $t = 0$, the solution of the non-homogeneous state equation, also called the state transition equation becomes

$$\mathbf{x}(t) = \phi(t - t_0)\mathbf{x}(t_0) + \int_0^t \phi(t - \tau)\mathbf{B}\mathbf{u}(\tau)\,d\tau$$

Significance of the STM: Since the STM satisfies the homogeneous state equations, it represents the free response of the system. In other words, it governs the response that is excited by the initial conditions only. The STM is dependent only on the system matrix $\mathbf{A}$, and therefore it is sometimes referred to as the STM of $\mathbf{A}$. As the name implies, the STM describes the change of state from the initial time $t = 0$, to any time t, when the inputs are zero.

Properties of STM

1. $\phi(0) = \mathbf{I}$, *Proof:* $\phi(0) = e^{A \times 0} = \mathbf{I}$

2. $\phi^{-1}(t) = \phi(-t)$ *Proof:* $\phi^{-1}(t) = \dfrac{1}{\phi(t)} = \dfrac{1}{e^{At}} = e^{-At} = \phi(-t)$

3. $\phi(t_2 - t_1)\phi(t_1 - t_0) = \phi(t_2 - t_0)$ for any t_2, t_1, t_0

   Proof: $[\phi(t_2 - t_1)\phi(t_1 - t_0) = e^{A(t_2 - t_1)} \cdot e^{A(t_1 - t_0)} = e^{A(t_2 - t_1 + t_1 - t_0)} = e^{A(t_2 - t_0)} = \phi(t_2 - t_0)]$

4. $[\phi(t)]^k = \phi(kt)$ *Proof:* $[\phi(t)]^k = \phi(t) \cdot \phi(t) \cdots k$ times $= e^{At} \cdot e^{At} \cdots k$ times $= e^{Akt} = \phi(kt)$

5. $\phi(t_1 + t_2) = \phi(t_1)\phi(t_2) = \phi(t_2)\phi(t_1)$

   Proof: $\phi(t_1 + t_2) = e^{A(t_1 + t_2)} = e^{At_1} \cdot e^{At_2} = e^{At_2} \cdot e^{At_1} = \phi(t_1) \cdot \phi(t_2) = \phi(t_2) \cdot \phi(t_1)$

10.7 COMPUTATION OF THE STATE TRANSITION MATRIX

10.7.1 Computation of the STM by Infinite Series Method

Example 10.22 Compute the STM by infinite series method.

(a) $\mathbf{A} = \begin{bmatrix} 0 & 1 \\ -1 & -2 \end{bmatrix}$ (b) $\mathbf{A} = \begin{bmatrix} 1 & 1 \\ 0 & 1 \end{bmatrix}$

Solution: (a) For the given system matrix **A**, the state transition matrix (STM) is

$$\phi(t) = e^{\mathbf{A}t} = \mathbf{I} + \mathbf{A}t + \frac{\mathbf{A}^2 t^2}{2!} + \frac{\mathbf{A}^3 t^3}{3!} + \cdots$$

$$\mathbf{A}^2 = \begin{bmatrix} 0 & 1 \\ -1 & -2 \end{bmatrix}\begin{bmatrix} 0 & 1 \\ -1 & -2 \end{bmatrix} = \begin{bmatrix} -1 & -2 \\ 2 & 3 \end{bmatrix}, \mathbf{A}^3 = \mathbf{A}^2 . \mathbf{A} = \begin{bmatrix} -1 & -2 \\ 2 & 3 \end{bmatrix}\begin{bmatrix} 0 & 1 \\ -2 & -3 \end{bmatrix} = \begin{bmatrix} 2 & 3 \\ -3 & -4 \end{bmatrix}$$

$$\therefore \quad \phi(t) = \begin{bmatrix} 1 & 0 \\ 0 & 1 \end{bmatrix} + \begin{bmatrix} 0 & 1 \\ -1 & -2 \end{bmatrix}t + \begin{bmatrix} -1 & -2 \\ 2 & 3 \end{bmatrix}\frac{t^2}{2!} + \begin{bmatrix} 2 & 3 \\ -3 & -4 \end{bmatrix}\frac{t^3}{3!} + \cdots$$

$$= \begin{bmatrix} 1 - \dfrac{t^2}{2} + \dfrac{t^3}{3} + \cdots & t - t^2 + \dfrac{t^3}{2} + \cdots \\ -t + t^2 - \dfrac{t^3}{2} + \cdots & 1 - 2t + \dfrac{3t^2}{2} - \dfrac{2t^3}{3} + \cdots \end{bmatrix}$$

$$= \begin{bmatrix} e^{-t} + te^{-t} & te^{-t} \\ -te^{-t} & e^{-t} - te^{-t} \end{bmatrix}$$

(b) For the given system matrix **A**, the state transition matrix (STM) is

$$\phi(t) = e^{\mathbf{A}t} = \mathbf{I} + \mathbf{A}t + \frac{\mathbf{A}^2 t^2}{2!} + \frac{\mathbf{A}^3 t^3}{3!} + \cdots$$

$$\mathbf{A}^2 = \begin{bmatrix} 1 & 1 \\ 0 & 1 \end{bmatrix}\begin{bmatrix} 1 & 1 \\ 0 & 1 \end{bmatrix} = \begin{bmatrix} 1 & 2 \\ 0 & 1 \end{bmatrix}, \quad \mathbf{A}^3 = \mathbf{A}^2 \cdot \mathbf{A} = \begin{bmatrix} 1 & 2 \\ 0 & 1 \end{bmatrix}\begin{bmatrix} 1 & 1 \\ 0 & 1 \end{bmatrix} = \begin{bmatrix} 1 & 3 \\ 0 & 1 \end{bmatrix}$$

$$\therefore \quad \phi(t) = \begin{bmatrix} 1 & 0 \\ 0 & 1 \end{bmatrix} + \begin{bmatrix} 1 & 1 \\ 0 & 1 \end{bmatrix}t + \begin{bmatrix} 1 & 2 \\ 0 & 1 \end{bmatrix}\frac{t^2}{2!} + \begin{bmatrix} 1 & 3 \\ 0 & 1 \end{bmatrix}\frac{t^3}{3!} + \cdots$$

$$= \begin{bmatrix} 1 + t + \dfrac{t^2}{2!} + \dfrac{t^3}{3!} + \cdots & t + t^2 + \dfrac{t^3}{2} + \cdots \\ 0 & 1 + t + \dfrac{t^2}{2!} + \dfrac{t^3}{3!} + \cdots \end{bmatrix}$$

$$= \begin{bmatrix} 1+t+\dfrac{t^2}{2!}+\dfrac{t^3}{3!}+\cdots & t\left(1+t+\dfrac{t^2}{2!}+\dfrac{t^3}{3!}+\cdots\right) \\ 0 & 1+t+\dfrac{t^2}{2!}+\dfrac{t^3}{3!}+\cdots \end{bmatrix} = \begin{bmatrix} e^t & te^t \\ 0 & e^t \end{bmatrix}$$

10.7.2 Computation of the STM by Laplace Transformation

Consider an unforced system. Its homogeneous state equation is

$$\dot{x}(t) = Ax(t)$$

where **A** is a constant matrix. Taking the Laplace transform of this equation,

$$sX(s) - x(0) = AX(s)$$

where $X(s)$ is the Laplace transform of the free response, and $x(0)$ is the initial condition vector. The above equation may be arranged as

$$[sI - A]\ X(s) = x(0)$$

Pre-multiplying both sides by $[sI - A]^{-1}$

$$X(s) = [sI - A]^{-1}\ x(0)$$

$$= \phi(s)x(0)$$

where $\phi(s) = [sI - A]^{-1}$ is called the resolvent matrix.

Taking the inverse Laplace transform, we get

$$x(t) = L^{-1}[sI - A]^{-1}\ x(0)$$

where $x(t)$ is the free response of the system. This solution must be identical with the one obtained earlier. Comparing them

$$\phi(t) = e^{At} = L^{-1}\ [sI - A]^{-1} = L^{-1}\ [\phi(s)]$$

we can say, the state transition matrix STM is the inverse Laplace transform of the resolvent matrix.

Let us now consider the forced response of the system.

The non homogeneous state equation of the system is

$$\dot{x}(t) = Ax(t) + Bu(t)$$

Taking the Laplace transform on both sides,

$$sX(s) - x(0) = AX(s) + BU(s)$$

or

$$[sI - A\ ]\ X(s) = x(0) + BU(s)$$

Pre-multiplying both sides by $[sI - A]^{-1}$,

$$X(s) = [sI - A]^{-1}\ x(0) + [sI - A]^{-1}\ BU(s)$$

$$= \phi(s)\, \mathbf{x}(0) + \phi(s)\, \mathbf{BU}(s)$$

$$= \phi(s)\, [\mathbf{x}(0) + \mathbf{BU}(s)]$$

Taking the inverse Laplace transform on both sides,

$$\mathbf{x}(t) = L^{-1}[\phi(s)\, [\mathbf{x}(0) + \mathbf{BU}(s)]]$$

$$= \phi(t)\, [\mathbf{x}(0)] + L^{-1}\, [\phi(s)\, \mathbf{BU}(s)]$$

Applying convolution theorem,

$$\mathbf{x}(t) = \phi(t)\mathbf{x}(0) + \int_0^t \phi(t-\tau)\mathbf{Bu}(\tau)\,d\tau$$

$$= \phi(t)\left[\mathbf{x}(0) + \int_0^t \phi(-\tau)\mathbf{Bu}(\tau)\,d\tau\right]$$

This solution of linear non-homogeneous state equation is called the state transition equation.

Example 10.23   Obtain the STM for the state model whose **A** matrix is given by

(a) $\mathbf{A} = \begin{bmatrix} 1 & 1 \\ 0 & 1 \end{bmatrix}$ (b) $\mathbf{A} = \begin{bmatrix} 0 & 1 \\ -1 & -2 \end{bmatrix}$ (c) $\mathbf{A} = \begin{bmatrix} 0 & 1 \\ -2 & -3 \end{bmatrix}$

Solution: (a) For the given system matrix **A**

$$[s\mathbf{I} - \mathbf{A}] = \begin{bmatrix} s & 0 \\ 0 & s \end{bmatrix} - \begin{bmatrix} 1 & 1 \\ 0 & 1 \end{bmatrix} = \begin{bmatrix} s-1 & -1 \\ 0 & s-1 \end{bmatrix}$$

$\therefore$

$$\phi(s) = [s\mathbf{I} - \mathbf{A}]^{-1} = \frac{\text{adj}\,[s\mathbf{I} - \mathbf{A}]}{|s\mathbf{I} - \mathbf{A}|} = \frac{\begin{bmatrix} s-1 & 0 \\ 1 & s-1 \end{bmatrix}^T}{(s-1)^2} = \frac{\begin{bmatrix} s-1 & 1 \\ 0 & s-1 \end{bmatrix}}{(s-1)^2}$$

$\therefore$

$$\text{STM} = \phi(t) = L^{-1}[\phi(s)] = L^{-1}[s\mathbf{I} - \mathbf{A}]^{-1} = L^{-1}\begin{bmatrix} \dfrac{1}{s-1} & \dfrac{1}{(s-1)^2} \\ 0 & \dfrac{1}{s-1} \end{bmatrix} = \begin{bmatrix} e^t & te^t \\ 0 & e^t \end{bmatrix}$$

(b) For the given system matrix **A**

$$[s\mathbf{I} - \mathbf{A}] = \begin{bmatrix} s & 0 \\ 0 & s \end{bmatrix} - \begin{bmatrix} 0 & 1 \\ -1 & -2 \end{bmatrix} = \begin{bmatrix} s & -1 \\ 1 & s+2 \end{bmatrix}$$

$$\phi(s) = [s\mathbf{I} - \mathbf{A}]^{-1} = \frac{\text{Adj}\,[s\mathbf{I} - \mathbf{A}]}{|s\mathbf{I} - \mathbf{A}|} = \frac{\begin{bmatrix} s+2 & -1 \\ 1 & s \end{bmatrix}^T}{|s\mathbf{I} - \mathbf{A}|} = \frac{\begin{bmatrix} s+2 & 1 \\ -1 & s \end{bmatrix}}{(s+1)^2}$$

$$\therefore \quad \text{STM} = \phi(t) = L^{-1}\phi(s) = L^{-1}[s\mathbf{I} - \mathbf{A}]^{-1} = L^{-1}\begin{bmatrix} \dfrac{s+2}{(s+1)^2} & \dfrac{1}{(s+1)^2} \\ \dfrac{-1}{(s+1)^2} & \dfrac{s}{(s+1)^2} \end{bmatrix}$$

$$= \begin{bmatrix} (1+t)e^{-t} & te^{-t} \\ -te^{-t} & (1-t)e^{-t} \end{bmatrix}$$

(c) For the given system matrix **A**

$$[s\mathbf{I} - \mathbf{A}] = \begin{bmatrix} s & 0 \\ 0 & s \end{bmatrix} - \begin{bmatrix} 0 & 1 \\ -2 & -3 \end{bmatrix} = \begin{bmatrix} s & -1 \\ 2 & s+3 \end{bmatrix}$$

$$\phi(s) = [s\mathbf{I} - \mathbf{A}]^{-1} = \frac{\text{Adj}\,[s\mathbf{I} - \mathbf{A}]}{|s\mathbf{I} - \mathbf{A}|} = \frac{\begin{bmatrix} s+3 & -2 \\ 1 & s \end{bmatrix}^T}{|s\mathbf{I} - \mathbf{A}|} = \frac{\begin{bmatrix} s+3 & 1 \\ -2 & s \end{bmatrix}}{s^2 + 3s + 2}$$

$$\therefore \quad \text{STM} = \phi(t) = L^{-1}\phi(s) = L^{-1}[s\mathbf{I} - \mathbf{A}]^{-1} = L^{-1}\begin{bmatrix} \dfrac{s+3}{(s+1)(s+2)} & \dfrac{1}{(s+1)(s+2)} \\ \dfrac{-2}{(s+1)(s+2)} & \dfrac{s}{(s+1)(s+2)} \end{bmatrix}$$

$$= \begin{bmatrix} L^{-1}\left(\dfrac{s+3}{(s+1)(s+2)}\right) & L^{-1}\left(\dfrac{1}{(s+1)(s+2)}\right) \\ L^{-1}\left(\dfrac{-2}{(s+1)(s+2)}\right) & L^{-1}\left(\dfrac{s}{(s+1)(s+2)}\right) \end{bmatrix}$$

$$= \begin{bmatrix} L^{-1}\left(\dfrac{2}{s+1} - \dfrac{1}{s+2}\right) & L^{-1}\left(\dfrac{1}{s+1} - \dfrac{1}{s+2}\right) \\ L^{-1}\left(\dfrac{-2}{s+1} + \dfrac{2}{s+2}\right) & L^{-1}\left(\dfrac{-1}{s+1} + \dfrac{2}{s+2}\right) \end{bmatrix}$$

$$= \begin{bmatrix} 2e^{-t} - e^{-2t} & e^{-t} - e^{-2t} \\ -2e^{-t} + 2e^{-2t} & -e^{-t} + 2e^{-2t} \end{bmatrix}$$

10.7.3 Computation of the STM using Cayley–Hamilton Theorem

The STM may be computed using the technique based on the Cayley–Hamilton theorem. For large systems this method is far more convenient computationally compared to other methods.

The Cayley–Hamilton theorem states that every square matrix **A** satisfies its own characteristic equation. This theorem provides a simple procedure for evaluating the function of a matrix.

If **A** is a nonsingular $n \times n$ matrix, then to determine the matrix polynomial

$$f(\mathbf{A}) = \alpha_0\mathbf{I} + \alpha_1\mathbf{A} + \alpha_2\mathbf{A}^2 + \cdots + \alpha_{n-1}\mathbf{A}^{n-1}$$

first determine α_0, $\alpha_1,\ldots$, α_{n-1} by considering the scalar case

$$f(\lambda_i) = \alpha_0 + \alpha_1\lambda_i + \alpha_2\lambda_i^2 + \cdots + \alpha_{n-1}\lambda_i^{n-1}$$

and write simultaneous equations for $i = 1, 2,\ldots, n-1$ and solve them.

The formal procedure to determine a matrix polynomial is

Step 1. Find the eigenvalues of system matrix **A**.

Step 2. If all the eigenvalues are distinct, solve n simultaneous equations given by the equation

$$f(\lambda_i) = \alpha_0 + \alpha_1\lambda_i + \alpha_2\lambda_i^2 + \cdots + \alpha_{n-1}\lambda_i^{n-1}$$

for the coefficients α_0, α_1, ..., α_{n-1}. If any of the eigenvalues are repeated, then obtain one independent equation by substituting that eigenvalue in the above equation.

Step 3. Substitute the coefficients α_i obtained in step 2 in equation

$\boldsymbol{f}(\mathbf{A}) = \alpha_0\mathbf{I} + \alpha_1\mathbf{A} + \alpha_2\mathbf{A}^2 + \cdots + \alpha_{n-1}\mathbf{A}^{n-1}$ to obtain the matrix polynomial.

Example 10.24 Find $f(\mathbf{A}) = \mathbf{A}^{10}$ for

$$\mathbf{A} = \begin{bmatrix} 0 & 1 \\ -1 & -2 \end{bmatrix}$$

Solution: The characteristic equation is

$$|\lambda\mathbf{I} - \mathbf{A}| = \left| \lambda\begin{bmatrix} 1 & 0 \\ 0 & 1 \end{bmatrix} - \begin{bmatrix} 0 & 1 \\ -1 & -2 \end{bmatrix} \right| = \begin{bmatrix} \lambda & -1 \\ 1 & \lambda+2 \end{bmatrix} = (\lambda+1)^2 = 0$$

Matrix **A** has repeated eigenvalues $\lambda_1 = -1$, $\lambda_2 = -1$. So we can get only one independent equation. Since **A** is of second-order,

$$f(\lambda) = \lambda^{10} = \alpha_0 + \alpha_1\lambda$$

Putting $\lambda = \lambda_1 = -1$ in the above equation, we get

$$f(\lambda_1) = \lambda_1^{10} = \alpha_0 + \alpha_1\lambda_1$$

i.e. $$(-1)^{10} = \alpha_0 - \alpha_1$$

i.e. $$\alpha_0 - \alpha_1 = 1$$

To obtain the second equation, differentiating the expression for $f(\lambda)$ on both sides,

$$\frac{d}{d\lambda}[\lambda^{10}]\bigg|_{\lambda=-1} = \alpha_1$$

i.e.
$$10\lambda^9\Big|_{\lambda=-1} = \alpha_1$$

i.e.
$$\alpha_1 = -10$$

$$\alpha_0 = 1 + \alpha_1 = 1 - 10 = -9$$

$$\therefore \qquad f(\mathbf{A}) = \mathbf{A}^{10} = \alpha_0\mathbf{I} + \alpha_1\mathbf{A}$$

$$= \alpha_0 \begin{bmatrix} 1 & 0 \\ 0 & 1 \end{bmatrix} + \alpha_1 \begin{bmatrix} 0 & 1 \\ -1 & -2 \end{bmatrix}$$

$$= \begin{bmatrix} \alpha_0 & \alpha_1 \\ -\alpha_1 & \alpha_0 - 2\alpha_1 \end{bmatrix} = \begin{bmatrix} -9 & -10 \\ 10 & 11 \end{bmatrix}$$

Example 10.25 Obtain the STM for the state model whose **A** matrix is given below using Cayley–Hamilton theorem.

(a) $\mathbf{A} = \begin{bmatrix} 1 & 1 \\ 0 & 1 \end{bmatrix}$ (b) $\mathbf{A} = \begin{bmatrix} 0 & 1 \\ -1 & -2 \end{bmatrix}$ (c) $\mathbf{A} = \begin{bmatrix} 0 & 1 \\ -2 & -3 \end{bmatrix}$

Solution: (a) The eigenvalues of the system matrix **A** are the roots of the characteristic equation

$$|\lambda\mathbf{I} - \mathbf{A}| = \left\| \begin{bmatrix} \lambda & 0 \\ 0 & \lambda \end{bmatrix} - \begin{bmatrix} 1 & 1 \\ 0 & 1 \end{bmatrix} \right\| = \begin{vmatrix} \lambda - 1 & -1 \\ 0 & \lambda - 1 \end{vmatrix} = \lambda^2 - 2\lambda + 1 = (\lambda - 1)(\lambda - 1) = 0$$

Therefore, the eigenvalues are $\lambda_1 = 1$, $\lambda_2 = 1$.

We know that

$$e^{\lambda t} = \alpha_0 + \alpha_1\lambda$$

Substituting $\lambda = 1$ in the above equation, we have

$$e^t = \alpha_0 + \alpha_1$$

Differentiating the equation $e^{\lambda t} = \alpha_0 + \alpha_1\lambda$, with respect to λ

$$te^{\lambda t}\Big|_{\lambda=1} = te^t = \alpha_1$$

Substituting this value of α_1 in the expression for $e^t = \alpha_0 + \alpha_1$, we have

$$\alpha_0 = -\alpha_1 + e^t = -te^t + e^t$$

Therefore, the STM is given by

$$\phi(t) = e^{\mathbf{A}t} = \alpha_0\mathbf{I} + \alpha_1\mathbf{A}$$

$$= \alpha_0 \begin{bmatrix} 1 & 0 \\ 0 & 1 \end{bmatrix} + \alpha_1 \begin{bmatrix} 1 & 1 \\ 0 & 1 \end{bmatrix} = \begin{bmatrix} \alpha_0 & 0 \\ 0 & \alpha_0 \end{bmatrix} + \begin{bmatrix} \alpha_1 & \alpha_1 \\ 0 & \alpha_1 \end{bmatrix} = \begin{bmatrix} \alpha_0 + \alpha_1 & \alpha_1 \\ 0 & \alpha_0 + \alpha_1 \end{bmatrix} = \begin{bmatrix} e^t & te^t \\ 0 & e^t \end{bmatrix}$$

(b) For the given system matrix **A**, the characteristic equation is

$$|\lambda\mathbf{I} - \mathbf{A}| = 0$$

i.e.

$$\begin{bmatrix} \lambda & 0 \\ 0 & \lambda \end{bmatrix} - \begin{bmatrix} 0 & 1 \\ -1 & -2 \end{bmatrix} = \begin{bmatrix} \lambda & -1 \\ 1 & \lambda+2 \end{bmatrix} = \lambda^2 + 2\lambda + 1 = 0$$

The roots of this equation are the eigenvalues. Therefore, the eigenvalues are $\lambda_1 = -1$ and $\lambda_2 = -1$, i.e. the eigenvalues are repeated.

For the second-order system

$$f(\lambda) = e^{\lambda t} = \alpha_0 + \alpha_1 \lambda$$

∴

$$f(\lambda_1) = e^{\lambda_1 t} = e^{-t} = \alpha_0 - \alpha_1$$

Differentiating $f(\lambda)$ with respect to λ,

$$te^{\lambda t} = \alpha_1$$

For $\lambda = \lambda_1 = -1$,

$$\alpha_1 = te^{-t}$$

∴

$$\alpha_0 = \alpha_1 + e^{-t} = te^{-t} + e^{-t} = e^{-t}(1 + t)$$

The state transition matrix is

∴

$$f(\mathbf{A}) = e^{\mathbf{A}t} = \alpha_0 \mathbf{I} + \alpha_1 \mathbf{A}$$

$$= \alpha_0 \begin{bmatrix} 1 & 0 \\ 0 & 1 \end{bmatrix} + \alpha_1 \begin{bmatrix} 0 & 1 \\ -1 & -2 \end{bmatrix}$$

$$= \begin{bmatrix} \alpha_0 & 0 \\ 0 & \alpha_0 \end{bmatrix} + \begin{bmatrix} 0 & \alpha_1 \\ -\alpha_1 & -2\alpha_1 \end{bmatrix} = \begin{bmatrix} \alpha_0 & \alpha_1 \\ -\alpha_1 & \alpha_0 - 2\alpha_1 \end{bmatrix}$$

$$= \begin{bmatrix} (1+t)e^{-t} & te^{-t} \\ -te^{-t} & (1-t)e^{-t} \end{bmatrix}$$

(c) For the given system matrix **A**, the eigenvalues are the roots of the characteristic equation

$$|\lambda\mathbf{I} - \mathbf{A}| = 0$$

i.e.

$$\begin{bmatrix} \lambda & 0 \\ 0 & \lambda \end{bmatrix} - \begin{bmatrix} 0 & 1 \\ -2 & -3 \end{bmatrix} = \begin{vmatrix} \lambda & -1 \\ 2 & \lambda+3 \end{vmatrix} = 0$$

i.e.

$$\lambda^2 + 3\lambda + 2 = 0$$

i.e.

$$(\lambda + 1)(\lambda + 2) = 0$$

∴

$$\lambda_1 = -1, \lambda_2 = -2 \text{ are the eigenvalues.}$$

For a second-order system,

$$f(\lambda) = e^{\lambda t} = \alpha_0 + \alpha_1 \lambda$$

$\therefore$

$$f(\lambda_1) = e^{\lambda_1 t} = \alpha_0 + \alpha_1 \lambda_1$$

i.e.

$$e^{-t} = \alpha_0 - \alpha_1$$

$$f(\lambda_2) = e^{\lambda_2 t} = \alpha_0 + \alpha_1 \lambda_2$$

i.e.

$$e^{-2t} = \alpha_0 - 2\alpha_1$$

Solving the equations for $f(\lambda_1)$ and $f(\lambda_2)$,

$$\alpha_0 = 2e^{-t} - e^{-2t}$$

$$\alpha_1 = e^{-t} - e^{-2t}$$

$\therefore$

$$f(\mathbf{A}) = e^{\mathbf{A}t} = \alpha_0 \mathbf{I} + \alpha_1 \mathbf{A} = \alpha_0 \begin{bmatrix} 1 & 0 \\ 0 & 1 \end{bmatrix} + \alpha_1 \begin{bmatrix} 0 & 1 \\ -2 & -3 \end{bmatrix}$$

$$= \begin{bmatrix} \alpha_0 & 0 \\ 0 & \alpha_0 \end{bmatrix} + \begin{bmatrix} 0 & \alpha_1 \\ -2\alpha_1 & -3\alpha_1 \end{bmatrix} = \begin{bmatrix} \alpha_0 & \alpha_1 \\ -2\alpha_1 & \alpha_0 - 3\alpha_1 \end{bmatrix}$$

$$= \begin{bmatrix} 2e^{-t} - e^{-2t} & e^{-t} - e^{-2t} \\ -2e^{-t} + 2e^{-2t} & -e^{-t} + 2e^{-2t} \end{bmatrix}$$

10.7.4 Computation of STM by Canonical Transformation

The STM can be computed by using the modal matrix. Consider the homogeneous state equation

$$\dot{\mathbf{x}}(t) = \mathbf{A}\mathbf{x}(t)$$

with initial condition vector $\mathbf{x}(0) = \mathbf{x_0}$.

The solution vector is

$$\mathbf{x}(t) = e^{\mathbf{A}t}\mathbf{x_0}$$

Suppose the matrix $\mathbf{A}$ is non-diagonal and has distinct eigenvalues, $\lambda_1, \lambda_2, \ldots, \lambda_n$. Then the above state equation can be transformed into another state equation using the linear transformation

$$\mathbf{x}(t) = \mathbf{M}\mathbf{z}(t)$$

where $\mathbf{M}$ is the diagonalizing or modal matrix. Substitution of this value of $\mathbf{x}(t)$ in the original state equation yields

$$\mathbf{M}\dot{\mathbf{z}}(t) = \mathbf{A}\mathbf{M}\mathbf{z}(t)$$

Pre-multiplying both sides by $\mathbf{M}^{-1}$, the transformed homogeneous state equation is

$$\dot{\mathbf{z}}(t) = \mathbf{M}^{-1}\mathbf{A}\mathbf{M}\mathbf{z}(t) = \bar{\mathbf{A}}\mathbf{z}(t)$$

where $\overline{\mathbf{A}}$ is a diagonal matrix with the eigenvalues of $\mathbf{A}$ as its main diagonal elements.

$$\overline{\mathbf{A}} = \begin{bmatrix} \lambda_1 & 0 & 0 & \cdots & 0 \\ 0 & \lambda_2 & 0 & \cdots & 0 \\ \vdots & & & & \\ 0 & 0 & 0 & \cdots & \lambda_n \end{bmatrix}$$

The new solution vector is

$$\mathbf{z}(t) = e^{\overline{\mathbf{A}}t}\mathbf{z}(0)$$

where $\mathbf{z}(0)$ is the transformed initial condition vector.

Since

$$\mathbf{x}(t) = \mathbf{Mz}(t)$$

$$\mathbf{z}(t) = \mathbf{M}^{-1}\mathbf{x}(t)$$

Substituting this value of $\mathbf{z}(t)$ in the new solution vector,

$$\mathbf{M}^{-1}\mathbf{x}(t) = e^{\overline{\mathbf{A}}t}\mathbf{M}^{-1}\mathbf{x}(0)$$

Pre-multiplying both sides by $\mathbf{M}$

$$\mathbf{x}(t) = \mathbf{M}e^{\overline{\mathbf{A}}t}\mathbf{M}^{-1}\mathbf{x}(0)$$

Comparison of this with the original solution vector yields

$$e^{\mathbf{A}t} = \mathbf{M}e^{\overline{\mathbf{A}}t}\mathbf{M}^{-1}$$

Since

$$\overline{\mathbf{A}} = \begin{bmatrix} \lambda_1 & 0 & 0 & \cdots & 0 \\ 0 & \lambda_2 & 0 & \cdots & 0 \\ \vdots & & & & \\ 0 & 0 & 0 & \cdots & \lambda_n \end{bmatrix}$$

$$e^{\overline{\mathbf{A}}t} = \begin{bmatrix} e^{\lambda_1 t} & 0 & \cdots & 0 \\ 0 & e^{\lambda_2 t} & \cdots & 0 \\ 0 & 0 & \cdots & e^{\lambda_n t} \end{bmatrix}$$

If the system matrix $\mathbf{A}$ involves multiple eigenvalues, then $\mathbf{M}^{-1}\mathbf{AM}$ will not yield a diagonal matrix. The resulting state equation is in Jordan canonical form. Suppose the matrix $\mathbf{A}$ has eigenvalues as $\lambda_1, \lambda_1, \lambda_1, \lambda_4, \ldots, \lambda_n$ then

$$\dot{\mathbf{z}}(t) = \mathbf{M}^{-1}\mathbf{AMz}(t) = \mathbf{Jz}(t)$$

where

$$\mathbf{J} = \begin{bmatrix} \lambda_1 & 1 & 0 & 0 & \cdots & 0 \\ 0 & \lambda_1 & 1 & 0 & \cdots & 0 \\ 0 & 0 & \lambda_1 & 0 & \cdots & 0 \\ 0 & 0 & 0 & \lambda_4 & \cdots & 0 \\ \vdots & & & & & \\ 0 & 0 & 0 & 0 & \cdots & \lambda_n \end{bmatrix}$$

and the STM is

$$e^{\mathbf{A}t} = \mathbf{M}e^{\mathbf{J}t}\mathbf{M}^{-1}$$

where

$$e^{\mathbf{J}t} = \begin{bmatrix} e^{\lambda_1 t} & te^{\lambda_1 t} & \frac{1}{2}t^2 e^{\lambda_1 t} & 0 & \cdots & 0 \\ 0 & e^{\lambda_1 t} & te^{\lambda_1 t} & 0 & \cdots & 0 \\ 0 & 0 & e^{\lambda_1 t} & 0 & \cdots & 0 \\ 0 & 0 & 0 & e^{\lambda_4 t} & \cdots & 0 \\ \vdots & & & & & \\ 0 & 0 & 0 & 0 & \cdots & e^{\lambda_n t} \end{bmatrix}$$

Example 10.26 Obtain the STM for the state model whose **A** matrix is given below using canonical transformation method.

(a) $\mathbf{A} = \begin{bmatrix} 1 & 1 \\ 0 & 1 \end{bmatrix}$ (b) $\mathbf{A} = \begin{bmatrix} 0 & 1 \\ -1 & -2 \end{bmatrix}$ (c) $\mathbf{A} = \begin{bmatrix} 0 & 1 \\ -2 & -3 \end{bmatrix}$

Solution: (a) Since the matrix **A** is not in companion form, the modal matrix can not be written directly. It can be determined by obtaining eigenvectors either by obtaining the co-factors along the rows or by the solution of simultaneous equations.

The eigenvalues of **A** are nothing but the roots of the characteristic equation

$$|\lambda\mathbf{I} - \mathbf{A}| = \left\| \begin{bmatrix} \lambda & 0 \\ 0 & \lambda \end{bmatrix} - \begin{bmatrix} 1 & 1 \\ 0 & 1 \end{bmatrix} \right\| = \begin{vmatrix} \lambda-1 & -1 \\ 0 & \lambda-1 \end{vmatrix} = \lambda^2 - 2\lambda + 1 = (\lambda-1)(\lambda-1) = 0$$

Therefore, the eigenvalues are $\lambda_1 = 1$, $\lambda_2 = 1$.

$$[\lambda\mathbf{I} - \mathbf{A}] = \begin{bmatrix} \lambda-1 & -1 \\ 0 & \lambda-1 \end{bmatrix}$$

To determine the eigenvector associated with $\lambda_1 = 1$, find the co-factors along any row of

$$[\lambda_1 I - A] = \begin{bmatrix} 0 & -1 \\ 0 & 0 \end{bmatrix}$$

The co-factors along the first row are $C_{11} = 0$, $C_{12} = 0$. Since all the co-factors along the first row are zeros, this eigenvector is a null vector and is not valid. Taking the co-factors along the second row, $C_{21} = 1$ and $C_{22} = 0$. Therefore, eigenvector $= [1 \quad 0]^T$.

Since the eigenvalues are repeated, the second eigenvector can be obtained by taking the first derivative of the co-factors C_{21} and C_{22} expressed in terms of λ. The co-factors along the first row should not be differentiated because the co-factors along that row turned out to be zeros. Therefore, the second eigenvector is given by

$$\begin{bmatrix} \dfrac{d}{d\lambda} C_{21} \\ \dfrac{d}{d\lambda} C_{22} \end{bmatrix} = \begin{bmatrix} \dfrac{d}{d\lambda}(1) \\ \dfrac{d}{d\lambda}(\lambda - 1) \end{bmatrix}_{\lambda = \lambda_2 = 1} = \begin{bmatrix} 0 \\ 1 \end{bmatrix}$$

Hence the modal matrix $M = \begin{bmatrix} 1 & 0 \\ 0 & 1 \end{bmatrix}$ and therefore $M^{-1} = \begin{bmatrix} 1 & 0 \\ 0 & 1 \end{bmatrix}$

Since the eigenvalues are repeated, $M^{-1}AM$ gives the diagonal matrix in Jordan canonical form

$$M^{-1}AM = \begin{bmatrix} 1 & 0 \\ 0 & 1 \end{bmatrix}\begin{bmatrix} 1 & 1 \\ 0 & 1 \end{bmatrix}\begin{bmatrix} 1 & 0 \\ 0 & 1 \end{bmatrix} = \begin{bmatrix} 1 & 1 \\ 0 & 1 \end{bmatrix} = J \text{ (Jordan canonical form)}$$

The state transition matrix $\phi(t)$ is

$$\phi(t) = e^{\bar{A}t} = Me^{Jt}M^{-1}$$

$$= \begin{bmatrix} 1 & 0 \\ 0 & 1 \end{bmatrix}\begin{bmatrix} e^t & te^t \\ 0 & e^t \end{bmatrix}\begin{bmatrix} 1 & 0 \\ 0 & 1 \end{bmatrix} = \begin{bmatrix} e^t & te^t \\ 0 & e^t \end{bmatrix}$$

(b) For the given system matrix A, the eigenvalues are given by the roots of the characteristic equation

$$|\lambda I - A| = \left|\lambda \begin{bmatrix} 1 & 0 \\ 0 & 1 \end{bmatrix} - \begin{bmatrix} 0 & 1 \\ -1 & -2 \end{bmatrix}\right| = \begin{vmatrix} \lambda & -1 \\ 1 & \lambda + 2 \end{vmatrix} = \lambda^2 + 2\lambda + 1 = (\lambda + 1)(\lambda + 1) = 0$$

Therefore, $\lambda_1 = -1$ and $\lambda_2 = -1$ are the eigenvalues of A. Since the matrix A is in companion form and the eigenvalues are repeated, the modal matrix M will be in the modified Vander Monde form. Therefore,

$$M = \begin{bmatrix} 1 & \dfrac{d}{d\lambda_1}(1) \\ \lambda_1 & \dfrac{d}{d\lambda_1}(\lambda_1) \end{bmatrix} = \begin{bmatrix} 1 & 0 \\ \lambda_1 & 1 \end{bmatrix} = \begin{bmatrix} 1 & 0 \\ -1 & 1 \end{bmatrix}$$

$$\mathbf{M}^{-1} = \begin{bmatrix} 1 & 1 \\ 0 & 1 \end{bmatrix}^T = \begin{bmatrix} 1 & 0 \\ 1 & 1 \end{bmatrix}$$

The diagonal matrix will be in Jordan canonical form

$$\mathbf{J} = \mathbf{M}^{-1}\mathbf{A}\mathbf{M} = \begin{bmatrix} 1 & 0 \\ 1 & 1 \end{bmatrix}\begin{bmatrix} 0 & 1 \\ -1 & -2 \end{bmatrix}\begin{bmatrix} 1 & 0 \\ -1 & 1 \end{bmatrix} = \begin{bmatrix} -1 & 1 \\ 0 & -1 \end{bmatrix}$$

$$\therefore \qquad e^{\mathbf{J}t} = \begin{bmatrix} e^{-t} & te^{-t} \\ 0 & e^{-t} \end{bmatrix}$$

The state transition matrix is given by

$$\phi(t) = \mathbf{M}e^{\mathbf{J}t}\mathbf{M}^{-1}$$

$$= \begin{bmatrix} 1 & 0 \\ -1 & 1 \end{bmatrix}\begin{bmatrix} e^{-t} & te^{-t} \\ 0 & e^{-t} \end{bmatrix}\begin{bmatrix} 1 & 0 \\ 1 & 1 \end{bmatrix} = \begin{bmatrix} e^{-t} + te^{-t} & te^{-t} \\ -te^{-t} & e^{-t} - te^{-t} \end{bmatrix}$$

(c) The eigenvalues are given by the roots of the characteristic equation

$$|\lambda\mathbf{I} - \mathbf{A}| = \left\|\begin{bmatrix} \lambda & 0 \\ 0 & \lambda \end{bmatrix} - \begin{bmatrix} 0 & 1 \\ -2 & -3 \end{bmatrix}\right\| = \begin{vmatrix} \lambda & -1 \\ 2 & \lambda+3 \end{vmatrix} = \lambda^2 + 3\lambda + 2 = (\lambda+1)(\lambda+2) = 0$$

$\lambda_1 = -1$ and $\lambda_2 = -2$ are the eigenvalues.
The matrix **A** is in companion form. So the modal matrix is in Vander Monde form, i.e.

$$\mathbf{M} = \begin{bmatrix} 1 & 1 \\ \lambda_1 & \lambda_2 \end{bmatrix} = \begin{bmatrix} 1 & 1 \\ -1 & -2 \end{bmatrix}$$

$$\mathbf{M}^{-1} = \frac{\begin{bmatrix} -2 & 1 \\ -1 & 1 \end{bmatrix}^T}{-1} = \begin{bmatrix} 2 & 1 \\ -1 & -1 \end{bmatrix}$$

$$\overline{\mathbf{A}} = \mathbf{M}^{-1}\mathbf{A}\mathbf{M} = \begin{bmatrix} 2 & 1 \\ -1 & -1 \end{bmatrix}\begin{bmatrix} 0 & 1 \\ -2 & -3 \end{bmatrix}\begin{bmatrix} 1 & 1 \\ -1 & -2 \end{bmatrix} = \begin{bmatrix} -1 & 0 \\ 0 & -2 \end{bmatrix}$$

Therefore, the state transition matrix is

$$\phi(t) = \mathbf{M}e^{\overline{\mathbf{A}}t}\mathbf{M}^{-1}$$

$$= \begin{bmatrix} 1 & 1 \\ -1 & -2 \end{bmatrix}\begin{bmatrix} e^{-t} & 0 \\ 0 & e^{-2t} \end{bmatrix}\begin{bmatrix} 2 & 1 \\ -1 & -1 \end{bmatrix}$$

$$= \begin{bmatrix} 2e^{-t} - e^{-t} & e^{-t} - e^{-t} \\ -2e^{-t} + 2e^{-2t} & -e^{-t} + 2e^{-2t} \end{bmatrix}$$

10.7.5 Computation of STM by Sylvester's Method

Case 1: If the matrix **A** ($n \times n$ square matrix) has distinct eigenvalues $\lambda_1, \lambda_2, ..., \lambda_m$, the STM $e^{\mathbf{A}t}$ can be obtained by solving the following determinant equation:

$$
\begin{vmatrix}
1 & \lambda_1 & \lambda_1^2 & \cdots & \lambda_1^{n-1} & e^{\lambda_1 t} \\
1 & \lambda_2 & \lambda_2^2 & \cdots & \lambda_2^{n-1} & e^{\lambda_2 t} \\
\vdots & & & & & \\
1 & \lambda_n & \lambda_n^2 & \cdots & \lambda_n^{n-1} & e^{\lambda_n t} \\
\mathbf{I} & \mathbf{A} & \mathbf{A}^2 & \cdots & \mathbf{A}^{n-1} & e^{\mathbf{A}t}
\end{vmatrix} = 0
$$

By solving the above equation for $e^{\mathbf{A}t}$, $e^{\mathbf{A}t}$ can be obtained in terms of $\mathbf{A}^k$ ($k = 0, 1, 2, ..., n - 1$) and $e^{\lambda_i t}$ ($i = 1, 2, ..., n$).

Case 2: If the matrix **A** has repeated eigenvalues (suppose the eigenvalue λ_1 is repeated thrice), the state transition matrix, STM can be determined by solving the following modified determinant.

$$
\begin{vmatrix}
0 & 0 & 1 & 3\lambda_1 & \cdots & \dfrac{(n-1)(n-2)}{2}\lambda_1^{n-3} & \dfrac{t^2}{2}e^{\lambda_1 t} \\
0 & 1 & 2\lambda_1 & 3\lambda_1^2 & \cdots & (n-1)\lambda_1^{n-2} & te^{\lambda_1 t} \\
1 & \lambda_1 & \lambda_1^2 & \lambda_1^3 & \cdots & \lambda_1^{n-1} & e^{\lambda_1 t} \\
1 & \lambda_4 & \lambda_4^2 & \lambda_4^3 & \cdots & \lambda_4^{n-1} & e^{\lambda_4 t} \\
\vdots & & & & & & \\
1 & \lambda_n & \lambda_n^2 & \lambda_n^3 & \cdots & \lambda_n^{n-1} & e^{\lambda_n t} \\
\mathbf{I} & \mathbf{A} & \mathbf{A}^2 & \mathbf{A}^3 & \cdots & \mathbf{A}^{n-1} & e^{\mathbf{A}t}
\end{vmatrix}
$$

Example 10.27 Compute the STM $e^{\mathbf{A}t}$ by Sylvester's method for the state model whose system matrix **A** is

(a) $\mathbf{A} = \begin{bmatrix} 1 & 1 \\ 0 & 1 \end{bmatrix}$ (b) $\mathbf{A} = \begin{bmatrix} 0 & 1 \\ -1 & -2 \end{bmatrix}$ (c) $\mathbf{A} = \begin{bmatrix} 0 & 1 \\ -2 & -3 \end{bmatrix}$ (d) $\mathbf{A} = \begin{bmatrix} -1 & 0 \\ 1 & -1 \end{bmatrix}$

Solution: (a) For the given system matrix **A**, the eigenvalues are given by the roots of the characteristic equation

$$
|\lambda \mathbf{I} - \mathbf{A}| = \left| \lambda \begin{bmatrix} 1 & 0 \\ 0 & 1 \end{bmatrix} - \begin{bmatrix} 1 & 1 \\ 0 & 1 \end{bmatrix} \right| = \begin{vmatrix} \lambda - 1 & -1 \\ 0 & \lambda - 1 \end{vmatrix} = \lambda^2 - 2\lambda + 1 = (\lambda - 1)(\lambda - 1) = 0
$$

Therefore, the eigenvalues are $\lambda_1 = 1$, $\lambda_2 = 1$.

Since the eigenvalues are repeated, the STM $e^{\mathbf{A}t}$ can be computed by solving the determinant

$$\begin{vmatrix} 0 & 1 & te^{\lambda_1 t} \\ 1 & \lambda_1 & e^{\lambda_1 t} \\ \mathbf{I} & \mathbf{A} & e^{\mathbf{A}t} \end{vmatrix} = \begin{vmatrix} 0 & 1 & te^t \\ 1 & 1 & e^t \\ \mathbf{I} & \mathbf{A} & e^{\mathbf{A}t} \end{vmatrix} = 0$$

i.e.
$$-1(e^{\mathbf{A}t} - \mathbf{I}e^t) + te^t(\mathbf{A} - \mathbf{I}) = 0$$

$$\therefore \qquad e^{\mathbf{A}t} = \mathbf{I}e^t + te^t(\mathbf{A} - \mathbf{I})$$

$$= \begin{bmatrix} 1 & 0 \\ 0 & 1 \end{bmatrix} e^t + te^t \left[\begin{bmatrix} 1 & 1 \\ 0 & 1 \end{bmatrix} - \begin{bmatrix} 1 & 0 \\ 0 & 1 \end{bmatrix} \right]$$

$$= \begin{bmatrix} e^t & te^t \\ 0 & e^t \end{bmatrix}$$

(b) For the given system matrix $\mathbf{A}$, the eigenvalues are given by the roots of the characteristic equation

$$|\lambda\mathbf{I} - \mathbf{A}| = \begin{vmatrix} \lambda\begin{bmatrix} 1 & 0 \\ 0 & 1 \end{bmatrix} - \begin{bmatrix} 0 & 1 \\ -1 & -2 \end{bmatrix} \end{vmatrix} = \begin{vmatrix} \lambda & -1 \\ 1 & \lambda+2 \end{vmatrix} = \lambda^2 + 2\lambda + 1 = (\lambda+1)(\lambda+1) = 0$$

$\lambda_1 = -1$ and $\lambda_2 = -1$ are the eigenvalues of $\mathbf{A}$.

Since the eigenvalues of $\mathbf{A}$ are repeated, the STM $e^{\mathbf{A}t}$ can be computed by solving the determinant

$$\begin{vmatrix} 0 & 1 & te^{\lambda_1 t} \\ 1 & \lambda_1 & e^{\lambda_1 t} \\ \mathbf{I} & \mathbf{A} & e^{\mathbf{A}t} \end{vmatrix} = \begin{vmatrix} 0 & 1 & te^{-t} \\ 1 & -1 & e^{-t} \\ \mathbf{I} & \mathbf{A} & e^{\mathbf{A}t} \end{vmatrix} = 0$$

i.e.
$$-1(e^{\mathbf{A}t} - \mathbf{I}e^{-t}) + te^{-t}(\mathbf{A} + \mathbf{I}) = 0$$

$$\therefore \qquad e^{\mathbf{A}t} = \mathbf{I}e^{-t} + te^{-t}(\mathbf{A} + \mathbf{I}) = \begin{bmatrix} 1 & 0 \\ 0 & 1 \end{bmatrix} e^{-t} + te^{-t}\left[\begin{bmatrix} 0 & 1 \\ -1 & -2 \end{bmatrix} + \begin{bmatrix} 1 & 0 \\ 0 & 1 \end{bmatrix}\right]$$

$$= \begin{bmatrix} e^{-t} & 0 \\ 0 & e^{-t} \end{bmatrix} + \begin{bmatrix} 1 & 1 \\ -1 & -1 \end{bmatrix} te^{-t} = \begin{bmatrix} e^{-t} + te^{-t} & te^{-t} \\ -te^{-t} & e^{-t} - te^{-t} \end{bmatrix}$$

(c) The eigenvalues of the given $\mathbf{A}$ matrix are obtained by solving the characteristic equation

$$|\lambda\mathbf{I} - \mathbf{A}| = \begin{vmatrix} \lambda\begin{bmatrix} 1 & 0 \\ 0 & 1 \end{bmatrix} - \begin{bmatrix} 0 & 1 \\ -2 & -3 \end{bmatrix} \end{vmatrix} = \begin{vmatrix} \lambda & -1 \\ 2 & \lambda+3 \end{vmatrix} = \lambda^2 + 3\lambda + 2 = (\lambda+1)(\lambda+2) = 0$$

Therefore, the eigenvalues are $\lambda_1 = -1$ and $\lambda_2 = -2$.

Using Sylvester's method, the STM, e^{At}, can be computed by solving the determinant

$$\begin{vmatrix} 1 & \lambda_1 & e^{\lambda_1 t} \\ 1 & \lambda_2 & e^{\lambda_2 t} \\ \mathbf{I} & \mathbf{A} & e^{At} \end{vmatrix} = \begin{vmatrix} 1 & -1 & e^{-t} \\ 1 & -2 & e^{-2t} \\ \mathbf{I} & \mathbf{A} & e^{At} \end{vmatrix} = 0$$

$$1(-2e^{At} - \mathbf{A}e^{-2t}) + (e^{At} - \mathbf{I}e^{-2t}) + e^{-t}(\mathbf{A} + 2\mathbf{I}) = 0$$

Therefore, the STM $= e^{At} = -\mathbf{A}e^{-2t} - \mathbf{I}e^{-2t} + (2\mathbf{I} + \mathbf{A})e^{-t}$

$$= \left[\begin{bmatrix} 0 & -1 \\ 2 & 3 \end{bmatrix} + \begin{bmatrix} -1 & 0 \\ 0 & -1 \end{bmatrix} \right] e^{-2t} + \left[\begin{bmatrix} 2 & 0 \\ 0 & 2 \end{bmatrix} + \begin{bmatrix} 0 & 1 \\ -2 & -3 \end{bmatrix} \right] e^{-t}$$

$$= \begin{bmatrix} -1 & -1 \\ 2 & 2 \end{bmatrix} e^{-2t} + \begin{bmatrix} 2 & 1 \\ -2 & -1 \end{bmatrix} e^{-t}$$

$$= \begin{bmatrix} 2e^{-t} - e^{-2t} & e^{-t} - e^{-2t} \\ -2e^{-t} + 2e^{-2t} & -e^{-t} + 2e^{-2t} \end{bmatrix}$$

(d) The eigenvalues of the given $\mathbf{A}$ matrix are obtained by solving the characteristic equation.

$$|\lambda\mathbf{I} - \mathbf{A}| = \left| \lambda \begin{bmatrix} 1 & 0 \\ 0 & 1 \end{bmatrix} - \begin{bmatrix} -1 & 0 \\ 0 & -1 \end{bmatrix} \right| = \begin{vmatrix} \lambda+1 & 0 \\ -1 & \lambda+1 \end{vmatrix} = (\lambda+1)(\lambda+1) = 0$$

Therefore, the eigenvalues are $\lambda_1 = -1$ and $\lambda_2 = -1$. Since the eigenvalues are repeated, using Sylvester's method, e^{At} can be computed by solving the determinant

$$\begin{vmatrix} 0 & 1 & te^{\lambda_1 t} \\ 1 & \lambda_1 & e^{\lambda_1 t} \\ \mathbf{I} & \mathbf{A} & e^{At} \end{vmatrix} = \begin{vmatrix} 0 & 1 & te^{-t} \\ 1 & -1 & e^{-t} \\ \mathbf{I} & \mathbf{A} & e^{At} \end{vmatrix} = 0$$

i.e.

$$-1(e^{At} - \mathbf{I}e^{-t}) + te^{-t}(\mathbf{A} + \mathbf{I}) = 0$$

$\therefore$

$$e^{At} = \mathbf{I}e^{-t} + [\mathbf{A} + \mathbf{I}]te^{-t}$$

Therefore, the STM

$$e^{At} = \begin{bmatrix} 1 & 0 \\ 0 & 1 \end{bmatrix} e^{-t} + \left[\begin{bmatrix} -1 & 0 \\ 1 & -1 \end{bmatrix} + \begin{bmatrix} 1 & 0 \\ 0 & 1 \end{bmatrix} \right] te^{-t} = \begin{bmatrix} e^{-t} & 0 \\ 0 & e^{-t} \end{bmatrix} + \begin{bmatrix} 0 & 0 \\ 1 & 0 \end{bmatrix} te^{-t}$$

$$e^{At} = \begin{bmatrix} e^{-t} & 0 \\ te^{-t} & e^{-t} \end{bmatrix}$$

Example 10.28 Given, $\mathbf{A}_1 = \begin{bmatrix} \sigma & 0 \\ 0 & \sigma \end{bmatrix}$; $\mathbf{A}_2 = \begin{bmatrix} 0 & \omega \\ -\omega & 0 \end{bmatrix}$; $\mathbf{A} = \begin{bmatrix} \sigma & \omega \\ -\omega & \sigma \end{bmatrix}$ compute $e^{\mathbf{A}t}$.

Solution: Looking at the matrices $\mathbf{A}_1$, $\mathbf{A}_2$ and $\mathbf{A}$, we see that, $\mathbf{A}_1 + \mathbf{A}_2 = \mathbf{A}$. Therefore,

$$e^{\mathbf{A}t} = e^{(\mathbf{A}_1 + \mathbf{A}_2)t} = e^{\mathbf{A}_1 t} \cdot e^{\mathbf{A}_2 t}$$

Since the matrix $\mathbf{A}_1$ is in diagonal form, $e^{\mathbf{A}_1 t}$ can be written directly as

$$e^{\mathbf{A}_1 t} = \begin{bmatrix} e^{\sigma t} & 0 \\ 0 & e^{\sigma t} \end{bmatrix}$$

$$e^{\mathbf{A}_2 t} = \mathbf{I} + \mathbf{A}_2 t + \frac{\mathbf{A}_2^2 t^2}{2!} + \frac{\mathbf{A}_2^3 t^3}{3!} + \cdots$$

$$= \begin{bmatrix} 1 & 0 \\ 0 & 1 \end{bmatrix} + \begin{bmatrix} 0 & \omega \\ -\omega & 0 \end{bmatrix} t + \begin{bmatrix} -\omega^2 & 0 \\ 0 & -\omega^2 \end{bmatrix}\frac{t^2}{2!} + \begin{bmatrix} 0 & -\omega^3 \\ \omega^3 & 0 \end{bmatrix}\frac{t^3}{3!}$$

$$+ \begin{bmatrix} \omega^4 & 0 \\ 0 & \omega^4 \end{bmatrix}\frac{t^4}{4!} + \begin{bmatrix} 0 & \omega^5 \\ -\omega^5 & 0 \end{bmatrix}\frac{t^5}{5!} + \cdots$$

$$= \begin{bmatrix} 1 - \dfrac{\omega^2 t^2}{2!} + \dfrac{\omega^4 t^4}{4!} + \cdots & \omega t\left(1 - \dfrac{\omega^2 t^2}{3!} + \dfrac{\omega^4 t^4}{5!} + \cdots\right) \\ -\omega t\left(1 - \dfrac{\omega^2 t^2}{3!} + \dfrac{\omega^4 t^4}{5!} + \cdots\right) & 1 - \dfrac{\omega^2 t^2}{2!} + \dfrac{\omega^4 t^4}{4!} + \cdots \end{bmatrix}$$

$$= \begin{bmatrix} \cos \omega t & \sin \omega t \\ -\sin \omega t & \cos \omega t \end{bmatrix}$$

$$\therefore \qquad e^{\mathbf{A}t} = \begin{bmatrix} e^{\sigma t} & 0 \\ 0 & e^{\sigma t} \end{bmatrix}\begin{bmatrix} \cos \omega t & \sin \omega t \\ -\sin \omega t & \cos \omega t \end{bmatrix} = \begin{bmatrix} e^{\sigma t} \cos \omega t & e^{\sigma t} \sin \omega t \\ -e^{\sigma t} \sin \omega t & e^{\sigma t} \cos \omega t \end{bmatrix}$$

Example 10.29 For a system described by the state equation

$$\dot{\mathbf{x}}(t) = \mathbf{A}\mathbf{x}(t)$$

The response is $\qquad \mathbf{x}(t) = \begin{pmatrix} e^{-2t} \\ -2e^{-2t} \end{pmatrix}$, when $\mathbf{x}(0) = \begin{pmatrix} 1 \\ -2 \end{pmatrix}$

and $\qquad \mathbf{x}(t) = \begin{pmatrix} e^{-t} \\ -e^{-t} \end{pmatrix}$, when $\mathbf{x}(0) = \begin{pmatrix} 1 \\ -1 \end{pmatrix}$

Determine the system matrix $\mathbf{A}$ and the state transition matrix $\phi(t)$.

Solution: Let the STM be $\phi(t) = \begin{bmatrix} \phi_{11}(t) & \phi_{12}(t) \\ \phi_{21}(t) & \phi_{22}(t) \end{bmatrix}$, we know that $\mathbf{x}(t) = \phi(t)\,\mathbf{x}(0)$

$\therefore$

$$\begin{bmatrix} e^{-2t} \\ -2e^{-2t} \end{bmatrix} = \begin{bmatrix} \phi_{11}(t) & \phi_{12}(t) \\ \phi_{21}(t) & \phi_{22}(t) \end{bmatrix} \begin{bmatrix} 1 \\ -2 \end{bmatrix}$$

and

$$\begin{bmatrix} e^{-t} \\ -e^{-t} \end{bmatrix} = \begin{bmatrix} \phi_{11}(t) & \phi_{12}(t) \\ \phi_{21}(t) & \phi_{22}(t) \end{bmatrix} \begin{bmatrix} 1 \\ -1 \end{bmatrix}$$

Therefore, $e^{-2t} = \phi_{11}(t) - 2\phi_{12}(t)$ and $e^{-t} = \phi_{11}(t) - \phi_{12}(t)$

$-2e^{-2t} = \phi_{21}(t) - 2\phi_{22}(t)$ and $-e^{-t} = \phi_{21}(t) - \phi_{22}(t)$

Solving the above equations, we get

$\phi_{11}(t) = 2e^{-t} - e^{2t}$, $\phi_{12}(t) = e^{-t} - e^{-2t}$, $\phi_{21}(t) = 2e^{-t} + 2e^{-2t}$, $\phi_{22}(t) = -e^{-t} + 2e^{-2t}$

Hence, the state transition matrix is

$$\phi(t) = \begin{bmatrix} 2e^{-t} - e^{-2t} & e^{-t} - e^{-2t} \\ 2e^{-2t} - 2e^{-t} & -e^{-t} + 2e^{-2t} \end{bmatrix}$$

Taking the Laplace transform on both sides

$$\therefore \qquad \phi(s) = [s\mathbf{I} - \mathbf{A}]^{-1} = \begin{bmatrix} \dfrac{2}{s+1} - \dfrac{1}{s+2} & \dfrac{1}{s+1} - \dfrac{1}{s+2} \\ \dfrac{2}{s+2} - \dfrac{2}{s+1} & -\dfrac{1}{s+1} + \dfrac{2}{s+2} \end{bmatrix}$$

$$= \frac{\begin{bmatrix} s+3 & 1 \\ -2 & s \end{bmatrix}}{\Delta}$$

$$\therefore \qquad [s\mathbf{I} - \mathbf{A}] = \begin{bmatrix} s & -1 \\ 2 & s+3 \end{bmatrix} = \begin{bmatrix} s & 0 \\ 0 & s \end{bmatrix} - \mathbf{A}$$

$$\mathbf{A} = [s\mathbf{I} - [s\mathbf{I} - \mathbf{A}]] = \begin{bmatrix} s & 0 \\ 0 & s \end{bmatrix} - \begin{bmatrix} s & -1 \\ 2 & s+3 \end{bmatrix} = \begin{bmatrix} 0 & 1 \\ -2 & -3 \end{bmatrix}$$

Example 10.30   Obtain the time response of the system described by

$$\begin{bmatrix} \dot{x}_1 \\ \dot{x}_2 \end{bmatrix} = \begin{bmatrix} 0 & 1 \\ -1 & -2 \end{bmatrix} \begin{bmatrix} x_1 \\ x_2 \end{bmatrix} + \begin{bmatrix} 1 \\ -1 \end{bmatrix} u$$

with the initial conditions $\begin{bmatrix} x_1(0) \\ x_2(0) \end{bmatrix} = \begin{bmatrix} 0 \\ 1 \end{bmatrix}$, $y = \begin{bmatrix} 0 & 1 \end{bmatrix} \begin{bmatrix} x_1 \\ x_2 \end{bmatrix}$

Solution: The response of the system in s-domain is given by

$$X(s) = [sI - A]^{-1} X(0^+) + [sI - A]^{-1} BU(s)$$

$$X(s) = \phi(s) X(0^+) + \phi(s) BU(s)$$

where $\phi(s) = [sI - A]^{-1}$ is called the resolvent matrix.

$$X(s) = \phi(s)[X(0) + BU(s)]$$

$$= \phi(s)\left[\begin{bmatrix} 0 \\ 1 \end{bmatrix} + \begin{bmatrix} 1 \\ -1 \end{bmatrix}\frac{1}{s}\right] = \phi(s)\begin{bmatrix} \dfrac{1}{s} \\ 1 - \dfrac{1}{s} \end{bmatrix}$$

Given, $A = \begin{bmatrix} 0 & 1 \\ -1 & -2 \end{bmatrix}$, $[sI - A] = \begin{bmatrix} s & 0 \\ 0 & s \end{bmatrix} - \begin{bmatrix} 0 & 1 \\ -1 & -2 \end{bmatrix} = \begin{bmatrix} s & -1 \\ 1 & s+2 \end{bmatrix}$

$$\therefore \quad \phi(s) = [sI - A]^{-1} = \begin{bmatrix} s & -1 \\ 1 & s+2 \end{bmatrix}^{-1} = \frac{\begin{bmatrix} s+2 & -1 \\ 1 & s \end{bmatrix}^{T}}{\Delta} = \frac{\begin{bmatrix} s+2 & 1 \\ -1 & s \end{bmatrix}}{\Delta} = \frac{\begin{bmatrix} s+2 & 1 \\ -1 & s \end{bmatrix}}{(s+1)^2}$$

$$\therefore \quad X(s) = \frac{\begin{bmatrix} s+2 & 1 \\ -1 & s \end{bmatrix}}{(s+1)^2}\begin{bmatrix} \dfrac{1}{s} \\ 1 - \dfrac{1}{s} \end{bmatrix} = \frac{\begin{bmatrix} 1 + \dfrac{2}{s} + 1 - \dfrac{1}{s} \\ -\dfrac{1}{s} + s - 1 \end{bmatrix}}{(s+1)^2} = \frac{\begin{bmatrix} 2 + \dfrac{1}{s} \\ -1 + s - \dfrac{1}{s} \end{bmatrix}}{(s+1)^2}$$

$$= \begin{bmatrix} \dfrac{2s+1}{s(s+1)^2} \\ \dfrac{s^2 - s - 1}{s(s+1)^2} \end{bmatrix} = \begin{bmatrix} \dfrac{1}{s} - \dfrac{1}{s+1} + \dfrac{1}{(s+1)^2} \\ -\dfrac{1}{s} + \dfrac{2}{s+1} - \dfrac{1}{(s+1)^2} \end{bmatrix}$$

Taking the inverse Laplace transform, the time response is

$$x(t) = \begin{bmatrix} 1 - e^{-t} + te^{-t} \\ -1 + 2e^{-t} - te^{-t} \end{bmatrix}$$

The output response is given by

$$Y(s) = \begin{bmatrix} 0 & 1 \end{bmatrix}\begin{bmatrix} X_1(s) \\ X_2(s) \end{bmatrix} = X_2(s) = -\frac{1}{s} + \frac{2}{s+1} - \frac{1}{(s+1)^2}$$

Taking the inverse Laplace transform, the output response is

$$y(t) = -1 + 2e^{-t} - te^{-t} = x_2(t)$$

The time response of the above system can also be determined by using the state transition matrix.

For the given system matrix, the STM has already been computed earlier as

$$\phi(t) = \begin{bmatrix} e^{-t} + te^{-t} & te^{-t} \\ -te^{-t} & e^{-t} - te^{-t} \end{bmatrix}$$

The state transition equation is

$$\mathbf{x}(t) = \phi(t) \left[\mathbf{x}(0) + \int_0^t \phi(-\tau) \mathbf{BU}(\tau) d\tau \right]$$

$$= \phi(t) \left[\begin{bmatrix} 0 \\ 1 \end{bmatrix} + \int_0^t \begin{bmatrix} e^{\tau} - \tau e^{\tau} & -\tau e^{\tau} \\ \tau e^{\tau} & e^{\tau} + \tau e^{\tau} \end{bmatrix} \begin{bmatrix} 1 \\ -1 \end{bmatrix} d\tau \right]$$

$$= \phi(t) \left[\begin{bmatrix} 0 \\ 1 \end{bmatrix} + \int_0^t \begin{bmatrix} e^{\tau} \\ -e^{\tau} \end{bmatrix} d\tau \right] = \phi(t) \left[\begin{bmatrix} 0 \\ 1 \end{bmatrix} + \begin{bmatrix} e^{\tau} \\ -e^{\tau} \end{bmatrix}_0^t \right] = \phi(t) \left[\begin{bmatrix} 0 \\ 1 \end{bmatrix} + \begin{bmatrix} e^t - 1 \\ 2 - e^t \end{bmatrix} \right]$$

$$= \begin{bmatrix} e^{-t} + te^{-t} & te^{-t} \\ -te^{-t} & e^{-t} - te^{-t} \end{bmatrix} \begin{bmatrix} e^t - 1 \\ 2 - e^t \end{bmatrix} = \begin{bmatrix} 1 - e^{-t} + te^{-t} \\ -1 + 2e^{-t} - te^{-t} \end{bmatrix}$$

The time response of the system is therefore

$$\mathbf{x}(t) = \begin{bmatrix} x_1(t) \\ x_2(t) \end{bmatrix} = \begin{bmatrix} 1 - e^{-t} + te^{-t} \\ -1 + 2e^{-t} - te^{-t} \end{bmatrix}$$

The output is given by

$$y(t) = [0 \quad 1] \begin{bmatrix} x_1 \\ x_2 \end{bmatrix} = x_2 = -1 + 2e^{-t} - te^{-t}$$

Example 10.31   A linear time-invariant system is characterized by the homogeneous state equation.

$$\begin{bmatrix} \dot{x}_1 \\ \dot{x}_2 \end{bmatrix} = \begin{bmatrix} 1 & 0 \\ 1 & 1 \end{bmatrix} \begin{bmatrix} x_1 \\ x_2 \end{bmatrix}$$

(a) Compute the solution of the homogeneous equation assuming the initial state vector

$$\mathbf{x}_0 = \begin{bmatrix} 1 \\ 0 \end{bmatrix}.$$

(b) Consider now that the system has a forcing function and is represented by the following nonhomogeneous state equation.

$$\begin{bmatrix} \dot{x}_1 \\ \dot{x}_2 \end{bmatrix} = \begin{bmatrix} 1 & 0 \\ 1 & 1 \end{bmatrix} \begin{bmatrix} x_1 \\ x_2 \end{bmatrix} + \begin{bmatrix} 0 \\ 1 \end{bmatrix} u$$

where u is a unit-step function. Compute the solution of this equation assuming initial conditions of part (a).

Solution: (a) The solution of the homogeneous state equation is given by

$$\mathbf{x}(t) = \boldsymbol{\phi}(t)\,\mathbf{x}(0)$$

$\boldsymbol{\phi}(t)$, the STM is computed as follows

$$[s\mathbf{I} - \mathbf{A}] = \left[s\begin{bmatrix} 1 & 0 \\ 0 & 1 \end{bmatrix} - \begin{bmatrix} 1 & 0 \\ 1 & 1 \end{bmatrix} \right] = \begin{bmatrix} s-1 & 0 \\ -1 & s-1 \end{bmatrix}$$

$$\therefore \quad [s\mathbf{I} - \mathbf{A}]^{-1} = \frac{\begin{bmatrix} s-1 & 1 \\ 0 & s-1 \end{bmatrix}^T}{s^2 - 2s + 1} = \frac{\begin{bmatrix} s-1 & 0 \\ 1 & s-1 \end{bmatrix}}{(s-1)^2} = \boldsymbol{\phi}(s), \text{ the resolvent matrix.}$$

$$\boldsymbol{\phi}(t) = L^{-1}[s\mathbf{I} - \mathbf{A}]^{-1} = L^{-1}\begin{bmatrix} \dfrac{1}{s-1} & 0 \\ \dfrac{1}{(s-1)^2} & \dfrac{1}{s-1} \end{bmatrix} = \begin{bmatrix} e^t & 0 \\ te^t & e^t \end{bmatrix}$$

The solution of the homogeneous state equation is given by

$$\therefore \quad \mathbf{x}(t) = \boldsymbol{\phi}(t)\,\mathbf{x}(0) = \begin{bmatrix} e^t & 0 \\ te^t & e^t \end{bmatrix}\begin{bmatrix} 1 \\ 0 \end{bmatrix} = \begin{bmatrix} e^t \\ te^t \end{bmatrix} = \begin{bmatrix} x_1(t) \\ x_2(t) \end{bmatrix}$$

This can also be obtained by finding $\mathbf{X}(s)$ and taking its inverse Laplace transform.

$$\mathbf{X}(s) = \boldsymbol{\phi}(s)\,\mathbf{x}(0) = \frac{\begin{bmatrix} s-1 & 0 \\ 1 & s-1 \end{bmatrix}\begin{bmatrix} 1 \\ 0 \end{bmatrix}}{(s-1)^2} = \frac{\begin{bmatrix} s-1 \\ 1 \end{bmatrix}}{(s-1)^2} = \begin{bmatrix} \dfrac{1}{s-1} \\ \dfrac{1}{(s-1)^2} \end{bmatrix}$$

$$\therefore \quad \mathbf{x}(t) = \begin{bmatrix} x_1(t) \\ x_2(t) \end{bmatrix} = L^{-1}[\mathbf{X}(s)] = L^{-1}\begin{bmatrix} \dfrac{1}{s-1} \\ \dfrac{1}{(s-1)^2} \end{bmatrix} = \begin{bmatrix} e^t \\ te^t \end{bmatrix}$$

(b) The solution of the nonhomogeneous state equation called the state transition equation is

$$\mathbf{x}(t) = \phi(t)\mathbf{x}(0) + \int_0^t \phi(t-\tau)\mathbf{Bu}(\tau)\,d\tau$$

$$= \phi(t)\left[\mathbf{x}(0) + \int_0^t \phi(-\tau)\mathbf{Bu}(\tau)\,d\tau\right]$$

The input is a unit-step function. Therefore $u(t) = 1$.

$$\mathbf{x}(t) = \phi(t)\left[\begin{bmatrix}1\\0\end{bmatrix} + \int_0^t \begin{bmatrix}e^{-\tau} & 0\\-\tau e^{-\tau} & e^{-\tau}\end{bmatrix}\begin{bmatrix}0\\1\end{bmatrix}d\tau\right]$$

$$= \phi(t)\left[\begin{bmatrix}1\\0\end{bmatrix} + \int_0^t \begin{bmatrix}0\\e^{-\tau}\end{bmatrix}d\tau\right] = \phi(t)\left[\begin{bmatrix}1\\0\end{bmatrix} + \begin{bmatrix}0\\-e^{-\tau}\end{bmatrix}_0^t\right]$$

$$= \phi(t)\left[\begin{bmatrix}1\\0\end{bmatrix} + \begin{bmatrix}0\\-e^{-t}+1\end{bmatrix}\right] = \phi(t)\begin{bmatrix}1\\1-e^{-t}\end{bmatrix}$$

$$= \begin{bmatrix}e^t & 0\\te^t & e^t\end{bmatrix}\begin{bmatrix}1\\1-e^{-t}\end{bmatrix} = \begin{bmatrix}e^t\\te^t+e^t-1\end{bmatrix} = \begin{bmatrix}x_1(t)\\x_2(t)\end{bmatrix}$$

The time response can also be calculated as given below.

$$\mathbf{X}(s) = \phi(s)[\mathbf{x}(0) + \mathbf{BU}(s)]$$

$$= \begin{bmatrix}\dfrac{1}{s-1} & 0\\[2mm]\dfrac{1}{(s-1)^2} & \dfrac{1}{s-1}\end{bmatrix}\left[\begin{bmatrix}1\\0\end{bmatrix} + \begin{bmatrix}0\\1\end{bmatrix}\dfrac{1}{s}\right]$$

$$= \begin{bmatrix}\dfrac{1}{s-1} & 0\\[2mm]\dfrac{1}{(s-1)^2} & \dfrac{1}{s-1}\end{bmatrix}\begin{bmatrix}1\\[2mm]\dfrac{1}{s}\end{bmatrix} = \begin{bmatrix}\dfrac{1}{s-1}\\[3mm]\dfrac{1}{(s-1)^2} + \dfrac{1}{s(s-1)}\end{bmatrix}$$

$$= \begin{bmatrix}\dfrac{1}{s-1}\\[3mm]\dfrac{1}{(s-1)^2} + \dfrac{1}{(s-1)} - \dfrac{1}{s}\end{bmatrix}$$

$$\therefore \qquad \mathbf{x}(t) = L^{-1}[\mathbf{X}(s)] = \begin{bmatrix}e^t\\te^t+e^t-1\end{bmatrix} = \begin{bmatrix}x_1(t)\\x_2(t)\end{bmatrix}$$

10.8 TRANSFER FUNCTION FROM THE STATE MODEL

In the previous sections, we discussed how to obtain the state model of a system from its transfer function. Here we discuss how to obtain the transfer function of the system from its state model. If the state model is using phase variables, the transfer function can be obtained directly by inspection of dynamic equations. Another way is to draw a signal flow graph for the given phase variable state model and then obtain the transfer function by using Mason's gain formula. In general, given a state model, the transfer function can be obtained algebraically as shown below.

The state model is given by

$$\dot{x}(t) = Ax(t) + Bu(t) \tag{10.19}$$

$$y(t) = Cx(t) + Du(t) \tag{10.20}$$

Taking the Laplace transform of Eqs. (10.19) and (10.20), we get

$$sX(s) - x(0) = AX(s) + BU(s)$$

i.e.

$$[sI - A]X(s) = x(0) + BU(s)$$

i.e.

$$X(s) = [sI - A]^{-1} x(0) + [sI - A]^{-1} BU(s) \tag{10.21}$$

Substituting the value of $X(s)$ from Eq. (10.21) in the expression $Y(s) = CX(s) + DU(s)$, we get

$$Y(s) = C[sI - A]^{-1} x(0) + C[sI - A]^{-1} BU(s) + DU(s) \tag{10.22}$$

Since transfer function is defined under zero initial conditions, neglecting $x(0)$, Eq. (10.22) becomes

$$Y(s) = [C[sI - A]^{-1}B + D] \, U(s)$$

Therefore, the transfer function

$$\frac{Y(s)}{U(s)} = T(s) = C[sI - A]^{-1} B + D$$

Eventhough the state model of a system is not unique, the transfer function of a system is unique that means all the state models of a system result in the same transfer function.

Example 10.32   Obtain the transfer function of a system described by the state model

$$\begin{bmatrix} \dot{x}_1(t) \\ \dot{x}_2(t) \\ \dot{x}_3(t) \end{bmatrix} = \begin{bmatrix} 0 & 1 & 0 \\ 0 & 0 & 1 \\ -1 & -2 & -3 \end{bmatrix} \begin{bmatrix} x_1(t) \\ x_2(t) \\ x_3(t) \end{bmatrix} + \begin{bmatrix} 0 & 0 \\ 1 & 0 \\ 0 & 1 \end{bmatrix} \begin{bmatrix} u_1(t) \\ u_2(t) \end{bmatrix}$$

$$\begin{bmatrix} y_1(t) \\ y_2(t) \end{bmatrix} = \begin{bmatrix} 1 & 0 & 0 \\ 0 & 0 & 1 \end{bmatrix} \begin{bmatrix} x_1(t) \\ x_2(t) \\ x_3(t) \end{bmatrix}$$

Solution: Given the system matrix **A**

$$[s\mathbf{I} - \mathbf{A}] = s \begin{bmatrix} 1 & 0 & 0 \\ 0 & 1 & 0 \\ 0 & 0 & 1 \end{bmatrix} - \begin{bmatrix} 0 & 1 & 0 \\ 0 & 0 & 1 \\ -1 & -2 & -3 \end{bmatrix} = \begin{bmatrix} s & -1 & 0 \\ 0 & s & -1 \\ 1 & 2 & s+3 \end{bmatrix}$$

$$\therefore \quad [s\mathbf{I} - \mathbf{A}]^{-1} = \frac{\begin{bmatrix} (s+2)(s+1) & -1 & -s \\ (s+3) & s(s+3) & -(2s+1) \\ 1 & s & s^2 \end{bmatrix}^{T}}{s(s^2 + 3s + 2) + 1(1)} = \frac{\begin{bmatrix} (s+2)(s+1) & (s+3) & 1 \\ -1 & s(s+3) & s \\ -s & -(2s+1) & s^2 \end{bmatrix}}{s^3 + 3s^2 + 2s + 1}$$

The transfer function of the system is given by

$$\frac{Y(s)}{U(s)} = T(s) = C[s\mathbf{I} - \mathbf{A}]^{-1} B + D$$

$$\therefore \quad T(s) = \frac{\begin{bmatrix} 1 & 0 & 0 \\ 0 & 0 & 1 \end{bmatrix} \begin{bmatrix} (s+2)(s+1) & (s+3) & 1 \\ -1 & s(s+3) & s \\ -s & -(2s+1) & s^2 \end{bmatrix} \begin{bmatrix} 0 & 0 \\ 1 & 0 \\ 0 & 1 \end{bmatrix}}{s^3 + 3s^2 + 2s + 1}$$

$$= \frac{\begin{bmatrix} 1 & 0 & 0 \\ 0 & 0 & 1 \end{bmatrix} \begin{bmatrix} s+3 & 1 \\ s(s+3) & s \\ -(2s+1) & s^2 \end{bmatrix}}{s(s+1)(s+2)} = \frac{\begin{bmatrix} s+3 & 1 \\ -(2s+1) & s^2 \end{bmatrix}}{s^3 + 3s^2 + 2s + 1}$$

Example 10.33 Obtain the transfer function of the system described by

$$\begin{bmatrix} \dot{x}_1 \\ \dot{x}_2 \end{bmatrix} = \begin{bmatrix} 0 & 1 \\ -2 & -3 \end{bmatrix} \begin{bmatrix} x_1 \\ x_2 \end{bmatrix} + \begin{bmatrix} 0 \\ 1 \end{bmatrix} u; \quad x(0) = \begin{bmatrix} 1 \\ 1 \end{bmatrix}, \quad y = \begin{bmatrix} 1 & 0 \end{bmatrix} \begin{bmatrix} x_1 \\ x_2 \end{bmatrix}$$

Solution: The transfer function of the system is given by

$$\frac{Y(s)}{U(s)} = T(s) = C[s\mathbf{I} - \mathbf{A}]^{-1} B + D$$

$$\therefore \quad T(s) = \begin{bmatrix} 1 & 0 \end{bmatrix} \begin{bmatrix} s & -1 \\ 2 & s+3 \end{bmatrix}^{-1} \begin{bmatrix} 0 \\ 1 \end{bmatrix} = \frac{\begin{bmatrix} 1 & 0 \end{bmatrix} \begin{bmatrix} s+3 & -2 \\ 1 & s \end{bmatrix}^{T} \begin{bmatrix} 0 \\ 1 \end{bmatrix}}{s^2 + 3s + 2}$$

$$= \begin{bmatrix} 1 & 0 \end{bmatrix} \frac{\begin{bmatrix} s+3 & 1 \\ -2 & s \end{bmatrix} \begin{bmatrix} 0 \\ 1 \end{bmatrix}}{(s+1)(s+2)}$$

$$= \frac{\begin{bmatrix} 1 & 0 \end{bmatrix} \begin{bmatrix} 1 \\ s \end{bmatrix}}{(s+1)(s+2)} = \frac{1}{s^2 + 3s + 2}$$

10.9 STABILITY

Stability of a system represented by its state model: Since the eigenvalues of the system matrix **A** are the same as the roots of the characteristic equation which are nothing but the poles of the closed-loop transfer function, the stability of a system can be determined by determining the location of the eigenvalues.

Example 10.34   Determine the stability of the system whose **A** matrix is

(a) $\mathbf{A} = \begin{bmatrix} 0 & -2 \\ 1 & -3 \end{bmatrix}$ (b) $\mathbf{A} = \begin{bmatrix} 1 & 1 \\ 0 & 1 \end{bmatrix}$ (c) $\mathbf{A} = \begin{bmatrix} 0 & 0 \\ -1 & -1 \end{bmatrix}$ (d) $\mathbf{A} = \begin{bmatrix} 0 & 2 \\ -2 & 0 \end{bmatrix}$

(e) $\mathbf{A} = \begin{bmatrix} 0 & 1 & 0 \\ 0 & 0 & 1 \\ -2 & -5 & -4 \end{bmatrix}$ (f) $\mathbf{A} = \begin{bmatrix} 0 & 1 & 0 \\ 0 & 0 & 1 \\ -6 & -11 & -6 \end{bmatrix}$ (g) $\mathbf{A} = \begin{bmatrix} 0 & 1 & 0 \\ 0 & 0 & 1 \\ -1 & -3 & 3 \end{bmatrix}$

Solution: (a) The characteristic equation of the system is

$$|\lambda \mathbf{I} - \mathbf{A}| = \begin{vmatrix} \begin{bmatrix} \lambda & 0 \\ 0 & \lambda \end{bmatrix} - \begin{bmatrix} 0 & -2 \\ 1 & -3 \end{bmatrix} \end{vmatrix} = \begin{vmatrix} \lambda & 2 \\ -1 & \lambda+3 \end{vmatrix} = \lambda^2 + 3\lambda + 2 = (\lambda+1)(\lambda+2) = 0$$

The roots of this characteristic equation, i.e. the eigenvalues of **A** are $\lambda_1 = -1$ and $\lambda_2 = -2$. Since all the eigenvalues have only negative real parts, the system represented by the state model is stable.

(b) For the given system matrix **A**, the eigenvalues are given by the roots of the characteristic equation

$$|\lambda \mathbf{I} - \mathbf{A}| = \begin{vmatrix} \lambda \begin{bmatrix} 1 & 0 \\ 0 & 1 \end{bmatrix} - \begin{bmatrix} 1 & 1 \\ 0 & 1 \end{bmatrix} \end{vmatrix} = \begin{vmatrix} \lambda-1 & -1 \\ 0 & \lambda-1 \end{vmatrix} = \lambda^2 - 2\lambda + 1 = (\lambda-1)(\lambda-1) = 0$$

Therefore, the eigenvalues of **A** are $\lambda_1 = 1$ and $\lambda_2 = 1$. Since the eigenvalues have positive real parts, the system represented by that state model is unstable.

(c) For the given system matrix **A**, the eigenvalues are given by the roots of the characteristic equation

$$|\lambda \mathbf{I} - \mathbf{A}| = \left|\lambda \begin{bmatrix} 1 & 0 \\ 0 & 1 \end{bmatrix} - \begin{bmatrix} 0 & 0 \\ -1 & -1 \end{bmatrix}\right| = \begin{vmatrix} \lambda & 0 \\ 1 & \lambda+1 \end{vmatrix} = \lambda^2 + \lambda = \lambda(\lambda+1) = 0$$

Hence, $\lambda_1 = 0$ and $\lambda_2 = -1$ are the eigenvalues of **A**. Since one eigenvalue has zero real part and the other one has negative real part, the system represented by that state model is limitedly stable (unstable).

(d) For the given system matrix **A**, the eigenvalues are given by the roots of the characteristic equation

$$|\lambda \mathbf{I} - \mathbf{A}| = \left|\lambda \begin{bmatrix} 1 & 0 \\ 0 & 1 \end{bmatrix} - \begin{bmatrix} 0 & 2 \\ -2 & 0 \end{bmatrix}\right| = \begin{vmatrix} \lambda & -2 \\ 2 & \lambda \end{vmatrix} = \lambda^2 + 4 = (\lambda + j2)(\lambda - j2) = 0$$

Therefore, $\lambda_1 = j2$ and $\lambda_2 = -j2$ are the eigenvalues of **A**. Since the eigenvalues are on the imaginary axis of the *s*-plane, the system represented by that state model is limitedly stable (unstable).

(e) The eigenvalues of the system matrix **A** are the roots of the characteristic equation

$$|\lambda \mathbf{I} - \mathbf{A}| = \begin{bmatrix} \lambda & 0 & 0 \\ 0 & \lambda & 0 \\ 0 & 0 & \lambda \end{bmatrix} - \begin{bmatrix} 0 & 1 & 0 \\ 0 & 0 & 1 \\ -2 & -5 & -4 \end{bmatrix} = \begin{vmatrix} \lambda & -1 & 0 \\ 0 & \lambda & -1 \\ 2 & 5 & \lambda+4 \end{vmatrix}$$

$$= \lambda^3 + 4\lambda^2 + 5\lambda + 2 = (\lambda + 1)(\lambda + 1)(\lambda + 2) = 0$$

Hence, the eigenvalues of **A** are $\lambda_1 = -1$, $\lambda_2 = -1$, $\lambda_3 = -2$. Since all the eigenvalues have only negative real parts, the system represented by that state model is stable.

(f) The eigenvalues of the system matrix **A** are the roots of the characteristic equation

$$|\lambda \mathbf{I} - \mathbf{A}| = \lambda \begin{bmatrix} 1 & 0 & 0 \\ 0 & 1 & 0 \\ 0 & 0 & 1 \end{bmatrix} - \begin{bmatrix} 0 & 1 & 0 \\ 0 & 0 & 1 \\ -6 & -11 & -6 \end{bmatrix} = \begin{bmatrix} \lambda & -1 & 0 \\ 0 & \lambda & -1 \\ 6 & 11 & \lambda+6 \end{bmatrix}$$

$$= \lambda^3 + 6\lambda^2 + 11\lambda + 6 = (\lambda + 1)(\lambda + 2)(\lambda + 3) = 0$$

Therefore, the eigenvalues of **A** are $\lambda_1 = -1$, $\lambda_2 = -2$, $\lambda_3 = -3$. Since all the eigenvalues have only negative real parts, the system represented by that state model is stable.

(g) The eigenvalues of the system matrix **A** are the roots of the characteristic equation

$$|\lambda \mathbf{I} - \mathbf{A}| = \left| \lambda \begin{bmatrix} 1 & 0 & 0 \\ 0 & 1 & 0 \\ 0 & 0 & 1 \end{bmatrix} - \begin{bmatrix} 0 & 1 & 0 \\ 0 & 0 & 1 \\ 1 & -3 & 3 \end{bmatrix} \right| = \left| \begin{bmatrix} \lambda & -1 & 0 \\ 0 & \lambda & -1 \\ -1 & 3 & \lambda - 3 \end{bmatrix} \right|$$

$$= \lambda^3 - 3\lambda^2 + 3\lambda - 1 = (\lambda - 1)(\lambda - 1)(\lambda - 1) = 0$$

Therefore, the eigenvalues are $\lambda_1 = 1$, $\lambda_2 = 1$, $\lambda_3 = 1$. Since the eigenvalues have positive real parts, the system represented by that state model is unstable.

10.10   CONTROLLABILITY OF LINEAR SYSTEMS

A system is said to be completely state controllable at time t_0, if it is possible by means of an unconstrained control vector $u(t)$ to transfer the system from an initial state $x(t_0)$ to any other desired state in a finite interval of time.

In other words, a process is said to be completely controllable, if every state variable of the process can be controlled to reach a certain objective in a finite time by some unconstrained control $\mathbf{u}(t)$. If any one of the state variables is independent of the control $\mathbf{u}(t)$, there would be no way of driving this particular state variable to a desired state in a finite time by means of a control effort. Therefore, this particular state is said to be uncontrollable and as long as there is atleast one uncontrollable state, the system is said not to be completely controllable or simply uncontrollable.

A system is said to be observable at time t_0, if with the system in state $x(t_0)$, it is possible to determine this state from the observation of the output over a finite time interval.

The concepts of controllability and observability were introduced by Kalman. They play an important role in the design of control systems in state-space.

Figure 10.32 illustrates the state diagram of an uncontrollable linear system with two state variables. Since the control $\mathbf{u}(t)$ effects only the state $\mathbf{x}_1(t)$, the state $\mathbf{x}_2(t)$ is uncontrollable. In other words, it would be impossible to drive $\mathbf{x}_2(t)$ from an initial state $\mathbf{x}_2(t_0)$ to a desired state $\mathbf{x}_2(t_f)$ in a finite time interval $t_f - t_0$ by the control $\mathbf{u}(t)$. Therefore, the entire system is said to be uncontrollable.

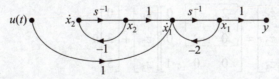

Figure 10.32   State diagram of an uncontrollable system.

Controllability can also be defined for the outputs of the system, so there is a difference between state controllability and output controllability.

For a linear time-invariant system described by the following dynamic equations.

$$\dot{x}(t) = Ax(t) + Bu(t)$$

$$y(t) = Cx(t) + Du(t)$$

where $x(t)$ is an $n \times 1$ state vector and $u(t)$ is a scalar to be completely state controllable, it is necessary and sufficient that the following $n \times n$ controllability matrix has a rank of n.

$$S = [B \quad AB \quad A^2B \quad ... \quad A^{n-1}B]$$

Since the matrices A and B are involved, sometimes we say that the pair $[A, B]$ is controllable which implies that S is of rank n.

10.10.1 Alternative Form of the Condition for Complete State Controllability

The necessary and sufficient condition for the system described by

$$\dot{x}(t) = Ax(t) + Bu(t)$$

to be state controllable is that no row of $M^{-1}B$ has all zero elements, where the matrix A has distinct eigenvalues and M is the transformation matrix such that $M^{-1}AM$ is a diagonal matrix with the distinct eigenvalues as the diagonal elements.

If the matrix A does not posses distinct eigenvalues, then diagonalization is impossible. So transform A into Jordan canonical form using the transformation matrix M. Then the system is completely state controllable, if and only if

1. No two Jordan blocks in $M^{-1}AM$ are associated with the same eigenvalues
2. The elements of any row of $M^{-1}B$ that correspond to last row of each Jordan block are not all zeors.
3. The elements of each row of $M^{-1}B$ that correspond to distinct eigenvalues are not all zero.

For example, he following systems are completely state controllable.

$$\begin{bmatrix} \dot{z}_1 \\ \dot{z}_2 \end{bmatrix} = \begin{bmatrix} -1 & 0 \\ 0 & -3 \end{bmatrix} \begin{bmatrix} z_1 \\ z_2 \end{bmatrix} + \begin{bmatrix} 4 \\ 2 \end{bmatrix} u$$

$$\begin{bmatrix} \dot{z}_1 \\ \dot{z}_2 \\ \dot{z}_3 \end{bmatrix} = \begin{bmatrix} -2 & 1 & 0 \\ 0 & -2 & 0 \\ 0 & 0 & -1 \end{bmatrix} \begin{bmatrix} z_1 \\ z_2 \\ z_3 \end{bmatrix} + \begin{bmatrix} 0 \\ 3 \\ 5 \end{bmatrix} u$$

$$\begin{bmatrix} \dot{z}_1 \\ \dot{z}_2 \\ \dot{z}_3 \\ \dot{z}_4 \\ \dot{z}_5 \end{bmatrix} = \begin{bmatrix} -1 & 1 & 0 & 0 & 0 \\ 0 & -1 & 1 & 0 & 0 \\ 0 & 0 & -1 & 0 & 0 \\ 0 & 0 & 0 & -4 & 1 \\ 0 & 0 & 0 & 0 & -4 \end{bmatrix} \begin{bmatrix} z_1 \\ z_2 \\ z_3 \\ z_4 \\ z_5 \end{bmatrix} + \begin{bmatrix} 0 & 1 \\ 0 & 0 \\ 2 & 0 \\ 0 & 0 \\ 2 & 1 \end{bmatrix} \begin{bmatrix} u_1 \\ u_2 \end{bmatrix}$$

The following systems are not completely state controllable:

$$\begin{bmatrix} \dot{z}_1 \\ \dot{z}_2 \end{bmatrix} = \begin{bmatrix} -1 & 0 \\ 0 & -2 \end{bmatrix} \begin{bmatrix} z_1 \\ z_2 \end{bmatrix} + \begin{bmatrix} 3 \\ 0 \end{bmatrix} u$$

$$\begin{bmatrix} \dot{z}_1 \\ \dot{z}_2 \\ \dot{z}_3 \end{bmatrix} = \begin{bmatrix} -2 & 1 & 0 \\ 0 & -2 & 0 \\ 0 & 0 & -1 \end{bmatrix} \begin{bmatrix} z_1 \\ z_2 \\ z_3 \end{bmatrix} + \begin{bmatrix} 3 & 2 \\ 0 & 0 \\ 1 & 0 \end{bmatrix} \begin{bmatrix} u_1 \\ u_2 \end{bmatrix}$$

$$\begin{bmatrix} \dot{z}_1 \\ \dot{z}_2 \\ \dot{z}_3 \\ \dot{z}_4 \\ \dot{z}_5 \end{bmatrix} = \begin{bmatrix} -3 & 1 & 0 & 0 & 0 \\ 0 & -3 & 1 & 0 & 0 \\ 0 & 0 & -3 & 0 & 0 \\ 0 & 0 & 0 & -4 & 1 \\ 0 & 0 & 0 & 0 & -4 \end{bmatrix} \begin{bmatrix} z_1 \\ z_2 \\ z_3 \\ z_4 \\ z_5 \end{bmatrix} + \begin{bmatrix} 3 \\ 2 \\ 1 \\ 4 \\ 0 \end{bmatrix} u$$

10.10.2 Condition for Complete State Controllability in the *s*-Plane

The condition for complete state controllability can be stated in terms of transfer functions or transfer matrices.

A necessary and sufficient condition for complete state controllability is that no cancellation occurs in the transfer function or transfer matrix. If cancellation occurs, the system can not be controlled in the direction of the cancelled mode.

10.10.3 Output Controllability

In the practical design of a control system, we may want to control the output rather than the state of the system. Complete state controllability is neither necessary nor sufficient for controlling the output of the system. For this reason, it is desirable to define separately complete output controllability.

The system described by

$$\dot{x}(t) = Ax(t) + Bu(t)$$

$$y(t) = Cx(t) + Du(t)$$

is said to be completely output controllable, if it is possible to construct an unconstrained controlled vector $u(t)$ that will transfer any given initial output $y(t_0)$ to any final output $y(t_f)$ in a finite time interval $t_0 \leq t \leq t_f$.

The condition for complete output controllability is – the system described by the state model

$$\dot{x}(t) = Ax(t) + Bu(t)$$

$$y(t) = Cx(t) + Du(t)$$

is completely output controllable, if and only if the $m \times (n + 1)$ matrix

$$[CB \quad CAB \quad CA^2B \; ... \; CA^{n-1}B \quad D]$$

is of rank m, where m is the number of outputs.

The presence of the **Du** term in the output equation always helps to establish controllability.

Uncontrollable system: An uncontrollable system has a sub-system that is physically disconnected from the input.

Example 10.35 Determine whether the system described by the state equation

$$\begin{bmatrix} \dot{x}_1 \\ \dot{x}_2 \\ \dot{x}_3 \end{bmatrix} = \begin{bmatrix} 0 & 1 & 0 \\ 0 & 0 & 1 \\ 0 & -2 & -3 \end{bmatrix} \begin{bmatrix} x_1 \\ x_2 \\ x_3 \end{bmatrix} + \begin{bmatrix} 0 \\ 0 \\ 1 \end{bmatrix} u$$

is completely state controllable.

Solution: First transform this state equation into canonical form. The characteristic equation is given by

$$|\lambda I - A| = \begin{vmatrix} \lambda & -1 & 0 \\ 0 & \lambda & -1 \\ 0 & 2 & \lambda+3 \end{vmatrix} = \lambda^3 + 3\lambda^2 + 2\lambda + 2 = \lambda(\lambda+1)(\lambda+2) = 0$$

Therefore, the eigenvalues are $\lambda_1 = 0$, $\lambda_2 = -1$ and $\lambda_3 = -2$. Since the eigenvalues are distinct, choosing Vander Monde matrix as modal matrix, we have

$$M = \begin{bmatrix} 1 & 1 & 1 \\ \lambda_1 & \lambda_2 & \lambda_3 \\ \lambda_1^2 & \lambda_2^2 & \lambda_3^2 \end{bmatrix} = \begin{bmatrix} 1 & 1 & 1 \\ 0 & -1 & -2 \\ 0 & 1 & 4 \end{bmatrix}$$

$$M^{-1} = \frac{\begin{bmatrix} -2 & 0 & 0 \\ -3 & 4 & -1 \\ -1 & 2 & -1 \end{bmatrix}^T}{-2} = \frac{\begin{bmatrix} -2 & -3 & -1 \\ 0 & 4 & 2 \\ 0 & -1 & -1 \end{bmatrix}}{-2}$$

$$\therefore \quad \overline{B} = M^{-1}B = \frac{\begin{bmatrix} -2 & -3 & -1 \\ 0 & 4 & 2 \\ 0 & -1 & -1 \end{bmatrix} \begin{bmatrix} 0 \\ 0 \\ 1 \end{bmatrix}}{-2} = \frac{\begin{bmatrix} -1 \\ 2 \\ -1 \end{bmatrix}}{-2} = \begin{bmatrix} 1/2 \\ -1 \\ 1/2 \end{bmatrix}$$

$$M^{-1}AM = -\frac{1}{2} \begin{bmatrix} -2 & -3 & -1 \\ 0 & 4 & 2 \\ 0 & -1 & -1 \end{bmatrix} \begin{bmatrix} 0 & 1 & 0 \\ 0 & 0 & 1 \\ 0 & -2 & -3 \end{bmatrix} \begin{bmatrix} 1 & 1 & 1 \\ 0 & -1 & -2 \\ 0 & 1 & 4 \end{bmatrix} = \begin{bmatrix} 0 & 0 & 0 \\ 0 & -1 & 0 \\ 0 & 0 & -2 \end{bmatrix}$$

Therefore, the state equation in canonical form is given by

$$\begin{bmatrix} \dot{z}_1 \\ \dot{z}_2 \\ \dot{z}_3 \end{bmatrix} = \begin{bmatrix} 0 & 0 & 0 \\ 0 & -1 & 0 \\ 0 & 0 & -2 \end{bmatrix} \begin{bmatrix} z_1 \\ z_2 \\ z_3 \end{bmatrix} + \begin{bmatrix} 1/2 \\ -1 \\ 1/2 \end{bmatrix} u$$

Since no element of $\overline{\mathbf{B}}$ is zero, the system is completely controllable.

Testing the controllability of the system by Kalaman's test, we have

$$\mathbf{B} = \begin{bmatrix} 0 \\ 0 \\ 1 \end{bmatrix}; \quad \mathbf{A} = \begin{bmatrix} 0 & 1 & 0 \\ 0 & 0 & 1 \\ 0 & -2 & -3 \end{bmatrix}$$

Then,

$$\mathbf{AB} = \begin{bmatrix} 0 & 1 & 0 \\ 0 & 0 & 1 \\ 0 & -2 & -3 \end{bmatrix} \begin{bmatrix} 0 \\ 0 \\ 1 \end{bmatrix} = \begin{bmatrix} 0 \\ 1 \\ -3 \end{bmatrix}$$

$$\mathbf{A}^2\mathbf{B} = \begin{bmatrix} 0 & 1 & 0 \\ 0 & 0 & 1 \\ 0 & -2 & -3 \end{bmatrix} \begin{bmatrix} 0 \\ 1 \\ -3 \end{bmatrix} = \begin{bmatrix} 1 \\ -3 \\ 7 \end{bmatrix}$$

The controllability matrix $\mathbf{S}$ is given by

$$\mathbf{S} = [\mathbf{B} \quad \mathbf{AB} \quad \mathbf{A}^2\mathbf{B}]$$

$$= \begin{bmatrix} 0 & 0 & 1 \\ 0 & 1 & -3 \\ 1 & -3 & -7 \end{bmatrix}$$

It is easily seen that det. $\mathbf{S} \neq 0$, i.e. its rank is $r = n = 3$. The system is therefore completely controllable.

Controllable phase variable form: If the system equation is given by

$$\dot{\mathbf{z}}(t) = \mathbf{A}_c \mathbf{z}(t) + \mathbf{B}_c \mathbf{u}(t)$$

where $\mathbf{z}(t)$ is $n \times 1$ vector and $u(t)$ is a scalar, and

$$\mathbf{A}_c = \begin{bmatrix} 0 & 1 & 0 & \cdots & 0 \\ 0 & 0 & 1 & \cdots & 0 \\ \vdots & & & \cdots & \vdots \\ 0 & 0 & 0 & \cdots & 1 \\ -a_n & -a_{n-1} & -a_{n-2} & \cdots & -a_1 \end{bmatrix}; \quad \mathbf{B}_c = \begin{bmatrix} 0 \\ 0 \\ \vdots \\ 0 \\ 1 \end{bmatrix}$$

Then, it is easily verified that the rank of the matrix $[\mathbf{B}_c \quad \mathbf{A}_c\mathbf{B}_c \quad \ldots \quad \mathbf{A}_c^{n-1}\mathbf{B}_c]$ is n. Therefore, a system described by state equations of the form

$$\dot{z}(t) = \mathbf{A}_c z(t) + \mathbf{B}_c u(t)$$

is always controllable.

The converse is also true that, if a linear time-invariant system given by

$$\dot{x}(t) = \mathbf{A}x(t) + \mathbf{B}u(t)$$

where $\mathbf{x}(t)$ is $n \times 1$ state vector, $\mathbf{A}$ is $n \times n$ system matrix, $\mathbf{B}$ is $n \times 1$ control vector, u is a scalar control input, is controllable, then it can be transformed into the form

$$\dot{z}(t) = \mathbf{A}_c z(t) + \mathbf{B}_c u(t)$$

For example, consider a linear system described by the differential equation

$$\ddot{y} + 3\dot{y} + 2y = \dot{u} + u$$

with $x_1 = y$, $x_2 = \dot{y} - u$ as the state variables, we get the state model

$$y = x_1$$
$$\dot{x}_1 = \dot{y} = x_2 + u$$
$$\dot{x}_2 = \ddot{y} - \dot{u} = u - 3\dot{y} - 2y = u - 3x_2 - 3u - 2x_1 = -2x_1 - 3x_2 - 2u$$

Therefore, the state model is

$$\begin{bmatrix} \dot{x}_1 \\ \dot{x}_2 \end{bmatrix} = \begin{bmatrix} 0 & 1 \\ -2 & -3 \end{bmatrix}\begin{bmatrix} x_1 \\ x_2 \end{bmatrix} + \begin{bmatrix} 1 \\ -2 \end{bmatrix}u; \quad y = x_1$$

Test for controllability of system using Kalman's test: Given

$$\mathbf{B} = \begin{bmatrix} 1 \\ -1 \end{bmatrix}; \quad \mathbf{A} = \begin{bmatrix} 0 & 1 \\ -2 & -3 \end{bmatrix}$$

Then,

$$\mathbf{AB} = \begin{bmatrix} 0 & 1 \\ -2 & -3 \end{bmatrix}\begin{bmatrix} 1 \\ -1 \end{bmatrix} = \begin{bmatrix} -1 \\ 1 \end{bmatrix}$$

The controllability matrix is given by

$$\mathbf{S} = [\mathbf{B} \quad \mathbf{AB}] = \begin{bmatrix} 1 & -1 \\ -1 & 1 \end{bmatrix}$$

The rank of this matrix is one. The system is therefore not completely controllable. One state of the system is uncontrollable (r out of n states are controllable).

The given differential equation can be transformed into the following controllable phase variable model

$$\begin{bmatrix} \dot{x}_1 \\ \dot{x}_2 \end{bmatrix} = \begin{bmatrix} 0 & 1 \\ -1 & -2 \end{bmatrix} \begin{bmatrix} x_1 \\ x_2 \end{bmatrix} + \begin{bmatrix} 0 \\ 1 \end{bmatrix} u \qquad y = [1 \quad 1] \begin{bmatrix} x_1 \\ x_2 \end{bmatrix}$$

Thus state controllability depends on how the state variables are defined for a given system.

Example 10.36   Given the system

$$\dot{x}(t) = Ax(t) + Bu(t), \quad y(t) = Cx(t)$$

where $\qquad A = \begin{bmatrix} 0 & 1 \\ -1 & -3 \end{bmatrix}, \qquad B = \begin{bmatrix} 1 \\ 2 \end{bmatrix}, \qquad C = [1 \quad 1]$

Determine the state and output controllability.

Solution: Given **A** and **B**

$$AB = \begin{bmatrix} 0 & 1 \\ -1 & -3 \end{bmatrix} \begin{bmatrix} 1 \\ 2 \end{bmatrix} = \begin{bmatrix} 2 \\ -7 \end{bmatrix}$$

The controllability matrix is

$$S = [B \quad AB] = \begin{bmatrix} 1 & 2 \\ 2 & -7 \end{bmatrix}$$

The rank of the controllability matrix is $r = n = 2$. Hence the system is completely state controllable.

For output controllability

$$CB = [1 \quad 1] \begin{bmatrix} 1 \\ 2 \end{bmatrix} = 3$$

$$CAB = [1 \quad 1] \begin{bmatrix} 0 & 1 \\ -1 & -3 \end{bmatrix} \begin{bmatrix} 1 \\ 2 \end{bmatrix} = -5$$

The rank of

$$[CB \quad CAB] = [3 \quad -5] \text{ is } 1 \ (= m)$$

So the system is completely output controllable.

Example 10.37   A third-order system has the coefficient matrices

$$A = \begin{bmatrix} 1 & 2 & 1 \\ 0 & 1 & 0 \\ 1 & -4 & 3 \end{bmatrix}, \qquad B = \begin{bmatrix} 0 \\ 0 \\ 1 \end{bmatrix}, \qquad C = [1 \quad 1 \quad 0]$$

Determine the state and output controllability.

Solution: Given the matrices **A** and **B**

$$\mathbf{AB} = \begin{bmatrix} 1 & 2 & 1 \\ 0 & 1 & 0 \\ 1 & -4 & 3 \end{bmatrix} \begin{bmatrix} 0 \\ 0 \\ 1 \end{bmatrix} = \begin{bmatrix} 1 \\ 0 \\ 3 \end{bmatrix}$$

$$\mathbf{A^2B} = \begin{bmatrix} 1 & 2 & 1 \\ 0 & 1 & 0 \\ 1 & -4 & 3 \end{bmatrix} \begin{bmatrix} 1 \\ 0 \\ 3 \end{bmatrix} = \begin{bmatrix} 4 \\ 0 \\ 10 \end{bmatrix}$$

The controllability matrix is

$$\mathbf{S} = [\mathbf{B} \quad \mathbf{AB} \quad \mathbf{A^2B}] = \begin{bmatrix} 0 & 1 & 4 \\ 0 & 0 & 0 \\ 1 & 3 & 10 \end{bmatrix}$$

which is singular (the rank $r = 1$). Thus the system is not completely state controllable.

For the given matrices **A**, **B**, and **C**

$$\mathbf{CB} = [1 \quad 1 \quad 0] \begin{bmatrix} 0 \\ 0 \\ 1 \end{bmatrix} = 0$$

$$\mathbf{CAB} = [1 \quad 1 \quad 0] \begin{bmatrix} 1 & 2 & 1 \\ 0 & 1 & 0 \\ 1 & -4 & 3 \end{bmatrix} \begin{bmatrix} 0 \\ 0 \\ 1 \end{bmatrix} = -1$$

$$\mathbf{CA^2B} = [1 \quad 1 \quad 0] \begin{bmatrix} 4 \\ 0 \\ 10 \end{bmatrix} = 4$$

The rank of $[\mathbf{CB} \quad \mathbf{CAB} \quad \mathbf{CA^2B}] = [0 \quad -1 \quad 4]$ is 1 ($= m$).

Thus, the system is completely output controllable.

10.11 OBSERVABILITY OF LINEAR SYSTEMS

A system is completely observable, if every state variable of the system affects some of the outputs. In other words, it is often desirable to obtain information on the state variables from the measurements of the outputs and the inputs. If any one of the states cannot be observed from the measurements of the output, the state is said to be unobservable and the system is not completely observable or simply unobservable. Figure 10.33 shows the state diagram of a linear system in which the state x_2 is not connected to the output $y(t)$ in any way. Once we have measured $y(t)$, we can observe the state $x_1(t)$, since $x_1(t) = y(t)$. However, the state $x_2(t)$ cannot be observed from the information on $y(t)$. Thus, the system is unobservable.

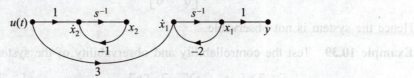

Figure 10.33 State diagram of an unobservable system.

10.11.1 Definition of Observability

A linear time-invariant system described by the state and output equations.

$$\dot{\mathbf{x}}(t) = \mathbf{A}\mathbf{x}(t) + \mathbf{B}\mathbf{u}(t)$$

$$\mathbf{y}(t) = \mathbf{C}\mathbf{x}(t) + \mathbf{D}\mathbf{u}(t)$$

is said to be completely observable, if every state $x(t_0)$ can be determined from the observation of the output $y(t)$ over a finite time interval, $t_0 \le t \le t_1$. The system is therefore completely observable if every transition of the state eventually affects every element of the output vector. The concept of observability is useful in solving the problem of reconstructing unmeasurable state variables from measurable state variables in the minimum possible length of the time.

The condition of observability depends on the matrices $\mathbf{A}$ and $\mathbf{C}$ of the system. Kalman's test of observability is–a general nth-order multi-input-multi-output linear time-invariant system described by

$$\dot{\mathbf{x}}(t) = \mathbf{A}\mathbf{x}(t) + \mathbf{B}\mathbf{u}(t)$$

$$\mathbf{y}(t) = \mathbf{C}\mathbf{x}(t) + \mathbf{D}\mathbf{u}(t)$$

is completely observable, if and only if, the rank of the observability matrix

$$\mathbf{S}_0 = [\mathbf{C}^T \ \mathbf{A}^T\mathbf{C}^T \ ... \ (\mathbf{A}^T)^{n-1}\mathbf{C}^T] \text{ is } n$$

This condition is also referred as the pair $[\mathbf{AC}]$ being observable.

Example 10.38 Test the observability of the system described by

$$\mathbf{A} = \begin{bmatrix} -2 & 0 \\ 0 & -1 \end{bmatrix}, \quad \mathbf{B} = \begin{bmatrix} 3 \\ 1 \end{bmatrix}, \quad \mathbf{C} = [1 \ \ 0]$$

Solution: Given the matrices $\mathbf{A}$ and $\mathbf{C}$

$$\mathbf{C}^T = \begin{bmatrix} 1 \\ 0 \end{bmatrix}$$

$$\mathbf{A}^T\mathbf{C}^T = \begin{bmatrix} -2 & 0 \\ 0 & -1 \end{bmatrix} \begin{bmatrix} 1 \\ 0 \end{bmatrix} = \begin{bmatrix} -2 \\ 0 \end{bmatrix}$$

The observability matrix

$$\mathbf{S}_0 = [\mathbf{C}^T \quad \mathbf{A}^T\mathbf{C}^T] = \begin{bmatrix} 1 & -2 \\ 0 & 0 \end{bmatrix} \text{ is of rank 1, i.e. it is singular}$$

Hence the system is not observable.

Example 10.39 Test the controllability and observability of the system described by

$$\begin{bmatrix} \dot{x}_1 \\ \dot{x}_2 \end{bmatrix} = \begin{bmatrix} 1 & 1 \\ -3 & -2 \end{bmatrix} \begin{bmatrix} x_1 \\ x_2 \end{bmatrix} + \begin{bmatrix} 0 \\ 1 \end{bmatrix} u, \qquad y = \begin{bmatrix} 1 & 0 \end{bmatrix} \begin{bmatrix} x_1 \\ x_2 \end{bmatrix}$$

Solution: Given the matrices **A**, **B**, and **C**.

$$\mathbf{AB} = \begin{bmatrix} 1 & 1 \\ -3 & -2 \end{bmatrix} \begin{bmatrix} 0 \\ 1 \end{bmatrix} = \begin{bmatrix} 1 \\ -2 \end{bmatrix}$$

Since the rank of the controllability matrix

$$\mathbf{S} = [\mathbf{B} \quad \mathbf{AB}] = \begin{bmatrix} 0 & 1 \\ 1 & -2 \end{bmatrix} \text{ is 2, the system is completely state controllable.}$$

$$\mathbf{CB} = \begin{bmatrix} 1 & 0 \end{bmatrix} \begin{bmatrix} 0 \\ 1 \end{bmatrix} = 0$$

$$\mathbf{CAB} = \begin{bmatrix} 1 & 0 \end{bmatrix} \begin{bmatrix} 1 \\ -2 \end{bmatrix} = 1$$

Since the rank of the matrix

$\mathbf{S}_0 = [\mathbf{CB} \quad \mathbf{CAB}] = [0 \quad 1]$ is $1 (= m)$, the system is completely output controllable.

$$\mathbf{C}^T = \begin{bmatrix} 0 \\ 1 \end{bmatrix}$$

$$\mathbf{A}^T\mathbf{C}^T = \begin{bmatrix} 1 & -3 \\ 1 & -2 \end{bmatrix} \begin{bmatrix} 1 \\ 0 \end{bmatrix} = \begin{bmatrix} 1 \\ 1 \end{bmatrix}$$

Since the rank of the observability matrix

$$\mathbf{S}_0 = [\mathbf{C}^T \quad \mathbf{A}^T\mathbf{C}^T] = \begin{bmatrix} 1 & 1 \\ 0 & 1 \end{bmatrix} \text{ is 2, the system is completely observable.}$$

10.11.2 Conditions for Complete Observability in the *s*-Plane

The necessary and sufficient condition for complete observability is that no cancellation occurs in the transfer function or transfer matrix. If cancellation occurs, the cancelled mode cannot be observed in the output.

The transfer function has no cancellation, if and only if, the system is completely state controllable and completely observable.

For example, the transfer function

$$\frac{Y(s)}{U(s)} = \frac{(s+1)(s+4)}{(s+2)(s+3)(s+4)}$$

is not completely observable.

10.11.3 Alternative Condition for Observability

For an *n*th-order system represented by the state model

$$\dot{x}(t) = Ax(t) + Bu(t)$$

$$y(t) = Cx(t) + Du(t)$$

If the eigenvalues of system matrix **A** are distinct and if **M** is the transformation matrix such that $M^{-1}AM$ is a diagonal matrix with eigenvalues as its diagonal elements, then the necessary and sufficient condition for complete state controllability is that, none of the columns of the matrix **CM** should be zero.

If the matrix **A** cannot be transformed into a diagonal matrix, then by use of a suitable transformation matrix **M**, we can transform **A** into a Jordan canonical form, or

$$M^{-1}AM = J$$

where **J** is in Jordan canonical form, then **y = CMz**.

The system is completely observable if

1. No two Jordan blocks in **J** are associated with the same eigenvalues.
2. No columns of **CM** that correspond to the first row of each Jordan block consists of zero elements.
3. No columns of **CM** that correspond to distinct eigenvalues consist of zero elements.

To clarify condition 2, in the example below, we have encircled by dashed lines the columns of **CM** that correspond to the first row of each Jordan block.

The following systems are completely observable.

$$\begin{bmatrix} \dot{z}_1 \\ \dot{z}_2 \end{bmatrix} = \begin{bmatrix} -2 & 0 \\ 0 & -3 \end{bmatrix} \begin{bmatrix} z_1 \\ z_2 \end{bmatrix} \qquad y = \begin{bmatrix} 1 & 2 \end{bmatrix} \begin{bmatrix} z_1 \\ z_2 \end{bmatrix}$$

$$\begin{bmatrix} \dot{z}_1 \\ \dot{z}_2 \\ \dot{z}_3 \end{bmatrix} = \begin{bmatrix} 3 & 1 & 0 \\ 0 & 3 & 1 \\ 0 & 0 & 3 \end{bmatrix} \begin{bmatrix} z_1 \\ z_2 \\ z_3 \end{bmatrix} \qquad \begin{bmatrix} y_1 \\ y_2 \end{bmatrix} = \begin{bmatrix} 2 & 0 & 0 \\ 4 & 0 & 0 \end{bmatrix} \begin{bmatrix} z_1 \\ z_2 \\ z_3 \end{bmatrix}$$

$$\begin{bmatrix} \dot{z}_1 \\ \dot{z}_2 \\ \dot{z}_3 \\ \dot{z}_4 \\ \dot{z}_5 \end{bmatrix} = \begin{bmatrix} 3 & 1 & 0 & 0 & 0 \\ 0 & 3 & 1 & 0 & 0 \\ 0 & 0 & 3 & 0 & 0 \\ 0 & 0 & 0 & -4 & 1 \\ 0 & 0 & 0 & 0 & -4 \end{bmatrix} \begin{bmatrix} z_1 \\ z_2 \\ z_3 \\ z_4 \\ z_5 \end{bmatrix} \qquad \begin{bmatrix} y_1 \\ y_2 \end{bmatrix} = \begin{bmatrix} 1 & 1 & 1 & 0 & 0 \\ 0 & 1 & 1 & 1 & 0 \end{bmatrix} \begin{bmatrix} z_1 \\ z_2 \\ z_3 \\ z_4 \\ z_5 \end{bmatrix}$$

The following systems are not completely observable

$$\begin{bmatrix} \dot{z}_1 \\ \dot{z}_2 \end{bmatrix} = \begin{bmatrix} -2 & 0 \\ 0 & -3 \end{bmatrix} \begin{bmatrix} z_1 \\ z_2 \end{bmatrix} \qquad y = \begin{bmatrix} 0 & 1 \end{bmatrix} \begin{bmatrix} z_1 \\ z_2 \end{bmatrix}$$

$$\begin{bmatrix} \dot{z}_1 \\ \dot{z}_2 \\ \dot{z}_3 \end{bmatrix} = \begin{bmatrix} 3 & 1 & 0 \\ 0 & 3 & 1 \\ 0 & 0 & 3 \end{bmatrix} \begin{bmatrix} z_1 \\ z_2 \\ z_3 \end{bmatrix} \qquad \begin{bmatrix} y_1 \\ y_2 \end{bmatrix} = \begin{bmatrix} 0 & 1 & 3 \\ 0 & 2 & 4 \end{bmatrix} \begin{bmatrix} z_1 \\ z_2 \\ x_3 \end{bmatrix}$$

$$\begin{bmatrix} \dot{z}_1 \\ \dot{z}_2 \\ \dot{z}_3 \\ \dot{z}_4 \\ \dot{z}_5 \end{bmatrix} = \begin{bmatrix} 3 & 1 & 0 & 0 & 0 \\ 0 & 3 & 1 & 0 & 0 \\ 0 & 0 & 3 & 0 & 0 \\ 0 & 0 & 0 & -4 & 1 \\ 0 & 0 & 0 & 0 & -4 \end{bmatrix} \begin{bmatrix} z_1 \\ z_2 \\ z_3 \\ z_4 \\ z_5 \end{bmatrix} \qquad \begin{bmatrix} y_1 \\ y_2 \end{bmatrix} = \begin{bmatrix} 1 & 1 & 1 & 0 & 0 \\ 0 & 1 & 1 & 0 & 0 \end{bmatrix} \begin{bmatrix} z_1 \\ z_2 \\ z_3 \\ z_4 \\ z_5 \end{bmatrix}$$

Duality property

1. The pair (**AB**) is controllable implies that the pair ($\mathbf{A}^T \mathbf{B}^T$) is observable.
2. The pair (**AC**) is observable implies that the pair ($\mathbf{A}^T \mathbf{C}^T$) is controllable.

Thus, the concepts of controllability and observability are dual concepts.

Example 10.40 Show that the following system is not completely observable.

$$\dot{\mathbf{x}}(t) = \mathbf{A}\mathbf{x}(t) + \mathbf{B}\mathbf{u}(t)$$

$$\mathbf{y}(t) = \mathbf{C}\mathbf{x}(t)$$

where $\mathbf{x}(t) = \begin{bmatrix} x_1(t) \\ x_2(t) \\ x_3(t) \end{bmatrix}$, $\mathbf{A} = \begin{bmatrix} 0 & 1 & 0 \\ 0 & 0 & 1 \\ -6 & -11 & -6 \end{bmatrix}$, $\mathbf{B} = \begin{bmatrix} 0 \\ 0 \\ 1 \end{bmatrix}$, $\mathbf{C} = \begin{bmatrix} 4 & 5 & 1 \end{bmatrix}$

Solution: The control function $\mathbf{u}(t)$ does not affect the complete observability of the system. To examine complete observability, we may simply set $\mathbf{u}(t) = 0$.

Therefore, for this system we have

$$\mathbf{C}^T = \begin{bmatrix} 4 \\ 5 \\ 1 \end{bmatrix} \quad \mathbf{A}^T\mathbf{C}^T = \begin{bmatrix} 0 & 0 & -6 \\ 1 & 0 & -11 \\ 0 & 1 & -6 \end{bmatrix} \begin{bmatrix} 4 \\ 5 \\ 1 \end{bmatrix} = \begin{bmatrix} 6 \\ -7 \\ -1 \end{bmatrix}, \quad (\mathbf{A}^T)^2\mathbf{C}^T = \begin{bmatrix} 0 & 0 & -6 \\ 1 & 0 & -11 \\ 0 & 1 & -6 \end{bmatrix} \begin{bmatrix} 6 \\ -7 \\ -1 \end{bmatrix} = \begin{bmatrix} -6 \\ 5 \\ -1 \end{bmatrix}$$

The rank of the observability matrix

$$\mathbf{S}_0 = [\mathbf{C}^T \quad \mathbf{A}^T\mathbf{C}^T \quad (\mathbf{A}^T)^2\mathbf{C}^T] = \begin{bmatrix} 4 & -6 & -6 \\ 5 & -7 & 5 \\ 1 & -1 & -1 \end{bmatrix} \text{ is } 2, \, (<3)$$

Therefore, the system is not completely observable.

To test the observability using alternative condition, first transform the state equation into canonical form. The characteristic equation is given by

$$|\lambda\mathbf{I} - \mathbf{A}| = \begin{vmatrix} \lambda & -1 & 0 \\ 0 & \lambda & -1 \\ 6 & 11 & \lambda+6 \end{vmatrix} = \lambda^3 + 6\lambda^2 + 11\lambda + 6 = (\lambda + 1)(\lambda + 2)(\lambda + 3) = 0$$

Hence, the eigenvalues are $\lambda_1 = -1$, $\lambda_2 = -2$, $\lambda_3 = -3$

Choosing the Vander Monde matrix as modal matrix, we have

$$\mathbf{M} = \begin{bmatrix} 1 & 1 & 1 \\ \lambda_1 & \lambda_2 & \lambda_3 \\ \lambda_1^2 & \lambda_2^2 & \lambda_3^2 \end{bmatrix} = \begin{bmatrix} 1 & 1 & 1 \\ -1 & -2 & -3 \\ 1 & 4 & 9 \end{bmatrix}$$

Under the linear transformation $\mathbf{x} = \mathbf{Mz}$, the output is given by

$$\mathbf{y} = \mathbf{CMz} = [4 \quad 5 \quad 1] \begin{bmatrix} 1 & 1 & 1 \\ -1 & -2 & -3 \\ 1 & 4 & 9 \end{bmatrix} \begin{bmatrix} z_1 \\ z_2 \\ z_3 \end{bmatrix} = [0 \quad -2 \quad -2] \begin{bmatrix} z_1 \\ z_2 \\ z_3 \end{bmatrix}$$

It is found that the system is not completely observable, since the state variable z_1 is completely hidden from observation.

10.11.4 Observable Phase Variable Form

If the system equations are given by

$$\dot{z}(t) = \mathbf{A}_0 z(t) + \mathbf{B}_0 u(t)$$
$$y(t) = \mathbf{C}_0 z(t) + \mathbf{D}_0 u(t)$$

where $\mathbf{z}$ is $n \times 1$ vector, $\mathbf{y}$ and $\mathbf{u}$ are scalars, and

$$\mathbf{A}_0 = \begin{bmatrix} 0 & 0 & \cdots & 0 & -a_n \\ 1 & 0 & \cdots & 0 & -a_{n-1} \\ \vdots & & \cdots & & \vdots \\ 0 & 0 & \cdots & 0 & -a_2 \\ 0 & 0 & \cdots & 1 & -a_1 \end{bmatrix}, \quad \mathbf{B}_0 = \begin{bmatrix} \beta_n \\ \beta_{n-1} \\ \vdots \\ \beta_2 \\ \beta_1 \end{bmatrix}, \quad \mathbf{C}_0 = [0 \quad 0 \quad \cdots \quad 0 \quad 1]$$

then the system is always observable. The converse is also true, i.e. a linear time-invariant observable system can be transformed into the above form. The above equations are said to be in the observable phase variable form.

If the input-output transfer function of a linear system has pole-zero cancellation, the system will be either uncontrollable or unobservable, or both depending on how the state variables are defined. On the other hand, if the input-output transfer function does not have pole-zero cancellation, we are assured that it is a controllable and observable system, no mater how the state variable model is defined.

Consider the following SISO system:

$$\mathbf{A} = \begin{bmatrix} -2 & 0 & 0 & 0 \\ 0 & -3 & 0 & 0 \\ 0 & 0 & -4 & 0 \\ 0 & 0 & 0 & -5 \end{bmatrix}, \quad \mathbf{B} = \begin{bmatrix} 1 \\ 1 \\ 0 \\ 0 \end{bmatrix}, \quad \mathbf{C} = [1 \quad 0 \quad 1 \quad 0], \quad \mathbf{D} = 0$$

Since $\mathbf{A}$ is a diagonal matrix, the controllability and observability conditions of the four states are determined by inspection. They are as follows:

x_1: Controllable and observable (C and O)
x_2: Controllable but unobservable (C but UO)
x_3: Uncontrollable but observable (UC but O)
x_4: Uncontrollable and unobservable (UC and UO)

The block diagram of the system in Figure 10.34 shows the DCF decomposition of the system. Clearly, the transfer function of the controllable and observable system should be

$$\frac{Y(s)}{U(s)} = \frac{1}{s+2}$$

whereas the transfer function that corresponds to the dynamics described above is

$$\frac{Y(s)}{U(s)} = \mathbf{C}[s\mathbf{I} - \mathbf{A}]^{-1}\mathbf{B} = \frac{(s+3)(s+4)(s+5)}{(s+2)(s+3)(s+4)(s+5)}$$

which has three pole-zero cancellations. This example illustrates that 'minimum order transfer function without pole-zero cancellation is the only component that corresponds to a system that is controllable and observable'.

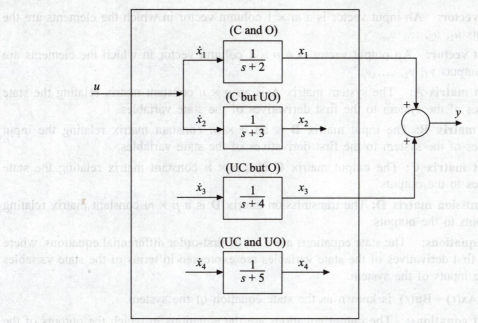

Figure 10.34 Block diagram showing the controllable, uncontrollable, observable, unobservable components of the system.

In fact, given a system that is modelled by a transfer function, the controllability and observability conditions of the system depend on how the state variables are defined.

SHORT QUESTIONS AND ANSWERS

1. Define the following terms with respect to state variable approach.

A. **State:** The state of a dynamic system is the smallest set of variables called the state variables such that the knowledge of these variables at $t = t_0$, together with the knowledge of the inputs for $t \geq t_0$, completely determines the behaviour of the system for $t \geq t_0$. The state of a system refers to the past, present and future conditions of the system.

State variables: The state variables of a dynamic system are the minimal set of variables selected such that the knowledge of these variables at any time $t = t_0$, together with the knowledge of the inputs for $t \geq t_0$ completely determine the dynamic behaviour of the system for $t \geq t_0$, i.e. the state variables of a dynamic system are the smallest set of variables that determine the state of the dynamic system.

State-space: The n dimensional space whose coordinate axes consists of the x_1 axis, x_2 axis, ..., x_n axis where $x_1, x_2, ..., x_n$ are state variables is called a state-space. Any state can be represented by a point in the state-space.

State vector: A state vector is an $n \times 1$ vector that determines uniquely the system state $\mathbf{x}(t)$ for any time $t \geq t_0$, once the state at $t = t_0$ is given and the input $\mathbf{u}(t)$ for $t \geq t_0$ is specified.

Input vector: An input vector is a $m \times 1$ column vector in which the elements are the m inputs $u_1, u_2, \ldots, u_m$.

Output vector: An output vector is a $p \times 1$ column vector in which the elements are the p outputs $y_1, y_2, \ldots, y_p$.

System matrix A: The system matrix $\mathbf{A}$ is an $n \times n$ constant matrix relating the state variables of the system to the first derivatives of the state variables.

Input matrix B: The input matrix $\mathbf{B}$ is an $n \times m$ constant matrix relating the input variables of the system to the first derivatives of the state variables.

Output matrix C: The output matrix $\mathbf{C}$ is a $p \times n$ constant matrix relating the state variables to the outputs.

Transmission matrix D: The transmission matrix $\mathbf{D}$ is a $p \times m$ constant matrix relating the inputs to the outputs.

State equations: The state equations are a set of first-order differential equations, where in, the first derivatives of the state variables are expressed in terms of the state variables and the inputs of the system.

$\dot{\mathbf{x}}(t) = \mathbf{A}\mathbf{x}(t) + \mathbf{B}\mathbf{u}(t)$ is known as the state equation of the system.

Output equations: The output equations are the equations in which the outputs of the system are expressed in terms of the state variables and the inputs of the system.

$\mathbf{y}(t) = \mathbf{C}\mathbf{x}(t) + \mathbf{D}\mathbf{u}(t)$ is known as the output equation of the system.

Dynamic equations: The state equations and the output equations together are called the dynamic equations of the system.

State Model: The state equations and the output equations together are called the state model of a system. It is a state variable representation of the system. It is given by

$$\dot{\mathbf{x}}(t) = \mathbf{A}\mathbf{x}(t) + \mathbf{B}\mathbf{u}(t)$$
$$\mathbf{y}(t) = \mathbf{C}\mathbf{x}(t) + \mathbf{D}\mathbf{u}(t)$$

Phase variables: The phase variables are defined as those particular state variables which are obtained from one of the system variables (usually the output variable) and its derivatives.

Companion form: The matrix $\mathbf{A}$ is said to be in Bush form or companion form when all its off diagonal elements are 1s and the last row is comprised of the negative of the coefficients of the original differential equation written in reverse order, and all other elements in the matrix are zero.

Bush form: This is the other name of companion form.

Normal form: The diagonal canonical form is also called the normal form. In this form, the matrix $\mathbf{A}$ will be a diagonal matrix, the main diagonal elements of the matrix $\mathbf{A}$ are the eigenvalues and all other elements in the matrix are zero.

Canonical form: The system matrix $\mathbf{A}$ is said to be in canonical form, if all its off diagonal elements are zero, and its main diagonal elements are equal to the roots of the characteristic equation.

Jordan canonical form: The matrix **A** is said to be in Jordan canonical form when it has Jordan blocks corresponding to the repeated poles in the system transfer function.

Jordan block: Jordan block is a square block in the matrix **A** in which all the diagonal elements are the same (value of the repeated poles) and the elements just above the main diagonal are all 1s and all other elements are 0s.

Eigenvalues: The roots of the characteristic equation of a state model, $|\lambda \mathbf{I} - \mathbf{A}| = 0$ are often called the eigenvalues of the matrix **A**.

Eigenvector: Any non-zero vector p_i that satisfies the matrix equation $|\lambda \mathbf{I} - \mathbf{A}|_{P_i} = 0$, where λ_i, $i = 1, 2, \ldots, m$ denotes the eigenvalues of **A** is called the eigenvector of **A** associated with the eigenvalue λ_i.

Modal matrix: The matrix formed by placing the eigenvectors together (column-wise) is called the modal matrix.

Diagonalizing matrix: The modal matrix used to diagonalize the system matrix **A** is called the diagonalizing matrix.

Resolvent matrix: $\phi(s) = [s\mathbf{I} - \mathbf{A}]^{-1}$ is called the resolvent matrix.

State transition matrix (STM): The state tranisition matrix is defined as a matrix that satisfies the linear homogeneous state equation $\dot{x}(t) = \mathbf{A}x(t)$. So it represents the free response of the system. The STM is the inverse Laplace transform of the resolvent matrix.

State transition equation: The solution of the linear nonhomogeneous state equation is called the state transition equation.

Forced response: The forced response is the response or output of the system when the inputs are present.

Free response: The free response is the response or output of the system when the inputs are zero. It is due to initial conditions only.

Vander Monde matrix: The Vander Monde matrix is a special form of modal matrix which can be written directly, if the system matrix **A** is in companion form and all its eigenvalues are distinct.

Modified Vander Monde matrix: The modified Vander Monde matrix is a special form of modal matrix which can be written directly, if the system matrix **A** is in companion form and some of its eigenvalues are repeated.

2. What are the basic approaches for the analysis and design of control systems?

A. The basic approaches for the analysis and design of control systems are (a) the transfer function approach and (b) the state variable approach.

3. Compare the conventional and modern control theories.

A. (a) The transfer function approach is also called the conventional approach or classical approach and the state variable approach is called the modern approach.

(b) The transfer function approach is applicable only to linear time-invariant single-input-single-output systems, whereas the state variable approach can handle linear as well as nonlinear, time-invariant as well time-varying, and single-input-single-output as well as multi-input-multi-output systems.

(c) The transfer function approach neglects initial conditions, whereas the state variable approach considers initial conditions.

(d) The transfer function approach is a frequency-domain approach, whereas the state variable approach is a time-domain approach.

(e) Classical design methods are based on trial and error procedures and do not result in optimal and adaptive systems, whereas design methods based on modern approach yield optimal systems.

(f) In transfer function approach, only the output can be fed back and it should be measurable and observable, whereas in state variable approach, even the internal variables can be fed back and they need not be measurable or observable.

(g) The transfer function formulation requires the Laplace transform for continuous-data control systems and z-transform for discrete-data control systems, whereas the state variable approach uses the same formulation for both those systems.

(h) The state variables of a system are not unique. So the state model of a system is not unique, whereas the transfer function of a system is unique.

(i) An nth-order differential equation can be converted into n first-order differential equations using state variable approach. So it can be solved easily using state variables.

4. Is conventional method of analysis and design obsolete? If not why?

A. No. The conventional method of analysis and design is not obsolete. It is very much in use because it provides the control engineer with a deep physical insight into the system and greatly aids the preliminary system design. It provides simple and powerful analysis and design techniques like root locus and frequency response methods.

5. Is the state-model of a system unique?

A. No. The state-model of a system is not unique. Many different state models can be obtained for a given system depending on the choice of state variables.

6. Is the transfer function of the system unique?

A. Yes. The transfer function of a system is unique. There can be only one transfer function for the given system.

7. In state-space analysis, how many types of variables are involved in the modelling of dynamic systems? What are they?

A. In state-space analysis, three types of variables are involved in the modelling of dynamic systems. They are (a) input variables, (b) output variables and (c) state variables.

8. What are the two conditions to be satisfied by the state variables?

A. The two conditions that must be satisfied by the state variables are as follows:

(a) At any initial time $t = t_0$, the state variables $x_1(t_0)$, $x_2(t_0)$, ..., $x_n(t_0)$ define the initial state of the system.

(b) Once the input of the system for $t \geq 0$ and the initial states are specified, the state variables should completely define the future behaviour of the system.

9. In the state-model with usual notation, what are $\mathbf{x}(t)$, $\mathbf{u}(t)$, $\mathbf{y}(t)$, **A**, **B**, **C**, **D** and what are their dimensions?

A. In the state model, $\mathbf{x}(t)$ is an $n \times 1$ state vector, $\mathbf{u}(t)$ is an $m \times 1$ input vector, $\mathbf{y}(t)$ is a $p \times 1$ output vector, **A** is an $n \times n$ system matrix, **B** is an $n \times m$ input matrix, **C** is a $p \times n$ output matrix, and **D** is a $p \times m$ transmission matrix.

10. Why outputs of the integrators are selected as the state variables?

A. The dynamic system must involve elements that memorize the values of the input for $t > t_0$. Since integrators in a continuous time control system serve as memory devices, the outputs of the integrators can be selected as the state variables.

11. How many state variables are required to completely define the dynamics of a system?

A. The number of state variables required to completely define the dynamics of a system are equal to the number integrators involved in the system. In state variable formulation, the outputs of the integrators are selected as the state variables.

12. What do you mean by a (a) homogeneous state equation (b) nonhomogeneous state equation?

A. (a) A homogeneous state equation is one in which the forcing function is zero.
(b) A nonhomogeneous state equation is one in which the forcing function is present.

13. How can you determine the order of a system from its state model?

A. All models of a system have the same number of elements in the state vector. The number of elements in the state vector, i.e. the number of state variables used to represent the system is refered to as the order of the system.

14. To obtain a state-model of an electrical network which variables are selected as state variables?

A. To obtain a state model of an electrical network, the currents through the inductors and the voltages across the capacitors are selected as the state variables.

15. What do you mean by decomposition of a transfer function? Name the methods of decomposition. Which one is preferred when? What is the advantage of each?

A. The process of obtaining the state diagram of a system from its transfer function is called decomposition. There are three basic methods of decomposition of transfer functions. They are (a) direct decomposition, (b) cascade decomposition and (c) parallel decomposition.

The direct decomposition is applied to transfer functions which are not in factored form. The advantage is that it is a general method and can be applied to any system. The resultant system matrix **A** will be in Bush form.

Cascade decomposition is applied to transfer functions that are written as products of simple first- or second-order components. The advantage of cascade decomposition is that the poles and zeros of the transfer function appear as isolated branch gains on the system diagram. This facilitates the study of the effects on the system when poles and zeros are varied.

Parallel decomposition is applied to transfer functions whose denominators are in factored form. The resulting state diagram will consist of simple first- and second-order systems connected in parallel. The advantage of parallel decomposition is that it leads to state equations in canonical form or Jordan canonical form.

16. How can the transfer function of a system be obtained from its state diagram?

A. The transfer function of a system can be obtained from its state diagram by use of the gain formula and by setting all other inputs and initial states to zero.

17. How is a state diagram constructed? What is its significance?

A. A state diagram is constructed following all the rules of the signal flow graph using the Laplace transformed state equations. The significance of the state diagram is that it forms a close relationship among the state equations, computer simulation and transfer functions.

18. How many canonical forms are there? Name them.

A. There are five canonical forms. They are (a) diagonal canonical form (DCF), (b) Jordan canonical form (JCF), (c) controllability canonical form (CCF), (d) observability canonical form (OCF) and (e) phase variable canonical form (PCF).

19. What is the advantage of canonical form?

A. The canonical form of a state model is most convenient for time-domain analysis, because each component state variable equation is decoupled from all other component state variable equations. But the disadvantage is canonical variables like phase variables are not physical variables.

20. What is the advantage and disadvantage of phase variables?

A. The phase variable formulation is simple. The phase variables establish a link between transfer function design approach and time-domain design approach, but the disadvantage is that the phase variables in general are not physical variables of the system and hence are not available for measurement and control purposes.

21. Write the properties of the eigenvalues.

A. Some of the important properties of eigenvalues are as follows:

(a) If the coefficients of $\mathbf{A}$ are all real, its eigenvalues are either real or in complex conjugate pairs.

(b) The trace [sum of the main diagonal elements] of $\mathbf{A}$ is the sum of all the eigenvalues of $\mathbf{A}$.

(c) The eigenvalues of the transpose of $\mathbf{A}$, i.e. of $\mathbf{A}^T$ are the same as the eigenvalues of $\mathbf{A}$.

(d) The eigenvalues of the inverse of $\mathbf{A}$, i.e. of $\mathbf{A}^{-1}$ are the inverse of the eigenvalues of $\mathbf{A}$.

22. Why STM is called STM of $\mathbf{A}$?

A. Since the STM depends only on the system matrix $\mathbf{A}$, it is called the STM of $\mathbf{A}$.

23. Why $e^{\mathbf{A}t}$ is known as the state transition matrix?

A. The matrix exponential $e^{\mathbf{A}t}$ carries out transition of state from the initial state $\mathbf{x}(0)$ at $t = 0$, to a state $\mathbf{x}(t)$ at time t. Hence it is known as the state transition matrix.

24. How do you obtain the characteristic equation of a system from its state model?

A. The characteristic equation of a system from its state model is given by

$$|\lambda \mathbf{I} - \mathbf{A}| = 0$$

25. What is the significance of STM?

A. The significance of STM is that since it satisfies the homogeneous state equations, it represents the free response of the system. In other words, STM governs the response that is excited by the initial conditions only. As the name implies, the STM describes the change of state from the initial time $t = 0$, to any time t, when the inputs are zero.

26. What are the properties of the STM?

A. The properties of STM are

(a) $\phi(0) = \mathbf{I}$

(b) $\phi^{-1}(t) = \phi(-t)$

(c) $\phi(t_2 - t_1)\, \phi(t_1 - t_0) = \phi(t_2 - t_0)$ for any t_2, t_1, t_0

(d) $[\phi(t)]^k = \phi(kt)$

(e) $\phi(t_1 + t_2) = \phi(t_1)\, \phi(t_2) = \phi(t_2)\, \phi(t_1)$

27. Are the eigenvalues of the state model and the poles of the system transfer function the same?

A. Yes. The eigenvalues of the state model and the poles of the system transfer function are the same.

28. In how many ways the STM can be computed? Name them?

A. The STM can be computed in five ways. They are: (a) infinite series method, (b) Laplace transform method, (c) using Cayley–Hamilton theorem, (d) using modal matrix, and (e) using Sylvester's theorem.

29. State the Cayley–Hamilton theorem.

A. The Cayley–Hamilton theorem states that every square matrix satisfies its own characteristic equation.

30. When is the modal matrix, the Vander Monde matrix?

A. The modal matrix will be the Vander Monde matrix, if the system matrix **A** is in companion form and all of its eigenvalues are distinct.

31. When is the modal matrix, the modified Vander Monde matrix?

A. The modal matrix will be the modified Vander Monde matrix, if the system matrix **A** is in companion form and some of its eigenvalues are repeated.

32. How do you prove the invariance of eigenvalues?

A. The invariance of the eigenvalues under a linear transformation can be proved by showing that the characteristic polynomials $|\lambda \mathbf{I} - \mathbf{A}|$ and $|\lambda \mathbf{I} - \mathbf{P}^{-1}\mathbf{AP}|$ are identical.

33. When do you say that the state model is stable?

A. The state model is said to be stable if all its eigenvalues have negative real parts.

34. What is the relation between the eigenvalues of the state model and the poles of the system transfer function?

A. The eigenvalues of the state model and the poles of the system transfer function are the same.

35. Under linear transformation of a state model, which parameters of the system are invariant?

A. In linear (similarity) transformation of the state model, the characteristic equation, eigenvalues, eigenvectors and the transfer function are all preserved, i.e. they are all invariant under a linear transformation.

36. How can you obtain the transfer function of a system from its state model?

A. The transfer function of a system can be obtained from its state model by using the formula

$$\frac{C(s)}{R(s)} = C[sI - A]^{-1} B + D$$

37. Given its state model, how can you determine the stability of a system?

A. Since the eigenvalues of the system matrix **A** are the same as the roots of the characteristic equation which are nothing but the poles of the closed-loop transfer function, the stability of a system represented by its state model can be determined by determining the location of the eigenvalues.

38. When do you say that the system is completely state controllable?

A. A system is said to be completely state controllable at time t_0, if it is possible by means of an un constrained control vector $u(t)$ to transfer the system from an initial state $x(t_0)$ to any other desired state $x(t)$ in a finite interval of time.

39. When do you say that the system is completely output controllable?

A. A system is said to be completely output controllable, if it is possible to construct an unconstrained control vector $u(t)$ that will transfer any given initial output $y(t_0)$ to a final output $y(t_f)$ in a finite time interval $t_0 \le t \le t_f$.

40. When do you say that the system is observable?

A. A system is said to be observable at time t_0, if with the system in state $x(t_0)$, it is possible to determine this state from the observation of the output over a finite time interval.

41. Who introduced the concepts of controllability and observability?

A. The concepts of controllability and observability were introduced by Kalman.

42. What is the necessary and sufficient condition for state controllability of a system?

A. The necessary and sufficient condition for complete state controllability of a system as per Kalman is that the rank of the controllability matrix $S_c = [B \quad AB \quad A^2B \quad \dots \quad A^{n-1}B]$ should be *n*.

43. What is the necessary and sufficient condition for output controllability of the system?

A. The necessary and sufficient condition for output controllability of a system is that the rank of the matrix $[CB \quad CAB \quad \dots \quad CA^{n-1}B \quad D]$ should be *m*.

44. What is the necessary and sufficient condition for observability of a system?

A. The necessary and sufficient condition for complete state observability of a system as per Kalman is that, the rank of the observability matrix $[\mathbf{C}^T \ \mathbf{A}^T\mathbf{C}^T \dots (\mathbf{A}^T)^{n-1}\mathbf{C}^T]$ should be n.

45. State the duality property.

A. Duality property is that (a) the pair $(\mathbf{AB})$ is controllable implies that the pair $(\mathbf{A}^T\mathbf{B}^T)$ is observable and (b) the pair $\mathbf{AC}$ is observable implies that the pair $(\mathbf{A}^T\mathbf{C}^T)$ is controllable.

46. What is the implication of pole-zero cancellation in a transfer function on controllability and observability?

A. If the input-output transfer function of a linear system has pole-zero cancellation, the system will be either uncontrollable or unobservable or both depending on how the state variables are defined. If the input-output transfer function of a linear system does not have pole-zero cancellation, we are assured that it is a controllable and observable system, no mater how the state variable model is defined.

47. When is the system always observable?

A. A system is always observable if it can be described in observable phase variable form.

48. When is the system always controllable?

A. A system is always controllable if it can be described in controllable canonical form.

49. What do you mean by an uncontrollable system?

A. An uncontrollable system is a system which has a sub-system that is physically disconnected from the input.

REVIEW QUESTIONS

1. Discuss the methods of decomposition of transfer functions.
2. Derive an expression for the solution of a homogeneous state equation.
3. Derive an expression for the solution of a non-homogeneous state equation.
4. Show that the eigenvalues are invariant under a linear transformation.
5. Obtain the transfer function of a system from its state model.

FILL IN THE BLANKS

1. The two basic approaches to the analysis and design of control systems are _____ and _state varied_

2. The transfer function approach is also called the _classic_ or _____ and the state variable approach is called the _____.

3. The transfer function approach is applicable only to _____ whereas the state variable approach can handle _____ as well as _____, _____ as well as _____, and _____ as well as _____ systems.

4. The transfer function approach _neglects_ the initial conditions whereas the state variable approach _consider_ the initial conditions.

5. The transfer function approach is a _freq_ approach whereas state variable approach is a _tm_ approach.

6. Classical design methods are based on _trailen_ procedure.

7. The state variables of a system are not _____.

8. The _state_ of a system is not unique, whereas the _t/f_ of a system is unique.

9. The number of elements in the state vector is refered to as the _order_ of the system.

10. To obtain a state model for electrical networks _____ and the _____ are selected as the state variables.

11. In state variable formulation, the _____ are selected as the state variables.

12. In state-space analysis, three types of variables are involved in the modelling of dynamic systems. They are _____, _____ and _____.

13. The number of state variables to completely define the dynamics of the system is equal to the number of _integrators_ involved in the system.

14. _integrators_ in a continuous time control system serve as memory devices.

15. The state of a system refers to the _____, _____ and _____ conditions of the system.

16. $\dot{x}(t) = Ax(t) + Bu(t)$ is known as the _____ of the system. **A** is called the _system mat_ and **B** is called the _i/p mat_.

17. $y(t) = Cx(t) + Du(t)$ is known as the _____ of the system. **C** is called the _o/p_ and **D** is called the _transmy_.

18. The state equations are a set of first-order differential equations, wherein the first derivatives of the state variables are expressed in terms of the _____ and the _____ of the system.

19. The output equations are the equations in which the outputs of the system are expressed in terms of the _____ and the _____ of the system.

20. The state equations and the output equations together are called the _____ of the system.

21. If the transfer function has distinct poles, the matrix $\bar{A}$ is in _canonical_ form.

22. If the transfer function has repeated poles, the matrix $\bar{A}$ will be in _____ form.

23. The five canonical forms are: (a) _____, (b) _____, (c) _____, (d) _____ and (e) _____.

24. The _____ are defined as those particular state variables, which are obtained from one of the system variables (usually the output variable) and its derivative.

25. A matrix is said to be in _____ or _____ form, if all its upper off dioganal elements are 1s, its last row is comprised of negative of the coefficients of the differential equation written in reverse order and all other elements are zero.

26. In state variable formulation, $\mathbf{x}(t)$ is an _____, $\mathbf{u}(t)$ is a _____, $\mathbf{y}(t)$ is a _____, $\mathbf{A}$ is an _____, $\mathbf{B}$ is a _____, $\mathbf{C}$ is a _____, and $\mathbf{D}$ is a _____.

27. The _____ is defined as a matrix that satisfies the linear homogeneous state equation.

28. The STM represents the _____ response of the system.

29. $\phi(s)$ is called the _____.

30. The STM can be computed in 5 ways. They are: (a) _____, (b) _____, (c) _____, (d) _____ and (e) _____.

31. The STM depends only on the _____ and not on the initial time t_0.

32. The STM depends only on the system matrix $\mathbf{A}$. Hence it is called the _____.

33. The characteristic equation of a state model is given by _____.

34. The solution of linear non-homogeneous state equation is called the _____.

35. The roots of the characteristic equation are often referred to as the _____ of the matrix $\mathbf{A}$.

36. The process of obtaining the state diagram of a system from its transfer function is called the _____.

37. There are three basic methods of decomposition of transfer functions. They are _____, _____, and _____.

38. Parallel decomposition leads to state equations in _____ form or _____ form.

39. A state model is stable if all of its _____ have negative real parts.

40. The eigenvalues of the state model and the ~~poles~~ of the system transfer function are the same.

41. The state equations and the output equations together are called the _____ of the system.

42. The matrix formed by placing the eigenvectors together (column-wise) is called the ~~modal matrix~~

43. The ~~Cayley Hamil~~ theorem states that every square matrix $\mathbf{A}$ satisfies its own characteristic equation.

44. The concepts of controllability and observability were introduced by ~~Kalman~~.

45. Controllability and observability can also be determined by ~~Gilberts~~ method.

46. If a system can be described in observable phase variable form, then the system is always _____.

47. If a system can be described in controllable phase variable form, then the sytem is always ~~controllable~~

48. The necessary and sufficient condition for complete state controllability is that the rank of the controllability matrix _____ should be n.

49. The necessary and sufficient condition for output controllability is that, the rank of the controllability matrix _____ should be *m*.

50. The necessary and sufficient condition for complete state observability is that, the rank of the observability matrix _____ shold be *n*.

51. Eventhough the model matrix is not _____, the resultant diagonal matrix is _____.

OBJECTIVE TYPE QUESTIONS

1. The transfer function approach is applicable to
   (a) only linear time-invariant systems
   (b) linear time-invariant as well as time-varying systems
   (c) linear as well as nonlinear systems
   (d) all systems

2. The state variable approach is applicable to
   (a) only linear time-invariant systems
   (b) linear time-invariant as well as time-varying systems
   (c) linear as well as nonlinear systems
   (d) all systems

3. The number of state variables of a system is equal to
   (a) the number of integrators present in the system
   (b) the number of differentiators present in the system
   (c) the sum of the number of integrators and differentiators present in the system
   (d) none of these

4. Using state variables, an *n*th-order differential equation can be decomposed into
   (a) *n* number of first-order differential equations
   (b) *n*/2 number of first-order differential equations
   (c) unlimited number of first-order differential equations
   (d) none of these

5. $\dot{x}(t) = Ax(t) + Bu(t)$ is called the
   (a) system equation   (b) state equation
   (c) state transition equation   (d) none of these

6. **A** is called the
   (a) system matrix   (b) input matrix
   (c) state matrix   (d) transmission matrix

7. **D** is called the
   (a) system matrix   (b) transmission matrix
   (c) transfer matrix   (d) output matrix

8. The number of canonical forms is
   (a) 2
   (b) 3
   (c) 4
   (d) 5

9. The number of ways in which STM can be computed is
   (a) 2
   (b) 3
   (c) 5
   (d) 6

10. $\phi(s)$ is called the
    (a) state transition matrix
    (b) resolution matrix
    (c) resolvent matrix
    (d) transfer matrix

11. An $n \times n$ matrix is said to be nonsingular if the rank of the matrix r is
    (a) $r \neq n$
    (b) $r = n$
    (c) $r = n/2$
    (d) $r = 2n$

12. Direct decomposition is applicable to transfer functions in which
    (a) denominator is in factored form
    (b) both numerator and denominator are in factored form
    (c) both numerator and denominator are not in factored form
    (d) all the above

13. The eigenvalues of the state model are the same as the
    (a) open-loop poles
    (b) closed-loop poles
    (c) both the open-loop and closed-loop poles
    (d) none of these

14. The concepts of controllability and observability were introduced by
    (a) Gilbert
    (b) Gibson
    (c) Kalman
    (d) none of these

PROBLEMS

10.1 A feedback system has a closed-loop transfer function

   (a) $\dfrac{10(s+3)}{s(s+2)(s+4)}$
   (b) $\dfrac{5}{(s+1)(s+2)^2}$
   (c) $\dfrac{(s+1)(s+3)(s+5)}{(s+2)(s+4)(s+6)}$

   Construct three different state models for this system and give block diagram representation for each state model.

10.2 Using parallel decomposition, construct state models for the systems represented by

   (a) $\dfrac{3s+4}{(s+1)^3(s+2)^2(s+3)}$
   (b) $\dfrac{1}{s(s+1)^3(s+2)}$
   (c) $\dfrac{5(s+1)}{s(s+3)^2}$

10.3 Construct state models for the following differential equations

(a) $2\ddot{y} + 3\ddot{y} + 5\dot{y} + 2y = u$

(b) $\ddot{y} + 5\dot{y} + 7y(t) + 3\int_0^t y(\tau)\,d\tau = \int_0^t u(\tau)\,d\tau$

(c) $3\dddot{y} + 5\ddot{y} + 6\ddot{y} + 7\dot{y} + 4y = 3u$

(d) $\dddot{y} + 6\ddot{y} + 11\dot{y} + 6y = \dddot{u} + 8\ddot{u} + 17\dot{u} + 8u$

(e) $\ddot{y} + 6\dot{y} + 3y = \ddot{u} + 4u$

(f) $\dddot{y} + 4\ddot{y} + 2y + \int_0^t y\,dt = 4u(t)$

10.4 The state equations of a linear time-invariant system are represented by

$$\dot{x}(t) = Ax(t) + Bu(t)$$

Find the state transition matrix $\phi(t)$, the characteristic equation and the eigenvalues of A and stability for the following cases.

(a) $A = \begin{bmatrix} 0 & 1 \\ -2 & -1 \end{bmatrix}$, $B = \begin{bmatrix} 0 \\ 1 \end{bmatrix}$

(b) $A = \begin{bmatrix} 0 & 1 \\ -4 & -5 \end{bmatrix}$, $B = \begin{bmatrix} 1 \\ 1 \end{bmatrix}$

(c) $A = \begin{bmatrix} 3 & 0 \\ 0 & -3 \end{bmatrix}$, $B = \begin{bmatrix} 0 \\ 1 \end{bmatrix}$

(d) $A = \begin{bmatrix} 0 & 2 \\ -2 & 0 \end{bmatrix}$, $B = \begin{bmatrix} 0 \\ 1 \end{bmatrix}$

(e) $A = \begin{bmatrix} -1 & 0 \\ 0 & -2 \end{bmatrix}$, $B = \begin{bmatrix} 1 \\ 0 \end{bmatrix}$

(f) $A = \begin{bmatrix} 0 & 1 \\ 0 & -2 \end{bmatrix}$, $B = \begin{bmatrix} 0 \\ 1 \end{bmatrix}$

(g) $A = \begin{bmatrix} -3 & 1 \\ -2 & 0 \end{bmatrix}$, $B = \begin{bmatrix} 0 \\ 1 \end{bmatrix}$

(h) $A = \begin{bmatrix} 0 & 1 \\ -10 & -7 \end{bmatrix}$, $B = \begin{bmatrix} 0 \\ 1 \end{bmatrix}$

(i) $A = \begin{bmatrix} 0 & -2 \\ 1 & -3 \end{bmatrix}$, $B = \begin{bmatrix} 1 \\ 0 \end{bmatrix}$

(j) $A = \begin{bmatrix} 0 & 0 \\ -1 & -1 \end{bmatrix}$, $B = \begin{bmatrix} 0 \\ 1 \end{bmatrix}$

(k) $A = \begin{bmatrix} 0 & 1 \\ -1 & -1 \end{bmatrix}$, $B = \begin{bmatrix} 1 \\ 0 \end{bmatrix}$

(l) $A = \begin{bmatrix} 0 & 1 \\ -3 & -2 \end{bmatrix}$, $B = \begin{bmatrix} 0 \\ 1 \end{bmatrix}$

(m) $A = \begin{bmatrix} 0 & 1 \\ 0 & -5 \end{bmatrix}$, $B = \begin{bmatrix} 1 \\ 0 \end{bmatrix}$

(n) $A = \begin{bmatrix} 0 & 1 \\ -2 & -2 \end{bmatrix}$, $B = \begin{bmatrix} 0 \\ 1 \end{bmatrix}$

(o) $A = \begin{bmatrix} 0 & 1 \\ -4 & 0 \end{bmatrix}$, $B = \begin{bmatrix} 1 \\ 0 \end{bmatrix}$

(p) $A = \begin{bmatrix} 1 & 2 \\ -4 & -3 \end{bmatrix}$, $B = \begin{bmatrix} 1 \\ 2 \end{bmatrix}$

10.5 The state equations of a linear time-invariant system are represented by

$$\dot{x}(t) = Ax(t) + Bu(t)$$

Find the state transition matrix $\phi(t)$, the characteristic equation, and the eigenvalues of **A**, and stability for the following cases.

(a) $\mathbf{A} = \begin{bmatrix} -1 & 0 & 0 \\ 0 & -2 & 1 \\ 0 & 0 & -2 \end{bmatrix}$, $\mathbf{B} = \begin{bmatrix} 0 \\ 1 \\ 0 \end{bmatrix}$ (b) $\mathbf{A} = \begin{bmatrix} -1 & 0 & 0 \\ 0 & -2 & 0 \\ 0 & 0 & -3 \end{bmatrix}$, $\mathbf{B} = \begin{bmatrix} 0 \\ 0 \\ 1 \end{bmatrix}$

(c) $\mathbf{A} = \begin{bmatrix} 0 & 1 & 0 \\ 0 & 0 & 1 \\ 0 & -2 & -3 \end{bmatrix}$, $\mathbf{B} = \begin{bmatrix} 0 \\ 0 \\ 1 \end{bmatrix}$ (d) $\mathbf{A} = \begin{bmatrix} 0 & 1 & 0 \\ 3 & 0 & 2 \\ -12 & -7 & -6 \end{bmatrix}$, $\mathbf{B} = \begin{bmatrix} 1 \\ 2 \\ 2 \end{bmatrix}$

(e) $\mathbf{A} = \begin{bmatrix} 0 & 1 & 0 \\ 0 & 0 & 1 \\ 1 & -3 & 3 \end{bmatrix}$, $\mathbf{B} = \begin{bmatrix} 1 \\ 1 \\ 1 \end{bmatrix}$ (f) $\mathbf{A} = \begin{bmatrix} 2 & 1 & 4 \\ 0 & 2 & 0 \\ 0 & 3 & 1 \end{bmatrix}$, $\mathbf{B} = \begin{bmatrix} 1 \\ 0 \\ 1 \end{bmatrix}$

(g) $\mathbf{A} = \begin{bmatrix} -1 & 0 & 1 \\ 1 & -2 & 0 \\ 0 & 0 & -3 \end{bmatrix}$, $\mathbf{B} = \begin{bmatrix} 0 \\ 0 \\ 1 \end{bmatrix}$ (h) $\mathbf{A} = \begin{bmatrix} 0 & 1 & 0 \\ -1 & -1 & 0 \\ 1 & 0 & 0 \end{bmatrix}$, $\mathbf{B} = \begin{bmatrix} 0 \\ 1 \\ 0 \end{bmatrix}$

10.6 Derive transfer functions corresponding to the following state models

(a) $\dot{\mathbf{x}} = \begin{bmatrix} 0 & 1 \\ -2 & -3 \end{bmatrix}\mathbf{x} + \begin{bmatrix} 1 \\ 0 \end{bmatrix}u$, $\mathbf{y} = \begin{bmatrix} 1 & 0 \end{bmatrix}\mathbf{x}$

(b) $\dot{\mathbf{x}} = \begin{bmatrix} -3 & 1 \\ -2 & 0 \end{bmatrix}\mathbf{x} + \begin{bmatrix} 0 \\ 1 \end{bmatrix}u$, $\mathbf{y} = \begin{bmatrix} 1 & 0 \end{bmatrix}\mathbf{x}$

(c) $\dot{\mathbf{x}} = \begin{bmatrix} -1 & 0 & 1 \\ 1 & -2 & 0 \\ 0 & 0 & -3 \end{bmatrix}\begin{bmatrix} x_1 \\ x_2 \\ x_3 \end{bmatrix} + \begin{bmatrix} 0 \\ 0 \\ 1 \end{bmatrix}u$, $\mathbf{y} = \begin{bmatrix} 1 & 1 & 0 \end{bmatrix}\begin{bmatrix} x_1 \\ x_2 \\ x_3 \end{bmatrix}$

(d) $\dot{\mathbf{x}} = \begin{bmatrix} 0 & 1 & 0 \\ -1 & -1 & 0 \\ 1 & 0 & 0 \end{bmatrix}\begin{bmatrix} x_1 \\ x_2 \\ x_3 \end{bmatrix} + \begin{bmatrix} 0 \\ 1 \\ 0 \end{bmatrix}u$, $\mathbf{y} = \begin{bmatrix} 0 & 0 & 1 \end{bmatrix}\begin{bmatrix} x_1 \\ x_2 \\ x_3 \end{bmatrix}$

(e) $\dot{\mathbf{x}} = \begin{bmatrix} 2 & 1 & 0 \\ 0 & 2 & 0 \\ 0 & 1 & 3 \end{bmatrix}\begin{bmatrix} x_1 \\ x_2 \\ x_3 \end{bmatrix} + \begin{bmatrix} 0 & 1 \\ 1 & 0 \\ 0 & 1 \end{bmatrix}u$, $\mathbf{y} = \begin{bmatrix} 1 & 0 & 0 \end{bmatrix}\begin{bmatrix} x_1 \\ x_2 \\ x_3 \end{bmatrix}$

(f) $\dot{\mathbf{x}} = \begin{bmatrix} -6 & 1 & 0 \\ -11 & 0 & 1 \\ -6 & 0 & 0 \end{bmatrix}\begin{bmatrix} x_1 \\ x_2 \\ x_3 \end{bmatrix} + \begin{bmatrix} 2 \\ 6 \\ 2 \end{bmatrix}u$, $\mathbf{y} = \begin{bmatrix} 1 & 0 & 0 \end{bmatrix}\begin{bmatrix} x_1 \\ x_2 \\ x_3 \end{bmatrix}$

(g) $\dot{\mathbf{x}} = \begin{bmatrix} 0 & 1 & 0 \\ 3 & 0 & 2 \\ -12 & -7 & -6 \end{bmatrix} \begin{bmatrix} x_1 \\ x_2 \\ x_3 \end{bmatrix} + \begin{bmatrix} 1 \\ 2 \\ 0 \end{bmatrix} u, \quad \mathbf{y} = \begin{bmatrix} 1 & 1 & 0 \end{bmatrix} \begin{bmatrix} x_1 \\ x_2 \\ x_3 \end{bmatrix}$

(h) $\dot{\mathbf{x}} = \begin{bmatrix} -1 & 0 & 0 \\ 0 & -2 & 1 \\ 0 & 0 & -2 \end{bmatrix} \begin{bmatrix} x_1 \\ x_2 \\ x_3 \end{bmatrix} + \begin{bmatrix} 0 \\ 1 \\ 1 \end{bmatrix} u, \quad \mathbf{y} = \begin{bmatrix} 1 & 1 & 0 \end{bmatrix} \begin{bmatrix} x_1 \\ x_2 \\ x_3 \end{bmatrix}$

10.7 (a) (i) Find $x_1(t)$ and $x_2(t)$ of the system described by

$$\begin{bmatrix} \dot{x}_1 \\ \dot{x}_2 \end{bmatrix} = \begin{bmatrix} 0 & 1 \\ -3 & -2 \end{bmatrix} \begin{bmatrix} x_1 \\ x_2 \end{bmatrix} \quad \text{where the initial conditions are} \quad \begin{bmatrix} x_1(0) \\ x_2(0) \end{bmatrix} = \begin{bmatrix} 1 \\ 0 \end{bmatrix}$$

(ii) If it has a forcing function and is represented by

$$\begin{bmatrix} \dot{x}_1 \\ \dot{x}_2 \end{bmatrix} = \begin{bmatrix} 0 & 1 \\ -3 & -2 \end{bmatrix} \begin{bmatrix} x_1 \\ x_2 \end{bmatrix} + \begin{bmatrix} 0 \\ 1 \end{bmatrix} u \quad \text{where } u \text{ is the unit-step function,}$$

Compute the solution using the same initial conditions.

(b) Find the state transition equations for the system described by

$$\begin{bmatrix} \dot{x}_1 \\ \dot{x}_2 \end{bmatrix} = \begin{bmatrix} 0 & 0 \\ -1 & -1 \end{bmatrix} \begin{bmatrix} x_1 \\ x_2 \end{bmatrix} + \begin{bmatrix} 0 \\ 1 \end{bmatrix} u \quad \text{with} \quad \begin{bmatrix} x_1(0) \\ x_2(0) \end{bmatrix} = \begin{bmatrix} 1 \\ 0 \end{bmatrix} \quad \text{where } u \text{ is a unit-step input.}$$

(c) (i) Find the solution of the homogeneous state equation

$$\begin{bmatrix} \dot{x}_1 \\ \dot{x}_2 \end{bmatrix} = \begin{bmatrix} 0 & 1 \\ -4 & -5 \end{bmatrix} \begin{bmatrix} x_1 \\ x_2 \end{bmatrix} \quad \text{with} \quad \begin{bmatrix} x_1(0) \\ x_2(0) \end{bmatrix} = \begin{bmatrix} 0 \\ 1 \end{bmatrix}$$

(ii) Find the state transition equation for the system

$$\begin{bmatrix} \dot{x}_1 \\ \dot{x}_2 \end{bmatrix} = \begin{bmatrix} 0 & 1 \\ -4 & -5 \end{bmatrix} \begin{bmatrix} x_1 \\ x_2 \end{bmatrix} + \begin{bmatrix} 1 \\ 1 \end{bmatrix} u \quad \text{with} \quad \begin{bmatrix} x_1(0) \\ x_2(0) \end{bmatrix} = \begin{bmatrix} 0 \\ 1 \end{bmatrix} \quad \text{where } u \text{ is a unit-step input.}$$

10.8 Consider the system

$$\dot{\mathbf{x}} = \begin{bmatrix} 0 & 1 \\ 0 & -2 \end{bmatrix} x + \begin{bmatrix} 0 \\ 1 \end{bmatrix} u, \quad \mathbf{x}(0) = \begin{bmatrix} 1 \\ 1 \end{bmatrix}; \quad \mathbf{y} = \begin{bmatrix} 1 & 0 \end{bmatrix} \begin{bmatrix} x_1 \\ x_2 \end{bmatrix} + \begin{bmatrix} 1 \\ 0 \end{bmatrix} u$$

(a) Determine the stability of the system
(b) Find the response of the system to a unit-step input
(c) Also determine the output of the system.

10.9 (a) Obtain the state variable model in Jordan canonical form, for the system with transfer function

$$\frac{Y(s)}{U(s)} = \frac{2s^2 + 6s + 5}{(s+1)^2 (s+2)}$$

(b) Find the response $y(t)$ to a unit-step input using the state variable model in (a)

(c) Give a block diagram for the analog computer simulation of the transfer function

10.10 Diagonalize the following system matrix.

(a) $A = \begin{bmatrix} 0 & 1 & 0 \\ 3 & 0 & 2 \\ -12 & -7 & -6 \end{bmatrix}$
(b) $A = \begin{bmatrix} 4 & 1 & -2 \\ 1 & 0 & 2 \\ 1 & -1 & 3 \end{bmatrix}$
(c) $A = \begin{bmatrix} 0 & 1 & 0 \\ 0 & 0 & 1 \\ 0 & -2 & -3 \end{bmatrix}$

(d) $A = \begin{bmatrix} 0 & 6 & -5 \\ 1 & 0 & 2 \\ 3 & 2 & 4 \end{bmatrix}$
(e) $A = \begin{bmatrix} 1 & 2 & -1 \\ 0 & 1 & 0 \\ 1 & -4 & 3 \end{bmatrix}$

10.11 Determine the state controllability, output controllability and observability of the system

$$\dot{x}(t) = Ax(t) + Bu(t), \qquad y(t) = Cx(t)$$

(a) $A = \begin{bmatrix} 0 & 1 \\ -1 & -3 \end{bmatrix}$, $B = \begin{bmatrix} 1 \\ 2 \end{bmatrix}$, $C = [1 \quad 1]$

(b) $A = \begin{bmatrix} 1 & 1 \\ -2 & -3 \end{bmatrix}$, $B = \begin{bmatrix} 0 \\ 1 \end{bmatrix}$, $C = [1 \quad 0]$

(c) $A = \begin{bmatrix} 0 & 2 & 0 \\ 1 & 2 & 0 \\ -1 & 0 & 1 \end{bmatrix}$, $B = \begin{bmatrix} 0 \\ 1 \\ 1 \end{bmatrix}$, $C = [1 \quad 0 \quad 1]$

(d) $A = \begin{bmatrix} 0 & 2 & 0 \\ 1 & 2 & 0 \\ -1 & 1 & 1 \end{bmatrix}$, $B = \begin{bmatrix} 1 \\ 1 \\ 0 \end{bmatrix}$, $C = [1 \quad 0 \quad 1]$

(e) $A = \begin{bmatrix} -2 & 1 & 0 \\ 0 & -2 & 0 \\ -1 & -2 & -3 \end{bmatrix}$, $B = \begin{bmatrix} 1 \\ 1 \\ 0 \end{bmatrix}$, $C = [1 \quad 0 \quad 0]$

(f) $A = \begin{bmatrix} -1 & 1 & 0 \\ 0 & -1 & 1 \\ 0 & 0 & -1 \end{bmatrix}$, $B = \begin{bmatrix} 0 \\ 1 \\ 1 \end{bmatrix}$, $C = [1 \quad 0 \quad 1]$

MATLAB PROGRAMS

PROGRAM 10.1

Matlab program to obtain the state transition matrix of

$$A = \begin{bmatrix} 1 & 1 \\ 0 & 1 \end{bmatrix}$$

```
Clc;clear all;close all
A=[1 1;0 1];
n= length(A);
a=poly(A);       %yes, poly() handles matrix too
F(:,1:n) =eye(n);
E1=F(:,1:n);
for i=1:n-1
   F(:,(i*n+1):(i+1)*n)=A*F(:,(i-1)*n+1:i*n)+a(i+1)*eye(n);
   E=F(:,(i*n+1):(i+1)*n);
  end
syms s
z1=(s*E1+E);
z2=tf(a,1);
disp('the numerator of STM  in S-transform is')
disp(z1)
disp('the denominator of STM in S-transform is')
disp(z2)
z=z1/z2;
y=ilaplace(z);
disp('y');
```

Output:

the numerator of STM in S-transform is
     [s - 1,   1]
     [0, s - 1]
the denominator of STM in S-transform is
Transfer function:
  $s^2 - 2s + 1$

PROGRAM 10.2

Matlab program to construct a state model for the system described by

$$\ddot{y} + 7\dot{y} + 5y + 6\int_0^t y \cdot dt = \dot{u} + 3u + 2\int_0^t u \, dt$$

```
clc;clear all;close all;
k=[1 3 2];
p=[1 7 5 6];
a=p;
n=length(a)-1;
I=eye(n-1);
z=zeros(n-1,1);
zi=[z,I];
for m=1:n
  an(m)=-a(n+2-m)/a(1);
end
A=[zi;an];
B=[k/a(1)];
C=[1 z'];
disp('The X dot matrix in terms of x')
disp(A)
disp('matrix beta')
disp(B)
disp('the y matrix in terms of x')
disp(C)
```

Output:

The *X* dot matrix in terms of *x*

```
   0    1    0
   0    0    1
  -6   -5   -7
```

matrix beta

```
   1    3    2
```

the *y* matrix in terms of *x*

```
   1    0    0
```

PROGRAM 10.3

Matlab program to obtain the transfer function for the state model

$$A = \begin{bmatrix} 0 & 1 & 0 \\ 0 & 0 & 1 \\ -9 & -11 & -6 \end{bmatrix}, B = \begin{bmatrix} 0 \\ 0 \\ 1 \end{bmatrix}, C = \begin{bmatrix} -10 & -10 & -5 \end{bmatrix}$$

```
% space state modal to transfer function
clc;clear all;close all;
A=[0 1 0; 0 0 1; -9 -11 -6];
B=[0 0 1]';
```

```
C=[-10 -10 -5];
D=2;
[b a]=ss2tf(A,B,C,D);
tf(b,a)
```

output:

Transfer function:

$$\frac{2s^3 + 7s^2 + 12s + 8}{s^3 + 6s^2 + 11s + 9}$$

PROGRAM 10.4

Matlab program to obtain the state model of the system

$$T(s) = \frac{Y(s)}{U(s)} = \frac{2s^3 + 7s^2 + 12s + 8}{s^3 + 6s^2 + 11s + 9}$$

```
% Transfer function to space state model
clc;clear all;close all;
a=[2 7 12 8 ];
b=[1 6 11 9];
c=tf(a,b)
[A,B,C,D]=tf2ss(a,b)
disp(A)
disp(B)
disp(C)
disp(D)
```

Output:

Transfer function:

$$\frac{2s^3 + 7s^2 + 12s + 8}{s^3 + 6s^2 + 11s + 9}$$

A =

−6	−11	−9
1	0	0
0	1	0

B =

```
    1
    0
    0
```

C =

−5	−10	−10

D =

```
    2
```

PROGRAM 10.5

Matlab program to determine the stability of a system with

$$A = \begin{bmatrix} 0 & 1 & 0 \\ 0 & 0 & 1 \\ -2 & -5 & -4 \end{bmatrix}$$

```
% Stability of a Matrix A
clc;clear all;close all;
a=[0 1 0;0 0 1; -2 -5 -4];
d=eig(a);
c=0;
c1=0;
for i=1:length(d)
   if d(i)<0
     c=c+1;
   else
     c1=c1+1;
   end
end
if c1>0
   disp('The system is unstable')
else
   disp('The System is stable')
end
```

Output:

The System is stable

PROGRAM 10.6

Matlab program to determine the state and output controllabity of a system with

$$A = \begin{bmatrix} 0 & 1 \\ -1 & -3 \end{bmatrix}, B = \begin{bmatrix} 1 \\ 2 \end{bmatrix}, C = \begin{bmatrix} 1 & 1 \end{bmatrix},$$

```
% state and output controllability
clc;clear all;close all;
A=[0 1; -1 -3];
B=[1;2];
C=[1 1];
r=rank ([B A*B A^2*B]);
```

```
n=rank ([C' A*C' A^2*C']);
m=rank ([C*B C*A*B C*A^2*B]);
if r==n
    disp('the system is completely state controllable')
else
    disp('the system is completely not state controllable')
end
if m==1
    disp('The system is completely output controllable')
else
    disp('The system is completely output controllable')
end
```

Output:

the system is completely state controllable
The system is completely output controllable

PROGRAM 10.7

Matlab program for diagonalization of the system matrix

$$A = \begin{bmatrix} 0 & 1 & 0 \\ 0 & 0 & 1 \\ -6 & -11 & -6 \end{bmatrix}$$

```
%diagonalization of system matrix
clc;clear all;close all;
A=[0 1 0; 0 0 1; -6 -11 -6];
[P,d]=eig(A);
Ad = inv (P) * A * P;
disp('The diagonal matrix is given by')
disp(Ad)
```

Output:

The diagonal matrix is given by

−1.0000	−0.0000	0.0000
−0.0000	−2.00000	
−0.0000	0.0000	−3.0000

Figure 11.1 Typical Sampled-data control system.

11

Digital Control Systems

11.1 INTRODUCTION

In the continuous time control systems discussed so far the signal at every point in the system is a continuous function of time. The controller elements are such that the controller produces continuous time control signals from continuous time input signals. Such a controller is called an analog controller. As the complexity of control system increases, severe demands of flexibility, adaptability and optimality and even demands to account for economic control function complexity arise. In fact, constructing a complex control function may even become technically infeasible, if one is restricted to use only analog elements. A digital controller in which either a special purpose computer or a general purpose computer forms the heart is, therefore, an ideal choice for complex control systems. Such systems are called digital control systems. A general purpose computer, when used as a digital controller, lends itself to time shared use for other control functions in the plant or process. A digital controller also has the versatality that its control function can be easily modified by changing a few program instructions or even the entire program and a change in instruction can even be accomplished either manually or automatically under control of a supervisor function. Moreover, the computers are able to receive and manipulate several inputs, so a digital computer control system can often be a multivariable system. Digital controllers used in control systems have the inherent characteristic that they accept the data as short duration pulses (i.e., sampled or discrete data) and produce a similar kind of output as control signal. In this chapter, we discuss the basics of digital control systems and the methods of determining the stability of these systems.

11.2 SAMPLED-DATA CONTROL SYSTEM

Figure 11.1 shows a typical sampled-data control scheme employing a digital controller.

A sampler and analog-to-digital converter (ADC) is needed at the computer input. The sampler converts the continuous time error signal into a sequence of pulses which are then expressed in numerical code (such as binary code). Numerically coded output data of digital computer are decoded into continuous time signal by digital-to-analog converter (DAC) and hold circuit. This continuous-time signal then controls the plant (continuous-time system). The overall system is hybrid in which the signal is in sampled form in the digital controller and in continuous form in the rest of the system. A system of this kind is referred to as a sampled-data control system.

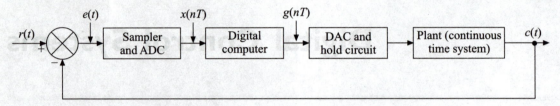

Figure 11.1 Typical Sampled-data control system.

Sampling is a necessity when a high degree of accuracy is required.

Sampled data technique is most appropriate for control systems requiring long distance data transmission. Pulses may be transmitted with little loss of accuracy, whereas analog form transmission involves distortion.

Time multiplexing decreases cost of transmission installation. Signal sampling reduces the power demand made on the signal and is, therefore, useful for signals of weak power origin. Some systems have signals which are inherently in sampled form only like radar tracking systems. So the circumstances that lead to the use of sampled data systems are as follows:

1. For using digital computer (or microprocessor) as part of the control loop.

2. For time sharing of control components.

3. Whenever a transmission channel forms part of the control loop.

4. Whenever the output of a control component is essentially in discrete form.

Sampling implies that the signal at the output end of the sampler is available in the form of short duration pulses each followed by a skip period. Uniform periodic sampling is illustrated in Figure 11.2.

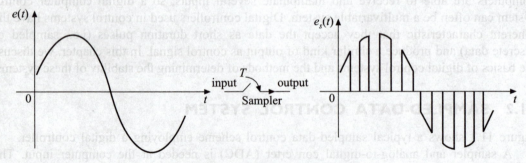

Figure 11.2 Uniform periodic sampling.

According to Shanon's sampling theorem, the information contained in a signal is fully preserved in the sampled version so long as the sampling frequency is atleast twice the maximum frequency contained in the signal.

Assuming sample width as fixed, following are the other forms of sampling:

Multi order sampling: A particular sampling pattern is repeated periodically.

Multirate sampling: In this case, two simultaneous sampling operations with different time periods are carried out on the signal to produce the sampled output.

Random sampling: In this case, sampling instants are random with a particular kind of distribution.

In this book we shall restrict ourselves to uniform periodic sampling.

11.3 SIGNAL RECONSTRUCTION

Sampled-data signal, which has been modified by a digital controller (or has been transmitted over a channel), must be converted into analog form for use in the continuous part of the system (the controlled plant). This is accomplished by means of various types of hold circuits (extrapolators). The simplest hold circuit is the zero-order-hold (ZOH) in which the reconstructed signal acquires the same value as the last received sample for the entire sampling period. The schematic diagram of the sampler and ZOH is shown in Figure11.3(a), while signal reconstruction is illustrated in Figures 11.3(b) and 11.3(c). The high frequencies present in the reconstructed signal are easily filtered out by the controlled elements of the system which are basically low-pass in frequency behaviour.

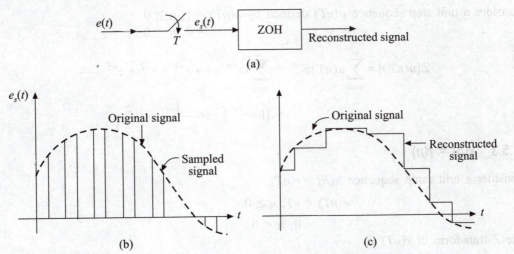

Figure 11.3   (a) Sampler and ZOH (b) Sampled signal and (c) Reconstructed signal.

In a first order hold, the last two signal samples are used to reconstruct the signal for the current sampling period. Similarly, higher holds can be devised. First or higher order holds offer no particular advantage over the ZOH. The simple ZOH used in conjunction with high sampling rate provides satisfactory performance.

11.4 THE Z-TRANSFORM

The one-sided Z-transform of a sequence

$$x(n) = [\ldots 0,\ x(0),\ x(1),\ x(2),\ \ldots]$$

which is defined for positive integers n, is defined as the weighted sum

$$Z[x(n)] = X(z) = \sum_{n=0}^{\infty} x(n)z^{-n}$$

where z is an arbitrary complex number. $X(z)$, a sum of complex numbers, is also a complex number.

11.5 Z-TRANSFORMS OF SOME COMMON SEQUENCES

11.5.1 $x(n) = \delta(n)$

Consider an impulse function $\delta(n)$.

$$Z[\delta(n)] = \sum_{n=0}^{\infty} \delta(n)z^{-n} = 1 + 0 + 0 + \ldots = 1$$

11.5.2 $x(n) = u(n)$

Consider a unit step sequence $u(nT)$ defined by $u(nT) = 1;\ n \geq 0$
$$= 0;\ n < 0$$

$$Z[u(nT)] = \sum_{n=0}^{\infty} u(nT)z^{-n} = \sum_{n=0}^{\infty} 1z^{-n} = 1 + z^{-1} + z^{-2} + z^{-3} + \cdots$$

$$= [1 - z^{-1}]^{-1} = \frac{1}{1 - z^{-1}} = \frac{z}{z - 1}$$

11.5.3 $x(n) = r(n)$

Consider a unit ramp sequence $x(n) = r(nT)$.
$$r(nT) = nT;\ n \geq 0$$
$$= 0;\ n < 0$$

The Z-transform of $r(nT)$ is:

$$Z[r(nT)] = \sum_{n=0}^{\infty} nT \times z^{-n} = Tz^{-1} + 2Tz^{-2} + 3Tz^{-3} + \cdots$$

$$= Tz^{-1}[1 + 2z^{-1} + 3z^{-2} + \ldots]$$

$$= Tz^{-1}[1 - z^{-1}]^{-2} = \frac{Tz^{-1}}{[1 - z^{-1}]^2} = \frac{Tz}{(z - 1)^2}$$

11.5.4 $x(n) = e^{j\omega n}$

Consider an exponential sequence $x(n) = e^{j\omega nT}$.

$$Z[e^{j\omega nT}] = \sum_{n=0}^{\infty} e^{j\omega nT} z^{-n} = \sum_{n=0}^{\infty} [e^{j\omega T} z^{-1}]^n$$

$$= 1 + (e^{j\omega T} z^{-1}) + (e^{j\omega T} z^{-1})^2 + \cdots$$

$$= [1 - e^{j\omega T} z^{-1}]^{-1} = \frac{1}{1 - e^{j\omega T} z^{-1}}$$

$$= \frac{z}{z - e^{j\omega T}}; |z| > 1$$

11.5.5 $x(n) = \sin \omega n$

Consider the sinusoidal sequence $x(n) = \sin n\omega T \, u(nT)$, i.e.,

$$x(n) = \sin n\omega T; \quad n \geq 0$$
$$= 0; \qquad n < 0$$

The Z-transform of $\sin n\omega T$ is:

$$Z[\sin n\omega T] = X(z) = \sum_{n=0}^{\infty} (\sin n\omega T) z^{-n}$$

$$= \sum_{n=0}^{\infty} \left[\frac{e^{j\omega nT} - e^{-jn\omega T}}{2j} \right] z^{-n}$$

$$= \frac{1}{2j} \sum_{n=0}^{\infty} (z^{-1} e^{j\omega T})^n - (z^{-1} e^{-j\omega T})^n$$

$$= \frac{1}{2j} \left[\frac{1}{1 - z^{-1} e^{j\omega T}} - \frac{1}{1 - z^{-1} e^{-j\omega T}} \right]$$

$$= \frac{1}{2j} \left[\frac{z}{z - e^{j\omega T}} - \frac{z}{z - e^{-j\omega T}} \right]$$

$$= \frac{z \sin \omega T}{z^2 - 2z \cos \omega T + 1}, |z| > 1$$

Convergence region of the Z-transform lies outside a circle of unit radius in the complex z-plane.

In general, the Z-transform of any sequence of numbers $x(n)$ will have a region of convergence specified by $|z| > R$, where the radius of convergence R depends upon the sequence $x(n)$.

11.5.6   x(n) = cos ωn

Consider the sequence $x(n) = \cos n\omega T\, u(nT)$, i.e.,

$$x(n) = \cos \omega nT; \quad n \geq 0$$
$$= 0; \qquad n < 0$$

The Z-transform of $\cos n\omega T$ is:

$$Z[\cos n\omega T] = Z\left[\frac{e^{jn\omega T} + e^{-jn\omega T}}{2}\right]$$

$$= \sum_{n=0}^{\infty}\left[\frac{e^{jn\omega T} + e^{-jn\omega T}}{2}\right]z^{-n}$$

$$= \frac{1}{2}\sum_{n=0}^{\infty}(z^{-1}e^{j\omega T})^n + (z^{-1}e^{-j\omega T})^n = \frac{1}{2}\left[\frac{1}{1-z^{-1}e^{j\omega T}} - \frac{1}{1-z^{-1}e^{-j\omega T}}\right]$$

$$= \frac{1}{2}\left[\frac{z}{z-e^{j\omega T}} + \frac{z}{z-e^{-j\omega T}}\right]$$

$$= \frac{z(z-\cos\omega T)}{z^2 - 2z\cos\omega T + 1}; |z| > 1$$

11.5.7   x(n) = aⁿ

Consider a geometric sequence

$$x(n) = (...0,\ 1,\ a,\ a^2,\ a^3,\ ...) = a^n;\ n \geq 0$$

where a is any real number.
The Z-transform of this sequence a^n is:

$$Z[a^n] = \sum_{n=0}^{\infty} a^n z^{-n} = \sum_{n=0}^{\infty}(az^{-1})^n$$

This infinite sum converges if

$$|az^{-1}| < 1 \quad \text{or} \quad |z| > |a|$$

and it diverges if

$$|z| < |a|$$

In the region of convergence,

$$Z(a^n) = \sum_{n=0}^{\infty}(az^{-1})^n = \frac{1}{1-az^{-1}} = \frac{z}{z-a}$$

11.6   PROPERTIES OF Z-TRANSFORM

In this section, we will study some of the important properties of the Z-transform which can be used to determine $F(z)$ and its inverse.

11.6.1 Linearity Property

The linearity property of Z-transform states that:

If $\qquad\qquad\qquad\qquad Z[x_1(n)] = X_1(z)$ and $Z[x_2(n)] = X_2(z)$

then $\qquad\qquad Z[ax_1(n) + bx_2(n)] = aX_1(z) + bX_2(z)$

$$Z[ax_1(n) + bx_2(n)] = \sum_{n=0}^{\infty} [ax_1(n) + bx_2(n)]z^{-n}$$

$$= a\sum_{n=0}^{\infty} x_1(n)z^{-n} + b\sum_{n=0}^{\infty} x_2(n)z^{-n}$$

$$= aX_1(z) + bX_2(z)$$

11.6.2 Shifting Property

The time shifting property of Z-transform states that:

If $\qquad\qquad Z[x(n)] = X(z)$, then $Z[x(n-m)] = z^{-m}X(z)$

$$Z[x(n-m)] = \sum_{n=0}^{\infty} x(n-m)z^{-n}$$

Let $n - m = p$ in the summation, then $n = m + p$.

$$\therefore \qquad\qquad Z[x(n-m)] = \sum_{p=-m}^{\infty} x(p)z^{-(m+p)}$$

$$= z^{-m}\sum_{p=0}^{\infty} x(p)z^{-p} = z^{-m}X(z) \text{ [Neglecting the initial conditions]}$$

Similarly, $\qquad\qquad\qquad\qquad Z[x(n+m)] = z^m X(z)$

If the initial conditions are not neglected,

$$Z[x(n-m)] = z^{-m}X(z) + z^{-m}\sum_{k=1}^{m} x(-k)z^k$$

$$= z^{-m}X(z) + z^{-(m-1)}x(-1) + z^{-(m-2)}x(-2) + z^{-(m-3)}x(-3) + \cdots$$

and $\qquad Z[x(n+m)] = z^m X(z) - z^m \sum_{p=0}^{m-1} x(p)z^{-p}$

$$= z^m X(z) - z^m x(0) - z^{m-1}x(1) - z^{m-2}x(2) - \cdots$$

11.6.3   Multiplication by an Exponential Sequence Property

If $Z[x(n)] = X(z)$, then $Z[a^n x(n)] = X\left(\dfrac{z}{a}\right)$

$$Z[a^n x(n)] = \sum_{n=0}^{\infty} a^n x(n) z^{-n}$$

$$= \sum_{n=0}^{\infty} x(n) \left(\frac{z}{a}\right)^{-n}$$

$$= X\left(\frac{z}{a}\right)$$

11.6.4   Time Reversal Property

If $Z[x(n)] = X(z)$, then $Z[x(-n)] = X(z^{-1}) = X\left(\dfrac{1}{z}\right)$

$$Z[x(-n)] = \sum_{n=0}^{\infty} x(-n) z^{-n}$$

Let $p = -n$ in the summation, then

$$Z[x(-n)] = \sum_{p=0}^{\infty} x(p) z^{p}$$

$$= \sum_{p=0}^{\infty} x(p)\, (z^{-1})^{-p}$$

$$= X(z^{-1}) = X\left(\frac{1}{z}\right)$$

11.6.5   Multiplication by *n* or Differentiation in z-domain Property

If $Z[x(n)] = X(z)$, then $Z[n\, x(n)] = -z\dfrac{d}{dz} X(z)$

We know that

$$X(z) = \sum_{n=0}^{\infty} x(n) z^{-n}$$

Differentiating both sides with respect to z, we get

$$\frac{d}{dz} X(z) = \frac{d}{dz} \left[\sum_{n=0}^{\infty} x(n) z^{-n} \right] = \sum_{n=0}^{\infty} x(n) \frac{d}{dz} (z^{-n})$$

$$= \sum_{n=0}^{\infty} x(n)\,(-n)z^{-n-1}$$

$$= -z^{-1} \sum_{n=0}^{\infty} [nx(n)]\,z^{-n}$$

$$= -z^{-1} Z[nx(n)]$$

$$\therefore \qquad Z[nx(n)] = -z\frac{d}{dz}\,X(z)$$

In the same way,
$$Z[n^k x(n)] = (-1)^k z^k \frac{d^k X(z)}{dz^k}$$

11.6.6 Convolution Property

The convolution property of Z-transform states that if $Z[x_1(n)] = X_1(z)$ and $Z[x_2(n)] = X_2(z)$, then $Z[x_1(n) * x_2(n)] = X_1(z)\,X_2(z)$. We know that:

$$x_1(n) * x_2(n) = \sum_{k=0}^{\infty} x_1(k)\,x_2(n-k)$$

$$\therefore \qquad Z[x_1(n) * x_2(n)] = \sum_{n=0}^{\infty} \left[\sum_{k=0}^{\infty} x_1(k)\,x_2(n-k) \right] z^{-n}$$

$$= \sum_{n=0}^{\infty} \sum_{k=0}^{\infty} x_1(k)\,x_2(n-k)z^{-(n-k)}z^{-k}$$

Interchanging the order of summations,

$$X(z) = \sum_{k=0}^{\infty} x_1(k)z^{-k} \sum_{n=0}^{\infty} x_2(n-k)\,z^{-(n-k)}$$

Replacing $(n-k)$ by p in the second summation, we get

$$X(z) = \sum_{k=0}^{\infty} x_1(k)z^{-k} \sum_{p=0}^{\infty} x_2(p)z^{-p}$$

$$= X_1(z)\,X_2(z)$$

This proves that $Z[x_1(n) * x_2(n)] = X_1(z)\,X_2(z)$

11.6.7 Initial Value Theorem

The initial value theorem of Z-transform states that, for a causal signal $x(n)$, if $Z[x(n)] = X(z)$, then

$$\underset{n\to 0}{\text{Lt}}\ x(n)\ =\ x(0) = \underset{z\to\infty}{\text{Lt}}\ X(z)$$

$$X(z)\ =\ \sum_{n=0}^{\infty} x(n)\,z^{-n} = x(0) + \frac{x(1)}{z} + \frac{x(2)}{z^2} + \cdots$$

Taking the limit $z \to \infty$ on both sides, we have

$$\underset{z\to\infty}{\text{Lt}}\ X(z)\ =\ \underset{z\to\infty}{\text{Lt}}\left[x(0) + \frac{x(1)}{z} + \frac{x(2)}{z^2} + \cdots\right] = x(0)$$

$\therefore$
$$\underset{n\to 0}{\text{Lt}}\ x(n)\ =\ x(0) = \underset{z\to\infty}{\text{Lt}}\ X(z)$$

11.6.8 Final Value Theorem

The final value theorem of Z-transform states that, for a causal signal, if $Z[x(n)] = X(z)$, then

$$\underset{n\to\infty}{\text{Lt}}\ x(n)\ =\ x(\infty) = \underset{z\to 1}{\text{Lt}}\ (z-1)\,X(z)$$

$$Z[x(n)]\ =\ X(z) = \sum_{n=0}^{\infty} x(n)\,z^{-n}$$

$$Z[x(n+1)]\ =\ zX(z) - zx(0) = \sum_{n=0}^{\infty} x(n+1)z^{-n}$$

$\therefore$
$$Z[x(n+1)] - Z[x(n)]\ =\ \sum_{n=0}^{\infty} x(n+1)\,z^{-n} - \sum_{n=0}^{\infty} x(n)\,z^{-n} = zX(z) - zx(0) - X(z)$$

$$(z-1)\,X(z) - zx(0)\ =\ \sum_{n=0}^{\infty} [x(n+1) - x(n)]z^{-n}$$

$$=\ [x(1) - x(0)] + [x(2) - x(1)]z^{-1} + [x(3) - x(2)]z^{-2} + \cdots$$

Taking the limit $z \to 1$ on both sides, we get

$$\underset{z\to 1}{\text{Lt}}\ (z-1)\,X(z) - x(0)\ = x(\infty) - x(0)$$

$\therefore$
$$x(\infty) = \underset{n\to\infty}{\text{Lt}}\ x(n) = \underset{z\to 1}{\text{Lt}}\ (z-1)\,X(z)$$

Table 11.1 shows some of the useful properties of Z-transforms. Table 11.2[(a) and (b)] shows some of the useful Z-transform pairs.

Table 11.1 Properties of the (one-sided) Z-transform

Property	*Discrete sequence*	*Z-transform*
Linearity	$ax_1(n) + bx_2(n)$	$aX_1(z) + bX_2(z)$
Shifting $m \geq 0$	$x(n + m)$	$z^m X(z) - z^m \sum_{p=0}^{m-1} x(p) z^{-p}$
	$x(n - m)$	$z^{-m} X(z) + z^{-m} \sum_{k=1}^{m} x(-k) z^k$
Multiplication by n^m	$n^m x(n)$	$(-1)^m z^m \dfrac{d^m X(z)}{dz^m}$
Scaling or multiplication by a^n	$a^n x(n)$	$X\left(\dfrac{z}{a}\right)$
Convolution	$\sum_{m=0}^{n} h(n - m)\, r(m)$	$H(z)\, R(z)$
Initial value	$x(0) = \underset{z \to \infty}{\text{Lt}}\ X(z)$	
Final value	$x(\infty) = \underset{z \to 1}{\text{Lt}}\ (z - 1)\, X(z)$	
	if $X(z)$ is analytical for $|z| > 1$	

Table 11.2(a) Z-transform (one-sided) pairs

$x(t)$	$x(n)/x(nT)$ $n \geq 0$	$X(z)$
$\delta(t)$	$\delta(n)$	1
$u(t)$	$u(n)$ or 1	$\dfrac{z}{z-1}$
	a^n	$\dfrac{z}{z-a}$
	na^n	$\dfrac{az}{(z-a)^2}$
	$n^2 a^n$	$\dfrac{az(z+a)}{(z-a)^3}$
	$(n+1)a^n$	$\dfrac{z^2}{(z-a)^2}$
	$\dfrac{(n+1)(n+2)a^n}{2!}$	$\dfrac{z^3}{(z-a)^3}$
	$\dfrac{(n+1)(n+2)(n+3)a^n}{3!}$	$\dfrac{z^4}{(z-a)^4}$
	$\dfrac{a^n}{n!}$	$e^{az^{-1}}$

Table 11.2(b) Z-transform (one-sided) pairs

$\dfrac{x(t)}{t \geq 0}$	$\dfrac{x(n)/x(nT)}{n \geq 0}$	$X(z)$
t	nT	$\dfrac{Tz}{(z-1)^2}$
t^2	$(nT)^2$	$\dfrac{T^2 z(z+1)}{(z-1)^3}$
e^{-at}	e^{-anT}	$\dfrac{z}{(z-e^{-aT})}$
te^{-at}	nTe^{-anT}	$\dfrac{zTe^{aT}}{(z-e^{-aT})^2}$
$a(1-e^{-at})$	$a(1-e^{-anT})$	$\dfrac{z(1-e^{-aT})}{(z-1)(z-e^{-aT})}$
$\sin \omega t$	$\sin \omega nT$	$\dfrac{z \sin \omega T}{z^2 - 2z \cos \omega T + 1}$
$\cos \omega t$	$\cos \omega nT$	$\dfrac{z(z-\cos \omega T)}{z^2 - 2z \cos \omega T + 1}$
$e^{-at} \sin \omega t$	$e^{-anT} \sin \omega nT$	$\dfrac{ze^{-aT} \sin \omega T}{z^2 - 2ze^{-aT} \cos \omega T + e^{-2aT}}$
$e^{-at} \cos \omega t$	$e^{-anT} \cos \omega nT$	$\dfrac{z(z-e^{-aT} \cos \omega T)}{z^2 - 2ze^{-aT} \cos \omega T + e^{-2aT}}$

Example 11.1 Find the Z-transform of

$$x(n) = 3 \left(\frac{5}{7} \right)^n u(n) + 2 \left(-\frac{1}{3} \right)^n u(n)$$

Solution:

$$Z[x(n)] = X(z) = \sum_{n=0}^{\infty} x(n) \, z^{-n} = \sum_{n=0}^{\infty} \left[3 \left(\frac{5}{7} \right)^n u(n) + 2 \left(-\frac{1}{3} \right)^n u(n) \right] z^{-n}$$

$$= 3 \sum_{n=0}^{\infty} \left[\left(\frac{5}{7} \right)^n u(n) \right] z^{-n} + 2 \sum_{n=0}^{\infty} \left[\left(-\frac{1}{3} \right)^n u(n) \right] z^{-n}$$

$$= 3 \sum_{n=0}^{\infty} \left[\frac{5}{7} z^{-1} \right]^n + 2 \sum_{n=0}^{\infty} \left[-\frac{1}{3} z^{-1} \right]^n$$

$$= 3 \frac{z}{z - \frac{5}{7}} + 2 \frac{z}{z + \frac{1}{3}}$$

$$= \frac{5z\left(z - \frac{3}{35}\right)}{\left(z - \frac{5}{7}\right)\left(z + \frac{1}{3}\right)}$$

Example 11.2 Find the Z-transform of the sequence

$$x(n) = \left(\frac{1}{4}\right)^n \cos\left(\frac{\pi}{3} n\right) u(n)$$

Solution:

Given

$$x(n) = \left(\frac{1}{4}\right)^n \cos\left(\frac{\pi}{3} n\right) u(n)$$

$$= \left(\frac{1}{4}\right)^n \left[\frac{e^{jn\frac{\pi}{3}} + e^{-jn\frac{\pi}{3}}}{2}\right] u(n)$$

$$= \frac{1}{2}\left[\left(\frac{1}{4} e^{j\frac{\pi}{3}}\right)^n + \left(\frac{1}{4} e^{-j\frac{\pi}{3}}\right)^n\right] u(n)$$

$$\therefore \quad Z[x(n)] = X(z) = \sum_{n=0}^{\infty} \frac{1}{2}\left[\left(\frac{1}{4} e^{j\frac{\pi}{3}}\right)^n + \left(\frac{1}{4} e^{-j\frac{\pi}{3}}\right)^n\right] u(n) \, z^{-n}$$

$$= \frac{1}{2} \sum_{n=0}^{\infty} \left(\frac{1}{4} e^{j\frac{\pi}{3}} z^{-1}\right)^n + \frac{1}{2} \sum_{n=0}^{\infty} \left(\frac{1}{4} e^{-j\frac{\pi}{3}} z^{-1}\right)^n$$

$$= \frac{1}{2}\left[\frac{1}{1 - \frac{1}{4} e^{j\frac{\pi}{3}} z^{-1}}\right] + \frac{1}{2}\left[\frac{1}{1 - \frac{1}{4} e^{-j\frac{\pi}{3}} z^{-1}}\right]$$

$$= \frac{1}{2}\left[\frac{z}{z - \frac{1}{4} e^{j\frac{\pi}{3}}}\right] + \frac{1}{2}\left[\frac{z}{z - \frac{1}{4} e^{-j\frac{\pi}{3}}}\right]$$

$$= \frac{z\left(z - \frac{1}{8}\right)}{\left(z - \frac{1}{8} - j \frac{\sqrt{3}}{8}\right)\left(z - \frac{1}{8} + j \frac{\sqrt{3}}{8}\right)}$$

Example 11.3   Determine the Z-transform of the signal

$$x(n) = \left(\frac{1}{3}\right)^n [u(n) - u(n-6)]$$

Solution:

$$Z[x(n)] = X(z) = \sum_{n=0}^{\infty} \left(\frac{1}{3}\right)^n [u(n) - u(n-6)]z^{-n}$$

$$= \sum_{n=0}^{5} \left(\frac{1}{3}z^{-1}\right)^n$$

$$= \frac{1 - \left(\frac{1}{3}z^{-1}\right)^6}{1 - \left(\frac{1}{3}z^{-1}\right)} = \frac{1}{z^5} \frac{z^6 - \left(\frac{1}{3}\right)^6}{z - \left(\frac{1}{3}\right)}$$

Example 11.4   Find the Z-transform of the sequence

$$x(n) = a^n \cos\frac{n\pi}{2}$$

Solution:

$$Z[x(n)] = X(z) = \sum_{n=0}^{\infty} a^n \cos\frac{n\pi}{2} z^{-n}$$

$$= \sum_{n=0}^{\infty} a^n \left[\frac{e^{jn\frac{\pi}{2}} + e^{-jn\frac{\pi}{2}}}{2}\right] z^{-n}$$

$$= \frac{1}{2}\left[\sum_{n=0}^{\infty} \left(ae^{j\frac{\pi}{2}}z^{-1}\right)^n + \sum_{n=0}^{\infty} \left(ae^{-j\frac{\pi}{2}}z^{-1}\right)^n\right]$$

$$= \frac{1}{2}\left[\frac{1}{1 - ae^{\left(j\frac{\pi}{2}\right)}z^{-1}} + \frac{1}{1 - ae^{\left(-j\frac{\pi}{2}\right)}z^{-1}}\right]$$

$$= \frac{1}{2}\left[\frac{z}{z - ae^{j\frac{\pi}{2}}} + \frac{z}{z - ae^{-j\frac{\pi}{2}}}\right]$$

$$= z\left[\frac{z - a\cos\frac{\pi}{2}}{z^2 - 2az\cos\left(\frac{\pi}{2}\right) + a^2}\right] = \frac{z^2}{z^2 + a^2}$$

Example 11.5 Using properties of Z-transform, find the Z-transform of the following signals:

(a) $x(n) = 2^n u(n - 2)$ (b) $x(n) = \alpha^{n-2} u(n - 2)$

(c) $x(n) = n2^n \sin\left(n\dfrac{\pi}{2}\right) u(n)$ (d) $x(n) = n^2 u(n)$

(e) $x(n) = n\left(\dfrac{1}{2}\right)^{n+2} u(n + 2)$

Solution:

(a) Given $x(n) = 2^n u(n - 2)$

Using time shifting property, we have

$$Z[u(n - 2)] = z^{-2} Z[u(n)] = z^{-2}\left[\frac{z}{z-1}\right] = \frac{z^{-1}}{z-1} = \frac{1}{z(z-1)}$$

Using multiplication by an exponential sequence property, we have

$$Z[2^n u(n - 2)] = Z[u(n - 2)]\Big|_{z=\frac{z}{2}} = \frac{1}{z(z-1)}\Big|_{z=\frac{z}{2}} = \frac{1}{\left(\frac{z}{2}\right)\left(\frac{z}{2}-1\right)} = \frac{4}{z(z-2)}$$

(b) Given $x(n) = \alpha^{n-2} u(n - 2)$

We know that $Z[u(n)] = \dfrac{z}{z-1}$

Using multiplication by an exponential sequence property, we have

$$Z[\alpha^n u(n)] = Z[u(n)]\Big|_{z=\frac{z}{\alpha}} = \frac{z}{z-1}\Big|_{z=\frac{z}{\alpha}} = \frac{z}{z-\alpha}$$

Using time shifting property, we have

$$Z[\alpha^{n-2} u(n - 2)] = z^{-2} Z[\alpha^n u(n)] = z^{-2} \frac{z}{z-\alpha} = \frac{1}{z(z-\alpha)}$$

(c) Given $x(n) = n2^n \sin\left(n\dfrac{\pi}{2}\right) u(n)$

We know that $Z\left[\sin\left(\dfrac{n\pi}{2}\right) u(n)\right] = \dfrac{z \sin\dfrac{\pi}{2}}{z^2 - 2z \cos\dfrac{\pi}{2} + 1} = \dfrac{z}{z^2 + 1}$

Using multiplication by an exponential sequence property, we have

$$Z\left[2^n \sin\left(\frac{n\pi}{2}\right) u(n)\right] = Z\left[\sin\left(\frac{n\pi}{2}\right) u(n)\right]\Big|_{z=\frac{z}{2}}$$

$$= \frac{z}{z^2 + 1}\bigg|_{z=\frac{z}{2}} = \frac{z/2}{(z/2)^2 + 1} = \frac{2z}{z^2 + 4}$$

Using differentiation in z-domain property, we have

$$Z\left[n2^n \sin\left(\frac{n\pi}{2}\right)u(n)\right] = -z\frac{d}{z}\left[Z\left[2^n \sin\left(\frac{n\pi}{2}\right)u(n)\right]\right]$$

$$= -z\frac{d}{dz}\left(\frac{2z}{z^2 + 4}\right) = -z\left[\frac{(z^2 + 4)(2) - 2z(2z)}{(z^2 + 4)^2}\right]$$

$$= \frac{2z(z^2 - 4)}{(z^2 + 4)^2}$$

(d) Given $x(n) = n^2u(n)$

We know that

$$Z[u(n)] = \frac{z}{z - 1}$$

Using the multiplication by n property, we have

$$Z[nu(n)] = -z\frac{d}{dz}[Z[u(n)]] = -z\frac{d}{dz}\left[\frac{z}{z-1}\right] = \frac{z}{(z-1)^2}$$

Again using the multiplication by n property, we have

$$Z[n^2u(n)] = -z\frac{d}{dz}[Z[nu(n)]] = -z\frac{d}{dz}\left[\frac{z}{(z-1)^2}\right] = \frac{z(z+1)}{(z-1)^3}$$

(e) $x(n) = n\left(\dfrac{1}{2}\right)^{n+2} u(n+2)$

We know that

$$Z[u(n)] = \frac{z}{z - 1}$$

Using multiplication by an exponential sequence property, we have

$$Z\left[\left(\frac{1}{2}\right)^n u(n)\right] = Z[u(n)]\bigg|_{z=\frac{z}{1/2}=2z} = \frac{z}{z-1}\bigg|_{z=2z}$$

$$= \frac{2z}{2z - 1} = \frac{z}{z - \dfrac{1}{2}}$$

Using time shifting property, we have

$$Z\left[\left(\frac{1}{2}\right)^{n+2} u(n+2)\right] = z^2 Z\left[\left(\frac{1}{2}\right)^n u(n)\right] = z^2\left(\frac{z}{z - \dfrac{1}{2}}\right) = \frac{z^3}{z - \dfrac{1}{2}}$$

Using the multiplication by n property, we have

$$Z\left[n\left(\frac{1}{2}\right)^{n+2} u(n+2)\right] = -z\frac{d}{dz}\left[Z\left[\left(\frac{1}{2}\right)^{n+2} u(n+2)\right]\right]$$

$$= -z\frac{d}{dz}\left[\frac{z^3}{z-\frac{1}{2}}\right] = \frac{1}{2}\frac{z^3(3-4z)}{\left(z-\frac{1}{2}\right)^2}$$

Example 11.6 Find the convolution of the sequences

$$x_1(n) = \left(\frac{1}{3}\right)^n u(n) \text{ and } x_2(n) = \left(\frac{1}{5}\right)^n u(n)$$

Solution:

$$Z[x_1(n)] = X_1(z) = \sum_{n=0}^{\infty}\left(\frac{1}{3}\right)^n u(n)\, z^{-n} = \frac{z}{z-\frac{1}{3}}$$

$$Z[x_2(n)] = X_2(z) = \sum_{n=0}^{\infty}\left(\frac{1}{5}\right)^n u(n)\, z^{-n} = \frac{z}{z-\frac{1}{5}}$$

We know that $x(n) = x_1(n) * x_2(n)$

$\therefore$
$$Z[x(n)] = X(z) = Z[x_1(n) * x_2(n)] = X_1(z)\, X_2(z)$$

$\therefore$
$$x_1(n) * x_2(n) = x(n) = Z^{-1}\left[\left(\frac{z}{z-\frac{1}{3}}\right)\left(\frac{z}{z-\frac{1}{5}}\right)\right]$$

$$= Z^{-1}\left[\frac{5}{2}\frac{z}{z-\frac{1}{3}} - \frac{3}{2}\frac{z}{z-\frac{1}{5}}\right]$$

$$= \frac{5}{2}\left(\frac{1}{3}\right)^n u(n) - \frac{3}{2}\left(\frac{1}{5}\right)^n u(n)$$

Example 11.7 Using final value theorem, find $x(\infty)$, if $X(z)$ is given by

(a) $\dfrac{z+1}{(z-0.6)^2}$

(b) $\dfrac{z+2}{4(z-1)(z+0.7)}$

(c) $\dfrac{2z+3}{(z+1)(z+3)(z-1)}$

Solution:

(a) $(z-1)X(z) = \dfrac{(z-1)(z+1)}{(z-0.6)^2}$ has no poles on or outside the unit circle. Therefore,

$$x(\infty) = \operatorname*{Lt}_{z \to 1} (z-1)X(z)$$

$$= \operatorname*{Lt}_{z \to 1} (z-1) \frac{(z+1)}{(z-0.6)^2} = 0$$

(b) $(z-1)X(z) = \dfrac{z+2}{4(z+0.7)}$ has no poles on or outside the unit circle. Therefore,

$$x(\infty) = \operatorname*{Lt}_{z \to 1} (z-1)X(z)$$

$$= \operatorname*{Lt}_{z \to 1} \frac{(z+2)}{4(z+0.7)} = \frac{3}{6.8} = 0.44$$

(c) $(z-1)[X(z)] = \dfrac{2z+3}{(z+1)(z+3)}$ has one pole on the unit circle and one pole outside the

unit circle. So, $x(\infty)$ tends to infinity as $n \to \infty$.

Example 11.8   Find $x(0)$ if $X(z)$ is given by

(a) $\dfrac{z^2 + 2z + 2}{(z+1)(z+0.5)}$ (b) $\dfrac{z+3}{(z+1)(z+2)}$

Solution:

(a) Given $X(z) = \dfrac{z^2 + 2z + 2}{(z+1)(z+0.5)} = \dfrac{1 + (2/z) + (2/z^2)}{[1 + (1/z)][1 + 0.5/z]}$

$$\therefore \qquad x(0) = \operatorname*{Lt}_{z \to \infty} X(z) = \operatorname*{Lt}_{z \to \infty} \frac{1 + (2/z) + (2/z^2)}{[1 + (1/z)][1 + 0.5/z]}$$

(b) Given $X(z) = \dfrac{z+3}{(z+1)(z+2)} = \dfrac{z[1 + (3/z)]}{z^2[1 + (1/z)][1 + (2/z)]}$

$$\therefore \qquad x(0) = \operatorname*{Lt}_{z \to \infty} X(z) = \operatorname*{Lt}_{z \to \infty} \frac{z[1 + (3/z)]}{z^2[1 + (1/z)][1 + (2/z)]}$$

11.7   INVERSE Z-TRANSFORM

The process of finding the time domain signal $x(n)$ from its Z-transform $X(z)$ is called the inverse Z-transform which is:

$$x(n) = Z^{-1}[X(z)]$$

Basically there are four methods that are often used to find the inverse Z-transform:

(a) Power series method or long division method

(b) Partial fraction expansion method

(c) Complex inversion integral method (also known as the residue method)

(d) Convolution integral method

Here we discuss only the first two methods.

The long division method is simple, but does not give a closed form expression for the signal. The partial fraction expansion method enables us to determine the time signal $x(n)$ making use of our knowledge of some basic Z-transform pairs and Z-transform theorems.

11.7.1 Long Division Method

If $X(z)$ is a ratio of two polynomials,

$$X(z) = \frac{N(z)}{D(z)} = \frac{b_0 + b_1 z^{-1} + b_2 z^{-2} + \cdots + b_M z^{-M}}{1 + a_1 z^{-1} + a_2 z^{-2} + \cdots + a_N z^{-N}}$$

for getting a causal sequence $x(n)$, first put $N(z)$ and $D(z)$ either in descending powers of z or in ascending powers of z^{-1} before long division and then perform long division. The coefficient of z^{-n} gives the value of the signal at the nth sampling instant.

Example 11.9   Using long division, determine the inverse Z-transform of

$$X(z) = \frac{z^2 + 2z}{z^3 - 3z^2 + 4z + 1}$$

Solution: To find the inverse Z-transform, express both $N(z)$ and $D(z)$ either in ascending powers of z^{-1} or in descending powers of z and then perform long division.

In the given $X(z)$, both $N(z)$ and $D(z)$ are already in descending powers of z. The long division is performed as follows:

$$
\begin{array}{r}
z^{-1} + 5z^{-2} + 11z^{-3} + 12z^{-4} - 13z^{-5} \\
z^3 - 3z^2 + 4z + 1 \overline{\smash{\big)}\, z^2 + 2z } \\
\underline{z^2 - 3z + 4 + z^{-1}} \\
5z - 4 - z^{-1} \\
\underline{5z - 15 + 20z^{-1} + 5z^{-2}} \\
11 - 21z^{-1} - 5z^{-2} \\
\underline{11 - 33z^{-1} + 44z^{-2} + 11z^{-3}} \\
12z^{-1} - 49z^{-2} - 11z^{-3} \\
\underline{12z^{-1} - 36z^{-2} + 48z^{-3} + 12z^{-4}} \\
-13z^{-2} - 59z^{-3} - 12z^{-4}
\end{array}
$$

$\therefore$ $X(z) = z^{-1} + 5z^{-2} + 11z^{-3} + 12z^{-4} - 13z^{-5} \cdots$

$\therefore$ $x(n) = \{0, 1, 5, 11, 12, -13, \ldots\}$

Writing $N(z)$ and $D(z)$ of $X(z)$ in ascending powers of z^{-1}, we have

$$X(z) = \frac{N(z)}{D(z)} = \frac{z^2 + 2z}{z^3 - 3z^2 + 4z + 1} = \frac{z^{-1} + 2z^{-2}}{1 - 3z^{-1} + 4z^{-2} + z^{-3}}$$

The long division is performed as follows:

$$
\begin{array}{r}
z^{-1} + 5z^{-2} + 11z^{-3} + 12z^{-4} - 13z^{-5} \\
1 - 3z^{-1} + 4z^{-2} + z^{-3} \overline{\smash{\big)}\, z^{-1} + 2z^{-2}} \\
\underline{z^{-1} - 3z^{-2} + 4z^{-3} + z^{-4}} \\
5z^{-2} - 4z^{-3} - z^{-4} \\
\underline{5z^{-2} - 15z^{-3} + 20z^{-4} + 5z^{-5}} \\
11z^{-3} - 21z^{-4} - 5z^{-5} \\
\underline{11z^{-3} - 33z^{-4} + 44z^{-5} + 11z^{-6}} \\
12z^{-4} - 49z^{-5} - 11z^{-6} \\
\underline{12z^{-4} - 36z^{-5} + 48z^{-6} + 12z^{-7}} \\
- 13z^{-5} - 59z^{-6} - 12z^{-7}
\end{array}
$$

$\therefore \quad X(z) = z^{-1} + 5z^{-2} + 11z^{-3} + 12z^{-4} - 13z^{-5} \ldots$

$\therefore \quad x(n) = \{0, 1, 5, 11, 12, -13, \ldots\}$

Observe that both the methods give the same sequence.

11.7.2 Partial Fraction Expansion Method

To find the inverse Z-transform of $X(z)$ using partial fraction expansion method, its denominator must be in factored form. Here we try to obtain the partial fraction expansion of $\dfrac{X(z)}{z}$ instead of $X(z)$. This is because the Z-transform of the time domain signals have z in their numerators. This method can be applied only if $\dfrac{X(z)}{z}$ is a proper rational function (i.e., the order of its denominator is greater than the order of its numerator). If $\dfrac{X(z)}{z}$ is not proper, then it should be written as the sum of a polynomial and a proper function before applying this method. The disadvantage of this method is that, the denominator must be factored. Using known Z-transform pairs and the properties of Z-transform, the inverse Z-transform of each partial fraction can be found.

Example 11.10   Find the inverse Z-transform of

$$X(z) = \frac{z^{-1}}{3 - 4z^{-1} + z^{-2}}$$

Solution:

Given $X(z) = \dfrac{z^{-1}}{3 - 4z^{-1} + z^{-2}} = \dfrac{z}{3z^2 - 4z + 1}$

$$= \frac{z}{3\left(z^2 - \frac{4}{3}z + \frac{1}{3}\right)} = \frac{1}{3}\frac{z}{(z-1)\left(z - \frac{1}{3}\right)}$$

$$\therefore \quad \frac{X(z)}{z} = \frac{1}{3}\frac{1}{(z-1)\left(z - \frac{1}{3}\right)} = \frac{A}{z-1} + \frac{B}{z - \frac{1}{3}}$$

where A and B can be evaluated as follows:

$$A = (z-1)\frac{X(z)}{z}\bigg|_{z=1} = (z-1)\frac{1}{3}\frac{1}{(z-1)\left(z - \frac{1}{3}\right)}\bigg|_{z=1} = \frac{1}{3}\frac{1}{1 - \frac{1}{3}} = \frac{1}{2}$$

$$B = \left(z - \frac{1}{3}\right)\frac{X(z)}{z}\bigg|_{z=\frac{1}{3}} = \left(z - \frac{1}{3}\right)\frac{1}{3}\frac{1}{(z-1)\left(z - \frac{1}{3}\right)}\bigg|_{z=\frac{1}{3}} = \frac{1}{3}\frac{1}{\frac{1}{3} - 1} = -\frac{1}{2}$$

$$\therefore \quad \frac{X(z)}{z} = \frac{1}{2}\frac{1}{z-1} - \frac{1}{2}\frac{1}{z - \frac{1}{3}}$$

or

$$X(z) = \frac{1}{2}\left[\frac{z}{z-1} - \frac{z}{z - \frac{1}{3}}\right]$$

Taking inverse Z-transform, we get

$$x(n) = \frac{1}{2}\left[u(n) - \left(\frac{1}{3}\right)^n u(n)\right]$$

Example 11.11 Find the inverse Z-transform of

$$X(z) = \frac{\frac{1}{6}z^{-1}}{\left[1 - \frac{1}{2}z^{-1}\right]\left[1 - \frac{1}{3}z^{-1}\right]}$$

Solution:

Given

$$X(z) = \frac{\frac{1}{6}z^{-1}}{\left[1 - \frac{1}{2}z^{-1}\right]\left[1 - \frac{1}{3}z^{-1}\right]} = \frac{\frac{1}{6}z}{\left(z - \frac{1}{2}\right)\left(z - \frac{1}{3}\right)}$$

The above equation can be expressed in partial fraction form as

$$\frac{X(z)}{z} = \frac{\frac{1}{6}}{\left(z - \frac{1}{2}\right)\left(z - \frac{1}{3}\right)} = \frac{C_1}{z - \frac{1}{2}} + \frac{C_2}{z - \frac{1}{3}}$$

where C_1 and C_2 can be evaluated as follows:

$$C_1 = \left(z - \frac{1}{2}\right)\frac{X(z)}{z}\bigg|_{z=\frac{1}{2}} = \frac{1}{6}\frac{1}{\left(z - \frac{1}{3}\right)}\bigg|_{z=\frac{1}{2}} = \frac{1}{6}\frac{1}{\left(\frac{1}{2} - \frac{1}{3}\right)} = 1$$

$$C_2 = \left(z - \frac{1}{3}\right)\frac{X(z)}{z}\bigg|_{z=\frac{1}{3}} = \frac{1}{6}\frac{1}{\left(z - \frac{1}{2}\right)}\bigg|_{z=\frac{1}{3}} = \frac{1}{6}\frac{1}{\left(\frac{1}{3} - \frac{1}{2}\right)} = -1$$

or

$$X(z) = \frac{z}{z - \frac{1}{2}} - \frac{z}{z - \frac{1}{3}}$$

Taking inverse Z-transform, we have

$$x(n) = \left(\frac{1}{2}\right)^n u(n) - \left(\frac{1}{3}\right)^n u(n)$$

Example 11.12 Find the inverse Z-transform of

$$X(z) = \frac{z(z-1)}{(z+1)^3(z+2)}$$

Solution:

Given

$$X(z) = \frac{z(z-1)}{(z+1)^3(z+2)}$$

$\therefore$

$$\frac{X(z)}{z} = \frac{z-1}{(z+1)^3(z+2)} = \frac{C_1}{(z+1)} + \frac{C_2}{(z+1)^2} + \frac{C_3}{(z+1)^3} + \frac{C_4}{z+2}$$

where the constants C_1, C_2, C_3 and C_4 can be obtained as follows:

$$C_4 = (z+2)\frac{X(z)}{z}\bigg|_{z=-2} = \frac{z-1}{(z+1)^3}\bigg|_{z=-2} = \frac{-2-1}{(-2+1)^3} = 3$$

$$C_3 = (z+1)^3\frac{X(z)}{z}\bigg|_{z=-1} = \frac{z-1}{z+2}\bigg|_{z=-1} = \frac{-1-1}{-1+2} = -2$$

$$C_2 = \frac{1}{1!}\frac{d}{dz}\left[(z+1)^3\frac{X(z)}{z}\right]\bigg|_{z=-1} = \frac{d}{dz}\left(\frac{z-1}{z+2}\right)\bigg|_{z=-1} = \frac{(z+2)1 - (z-1)1}{(z+2)^2}\bigg|_{z=-1} = 3$$

$$C_1 = \frac{1}{2!} \frac{d^2}{dz^2}\left[(z+1)^3 \frac{X(z)}{z}\right]\Bigg|_{z=-1} = \frac{1}{2!} \frac{d^2}{dz^2}\left(\frac{z-1}{z+2}\right)\Bigg|_{z=-1}$$

$$= \frac{1}{2}\frac{d}{dz}\left[\frac{3}{(z+2)^2}\right]\Bigg|_{z=-1} = \frac{1}{2}\frac{-3\times 2(z+2)}{(z+2)^4}\Bigg|_{z=-1} = \frac{-3(-1+2)}{(-1+2)^4} = -3$$

$$\therefore \quad \frac{X(z)}{z} = \frac{-3}{z+1} + \frac{3}{(z+1)^2} - \frac{2}{(z+1)^3} + \frac{3}{z+2}$$

$$\therefore \quad X(z) = -3\frac{z}{z+1} + 3\frac{z}{(z+1)^2} - 2\frac{z}{(z+1)^3} + 3\frac{z}{z+2}$$

Taking inverse Z-transform on both sides, we have

$$x(n) = -3(-1)^n u(n) + 3n(-1)^n u(n) - 2n(n-1)(-1)^n u(n) + 3(-2)^n u(n)$$

$$= [-3 + 3n - 2n(n-1)](-1)^n u(n) + 3(-2)^n u(n)$$

Example 11.13 Find the inverse Z-transform of

$$X(z) = \frac{2z^3 - 5z^2 + z + 4}{(z-1)(z-2)}$$

Solution:

Given
$$X(z) = \frac{2z^3 - 5z^2 + z + 4}{z^2 - 3z + 2}$$

$$\therefore \quad \frac{X(z)}{z} = \frac{2z^3 - 5z^2 + z + 4}{z^3 - 3z^2 + 2z}$$

Since the order of numerator and denominator are same, divide the numerator by the denominator and remove a constant term such that the remaining is a proper function.

$$\frac{X(z)}{z} = 2 + \frac{z^2 - 3z + 4}{z^3 - 3z^2 + 2z} = 2 + \frac{z^2 - 3z + 4}{z(z-1)(z-2)}$$

$$\frac{z^2 - 3z + 4}{z(z-1)(z-2)} = \frac{A}{z} + \frac{B}{z-1} + \frac{C}{z-2} = \frac{2}{z} - \frac{2}{z-1} + \frac{1}{z-2}$$

$$\therefore \quad \frac{X(z)}{z} = 2 + \frac{2}{z} - \frac{2}{z-1} + \frac{1}{z-2}$$

or
$$X(z) = 2z + 2 - 2\frac{z}{z-1} + \frac{z}{z-2}$$

Taking inverse Z-transform on both sides, we have

$$x(n) = 2\delta(n+1) + 2\delta(n) - 2u(n) + 2^n u(n)$$

11.8 THE Z-TRANSFER FUNCTION (PULSE TRANSFER FUNCTION)

Consider a linear time-invariant discrete system represented by the block diagram of Figure 11.4. The system produces an output sequence $y(n)$ for an input sequence $x(n)$. Such a system can be characterized by its response $h(n)$ (also called the weighting sequence) to unit discrete impulse.

$$\delta(n) = 1; \; n = 0$$
$$= 0; \; n \neq 0$$

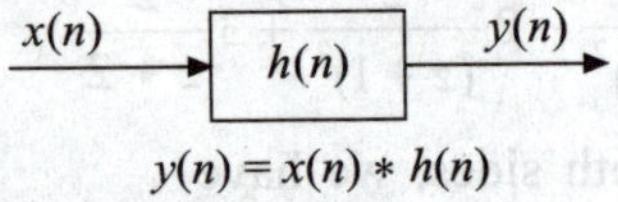

$$y(n) = x(n) * h(n)$$

Figure 11.4 LTI discrete-time system.

The input and output of the system are related as:

$$y(n) = x(n) * h(n)$$

Taking Z-transform of both sides, we get

$$Y(z) = X(z)\, H(z)$$

$$\therefore \qquad H(z) = \frac{Y(z)}{X(z)}$$

$H(z)$ is called the system function or the transfer function of the linear discrete system. If $x(n) = \delta(n)$, i.e., the input is a unit impulse function, then $X(z) = 1$.

$$\therefore \qquad Y(z) = H(z)$$

So the transfer function is also defined as the Z-transform of the impulse response of the system.

11.9 RELATIONSHIP BETWEEN TRANSFER FUNCTION AND DIFFERENCE EQUATION

In terms of a difference equation, an nth order discrete-time LTI system is specified as:

$$\sum_{k=0}^{N} a_k y(n-k) = \sum_{k=0}^{M} b_k x(n-k)$$

Expanding it, we have

$$a_0 y(n) + a_1 y(n-1) + a_2 y(n-2) + \cdots + a_N y(n-N)$$
$$= b_0 x(n) + b_1 x(n-1) + b_2 x(n-2) + \cdots + b_M x(n-M)$$

Taking Z-transform on both sides and neglecting the initial conditions, we obtain

$$a_0 Y(z) + a_1 z^{-1} Y(z) + a_2 z^{-2} Y(z) + \cdots + a_N z^{-N} Y(z)$$
$$= b_0 X(z) + b_1 z^{-1} X(z) + b_2 z^{-2} X(z) + \cdots + b_M z^{-M} X(z)$$

i.e.
$$Y(z) [a_0 + a_1 z^{-1} + a_2 z^{-2} + \cdots + a_N z^{-N}]$$
$$= X(z) [b_0 + b_1 z^{-1} + b_2 z^{-2} + \cdots + b_M z^{-M}]$$

$$\therefore \qquad \frac{Y(z)}{X(z)} = \frac{b_0 + b_1 z^{-1} + b_2 z^{-2} + \cdots + b_M z^{-M}}{a_0 + a_1 z^{-1} + a_2 z^{-2} + \cdots + a_N z^{-N}} = \frac{\displaystyle\sum_{k=0}^{M} b_k z^{-k}}{\displaystyle\sum_{k=0}^{N} a_k z^{-k}}$$

is the transfer function of the system.

Example 11.14   A casual system is represented by

$$H(z) = \frac{z+2}{2z^2 - 3z + 4}$$

Find the difference equation.

Solution: Given $H(z) = \dfrac{z+2}{2z^2 - 3z + 4} = \dfrac{Y(z)}{X(z)}$

Expressing in negative powers of z,

$$\frac{Y(z)}{X(z)} = \frac{z^{-1} + 2z^{-2}}{2 - 3z^{-1} + 4z^{-2}}$$

i.e.
$$2Y(z) - 3z^{-1} Y(z) + 4z^{-2} Y(z) = z^{-1} X(z) + 2z^{-2} X(z)$$

Taking inverse Z-transform on both sides, we have

$$2y(n) - 3y(n-1) + 4y(n-2) = x(n-1) + 2x(n-2)$$

which is the desired difference equation.

Example 11.15   Determine the impulse response of the system described by the difference equation

$$y(n) - 3y(n-1) - 4y(n-2) = x(n) + 2x(n-1)$$

using Z-transform.

Solution: Given difference equation is:

$$y(n) - 3y(n-1) - 4y(n-2) = x(n) + 2x(n-1)$$

Taking Z-transform on both sides and neglecting initial conditions we have

$$Y(z) - 3z^{-1} Y(z) - 4z^{-2} Y(z) = X(z) + 2z^{-1} X(z)$$

i.e.
$$Y(z)[1 - 3z^{-1} - 4z^{-2}] = X(z) [1 + 2z^{-1}]$$

The transfer function of the system is:

$$\frac{Y(z)}{X(z)} = H(z) = \frac{1 + 2z^{-1}}{1 - 3z^{-1} - 4z^{-2}} = \frac{z(z+2)}{z^2 - 3z - 4}$$

Taking partial fractions of $\dfrac{H(z)}{z}$, we have

$$\frac{H(z)}{z} = \frac{z+2}{z^2 - 3z - 4} = \frac{z+2}{(z+1)(z-4)} = \frac{A}{z+1} + \frac{B}{z-4} = \frac{1.2}{z-4} - \frac{0.2}{z+1}$$

$$\therefore \qquad H(z) = 1.2\frac{z}{z-4} - 0.2\frac{z}{z+1}$$

Taking inverse Z-transform on both sides, the impulse response $h(n)$ is given by

$$h(n) = 1.2(4)^n u(n) - 0.2(-1)^n u(n)$$

Example 11.16   Consider a discrete-time LTI system described by

$$y(n) - \frac{3}{4}y(n-1) + \frac{1}{8}y(n-2) = x(n) + \frac{1}{3}x(n-1)$$

Obtain the unit sample response of the system.

Solution: Taking Z-transform on both sides of the given difference equation and neglecting initial conditions we have

$$Y(z) - \frac{3}{4}z^{-1}Y(z) + \frac{1}{8}z^{-2}Y(z) = X(z) + \frac{1}{3}z^{-1}X(z)$$

i.e.

$$Y(z)\left[1 - \frac{3}{4}z^{-1} + \frac{1}{8}z^{-2}\right] = X(z)\left[1 + \frac{1}{3}z^{-1}\right]$$

The system function $H(z)$ is:

$$H(z) = \frac{Y(z)}{X(z)} = \frac{1 + \frac{1}{3}z^{-1}}{1 - \frac{3}{4}z^{-1} + \frac{1}{8}z^{-2}} = \frac{z\left(z + \frac{1}{3}\right)}{z^2 - \frac{3}{4}z + \frac{1}{8}}$$

Taking partial fractions of $\dfrac{H(z)}{z}$, we have

$$\frac{H(z)}{z} = \frac{z + \frac{1}{3}}{z^2 - \frac{3}{4}z + \frac{1}{8}} = \frac{z + \frac{1}{3}}{\left(z - \frac{1}{2}\right)\left(z - \frac{1}{4}\right)} = \frac{A}{z - \frac{1}{2}} + \frac{B}{z - \frac{1}{4}}$$

$$= \frac{\frac{10}{3}}{z - \frac{1}{2}} - \frac{\frac{7}{3}}{z - \frac{1}{4}}$$

$$\therefore \qquad H(z) = \frac{10}{3} \frac{z}{z - \frac{1}{2}} - \frac{7}{3} \frac{z}{z - \frac{1}{4}}$$

Taking inverse Z-transform on both sides, the unit sample response of the system is:

$$h(n) = \frac{10}{3} \left(\frac{1}{2}\right)^n u(n) - \frac{7}{3} \left(\frac{1}{4}\right)^n u(n)$$

Example 11.17 Solve the difference equation

$$y(n + 2) - 3y(n + 1) + 2y(n) = x(n); \ y(0) = 0, \ y(1) = 1, \ x(n) = 3^n$$

Solution: Taking Z-transform on both sides of the given difference equation, we have

$$[z^2 Y(z) - z^2 y(0) - zy(1)] - 3[zY(z) - zy(0)] + 2Y(z) = X(z) = \frac{z}{z - 3}$$

i.e. $$[z^2 - 3z + 2]Y(z) = z^2 y(0) + zy(1) - 3zy(0) + \frac{z}{z - 3}$$

or $$Y(z) = \frac{z^2 y(0) + z[y(1) - 3y(0)]}{z^2 - 3z + 2} + \frac{z}{(z - 3)(z^2 - 3z + 2)}$$

Substituting the initial conditions, we have

$$Y(z) = \frac{z}{(z - 1)(z - 2)} + \frac{z}{(z - 1)(z - 2)(z - 3)}$$

$$= \left[-\frac{z}{z - 1} + \frac{z}{z - 2} \right] + \left[\frac{1}{2} \frac{z}{z - 1} - \frac{z}{z - 2} + \frac{1}{2} \frac{z}{z - 3} \right]$$

Taking inverse z-transform, we have

$$y(n) = \underbrace{[-1 + 2^n] u(n)}_{\text{Free response}} + \underbrace{\left[\frac{1}{2} - 2^n + \frac{1}{2} 3^n \right] u(n)}_{\text{Forced response}}$$

$$\underbrace{\hphantom{\text{Total response}}}_{\text{Total response}}$$

$$= \underbrace{\frac{1}{2}[-1 + 3^n] u(n)}_{\text{Total response}}$$

Example 11.18 Solve the following difference equation using unilateral Z-transform.

$$y(n) - \frac{7}{12} y(n - 1) + \frac{1}{12} y(n - 2) = x(n)$$

with initial conditions

$$y(-1) = 2, \ y(-2) = 4 \text{ and } x(n) = \left(\frac{1}{5}\right)^n u(n)$$

Solution: The solution of the difference equation gives the total response of the system [i.e., the sum of the natural (free) response and the forced response].

Taking Z-transform on both sides of the given difference equation, we have

$$Y(z) - \frac{7}{12}[z^{-1}Y(z) + y(-1)] + \frac{1}{12}[z^{-2}Y(z) + z^{-1}y(-1) + y(-2)] = \frac{1}{1 - \left(\frac{1}{5}\right)z^{-1}}$$

i.e.

$$Y(z)\left(1 - \frac{7}{12}z^{-1} + \frac{1}{12}z^{-2}\right) = \frac{7}{12}(2) - \frac{1}{12}(2z^{-1}) - \frac{1}{12}(4) + \frac{1}{1 - \left(\frac{1}{5}\right)z^{-1}}$$

i.e.

$$Y(z)\left(1 - \frac{7}{12}z^{-1} + \frac{1}{12}z^{-2}\right) = \frac{5}{6}\left(1 - \frac{1}{5}z^{-1}\right) + \frac{1}{1 - \left(\frac{1}{5}\right)z^{-1}}$$

∴

$$Y(z) = \frac{\frac{5}{6}\left(1 - \frac{1}{5}z^{-1}\right)}{\left(1 - \frac{7}{12}z^{-1} + \frac{1}{12}z^{-2}\right)} + \frac{1}{\left[1 - \frac{1}{5}z^{-1}\right]\left[1 - \frac{7}{12}z^{-1} + \frac{1}{12}z^{-2}\right]}$$

$$= \underbrace{\frac{\frac{5}{6}\left(z - \frac{1}{5}\right)z}{\left[z - \frac{1}{3}\right]\left[z - \frac{1}{4}\right]}}_{\text{Free response}} + \underbrace{\frac{z^3}{\left(z - \frac{1}{5}\right)\left(z - \frac{1}{4}\right)\left(z - \frac{1}{3}\right)}}_{\text{Forced response}}$$

$$= \frac{z\left[\frac{11}{6}z^2 - \frac{1}{3}z + \frac{1}{30}\right]}{\left(z - \frac{1}{5}\right)\left(z - \frac{1}{4}\right)\left(z - \frac{1}{3}\right)}$$

Taking partial fractions of $\dfrac{Y(z)}{z}$, we have

$$\frac{Y(z)}{z} = \frac{A}{z - \frac{1}{5}} + \frac{B}{z - \frac{1}{4}} + \frac{C}{z - \frac{1}{3}} = \frac{6}{5}\frac{1}{z - \frac{1}{5}} + \frac{1}{8}\frac{1}{z - \frac{1}{4}} + \frac{100}{27}\frac{1}{z - \frac{1}{3}}$$

Multiplying both sides by z, we have

$$Y(z) = \frac{6}{5}\frac{z}{z - \frac{1}{5}} + \frac{1}{8}\frac{z}{z - \frac{1}{4}} + \frac{100}{27}\frac{z}{z - \frac{1}{3}}$$

Taking inverse Z-transform on both sides, the solution of the difference equation is:

$$y(n) = \frac{6}{5}\left(\frac{1}{5}\right)^n u(n) + \frac{1}{8}\left(\frac{1}{4}\right)^n u(n) + \frac{100}{27}\left(\frac{1}{3}\right)^n u(n)$$

11.10 THE Z-TRANSFORM ANALYSIS OF SAMPLED-DATA CONTROL SYSTEMS

Sampled-data control systems are in fact hybrid systems as they have both discrete-time and continuous-time signals. Special techniques are, therefore, required for analysis of these systems.

11.10.1 Analysis of Sampler and Zero-Order Hold (ZOH)

Figure 11.5(a) shows a sampler with ZOH. As ZOH holds the input signal value for a period T, it means that for a short duration (Δ) input pulse, it produces an output pulse of duration T, the sampling period. This is illustrated in Figure 11.5(b).

The ZOH output pulse appearing at kT instant can be expressed as:

$$i(nT)\,[u(t - nT) - u(t - (n + 1)T)]$$

We can, therefore, write the ZOH output as:

$$o(t) = \sum_{n=0}^{\infty} i(nT)\,[u(t - nT) - u(t - (n+1)T)]$$

Taking the Laplace transform, we have

$$O(s) = \sum_{n=0}^{\infty} i(nT)\left[\frac{e^{-snT} - e^{-s(n+1)T}}{s}\right]$$

$$= \left(\frac{1 - e^{-sT}}{s}\right)\sum_{n=0}^{\infty} i(nT)\,e^{-snT}$$

Taking the inverse Laplace transform of the infinite sum, we get

$$L^{-1}\left[\sum_{n=0}^{\infty} i(nT)\,e^{-snT}\right] = \sum_{n=0}^{\infty} i(nT)\,\delta(t - nT) = i(t)\,\delta_T(t)$$

Thus the output $o(t)$ of pulse sampler and ZOH can be produced by impulse sampled $i(t)$ when passed through a transfer function

$$G_0(s) = \frac{1 - e^{-sT}}{s}$$

This is illustrated in Figure 11.5(c). Figure 11.5 [(a) and (c)] represents equivalent operations, but the operation of Figure 11.5(c) offers ease of analysis.

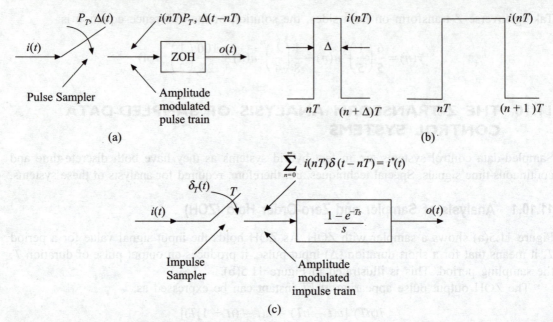

Figure 11.5 (a) Pulse sampler with ZOH (b) ZOH input and output pulses (c) Equivalent representation of pulse sampler and ZOH.

11.10.2 Analysis of Systems with Impulse Sampling

In sampled-data systems, our interest generally is to obtain the values of the output at the sampling instants. Pulse sampling and ZOH can be replaced by impulse sampling and $G_0(s)$.

Consider the linear continuous system shown in Figure 11.6. Here the continuous system has sampled input. The output signal $c(t)$ is read off at discrete sampling instants (kT) by means of a mathematical sampler $T(M)$.

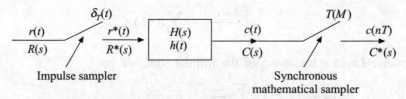

Figure 11.6 Linear continuous system with impulse sampled input.

The continuous output of the system

$$C(s) = R^*(S)\, H(s)$$

$$\therefore \qquad C^*(s) = [R^*(s)\, H(s)]^* = R^*(s)\, H^*(s)$$

Taking Z-transform on both sides, we have

$$C(z) = R(z)\, H(z)$$

where

$$H(z) = Z[h(nT)] = Z[L^{-1}[H(s)]]|_{t=nT}$$

To find $H(z)$, given $H(s)$

Find $h(t) = L^{-1}[H(s)]$

Find $h(nT) = h(t)|_{t=nT}$

Find $Z[h(nT)]$

Example 11.19 Find Z-transform of

$$H(s) = \frac{1}{s(s+1)(s+2)}$$

Solution: Given

$$H(s) = \frac{1}{s(s+1)(s+2)} = \frac{A}{s} + \frac{B}{s+1} + \frac{C}{s+2}$$

$$= \frac{1}{2}\frac{1}{s} - \frac{1}{s+1} + \frac{1}{2}\frac{1}{s+2}$$

Taking inverse Laplace transform, we have

$$h(t) = \left[\frac{1}{2} - e^{-t} + \frac{1}{2}e^{-2t}\right]u(t)$$

Putting $t = nT$, we have

$$h(nT) = \frac{1}{2}u(nT) - e^{-nT}u(nT) + \frac{1}{2}e^{-2nT}u(nT)$$

Taking Z-transform, we have

$$H(z) = \frac{1}{2}\frac{z}{z-1} - \frac{z}{z-e^{-T}} + \frac{1}{2}\frac{z}{z-e^{-2T}}$$

Now, consider Figure 11.7(a), a continuous system $h(t)$ with continuous input $r(t)$. If we want the output at the sampling instants, we can assume a mathematical sampler at the output. We can represent now $H(s)\,R(s)$ as a single block with impulse input as shown in Figure 11.7(b). Equivalently, we can represent, as shown in Figure 11.7(c), by imagining a fictitious sampler at the input through which $\delta(t)$ is applied to $H(s)\,R(s)$.

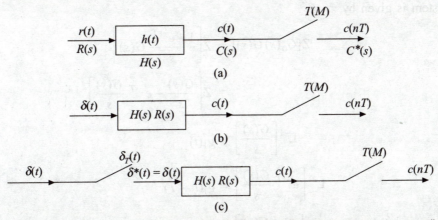

Figure 11.7 (a) Continuous system with continuous input (b) its equivalent (c) impulse input applied through fictitious sampler.

Now,
$$C(s) = \delta^*(t)\, H(s)\, R(s)$$

Taking sampled version, we get
$$C^*(s) = [\delta(nT)\, H(s)\, R(s)]^* = \delta(nT)\, HR^*(s)$$

Taking Z-transform, we get
$$C(z) = HR(z)\, Z[\delta(nT)] = HR(z)$$

Consider the case shown in Figure 11.8(a) where the impulse sampled input is applied to two s-domain transfer functions in tandem. Its z-domain transfer function is shown in Figure 11.8(b) where

$$H(z) = H_1 H_2(z)$$

However, if the blocks are separated by an impulse sampler as shown in Figure 11.8(c), it obviously follows that

$$H(z) = H_1(z)\, H_2(z)$$

as shown in Figure 11.8(d).

$$H_1(z)H_2(z) \neq H_1 H_2(z)$$

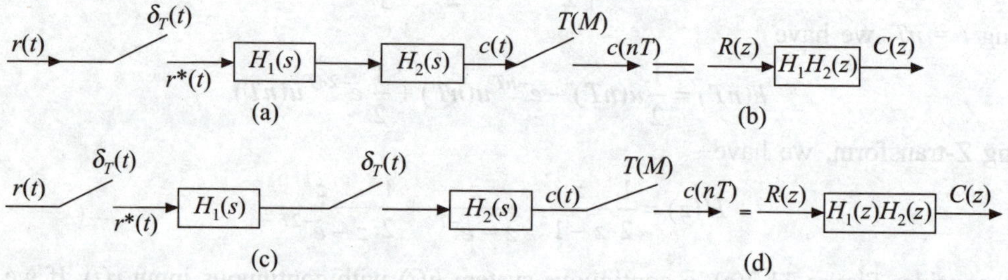

Figure 11.8   (a) Blocks in cascade (b) Its equivalent (c) Blocks separated by an impulse sampler (d) Its equivalent.

Now, consider a linear continuous part $G(s)$ of a system which is fed from a sampler and ZOH as shown in Figure 11.9(a). Its equivalent impulse sampled system is shown in Figure 11.9(b). The corresponding z-domain block diagram is shown in Figure 11.9(c). The z-transfer function of the system is given by

$$Z[G_0(s)\, G(s)] = Z\left[\frac{1 - e^{-sT}}{s}\, G(s)\right]$$

$$= Z\left[\frac{G(s)}{s} - e^{-sT}\,\frac{G(s)}{s}\right]$$

Let
$$L^{-1}\left[\frac{G(s)}{s}\right] = g_1(t)$$

$\therefore$
$$L^{-1}\left[e^{-sT}\,\frac{G(s)}{s}\right] = g_1(t - T)$$

Hence,
$$Z\left[e^{-sT}\,\frac{G(s)}{s}\right] = Z[g_1(t - T)]$$

$$Z[g_1(nT - T)] = z^{-1}Z[g_1(nT)]$$

$$= z^{-1}Z\left[\frac{G(s)}{s}\right]$$

Therefore,

$$Z[G_0(s)\,G(s)] = [1 - z^{-1}]\,Z\left[\frac{G(s)}{s}\right]$$

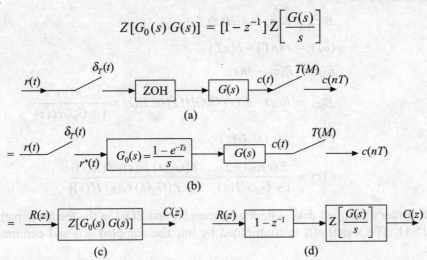

(a)

(b)

(c)

(d)

Figure 11.9 (a) $G(s)$ fed from a sampler and ZOH (b) Its equivalent impulse sampled system (c) and (d) Corresponding z-domain transfer function.

Consider now the basic sampled-data feedback control system whose block diagram is shown in Figure 11.10.

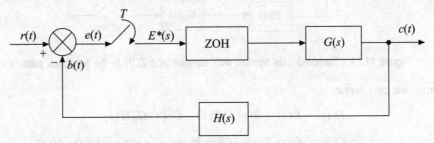

Figure 11.10 Basic sampled data feedback control system.

The transfer function of the above system is obtained as follows:

$$C(s) = E^*(s)\,G_0(s)\,G(s)$$

∴

$$C^*(s) = [E^*(s)\,G_0G(s)]^* = E^*(s)\,G_0G^*(s)$$

∴

$$C(z) = E(z)\,Z[G_0G(s)] = E(z)\,(1 - z^{-1})\,Z\left[\frac{G(s)}{s}\right]$$

$$= E(z)\, G_0 G(z)$$

$$B(s) = C(s)\, H(s) = E^*(s)\, G_0(s)\, G(s)\, H(s)$$

$$\therefore \qquad B^*(s) = [E^*(s)\, G_0 GH(s)]^* = E^*(s)\, G_0 GH^*(s)$$

Taking Z-transform, we get

$$B(z) = E(z)\, G_0 GH(z)$$

$$e(nT) = r(nT) - b(nT)$$

$$\therefore \qquad E(z) = R(z) - B(z)$$

i.e. $\qquad E(z) = R(z) - E(z)\, G_0 GH(z)$ or $E(z) = \dfrac{R(z)}{1 + G_0 GH(z)}$

But $\qquad C(z) = E(z)\, G_0 G(z)$

$$\therefore \qquad C(z) = \frac{R(z) G_0 G(z)}{1 + G_0 GH(z)} = \frac{Z[G_0(s)\, G(s)]\, Z(R(s))}{1 + Z[G_0(s)\, G(s)\, H(s)]}$$

Now, consider a sampled-data system with sampler and ZOH in the feedback path as shown in Figure 11.11. The signal $e(t)$ is contributed by impulse sampled $c(t)$ and continuous output signal $r(t)$.

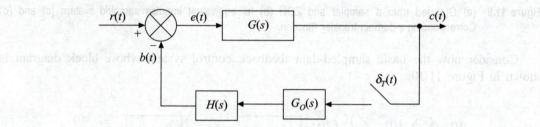

Figure 11.11   Sampled-data system with sampler and ZOH in the feedback path.

In s-domain, we can write

$$E(s) = R(s) - B(s) = R(s) - C^*(s)\, G_0 H(s)$$

$$C(s) = G(s)\, E(s) = G(s)\, R(s) - C^*(s)\, G_0(s)\, G(s)\, H(s)$$

$$\therefore \qquad C^*(s) = [G(s)\, R(s)]^* - C^* G_0 GH^*(s)$$

$$C^*(s) = \frac{GR^*(s)}{1 + G_0 GH^*(s)}$$

i.e. $\qquad C(z) = \dfrac{GR(z)}{1 + G_0 GH(z)}$

Here the input is combined with $G(s)$, so we cannot get a transfer function. We get a term $GR(z)$.

11.10.3 The *z*-transfer Function of a Digital Computer

Consider the system shown in Figure 11.12(a) in which a digital computer or a digital network is included after the sampler. It modifies the strength of the pulses from the sampler. The action of the digital computer in the z-domain is, therefore, that of a transfer function

$$D(z) = \frac{V(z)}{R(z)}$$

Thus the system can be represented by the block diagram of Figure 11.12(b).

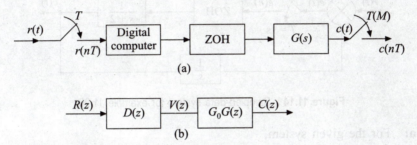

(a)

(b)

Figure 11.12 (a) A system with digital computer included after the sampler (b) Its equivalent.

Now, consider another system in which digital controller is a part of the system as shown in Figure 11.13.

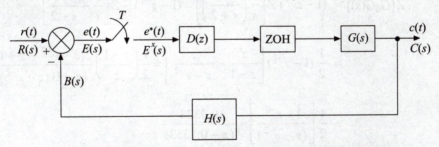

Figure 11.13 System with digital computer as a part of it.

The transfer function of the above system is obtained as follows:

$$C(s) = E^*(s)\, D(z)\, G_0 G(s)$$

or

$$C(z) = E(z)\, D(z)\, G_0 G(z)$$

$$B(s) = E^*(s)\, D(z)\, G_0 GH(s)$$

$$B(z) = E(z)\, D(z)\, G_0 GH(z)$$

$$E(z) = R(z) - B(z) = R(z) - E(z)\, D(z)\, G_0 GH(z)$$

or
$$E(z) = \frac{R(z)}{1 + D(z)\,G_0GH(z)}$$

$\therefore$
$$C(z) = \frac{R(z)\,D(z)\,G_0G(z)}{1 + D(z)\,G_0GH(z)}$$

$\therefore$
$$\frac{C(z)}{R(z)} = \frac{D(z)\,G_0G(z)}{1 + D(z)\,G_0GH(z)}$$

Example 11.20 For the sampled-data control system shown in Figure 11.14, find the output $c(n)$ for $r(t)$ unit step.

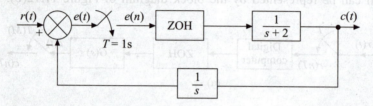

Figure 11.14 Sampled-data system for example 11.20.

Solution: For the given system,

$$\frac{C(z)}{R(z)} = \frac{Z[G_0G(s)]}{1 + Z[G_0GH(s)]}$$

$$Z[G_0G(s)] = (1 - z^{-1})\,Z\left[\frac{1}{s}\left(\frac{1}{s+2}\right)\right] = (1 - z^{-1})\frac{1}{2}Z\left[\frac{1}{s} - \frac{1}{s+2}\right]$$

$$= \frac{1}{2}(1 - z^{-1})\left[\frac{z}{z-1} - \frac{z}{z-e^{-2}}\right] = \frac{1}{2}\left(\frac{z-1}{z}\right)\frac{z(z - e^{-2} - z + 1)}{(z-1)\,(z - e^{-2})}$$

$$= \frac{1}{2}\left[\frac{1 - e^{-2}}{(z - e^{-2})}\right] = \frac{0.4323}{(z - 0.1353)}$$

Now,
$$Z(G_0GH(s)) = Z\left[\text{ZOH}\left(\frac{1}{s(s+2)}\right)\right]$$

$$= (1 - z^{-1})\,Z\left[\frac{1}{s^2(s+2)}\right]$$

$$= (1 - z^{-1})\,Z\left[\frac{1/2}{s^2} - \frac{1/4}{s} + \frac{1/4}{s+2}\right]$$

$$= (1 - z^{-1}) Z\left(\frac{1}{2} t\, u(t) - \frac{1}{4} u(t) + \frac{1}{4} e^{-2t} u(t)\right)$$

$$= (1 - z^{-1})\left[\frac{1}{2} \frac{z}{(z-1)^2} - \frac{1}{4} \frac{z}{z-1} + \frac{1}{4} \frac{z}{z - e^{-2T}}\right]$$

$$= \frac{0.2838z + 0.1485}{(z-1)(z-0.1353)}$$

$$\therefore \quad \frac{C(z)}{R(z)} = \frac{\dfrac{0.4323}{(z - 0.1353)}}{1 + \dfrac{0.283z + 0.1485}{(z-1)(z-0.1353)}}$$

$$= \frac{0.4323\,(z - 1)}{z^2 - 0.8523z + 0.2838}$$

$$= \frac{0.4323\,(z - 1)}{(z - 0.4262 - j0.2659)(z - 0.4262 + j0.2659)}$$

For a unit step intput

$$\therefore \quad C(z) = \frac{0.4323z}{(z - 0.4262 - j0.2659)(z - 0.4262 + j0.2659)}$$

$$= \left(\frac{-j0.8129z}{z - 0.4262 - j0.2659} + \frac{j0.8192z}{z - 0.4262 + j0.2659}\right)$$

Taking the inverse Z-transform, we get

$$C(n) = -j0.8129(0.4262 + j0.2659)^n + j0.8192(0.4262 - j0.2659)^n$$

11.11   THE z- AND s-DOMAIN RELATIONSHIP

Consider a signal $r(t)$ which has discrete values $r(nT)$ at a sampling rate $\dfrac{1}{T}$. The Z-transform of these discrete values is:

$$R(z) = \sum_{n=0}^{\infty} r(nT)\, z^{-n}$$

If the signal $r(t)$ is imagined to be impulse sampled at the same rate, it becomes

$$r^*(t) = \sum_{n=0}^{\infty} r(nT)\, \delta(t - nT)$$

Taking the Laplace transform, we have

$$R^*(s) = \sum_{n=0}^{\infty} r(nT)e^{-nTs}$$

If we let $z = e^{Ts}$ or $s = \dfrac{1}{T}\ln z$, we get

$$R^*(s)\Big|_{s=\frac{1}{T}\ln z} = \sum_{n=0}^{\infty} r(nT)z^{-n} = R(z)$$

This shows that the Z-transform for a set of discrete values can be obtained by imagining these to be impulses, Laplace transforming and then using the information $z = e^{Ts}$ or $s = \dfrac{1}{T}\ln z$.

The transformation $z = e^{sT}$ maps the s-plane into z-plane. Consider the mapping of the $j\omega$ axis in the s-plane, i.e.,

$$z = e^{j\omega T} = e^{j2\pi\omega/\omega_s} = 1 \angle \pi(\omega/\omega_s)$$

where $\omega_s = \dfrac{2\pi}{T}$, the sampling frequency.

Thus the section $(-j\omega_s/2) - 0 - (+j\omega_s/2)$ of the $j\omega$-axis maps into the unit circle in the anticlockwise direction as shown in Figure 11.15.

In fact, every section of the $j\omega$-axis, which is an integral multiple of ω_s, maps into the unit circle. With the direction of mapping indicated it is then obvious that the left half s-plane can be divided into strips of width ω_s each of which maps into the interior of the unit circle. It suggests that the s-plane stability criterion of the poles of s-plane will become the z-plane stability criterion that all the poles of the z-transfer function would lie within the unit circle.

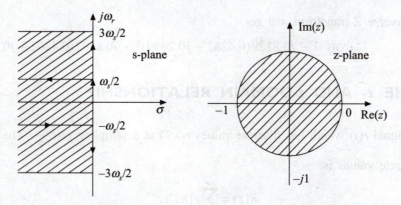

Figure 11.15 Relationship between the s- and z-domains.

11.12 STABILITY

We know that the necessary and sufficient condition for a causal linear time invariant discrete-time system to be BIBO stable is:

$$\sum_{n=0}^{\infty} |h(n)| < \infty$$

i.e., an LTI discrete-time system is BIBO stable if the impulse response is absolutely summable.

For a causal LTI system to be stable, all the poles of $H(z)$ must lie inside the unit circle centred at the origin of the z-plane.

Example 11.21 Determine the stability of the system described by

(a) $y(n) = y(n-1) - 0.8y(n-2) + x(n) + x(n-2)$

(b) $y(n) = 2y(n-1) - 0.8y(n-2) + x(n) + 0.8x(n-1)$

Solution:

(a) Given $y(n) = y(n-1) - 0.8y(n-2) + x(n) + x(n-2)$

Taking Z-transform on both sides and neglecting the initial conditions, we have

$$Y(z) = z^{-1} Y(z) - 0.8z^{-2} Y(z) + X(z) + z^{-2} X(z)$$

i.e. $Y(z)[1 - z^{-1} + 0.8z^{-2}] = X(z)[1 + z^{-2}]$

The transfer function of the system is:

$$H(z) = \frac{Y(z)}{X(z)} = \frac{1 + z^{-2}}{1 - z^{-1} + 0.8z^{-2}} = \frac{z^2 + 1}{z^2 - z + 0.8} = \frac{(z+j)(z-j)}{(z - 0.5 - j0.74)(z - 0.5 + j0.74)}$$

The poles of $H(z)$ are $z = 0.5 - j0.74$ and $z = 0.5 + j0.74$. All the poles are inside the unit circle. Hence the system is stable.

(b) Taking Z-transform on both sides of the given difference equation, and neglecting the initial conditions, we have

$$Y(z) = 2z^{-1} Y(z) - 0.8z^{-2} Y(z) + X(z) + 0.8z^{-1} X(z)$$

i.e. $Y(z)[1 - 2z^{-1} + 0.8z^{-2}] = X(z)[1 + 0.8z^{-1}]$

The transfer function of the system is:

$$H(z) = \frac{Y(z)}{X(z)} = \frac{1 + 0.8z^{-1}}{1 - 2z^{-1} + 0.8z^{-2}} = \frac{z(z + 0.8)}{z^2 - 2z + 0.8}$$

$$= \frac{z(z + 0.8)}{(z - 1.445)(z - 0.555)}$$

The poles of $H(z)$ are $z = 1.445$. and $z = 0.555$. One pole is outside the unit circle. Therefore, the system is unstable.

11.12.1 Methods of Stability Analysis

Jury's stability test: It is an algebraic criterion for determining whether or not the roots of the characteristic polynomial lie within the unit circle thereby determining system stability. Consider the characteristic polynomial

$$F_1(z) = a_n z^n + a_{n-1} z^{n-1} + \cdots + a_0 = 0; \ a_n > 0$$

Like the Routh's method, the Jury's test consists of two parts; a simple test for necessary conditions and a second test for sufficiency. The necessary conditions for stability are:

$$F_1(1) > 0; \ (-1)^n F_1(-1) > 0$$

The sufficient conditions for stability can be established through the following method:

Method: Prepare a table of coefficients of the characteristic polynomial as shown below:

Row	z^0	z^1	z^2	z^3	$\ldots$	z^{n-k}	$\ldots$	z^{n-2}	z^{n-1}	z^n
1	a_0	a_1	a_2	a_3	$\cdots$	a_{n-k}	$\cdots$	a_{n-2}	a_{n-1}	a_n
2	a_n	a_{n-1}	a_{n-2}	a_{n-3}	$\cdots$	a_k	$\cdots$	a_2	a_1	a_0
3	b_0	b_1	b_2	b_3	$\cdots$	b_{n-k}	$\cdots$	b_{n-2}	b_{n-1}	
4	b_{n-1}	b_{n-2}	b_{n-3}	b_{n-4}	$\cdots$	b_{k-1}	$\cdots$	b_1	b_0	
5	c_0	c_1	c_2	c_3	$\cdots$	c_{n-k}	$\cdots$	c_{n-2}		
6	c_{n-2}	c_{n-3}	c_{n-4}	c_{n-5}	$\cdots$	c_{k-2}	$\cdots$	c_0		
$\vdots$	$\vdots$	$\vdots$	$\vdots$	$\vdots$		$\vdots$				
$2n-5$	s_0	s_1	s_2	s_3						
$2n-4$	s_3	s_2	s_1	s_0						
$2n-3$	r_0	r_1	r_2							

where

$$b_k = \begin{vmatrix} a_0 & a_{n-k} \\ a_n & a_k \end{vmatrix}$$

$$c_k = \begin{vmatrix} b_0 & b_{n-1-k} \\ b_{n-1} & b_k \end{vmatrix}$$

$$d_k = \begin{vmatrix} c_0 & c_{n-2-k} \\ c_{n-2} & c_k \end{vmatrix}$$

The sufficient conditions for stability are:

$$\left.\begin{aligned} |a_0| &< |a_n| \\ |b_0| &> |b_{n-1}| \\ |c_0| &> |c_{n-2}| \\ |r_0| &> |r_2| \end{aligned}\right\} (n-1) \text{ constraints.}$$

Example 11.22 What are the constraints for stability of the system given by

$$F_1(z) = b_2 z^2 + b_1 z + b_0 = 0; \ b_2 > 0$$

Solution: The stability constraints are:

$$F_1(1) = b_2 + b_1 + b_0 > 0$$
$$(-1)^n F_1(-1) = b_2 - b_1 + b_0 > 0$$
$$|b_0| < b_2$$

Example 11.23 Test for stability

$$F_1(z) = 2z^4 + 5z^3 + 10z^2 + 2z + 1$$

Solution: Given

$$F_1(z) = 2z^4 + 5z^3 + 10z^2 + 2z + 1$$

$$F_1(1) = 2 + 5 + 10 + 2 + 1 = 20 > 0; \text{ (Satisfied)}$$

$$(-1)^4 F_1(-1) = 2 - 5 + 10 - 2 + 1 = 6 > 0; \text{ (Satisfied)}$$

Row	z^0	z^1	z^2	z^3	z^4
1	1	2	10	5	2
2	2	5	10	2	1
3	-3	-8	-10	1	
4	1	-10	-8	-3	
5	8	34	38		

Employing stability constraints

$$|a_0| < |a_n|; |1| < 2 \qquad \text{(Satisfied)}$$
$$|b_0| > |b_{n-1}|; |-3| > |1| \qquad \text{(Satisfied)}$$
$$|c_0| > |c_{n-2}|; |8| > |38| \qquad \text{(Not satisfied)}$$

The system, is therefore, unstable.

Example 11.24 Find the stability using Jury's method.

$$F_1(z) = 2z^4 + 10z^3 + 4z^2 + 6z + 1 = 0$$

Solution: For the given $F(z)$

$$F_1(1) = 2 + 10 + 4 + 6 + 1 = 23 > 0; \qquad \text{(Satisfied)}$$
$$(-1)^4 F_1(-1) = 2 - 10 + 4 - 6 + 1 = -9 > 0; \qquad \text{(Not satisfied)}$$

The system is, therefore, unstable.

Bilinear Transformation

We have seen earlier that in determining the stability of a discrete-time system, we need to find if all the roots of the characteristic equation lie within the unit circle in z-plane. So standard methods of testing stability of continuous-time systems like Routh and Nyquist cannot be applied. Routh and Nyquist methods could be applied to this problem if we could find a complex transformation which maps the interior of the unit circle into the left half of the new plane. The transformation $z = e^{TS} \left[s = \frac{1}{T} \ln z \right]$ cannot be used for this purpose because of the periodicity of e^{sT} and the multiple strips of the left half s-plane into which the interior of the unit circle maps. A simple transformation which uniquely maps the interior of the unit circle in the z-plane into the left half of the r-plane is the bilinear transformation.

$$r = \frac{z-1}{z+1}; z = \frac{1+r}{1-r}$$

On the unit circle in the z-plane $z = e^{j\theta}$ (θ varying anticlockwise from $-\pi$ through 0 to $+\pi$).

$$r = \frac{e^{j\theta} - 1}{e^{j\theta} + 1} = \frac{e^{j\theta/2} - e^{-j\theta/2}}{e^{j\theta/2} + e^{-j\theta/2}}$$

$$= \tan h \, j\frac{\theta}{2} = j \tan\frac{\theta}{2} = j\omega_r$$

where $\omega_r = \tan\frac{\theta}{2}$ varies from $-\infty$ through 0 to $+\infty$.

This mapping is indicated in Figure 11.16.

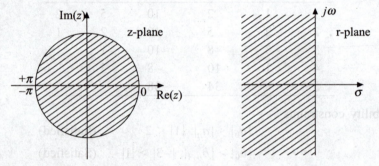

Figure 11.16   Transformation from z-plane to r-plane.

Routh's Stability Criterion

Through the use of the bilinear transformation, the characteristic equation

$$a_n z^n + a_{n-1} z^{n-1} + \cdots + a_1 z + a_0 = 0$$

is transformed into

$$a_n \left(\frac{1+r}{1-r}\right)^n + a_{n-1} \left(\frac{1+r}{1-r}\right)^{n-1} + \cdots + a_1 \left(\frac{1+r}{1-r}\right) + a_0 = 0$$

This can be organized into the form

$$b_n r^n + b_{n-1} r^{n-1} + \cdots + b_1 r + b_0 = 0$$

Now, the Routh criterion can be applied to the new characteristic equation to determine if all its roots lie in the left half of the r-plane. All the roots lie in the left half of the r-plane, implies that all the poles of $F(z)$ lie inside the unit circle in z-plane and so the system is stable. Nyquist criterion can also be applied.

Example 11.25   Determine the stability of the system

$$F(z) = z^3 + 3z^2 + 2z + 1 = 0$$

using Routh's criterion

Solution: For the given $F(z)$,

$$F(r) = \left(\frac{1+r}{1-r}\right)^3 + 3\left(\frac{1+r}{1-r}\right)^2 + 2\left(\frac{1+r}{1-r}\right) + 1 = 0$$

i.e. $$F(r) = r^3 - r^2 - r - 7 = 0$$

Since some of the coefficients of the characteristic equation in r-plane are negative, the given discrete system will not have all its poles inside the unit circle in the z-plane, and hence the system is unstable. The number of poles in the right half of r-plane, i.e., the number of poles outside the unit circle in z-plane can be determined using Routh's criterion as shown below.

$$
\begin{array}{ccc}
r^3 & 1 & -1 \\
r^2 & -1 & -7 \\
r^1 & -8 & \\
r^0 & -7 & \\
\end{array}
$$

Since there is one sign change in the elements of the first column of the Routh array, there is one pole in the right half of r-plane, i.e., there is one pole outside the unit circle in z-plane, and hence the system is unstable.

Example 11.26 Determine the stability of the system

$$F(z) = 2z^4 + 5z^3 + 10z^2 + 2z + 1 = 0$$

using Routh's criterion.

Solution: For the given $F(z)$,

$$F(r) = 2\left(\frac{1+r}{1-r}\right)^4 + 5\left(\frac{1+r}{1-r}\right)^3 + 10\left(\frac{1+r}{1-r}\right)^2 + 2\left(\frac{1+r}{1-r}\right) + 1 = 0$$

i.e. $$F(r) = 3r^4 - r^3 - r^2 + 5r + 10 = 0$$

is the characteristic equation in r-plane. Since some of its coefficients are negative, the system is unstable. The number of poles lying outside the unit circle in z-plane can be determined using Routh's criterion as shown below.

$$
\begin{array}{cccc}
r^4 & 3 & -1 & 10 \\
r^3 & -1 & 5 & \\
r^2 & 14 & 10 & \\
r^1 & \dfrac{40}{7} & & \\
r^0 & 10 & & \\
\end{array}
$$

There are two sign changes in the elements of the first column of the Routh array. So there are two roots of $F(r)$ in the right half of the r-plane, i.e., two poles of $F(z)$ are outside the unit circle in the z-plane, and hence the given discrete system is unstable.

Example 11.27 Determine the stability of the system

$$F(z) = 2z^3 + z^2 + 2z + 1 = 0$$

Solution: For the given $F(z)$

$$F(r) = 2\left(\frac{1+r}{1-r}\right)^3 + \left(\frac{1+r}{1-r}\right)^2 + 2\left(\frac{1+r}{1-r}\right) + 1 = 0$$

i.e.
$$F(r) = r^3 + 7r^2 + 3r + 5 = 0$$

Since all the coefficients of $F(r)$ are positive, the necessary condition for stability is satisfied. The Routh's table is formulated as shown below.

r^3	1	3
r^2	7	5
r^1	$\dfrac{16}{7}$	
r^0	5	

Since all the elements in the first column of the Routh array are positive, all the poles of $F(r)$ are in the left half of r-plane, i.e., all the poles of $F(z)$ are inside the unit circle in z-plane, and so the given discrete system is stable.

Example 11.28 For the sampled-data system, shown in Figure 11.17, determine the characteristic equation in the z-domain and ascertain its stability via the bilinear transformation.

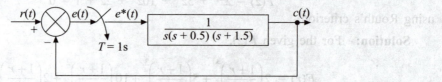

Figure 11.17 Sampled-data system for Example 11.28.

Solution: Given $GH(s) = \dfrac{1}{s(s+0.5)(s+1.5)}$

$$\therefore \quad GH(z) = Z\left[\frac{1}{s(s+0.5)(s+1.5)}\right] = Z\left[\frac{1.333}{s} - \frac{2}{s+0.5} + \frac{0.666}{s+1.5}\right]$$

$$= Z[1.33u(t) - 2e^{-0.5t}u(t) + 0.666e^{-1.5t}u(t)]$$

$$= 1.33\frac{z}{z-1} - 2\frac{z}{z-e^{-0.5}} + 0.666\frac{z}{z-e^{-1.5}}$$

$$= 1.33\frac{z}{z-1} - 2\frac{z}{z-0.606} + 0.666\frac{z}{z-0.223}$$

$$= \frac{z(0.402z + 0.113)}{(z-1)(z-0.606)(z-0.223)}$$

The characteristic equation is:

$$1 + GH(z) = 0$$

i.e.

$$1 + \frac{z(0.402z + 0.113)}{(z-1)(z-0.606)(z-0.223)} = 0$$

i.e.

$$z^3 - 1.427z^2 + 1.077z - 0.1352 = 0 = F(z)$$

Using bilinear transformation $\left[z = \dfrac{1+r}{1-r} \right]$ transform $1 + GH(z)$ into r-plane.

$$\therefore \quad F(r) = \left(\frac{1+r}{1-r}\right)^3 - 1.427\left(\frac{1+r}{1-r}\right)^2 + 1.077\frac{1+r}{1-r} - 0.1352 = 0$$

i.e., the characteristic equation in r-domain is

$$r^3 + 0.1146r^2 + 4.77r + 4.29 = 0$$

Formulating the Routh array, we have

r^3	1	4.77
r^2	0.1146	4.29
r^1	−32.86	
r^0	4.29	

There are two sign changes in the elements of the first column of the Routh array. So there are two poles of $F(z)$ outside the unit circle in z-plane and the given sampled data system is unstable.

Let us check the stability if the system were linear continuous, i.e.,

$$1 + GH(s) = 0$$

$$1 + \frac{1}{s(s+0.5)(s+1.5)} = 0$$

$$s^3 + 2s^2 + 0.75s + 1 = 0$$

Formulating the Routh array, we have

s^3	1	0.75
s^2	2	1
s^1	0.25	
s^0	1	

All the elements in the first column of the Routh array are positive. So the continuous system is stable.

We can conclude that a stable linear continuous system may become unstable upon introduction of sampler and ZOH in the forward path. It can, therefore, be concluded that sampling has a destabilizing effect on a system.

The Root Locus Technique

The root locus technique can be easily adopted to stability analysis and design of sampled-data feed back control systems. The characteristic equation of these systems is of the form

$$1 + F(z) = 0$$

where $F(z)$ is a rational function of z. It can be written in the standard pole-zero form

$$1 + \frac{K\pi(z + z_i)}{\pi(z + p_j)} = 0$$

for drawing the root locus in the z-plane when the gain K is varied.

Examination of the root locus with respect to the unit circle reveals information on system stability and the range of K for the system to be stable can also be determined.

Example 11.29 Draw the root locus for the system with

$$GH(z) = \frac{K(z + 0.2)}{(z - 1)(z - 0.5)}$$

Show that part of the root locus is a circle.

Solution: The root locus for a discrete system can be constructed on the same lines as that for a continuous time system.

1. The root locus is symmetrical about the real axis because the pole-zero configuration is symmetrical about the real axis.
2. The root locus starts at the open loop poles $z = 1$ and $z = 0.5$ and terminates at the open loop zero $z = -0.2$ and at $z = \infty$.
3. No. of asymptotes $= 2 - 1 = 1$ and the angle of the asymptote is $\theta_0 = \dfrac{(2q + 1)\pi}{n - m} = \pi$.
4. The centroid $-\sigma = \dfrac{(1 + 0.5) - (-0.2)}{2 - 1} = 1.7$.
5. Root locus exists on the real axis from $z = 1$ to $z = 0.5$ and to the left of $z = -0.2$.
6. The break points are given by the solution of

$$\frac{dK}{dz} = 0$$

$$\frac{d}{dz}\left[\frac{(z - 1)(z - 0.5)}{z + 0.2}\right] = \frac{d}{dz}\left[\frac{z^2 - 1.5z + 0.5}{z + 0.2}\right] = 0$$

i.e., $z = 0.716$ and $z = -1.16$ are the break points. The break angles are $\pm\dfrac{180°}{2} = \pm 90°$.

7. There are no angles of departures and no angles of arrivals as there are no complex poles or complex zeros.

8. The complete root locus is shown in Figure 11.18. The value of K at $z = 1$ i.e., at the point of intersection of root locus with unit circle is

$$K = 2.72 \left(K = \frac{1.36 \times 1.8}{0.9} = 2.72 \right)$$

So the range of values of K for stability is $K < 2.72$.

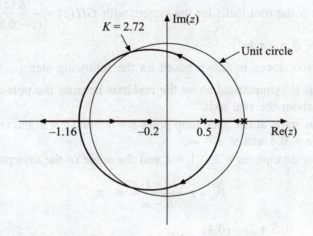

Figure 11.18 Root locus for $GH(z) = \dfrac{K(z + 0.2)}{(z - 1)(z - 0.5)}$.

We can show that part of the root locus is a circle. Let $Re(z) = p$ and $Im(z) = q$. So it is p–q axis and $z = p + jq$.

$$GH(z) = \frac{K(z + 0.2)}{(z - 1)(z - 0.5)} = \frac{K(p + jq + 0.2)}{(p + jq - 1)(p + jq - 0.5)}$$

$$\angle GH(z) = \tan^{-1} \frac{q}{p + 0.2} - \tan^{-1} \frac{q}{p - 1} - \tan^{-1} \frac{q}{p - 0.5} = -\pi$$

$$\therefore \quad \pi + \tan^{-1} \frac{q}{p + 0.2} = \tan^{-1} \frac{q}{p - 1} + \tan^{-1} \frac{q}{p - 0.5}$$

Taking tangent on both sides,

$$\frac{\tan \pi + \dfrac{q}{p + 0.2}}{1 - \tan \pi \tan \dfrac{q}{p + 0.2}} = \frac{\dfrac{q}{p - 1} + \dfrac{q}{p - 0.5}}{1 - \dfrac{q}{p - 1} \dfrac{q}{p - 0.5}}$$

$$\frac{q}{p + 0.2} = \frac{q(p - 0.5 + p - 1)}{(p - 1)(p - 0.5) - q^2} = \frac{q(2p - 1.5)}{p^2 - 1.5p + 0.5 - q^2}$$

i.e.
$$p^2 - 1.5p + 0.5 - q^2 = (2p - 15)(p + 0.2) = 2p^2 - 1.1p - 0.3$$

i.e.
$$p^2 + 0.4p + \omega^2 = 0.8$$

or
$$(p + 0.2)^2 + \omega^2 = (0.916)^2$$

This is the equation of a circle with centre at $(-0.2, 0)$ and radius $= 0.916$ as shown in Figure 11.18.

Example 11.30   Draw the root locus for the system with $GH(z) = \dfrac{K(z - 0.4)}{(z - 0.5)(z - 2)}$. Show that

part of the root locus is a circle.

Solution: The root locus is drawn based on the following steps:

1. The root locus is symmetrical about the real axis because the pole-zero configuration is symmetrical about the real axis.
2. The root locus starts at the open loop poles $z = 0.5$ and $z = 2$ and terminates at the open loop zero at $z = 0.4$ and at $z = \infty$.
3. The number of asymptotes $= 2 - 1 = 1$ and the angle of the asymptotes

$$\theta_0 = \pm \frac{(2q + 1)\pi}{n - m} = -\pi.$$

4. The centroid $= \dfrac{(0.5 + 2) - (0.4)}{2 - 1} = 2.1.$

5. Root locus exists on the real axis between $z = 2$ to $z = 0.5$ and to the left of $z = 0.4$.
6. The break points are given by the solution of

$$\frac{dK}{dz} = 0, \text{i.e. } \frac{d}{dz}\left[\frac{(z - 2)(z - 0.5)}{z - 0.4}\right] = \frac{d}{dz}\left[\frac{z^2 - 2.5z + 1}{z - 0.4}\right]$$

i.e.
$$(z - 0.4)(2z - 2.5) - (z^2 - 2.5z + 1)(1) = 0$$

i.e.
$$z^2 - 0.8z = 0$$

i.e. the break points are $z = 0$ and $z = 0.8$.

7. There are no angles of departures and angles of arrivals as there are no complex poles or complex zeros.

We can show that part of the root locus is a circle. Let $\text{Re}(z) = p$ and $\text{Im}(z) = q$. So it is p–q axis and $z = p + jq$.

$\therefore$
$$\angle GH(z) = \angle \frac{K(z - 0.4)}{(z - 2)(z - 0.5)} = \angle p + jq - 0.4 - \angle p + jq - 2 - \angle p + jq - 0.5 = -\pi$$

i.e.
$$\tan^{-1}\frac{q}{p - 0.4} - \tan^{-1}\frac{q}{p - 2} - \tan^{-1}\frac{q}{p - 0.5} = -\pi$$

i.e.
$$\pi + \tan^{-1}\frac{q}{p - 0.4} = \tan^{-1}\frac{q}{p - 2} + \tan^{-1}\frac{q}{p - 0.5}$$

Taking tangent on both sides, we have

$$\frac{q}{p-0.4} = \frac{\dfrac{q}{p-2} + \dfrac{q}{p-0.5}}{1 - \dfrac{q}{p-2}\dfrac{q}{p-0.5}} = q\frac{(2p-2.5)}{p^2 - 2.5p + 1 - q^2}$$

i.e. $\qquad\qquad p^2 - 2.5p + 1 - q^2 = 2p^2 - 2.5p - 0.8p + 1$

i.e. $\qquad\qquad p - 0.8p + q^2 = 0$, i.e. $(p - 0.4)^2 + (q - 0)^2 = (0.4)^2$

This is the equation of a circle with centre at (0.4, 0) and radius = 0.4.

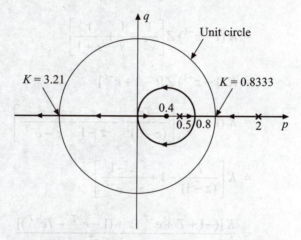

Figure 11.19 Root locus for $GH(z) = \dfrac{K(z-0.4)}{(z-0.5)(z-2)}$.

The value of K at $z = 1$ is $K_1 = \dfrac{(1)(0.5)}{0.6} = 0.8333$.

The value of K at $z = -1$ is $K_2 = \dfrac{(3)(1.5)}{1.4} = 3.21$.

So the given discrete system is stable for $0.833 < K < 3.21$.
The complete root locus is drawn in Figure 11.19.

Example 11.31 Investigate the stability of the system shown in Figure 11.20 for sampling period $T = 0.5s, 2s$.

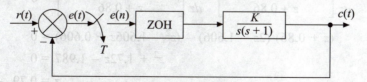

Figure 11.20 Sampled-data system for Example 11.31.

Solution: The characteristic equation of the sampled data system is:

$$1 + G_0G(z) = 0$$

The open loop transfer function of the system is:

$$G_0G(z) = Z\left[\frac{1-e^{-sT}}{s}\frac{K}{s(s+1)}\right]$$

$$= K(1-z^{-1})Z\left[\frac{1}{s^2(s+1)}\right]$$

$$= K(1-z^{-1})Z\left[\frac{1}{s^2}-\frac{1}{s}+\frac{1}{s+1}\right]$$

$$= K(1-z^{-1})Z[t-1+e^{-t}]$$

$$= K(1-z^{-1})\left[\frac{Tz}{(z-1)^2}-\frac{z}{z-1}+\frac{z}{z-e^{-T}}\right]$$

$$= K\left[\frac{T}{(z-1)}-1+\frac{z-1}{z-e^{-T}}\right]$$

$$= \frac{K[(-1+T+e^{-T})z+(1-e^{-T}-Te^{-T})]}{(z-1)(z-e^{-T})}$$

Case 1 $T = 0.5\ s$

$$G_0G(z) = (0.106K)\frac{z+0.86}{(z-1)(z-0.606)}$$

$$= K'\frac{z+0.86}{(z-1)(z-0.606)}$$

The root locus for this $G_0G(z)$ is shown in Figure 11.21.

Root locus exists on the real axis between $z = 1$ to $z = 0.616$ and to the left of $z = -0.86$.

The break points are given by

$$\frac{d}{dz}\left[\frac{(z-1)(z-0.606)}{z+0.86}\right] = \frac{d}{dz}\left[\frac{z^2-1.606z+0.606}{z+0.86}\right] = 0$$

i.e. $$(z+0.86)(2z-1.606)-(z^2-1.606z+0.606) = 0$$

or $$z^2 + 1.72z - 1.987 = 0$$

$$z = 0.79, -2.51$$

Using the angle criterion, we can show that part of the root locus is a circle centred at $z = -0.86$ (zero) and of radius 1.65. The complete root locus is drawn as shown in Figure 11.21. The root locus crosses the unit circle at $K' = 0.59 \left(K' = \dfrac{1.04 \times 0.9}{1.6} = 0.59 \right)$. So the range of values of K for stability is $K < \dfrac{0.59}{0.106} = 5.566$.

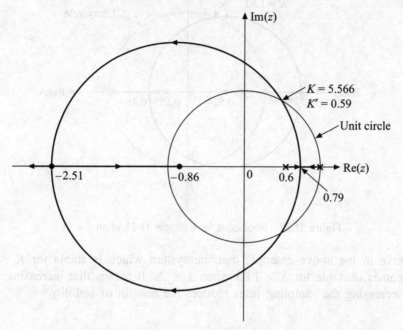

Figure 11.21 Root locus for Example 11.31 when $T = 0.5$s.

Case 2 $T = 2$s

$$G_0G(z) = (1.135K) \frac{z + 0.524}{(z-1)(z - 0.135)}$$

The root locus for this $G_0G(z)$ is shown in Figure 11.22.

The root locus exists on the real axis between $z = 1$ to $z = 0.135$ and to the left of $z = -0.524$.

The break points are given by the solution of

$$\frac{d}{dz}\left[\frac{(z-1)(z-0.135)}{z+0.524} \right] = \frac{d}{dz}\left[\frac{(z^2 - 1.135z + 0.135)}{z + 0.524} \right] = 0$$

i.e. $z^2 + 1.048z - 0.7297 = 0$

i.e. $z = -1.526, \ 0.478$

are the break points.

Using the angle criterion we can show that part of the root locus is a circle centred at $z = -0.524$ (zero) and of radius 1.002.

The complete root locus is drawn in Figure 11.22. The root locus crosses the unit circle at $K = 1.85 \left(K = \dfrac{1.68 \times 1.1}{1} = 1.85 \right)$. So the range of values of K for stability is $K < \dfrac{1.85}{1.135} = 1.63$.

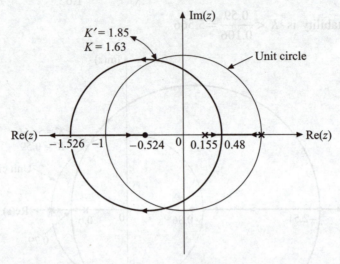

Figure 11.22   Root locus for Example 11.31 when $T = 2s$.

We observe in the above example that the system which is stable for $K < 5.566$ when $T = 0.5s$ becomes unstable for $K > 1.63$ when $T = 2s$. It means that increasing the sampling period, (or decreasing the sampling rate) reduces the margin of stability.

SHORT QUESTIONS AND ANSWERS

1. What is an analog controller?
A. An analog controller is one in which the controller elements are such that the controller produces continuous-time control signals from continuous-time input signals.

2. What is a digital controller?
A. A digital controller is one in which either a special purpose computer or a general purpose computer forms the heart. Its input and output both are in digital form.

3. What does the term sampling imply?
A. Sampling implies that the signal at the output end of the sampler is available in the form of short duration pulses each followed by a skip period when no signal is available.

4. With fixed sample width what are the methods of sampling?
A. With fixed sample width the common methods of sampling are
   (i) Uniform periodic sampling
   (ii) Multi-order sampling

(iii) Multiple-rate sampling

(iv) Random sampling

5. What is uniform periodic sampling?

A. Uniform periodic sampling is one in which the sample width is fixed and sampling period is uniform.

6. What is multi-order sampling?

A. Multi-order sampling is one in which a particular sampling pattern is repeated periodically.

7. What is multiple-rate sampling?

A. Multiple-rate sampling is one in which two simultaneous sampling operations with different time periods are carried out on the signal to produce the sampled output.

8. What is random sampling?

A. Random sampling is one in which the sampling instants are random with a particular kind of distribution.

9. What for a sampler is used?

A. A sampler is used to convert a continuous-time signal into a sequence of pulses.

10. What is a sampled-data control system?

A. A hybrid control system in which signals at some points in the system are continuous and at some points they are digital is called a sampled-data control system.

11. State Shanon's sampling theorem.

A. The Shanon's sampling theorem states that the information contained in a signal is fully preserved in the sampled version so long as the sampling frequency is atleast twice the maximum frequency contained in the signal.

12. What are the advantages of sampling?

A. The advantages of sampling are

1. Sampling improves the accuracy of the system.
2. Sampled data technique is most appropriate for control systems requiring long distance data transmission.
3. Using sampled data technique, time multiplexing is possible and this reduces the cost of transmission installation.
4. Signal sampling reduces the power demand made on the signal and is therefore helpful for signals of weak power origin.

13. What are the circumstances that lead to the use of sampled data control systems?

A. The circumstances that lead to the use of sampled data control systems are

1. For using digital computer (or microprocessor) as part of the control loop.
2. For time sharing of control components.
3. Whenever a transmission channel forms part of the control loop.
4. Whenever the output of a control component is essentially in discrete form.

14. What is a hold circuit?

A. A hold circuit is an extrapolator which converts a sampled data signal into analog form.

15. What is a zero order hold?

A. A zero order hold is the simplest hold circuit in which the reconstructed signal acquires the same value as the last received sample for the entire sampling period.

16. What is a first order hold?

A. A first order hold is an extrapolator in which the last two signal samples are used to reconstruct the signal for the current sampling period.

17. How are sampled-data systems analysed using Z-transforms?

A. Sampled data systems are described by difference equations. The difference equations, which are in time domain, are converted into algebraic equations in z-domain using Z-transforms. Those algebraic equations are manipulated and result is obtained in z-domain. Using inverse Z-transform, the result is converted into time domain.

18. Define Z-transform.

A. The Z-transform of a unilateral discrete-time signal $x(nT)$ is defined as

$$X(z) = \sum_{n=0}^{\infty} x(nT) z^{-n}$$

19. What is inverse Z-transform?

A. The process of finding the time domain signal $x(n)$ from its Z-transform $X(z)$ is called the inverse Z-transform.

20. State the linearity property of Z-transforms?

A. The linearity property of Z-transforms states that the Z-transform of a weighted sum of two signals is equal to the weighted sum of individual Z-transforms.

i.e. $\qquad Z[ax_1(n) + bx_2(n)] = aX_1(z) + bX_2(z)$

21. State the shifting property of Z-transforms.

A. The time shifting property of Z-transforms states that

$$Z[x(n - m)] = z^{-m} X(z)$$
$$Z[x(n + m)] = z^{m} X(z)$$

22. State the multiplication by an exponential sequence property of Z-transforms.

A. The multiplication by an exponential sequence property of Z-transform states that

$$Z[a^n x(n)] = X\left(\frac{z}{a}\right)$$

23. State the multiplication by n property of Z-transforms.

A. The multiplication by n property of Z-transforms states that

$$Z[nx(n)] = -z\frac{d}{dz}[X(z)]$$

24. State the convolution property of Z-transforms.

A. The convolution property of Z-transforms states that

$$Z[x_1(n) * x_2(n)] = X_1(z) \, X_2(z)$$

25. State the initial value theorem of Z-transforms.

A. The initial value theorem of Z-transforms states that

$$x(0) = \mathop{\mathrm{Lt}}_{n \to 0} x(n) = \mathop{\mathrm{Lt}}_{z \to \infty} X(z)$$

26. State the final value theorem of Z-transforms.

A. The final value theorem of Z-transforms states that

$$x(\infty) = \mathop{\mathrm{Lt}}_{n \to \infty} x(n) = \mathop{\mathrm{Lt}}_{z \to 1} (z - 1) \, X(z)$$

27. Define transfer function of a discrete-time system.

A. The transfer function of a discrete-time system is defined as the ratio of the Z-transform of the output to the Z-transform of the input when the initial conditions are neglected.

The transfer function of a system is also defined as the impulse response of the system.

28. What is the condition for the stability of sampled-data systems?

A. The condition for the stability of sampled-data systems is – All the poles of the closed-loop transfer function must lie within the unit circle centred at the origin of the z-plane. Its impulse response must be absolutely summable.

29. How is s-plane mapped into z-plane?

A. The right half of the s-plane is mapped into the outside of the unit circle centred at the origin of the z-plane. The left half of the s-plane is mapped into the interior of the unit circle and the imaginary axis of s-plane is mapped onto the circumference of the unit circle.

30. What is Jury's stability test?

A. Jury's stability test is an algebraic criterion for determining whether or not the roots of the characteristic polynomial lie within the unit circle thereby determining system stability.

31. What is bilinear transformation?

A. Bilinear transformation is a complex transformation which maps the interior of the unit circuit in z-plane into the left half of the r-plane.

32. What is the effect of sampling on the stability of a system?

A. Sampling has a destabilizing effect on a system.

33. What is the effect of sampling period on the stability of a system?

A. The effect of sampling period on the stability of a system is that increasing the sampling period (or decreasing the sampling rate) reduces the margin of stability.

34. How is root locus applied to digital systems?

A. For digital systems, root locus is drawn in z-plane considering $GH(z)$ just like the root locus is drawn in s-plane considering $G(s)H(s)$. Examination of the root locus with reference to the unit circle reveals information on system stability and the range of K for the system to be stable can also be determined.

REVIEW QUESTIONS

1. What are the advantages of sampling?

2. What are the circumstances that lead to the use of sampled-data control systems?

3. State and prove (1) time shifting (2) multiplication by an exponential sequence (3) multiplication by n and (4) convolution properties of Z-transforms.

4. State and prove the initial and final value theorems of Z-transforms.

5. Explain Jury's stability criterion for determining the stability of discrete-time systems.

6. Explain how bilinear transformation can be used to determine the stability of discrete systems.

FILL IN THE BLANKS

1. A linear shift invariant discrete-time system is represented by _____ equations.

2. The Z-transform converts _____ equations into _____ equations.

3. Initial value theorem states that for a causal signal $x(0)$ = _____.

4. Final value theorem states that for a causal signal $x(\infty)$ = _____.

5. The transfer function is defined as the Z-transform of the _____ of the system.

6. For a casual LTI system to be stable, all the poles of $H(z)$ must lie _____ in the plane.

7. The response of the system due to input alone when the initial conditions are neglected is called the _____ of the system.

8. The response of the system due to initial conditions alone, when the input is neglected is called the _____ of the system.

9. The response due to input and initial conditions considered simultaneously is called the _____ of the system.

10. The output due to unit sample sequence is called the _____ of the system.

11. The sampler converts the continuous-time signals into a _____.

12. A sampled-data control system is one in which the signals are _____ at some points and _____ at other points in the system.

13. Signal sampling _____ the power demand made on the signal.

14. The signal at the output of the sampler is available in the form of _____.

15. For fully preserving the information contained in a signal in the sampled version, the sampling frequency must be _____ the maximum frequency contained in the signal.

16. In a _____ order hold the last signal sample is used to reconstruct the signal for the current sampling period.

17. In a _____ order hold, the last two signal samples are used to reconstruct the signal for the current sampling period.

18. For sampled data system analysis we use _____ sided Z-transform.

19. The _____ is a process of determining the sequence which generates a given Z-transform.

20. Time shifting property of Z-transform states that $Z[x(n - m)] =$ _____ and $Z[x(n + m)]=$ _____ neglecting initial conditions.

21. For a closed-loop sampled-data system to be stable, all the poles must be _____ in z-plane.

22. Jury's stability test is _____ criterion.

23. If $F(z)$ is the characteristic polynomial then as per Jury, the necessary conditions for stability are _____, _____.

24. $F(z)$ is converted into $F(r)$ using _____ transformation.

25. Sampling has _____ effect on a system.

26. Sampling period _____ the margin of stability.

OBJECTIVE TYPE QUESTIONS

1. Signal sampling _____ the power demand made on the signal
   - (a) reduces
   - (b) increases
   - (c) does not alter
   - (d) makes zero

2. The signal at the output of a sampler is available in the form of
   - (a) short duration pulses
   - (b) square waves
   - (c) long duration pulses
   - (d) impulses

3. Shanon's sampling theorem states that for signal recovery
   - (a) $\omega_s < 2\omega_m$
   - (b) $\omega_s > 2\omega_m$
   - (c) $\omega_s = \infty$
   - (d) $\omega_s = 0$

4. Sampled-data signal is converted into analog signal using
   - (a) filters
   - (b) hold circuits
   - (c) samplers
   - (d) R–L circuits

5. Bilinear transformation is performed using
   - (a) $z = \dfrac{r+1}{r-1}$
   - (b) $z = \dfrac{r-1}{r+1}$
   - (c) $z = \dfrac{1+r}{1-r}$
   - (d) $z = \dfrac{1-r}{1+r}$

6. Sampling has _____ effect on a system
   (a) stabilizing   (b) destabilizing
   (c) no   (d) compensating
7. Increasing the sampling period _____ the margin of stability
   (a) reduces   (b) increases
   (c) does not alter   (d) makes ∞

PROBLEMS

11.1 Find the Z-transform of

(a) $x_1(n) = a^n \sin(n\pi)\, u(n)$ (b) $x_2(n) = u(n) - u(n-4)$

(c) $x_3(n) = [u(n) - u(n-3)]$ (d) $x_4(n) = \left(\dfrac{1}{4}\right)^n u(n) + \left(\dfrac{1}{5}\right)^n u(n)$

11.2 Using properties of Z-transform, find the Z-transform of the following sequences

(a) $x_1(n) = n\, u(n-1)$ (b) $x_2(n) = n^2 u(n)$

(c) $x_3(n) = \left(\dfrac{1}{3}\right)^n \sin\left(\dfrac{\pi}{4}n\right) u(n)$ (d) $x_4(n) = 2^n \cos 3n\, u(n)$

11.3 Find the Z-transforms of the discrete sequences generated by mathematically sampling (at uniform time interval *T*) the following continuous-time functions:

(a) t^2 (b) e^{-at}

(c) $e^{-at} \cos \omega t$ (d) $e^{-at} \sin \omega t$

11.4 Find the z-domain transfer functions of the following s-domain transfer functions:

(a) $\dfrac{a}{(s+a)^2}$ (b) $\dfrac{s}{s^2 + \omega^2}$

(c) $\dfrac{a}{(s+b)^2 + a^2}$ (d) $\dfrac{s+b}{(s+b)^2 + a^2}$

11.5 Find the inverse Z-transform of the following.

(a) $\dfrac{z^2 + 2z + 1}{z^2 + 3z + 2}$ (b) $\dfrac{z - 0.2}{z^2 + z + 1}$

(c) $\dfrac{z}{(z-1)^2 (z-2)}$ (d) $\dfrac{\dfrac{1}{4}z}{\left(z - \dfrac{1}{2}\right)\left(z - \dfrac{1}{4}\right)}$

11.6 The input–output of a sampled-data system is described by the difference equation

$$c(n+2) + 4c(n+1) + 5c(n) = r(n+1) - 2r(n)$$

Determine the Z-transfer function. Also obtain the weighting sequence (discrete impulse response) of the system.

11.7 Find $\dfrac{C(z)}{R(z)}$ for the sampled-data closed loop system shown in Figure 11.23.

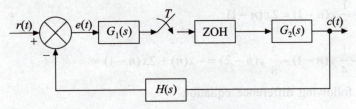

Figure 11.23 Sampled data system.

11.8 Find $\dfrac{C(z)}{R(z)}$ for the sampled-data closed loop system shown in Figure 11.24.

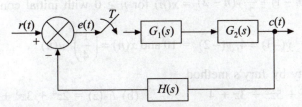

Figure 11.24 Sampled data system.

11.9 For the sampled-data feedback system with a digital network in the feedback path as shown in Figure 11.25, find $\dfrac{C(z)}{R(z)}$.

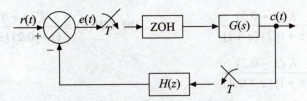

Figure 11.25 Sampled dats system.

11.10 For the sampled-data system shown in Figure 11.26, find the response to unit step input.

Given $G(s) = \dfrac{1}{s+1}$.

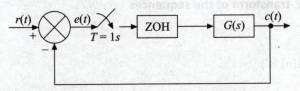

Figure 11.26 Sampled data system.

11.11 Find the transfer function and the impulse response of the system described by the following difference equations:

(a) $y(n) - \dfrac{1}{2} y(n-1) = 2x(n-1)$

(b) $y(n) - \dfrac{1}{4} y(n-1) - \dfrac{3}{8} y(n-2) = -x(n) + 2x(n-1)$

11.12 Solve the following difference equation

$y(n) + 3y(n-1) = x(n)$ with $x(n) = u(n)$ and the initial condition $y(-1) = 1$.

11.13 Solve the following difference equation using unilateral Z-transform

$$y(n) - \dfrac{3}{2} y(n-1) + \dfrac{1}{2} y(n-2) = x(n) \text{ for } n \geq 0 \text{ with initial conditions}$$

$$y(-1) = 4,\ y(-2) = 10 \text{ and } x(n) = \left(\dfrac{1}{4}\right)^n u(n)$$

11.14 Test for stability by Jury's method

(a) $F_1(z) = 2z^3 + 5z^2 + 3z + 4$ (b) $F_2(z) = 2z^4 + 3z^3 + 4z^2 + 5z + 1$

(c) $F_3(z) = 3z^4 + 4z^3 + 3z^2 + 2z + 4$

11.15 Test for stability using Routh's method.

(a) $F_1(z) = 2z^3 + 3z^2 + z + 1$ (b) $F_2(z) = 2z^2 + 4z + 1$

(c) $F_3(z) = 3z^4 + 2z^3 + z^2 + 3z + 2$

11.16 Draw the root locus for the following systems:

(a) $GH(z) = \dfrac{K(z + 0.5)}{(z + 0.2)(z + 1)}$ (b) $GH(z) = \dfrac{K(z + 0.4)}{(z - 0.2)(z - 1)}$

(c) $GH(z) = \dfrac{K(z - 0.2)}{(z + 1)(z + 0.4)}$

and determine the range of values of K for stability

MATLAB PROGRAM

PROGRAM 11.1

% Generation of the Z-transform of the sequences

```
clc;close all; clear all;
syms a b w0 n;
disp('the sequence x1(n) is')
x1=sin(w0*n)
X1=ztrans(x1);
```

```
disp('the Z-Transform of x1(n) is');
X1=simplify(X1)
disp('the sequence x2(n) is')
x2=cos(w0*n)
X2=ztrans(x2);
disp('the Z-Transform of x2(n) is');
X2=simplify(X2)
disp('the sequence x3(n) is')
x3=a.^n+b.^n
X3=ztrans(x3);
disp('the Z-Transform of x3(n) is');
X3=simplify(X3)
```

Output:

the sequence $x1(n)$ is

$$x1 = \sin(n*w0)$$

the Z-Transform of $x1(n)$ is

$$X1 = \frac{(z*\sin(w0))}{(z^2 - 2*\cos(w0)*z + 1)}$$

the sequence $x2(n)$ is

$$x2 = \cos(n*w0)$$

the Z-Transform of $x2(n)$ is

$$X2 = \frac{\left(\dfrac{z^2}{2} - \dfrac{1}{2}\right)}{(z^2 - 2*\cos(w0)*z + 1)} + \left(\dfrac{1}{2}\right)$$

the sequence $x3(n)$ is

$$x3 = a^n + b^n$$

the Z-Transform of $x3(n)$ is

$$X3 = -\frac{z}{(a-z)} - \frac{z}{(b-z)}$$

PROGRAM 11.2

% Z-transform and Inverse Z-transform of given sequences

```
clc; clear all; close all;
syms n wo
% first signal x1(n)
x1=n+1;
disp('The input equation is')
disp(x1)
X1=ztrans(x1);
```

```
disp('The z-transform is')
disp(X1)
x11=iztrans(X1);
disp('The inverse z-transform is')
disp(x11')
% second signal x2(n)
x2=cos(wo*n);
disp('The input equation is')
disp(x2)
X2=ztrans(x2);
disp('The z-transform is')
disp(X2)
x22=iztrans(X2);
disp('The inverse z-transform is')
disp(x22)
```

Output:

The input equation is

$$n + 1$$

The z-transform is

$$\frac{z}{(z-1)} + \frac{z}{(z-1)^2}$$

The inverse z-transform is

$$n + 1$$

The input equation is

$$\cos(n*wo)$$

The z-transform is

$$\frac{(z*(z-\cos(wo)))}{(z^2 - 2*\cos(wo)*z + 1)}$$

The inverse z-transform is

$$\cos(n*a\cos(\cos(wo)))$$

PROGRAM 11.3

%Finding the poles and residues and polo-zero plot of the function

$$X(z) = \frac{z^3}{(z-0.5)(z-0.75)(z-1)}$$

```
clc; clear all; close all;
syms z
% The denominator of X(Z)
d=(z-0.5)*(z-0.75)*(z-1);
```

```
a1=collect(d);
den=sym2poly(a1);
% The numarator of X(Z)
num=[0 1 0 0];
% residues and poles of X(Z)
[num1,den1]=residue(num,den);
fprintf('r1 = %4.2f \t', num(1));
fprintf('p1 = %4.2f \t', den(1));
fprintf('r2 = %4.2f \t', num(2));
fprintf('p2 = %4.2f \t', den(2));
fprintf('r3 = %4.2f \t', num(3));
fprintf('p3 = %4.2f \t', den(3));
% Pole-zero plot
Ts=0.2;
H=tf('z');
H=tf(num,den,Ts);
pzmap(H);
```

Output:

r1 = 0.00	p1 = 1.00
r2 = 1.00	p2 = -2.25
r3 = 0.00	p3 = 1.63

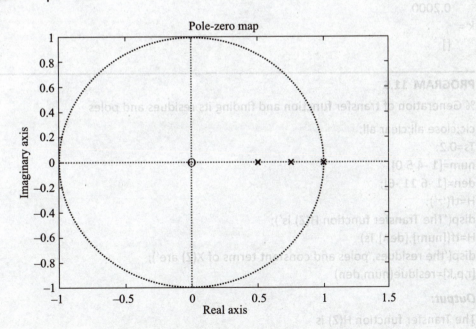

Pole-zero map

PROGRAM 11.4

% Generation of partial fraction expansion and pole-zero plot of a function

```
clc;clear all;close all;
% partial fraction expansion of X(Z)
num=input('enter the numarator coefficients');
den=input('enter the denominator coefficients');
disp('residues,poles and constant terms of the given ZT are')
[r,p,k]=residue(num,den)
% pole-zero plot of X(Z)
zplane(num,den);
title('pole-zero plot')
```

Output:

Enter the numarator coefficients[1 1/2]
Enter the denominator coefficients[1 -3/5 2/25]
Residues,poles and constant terms of the given *ZT* are
r =

    4.5000
    −3.5000

p =

    0.4000
    0.2000

k =

    []

PROGRAM 11.5

% Generation of transfer function and finding its residues and poles

```
clc;close all;clear all;
Ts=0.2;
num=[1 -4 5 0];
den=[1 -6 11 -6];
H=tf('z');
disp('The Transfer function H(Z) is');
H=tf([num],[den],Ts)
disp('the residues, poles and constant terms of X(Z) are');
[r,p,k]=residue(num,den)
```

Output:

The Transfer function H(Z) is
Transfer function:

$$\frac{z^3 - 4z^2 + 5z}{z^3 - 6z^2 + 11z - 6}$$

Sampling time: 0.2

The residues, poles and constant terms of $X(Z)$ are

r =

3.0000

−2.0000

1.0000

p =

3.0000

2.0000

1.0000

k =

1

PROGRAM 11.6

% Inverse Z-transform by the polynomial division method

$$x(z) = \frac{(1 + 2 * z^{(-1)} + z^{(-2)})}{(1 - z^{(-1)} + 0.3561 * z^{(-2)})}$$

```
clc; clear all; close all;
b=[1 2 1];
a=[1 -1 0.3561];
%number of power series points
n=5;
b=[b zeros(1,n-1)];
[h,om]=deconv(b,a);
disp('The terms of inverse z-transforms are')
disp(h)
```

Output:

The terms of inverse z-transforms are

    1.0000   3.0000   3.6439   2.5756   1.2780

PROGRAM 11.7

% The convolution property of Z-transform

```
clc;close all;clear all;
syms n z
disp('the first sequence x1(n) is')
x1n=2.^n
```

```
disp('the second sequence x2(n) is')
x2n=(1/3).^n
X1Z=ztrans(x1n);
X2Z=ztrans(x2n);
XZ=X1Z*X2Z;
yn=iztrans(XZ);
disp('convolution of two sequences is')
simplify(yn)
```

Output:

The first sequence $x1(n)$ is

$$x1n = 2^n$$

The second sequence $x2(n)$ is

$$x2n = \left(\frac{1}{3}\right)^n$$

Convolution of two sequences is

$$ans = \frac{\dfrac{(6*2^n)}{5-1}}{(5*3^n)}$$

PROGRAM 11.8

% Convolution using Z-transform

```
clc; clear all; close all;
% X1Z=2+z^(-1)-z^(-3)+3*z^(-4)
disp('coefficients of X1(Z) represents x1(n) and is')
x1=[2 1 0 -1 3]
subplot(2,1,1);stem(x1);
title('first sequence x1(n)')
%X2Z=1-3*z^(-1)+2*z^(-2)
disp('coefficients of X2(Z) represents x2(n) and is')
x2=[1 -3 2]
subplot(2,1,2);stem(x2);
title('second sequence x2(n)')
disp('convolution of x1(n) and x2(n) is')
y=conv(x1,x2)
figure;stem(y);
title('convolution of x1(n) and x2(n)')
```

Output:

Coefficients of $X1(Z)$ represents $x1(n)$ and is

$$x1 = 2 \quad 1 \quad 0 \quad -1 \quad 3$$

Coefficients of $X2(Z)$ represents $x2(n)$ and is

$$x2 = 1 \quad -3 \quad 2$$

Convolution of $x1(n)$ and $x2(n)$ is

$$y = 2 \quad -5 \quad 1 \quad 1 \quad 6 \quad -11 \quad 6$$

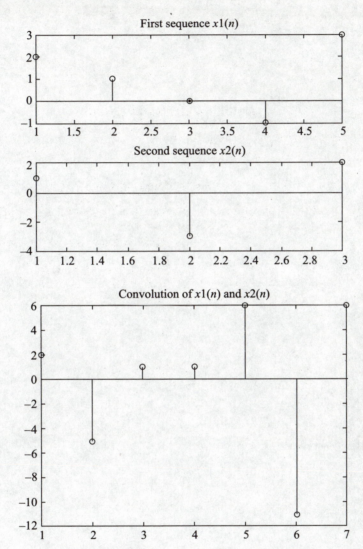

First sequence $x1(n)$

Second sequence $x2(n)$

Convolution of $x1(n)$ and $x2(n)$

Glossary

A.C. control system A control system in which the signals are modulated by some form of modulation scheme.

Analogous systems Systems whose differential equations are of identical form.

Absolute stability A qualitative measure of stability which is an yes or no answer, i.e., which tells whether the system is stable or not.

Acceleration error constant A static error constant which is indicative of the error in output for a unit-parabolic input.

Aligned position of a synchro pair The position in which both the synchro transmitter and the synchro control transmitter are in their electrical zero position.

All-pass system A system with transfer function having a pole-zero pattern which is anti symmetric about the imaginary axis. The magnitude of the All-pass transfer function is unity at all frequencies.

Analog controller A controller which produces continuous time output signals from continuous time input signals.

Analytic function A function which along with all its derivatives exists.

Angle of arrival The angle at which the root locus arrives at a complex zero.

Angle of departure The angle at which the root locus departs from a complex pole.

Approximate Bode plot A Bode plot drawn using straight line asymptotes.

Asymptote A straight line along which the root locus is expected to travel to reach the zero at infinity.

Asymptotic stability A criterion which says that the output tends to zero irrespective of initial conditions in the absence of any input.

Automatic control system See closed-loop control system.

Auxiliary polynomial The polynomial whose coefficients are the elements of the row just above the row of zeros in the Routh array.

Bandwidth   The range of the frequencies for which the system gain is more than –3 dB.

BIBO stability   A criterion which says that the output of the system will be bounded for a bounded input.

Bilinear transformation   A complex transformation which maps the interior of the unit circle in z-plane into the left half of the r-plane.

Block   A symbol for the mathematical operation on the input signal to the block that produces the output.

Block diagram   A pictorial representation of the functions performed by each component of the system and of the flow of signals. It depicts the interrelationships that exist among the various components.

Bode plot   (Also called the logarithmic plot) It is a frequency response plot of the transfer function of a system.

Branch   A line segment of the signal flow graph joining two nodes along which a signal travels from one node to the other in the direction indicated by the branch arrow.

Break angle   The angle at which the root locus branches travel immediately after breaking away.

Break points   The points in the s-plane where multiple roots of the characteristic equation exist.

Bush form   Other name of companion form.

Canonical form   A form of representation of system matrix where all its off diagonal elements are zero, and its main diagonal elements are equal to the roots of the characteristic equation.

Cascade compensation   The compensation in which the compensator transfer function is placed in cascade with the plant transfer function.

Cayley-Hamilton theorem   A theorem which states that every square matrix satisfies its own characteristic equation.

Centroid   The point of intersection of the asymptotes on the real axis.

Characteristic equation   The denominator of the closed-loop transfer function equated to zero. *or*

The equation obtained by setting the denominator polynomial of the transfer function to zero.

Characteristic polynomial   The denominator polynomial of the closed-loop transfer function.

Closed-loop control system   A control system in which the output has an effect on the input. The output is fed back, compared with the reference input and the difference between them is used to control and bring the output of the system to a desired level.

Companion form   A form of representation of system matrix where all its off diagonal elements are 1s and the last row is comprised of the negative of the coefficients of the original differential equation written in reverse order and all other elements in the matrix are zero.

Compensators   Corrective sub systems used to compensate for the deficiency in the performance of the plant.

Constant *M* circles   The family of the circles with constant amplitude.

Constant *N* circles   The family of the circles with constant phase shift.

Continuous-data control system   A control system in which the signals at various parts of the system are all functions of the continuous time variable.

Control system   The means by which any quantity of interest in a machine, mechanism, or some other equipment is maintained or altered in accordance with a desired manner. *or,*

A system in which the output quantity is controlled by varying the input quantity.

Corner frequency   The frequency at which the low frequency and high frequency asymptotes meet.

Coulomb friction   The force of sliding friction between dry surfaces.

Critical value of *K*   The value of *K* at the point of intersection of the root locus with the imaginary axis of s-plane.

Critically damped systems   Systems with exponentially rising response.

Cut-off rate   The slope of the log-magnitude curve near the cut-off frequency.

D.C. control system   A control system in which the signals are not pure D.C., but they are unmodulated.

Damped frequency of oscillations   The frequency of damped oscillations of an underdamped system.

Damping ratio   The ratio of actual damping to critical damping.

Decomposition of a transfer function   The process of obtaining the state diagram of a system from its transfer function.

Delay time   The time required for the response to reach 50% of the final value in the first attempt.

Derivative control   A type of control in which the actuating error signal consists of proportional error signal added to the derivative of error signal.

Derivative feedback control   A type of control in which the actuating signal is the difference of proportional error signal and the derivative of the output.

Diagonalizing matrix   The modal matrix used to diagonalize the system matrix A.

Difficulty-1 in Routh method   The difficulty which arises when the first element in any row of the Routh array is zero, while the rest of the row has at least one non zero element.

Difficulty-2 in Routh method   The difficulty which arises when all the elements in any particular row of the Routh array are zeros.

Digital control system   A class of discrete-data control systems which uses a digital computer or controller so that the signals are digitally coded.

Digital controller   A controller which produces digital output signals from digital input signals.

Discrete-data control system   A control system in which the signals at one or more points in the system are either in the form of a pulse train or a digital code.

Dominant poles   The poles that are close to the imaginary axis in the left-half s-plane.

Duality property   The property which says that (i) The pair (AB) is controllable implies that the pair (A^TB^T) is observable. (ii) The pair A.C. is observable implies that the pair (A^TC^T) is controllable.

Dynamic equations   The state equations and the output equations together.

Dynamic error coefficients   The coefficients used to express the dynamic error.

Eigen Values   The roots of the characteristic equation of a state model.

Eigen Vector   Any non zero vector p_i that satisfies the matrix equation $|\lambda_i - A|p_i = 0$, where λ_i, $i = 1, 2, ..., m$ denotes the eigenvalues of A is the eigenvector of A associated with the eigenvalue.

Encircled region   The region which lies inside the closed path.

Enclosed region   The region which lies to the right of the path of traversal when the contour is traversed in the clockwise direction.

Error signal   The difference between input signal and feedback signal.

Feedback   A control action in which the output is sampled and a proportional signal is given to input for automatic correction of any changes in system output.

Feedback compensation   The compensation in which the compensator transfer function is placed in the feedback path.

Feedback control system   See closed-loop control system.

First order hold   An extrapolator in which the last two signal samples are used to reconstruct the signal for the current sampling period.

Forced response   The response or output of the system when the inputs are present.

Forward path   A path that starts from the input node and ends at the output node.

Forward path gain   The product of the branch gains encountered in traversing a forward path.

Free response   The response or output of the system when the inputs are zero.

Free-body diagram   A diagram showing each mass separately, with all forces acting on the mass marked on it.

Frequency response   The magnitude and phase relationship between the sinusoidal input and the steady-state output of a system.

Gain crossover frequency   The frequency at which the resultant magnitude is zero dB.

Gain margin   The margin between the actual gain and the critical gain which causes sustained oscillations.

Gear ratio   The ratio of torque, speed, angular displacement, velocity and acceleration between any two gear wheels in that gear train.

Gear trains   The devices used in control systems to obtain mechanical matching of motor to load.

Hold circuit   An extrapolator which converts a sampled data signal into analog form.

Homogeneous state equation   State equation in which the forcing function is zero.

Improper transfer function   A transfer function in which the order of the denominator polynomial is less than that of the numerator polynomial.

Impulse response of a system   The output of the system when it is exited by a unit impulse signal.

Inertia   The property of an element that stores the kinetic energy of rotational motion.

Input matix   An $n \times m$ constant matrix relating the input variables of the system to the first derivatives of the state variables.

Input node   A node with only outgoing branches.

Input vector   An $m \times 1$ column vector in which the elements are the m inputs $u_1, u_2, ..., u_m$.

Insignificant poles   The poles that are far away from the imaginary axis in the left half s-plane.

Integral control   A type of control in which the actuating signal consists of proportional error signal added to the integral of error signal.

Inverse Z-transform   The process of obtaining a time domain function from its Z-transform.

Jordan block   A square block in the A matrix in which all the diagonal elements are the same (value of the repeated poles) and the elements just above the main diagonal are all $1s$ and all other elements are $0s$.

Jordan canonical form   A form of representation of system matrix where it has Jordan blocks corresponding to the repeated poles in the system transfer function.

Jury's stability test   An algebraic criterion for determining whether or not the roots of the characteristic polynomial lie within the unit circle there by determining the stability of the system.

Lag compensator   A compensator with pole located to the right of the zero.

Lag–lead compensator   A cascade connection of a lag compensator and a lead compensator.

Lead compensator   A compensator with pole located to the left of the zero.

Linear mathematical model   A model described by a differential equation with coefficients which are either functions only of the independent variable or are constants.

Linear control system   A control system for which the principle of superposition and the principle of homogeneity are valid.

Linear time-invariant model   A model described by constant coefficient differential equation.

Linear time-varying model   A model described by differential equations with coefficients which are functions of time.

Loading   Loading in electrical systems means drawing the current.

Log-magnitude versus phase plot   A plot of magnitude in dB versus phase angle in degrees with frequency ω as the running parameter.

Loop   A path which originates and terminates at the same node and along which no node is traversed more than once.

Loop gain   The product of the branch gains encountered in traversing the loop.

Marginally or limitedly stable system   A system with non repeated poles at the origin or/and on the imaginary axis.

Mason's gain formula   A formula developed by S.J. Mason for reducing large and complex system diagrams in one step, without requiring step-by-step reductions.

Mass   A property of an element that stores the kinetic energy of translational motion.

Mathematical model   The mathematical representation of the physical model through use of appropriate physical laws.

Mechanical network   A diagram indicating the interconnection of sources and components of the mechanical system in which one end of the force or torque sources and the mass or inertia elements is connected to ground.

Mechanical rotational system   A mechanical system in which the motion takes place about a fixed axis.

Mechanical translational system   A mechanical system in which the motion takes place along a straight line.

Minimum-phase system   A system whose transfer function is of minimum-phase type.

Mixed node   A node that has both incoming and outgoing branches.

Modal matrix   The matrix formed by placing the eigenvectors together.

Multi-order sampling   A type of sampling in which a particular sampling pattern is repeated periodically.

Multi-rate sampling   A type of sampling in which two simultaneous sampling operations with different time periods are carried out on the signal to produce the sampled output.

Multi-variable system   A multi-input-multi-output system.

Necessary and sufficient condition for stability using the Routh method   The condition that each term of the first column of the Routh array of its characteristic equation be positive if $a_0 > 0$.

Newton's law of motion for mechanical rotational systems   A law which states that, the algebraic sum of the moments or Torques about a fixed axis is equal to the product of the inertia and the angular acceleration about the axis.

Newton's law of motion for mechanical translational systems   A law which states that, the algebraic sum of the forces acting on a rigid body in a given direction is equal to the product of the mass of the body and its acceleration in the same direction.

Nichol's chart   A chart consisting of constant M and N contours superimposed on ordinary graph. It is used to find the closed-loop frequency response from the open-loop frequency response.

Node   A junction point to represent a system variable which is equal to the sum of all the incoming signals.

Nonhomogeneous state equation   State equation in which the forcing function is present.

Nonlinear control system   A control system for which the principle of superposition and the principle of homogeneity are not valid.

Nonminimum-phase transfer function   A transfer function which has one or more zeros in the right-half s-plane.

Nontouching loops   Loops which do not possess any common node.

Nyquist stability criterion   A criterion which relates the stability of a closed-loop system to the encirclement of the $(-1 + j0)$ point of the s-plane by the contour Γ_{GH} of the open-loop transfer function $G(s)\,H(s)$ corresponding to the Nyquist contour.

Open-loop control system   A control system in which the output quantity has no effect on the input quantity, i.e. a system in which there is no feedback.

Order of a system   The order of the differential equation used to describe the system.

Output equations   The equations in which the outputs of the system are expressed in terms of the state variables and the inputs of the system.

Output matrix   A $p \times n$ constant matrix relating the state variables to the outputs.

Output node   A node with only incoming branches.

Output vector   A $p \times 1$ column vector in which the elements are the p outputs $y_1, y_2, ..., y_p$.

Overdamped systems   Systems with exponentially rising response but the rise time will be very large.

Path   The traversal of connected branches in the direction of the branch arrows such that no node is traversed more than once.

Path gain   The product of the branch gains encountered in traversing a path.

Peak overshoot   The difference between the time response peak and the steady-state output.

Peak time   The time required for the response to reach the peak of the time response or the peak overshoot.

Phase crossover frequency   The frequency at which the resultant phase is $-180°$.

Phase margin   The amount of additional phase lag that should be added at the gain crossover frequency to bring the system to the verge of instability.

Phase variables   Those particular state variables which are obtained from one of the system variables and its derivatives.

Physical model   An idealized physical system.

Physical system   A collection of physical objects connected together to serve an objective.

PID controller   A controller in which the actuating signal consists of proportional error signal added with derivative and integral of error signal.

Polar plot   The locus traced by the tip of the phasor $G(j\omega)$, as the frequency ω is varied from 0 to ∞.

Pole   The value of s for which the function $F(s)$ becomes infinite.

Position error constant   A static error constant which is indicative of the error in output for a unit-step input.

Principle of argument   The relation between the enclosure of poles and zeros of $q(s)$ by the s-plane contour and the corresponding encirclements of the origin by the $q(s)$-plane contour.

Principle of superposition   A statement which says that the response produced by the simultaneous application of two different forcing functions is equal to the sum of the two individual responses.

Proper transfer function A transfer function in which the order of the numerator polynomial is equal to that of the denominator polynomial.

Proportional control A type of control in which the actuating signal for the control action is proportional to the error signal.

Quadrantal symmetry A type of symmetry with symmetrical roots in all four quadrants.

Random sampling A type of sampling in which the sampling instants are random with a particular kind of distribution.

Relative damping ratio The damping ratio corresponding to a pair of complex conjugate dominant poles if those poles can accurately represent the dynamics of a higher order system.

Relative stability A quantitative measure of stability which tells how much stable or unstable a system is.

Resolvent matrix $\phi(s) = [sI - A]^{-1}$ is the resolvent matrix.

Resonant frequency The frequency at which the resonant peak occurs.

Resonant peak The maximum value of the magnitude of the closed-loop frequency response.

Rise time The time required for the response to rise from 10% to 90% of the final value for overdamped systems and 0 to 100% of the final value for underdamped systems.

Root locus The locus of the roots of the characteristic equation when one of the system parameters is varied from 0 to ∞.

Routh stability criterion An algebraic method to test the stability of a control system by manipulating the coefficients of the characteristic equation.

Sampled-data control system A general class of discrete-data control systems in which the signals are in the form of pulsed-data.

Sampler A device used to convert a continuous time signal into a sequence of pulses.

Sampling The process of converting a continuous time signal into short duration pulses each followed by a skip period when no signal is available.

Self loop A loop consisting of a single branch.

Servomechanism A feedback control system in which the controlled variable is mechanical position or time derivatives of position.

Servomotors The motors which are used in automatic control systems.

Settling time The time required for the response to reach and stay within a particular percentage of its final value.

Shanon's sampling theorem A theorem which states that the information contained in a signal is fully preserved in the sampled version so long as the sampling frequency is at least twice the minimum frequency contained in the signal.

Singular points The points in the s-plane where the function or its derivatives do not exist.

Sinusoidal transfer function The transfer function obtained by replacing s with $j\omega$ in the original transfer function.

Speed of response The time for the output to become a particular percentage of its final value.

Stability criterion for discrete systems A criterion which states that for a closed loop discrete time system to be stable all the poles of the closed loop transfer function in z-domain must lie inside the unit circle centred at the origin of the z-plane.

Stability of a control system Stability of a control system implies that small changes in the system input, in initial conditions, or in system parameters do not result in large changes in system output.

State The smallest set of variables called the state variables such that the knowledge of these variables at $t = t_0$, together with the knowledge of the inputs for $t \geq t_0$, completely determine the behaviour of the system for $t \geq t_0$.

State equations A set of first-order differential equations, wherein, the first derivatives of the state variables are expressed in terms of the state variables and the inputs of the system.

State Model The state equations and the output equations together.

State space The n dimensional space whose coordinate axes consists of the x_1 axis, x_2 axis, ..., x_n axis where x_1, x_2, ..., x_n are state variables.

State transition equation The solution of the linear non-homogeneous state equation.

State transition matrix STM The matrix that satisfies the linear homogeneous state equation.

State variables The smallest set of variables that determine the state of the dynamic system.

State vector An $n \times 1$ vector that determines uniquely the system state $\mathbf{x(t)}$ for any time $t \geq t_0$, once the state at $t = t_0$ is given and the input $\mathbf{u(t)}$ for $t \geq t_0$ is specified.

Static error constants The constants associated with steady-state error in a particular type of system and for a standard input.

Steady-state error The error between the actual output and the desired output as t tends to infinity.

Steady-state response That part of the time response which remains constant as $t \rightarrow \infty$.

Stiction The force required to initiate motion between two contacting surfaces.

Strictly proper transfer function A transfer function in which the order of the denominator polynomial is greater than that of the numerator polynomial.

Summing point A point at which all the incoming signals are added.

Synchro An electromagnetic transducer commonly used to convert an angular position of a shaft into an electrical signal.

Synchro pair A system formed by interconnection of the devices-synchro transmitter and synchro control transformer.

System A collection of objects (components) connected together to serve an objective. *or* A combination of components that act together to perform a certain objective.

System matrix An $n \times n$ constant matrix relating the state variables of the system to the first derivatives of the state variables.

Take off point A point from which the signal from a block goes concurrently to other blocks or summing points.

Signal flow graph A graphical representation of the relationships between the variables of a set of linear algebraic equations written in the form of cause-and-effect relations.

Test signals   The signals used to test the performance of a system.

Time constant of a system   The time taken by the output of a system to reach 100% of the input step if the initial slope of the output is maintained constant.

Time response   The output of the system as a function of time.

Time-invariant system   A system whose parameters are stationary with respect to time during the operation of the system.

Time-varying system   A system whose parameters vary with respect to time during the operation of the system.

Transfer function   The Laplace transform of the impulse response of the system. *or*

The ratio of the Laplace transform of the output to the Laplace transform of the input with all initial conditions neglected.

Transfer function of a discrete time system   The ratio of the Z-transform of the output to the Z-transform of the input when the initial conditions are neglected.

Transient response   Also called the dynamic response is that part of the time response which tends to zero as t tends to infinity.

Transmission matrix   A $p \times m$ constant matrix that relates the inputs to the outputs.

Type of a system   The number which indicates the number of open-loop poles present at the origin of the s-plane.

Type-0 system   A system with no open-loop pole at the origin of the s-plane.

Type-1 system   A system with one open-loop pole at the origin of the s-plane.

Type-2 system   A system with two open-loop poles at the origin of the s-plane.

Uncontrollable system   A system which has a sub system that is physically disconnected from the input.

Undamped natural frequency   The frequency at which the system will oscillate in the absence of any damping.

Undamped systems   Systems with purely oscillatory response.

Underdamped systems   Systems with damped oscillatory response.

Uniform periodic sampling   A type of sampling in which sample width is fixed and sampling period is uniform.

Unit-impulse signal   A signal which has zero value everywhere except at $t = 0$, where its magnitude is infinity.

Unit-parabolic signal   A signal which remains at zero level for $t < 0$ and increases as per the equation $t^2/2$ for $t > 0$ i.e. $r(t) = 0$, for $t < 0$, and $r(t) = t^2/2$ for $t > 0$

Unit-ramp signal   A signal which remains at zero level for $t < 0$ and increases linearly with time for $t > 0$. i.e. $r(t) = 0$, for $t < 0$ and $r(t) = t$ for $t > 0$

Unit-step signal   A signal which remains at zero level for $t < 0$ and changes suddenly to a level of unity at $t = 0$ and remains at 1 for $t > 0$. i.e. $u(t) = 0$ for $t < 0$ and $u(t) = 1$, for $t > 0$.

Vander Monde matrix   It is a special form of model matrix which can be written directly, if the system matrix A is in companion form and all its eigenvalues are distinct.

Velocity error constant A static error constant which is indicative of the error in output for a unit-ramp input.

Viscous friction The force of friction between moving surfaces separated by viscous fluid or the force between a solid body and a fluid medium.

Weighing function The system's impulse response.

Zero The value of s for which the function $F(s)$ becomes zero.

Zero order hold A hold circuit in which the reconstructed signal acquires the same value as the last received sample for the entire sampling period.

Zero-input response The response of the system due to initial conditions only.

Zero-state response The response of the system due to inputs only.

Z-transform A transformation technique to transform a time domain function into a complex z-domain function.

Answers

CHAPTER 1

Answers to Fill in the Blanks

1. physical objects **2.** physical model **3.** physical model **4.** (i) open-loop control systems, (ii) closed-loop control systems, (iii) optimal control systems, (iv) adaptive control systems, (v) learning control systems **5.** (i) manually controlled systems, (ii) automatic control systems **6.** (i) open-loop control systems, (ii) closed-loop control systems **7.** (i) position control systems, (ii) velocity control systems, (iii) traffic control systems, etc. **8.** (i) linear control systems, (ii) nonlinear control systems **9.** (i) time-varying control systems, (ii) time-invariant control systems **10.** (i) continuous-data control systems, (ii) discrete-data control systems, or (i) ac control systems, (ii) dc control systems **11.** (i) position control systems, (ii) velocity control systems, (iii) traffic control systems, etc. **12.** (i) single-input-single-output control systems, (ii) multi-input-multi-output control systems **13.** (i) type-0, (ii) type-1, (iii) type-2 **14.** (i) first-order control systems, (ii) second-order control systems, (iii) third-order control systems, etc. **15.** (i) undamped systems, (ii) underdamped systems, (iii) critically-damped systems, (iv) overdamped systems **16.** (i) open-loop control systems, (ii) closed-loop control systems **17.** output quantity, input quantity **18.** output, input **19.** negative **20.** (i) plant, (ii) feedback path elements, (iii) error detector, (iv) controller **21.** principle of superposition, principle of homogeneity **22.** modulated, unmodulated **23.** intentional, inherent.

CHAPTER 2

Answers to Fill in the Blanks

1. mechanical, electrical **2.** analogous **3.** translational, rotational, combinations of both **4.** translational **5.** rotational **6.** displacement, velocity, acceleration **7.** mass **8.** spring

9. coulomb   **10.** stiction   **11.** dash pot   **12.** viscous friction   **13.** inertia   **14.** analogous
15. transfer function   **16.** linear time-invariant, nonlinear   **17.** initial conditions   **18.** input
19. impulse response   **20.** Laplace transform of the output, Laplace transform of the input,
initial conditions   **21.** strictly proper   **22.** proper   **23.** improper   **24.** denominator polynomial,
transfer function   **25.** sinusoidal transfer function   **26.** dc motors   **27.** (a) armature control
mode with fixed field current, (b) field control mode with fixed armature current **28.** linear
29. field control, armature control   **30.** motor, load   **31.** transformers   **32.** servomotors
33. electrical signal, angular motion   **34.** ac, dc   **35.** ac, dc   **36.** dc, ac **37.** low, large **38.** synchro
39. selsyn, autosyn   **40.** Synchro transmitter, synchro control transformer   **41.** Dumb-bell,
cylindrical   **42.** Electrical zero position.

Answers to Objective Type Questions

1. c   **2.** a   **3.** b   **4.** a   **5.** b   **6.** a   **7.** c   **8.** a   **9.** b   **10.** a   **11.** b   **12.** b   **13.** a   **14.** c
15. a   **16.** b

Answers to Problems

2.1 (a) $M\ddot{y}_1 + f\dot{y}_1 + K(y_1 - y_2) = 0$, $F(t) = K(y_2 - y_1)$

(b)

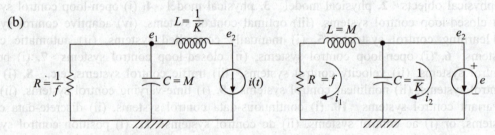

(c) (i) $C\dfrac{de_1}{dt} + \dfrac{e_1}{R} + \dfrac{1}{L}\displaystyle\int (e_1 - e_2)\, dt = 0$, $i(t) = \dfrac{1}{L}\displaystyle\int (e_2 - e_1)\, dt$

(ii) $e(t) = \dfrac{1}{C}\displaystyle\int (i_2 - i_1)\, dt$, $L\dfrac{di_1}{dt} + Ri_1 + \dfrac{1}{C}\displaystyle\int (i_1 - i_2)\, dt = 0$

2.2 (a) $F(t) = M_1\ddot{y}_1 + K(y_1 - y_2) + f_3(\dot{y}_1 - \dot{y}_2) + f_1\dot{y}_1$

$M_2\ddot{y}_2 + f_2\dot{y}_2 + f_3(\dot{y}_2 - \dot{y}_1) + K(y_2 - y_1) = 0$

(b)

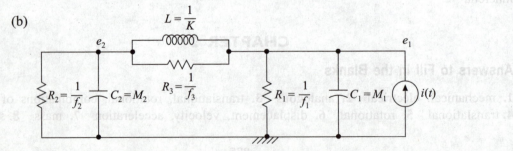

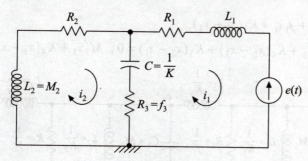

(c) (i) $i(t) = C_1 \dot{e}_1 + \dfrac{e_1}{R_1} + \dfrac{e_1 - e_2}{R_3} + \dfrac{1}{L} \displaystyle\int (e_1 - e_2)\, dt$

$\dfrac{e_2}{R_2} + \dfrac{e_2 - e_1}{R_3} + C_2 \dot{e}_2 + \dfrac{1}{L} \displaystyle\int (e_2 - e_1)\, dt = 0$

(ii) $e(t) = L_1 \dfrac{di_1}{dt} + \dfrac{1}{C} \displaystyle\int (i_1 - i_2)\, dt + R_3 (i_1 - i_2) + R_1 i_1$

$L_2 \dfrac{di_2}{dt} + R_2 i_2 + R_3 (i_2 - i_1) + \dfrac{1}{C} \displaystyle\int (i_2 - i_1)\, dt = 0$

2.3 (a) $F(t) + Mg = K_2 [y_1 - y_2],\ M \ddot{y}_2 + f \dot{y}_2 + K_2 (y_2 - y_1) + K_1 y_2 = 0$

(b)

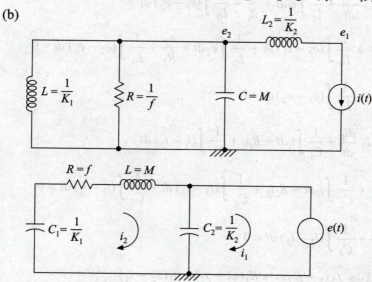

(c) (i) $i(t) = \dfrac{1}{L_2} \displaystyle\int (e_1 - e_2)\, dt,\quad \dfrac{1}{L_2} \displaystyle\int (e_2 - e_1)\, dt + \dfrac{1}{L_1} \displaystyle\int e_2\, dt + \dfrac{e_2}{R} + C \dot{e}_2 = 0$

(ii) $e(t) = \dfrac{1}{C_2} \displaystyle\int (i_1 - i_2)\, dt,\quad L \dfrac{di_2}{dt} + R i_2 + \dfrac{1}{C_1} \displaystyle\int i_2\, dt + \dfrac{1}{C_2} \displaystyle\int (i_2 - i_1)\, dt = 0$

2.4 (a) $F(t) = M_1\ddot{x}_1 + K_1x_1 + f_1\dot{x}_1 + K_3(x_1 - x_2)$

$M_2\ddot{x}_2 + K_2x_2 + f_2\dot{x}_2 + K_4(x_2 - x_3) + K_3(x_2 - x_1) = 0$, $M_3\ddot{x}_3 + K_4(x_3 - x_2) = 0$

(b)

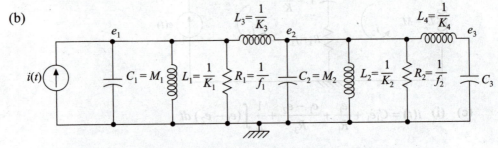

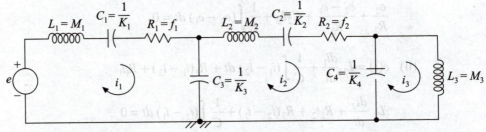

(c) (i) $i(t) = C_1\dfrac{de_1}{dt} + \dfrac{1}{L_1}\int e_1 dt + \dfrac{e_1}{R_1} + \dfrac{1}{L_3}\int(e_1 - e_2)\,dt$

$C_2\dfrac{de_2}{dt} + \dfrac{1}{L_3}\int(e_2 - e_1)\,dt + \dfrac{1}{L_2}\int e_2 dt + \dfrac{e_2}{R_2} + \dfrac{1}{L_4}\int(e_2 - e_3)\,dt = 0$

$C_3\dfrac{de_3}{dt} + \dfrac{1}{L_4}\int(e_3 - e_2)\,dt = 0$

(ii) $e(t) = L_1\dfrac{di_1}{dt} + \dfrac{1}{C_1}\int i_1 dt + R_i i_1 + \dfrac{1}{C_3}\int(i_1 - i_2)\,dt$

$L_2\dfrac{di_2}{dt} + \dfrac{1}{C_2}\int i_2 dt + R_2 i_2 + \dfrac{1}{C_4}\int(i_2 - i_3)\,dt + \dfrac{1}{C_3}\int(i_2 - i_1)\,dt = 0$

$L_2\dfrac{di_3}{dt} + \dfrac{1}{C_4}\int(i_3 - i_2)\,dt = 0$

2.5 (a) $F(t) = M_2\ddot{x}_2 + f_2\dot{x}_2 + K_2x_2 + K_1(x_2 - x_1) + f_1(\dot{x}_2 - \dot{x}_1)$

$M_1\ddot{x}_1 + K_1(x_1 - x_2) + f_1(\dot{x}_1 - \dot{x}_2) = 0$

(b)

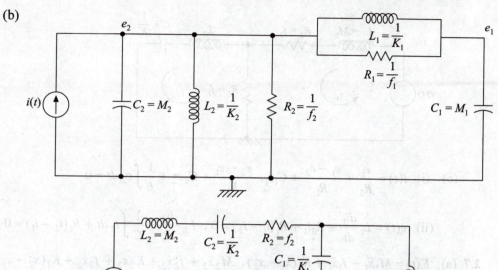

(c) (i) $i(t) = C_2\dot{e}_2 + \dfrac{1}{L_2}\displaystyle\int e_2\,dt + \dfrac{e_2}{R_2} + \dfrac{e_2 - e_1}{R_1} + \dfrac{1}{L_1}\displaystyle\int (e_2 - e_1)\,dt$

$C_1\dot{e}_1 + \dfrac{1}{L_1}\displaystyle\int (e_1 - e_2)\,dt + \dfrac{e_1 - e_2}{R_1} = 0$

(ii) $e(t) = L_2\dfrac{di_2}{dt} + \dfrac{1}{C_2}\displaystyle\int i_2\,dt + R_2 i_2 + \dfrac{1}{C_1}\displaystyle\int (i_2 - i_1)\,dt + R_1(i_2 - i_1)$

$L_1\dfrac{di_1}{dt} + R_1(i_1 - i_2) + \dfrac{1}{C_1}\displaystyle\int (i_1 - i_2)\,dt = 0$

2.6 (a) $F(t) = M_1\ddot{x}_1 + f_2\dot{x}_1 + f_1(\dot{x}_1 - \dot{x}_2),\quad M_2\ddot{x}_2 + f_1(\dot{x}_2 - \dot{x}_1) + Kx_2 = 0$

(b)

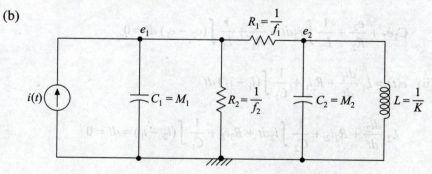

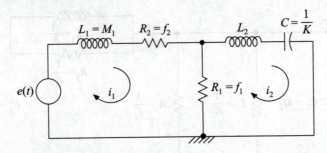

(c) (i) $i(t) = \dfrac{e_1}{R_2} + \dfrac{e_1 - e_2}{R_1} + C_1\dot{e}_1, \quad \dfrac{e_2 - e_1}{R_1} + C_2\dot{e}_2 + \dfrac{1}{L}\int e_2\, dt = 0$

(ii) $e(t) = L_1\dfrac{di_1}{dt} + R_2i_1 + R_1(i_1 - i_2) = 0, \quad L_2\dfrac{di_2}{dt} + \dfrac{1}{C}\int i_2\, dt + R_1(i_2 - i_1) = 0$

2.7 (a) $F(t) = M_1\ddot{x}_1 + f_1\dot{x}_1 + K_1(x_1 - x_2), \quad M_2\ddot{x}_2 + f_2\dot{x}_2 + K_2x_2 + f_3\dot{x}_2 + K_1(x_2 - x_1) = 0$

(b)

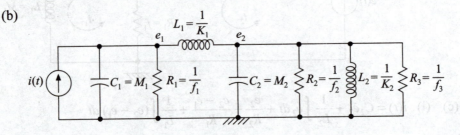

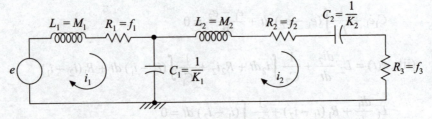

(c) (i) $i(t) = C_1\dot{e}_1 + \dfrac{e_1}{R_1} + \dfrac{1}{L_1}\int(e_1 - e_2)\, dt$

$C_2\dot{e}_2 + \dfrac{e_2}{R_2} + \dfrac{1}{L_2}\int e_2\, dt + \dfrac{e_2}{R_3} + \dfrac{1}{L_1}\int(e_2 - e_1)\, dt = 0$

(ii) $e(t) = L_1\dfrac{di_1}{dt} + R_1i_1 + \dfrac{1}{C_1}\int(i_1 - i_2)\, dt$

$L_2\dfrac{di_2}{dt} + R_2i_2 + \dfrac{1}{C_2}\int i_2\, dt + R_3i_2 + \dfrac{1}{C_1}\int(i_2 - i_1) = dt = 0$

2.8 (a) $F(t) = M_1\ddot{x}_1 + K_1 x_1 + f_1\dot{x}_1 + K_3(x_1 - x_3) + K_2(x_1 - x_2)$

$K_3(x_3 - x_1) + f_3(\dot{x}_3 - \dot{x}_2) = 0, \quad M_2\ddot{x}_2 + f_3(\dot{x}_2 - \dot{x}_3) + K_2(x_2 - x_1) = 0$

(b)

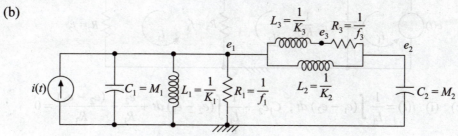

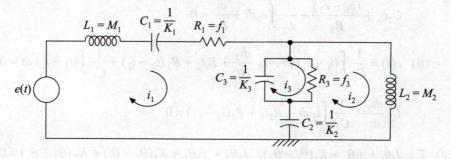

(c) (i) $i(t) = C_1\dot{e}_1 + \dfrac{1}{L_1}\int e_1 dt + \dfrac{e_1}{R_1} + \dfrac{1}{L_3}\int(e_1 - e_3)\,dt + \dfrac{1}{L_2}\int(e_1 - e_2)\,dt$

$\dfrac{1}{L_3}\int(e_3 - e_1)\,dt + \dfrac{(e_3 - e_2)}{R_3} = 0, \quad C_2\dot{e}_2 + \dfrac{1}{L_2}\int(e_2 - e_1)\,dt + \dfrac{(e_2 - e_3)}{R_3} = 0$

(ii) $e(t) = L_1\dfrac{di_1}{dt} + \dfrac{1}{C_1}\int i_1 dt + R_1 i_1 + \dfrac{1}{C_3}\int(i_1 - i_3)\,dt + \dfrac{1}{C_2}\int(i_1 - i_2)\,dt$

$\dfrac{1}{C_3}\int(i_3 - i_1)\,dt + R_3(i_3 - i_2) = 0, \quad L_2\dfrac{di_2}{dt} + \dfrac{1}{C_2}\int(i_2 - i_1)\,dt + R_3(i_2 - i_3) = 0$

2.9 (a) $T(t) = K_1(\theta_1 - \theta_2), \quad J_1\ddot{\theta}_2 + K_1(\theta_2 - \theta_1) + f_1\dot{\theta}_2 + f_3(\dot{\theta}_2 - \dot{\theta}_3) = 0$

$J_2\ddot{\theta}_3 + f_3(\dot{\theta}_3 - \dot{\theta}_2) + K_2\theta_3 + f_2\dot{\theta}_3 = 0$

(b)

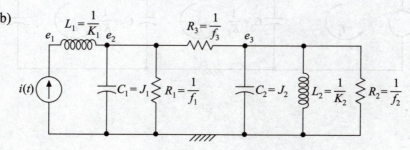

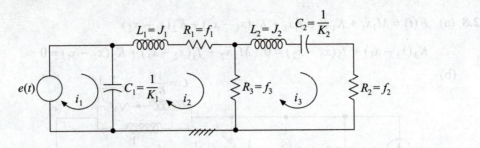

(c) (i) $i(t) = \dfrac{1}{L_1} \displaystyle\int (e_1 - e_2)\, dt$, $\quad C_1 \dot{e}_2 + \dfrac{1}{L_1} \displaystyle\int (e_2 - e_1)\, dt + \dfrac{e_2}{R_1} + \dfrac{(e_2 - e_3)}{R_3} = 0$

$$C_2 \dot{e}_3 + \dfrac{(e_3 - e_2)}{R_3} + \dfrac{1}{L_2} \int e_3 dt + \dfrac{e_3}{R_2} = 0$$

(ii) $e(t) = \dfrac{1}{C_1} \displaystyle\int (i_1 - i_2)\, dt$, $\quad L_1 \dfrac{di_2}{dt} + R_1 i_2 + R_3 (i_2 - i_3) + \dfrac{1}{C_1} \displaystyle\int (i_2 - i_1)\, dt = 0$

$$L_2 \dfrac{di_3}{dt} + \dfrac{1}{C_2} \int i_3 \, dt + R_2 i_3 + R_3 (i_3 - i_2) = 0$$

2.10 (a) $T = J_1 \ddot{\theta}_1 + f_1 \dot{\theta}_1 + K_1 (\theta_1 - \theta_2)$, $\quad J_2 \ddot{\theta}_2 + f_2 \dot{\theta}_2 + K_1 (\theta_2 - \theta_1) + K_2 (\theta_2 - \theta_3) = 0$

$J_3 \ddot{\theta}_3 + f_3 \dot{\theta}_3 + K_3 \theta_3 + K_2 (\theta_3 - \theta_2) = 0$

(b)

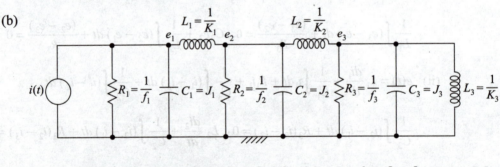

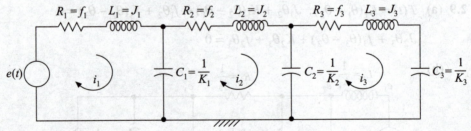

(c) (i) $i(t) = \dfrac{e_1}{R_1} + C_1\dot{e}_1 + \dfrac{1}{L_1}\displaystyle\int (e_1 - e_2)\,dt,$

$$C_2\dot{e}_2 + \dfrac{e_2}{R_2} + \dfrac{1}{L_1}\int (e_2 - e_1)\,dt + \dfrac{1}{L_2}\int (e_2 - e_3)\,dt = 0$$

$$C_3\dot{e}_3 + \dfrac{e_3}{R_3} + \dfrac{1}{L_3}\int e_3\,dt + \dfrac{1}{L_2}\int (e_3 - e_2)\,dt = 0$$

(ii) $e(t) = R_1 i_1 + L_1 \dfrac{di_1}{dt} + \dfrac{1}{C_1}\displaystyle\int (i_1 - i_2)\,dt = 0$

$$R_2 i_2 + L_2 \dfrac{di_2}{dt} + \dfrac{1}{C_2}\int (i_2 - i_3)\,dt + \dfrac{1}{C_1}\int (i_2 - i_1)\,dt = 0$$

$$R_3 i_3 + L_3 \dfrac{di_3}{dt} + \dfrac{1}{C_3}\int i_3\,dt + \dfrac{1}{C_2}\int (i_3 - i_2)\,dt = 0$$

2.11 (a) $M\ddot{x}_2 + f_2\dot{x}_2 + K_1(x_2 - x_1) + f_1(\dot{x}_2 - \dot{x}_1) = 0,\quad F(t) + Mg = K_1(x_1 - x_2) + f_1(\dot{x}_1 - \dot{x}_2)$

(b)

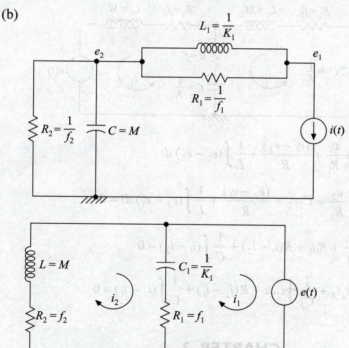

(c) (i) $C\dot{e}_2 + \dfrac{e_2}{R_2} + \dfrac{(e_2 - e_1)}{R_1} + \dfrac{1}{L_1}\displaystyle\int (e_2 - e_1)\,dt = 0$, $i(t) = \dfrac{1}{L_1}\displaystyle\int (e_1 - e_2)\,dt + \dfrac{(e_1 - e_2)}{R_1}$

(ii) $\quad L\dfrac{di_2}{dt} + R_2 i_2 + \dfrac{1}{C_1}\displaystyle\int (i_2 - i_1)\,dt + R_1(i_2 - i_1) = 0,$

$\qquad e(t) = \dfrac{1}{C_1}\displaystyle\int (i_1 - i_2)\,dt + R_1(i_1 - i_2)$

2.12 (a) $\quad F(t) = M_1\ddot{x} + f_1\dot{x} + f(\dot{x} - \dot{y}) + K(x - y)$

$\qquad M_2\ddot{y} + f_2\dot{y} + K_2 y + f(\dot{y} - \dot{x}) + K(y - x) = 0$

(b)

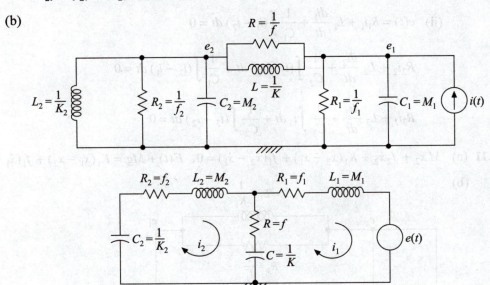

(c) (i) $\quad i(t) = C_1\dot{e}_1 + \dfrac{e_1}{R_1} + \dfrac{(e_1 - e_2)}{R} + \dfrac{1}{L}\displaystyle\int (e_1 - e_2)\,dt$

$\qquad \dfrac{1}{L_2}\displaystyle\int e_2\,dt + \dfrac{e_2}{R_2} + C_2\dot{e}_2 + \dfrac{(e_2 - e_1)}{R} + \dfrac{1}{L}\displaystyle\int (e_2 - e_1)\,dt = 0$

(ii) $\quad e(t) = L_1\dfrac{di_1}{dt} + R_1 i_1 + R(i_1 - i_2) + \dfrac{1}{C}\displaystyle\int (i_1 - i_2) = 0$

$\qquad L_2\dfrac{di_2}{dt} + R_2 i_2 + \dfrac{1}{C_2}\displaystyle\int i_2\,dt + R(i_2 - i_1) + \dfrac{1}{C}\displaystyle\int (i_2 - i_1) = 0$

CHAPTER 3

Answers to Fill in the Blanks

1. pictorial **2.** linear, nonlinear **3.** input, output **4.** block diagram **5.** summing point
6. take-off, branch **7.** $G(s)H(s)$ **8.** linear systems **9.** algebraic, cause, effect **10.** Nodes

11. arrows   **12.** simplified version   **13.** S.J. Mason   **14.** Mason's gain formula   **15.** same information, superior   **16.** signal flow graph, block diagram   **17.** algebraic equations, cause-and-effect   **18.** unique   **19.** node, node   **20.** input, source   **21.** output, sink   **22.** mixed node   **23.** nontouching loops   **24.** self loop   **25.** self

Answers to Objective Type Questions

1. c   **2.** a   **3.** c   **4.** a   **5.** b   **6.** c   **7.** b   **8.** a   **9.** c   **10.** c

Answers to Problems

3.1

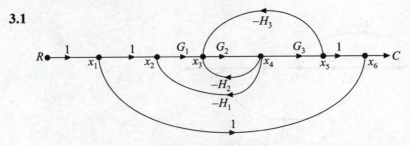

$$\frac{G_1 G_2 G_3 + 1 + G_2 H_2 + G_1 G_2 H_1 + G_2 G_3 H_3}{1 + G_2 H_2 + G_1 G_2 H_1 + G_2 G_3 H_3}$$

3.2

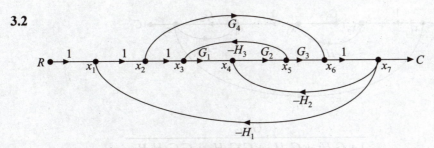

$$\frac{G_1 G_2 G_3 + G_4 (1 + G_1 G_2 H_3)}{1 + G_1 G_2 H_3 + G_2 G_3 H_2 + G_1 G_2 G_3 H_1 + G_4 H_1 + G_1 G_2 G_4 H_1 H_3}$$

3.3

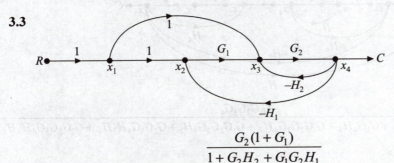

$$\frac{G_2 (1 + G_1)}{1 + G_2 H_2 + G_1 G_2 H_1}$$

3.4

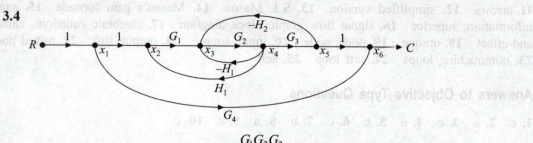

$$\frac{G_1 G_2 G_3}{1 + G_2 H_1 + G_2 G_3 H_2 - G_1 G_2 H_1} + G_4$$

3.5

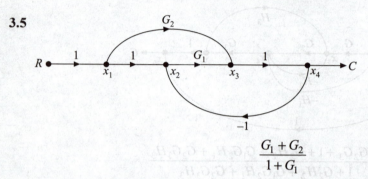

$$\frac{G_1 + G_2}{1 + G_1}$$

3.6

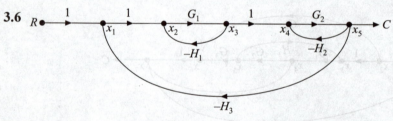

$$\frac{G_1 G_2}{1 + G_1 H_1 + G_2 H_2 + G_1 G_2 H_3 + G_1 G_2 H_1 H_2}$$

3.7

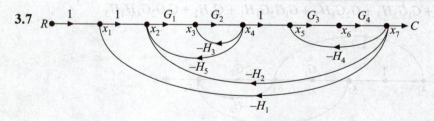

$$\frac{G_1 G_2 G_3 G_4}{1 + G_2 H_3 + G_1 G_2 H_5 + G_3 G_4 H_4 + G_1 G_2 G_3 G_4 H_2 + G_1 G_2 G_3 G_4 H_1 + G_2 G_3 G_4 H_3 H_4 + G_1 G_2 G_3 G_4 H_4 H_5}$$

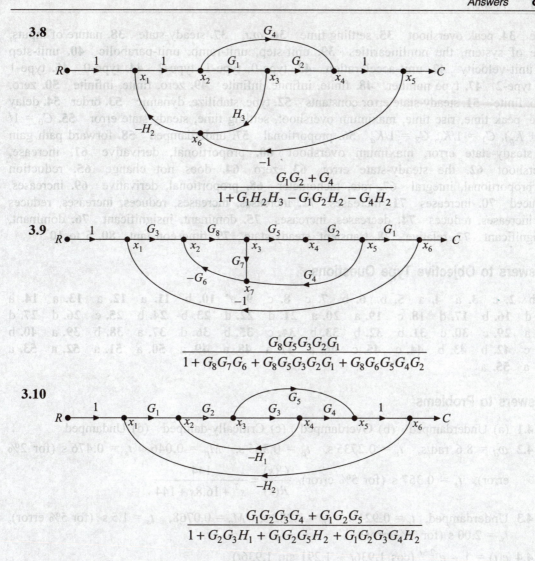

3.8

$$\frac{G_1 G_2 + G_4}{1 + G_1 H_2 H_3 - G_1 G_2 H_2 - G_4 H_2}$$

3.9

$$\frac{G_8 G_5 G_3 G_2 G_1}{1 + G_8 G_7 G_6 + G_8 G_5 G_3 G_2 G_1 + G_8 G_6 G_5 G_4 G_2}$$

3.10

$$\frac{G_1 G_2 G_3 G_4 + G_1 G_2 G_5}{1 + G_2 G_3 H_1 + G_1 G_2 G_5 H_2 + G_1 G_2 G_3 G_4 H_2}$$

CHAPTER 4

Answers to Fill in the Blanks

1. parameters **2.** not known **3.** a sudden shock, a sudden change, a constant velocity and a constant acceleration **4.** system poles, input **5.** system poles, input **6.** unit-impulse, unit-step, unit-ramp, unit-parabolic, sinusoidal **7.** impulse response **8.** impulse **9.** weighting function **10.** step **11.** ramp **12.** parabolic **13.** transient response, steady-state response **14.** dynamic response **15.** transient **16.** how fast **17.** sluggish, fast **18.** damping ratio **19.** undamped natural frequency **20.** characteristic polynomial **21.** characteristic equation **22.** poles **23.** characterize **24.** damped **25.** < **26.** undamped **27.** underdamped **28.** critically-damped **29.** overdamped **30.** less **31.** delay time **32.** rise time **33.** peak time **34.** peak overshoot **35.** settling time **36.** $\omega_n t_s$ **37.** steady-state **38.** nature of inputs, type of system, the nonlinearities **39.** unit-step, unit-ramp, unit-parabolic **40.** unit-step **41.** unit-velocity **42.** unit-acceleration **43.** type-0, type-1, type-2 **44.** type-0 **45.** type-1 **46.** type-2 **47.** type number **48.** finite, infinite, infinite **49.** zero, finite, infinite **50.** zero, zero, finite **51.** steady-state error constants **52.** type, stabilize, dynamic **53.** order **54.** delay time, peak time, rise time, maximum overshoot, settling time, steady-state error **55.** $C_0 = 1/(1 + K_p)$, $C_1 = 1/K_v$, $C_2 = 1/K_a$ **56.** proportional **57.** underdamped **58.** forward path gain **59.** steady-state error, maximum overshoot **60.** proportional, derivative **61.** increase, overshoot **62.** the steady-state error **63.** zero **64.** does not change **65.** reduction **66.** proportional, integral **67.** rate, tachometer **68.** proportional, derivative **69.** increases, reduced **70.** increases **71.** increases **72.** increases, increases, reduces, increases, reduces **73.** increases, reduces **74.** decreases, increases **75.** dominant, insignificant **76.** dominant, insignificant **77.** relative **78.** transient, steady-state **79.** time constant **80.** 5 to 10.

Answers to Objective Type Questions

1. b **2.** c **3.** a **4.** a **5.** b **6.** b **7.** c **8.** c **9.** a **10.** b **11.** a **12.** a **13.** a **14.** a
15. d **16.** b **17.** d **18.** c **19.** a **20.** a **21.** d **22.** d **23.** b **24.** b **25.** c **26.** d **27.** d
28. a **29.** c **30.** c **31.** b **32.** b **33.** b **34.** c **35.** b **36.** d **37.** a **38.** b **39.** a **40.** b
41. c **42.** b **43.** b **44.** c **45.** c **46.** a **47.** a **48.** a **49.** a **50.** a **51.** a **52.** a **53.** a
54. a **55.** a

Answers to Problems

4.1 (a) Underdamped (b) Overdamped (c) Critically-damped (d) Undamped

4.2 $\omega_d = 8.6$ rad/s, $t_r = 0.2735$ s, $t_p = 0.365$ s, $M_p = 0.046$, $t_s = 0.476$ s (for 2% error), $t_s = 0.357$ s (for 5% error), $\dfrac{C(s)}{R(s)} = \dfrac{144}{s^2 + 16.8s + 144}$

4.3 Underdamped, $t_r = 0.921$ s, $t_p = 1.282$ s, $M_p = 0.0768$, $t_s = 1.5$ s (for 5% error), $t_s = 2.00$ s (for 2% error).

4.4 $c(t) = 1 - e^{-2.5t}$ (cos $1.936t$ – 1.291 sin $1.936t$)

4.5 $\omega_d = 3.464$ rad/s, $t_r = 0.6046$ s, $t_p = 0.906$ s, $M_p = 0.163$ s, $t_s = 1.5$ s (for 5% error), $t_s = 2$ s (for 2% error).

4.6 $\dfrac{C(s)}{R(s)} = \dfrac{300}{s^2 + 40s + 300}$, $\omega_n = 17.32$ rad/s, $\xi = 1.155$

4.7 4.989

4.8 $\omega_n = 4.472$ rad/s, $\xi = 0.67$, % $M_p = 5.87\%$

4.9 $t_r = 1.209$ s, $t_p = 1.813$ s, $M_p = 2.445$, % $M_p = 16.3\%$, $t_s = 3$ s (for 5% error), $t_s = 4$ s (for 2% error).

4.10 $K = 5.514$, $T = 0.388$

4.11 e_{ss} (step) = 0, e_{ss} (velocity) = 1, e_{ss} (acceleration) = ∞

4.12 $e_{ss} = \infty$

4.13 $C_0 = 0$, $C_1 = 0.2$, $C_2 = 1.2$, $e_{ss}(t) = 0.2$

4.14 Type-2 system, $K_p = \infty$, $K_v = \infty$, $K_a = \dfrac{6K}{15}$, e_{ss} (step) = 0, e_{ss} (ramp) = 0,

e_{ss} (parabolic) = $\dfrac{15}{6K}$

4.15 (a) $K_p = 25$, $K_v = 0$, $K_a = 0$ (b) $K_p = \infty$, $K_v = 20$, $K_a = 0$

    (c) $K_p = \infty$, $K_v = \infty$, $K_a = 5$ (d) $K_p = \infty$, $K_v = \infty$, $K_a = \infty$

4.16 $e(t) = \dfrac{3}{13}r(t) + \dfrac{25}{169}\dot{r}(t) - \dfrac{95}{2197}\ddot{r}(t)$

    (a) $e(t) = \dfrac{3}{13}$, $e_{ss}(t) = \dfrac{3}{13}$

    (b) $e(t) = \dfrac{3}{13}(2t) + \dfrac{50}{169}$; $e_{ss}(t) = \infty$

    (c) $e(t) = \dfrac{3}{13}\dfrac{t^2}{2} + \dfrac{25}{169}t - \dfrac{95}{2197}$, $e_{ss}(t) = \infty$

    (d) $e(t) = \dfrac{3}{13}\left(1 + 2t + \dfrac{t^2}{2}\right) + \dfrac{25}{169}(2 + t) - \dfrac{95}{2197}$, $e_{ss}(t) = \infty$

CHAPTER 5

Answers to Fill in the Blanks

1. linear time-invariant   **2.** linear   **3.** nonlinear   **4.** (a) when the system is excited by a bounded input, the output is bounded (b) in the absence of the input, the output tends to zero irrespective of the initial conditions   **5.** inputs, initial conditions, system parameters **6.** qualitative, quantitative   **7.** negative real parts   **8.** positive real part   **9.** inversely **10.** all values of that parameter   **11.** a range of values of that parameter   **12.** first, second **13.** transient   **14.** unstable   **15.** symmetrically   **16.** real, complex   **17.** right-half **18.** absolute, relative.

Answers to Objective Type Questions

1. c   **2.** b   **3.** a   **4.** c   **5.** c   **6.** d   **7.** a   **8.** a   **9.** a   **10.** a   **11.** b   **12.** a   **13.** a   **14.** a **15.** b   **16.** a   **17.** b   **18.** b   **19.** a   **20.** d   **21.** c   **22.** b   **23.** b   **24.** b   **25.** c   **26.** b

Answers to Problems

5.1 (a) Unstable, one root in RH of s-plane   (b) Unstable, one root in RHS, two roots on $j\omega$ axis and two roots in LHS   (c) Stable, all roots in LHS   (d) Unstable, two roots in RHS (e) Unstable, two roots in RHS   (f) Stable, all roots in LHS   (g) Unstable, two roots in RHS and five roots in LHS   (h) Unstable, two roots in LHS, two roots on $j\omega$-axis and two roots in RHS   (i) Unstable, two roots in RHS   (j) Unstable, two roots in RHS, 5 roots in LHS   (k) Unstable, no root in RHS, two pairs of roots on $j\omega$-axis

5.2   (i) (a) $K > 0.73$,   (b) Yes, $K = 0.73$, $\omega = 1.65$ rad/s,

   (ii) (a) $0 < K < 80$,   (b) Yes, $K = 80$, $\omega = 2$ rad/s

   (iii) (a) $0 < K < 11.36$,   (b) Yes, $K = 11.36$, $\omega = 0.88$ rad/s,

   (iv) (a) No value of K,   (b) No.

   (v) (a) $K > 1.45$,   (b) Yes, $K = 1.45$, $\omega = 1.7$ rad/s

   (vi) (a) $0 < K < 10$,   (b) Yes, $K = 10$, $\omega = 2.236$ rad/s

   (vii) (a) No value of K (b) No

   (viii) (a) $0 < K < 0.0384$ (b) Yes, $K = 0.384$, $\omega = 0.2$ rad/s.

5.3 $0 < K < \dfrac{60}{121}, K_m = \dfrac{60}{121}, \omega = \dfrac{1}{\sqrt{11}}$ rad/s

5.4 (a) $0 < K < 11.56$ (b) Stability is reduced ($0 < K < 4$)

5.5 $0 < K < \dfrac{14}{9}, K_m = \dfrac{14}{9}, \omega = 0.816$ rad/s

5.6 No

5.7 Unstable

5.8 $0 < K < 6$

5.9 (a) $0 < K < 20$,   (b) $K > 0$

5.10 (a) No. Unstable   (b) $K_m = 0.46$

5.11 $K < 6.5$

5.12 $0 < K < 0.9$, $K_m = 0.9$, $\omega = 0.3013$ rad/s

5.13 $0 < K < 3.36$

5.14 (a) $0 < K < 7644$, $K_m = 7644$, $\omega = 7.874$ rad/s

   (b) $K > 1.40$, $K_m = 1.40$, $\omega = 2.37$ rad/s

5.15 $0 < K < 22.75$, $K_m = 22.75$, $\omega = 2.55$ rad/s

5.16 $K > 0$

5.17 $K_m = \dfrac{1}{T}$

5.18 Stable for $K > 0.5$ in both cases

5.19 $K_m = \dfrac{1}{3}$

CHAPTER 6

Answers to Fill in the Blanks

1. W.R. Evans   **2.** algebraic   **3.** dynamic response   **4.** independent, implies   **5.** $\angle G(s_0)H(s_0)$ $= \pm(2q + 1)\pi$; $q = 0, 1, 2,...$ **6.** $|G(s)H(s)|_{s=s_0} = 1$ **7.** root locus   **8.** absolute, relative **9.** symmetrical   **10.** the open-loop gain K **11.** an open-loop pole, $K = 0$, open-loop zero, zero at infinity, $K = \infty$.   **12.** no. of open-loop poles minus no. of open-loop zeros   **13.** no. of open-loop poles minus no. of open-loop zeros   **14.** odd   **15.** straight line   **16.** centroid, (sum of real parts of poles – sum of real parts of zeros)/(no. of poles – no. of zeros)   **17.** break points

18. real, complex   **19.** $\dfrac{dK}{ds} = 0$ **20.** 0° or 180°   **21.** $\pm(2q + 1)\pi + \phi$, net angle contribution made at that pole by all other open-loop poles and zeros.   **22.** $\pm(2q + 1)\pi - \phi$, net angle contribution made at that zero by all other open-loop poles and zeros.

23. $\dfrac{\text{product of phasor lengths from } s_0 \text{ to all the open-loop poles}}{\text{product of phasor lengths from } s_0 \text{ to all the open-loop zeros}}$ **24.** Routh stability criterion

25. very near to the origin.

Answers to Objective Type Questions

1. b   **2.** a   **3.** a   **4.** c   **5.** a   **6.** a   **7.** b   **8.** a   **9.** a   **10.** c   **11.** c   **12.** b   **13.** c   **14.** a **15.** c   **16.** c   **17.** b   **18.** c

Answers to Problems

6.1 $\theta_0 = \pi$, $-\sigma = 2$, break points at $s = -1.18$ and $s = -6.82$, No θ_d or θ_a, circle with centre at $(-4, 0)$ radius $= 2.82$, overdamped for $0 < K < 0.343$ and $11.65 < K < \infty$, critically damped for $K = 0.343$ and $K = 11.65$, underdamped for $0.343 < K < 11.65$, $\xi_{min} = 0.707$, K for $\xi_{min} = 2$, roots are $s = -2 + j2$ and $s = -2 -j2$, on real axis RL exists between $s = 0$ to $s = -2$ and to the left of $s = -4$.

6.2 $\theta_0 = \pi$, $-\sigma = 0$, break point at $s = -3.414$, $\theta_d = 135°, -135°$, circle of radius $\sqrt{2}$; centred at $(-2, 0)$, on real axis RL exists to the left of $s = -2$.

6.3 $\theta_0 = \dfrac{\pi}{2}$, $\theta_1 = \dfrac{3\pi}{2}$, $-\sigma = -1$, No θ_d, break point at $s = -0.44$, $\omega_0 = 2.23$ rad/s, $K_m = 3$, overdamped for $0 < K < 0.083$, underdamped for $0.083 < K < 3$, critically damped for $K = 0.083$, $K = 0.26$ for $\xi = 0.5$, $\dfrac{C(s)}{R(s)} = \dfrac{0.26}{(s + 4 + j0.6)(s + 4 - j0.6)(s + 2.25)}$, on real axis RL exists between $s = 0$ to -1 and from $s = -2$ to $s = -5$.

6.4 $\theta_0 = \dfrac{\pi}{2}$, $\theta_1 = \dfrac{3\pi}{2}$, $-\sigma = 1$, no break points, $\omega_0 = 1.71$ rad/s, $K_m = 1$, $\theta_d = 7.3°, -7.3°$, on real axis RL exists from $s = 0$ to $s = -3$.

6.5 $\theta_0 = \dfrac{\pi}{2}$, $\theta_1 = \dfrac{3\pi}{2}$, $-\sigma = -1$, no break points, $\theta_d = 90°$, $-90°$, no RL on real axis.

6.6 $\theta_0 = \dfrac{\pi}{2}$, $\theta_1 = \dfrac{3\pi}{2}$, $-\sigma = -1$, break points at $s = 0$, $s = -3$, $\theta_a = 126.86°$, $-126.86°$. No RL on real axis.

6.7 $\theta_0 = \pi$, $-\sigma = -5$, break points at $s = 0.625$ and $s = -8.32$, $\omega_0 = 2$ rad/s, $K_m = 1.2$ (for stability $K > 1.2$). On real axis RL exists from $s = 1.414$ to $s = 0$, from $s = -1$ to -1.414 and to the left of $s = -4$.

6.8 No asymptote, no centroid, break point at $s = -1.38$, unstable for all values of K, $\theta_d = -116.6°$, $116.6°$, on real axis RL exists from $s = 1$ to $s = 0$ and $s = -1$ to $s = -2$.

6.9 $\theta_0 = \pi$, $-\sigma = 2.5$, break points at $s = 0.41$ and $s = -4$, $\omega_0 = 1$ rad/s, $K_m = 0.8$ (for stability $K > 0.8$), no θ_d, on real axis RL exists from $s = 1$ to $s = 0$, $s = -0.5$ to $s = -1$ and to the left of $s = -2$.

6.10 $\theta_0 = \dfrac{\pi}{3}$, $\theta_1 = \pi$, $\theta_2 = \dfrac{5\pi}{3}$, $-\sigma = 1$, break points at $s = 0$ and $s = -3.26$, $\theta_d = -164°$, $164°$, on the real axis RL exists to the left of $s = -5$.

6.11 $\theta_0 = \dfrac{\pi}{2}$, $\theta_1 = \dfrac{3\pi}{2}$, $-\sigma = -4$, break point at $s = 0$, stable for $K > 0$. No θ_d or θ_a, on real axis RL exists from $s = -12$ to $s = -20$.

6.12 $\theta_0 = \dfrac{\pi}{3}$, $\theta_1 = \pi$, $\theta_2 = \dfrac{5\pi}{3}$, $-\sigma = -2$, no break point, $\theta_d = -56.°$, $56°$, $\omega_0 = 3.46$ rad/s, $K_m - 78$, for stability $0 < K < 78$, on real axis RL exists to the left of $s = 0$.

6.13 No asymptotes, no centroid, break points at $s = -0.42$ and $s = -2.38$, circle of radius 1 with centre $(-1, 0)$, $K_m = \dfrac{1}{6}$, $K > \dfrac{1}{6}$ for stability, on real axis RL exists from $s = +1$ to $s = -1$ and $s = -2$ to $s = -3$.

6.14 $\theta_0 = 180°$, $-\sigma = 0$, break points at $s = -1$ and $s = -3$, circle of radius 1.12 centred at $(-1.5, 0)$, no θ_d or θ_a, undampled for $0 < K < 4$, critically dampled for $K = 0$ and $K = 4$, overdamped for $K > 4$, $\xi_{min} = 0.866$. K for ξ_{min} is 1, on real axis RL exists to the left of $s = -2$. $\dfrac{C(s)}{R(s)} = \dfrac{1}{(s + 1.5 + j0.9)(s + 1.5 - j1.9)}$.

6.15 $\theta_0 = \dfrac{\pi}{3}$, $\theta_1 = \pi$, $\theta_2 = \dfrac{5\pi}{3}$, $-\sigma = -1.33$, no break points, $K_m = 52$, $\omega_0 = 3.6$ rad/s, $\theta_d = -33.7°$, $33.7°$, on real axis RL exists to the left of $s = 0$.

6.16 $\theta_0 = \pi$, $-\sigma = 0$, break point at $s = -6.83$, circle of radius $\sqrt{8}$ centred at $(-4, 0)$. $\theta_d = -135°$, $135°$, on real axis RL exists to the left of $s = -4$.

6.17 $\theta_0 = \pi$, $-\sigma = 3$, break point at $s = -0.348$, $\theta_a = 77.4°$, $-77.4°$, for stability $K > 0$, on real axis RL exists from $s = 0$ to $s = -1$ and to the left of $s = -2$.

CHAPTER 7

Answers to Fill in the Blanks

1. sinusoidal, steady-state   **2.** resonant peak   **3.** resonant peak   **4.** bandwidth   **5.** cut-off rate
6. increase   **7.** less, decreasing   **8.** inversely   **9.** directly   **10.** faster   **11.** increases, decreases
12. inversely   **13.** ξ **14.** polar   **15.** logarithmic   **16.** semi log   **17.** straight line asymptotes   **18.** corner frequency   **19.** gain crossover   **20.** phase crossover   **21.** phase margin   **22.** gain
margin   **23.** positive   **24.** sluggish   **25.** minimum-phase   **26.** antisymmetric   **27.** nonminimum-
phase   **28.** minimum-phase, all-pass   **29.** nonminimum-phase

Answers to Objective Type Questions

1. c   **2.** b   **3.** c   **4.** b   **5.** b   **6.** d   **7.** d   **8.** c   **9.** b   **10.** b   **11.** b   **12.** a   **13.** a   **14.** b
15. c   **16.** b   **17.** b   **18.** c   **19.** b   **20.** a   **21.** c   **22.** b   **23.** a

Answers to Problems

7.1 $K = 353.47$, $b = 17.74$, $t_s = 0.45$ s (2%), $t_s = 0.338$ s (5%), $\omega_b = 24.51$ rad/s

7.2 $M_r = 1.24$, $\omega_r = 8.99$ rad/s, $\omega_b = 15.52$ rad/s

7.3 (a) $G(j0) = 1 - j0$, $G(j\infty) = -0 - j0$, plot does not cross the real axis. It crosses the
imaginary axis at $\omega = 1/2$ with $|G(j\omega)| = 0.4$.

(b) $G(j0) = -5 - j\infty$, $G(j\infty) = -0 + j0$, plot crosses the real axis at $\omega = 1/2$ with
$|G(j\omega)| = 0.8$

(c) $G(j0) = -\infty + j\infty$, $G(j\infty) = 0 + j0$, plot does not cross the real axis. It crosses the
imaginary axis at $\omega = 1/2$ with $|G(j\omega)| = 1.6$.

(d) $G(j0) = -\infty + j\infty$, $G(j\infty) = -0 + j0$, plot does not cross the real axis.

7.4 (a) $\omega_g = 4.25$ rad/s, $\omega_p = 6.5$ rad/s, GM = 8 dB, PM = 13.5°, stable

(b) $\omega_g = 8.5$ rad/s, $\omega_p = 11$ rad/s, GM = 5 dB, PM = 7°, stable

7.5 (a) With $K = 1$, $\omega_g = 1.2$ rad/s, For $\omega_g = 10$ rad/s, $K = 0.14$, stable

(b) With $K = 1$, $\omega_g = 0.85$ rad/s, For $\omega_g = 10$ rad/s, $K = 250$, stable

7.6 (a) $G(s) = 0.67 (1 + 0.2s) (1 + 0.083s)/s (1 + 0.033s)$

(b) $G(s) = 800 (1 + 0.1s)^2/s (1 + 0.4s) (1 + 0.02s)$

(c) $G(s) = 252s^2/(1 + 2s) (1 + s) (1 + 0.2s) (1 + 0.05s)$

CHAPTER 8

Answers to Fill in the Blanks

1. location of the roots of the characteristic equation   **2.** absolute, relative   **3.** location
4. principle of argument   **5.** to the right   **6.** principle of argument   **7.** real axis   **8.** singular
points   **9.** analytic   **10.** infinite radius   **11.** stability   **12.** improves   **13.** relative stability,
instability   **14.** margin   **15.** reciprocal   **16.** constant ∞ **17.** Resonant peak M_r and resonant

frequency ω_r **18.** 35°   **19.** 0.25   **20.** 20 dB   **21.** –0.0315   **22.** oscillatory   **23.** 0   **24.** 0°
25. constant M **26.** constant N **27.** closed-loop frequency, open-loop frequency   **28.** constant
M and constant N circles   **29.** closed-loop frequency, open-loop frequency   **30.** frequency

Answers to Objective Type Questions

1. b   **2.** a   **3.** b   **4.** b   **5.** a   **6.** b   **7.** c   **8.** b   **9.** c   **10.** b   **11.** a   **12.** b   **13.** c   **14.** c
15. b   **16.** b   **17.** b   **18.** c   **19.** b   **20.** c   **21.** b   **22.** a   **23.** c   **24.** b   **25.** c.

Answers to Problems

8.1 (a) $G(-j\infty)\,H(-j\infty) = -0,\ G(j0^-)\,H(j0^-) = 0.01$

$G(j0^+)\,H(j0^+) = 0.01,\ G(j\infty)\,H(j\infty) = -0$

Nyquist plot is on x-axis from -0 to 0.01.
System is unstable, two poles on $j\omega$-axis.

(b) $G(-j\infty)\,H(-j\infty) = -0 - j0,\ G(j0^-)\,H(j0^-) = -5 + j\infty$

$G(j0^+)\,H(j0^+) = -5 - j\infty,\ G(j\infty)\,H(j\infty) = -0 + j0$

Nyquist plot intersects the real axis at -0.8 for $\omega = 0.5$. It does not encircle the
$-1 + j0$ point. System is stable.

(c) $G(-j\infty)\,H(-j\infty) = 0 - j0,\ G(j0^-)\,H(j0^-) = -\infty - j\infty$

$G(j0^+)\,H(j0^+) = -\infty + j\infty,\ G(j\infty)\,H(j\infty) = 0 + j0$

Nyquist plot encircles the $-1 + j0$ point twice in clockwise direction.
System is unstable, two poles in RH s-plane.

8.2 $G(-j\infty)\,H(-j\infty) = \dfrac{K}{16} + j0,\ G(j0^-)\,H(j0^-) = -\dfrac{K}{2} - j0$

$G(j0^+)\,H(j0^+) = -\dfrac{K}{2} + j0,\ G(j\infty)\,H(j\infty) = \dfrac{K}{16} - j0$

Nyquist plot intersects the real axis at $-0.0806\,K$ for $\omega = 0.06166$ rad/s. It encircles the
$-1 + j0$ point once in clockwise direction for $K > 12.4$.
System is stable for $K > 12.4$.

8.3 $G(-j\infty)\,H(-j\infty) = -0 + j0,\ G(j0^-)\,H(j0^-) = \dfrac{3}{2} + j0$

$G(j0^+)\,H(j0^+) = \dfrac{3}{2} - j0,\ G(j\infty)\,H(j\infty) = -0 - j0$

Nyquist plot does not encircle the $-1 + j0$ point.
System is stable.

8.4 $G(-j\infty)\,H(-j\infty) = -0 + j0,\ G(j0^-)\,H(j0^-) = -\dfrac{3}{2}K - j\infty$

$G(j0^+)\,H(j0^+) = -\dfrac{3}{2}K + j\infty,\ G(j\infty)\,H(j\infty) = -0 - j0$

Nyquist plot intersects the real axis at $-\dfrac{K}{2}$ for $\omega = \sqrt{8}$ rad/s.

It encircles the $-1 + j0$ point for $K > 2$.

The system is stable for $K > 2$.

8.5 $G(-j\infty)\ H(-j\infty) = 0 + j0$, $G(j0^-)\ H(j0^-) = -\dfrac{3}{2}K - j0$

$G(j0^+)\ H(j0^+) = -\dfrac{3}{2}K + j0$, $G(j\infty)\ H(j\infty) = 0 - j0$

Nyquist plot intersects the real axis at $\dfrac{K}{256}$ for $\omega = \sqrt{28}$ rad/s on the right side and at

$-\dfrac{3}{2}K$ for $\omega = 0$ on the left side. Nyquist plot encircles the $-1 + j0$ point for $K > \dfrac{2}{3}$.

System is stable for $K < \dfrac{2}{3}$.

8.6 $G(-j\infty)\ H(-j\infty) = -0 - j0$, $G(j0^-)\ H(j0^-) = -\infty - j\infty$

$G(j0^+)\ H(j0^+) = -\infty + j\infty$, $G(j\infty)\ H(j\infty) = -0 + j0$

Nyquist plot encircles the $-1 + j0$ point twice in the clockwise direction.
System is unstable, two poles in RH s-plane.

8.7 $G(-j\infty)\ H(-j\infty) = -0 - j0$, $G(j0^-)\ H(j0^-) = -\dfrac{K}{18} + j\infty$

$G(j0^+)\ H(j0^+) = -\dfrac{K}{18} - j\infty$, $G(j\infty)\ H(j\infty) = -0 + j0$

Nyquist plot intersects the real axis at $-\dfrac{K}{12}$ for $\omega = \sqrt{6}$ rad/s. It encircles the $-1 + j0$

point for $K > 12$.
System is unstable for $K < 12$.

8.8 $G(-j\infty)\ H(-j\infty) = -\infty - j\infty$, $G(j0^-)\ H(j0^-) = -0 - j0$

$G(j0^+)\ H(j0^+) = -0 + j0$, $G(j\infty)\ H(j\infty) = -\infty + j\infty$

Nyquist plot does not encircle the $-1 + j0$ point.
System is stable.

8.9 (a) $K = 5.208$, (b) $K = 5.5$

8.10 $\omega_g = 0.445$ rad/s, $\omega_p = 0.5$ rad/s, $GM = 1.94$ dB, $PM = 5.34°$, system is stable.

CHAPTER 9

Answers to Fill in the Blanks

1. damping ratio ξ, peak overshoot M_p **2.** rise time t_r, settling time t_s, undamped natural
frequency ω_n **3.** resonant peak M_r, phase margin ϕ_{pm} **4.** resonant frequency ω_r, bandwidth ω_b

5. series or cascade compensation, feedback or parallel compensation   **6.** transient   **7.** steady-state   **8.** transient, steady-state   **9.** lead, lag   **10.** zero   **11.** pole   **12.** attenuation, phase-lag   **13.** simplicity in analysis and design, ease in experimental determination of frequency response for real systems   **14.** Nyquist plots, Bode plots, Nichols chart   **15.** Bode plots   **16.** resonant peak M_r, resonant frequency ω_r **17.** phase margin ϕ_{pm}, bandwidth ω_b **18.** Nichols chart   **19.** gain crossover frequency   **20.** frequency, time   **21.** geometric mean   **22.** high-pass   **23.** low-pass   **24.** band-pass   **25.** reduced

Answers to Objective Type Questions

1. b   **2.** a   **3.** c   **4.** a   **5.** c   **6.** a   **7.** a   **8.** c   **9.** b   **10.** a   **11.** a or c   **12.** b or c   **13.** c

Answers to Problems

9.1 $G_c(s) = \left(\dfrac{1 + 0.285s}{1 + 0.091s} \right)$

For uncompensated system gcf = 4.5 rad/s, PM = 22°, pcf = ∞, GM = ∞
For lead compensated system gcf = 6.2 rad/s, PM = 49°, pcf = ∞, GM = ∞

9.2 $G_c(s) = \left(\dfrac{1 + 0.3972s}{1 + 0.0867s} \right)$

For uncompensated system gcf = 3 rad/s, PM = −30°, pcf = 0, GM = negative
For lead compensated system gcf = 5.7 rad/s, PM = 32°, pcf = 11.5 rad/s, GM = 4 dB

9.3 $G_c(s) = \left(\dfrac{1 + 5s}{1 + 50s} \right)$

For uncompensated system gcf = 3.2 rad/s, PM = 2°, pcf = 3.2 rad/s, GM = 1 dB
For lag compensated system gcf = 0.8 rad/s, PM = 34°, pcf = 2.8 rad/s, GM = 12 dB

9.4 $G_c(s) = \left(\dfrac{1 + s}{1 + 5.3s} \right) \left(\dfrac{1 + 0.46s}{1 + 0.086s} \right)$

For uncompensated system gcf = 8.5 rad/s, PM = −10°, pcf = 7.5 rad/s, GM = 1 dB
For lag compensated system gcf = 3.3 rad/s, PM = 22°, pcf = 6.8 rad/s, GM = 10 dB
For lag-lead compensated system gcf = 7 rad/s, PM = 40°, pcf = 9 rad/s, GM = 10 dB

CHAPTER 10

Answers to Fill in the Blanks

1. the transfer function approach, the state variable approach   **2.** conventional approach, classical approach, modern approach   **3.** linear time-invariant single-input-single-output systems, linear, nonlinear, time-invariant, time-varying, single-input-single-output, multi-input-multi-output   **4.** neglects, considers   **5.** frequency-domain, time-domain   **6.** trial and error   **7.** unique   **8.** state model, transfer function   **9.** order   **10.** currents through the inductors, voltages across the capacitors **11.** the outputs of the integrators **12.** input variables, output variables, state variables **13.** integrators **14.** Integrators **15.** past, present, future **16.** state equation, system matrix, input matrix **17.** output equation, output matrix, transmission matrix **18.** state variables, inputs **19.** state variables, inputs **20.** dynamic equations **21.** canonical **22.** Jordan canonical **23.** (a) diagonal canonical form (DCF), (b) Jordan canonical form (JCF), (c) controllability canonical form (CCF), (d) observability canonical form (OCF) and (e) phase variable canonical form (PCF) **24.** phase variables **25.** Bush, companion **26.** $n \times 1$ state vector, $m \times 1$ input vector, $p \times 1$ output vector, $n \times n$ system matrix, $n \times m$ input matrix, $p \times n$ output matrix, $p \times m$ transmission matrix **27.** STM **28.** free **29.** resolvent matrix **30.** (a) using exponential series, (b) using Laplace transform, (c) using Cayley–Hamilton theorem, (d) using modal matrix, (e) using Sylvester's method **31.** length of the time $(t - t_0)$ **32.** STM of $\mathbf{A}$ **33.** $|\lambda \mathbf{I} - \mathbf{A}| = 0$ **34.** state transition equation **35.** eigenvalues **36.** decomposition **37.** direct decomposition, cascade decomposition, parallel decomposition **38.** canonical, Jordan canonical **39.** eigenvalues **40.** poles **41.** state model or dynamic equations **42.** modal matrix **43.** Cayley–Hamilton theorem **44.** Kalman **45.** Gilbert's **46.** observable **47.** controllable **48.** $\mathbf{S} = [\mathbf{B} \ \mathbf{AB} \ \mathbf{A}^2\mathbf{B} \ \dots \ \mathbf{A}^{n-1}\mathbf{B}]$ **49.** $\mathbf{S} = [\mathbf{CB} \ \mathbf{CAB} \ \mathbf{CA}^2\mathbf{B} \ \dots \ \mathbf{CA}^{n-1}\mathbf{BD}]$ **50.** $\mathbf{S} = [\mathbf{C}^T \ \mathbf{A}^T\mathbf{C}^T \ \dots \ (\mathbf{A}^T)^{n-1}\mathbf{C}^T]$ **51.** unique, unique

Answers to Objective Type Questions

1. a **2.** d **3.** a **4.** a **5.** b **6.** a **7.** b **8.** d **9.** c **10.** c **11.** b **12.** c **13.** b **14.** c

Answers to Problems

10.1 (a) (i)
$$\begin{bmatrix} \dot{x}_1 \\ \dot{x}_2 \\ \dot{x}_3 \end{bmatrix} = \begin{bmatrix} 0 & 1 & 0 \\ 0 & 0 & 1 \\ 0 & -8 & -6 \end{bmatrix}\begin{bmatrix} x_1 \\ x_2 \\ x_3 \end{bmatrix} + \begin{bmatrix} 0 \\ 0 \\ 1 \end{bmatrix}u, \quad y = [30 \ \ 10 \ \ 0]\begin{bmatrix} x_1 \\ x_2 \\ x_3 \end{bmatrix}$$

(ii)
$$\begin{bmatrix} \dot{x}_1 \\ \dot{x}_2 \\ \dot{x}_3 \end{bmatrix} = \begin{bmatrix} -4 & 1 & 0 \\ 0 & -2 & 1 \\ 0 & 0 & 0 \end{bmatrix}\begin{bmatrix} x_1 \\ x_2 \\ x_3 \end{bmatrix} + \begin{bmatrix} 0 \\ 0 \\ 10 \end{bmatrix}u, \quad y = [-1 \ \ 1 \ \ 0]\begin{bmatrix} x_1 \\ x_2 \\ x_3 \end{bmatrix}$$

(iii)
$$\begin{bmatrix} \dot{x}_1 \\ \dot{x}_2 \\ \dot{x}_3 \end{bmatrix} = \begin{bmatrix} 0 & 0 & 0 \\ 0 & -2 & 0 \\ 0 & 0 & -4 \end{bmatrix}\begin{bmatrix} x_1 \\ x_2 \\ x_3 \end{bmatrix} + \begin{bmatrix} 1 \\ 1 \\ 1 \end{bmatrix}u, \quad y = [3.75 \ \ -2.5 \ \ -1.25]\begin{bmatrix} x_1 \\ x_2 \\ x_3 \end{bmatrix}$$

(b) (i)
$$\begin{bmatrix} \dot{x}_1 \\ \dot{x}_2 \\ \dot{x}_3 \end{bmatrix} = \begin{bmatrix} 0 & 1 & 0 \\ 0 & 0 & 1 \\ -4 & -8 & -5 \end{bmatrix}\begin{bmatrix} x_1 \\ x_2 \\ x_3 \end{bmatrix} + \begin{bmatrix} 0 \\ 0 \\ 1 \end{bmatrix}u, \quad y = [5 \ \ 0 \ \ 0]\begin{bmatrix} x_1 \\ x_2 \\ x_3 \end{bmatrix}$$

(ii)
$$\begin{bmatrix} \dot{x}_1 \\ \dot{x}_2 \\ \dot{x}_3 \end{bmatrix} = \begin{bmatrix} -2 & 1 & 0 \\ 0 & -2 & 1 \\ 0 & 0 & -1 \end{bmatrix}\begin{bmatrix} x_1 \\ x_2 \\ x_3 \end{bmatrix} + \begin{bmatrix} 0 \\ 0 \\ 5 \end{bmatrix}u, \quad y = [1 \ \ 0 \ \ 0]\begin{bmatrix} x_1 \\ x_2 \\ x_3 \end{bmatrix}$$

(iii) $\begin{bmatrix} \dot{x}_1 \\ \dot{x}_2 \\ \dot{x}_3 \end{bmatrix} = \begin{bmatrix} -1 & 0 & 0 \\ 0 & -2 & 1 \\ 0 & 0 & -2 \end{bmatrix} \begin{bmatrix} x_1 \\ x_2 \\ x_3 \end{bmatrix} + \begin{bmatrix} 1 \\ 0 \\ 1 \end{bmatrix} u, \quad y = [5 \quad -5 \quad -5] \begin{bmatrix} x_1 \\ x_2 \\ x_3 \end{bmatrix}$

(c) (i) $\begin{bmatrix} \dot{x}_1 \\ \dot{x}_2 \\ \dot{x}_3 \end{bmatrix} = \begin{bmatrix} 0 & 1 & 0 \\ 0 & 0 & 1 \\ -48 & -44 & -12 \end{bmatrix} \begin{bmatrix} x_1 \\ x_2 \\ x_3 \end{bmatrix} + \begin{bmatrix} 0 \\ 0 \\ 1 \end{bmatrix} u, \quad y = [-33 \quad -21 \quad -3] \begin{bmatrix} x_1 \\ x_2 \\ x_3 \end{bmatrix} + u$

(ii) $\begin{bmatrix} \dot{x}_1 \\ \dot{x}_2 \\ \dot{x}_3 \end{bmatrix} = \begin{bmatrix} -6 & -1 & -1 \\ 0 & -4 & -1 \\ 0 & 0 & -2 \end{bmatrix} \begin{bmatrix} x_1 \\ x_2 \\ x_3 \end{bmatrix} + \begin{bmatrix} 1 \\ 1 \\ 1 \end{bmatrix} u, \quad y = [-1 \quad -1 \quad -1] \begin{bmatrix} x_1 \\ x_2 \\ x_3 \end{bmatrix} + u$

(iii) $\begin{bmatrix} \dot{x}_1 \\ \dot{x}_2 \\ \dot{x}_3 \end{bmatrix} = \begin{bmatrix} -2 & 0 & 0 \\ 0 & -4 & 0 \\ 0 & 0 & -6 \end{bmatrix} \begin{bmatrix} x_1 \\ x_2 \\ x_3 \end{bmatrix} + \begin{bmatrix} 1 \\ 1 \\ 1 \end{bmatrix} u, \quad y = \left[-\dfrac{3}{8} \quad -\dfrac{3}{4} \quad -\dfrac{15}{8} \right] \begin{bmatrix} x_1 \\ x_2 \\ x_3 \end{bmatrix} + u$

10.2 (a) $\begin{bmatrix} \dot{x}_1 \\ \dot{x}_2 \\ \dot{x}_3 \\ \dot{x}_4 \\ \dot{x}_5 \\ \dot{x}_6 \end{bmatrix} = \begin{bmatrix} -1 & 1 & 0 & 0 & 0 & 0 \\ 0 & -1 & 1 & 0 & 0 & 0 \\ 0 & 0 & -1 & 0 & 0 & 0 \\ 0 & 0 & 0 & -2 & 1 & 0 \\ 0 & 0 & 0 & 0 & -2 & 0 \\ 0 & 0 & 0 & 0 & 0 & -3 \end{bmatrix} \begin{bmatrix} x_1 \\ x_2 \\ x_3 \\ x_4 \\ x_5 \\ x_6 \end{bmatrix} + \begin{bmatrix} 0 \\ 0 \\ 1 \\ 0 \\ 1 \\ 1 \end{bmatrix} u, \quad y = \left[\dfrac{1}{2} \quad \dfrac{1}{4} \quad \dfrac{-13}{4} \quad 2 \quad 5 \quad \dfrac{5}{8} \right] \begin{bmatrix} x_1 \\ x_2 \\ x_3 \\ x_4 \\ x_5 \\ x_6 \end{bmatrix}$

(b) $\begin{bmatrix} \dot{x}_1 \\ \dot{x}_2 \\ \dot{x}_3 \\ \dot{x}_4 \\ \dot{x}_5 \end{bmatrix} = \begin{bmatrix} -1 & 1 & 0 & 0 & 0 \\ 0 & -1 & 1 & 0 & 0 \\ 0 & 0 & -1 & 0 & 0 \\ 0 & 0 & 0 & -2 & 0 \\ 0 & 0 & 0 & 0 & 0 \end{bmatrix} \begin{bmatrix} x_1 \\ x_2 \\ x_3 \\ x_4 \\ x_5 \end{bmatrix} + \begin{bmatrix} 0 \\ 0 \\ 1 \\ 1 \\ 1 \end{bmatrix} u, \quad y = \left[-1 \quad 0 \quad -1 \quad \dfrac{1}{2} \quad \dfrac{1}{2} \right] \begin{bmatrix} x_1 \\ x_2 \\ x_3 \\ x_4 \\ x_5 \end{bmatrix}$

(c) $\begin{bmatrix} \dot{x}_1 \\ \dot{x}_2 \\ \dot{x}_3 \end{bmatrix} = \begin{bmatrix} -3 & 1 & 0 \\ 0 & -3 & 0 \\ 0 & 0 & 0 \end{bmatrix} \begin{bmatrix} x_1 \\ x_2 \\ x_3 \end{bmatrix} + \begin{bmatrix} 0 \\ 1 \\ 1 \end{bmatrix} u, \quad y = \left[\dfrac{10}{3} \quad \dfrac{-5}{9} \quad \dfrac{5}{9} \right] \begin{bmatrix} x_1 \\ x_2 \\ x_3 \end{bmatrix}$

10.3 (a) $\begin{bmatrix} \dot{x}_1 \\ \dot{x}_2 \\ \dot{x}_3 \end{bmatrix} = \begin{bmatrix} 0 & 1 & 0 \\ 0 & 0 & 1 \\ -1 & -2.5 & -1.5 \end{bmatrix} \begin{bmatrix} x_1 \\ x_2 \\ x_3 \end{bmatrix} + \begin{bmatrix} 0 \\ 0 \\ 0.5 \end{bmatrix} u, \quad y = [1 \quad 0 \quad 0] \begin{bmatrix} x_1 \\ x_2 \\ x_3 \end{bmatrix}$

(b) $\begin{bmatrix} \dot{x}_1 \\ \dot{x}_2 \\ \dot{x}_3 \end{bmatrix} = \begin{bmatrix} 0 & 1 & 0 \\ 0 & 0 & 1 \\ -3 & -7 & -5 \end{bmatrix} \begin{bmatrix} x_1 \\ x_2 \\ x_3 \end{bmatrix} + \begin{bmatrix} 0 \\ 0 \\ 1 \end{bmatrix} u, \quad y = [1 \quad 0 \quad 0] \begin{bmatrix} x_1 \\ x_2 \\ x_3 \end{bmatrix}$

(c) $\begin{bmatrix} \dot{x}_1 \\ \dot{x}_2 \\ \dot{x}_3 \\ \dot{x}_4 \end{bmatrix} = \begin{bmatrix} 0 & 1 & 0 & 0 \\ 0 & 0 & 1 & 0 \\ 0 & 0 & 0 & 1 \\ -\dfrac{4}{3} & -\dfrac{7}{3} & -2 & -\dfrac{5}{3} \end{bmatrix} \begin{bmatrix} x_1 \\ x_2 \\ x_3 \\ x_4 \end{bmatrix} + \begin{bmatrix} 0 \\ 0 \\ 0 \\ 1 \end{bmatrix} u, \quad y = \begin{bmatrix} 1 & 0 & 0 & 0 \end{bmatrix} \begin{bmatrix} x_1 \\ x_2 \\ x_3 \\ x_4 \end{bmatrix}$

(d) $\begin{bmatrix} \dot{x}_1 \\ \dot{x}_2 \\ \dot{x}_3 \end{bmatrix} = \begin{bmatrix} 0 & 1 & 0 \\ 0 & 0 & 1 \\ -6 & -11 & -6 \end{bmatrix} \begin{bmatrix} x_1 \\ x_2 \\ x_3 \end{bmatrix} + \begin{bmatrix} 2 \\ -6 \\ 16 \end{bmatrix} u, \quad y = \begin{bmatrix} 1 & 0 & 0 \end{bmatrix} \begin{bmatrix} x_1 \\ x_2 \\ x_3 \end{bmatrix} + u$

(e) $\begin{bmatrix} \dot{x}_1 \\ \dot{x}_2 \\ \dot{x}_3 \end{bmatrix} = \begin{bmatrix} 0 & 1 & 0 \\ 0 & 0 & 1 \\ -3 & 0 & -6 \end{bmatrix} \begin{bmatrix} x_1 \\ x_2 \\ x_3 \end{bmatrix} + \begin{bmatrix} 1 \\ -6 \\ 40 \end{bmatrix} u, \quad y = \begin{bmatrix} 1 & 0 & 0 \end{bmatrix} \begin{bmatrix} x_1 \\ x_2 \\ x_3 \end{bmatrix}$

(f) $\begin{bmatrix} \dot{x}_1 \\ \dot{x}_2 \\ \dot{x}_3 \\ \dot{x}_4 \end{bmatrix} = \begin{bmatrix} 0 & 1 & 0 & 0 \\ 0 & 0 & 1 & 0 \\ 0 & 0 & 0 & 1 \\ -1 & -2 & 0 & -4 \end{bmatrix} \begin{bmatrix} x_1 \\ x_2 \\ x_3 \\ x_4 \end{bmatrix} + \begin{bmatrix} 0 \\ 0 \\ 4 \\ -16 \end{bmatrix} u, \quad y = \begin{bmatrix} 1 & 0 & 0 & 0 \end{bmatrix} \begin{bmatrix} x_1 \\ x_2 \\ x_3 \\ x_4 \end{bmatrix}$

10.4 (a)

$$\begin{bmatrix} e^{-0.5t} \cos\sqrt{1.75}\,t + \dfrac{0.5}{\sqrt{1.75}} e^{-0.5t} \sin\sqrt{1.75}\,t & \dfrac{1}{\sqrt{1.75}} e^{-0.5t} \sin\sqrt{1.75}\,t \\[2mm] \dfrac{-2}{\sqrt{1.75}} e^{-0.5t} \sin\sqrt{1.75}\,t & e^{-0.5t} \cos\sqrt{1.75}\,t - \dfrac{0.5}{\sqrt{1.75}} e^{-0.5t} \sin\sqrt{1.75}\,t \end{bmatrix}$$

$s^2 + s + 2 = 0, \ \lambda_1 = \dfrac{-1 + j\sqrt{7}}{2}, \ \lambda_2 = \dfrac{-1 - j\sqrt{7}}{2}$; stable

(b) $\begin{bmatrix} \dfrac{4}{3}e^{-t} - \dfrac{1}{3}e^{-4t} & \dfrac{1}{3}e^{-t} - \dfrac{1}{3}e^{-4t} \\[2mm] -\dfrac{4}{3}e^{-t} + \dfrac{4}{3}e^{-4t} & -\dfrac{1}{3}e^{-t} + \dfrac{4}{3}e^{-4t} \end{bmatrix}$; $s^2 + 5s + 4 = 0, \ \lambda_1 = -1$ and $\lambda_2 = -4$; stable.

(c) $\begin{bmatrix} e^{3t} & 0 \\ 0 & e^{-3t} \end{bmatrix}$; $s^2 - 9 = 0, \ \lambda_1 = 3$ and $\lambda_2 = 3$; unstable.

(d) $\begin{bmatrix} \cos 2t & \sin 2t \\ -\sin 2t & \cos 2t \end{bmatrix}$; $s^2 + 4 = 0$; $\lambda_1 = j2, \ \lambda_2 = -j2$; limitedly stable (unstable)

(e) $\begin{bmatrix} e^{-t} & 0 \\ 0 & e^{-2t} \end{bmatrix}$; $s^2 + 3s + 2 = 0$; $\lambda_1 = -1$ and $\lambda_2 = -2$; stable

(f) $\begin{bmatrix} 1 & \dfrac{1}{2} - \dfrac{1}{2} e^{-2t} \\ 0 & e^{-2t} \end{bmatrix}$; $s^2 + 2s = 0$; $\lambda_1 = 0$ and $\lambda_2 = -2$; marginally stable.

(g) $\begin{bmatrix} -e^{-t} + 2e^{-2t} & e^{-t} - e^{-2t} \\ -2e^{-t} + 2e^{-2t} & 2e^{-t} - e^{-2t} \end{bmatrix}$; $s^2 + 3s + 2 = 0$; $\lambda_1 = 1$ and $\lambda_2 = -2$; stable

(h) $\begin{bmatrix} \dfrac{5}{3} e^{-2t} - \dfrac{2}{3} e^{-5t} & \dfrac{1}{3} e^{-2t} - \dfrac{1}{3} e^{-5t} \\ -\dfrac{10}{3} e^{-2t} + \dfrac{10}{3} e^{-5t} & -\dfrac{2}{3} e^{-2t} + \dfrac{5}{3} e^{-5t} \end{bmatrix}$; $s^2 + 7s + 10 = 0$; $\lambda_1 = -2$ and $\lambda_2 = -5$; stable.

(i) $\begin{bmatrix} 2e^{-t} - e^{-2t} & -2e^{-t} + 2e^{-2t} \\ e^{-t} - e^{-2t} & -e^{-t} + 2e^{-2t} \end{bmatrix}$; $s^2 + 3s + 2 = 0$; $\lambda_1 = -1$ and $\lambda_2 = -2$; stable

(j) $\begin{bmatrix} 1 & 0 \\ e^{-t} - 1 & e^{-t} \end{bmatrix}$; $s^2 + s = 0$; $\lambda_1 = 0$ and $\lambda_2 = 1$; Limitedly stable (unstable)

(k)

$\begin{bmatrix} e^{-0.5t} \cos \sqrt{0.75}\,t + \dfrac{0.5}{\sqrt{0.75}} e^{-0.5t} \sin \sqrt{0.75}\,t & \dfrac{1}{\sqrt{0.75}} e^{-0.5t} \sin \sqrt{0.75}\,t \\ \dfrac{-1}{\sqrt{0.75}} e^{-0.5t} \sin \sqrt{0.75}\,t & e^{-0.5t} \cos \sqrt{0.75}\,t - \dfrac{0.5}{\sqrt{0.75}} e^{-0.5t} \sin \sqrt{0.75}\,t \end{bmatrix}$

$s^2 + s + 1 = 0$; $\lambda_1 = -0.5 + j\sqrt{0.75}$ and $\lambda_2 = -0.5 - j\sqrt{0.75}$; stable

(l) $\begin{bmatrix} e^{-t} \cos \sqrt{2}t + \dfrac{1}{\sqrt{2}} e^{-t} \sin \sqrt{2}t & \dfrac{1}{\sqrt{2}} e^{-t} \sin \sqrt{2}t \\ -\dfrac{3}{\sqrt{2}} e^{-t} \sin \sqrt{2}t & e^{-t} \cos \sqrt{2}t - \dfrac{1}{\sqrt{2}} e^{-t} \sin \sqrt{2}t \end{bmatrix}$

$s^2 + 2s + 3 = 0$; $\lambda_1 = -1 + j\sqrt{2}$ and $\lambda_2 = -1 - j\sqrt{2}$; stable

(m) $\begin{bmatrix} 1 & \dfrac{1}{5}[1 - e^{-5t}] \\ 0 & e^{-5t} \end{bmatrix}$; $s^2 + 5s = 0$; $\lambda_1 = 0$ and $\lambda_2 = -5$; limitedly stable (unstable)

(n) $\begin{bmatrix} e^{-t} \cos t + e^{-t} \sin t & e^{-t} \sin t \\ -2e^{-t} \sin t & e^{-t} \cos t - e^{-t} \sin t \end{bmatrix}$;

$s^2 + 2s + 2 = 0$; $\lambda_1 = -1 - j1$ and $\lambda_2 = -1 + j1$; limitedly stable (unstable)

(o) $\begin{bmatrix} \cos 2t & \dfrac{1}{2}\sin 2t \\ -2\sin 2t & \cos 2t \end{bmatrix}$; $s^2 + 4 = 0$; $\lambda_1 = j2$ and $\lambda_2 = -j2$; limitedly stable (unstable)

(p) $\begin{bmatrix} e^{-t}\cos 2t + e^{-t}\sin 2t & e^{-t}\sin 2t \\ -2e^{-t}\sin 2t & e^{-t}\cos 2t - e^{-t}\sin 2t \end{bmatrix}$;

$s^2 + 2s + 5 = 0$; $\lambda_1 = -1 + j2$ and $\lambda_2 = -1 - j2$; stable.

10.5 (a) $\begin{bmatrix} e^{-t} & 0 & 0 \\ 0 & e^{-2t} & te^{-2t} \\ 0 & 0 & e^{-2t} \end{bmatrix}$; $s^3 + 5s^2 + 8s + 4$; $\lambda_1 = -1$, $\lambda_2 = -2$ and $\lambda_3 = -2$; stable.

(b) $\begin{bmatrix} e^{-t} & 0 & 0 \\ 0 & e^{-2t} & 0 \\ 0 & 0 & e^{-3t} \end{bmatrix}$; $s^3 + 6s^2 + 11s + 6 = 0$; $\lambda_1 = -1$, $\lambda_2 = -2$ and $\lambda_3 = -3$; stable.

(c) $\begin{bmatrix} 1 & \dfrac{3}{2} - 2e^{-t} + \dfrac{1}{2}e^{-2t} & \dfrac{1}{2} - e^{-t} + \dfrac{1}{2}e^{-2t} \\ 0 & 2e^{-t} - e^{-2t} & e^{-t} - e^{-2t} \\ 0 & -2e^{-t} + 2e^{-2t} & -e^{-t} + 2e^{-2t} \end{bmatrix}$;

$s^3 + 3s^2 + 2 = 0$; $\lambda_1 = 0$, $\lambda_2 = -1$ and $\lambda_3 = -2$; limitedly stable (unstable)

(d) $\begin{bmatrix} \dfrac{9}{2}e^{-t} - 6e^{-2t} + \dfrac{5}{2}e^{-3t} & \dfrac{5}{2}e^{-t} - 4e^{-2t} + \dfrac{3}{2}e^{-3t} & e^{-t} - 2e^{-2t} + e^{-3t} \\ -\dfrac{9}{2}e^{-t} + 12e^{-2t} - \dfrac{15}{2}e^{-3t} & -\dfrac{5}{2}e^{-t} + 8e^{-2t} - \dfrac{9}{2}e^{-3t} & -e^{-t} + 4e^{-2t} - 3e^{-3t} \\ -\dfrac{9}{2}e^{-t} - 3e^{-2t} + \dfrac{15}{2}e^{-3t} & -\dfrac{5}{2}e^{-t} - 2e^{-2t} + \dfrac{9}{2}e^{-3t} & -e^{-t} - e^{-2t} + 3e^{-3t} \end{bmatrix}$

$s^3 + 6s^2 + 11s + 6 = 0$. $\lambda_1 = -1$, $\lambda_2 = -2$ and $\lambda_3 = -3$; stable.

(e) $\begin{bmatrix} e^t - te^t + \dfrac{1}{2}t^2 e^t & te^t - t^2 e^t & \dfrac{1}{2}t^2 e^t \\ \dfrac{1}{2}t^2 e^t & e^t - te^t - t^2 e^t & te^t + \dfrac{1}{2}t^2 e^t \\ te^t + \dfrac{1}{2}t^2 e^t & -3te^t - t^2 e^t & e^t + 2te^t + \dfrac{1}{2}t^2 e^t \end{bmatrix}$;

$s^3 - 3s^2 + 3s - 1 = 0$; $\lambda_1 = 1$, $\lambda_2 = 1$ and $\lambda_3 = 1$; unstable.

(f) $\begin{bmatrix} e^{2t} & 12e^{t} - 12e^{2t} + 13te^{2t} & -4e^{t} + 4e^{2t} \\ 0 & e^{2t} & 0 \\ 0 & -3e^{t} + 3e^{2t} & e^{t} \end{bmatrix}$;

$s^3 - 5s^2 + 8s - 4 = 0$; $\lambda_1 = 1$, $\lambda_2 = 2$ and $\lambda_3 = 2$; unstable.

(g) $\begin{bmatrix} e^{-t} & 0 & \dfrac{1}{2}e^{-t} - \dfrac{1}{2}e^{-3t} \\ e^{-t} - e^{-2t} & e^{-2t} & \dfrac{1}{2}e^{-t} - e^{-2t} + \dfrac{1}{2}e^{-3t} \\ 0 & 0 & e^{-3t} \end{bmatrix}$;

$s^3 + 6s^2 + 11s + 6 = 0$; $\lambda_1 = -1$, $\lambda_2 = -2$ and $\lambda_3 = -3$; stable.

(h) $\begin{bmatrix} e^{-0.5t}\cos\sqrt{0.75}t + \dfrac{0.5}{\sqrt{0.75}}e^{-0.5t}\sin\sqrt{0.75}t & -\dfrac{1}{\sqrt{0.75}}e^{-0.5t}\sin\sqrt{0.75}t & 0 \\ -\dfrac{1}{\sqrt{0.75}}e^{-0.5t}\sin\sqrt{0.75}t & e^{-0.5t}\cos\sqrt{0.75}t - \dfrac{0.5}{\sqrt{0.75}}e^{-0.5t}\sin\sqrt{0.75}t & 0 \\ 1 - e^{-0.5t}\left(\cos\sqrt{0.75}t - \dfrac{0.5}{\sqrt{0.75}}\sin\sqrt{0.75}t\right) & 1 - e^{-0.5t}\left(\cos\sqrt{0.75}t + \dfrac{0.5}{\sqrt{0.75}}\sin\sqrt{0.75}t\right) & 1 \end{bmatrix}$

$s^3 + s^2 + s = 0$; $\lambda_1 = 0$, $\lambda_2 = -0.5 - j\sqrt{0.75}$

and $\lambda_3 = -0.5 + j\sqrt{0.75}$; limitedly stable (unstable)

10.6 (a) $\dfrac{s+3}{s^2 + 3s + 2}$

(b) $\dfrac{1}{s^2 + 3s + 2}$

(c) $\dfrac{s+3}{(s+1)(s+2)(s+3)}$

(d) $\dfrac{1}{s(s^2 + s + 1)}$

(e) $\left[\dfrac{(s-3)}{(s-2)(s-2)(s-3)} \quad \dfrac{(s-2)(s-3)}{(s-2)(s-2)(s-3)}\right]$

(f) $\dfrac{2s^2 + 6s + 2}{s^3 + 6s^2 + 11s + 6}$

(g) $\dfrac{3s^2 + 23s + 10}{s^3 + 6s^2 + 11s + 6}$

(h) $\dfrac{(s+1)(s+2)}{(s+1)(s+2)(s+2)}$

10.7 (a) (i) $x(t) = \begin{bmatrix} x_1(t) \\ x_2(t) \end{bmatrix} = \begin{bmatrix} e^{-t}\cos\sqrt{2}t + \dfrac{1}{\sqrt{2}}e^{-t}\sin\sqrt{2}t \\ \dfrac{-3}{\sqrt{2}}e^{-t}\sin\sqrt{2}t \end{bmatrix}$

(ii) $x(t) = \begin{bmatrix} x_1(t) \\ x_2(t) \end{bmatrix} = \begin{bmatrix} \dfrac{1}{3} + \dfrac{2}{3}\left[e^{-t}\cos\sqrt{2}t + \dfrac{1}{\sqrt{2}}e^{-t}\sin\sqrt{2}t\right] \\ -\sqrt{2}e^{-t}\sin\sqrt{2}t \end{bmatrix}$

(b) $\begin{bmatrix} x_1(t) \\ x_2(t) \end{bmatrix} = \begin{bmatrix} 1 \\ 0 \end{bmatrix}$

(c) (i) $\begin{bmatrix} x_1(t) \\ x_2(t) \end{bmatrix} = \begin{bmatrix} \dfrac{1}{3}(e^{-t} - e^{-4t}) \\ \dfrac{1}{3}(4e^{-4t} - e^{-t}) \end{bmatrix}$

(ii) $\begin{bmatrix} x_1(t) \\ x_2(t) \end{bmatrix} = \begin{bmatrix} \dfrac{3}{2} - \dfrac{4}{3}e^{-t} - \dfrac{1}{6}e^{-4t} \\ -1 + \dfrac{4}{3}e^{-t} - \dfrac{2}{3}e^{-4t} \end{bmatrix}$

10.8 (a) stable

(b) $\begin{bmatrix} x_1(t) \\ x_2(t) \end{bmatrix} = \begin{bmatrix} \dfrac{1}{2}t + \dfrac{5}{4} - \dfrac{1}{4}e^{-2t} \\ \dfrac{1}{2} + \dfrac{1}{2}e^{-2t} \end{bmatrix}$

(c) $y(t) = \dfrac{9}{4} + \dfrac{1}{2}t - \dfrac{1}{4}e^{-2t}$

10.9 (a) $\begin{bmatrix} \dot{x}_1 \\ \dot{x}_2 \\ \dot{x}_3 \end{bmatrix} = \begin{bmatrix} -1 & 1 & 0 \\ 0 & -1 & 0 \\ 0 & 0 & -2 \end{bmatrix} \begin{bmatrix} x_1 \\ x_2 \\ x_3 \end{bmatrix} + \begin{bmatrix} 0 \\ 1 \\ 1 \end{bmatrix} u, \quad y = \begin{bmatrix} 1 & 1 & 1 \end{bmatrix} \begin{bmatrix} x_1 \\ x_2 \\ x_3 \end{bmatrix}$

(b) $\begin{bmatrix} x_1 \\ x_2 \\ x_3 \end{bmatrix} = \begin{bmatrix} 1 - e^{-t} - te^{-t} \\ 1 - e^{-t} \\ \dfrac{1}{2} - \dfrac{1}{2}e^{-2t} \end{bmatrix}, \; y(t) = \dfrac{5}{2} - te^{-t} - 2e^{-t} - \dfrac{1}{2}e^{-2t}$

10.10 (a) $\begin{bmatrix} -1 & 0 & 0 \\ 0 & -2 & 0 \\ 0 & 0 & -6 \end{bmatrix}$ (b) $\begin{bmatrix} 1 & 0 & 0 \\ 0 & 3 & 1 \\ 0 & 0 & 3 \end{bmatrix}$ (c) $\begin{bmatrix} 0 & 0 & 0 \\ 0 & -1 & 0 \\ 0 & 0 & -2 \end{bmatrix}$

(d) $\begin{bmatrix} 1 & 1 & 0 \\ 0 & 1 & 0 \\ 0 & 0 & 2 \end{bmatrix}$ (e) $\begin{bmatrix} 1 & 0 & 0 \\ 0 & 2 & 1 \\ 0 & 0 & 2 \end{bmatrix}$

10.11 (a) completely state controllable, output controllable and observable.
(b) completely state controllable, output controllable and observable.
(c) completely state controllable, output controllable and observable.
(d) completely state controllable and output controllable but not observable.
(e) completely state controllable and output controllable but not observable.
(f) completely state controllable, output controllable and observable.

CHAPTER II

Answers to Fill in the Blanks

1. difference **2.** difference, algebraic **3.** $\underset{z\to\infty}{\text{Lt}}\, X(z)$ **4.** $\underset{z\to 1}{\text{Lt}}\, (z-1)\, X(z)$ **5.** impulse response **6.** inside the unit circle **7.** forced response **8.** free response **9.** total response **10.** impulse response **11.** sequence of pulses **12.** continuous, discrete **13.** reduces **14.** short duration pulses **15.** at least twice **16.** zero **17.** first **18.** one **19.** inverse Z-transformation **20.** $z^{-m} X(z), z^{m} X(z)$ **21.** $\underset{z\to\infty}{\text{Lt}}\, X(z)$ **22.** $\underset{z\to 1}{\text{Lt}}\, (z-1)\, X(z)$ **23.** inside the unit circle **24.** an algebraic **25.** $F(1) > 0,\ (-1)^n\, F(-1) > 0$ **26.** bilinear **27.** destabilizing **28.** reduces.

Answers to Objective Type Questions

1. a **2.** a **3.** b **4.** b **5.** c **6.** b **7.** a

Answers to Problems

11.1 (a) 0

(b) $\dfrac{z - z^3}{z - 1}$

(c) $\dfrac{2z^{-2} - 3z^{-1} + z}{(z-1)^2}$

(d) $\dfrac{z\left(2z - \dfrac{9}{20}\right)}{\left(z - \dfrac{1}{4}\right)\left(z - \dfrac{1}{5}\right)}$

11.2 (a) $\dfrac{z}{(z-1)^2}$

(b) $\dfrac{z(z+1)}{(z-1)^3}$

(c) $\dfrac{\dfrac{3}{\sqrt{2}}z}{9z^2 - \dfrac{6}{\sqrt{2}}z + 1}$

(d) $\dfrac{z(z - 2\cos 3)}{z^2 - 4z\cos 3 + 4}$

11.3 (a) $\dfrac{T^2 z(z+1)}{(z-1)^3}$

(b) $\dfrac{z}{z - e^{-aT}}$

(c) $\dfrac{ze^{aT}[ze^{aT} - \cos\omega T]}{z^2 e^{2aT} - 2ze^{aT}\cos\omega T + 1}$

(d) $\dfrac{ze^{aT}\sin\omega t}{z^2 e^{2aT} - 2ze^{aT}\cos\omega T + 1}$

11.4 (a) $\dfrac{z\,aTe^{-aT}}{[z - e^{-aT}]^2}$

(b) $\dfrac{z(z - \cos\omega T)}{z^2 - 2z\cos\omega T + 1}$

(c) $\dfrac{ze^{-bT}\sin aT}{z^2 - 2ze^{-bT}\cos aT + e^{-2bT}}$

(d) $\dfrac{z(z - e^{-bT}\cos aT)}{z^2 - 2ze^{-bT}\cos aT + e^{-2bT}}$

11.5 (a) $\{1, -1, 2, -4, 8, -16, \ldots\}$

(b) $\{0, 1, -1.2, 0.2, 1, -1.2, \ldots\}$

(c) $[-n + 1 - 2^n]\, u(n)$

(d) $\left(\dfrac{1}{2}\right)^n u(n) - \left(\dfrac{1}{4}\right)^n u(n)$

11.6 $\dfrac{z-2}{z^2 + 4z + 5}$, $\{0, 1, -6, 19, -46, 89, \ldots\}$

11.7 Not possible, $C(z) = \dfrac{G_0 G_2(z)\, G_1 R(z)}{1 + G_0 G_2 H G_1(z)}$

11.8 $\dfrac{G_1(z)\, G_2(z)}{1 + G_1(z)\, G_2 H(z)}$

11.9 $\dfrac{G_0 G(z)}{1 + G_0 G(z)\, H(z)}$

11.10 $0.5[1 - (0.2644)^n]\, u(n)$

11.11 (a) $\dfrac{2}{z - \dfrac{1}{2}}$, $\quad 2\left(\dfrac{1}{2}\right)^{n-1} u(n-1)$

(b) $\dfrac{z(-z+2)}{z^2 - \dfrac{1}{4}z - \dfrac{3}{8}}$, $(-2)\left(-\dfrac{1}{2}\right)^n u(n) + \left(\dfrac{3}{4}\right)^n u(n)$

11.12 $\dfrac{1}{4}u(n) - \dfrac{9}{4}(-3)^n u(n)$

11.13 $2u(n) + 3\left(\dfrac{1}{4}\right)^n u(n) - \left(\dfrac{1}{2}\right)^n u(n)$

11.14 (a) Unstable   (b) Unstable   (c) Unstable

11.15 (a) Unstable   (b) Unstable   (c) Unstable

11.16 (a) Unstable for all values of K

(b) $K < 2$

(c) Unstable for all values of K

Index